CHOICES

ANSWERING THE QUESTIONS,

QUESTIONING THE ANSWERS.

---

*Human Sexuality in
a World of Diversity,
Second Edition*

Jeffrey S. Nevid,
St. John's University,
Lois Fichner-Rathus,
Trenton State College, and
Spencer A. Rathus,
St. John's University

CHOICES

What Do Today's Students Need To Know About Sexuality?

. . .The Most Up-to-date Information to Make the Best Choices Possible.

- **Comprehensive updating** of scientific development in the field including topics such as contraception, AIDS, and STDs.

- **"What Do You Say Now Boxes"** focus on issues students are likely to face now, such as talking back to sexual pressure lines, talking to your partner about STDs,— or in the future, such as talking to your children about sex.

- **New student-oriented exercises** provide important and helpful suggestions for concerned students.

  — *Tracking Menstrual Complaints with the PMS Calendar* helps women track menstrual complaints through two full cycles and note patterns that they can bring to the attention of their health care providers.

  — *What To Do If You Suspect You Have Contracted an STD*

- **New Questionnaires:** "The Index of Sexual Satisfaction" and "Are You a Romantic or a Realist? The Love Attitudes Scale."

- **Discussion** of the genetics of homosexuality.

Teaching sexual and cultural diversity to a diverse student population.

- Female circumcision practices in the Middle East and Africa.
- The Liu report on sexual behavior in Chinese males and females.
- Cross-cultural perspectives on homosexual behavior.
- AIDS and prostitution in Thailand.
- The Warren survey of Native American women.

Beauty and Culture. Can you find Mr. or Ms. Right among these people? Are your judgments of physical beauty based on universal standards or on your cultural experiences?

ATTRACTION

Let us explore some of the factors that determine interpersonal attraction.

Looking at the complete range of human sexual behavior.

From the sexual experiences and practices of minority populations throughout the United States to cultural groups around the world, the Second Edition encourages respect for those who hold different beliefs and attitudes and prompts students to question social roles and sexual conduct in light of various cultural traditions and standards.

Timely information on sexual health issues, such as:

- The influence of religion, gender, and socioeconomic status
- HIV/AIDS
- Contraception and reproductive technologies
- Sexually transmitted diseases (STDs)
- Menstrual distress
- Breast cancer and self-examination
- Testicular self-examination
- Sexual functioning and disabilities

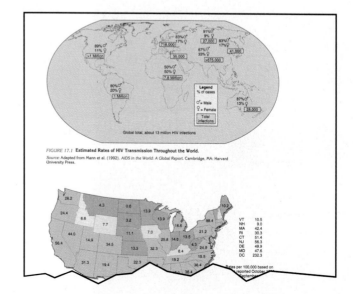

FIGURE 17.1 **Estimated Rates of HIV Transmission Throughout the World.**

Source: Adapted from Mann et al. (1992). *AIDS in the World: A Global Report.* Cambridge, MA: Harvard University Press.

CHOICES

Incorporating the latest research and most up-to-date coverage possible.

Many late-breaking developments in the field of human sexuality have been included in the Second Edition, such as:

- Effects of smoking during pregnancy
- Data on safer sex practices among college students in the U.S. and Canada
- Rates of teenage pregnancy
- Rates of sexual harassment in the workplace and in schools
- Reports on Prozac in the treatment of voyeurism and fetishism
- Biological factors in erectile dysfunction
- Reports on rates of cohabitation

More than 500 new citations to scientific research have been added, making this edition the most current resource to date.

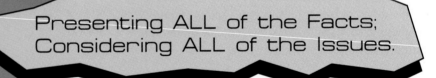

Presenting ALL of the Facts; Considering ALL of the Issues.

Chapter outlines. Examples. Special interest features. Exercises. Questionnaires. Illustrations. Chapter summaries.

This text has been carefully written, designed, and class tested to ensure information is presented in a way that makes sense to students. For instance, male and female anatomy is presented up front, setting the stage for following chapters. In addition, special pedagogical features and frequent examples illustrate key points while helping to stimulate student interest throughout. All of these different elements work in unison to encourage critical thinking skills and emphasize the importance of considering all of the facts. *Students learn to think beyond the obvious — to take an active role in making decisions.*

Informative and interesting ways of presenting information that students can relate to.

"A World of Diversity" boxes — Encourage students
to question what is appropriate for women and men in terms of social roles and sexual conduct in light of cultural traditions and standards

- The contraception revolution in the Third World.
- Japan's abortion agony
- Ethics differences in premarital intercourse, adolescent use of contraception, and resolution of unwanted pregnancies

"Truth or Fiction?" sections — Each chapter opens
with statements which are later debunked or verified in the context of the material presented. Examples include:

- Uncircumcised men are more sensitive than circumcised men to sexual stimulation.
- Orgasms attained through masturbation are more intense than those attained through coitus.
- When partners truly love one another, they instinctively know how to satisfy each other sexually.
- Gay males and lesbians would prefer to be members of the opposite gender.

"What Do You Say Now?" discussion boxes —
Encourage students to talk more freely about their personal views and attitudes.

- Talking to your partner about STDs
- Talking to your children about sex
- Talking back to sexual pressure lines

"A Closer Look" boxes — Stimulate group discussion
on a current social topic and provide practical information on sexual health and awareness.

- Is there *man*opause?
- Should schools distribute condoms?
- How to do a testicular self-exam.
- How to prevent rape.

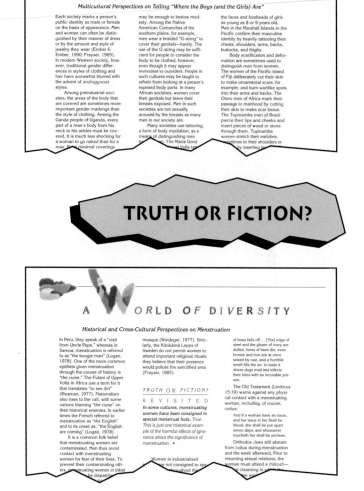

Self-Scoring Questionnaires — Encourages
students to examine their own sexual attitudes, knowledge, and beliefs.

- Triangular Love Scale
- Sexually-Transmitted Diseases Attitude Scale
- Reasoning About Abortion Scale

CHOICES

CNN

Tying It all together for your students.

CNN *Video*

Over 45 exclusive, specially edited, and current Cable News Network Video segments correlate directly to specific sections within the text — show students the connection between what they're learning in class and what's happening in the world around them. Plus, the Video User's Guide, included in the Instructor's Manual, helps you make the best use of these two- to six-minute segments.

Among the CNN "Connection" Video Topics

AIDS Moms • Breast Cancer • Elderly Divorce • Female Circumcision • Gay Bashing • Gender Equality • Lesbian Parents • Male Contraception Pill • Rape Reporting • Sex Survey Update • Sex Education and Morality • Sexual Harassment in Schools • Sexually Transmitted Diseases on the Rise • Sexy Foods • Teen AIDS

All-New

Test Bank and Computerized Test Bank —
Prepared by Sharon Ng, Yuba College
Over 2,000 multiple-choice questions and prepared tests for each chapter. All items are tied to chapter learning objectives and are referenced for cognitive type. (Computerized format for use with Macintosh and IBM-PC and compatibles.)

New

Color Transparencies —
48 new full-color transparencies of key illustrations, charts, and diagrams taken directly from the textbook — and from other related materials.

Instructor's Annotated Edition (IAE) —
The IAE provides you with in-text annotations that refer you to the numerous resources found in the Instructor's Manual, CNN videos and transparencies.

Instructor's Manual — Written by Beverly Drinnin, Des Moines Community College
The Instructor's Manual provides a wide range of questionnaires, classroom activities, mini-lectures for use throughout the course. Completely reorganized, the IM now includes chapter overviews, chapters-at-a-glance, lecture topics, student activities, and recommended readings and videos. A Video User's Guide suggests appropriate times to interject CNN video segments.

Student Study Guide — Prepared by Beverly A. Drinnin, Des Moines Community College
This easy-to-use student guide features learning objectives, exercises, glossary quizzes, sample tests, and much more.

Special Supplement — *CHOICES: Sex in the Age of STDs* by Jeffrey S. Nevid, St. Johns University, with Fern Gotfried, consulting medical editor
This special supplement puts crucial information at students' fingertips and provides chapters on condom use and safer sex, a directory of national health hotlines, and suggestions on how students can most effectively broach these controversial topics in their own lives.

CHOICES

You'll gain a whole new means of communication when you start to experience AMERICA ONLINE. Its award-winning interface makes navigating easy. Just point and click to download any of thousands of programs; attend real-time, online conferences and forums; keep in touch through electronic mail; and get the latest news and information from leading magazines and news wires.

Connect to a whole new world of teaching and learning!

Here's your key to the wonderful world of AMERICA ONLINE!

 We'll help you get started. Adopt this textbook and we'll waive the America Online membership fee for the first two months! Use this introductory membership to access a wide range of interactive services and educational information including a fast and easy gateway to the Internet. All you need is a computer and a modem. We'll make it easy for your students to get started too! What's more, Simon & Schuster Higher Education Group will be developing online services specifically for college and university faculty and student use!

Ask your local Representative for more details. Or, if you have already selected this textbook for your course adoption, please call at **1-800-827-6364, ext. 4314** and we'll send you your FREE America Online Faculty Starter Kit!

INSTRUCTOR'S ANNOTATED EDITION

Beverly Drinnin
Des Moines Community College

SECOND EDITION

HUMAN SEXUALITY IN A WORLD OF DIVERSITY

Jeffery S. **Nevid**
St. John's University

Lois **Fichner-Rathus**
Trenton State College

Spencer A. **Rathus**
St. John's University

ALLYN AND BACON
Boston • London • Toronto • Sydney • Tokyo • Singapore

Vice President and Publisher: Susan Badger
Executive Editor: Laura Pearson
Editorial Assistant: Jennifer Normandin
Marketing Manager: Joyce Nilsen
Production Administrator: Deborah Brown
Production Coordinator: Eleanor Sabini
Text Designer: Melinda Grosser (*Silk*)
Cover Administrator: Linda Knowles
Cover Designer: Susan Paradise
Composition Buyer: Linda Cox
Manufacturing Buyer: Louise Richardson
Manager, Electronic Production: Meredith Garniss
Electronic Project Manager: Gayle A. Robertson
Electronic Composition: Janine Hosseini, Nancy Jones, Stuart Cooke

Printed in the United States of America
10 9 8 7 6 5 4 3 2 1   100 99 98 97 96 95

ISBN 0-205-16545-1

BRIEF CONTENTS

CHAPTER

Introduction to the
Instructor's Annotated Edition

This introduction to the Instructor's Annotated Edition (IAE) is designed to provide a complete description of the outstanding package of supplementary materials available with the second edition of *Human Sexuality in a World of Diversity.*

THE WALK-THROUGH

The Walk-Through provides the instructor with step-by-step examples of the various features, pedagogy, and supplements that form the complete Allyn and Bacon teaching package for your human sexuality course. Sample pages demonstrate the layout of the text and how to use the complete package most effectively. A description of the supplements can be found at the end of the Walk-Through.

THE ANNOTATIONS

The Instructor's Annotated Edition is designed to ease the time-consuming demands of instructional preparation, and also to guide instructors through teaching human sexuality. Its elements appear in the margins in blue type. Within the constraints of the text layout, the annotations indicate where to use learning objectives, extra activities appearing in the Instructor's Manual, discussion questions, teaching tips, notes (extra informational "tidbits" on human sexuality), and CNN video connections.

CHAPTER-AT-A-GLANCE TABLES

Found in the Instructor's Section of the IAE as well as the Instructor's Manual, these charts coordinate each chapter with the corresponding lecture topics, transparencies, discussion questions, teaching tips, notes, and videos to cut back on your preparation time and simplify your presentation.

THE TEXT SUPPLEMENTS

AN INSTRUCTOR'S MANUAL Completely redesigned for the second edition, this guide for new instructors as well as experienced faculty includes an expanded discussion of ways to use the text and its ancillaries. Each chapter begins with a chapter summary, followed by a chapter-at-a-glance table — a tabular reference to all of the teaching aids and ancillaries that accompany the text. Instructors will also find the lecture outlines, list of transparencies, activities, and video user's guide.

CNN "CONNECTION" VIDEOS Exclusive Cable News Network Video "Connection" provides two hours of new edited segments on a wide variety of topics. These short video segments, each introduced by a commentator providing background information, correlate directly with specific sections in the textbook. Video "Connections" sections in the Instructor's Manual help you make best use of this unique teaching tool.

TEST BANK Includes over 2,000 multiple-choice questions and pre-made tests for each chapter. Items are tied to learning objectives and referenced for cognitive type.

COMPUTERIZED TEST BANK Available in the easy-to-use Test Manager format for both IBM-PCs and Macintosh computers.

STUDY GUIDE Reorganized to include chapter summaries, learning objectives, fill-in-the-blank questions, short answer questions, matching exercises, multiple choice questions, and vocabulary exercises. Also contains activities not contained in the book, such as "Talking to Your Partner about Contraception," and "How Should a Parent Respond to Childhood Masturbation."

TRANSPARENCY PACKAGE Contains 48 full-color transparencies of art from the text and related sources to enhance classroom lectures and discussions.

CHOICES: SEX IN THE AGE OF STDs
by Jeffrey S. Nevid with Fern Gotfried, Consulting Medical Editor
This book discusses the very real risks that STDs pose to students. Encourages sexually active students to adopt the responsible sexual practices described in the book. Contains four full chapters on AIDS, including the most current information about the AIDS epidemic, how it is transmitted, women and AIDS, and testing and treatment for AIDS. Describes over twelve additional STDs, offers health tips, common signs and symptoms, fact sheets, explanations, and treatments for each.

CHAPTER 1
Chapter-at-a-Glance
What is Human Sexuality?

Chapter Outline	Instructional Ideas	Supplemental Materials
What is Human Sexuality? p. 5 • The Study of Human Sexuality • Why Study Human Sexuality? • Sexuality and Values	L. O. 1.............................p. 5 L. O. 2.............................p. 5 Notes ....p. 6	**IM Activity:** *How Much Do You Know About Sex?* **IM Activity:** *The Sexual Permissiveness Scale*
Thinking Critically About Human Sexuality p. 7 • Some Features of Critical Thinking	L. O. 3.............................p. 7 L. O. 4 ....p. 7 Teaching Tip ....p. 10	**IM Activity:** *Thinking About Self-Help Books on Sex*
Perspectives On Human Sexuality p. 10 • The Historical Perspective • The Biological Perspective • The Cross-Species Perspective • The Cross-Cultural Perspective • Psychological Perspectives • Sociological Perspectives • Multiple Perspectives on Human Sexuality	L. O. 5.............................p. 11 Notes ....p. 12 L. O. 6.............................p. 18 Discussion Question.......p. 19 L. O. 7.............................p. 22 L. O. 8.............................p. 22 Notes ....p. 24 L. O. 9.............................p. 24 Notes ....p. 26 Teaching Tip ....p. 26 L. O. 10...........................p. 29 Discussion Question.......p. 30 L. O. 11...........................p. 31 Notes ....p. 31 L. O. 12...........................p. 31	**IM Lecture Material:** *Animal Sexual Behavior* **IM Activity:** *Changing Gender Roles (Small-Group Discussion)*

CHAPTER 2
Chapter-at-a-Glance
Research Methods in Human Sexuality

Chapter Outline	Instructional Ideas	Supplemental Materials
A Scientific Approach to Human Sexuality p. 36 • The Scientific Method • Goals and Methods of the Science of Human Sexuality • Operational Definitions	L. O. 1.............................p. 36 L. O. 2.............................p. 37 Teaching Tip ....p. 37 Teaching Tip ....p. 38 L. O. 3.............................p. 38	
Methods of Research in Human Sexuality p. 40 • The Survey Method • Observational Methods • The Experimental Method • The Correlational Method • The Case-Study Method	L. O. 4.............................p. 41 L. O. 5.............................p. 42 Discussion Question.......p. 44 L. O. 6.............................p. 45 Discussion Question.......p. 46 L. O. 7.............................p. 51 Discussion Question.......p. 52 L. O. 8.............................p. 53 L. O. 9.............................p. 54 Teaching Tip ....p. 55 L. O. 10...........................p. 55 L. O. 11...........................p. 56 L. O. 12...........................p. 57	**Transparency 1:** *Strengths and Limitations of General Research Design* **IM Activity:** *The Social-Desirability Scale* **IM Activity:** *Thinking About the Limitations of Sex Surveys* **IM Activity:** *Evaluating Scientific Claims*

CHAPTER 2 *(continued)*
Chapter-at-a-Glance
Research Methods in Human Sexuality

Chapter Outline	Instructional Ideas	Supplemental Materials
Ethics in Sex Research p. 58 • Pain and Stress • Confidentiality • Informed Consent • The Use of Deception • Debriefing	L. O. 13............p. 58 Notes ....p. 58	

CHAPTER 3
Chapter-at-a-Glance
Female Sexual Anatomy and Physiology

Chapter Outline	Instructional Ideas	Supplemental Materials
External Sexual Organs p. 65 • The Mons Veneris • The Labia Majora • The Labia Minora • The Clitoris • The Vestibule • The Urethral Opening • The Vaginal Opening • The Perineum • Structures That Underlie the External Sexual Organs	L. O. 1............p. 64 L. O. 2............p. 65 Discussion Question.......p. 66 L. O. 3............p. 66 L. O. 4............p. 67 Notes ....p. 70 L. O. 5............p. 70 Notes ....p. 71 Discussion Question.......p. 71	**Transparency 2:** *External Female Sexual Organs* **Transparency 3:** *Normal Variations in the Vulva* **CNN:** *Female Circumcision*
Internal Sexual Organs p. 73 • The Vagina • The Cervix • The Uterus • The Fallopian Tubes • The Ovaries • The Pelvic Examination	L. O. 6............p. 73 L. O. 7............p. 78 Teaching Tip ....p. 79	**Transparency 4:** *The Female Reproductive System* **Transparency 5:** *Internal Female Reproductive Organs* **IM Lecture Material:** *A Sexist Thing Happened on the Way to the Forum*
The Breasts p. 79 • Breast Cancer	L. O. 8............p. 79 L. O. 9............p. 81 Discussion Question.......p. 82 Teaching Tip ....p. 84 Notes ....p. 86	**Transparency 6:** *A Breast of an Adult Woman* **CNN:** *Breast Cancer* **CNN:** *Breast Implant Settlement*
The Menstrual Cycle p. 86 • Menstruation Versus Estrus • Regulation of the Menstrual Cycle • Phases of the Menstrual Cycle • Coitus During Menstruation • Menopause	L. O. 10............p. 86 Teaching Tip ....p. 94 L. O. 11............p. 94 L. O. 12............p. 96 Notes ....p. 96	**Transparency 7:** *Some Major Glands of the Endocrine System* **Transparency 8:** *Some of the Bodily Changes that Occur During the Menstrual Cycle*

Chapter-at-a-Glance
Female Sexual Anatomy and Physiology

Chapter Outline	Instructional Ideas	Supplemental Materials
Menstrual Problems p. 97 • Dysmenorrhea • Amenorrhea • Premenstrual Syndrome (PMS) • How to Handle Menstrual Discomfort	L. O. 13...........................p. 97 L. O. 14...........................p. 99 Notes ....p. 100	**IM Lecture Material:** *Religious Beliefs and Menstrual Discomfort*

CHAPTER 4
Chapter-at-a-Glance
Male Sexual Anatomy and Physiology

Chapter Outline	Instructional Ideas	Supplemental Materials
External Sexual Organs p. 107 • The Penis • The Scrotum	Notes ....p. 106 Notes ....p. 106 L. O. 1...........................p. 107 L. O. 2...........................p. 109 Teaching Tip ....p. 110 L. O. 3...........................p. 110 L. O. 4...........................p. 111	**Transparency 9:** *The Penis*
Internal Sexual Organs p. 112 • The Testes • The Vas Deferens • The Seminal Vesicles • The Prostate Gland • Cowper's Glands • Semen	L. O. 5...........................p. 113 L. O. 6...........................p. 116 Discussion Question.....p. 117	**Transparency 10:** *The Male Reproductive System*
Diseases of the Urogenital System p. 117 • Urethritis • Cancer of the Testes • Disorders of the Prostate	L. O. 7...........................p. 117 L. O. 8...........................p. 118 Discussion Question.....p. 118 L. O. 9...........................p. 118 Discussion Question.....p. 119	**CNN:** *Prostate Support Group*
Male Sexual Functions p. 120 • Erection • Spinal Reflexes and Sexual Response • Ejaculation	L. O. 10.........................p. 120 L. O. 11.........................p. 123 L. O. 12.........................p. 123 Notes ....p. 123 L. O. 13.........................p. 125 L. O. 14.........................p. 125	**Transparency 11:** *Reflexes* **IM Activity:** *Thinking About Whether the Penis Has a Mind of Its Own*

I N S T R U C T O R ' S   S E C T I O N

CHAPTER 5
Chapter-at-a-Glance
Sexual Arousal and Response

Chapter Outline	Instructional Ideas	Supplemental Materials
Making Sense of Sex: The Role of the Senses in Sexual Arousal p. 130 • Vision: The Better to See You With • Smell: Does the Nose Know Best? • The Skin Senses: Sex as a Touching Experience • Taste: On Savory Sex • Hearing: The Better to Hear You With	L. O. 1.........................p. 130 L. O. 2.........................p. 131 Discussion Question.....p. 132 Discussion Question.....p. 132 L. O. 3.........................p. 134 Teaching Tip ....p. 134 L. O. 4.........................p. 135	
Aphrodisiacs: Of Spanish Flies and Rhino Horns p. 135 • Psychoactive Drugs	L. O. 5.........................p. 135 Notes ....p. 137 L. O. 6.........................p. 137 Teaching Tip ....p. 138 Notes ....p. 139	**CNN:** *Weird Market in China* **CNN:** *Sexy Foods*
Sexual Response and the Brain p. 139 • The Geography of the Brain • Brain Mechanisms in Sexual Functioning • On Pushing the Right Buttons: Are There Pleasure Centers in the Brain? • Sex Hormones	Teaching Tip ....p. 139 L. O. 7.........................p. 142 L. O. 8.........................p. 144 Notes ....p. 144	**Transparency 12:** *The Geography of the Brain*
The Sexual Response Cycle p. 146 • Excitement Phase • Plateau Phase • Orgasmic Phase • Resolution Phase • Kaplan's Three Stages of Sexual Response: An Alternate Model	L. O. 9.........................p. 146 L. O. 10.......................p. 151	**Transparency 13:** *The Male Genitals During the Phases of the Sexual Response Cycle* **Transparency 14:** *The Female Genitals During the Phases of the Sexual Response Cycle* **IM Activity:** *Is the Orgasm Male or Female?*
Controversies About Orgasm p. 152 • Multiple Orgasms: When You're Having More Than One • How Many Kinds of Orgasms Do Women Have? One, Two, or Three? • The Grafenberg Spot	L. O. 11.......................p. 152 Discussion Question.....p. 153 L. O. 12.......................p. 154 L. O. 13.......................p. 156	**Transparency 15:** *The Grafenberg Spot*

CHAPTER 6
Chapter-at-a-Glance
Gender Identity and Gender Roles

Chapter Outline	Instructional Ideas	Supplemental Materials
Prenatal Sexual Differentiation p. 162 • The Role of Sex Hormones in Sexual Differentiation • Descent of the Testes and the Ovaries • Sex Chromosomal Abnormalities • Prenatal Sexual Differentiation of the Brain	L. O. 1..........................p. 162	**Transparency 16:** *Development of the Internal Sexual Organs from an Undifferentiated Stage at About 5 or 6 Weeks Following Conception* **Transparency 17:** *Development of the External Sexual Organs from an Undifferentiated Stage at About 5 or 6 Weeks Following Conception*
Gender Identity p. 165 • Nature and Nurture in Gender Identity • Hermaphroditism • Transsexualism	L. O. 2..........................p. 166 L. O. 3..........................p. 170 Notes ....p. 171 Discussion Question.....p. 171	**IM Activity:** *Thinking About Gender and Reality*
Gender Roles and Stereotypes p. 173		
Sexism p. 173	L. O. 4..........................p. 174 Teaching Tip ....p. 176	**IM Activity:** *What Do You Say Now? Handling a Sexist Remark* **CNN:** *Gender Equality* **CNN:** *Female Bias*
Gender Differences: *Vive La Différence or Vive La Similarité?* p. 176 • Differences in Cognitive Abilities • Differences in Personality	L. O. 5..........................p. 176 Teaching Tip ....p. 176 Discussion Question.....p. 177	**Transparency 18:** *Current Sex-Related Differences in Mental Abilities and Personality Traits*
On Becoming a Man or a Woman: Gender Typing p. 178 • Biological Perspectives • Cross-Cultural Perspectives • Psychological Perspectives	L. O. 6..........................p. 178 Notes ....p. 179 L. O. 7..........................p. 180 Notes ....p. 180 Notes ....p. 181 L. O. 8..........................p. 181 Notes ....p. 182 Discussion Question.....p. 183	**CNN:** *Girls' Education* **IM Lecture Material:** *A Mixed Blessing: Female Gender Roles and Religion*
Gender Roles and Sexual Behavior p. 185 • Men as Sexually Aggressive, Women as Sexually Passive • Men as Overaroused, Women as Underaroused	L. O. 9..........................p. 185	**IM Activity:** *Thinking About Sleeping Beauty and Other Fairy Tales*
Psychological Androgyny: The More Traits the Merrier? p. 186 • Psychological Androgyny, Psychological Well-Being, and Personal Development • Psychological Androgyny and Sexual Behavior • Who Is Androgynous?	L. O. 10..........................p. 186	**IM Activity:** *The ANDRO Scale: Assessing Your Masculinity and Femininity*

CHAPTER 7
Chapter-at-a-Glance
Attraction and Love

Chapter Outline	Instructional Ideas	Supplemental Materials

Attraction   p. 196
• Physical Attractiveness:
  How Important Is Looking Good?
• Attraction and Attitudinal Similarity:
  Do Opposites Attract?
• Reciprocity: If You Like Me,
  You Must Have Excellent Judgment
	L. O. 1...........................p. 196
	Teaching Tip ....p. 197
	Discussion Question.....p. 198
	Teaching Tip ....p. 199
	L. O. 2...........................p. 199
	L. O. 3...........................p. 201
	Discussion Question.....p. 202
	L. O. 4...........................p. 202
	L. O. 5...........................p. 203
	L. O. 6...........................p. 204
		IM Lecture Material:
		Body Image and the Idealization of Thinness
		CNN: *Love in the 90's*

Love   p. 204
• The Greek Heritage
• Romantic Love in Contemporary
  Western Culture
• Contemporary Models of Love:
  Dare Science Intrude?
	Teaching Tip ....p. 205
	L. O. 7...........................p. 205
	Discussion Question.....p. 205
	L. O. 8...........................p. 205
	Teaching Tip ....p. 208
	L. O. 9...........................p. 208
	L. O. 10.........................p. 212
		IM Activity: *Thinking About...Does Love Make the World Go 'Round?*
		IM Activity: *Thinking About Love and Gladiator Contests, or "Why I Took My Date to See 'Rocky 10'"*
		IM Activity: *Are You in Love? The Love Scale*
		IM Activity: *Thinking About Whether or Not All You Need is Love*

CHAPTER 8
Chapter-at-a-Glance
Relationships, Intimacy, and Communication

Chapter Outline	Instructional Ideas	Supplemental Materials
Stages in Romantic Relationships p. 218 • Attraction • Building • Continuation • Deterioration • Ending	L. O. 1...........................p. 218 Discussion Question.....p. 219 L. O. 2...........................p. 219 Discussion Question.....p. 219 L. O. 3...........................p. 220 Discussion Question.....p. 221 L. O. 4...........................p. 223 Discussion Question.....p. 223 L. O. 5...........................p. 224 Discussion Question.....p. 224	
Loneliness p. 225 • Causes of Loneliness • Coping with Loneliness	Notes ....p. 225 L. O. 6...........................p. 225	**IM Activity:** *The UCLA Loneliness Scale*

Chapter Outline	Instructional Ideas	Supplemental Materials
Intimacy p. 226 • Knowing and Liking Yourself • Trusting and Caring • Being Honest • Making a Commitment • Maintaining Individuality When the I Becomes We • Communicating	L. O. 7.........................p. 227 Discussion Question.....p. 228 L. O. 8.........................p. 229 Notes ....p. 229 Teaching Tip ....p. 231	**IM Activity:** *Conducting a Personal Experiment: Should You Be Completely Open With Your Partner?*
Communication Skills for Enhancing Relationships and Sexual Relations p. 232 • Common Difficulties in Sexual Communication • Getting Started • Listening to the Other Side • Learning About Your Partner's Needs • Providing Information • Making Requests • Delivering Criticism • Receiving Criticism • When Communication Is Not Enough: Handling Impasses	L. O. 9.........................p. 232 L. O. 10.......................p. 233 Notes ....p. 233 L. O. 11.......................p. 234 L. O. 12.......................p. 237 L. O. 13.......................p. 239 Teaching Tip ....p. 239	**IM Activity:** *What Do You Say Now? Delivering Criticism* **IM Activity:** *What Do You Say Now? Receiving Criticism*

CHAPTER 9
Chapter-at-a-Glance
Sexual Techniques and Behavior Patterns

Chapter Outline	Instructional Ideas	Supplemental Materials
Solitary Sexual Behavior p. 244 • Masturbation • Sexual Fantasy	L. O. 1.........................p. 244 Notes ....p. 246 Discussion Question.....p. 246 Notes ....p. 247 Teaching Tip ....p. 248 L. O. 2.........................p. 248 L. O. 3.........................p. 251 Notes ....p. 251 Notes ....p. 252	**CNN:** *Sex Survey Update* **IM Activity:** *Thinking About the Logic of Cultural Taboos Against Masturbation* **IM Lecture Material:** *Thinking About Sex and Athletic Performance* **CNN:** *Moscow Sex Shop*
Sex with Others p. 253 • Foreplay • Kissing • Touching • Breast Stimulation • Oral-Genital Stimulation • Sexual Intercourse: Positions and Techniques	L. O. 4.........................p. 254 Teaching Tip ....p. 254 L. O. 5.........................p. 256 Notes ....p. 258 L. O. 6.........................p. 260 Notes ....p. 261 Discussion Question.....p. 262 L. O. 7.........................p. 267 L. O. 8.........................p. 264 L. O. 9.........................p. 267 Notes ....p. 269	**IM Activity:** *Examining Correlations Between Cunnilingus and Psychosocial Characteristics* **Transparency 19:** *Sexual Intercourse Positions* **IM Activity:** *Index of Sexual Satisfaction*

CHAPTER 10
Chapter-at-a-Glance
Sexual Orientation

Chapter Outline	Instructional Ideas	Supplemental Materials
Sexual Orientation p. 272 • Classification of Sexual Orientation • Homosexuality and Bisexuality	L. O. 1 ....p. 272 Teaching Tip ....p. 273 Notes ....p. 273 Notes ....p. 274 L. O. 2 ....p. 277 L. O. 3 ....p. 278	**IM Lecture Material:** *Is Homosexuality a Sexual Orientation or a Sexual Preference?*
Perspectives on Homosexuality p. 279 • Historical Perspectives • Cross-Species Perspectives • Attitudes Toward Homosexuality in Contemporary Society • Biological Perspectives • Psychological Perspectives • Gender Nonconformity	L. O. 4 ....p. 279 L. O. 5 ....p. 281 L. O. 6 ....p. 282 Notes ....p. 284 Discussion Question.....p. 284 Notes ....p. 285 Discussion Question.....p. 285 Notes ....p. 286 Teaching Tip ....p. 287 L. O. 7 ....p. 288 Notes ....p. 289 Discussion Question.....p. 290 L. O. 8 ....p. 291 Discussion Question.....p. 294	**CNN:** *Gay Asylum* **CNN:** *Gay Bashing* **CNN:** *Gay Census* **IM Lecture Material:** *Freud on Homosexuality* **IM Lecture Material:** *A Panel Discussion: Common Questions About Homosexuality*
Adjustment of Gay Males and Lesbians p. 295	L. O. 9 ....p. 295	**IM Activity:** *Thinking About Whether Homosexuality is a Mental Disorder*
Gay Identity: Coming to Terms with Being Gay p. 297 • Coming Out	L. O. 10 ....p. 297 Notes ....p. 297 Discussion Question.....p. 298 Notes ....p. 298	
Patterns of Gay Male and Lesbian Sexual Activity p. 299 • Sexual Techniques	L. O. 11 ....p. 299	**IM Activity:** *Thinking About Whether or Not Gay Men and Lesbians Make Better Lovers*
Gay Lifestyles p. 299 • Lifestyle Differences Between Gay Males and Lesbians • Variations in Gay Lifestyles	L. O. 12 ....p. 299	**CNN:** *Lesbian Parents*

INSTRUCTOR'S SECTION

CHAPTER 11
Chapter-at-a-Glance
Conception, Pregnancy, and Childbirth

Chapter Outline	Instructional Ideas	Supplemental Materials
Conception: Against All Odds p. 306 • Optimizing the Chances of Conception • Selecting the Gender of Your Child	L. O. 1............................p. 306 L. O. 2............................p. 307 L. O. 3............................p. 309 Notes ....p. 309 Discussion Question......p. 309	**Transparency 20:** *Human Sperm Swarming Around an Ovum in a Fallopian Tube* **Transparency 21:** *The Ovarian Cycle, Conception, and the Early Days of the Germinal Stage* **Transparency 22:** *Determination of Gender*
Infertility and Alternative Ways of Becoming Parents p. 310 • Male Fertility Problems • Female Fertility Problems	Discussion Question......p. 311 L. O. 4............................p. 311 Discussion Question......p. 312 Notes ....p. 312 L. O. 5............................p. 313	**IM Activity:** *Thinking About Surrogate Motherhood: Who Is the "Real" Mother?* **CNN:** *Pregnant Grandmother* **CNN:** *My Mother the Fetus*
Pregnancy p. 314 • Early Signs of Pregnancy • Pregnancy Tests • Early Effects of Pregnancy • Miscarriage (Spontaneous Abortion) • Sex During Pregnancy • Psychological Changes During Pregnancy	L. O. 6............................p. 314 Teaching Tip ....p. 314	**IM Lecture Material:** *"France Wants Me to Have This Baby: The Story of a Pregnant Woman in Paris"*
Prenatal Development p. 321 • The Germinal Stage • The Embryonic Stage • The Fetal Stage • Environmental Influences on Prenatal Development • Chromosomal and Genetic Abnormalities	L. O. 7............................p. 321 L. O. 8............................p. 325 Notes ....p. 328 L. O. 9............................p. 331	**Transparency 23:** *Human Embryos and Fetuses* **Transparency 24:** *Changes in Body Proportions from the Early Prenatal Period to Adulthood* **Transparency 25:** *Prenatal Development* **Transparency 26:** *Amniocentesis and Chorionic Villus Sampling* **Transparency 27:** *Critical Periods in Prenatal Development*
Childbirth p. 334 • The Stages of Childbirth • Methods of Childbirth • Alternatives to the Hospital: Where Should a Child Be Born?	L. O. 10..........................p. 335 Notes ....p. 335 L. O. 11..........................p. 336 Notes ....p. 338 L. O. 12..........................p. 339 Discussion Question......p. 339	**Transparency 28:** *The Three Stages of Labor* **CNN:** *Midwives*

INSTRUCTORS' SECTION

CHAPTER 11 (continued)
Chapter-at-a-Glance
Conception, Pregnancy, and Childbirth

Chapter Outline	Instructional Ideas	Supplemental Materials
Birth Problems p. 339 • Anoxia • Preterm and Low-Birth-Weight Children	L. O. 13........................p. 339	**CNN:** *Black Health Care* **IM Lecture Material:** *Some Notes on Prenatal Care: A Tale of Three Neighborhoods and Two Countries*
The Postpartum Period p. 341 • Maternal Depression • Breast-Feeding Versus Bottle-Feeding • Resumption of Ovulation and Menstruation • Resumption of Sexual Activity	L. O. 14........................p. 341 L. O. 15........................p. 342 Notes ....p. 342 Notes ....p. 343	**CNN:** *Unequal Treatment*

CHAPTER 12
Chapter-at-a-Glance
Contraception and Abortion

Chapter Outline	Instructional Ideas	Supplemental Materials
Contraception p. 348 • Contraception in the United States: The Legal Battle • Selecting a Method of Contraception	Discussion Question.....p. 348 L. O. 1..........................p. 348 L. O. 2..........................p. 349 Notes ....p. 349 L. O. 3..........................p. 350 Notes ....p. 350 Notes ....p. 350	**Transparency 29:** *Contraception Methods Used by U.S. Women*
Methods of Contraception p. 351 • Oral Contraceptives (The Pill) • Intrauterine Devices • The Diaphragm • Spermicides • The Contraceptive Sponge • The Cervical Cap • Condoms • Douching • Withdrawal (Coitus Interruptus) • Fertility Awareness Methods (Rhythm Methods) • Sterilization • New Developments in Contraception	L. O. 4..........................p. 351 Teaching Tip ....p. 351 L. O. 5..........................p. 356 L. O. 6..........................p. 358 L. O. 7..........................p. 359 Notes ....p. 361 L. O. 8..........................p. 363 Teaching Tip ....p. 366 L. O. 9..........................p. 366 L. O. 10........................p. 367 Discussion Question.....p. 368 L. O. 11........................p. 369 Notes ....p. 370 Discussion Question.....p. 372 L. O. 12........................p. 372 Notes ....p. 374 Notes ....p. 375	**Transparency 30:** *Insertion and Checking of the Diaphragm* **Transparency 31:** *The Application of Spermicidal Foam* **Transparency 32:** *Vasectomy* **Transparency 33:** *Laparoscopy* **Transparency 34:** *The Female Condom* **CNN:** *Norplant* **CNN:** *Male Pill* **IM Lecture Material:** *Birth Control for Beavers?*

CHAPTER 12 *(continued)*
Chapter-at-a-Glance
Contraception and Abortion

Chapter Outline	Instructional Ideas	Supplemental Materials
Abortion p. 376 • Historical and Legal Perspectives on Abortion • Methods of Abortion • Psychological Consequences of Abortion	Notes ....p. 376 L. O. 13......................p. 378 Notes ....p. 379 Notes ....p. 379 Notes ....p. 380 Discussion Question.....p. 380 Notes ....p. 381 L. O. 14......................p. 381 Notes ....p. 383 L. O. 15......................p. 385 Notes ....p. 386	**Transparency 35:** *Legal Abortion in the United States by Age* **CNN:** *Russian Abortion* **CNN:** *Abortion Doctor* **IM Activity:** *Thinking About the Differences in African American and White Attitudes Toward Abortion* **Transparency 36:** *Vacuum Aspiration* **CNN:** *RU-486*

CHAPTER 13
Chapter-at-a-Glance
Sexuality in Childhood and Adolescence

Chapter Outline	Instructional Ideas	Supplemental Materials
Infancy (0 to 2 Years): A Search for the Origins of Human Sexuality p. 390 • The Infant's Capacity for Sexual Response • Masturbation • Genital Play	L. O. 1...........................p. 390 Discussion Question.....p. 392	**Early Childhood (3 to 8 Years)** p. 393 • Masturbation • Heterosexual Behavior
• Same-Gender Sexual Behavior	Teaching Tip ....p. 393 L. O. 2........................p. 394 L. O. 3........................p. 394	**IM Activity:** *Thinking About Childhood Messages About Sexuality*
Preadolescence (9 to 13 Years) p. 395 • Masturbation • Heterosexual Behavior • Same-Gender Sexual Behavior • Sources of Sexual Information	L. O. 4..........................p. 395 L. O. 5..........................p. 397 Discussion Question.....p. 398	**CNN:** *Chastity Class*

CHAPTER 13 *(continued)*
Chapter-at-a-Glance
Sexuality in Childhood and Adolescence

Chapter Outline	Instructional Ideas	Supplemental Materials
Adolescence p. 399 • Puberty • Masturbation • Heterosexual Behavior • Same-Gender Sexual Behavior	L. O. 6...........................p. 400 Discussion Question......p. 400 Teaching Tip ....p. 401 L. O. 7...........................p. 402 Teaching Tip ....p. 403 L. O. 8...........................p. 405 Discussion Question......p. 405 Notes ....p. 406 Notes ....p. 407 L. O. 9...........................p. 409 L. O. 10.........................p. 411 Discussion Question......p. 412 L. O. 11.........................p. 413 Discussion Question......p. 414 L. O. 12.........................p. 414 L. O. 13.........................p. 415 Discussion Question......p. 416 L. O. 14.........................p. 418 Notes ....p. 418	**Transparency 37:** *Stages of Pubertal Development (Part One)* **Transparency 38:** *Stages of Pubertal Development (Part Two)* **IM Activity:** *Thinking About Messages About Menstruation* **IM Activity:** *Thinking About Contraceptive Distribution in Schools* **CNN:** *Safe Sex Moms* **CNN:** *Education and Morality* **CNN:** *Israel, Pizza and Sex*

CHAPTER 14
Chapter-at-a-Glance
Sexuality in Adulthood

Chapter Outline	Instructional Ideas	Supplemental Materials
Singlehood p. 422	Teaching Tip ....p. 422 L. O. 1...........................p. 422	**IM Lecture Material:** *Snug in Their Beds for Christmas Eve—In Japan, December 24th Has Become the Hottest Night of the Year*
Cohabitation: Darling, Would You Be My POSSLQ? p. 423 • Who Are the Cohabitors? • Reasons for Cohabitation • Style of Cohabitation • Cohabitation and Later Marriage: A Benefit or a Risk?	L. O. 2...........................p. 423 Notes ....p. 424 Notes ....p. 424 Notes ....p. 425	
Marriage p. 426 • Historical Perspectives • Why Do People Marry? • Types of Marriage • Whom Do We Marry: Are Marriages Made in Heaven or in the Neighborhood?	L. O. 3...........................p. 426 Discussion Question......p. 427 L. O. 4...........................p. 428 Notes ....p. 428 L. O. 5...........................p. 429	**IM Lecture Material:** *Quotes About Marriage* **IM Activity:** *Do You Endorse Traditional or Liberal Marital Roles?* **IM Activity:** *Are People Naturally Monogamous*

Chapter Outline	Instructional Ideas	Supplemental Materials
Marital Sexuality p. 432 • The Sexual Revolution Hits Home • Sexual Satisfaction	L. O. 6..........................p. 432 Discussion Question......p. 434 Discussion Question......p. 434	
Extramarital Sex p. 435 • Patterns of Extramarital Sex • Attitudes Toward Extramarital Sex • Effects of Extramarital Sex • Swinging	L. O. 7..........................p. 436 Discussion Question......p. 437	
Divorce p. 438 • The Cost of Divorce	L. O. 8..........................p. 438 Notes ....p. 439 Notes ....p. 439 Teaching Tip ....p. 440	**CNN:** *Elderly Divorce*
Alternative Forms of Marriage p. 440 • Open Marriage • Group Marriage	L. O. 9..........................p. 440	**IM Lecture Material:** *Interracial Relationships: Race, Sex, and Stereotypes*
Sex in the Later Years p. 441 • Physical Changes • Patterns of Sexual Activity	L. O. 10........................p. 441 Teaching Tip ....p. 445	
Sex and Disability p. 446 • Cerebral Palsy • Spinal-Cord Injuries • Sensory Disabilities • Other Physical Disabilities and Impairments • Psychological Disabilities	L. O. 11........................p. 446 Discussion Question......p. 446 L. O. 12........................p. 447	

CHAPTER 15
Chapter-at-a-Glance
Sexual Dysfunctions and Sex Therapy

Chapter Outline	Instructional Ideas	Supplemental Materials
Types of Sexual Dysfunctions p. 455 • Sexual Desire Disorders • Sexual Arousal Disorders • Orgasm Disorders • Sexual Pain Disorders	Discussion Question......p. 454 Teaching Tip ....p. 455 L. O. 1..........................p. 456 Discussion Question......p. 456 L. O. 2..........................p. 458 L. O. 3..........................p. 460 L. O. 4..........................p. 462	**IM Lecture Material:** *On "Frigid" Women and "Impotent" Men*

CHAPTER 15 *(continued)*
Chapter-at-a-Glance
Sexual Dysfunctions and Sex Therapy

Chapter Outline	Instructional Ideas	Supplemental Materials
Origins of Sexual Dysfunctions p. 463 • Organic Causes • Psychosocial Causes	L. O. 5............................p. 463 L. O. 6............................p. 467	**IM Activity:** *The Sexual Anxiety Inventory* **IM Lecture Material:** *Does Anxiety Always Interfere with Sexual Performance?* **Transparency 39:** *Barlow's Model of Sexual Dysfunction*
Treatment of Sexual Dysfunctions p. 471 • The Masters-and-Johnson Approach • The Helen Singer Kaplan Approach • Disorders of Sexual Desire • Disorders of Sexual Arousal • Orgasm Disorders • Sexual Pain Disorders • Evaluation of Sex Therapy • Biological Treatments of Erectile Dysfunction	L. O. 7............................p. 471 Discussion•Question......p. 471 L. O. 8............................p. 472 L. O. 9............................p. 473 Discussion Question......p. 473 Teaching Tip ....p. 473 L. O. 10..........................p. 480 L. O. 11..........................p. 481 Discussion Question......p. 481	**IM Activity:** *Tracking the Thoughts that "Pop" into Your Head During Sex* **IM Lecture Material:** *The Use of Sexual Surrogates*
How Do You Find a Qualified Sex Therapist p. 483	L. O. 12..........................p. 483	

CHAPTER 16
Chapter-at-a-Glance
Sexually Transmitted Diseases

Chapter Outline	Instructional Ideas	Supplemental Materials
An Epidemic p. 489	L. O. 1............................p. 489 Teaching Tip ....p. 489 Teaching Tip ....p. 490	**CNN:** *Sex Disease*
Bacterial Diseases p. 492 • Gonorrhea • Syphilis • Chlamydia • Other Bacterial Diseases	L. O. 2............................p. 491 L. O. 3............................p. 498 Notes ....p. 500 L. O. 4............................p. 501 Notes ....p. 501 L. O. 5............................p. 502	**CNN:** *Syphilis Surge* **CNN:** *STD Increases*
Vaginal Infections p. 503 • Bacterial Vaginosis • Candidiasis • Trichomoniasis	L. O. 6............................p. 503	
Viral Diseases p. 506 • Herpes • Viral Hepatitis • Genital Warts • Molluscum Contagiosum	L. O. 7............................p. 506 Discussion Question......p. 510 L. O. 8............................p. 510 Notes ....p. 511 L. O. 9............................p. 511 Notes ....p. 511	

Chapter Outline	Instructional Ideas	Supplemental Materials
Ectoparasitic Infestations p. 512 • Pediculosis • Scabies	L. O. 10.........................p. 513 L. O. 11.........................p. 513	
Prevention of STDs: **It's More Than Safer Sex** p. 513	L. O. 12.........................p. 513 Notes ....p. 514 Teaching Tip ....p. 514 Notes ....p. 515 Teaching Tips...............p. 515	**CNN:** *Men, Sex and Condoms*

CHAPTER 17
Chapter-at-a-Glance
Acquired Immunodeficiency Syndrome (AIDS)

Chapter Outline	Instructional Ideas	Supplemental Materials
Prevalence of HIV Infection **and AIDS** p. 521	L. O. 1.........................p. 521 L. O. 2.........................p. 521 Notes ....p. 523 Notes ....p. 524	**Transparency 40:** *Estimated Rates of HIV Transmission Throughout the World* **Transparency 41:** *AIDS Cases Within the United States—Comparison of 1991 to 1993* **Transparency 42:** *AIDS Cases by Exposure Category (a)* **Transparency 43:** *AIDS Cases by Exposure Category (b)* **Transparency 44:** *AIDS Cases by Exposure Category (c)* **Transparency 45:** *AIDS Cases by Race* **Transparency 46:** *AIDS Cases by Gender* **Transparency 47:** *HIV and AIDS: A World Epidemic* **CNN:** *Asia AIDS* **CNN:** *AIDS India* **CNN:** *Japan World AIDS Day* **IM Activity:** *AIDS and Divine Retribution*
The Immune System and AIDS p. 525 • The Immune System • Effects of HIV on the Immune System	L. O. 3.........................p. 525 L. O. 4.........................p. 526	

CHAPTER 17 *(continued)*
Chapter-at-a-Glance
Acquired Immunodeficiency Syndrome (AIDS)

Chapter Outline	Instructional Ideas	Supplemental Materials
Progression of HIV Infection and AIDS p. 526	L. O. 5............................p. 526	
Transmission p. 529 • Factors Affecting the Risk of Sexual Transmission • How HIV Is Not Transmitted • Transmission via Medical or Dental Treatment • Women and AIDS	L. O. 6......................p. 529 Teaching Tip ....p. 530 L. O. 7......................p. 531 L. O. 8......................p. 532 L. O. 9......................p. 534 Teaching Tip ....p. 535	**IM Lecture Material:** *Women with AIDS: Agonizing Choices About Motherhood* **CNN:** *AIDS Watch: The Iron Curtain* **CNN:** *AIDS Mom*
Diagnosis of HIV Infection and AIDS p. 537 • Issues Concerning Testing for HIV Infection	L. O. 10......................p. 537 Discussion Question.....p. 539 Discussion Question.....p. 539	**IM Activity:** *Should You and Your Partner Be Tested for HIV?*
Treatment of HIV Infection and AIDS p. 540	L. O. 11......................p. 540 Notes ....p. 540	
Psychological Adjustment of Persons with HIV Infections and AIDS p. 541	L. O. 12......................p. 541	
Prevention p. 542 • Coming of Age in the Age of AIDS • Reducing the Risk of HIV Infection	L. O. 13......................p. 542 L. O. 14......................p. 544 Notes ....p. 545 Discussion Question.....p. 546 Discussion Question.....p. 548 L. O. 15......................p. 549	**IM Lecture Material:** *College Students: Knowledge and Risky Behavior* **IM Activity:** *What Do You Say Now? Making Sex Safe(r) in the Age of AIDS* **CNN:** *Teen AIDS*

CHAPTER 18
Chapter-at-a-Glance
Atypical Sexual Variations

Chapter Outline	Instructional Ideas	Supplemental Materials
Normal Versus Deviant Sexual Behavior p. 556		
The Paraphilias p. 557 • Fetishism • Transvestism • Exhibitionism • Obscene Telephone Calling • Voyeurism • Sexual Masochism • Sexual Sadism • Frotteurism • Other Paraphilias	L. O. 1......................p. 557 Teaching Tip ....p. 558 Discussion Question.....p. 558 L. O. 2......................p. 558 L. O. 3......................p. 559 Discussion Question.....p. 559 L. O. 4......................p. 560 Discussion Question.....p. 562 L. O. 5......................p. 563 L. O. 6......................p. 565 L. O. 7......................p. 566 L. O. 8......................p. 570 Notes ....p. 574	**IM Lecture Material:** *Cases of Fetishism* **IM Lecture Material:** *A Case of Exhibitionism* **IM Lecture Material:** *Exhibitionists, Masturbation, and Motivation* **IM Lecture Material:** *A Case of Voyeurism*

Chapter Outline		Instructional Ideas	Supplemental Materials
Theoretical Perspectives • Biological Perspectives • Psychoanalytic Perspectives • Learning Perspectives • Sociological Perspectives • An Integrated Perspective: The "Lovemap"	p. 574	L. O. 9..............................p. 574 L. O. 10...........................p. 575 L. O. 11...........................p. 575 L. O. 12...........................p. 577 L. O. 13...........................p. 578 Discussion Question.....p. 578	
Treatment of the Paraphilias • Psychotherapy • Behavior Therapy • Biochemical Approaches	p. 578	L. O. 14...........................p. 578	

CHAPTER 19
Chapter-at-a-Glance
Sexual Coercion

Chapter Outline		Instructional Ideas	Supplemental Materials
Rape • Incidence of Rape • Types of Rape • Social Attitudes and Myths That Encourage Rape • Sociocultural Factors in Rape • Psychological Characteristics of Rapists • Adjustment of Rape Survivors • Treatment of Rape Survivors • Rape Prevention	p. 586	L. O. 1.............................p. 586 L. O. 2.............................p. 589 Discussion Question.....p. 590 Teaching Tip ....p. 591 Notes ....p. 592 Notes ....p. 592 Discussion Question.....p. 593 Notes ....p. 594 L. O. 3.............................p. 594 Notes ....p. 595 L. O. 4.............................p. 595 L. O. 5.............................p. 598 L. O. 6.............................p. 601 Discussion Question.....p. 603	**Transparency 48:** *Age of Rape Survivors and Percentages Who Knew Their Assailants* **CNN:** *Rape Reporting* **CNN:** *Comfort Women in the Philippines* **IM Activity:** *Cultural Myths That Support Rape* **IM Lecture Material:** *Romance and a Little Rape*
Verbal Sexual Coercion	p. 605		
Sexual Abuse of Children • What Is Child Sexual Abuse? • Patterns of Abuse • Pedophilia • Incest • Effects of Child Sexual Abuse • Prevention of Child Sexual Abuse • Treatment of Survivors of Child Sexual Abuse	p. 605	L. O. 7.............................p. 605 Notes ....p. 607 L. O. 8.............................p. 608 L. O. 9.............................p. 609 Teaching Tip ....p. 609 Notes ....p. 610 L. O. 10...........................p. 611 L. O. 11...........................p. 612 Notes ....p. 613 Teaching Tip ....p. 613	
Treatment of Rapists and Child Molesters	p. 614	L. O. 12...........................p. 614	

CHAPTER 19 (continued)
Chapter-at-a-Glance
Sexual Coercion

Chapter Outline	Instructional Ideas	Supplemental Materials
Sexual Harassment p. 615 • Sexual Harassment in the Workplace • Sexual Harassment on Campus • Sexual Harassment in the Schools • How to Resist Sexual Harassment	L. O. 13.......................p. 615 Notes ....p. 615 Notes ....p. 616 Notes ....p. 616 Discussion Question.....p. 616 Notes ....p. 617 L. O. 14.......................p. 617 Notes ....p. 618 Teaching Tip ....p. 619	**IM Activity:** *Thinking Critically About Where to Draw the Line on Sexual Harassment* **CNN:** *Sexual Harassment in Schools*

CHAPTER 20
Chapter-at-a-Glance
Commercial Sex, Obscenity, and Censorship

Chapter Outline	Instructional Ideas	Supplemental Materials
The World of Commercial Sex: A Disneyland for Adults p. 624		
Prostitution p. 624 • Incidence of Prostitution in Contemporary U.S. Society • Types of Female Prostitution • Characteristics of Female Prostitutes • Customers of Female Prostitutes • Male Prostitution • HIV, AIDS, and Prostitution	L. O. 1.........................p. 625 Discussion Question.....p. 625 L. O. 2.........................p. 626 Notes ....p. 627 Notes ....p. 627 Discussion Question.....p. 628 L. O. 3.........................p. 629 Discussion Question.....p. 630 L. O. 4.........................p. 630 Notes ....p. 631 L. O. 5.........................p. 632 Notes ....p. 632 L. O. 6.........................p. 634	**IM Activity:** *Thinking Critically About Whether Prostitution Should Be Legalized* **CNN:** *Bangkok Sex Tours* **IM Lecture Material:** *Is the Parisian Romance with Prostitutes Drawing to an End?* **IM Lecture Material:** *A Cross-Cultural Comparison: The Danish Experience*
Pornography and Obscenity p. 635 • What Is Pornographic? • Pornography and the Law • Prevalence and Use of Erotica and Pornography • Pornography and Sexual Coercion	L. O. 7.........................p. 635 L. O. 8.........................p. 636 Teaching Tip ....p. 636 Notes ....p. 637 L. O. 9.........................p. 638 Notes ....p. 638 L. O. 10.......................p. 639 Notes ....p. 640 Notes ....p. 646	
Sex in Advertising p. 648 • Advertising and Gender-Role Stereotypes	L. O. 11.......................p. 648 L. O. 12.......................p. 649 Teaching Tip ....p. 649 Teaching Tip ....p. 649	

CHAPTER 21
Chapter-at-a-Glance
Making Responsible Sexual Decisions—An Epilogue

Chapter Outline		Instructional Ideas	Supplemental Materials
Choices, Information, and Decision Making • Conflict • Decisions, Decisions, Decisions…	p. 654	L. O. 1..........................p. 654 Discussion Question.....p. 654	
Value Systems • Legalism • Situation Ethics • Ethical Relativism • Hedonism • Asceticism • Utilitarianism • Rationalism	p. 655	L. O. 2..........................p. 655 Teaching Tip ....p. 658	
The Balance Sheet for Decision Making	p. 658		
Back to You	p. 660		**IM Activity:** *Balance Sheet for Decision Making*

INSTRUCTORS' SECTION

Jeffery S.
NEVID
St. John's University

Lois
FICHNER-RATHUS
Trenton State College

Spencer A.
RATHUS
St. John's University

SECOND EDITION

HUMAN SEXUALITY IN
A WORLD OF DIVERSITY

ALLYN AND BACON

Boston • London • Toronto • Sydney • Tokyo • Singapore

Vice President and Publisher: Susan Badger
Executive Editor: Laura Pearson
Editorial Assistant: Jennifer Normandin
Marketing Manager: Joyce Nilsen
Production Administrator: Deborah Brown
Production Coordinator: Eleanor Sabini
Text Designer: Melinda Grosser (*Silk*)
Cover Administrator: Linda Knowles
Cover Designer: Susan Paradise
Composition Buyer: Linda Cox
Manufacturing Buyer: Louise Richardson
Manager, Electronic Production: Meredith Garniss
Electronic Project Manager: Gayle A. Robertson
Electronic Composition: Janine Hosseini, Nancy Jones, Stuart Cooke

Library of Congress Cataloging-in-Publication Data

Nevid, Jeffrey S.
    Human sexuality in a world of diversity / Jeffrey S. Nevid,
Lois Fichner-Rathus, Spencer A. Rathus.   2nd ed.
        p.   cm.
    Spencer Rathus's name appears first on the earlier edition.
    Includes bibliographical references and index.
    ISBN 0-205-16407-2
    1. Sex. I. Fichner-Rathus, Lois, 1953–   II. Rathus, Spencer A.
HQ21.R23 1995   94-33693
306.7–dc 20   CIP

Printed in the United States of America

10 9 8 7 6 5 4 3 2 1   99 98 97 96 95

Photo Credits: **Chapter Opener Art:** Chapter 1: Ilona Anderson, *The Rites of Spring*; Chapter 2: Ilona Anderson, *The View Finder*; Chapter 3: Bonnie Griffith; Chapter 4: Bonnie Griffith; Chapter 5: Ilona Anderson, *Archeaology of Desire*; Chapter 6: Ilona Anderson, *Night in New Orleans*; Chapter 7: Ilona Anderson, *Saturday Afternoon*; Chapter 8: Ilona Anderson, *Riders in the Chariot*; Chapter 9: Ilona Anderson, *Les Demoiselles*; Chapter 10: Ilona Anderson, *In an African Tomb IV*; Chapter 11: Bonnie Griffith, *The Evolution of Forms*; Chapter 12: Bonnie Griffith; Chapter 13: Ilona Anderson, *Tears of Eros*; Chapter14: Ilona Anderson, *Palm Wine*; Chapter 15: Ilona Anderson, *Old Haunts*; Chapter16: Ilona Anderson, *Elle*; Chapter 17: Ilona Anderson, *Journal of the Plague Years*; Chapter 18: Ilona Anderson, *City of Night*; Chapter 19: Ilona Anderson, *Shout in the Street*; Chapter 20: Ilona Anderson, *Strawberry Ice*; Chapter 21: Ilona Anderson, *Le Cirque Magnifique*.
Chapter 1: p. 2: Courtesy of Cable News Network, Inc.; p. 9: D.H. Hessell /Stock Boston; p. 11: Ali Meyer/The Bridgeman Library Ltd; p. 13: North Wind Picture Archives; p. 20: Tom Sobolik/Black Star; p. 23: North Wind Picture Archives; p. 25: Wolfgang Kaehler; p. 27: Lyrl Ahern; **Chapter 2:** p. 39: Courtesy of Farrall Instruments; p. 42: Reprinted by permission of the Kinsey Institute for Research in Sex, Gender and Reproduction, Inc.; p. 47: (left) John

The photo credits are continued on page 733.

CONTENTS

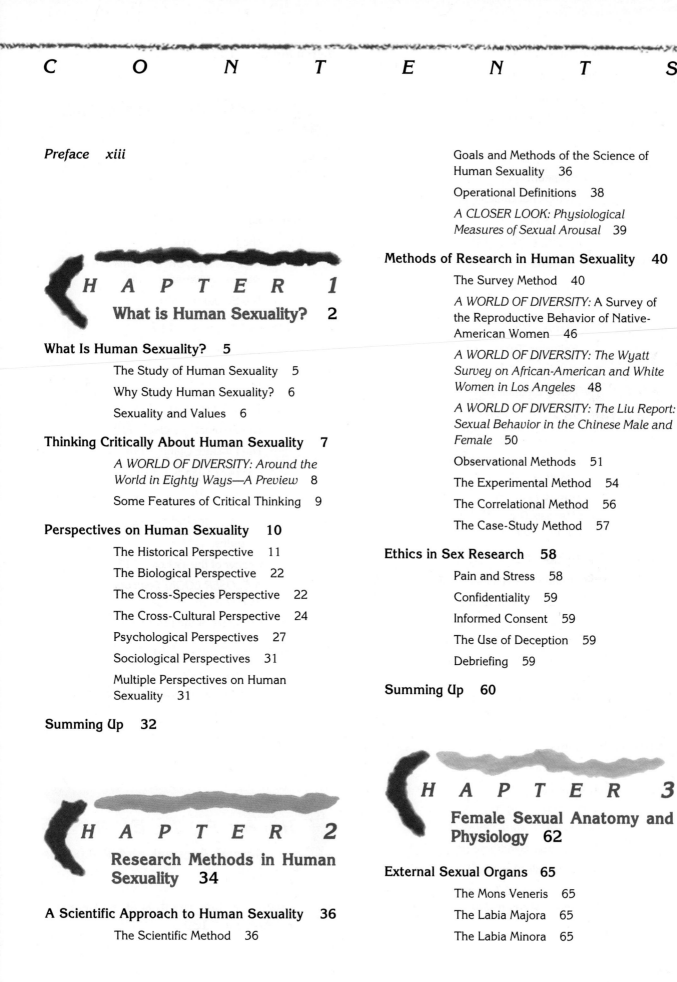

CHAPTER 4
Male Sexual Anatomy and Physiology   104

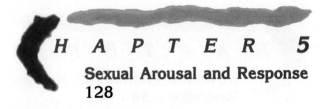

CHAPTER 5
Sexual Arousal and Response   128

C H A P T E R   6

Gender Identity and Gender Roles   160

C H A P T E R 7
Attraction and Love 192

C H A P T E R 8
Relationships, Intimacy, and Communication 216

C H A P T E R 9
Sexual Techniques and Behavior Patterns 242

C H A P T E R   10

Sexual Orientation   270

C H A P T E R   11

Conception, Pregnancy, and Childbirth   304

C H A P T E R   12

Contraception and Abortion
346

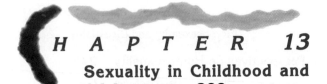

C H A P T E R   13

Sexuality in Childhood and
Adolescence   388

H A P T E R   14
Sexuality in Adulthood   420

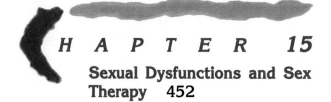

H A P T E R   15
Sexual Dysfunctions and Sex Therapy   452

H A P T E R 16
Sexually Transmitted Diseases 486

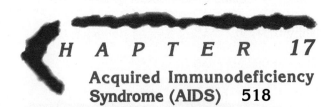

H A P T E R 17
Acquired Immunodeficiency Syndrome (AIDS) 518

C H A P T E R   18
Atypical Sexual Variations   554

C H A P T E R   19
Sexual Coercion   584

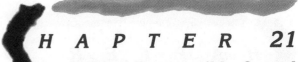

There are more things in heaven and earth, Horatio,
Than are dreamt of in your philosophy.
Shakespeare, *Hamlet*

There are indeed more kinds of people in this world, and more ways in which people experience their sexuality, than most of us might imagine. Human sexuality may be intimately related to human biology, but it is embedded within the sociocultural fabric of human society. For this reason, a core theme of the Second Edition of *Human Sexuality in a World of Diversity* remains its multicultural perspective.

THEMES

Four themes are threaded through the Second Edition of *Human Sexuality in a World of Diversity*: the rich diversity that exists in gender roles, sexual attitudes, and sexual behaviors and customs; critical thinking; making responsible sexual decisions; and sexual health.

FOCUS ON DIVERSITY

The United States is a nation of hundreds of different ethnic and religious groups, many of whom endorse culturally distinctive beliefs about appropriate gender roles for men and women and sexual practices and customs. Diversity is yet greater within the global village of the world's nearly 200 nations and those nations' own distinctive subcultures. *Human Sexuality in a World of Diversity* incorporates a multicultural, multiethnic perspective that reflects the diversity of sexual experience in our own society and around the world, thereby broadening a student's understanding of the range of cultural differences in sexual attitudes and behavior. Exploring diversity in human sexual experience can encourage respect for people who hold differing beliefs and attitudes. We encourage students to question what is appropriate for women and men in terms of social roles and sexual conduct in light of cultural traditions and standards.

FOCUS ON CRITICAL THINKING

Today's students are so inundated with information about gender and sexuality that it is difficult to sort truth from fiction. Not only do politicians, theologians, and community leaders influence our gender- and sex-related atti-

tudes and behaviors, but newspapers, television programs, and other media also brim with features about gender roles and issues concerning human sexuality.

Critical thinking involves being skeptical of information that is presented in print, or uttered by authority figures or celebrities, or passed along by friends. Critical thinking requires thoughtful analysis and probing of the claims and arguments of others in the light of the evidence. Moreover, it requires a willingness to challenge conventional wisdom and common knowledge that many of us take for granted. It means scrutinizing definitions of terms, evaluating the premises or assumptions that underlie arguments, and examining the logic of arguments.

Throughout the book we raise issues that demand critical thinking. These issues are intended to stimulate student interest in analyzing and evaluating their beliefs and attitudes toward gender roles and sexuality in light of the accumulated scientific evidence.

FOCUS ON RESPONSIBLE SEXUAL DECISION MAKING

Decision making is deeply intertwined with our sexual experiences. We can decide whom to date, how and when to become sexually intimate, and whether to practice contraception and which methods to use. We can (no, we must!) decide how we will protect ourselves against AIDS and other sexually transmitted diseases.

Responsible sexual decision making is based not only on acquiring accurate information, but also on carefully evaluating this information according to one's own moral values. We encourage students to make active sexual decisions based on the information presented and their own values, needs, and interests, rather than simply go along with the crowd or accede to the demands of one's partner.

Throughout the text we provide students with the information they need to make responsible decisions for themselves about matters such as sexual health, gender roles, sexual behavior, contraception, abortion, and ways of preventing sexually transmitted diseases, especially HIV infection and AIDS.

In the epilogue, "Making Responsible Sexual Decisions," we explain the major ethical systems that are used in moral reasoning and provide a decision-making model that will help students weigh the pluses and minuses of the choices they face.

FOCUS ON SEXUAL HEALTH

Human Sexuality in a World of Diversity places a strong emphasis on issues relating to sexual health, including extensive coverage of such topics as HIV/AIDS and other STDs, recent developments in contraception and reproductive technologies, breast cancer, menstrual distress, sexual functioning and disabilities, and diseases that affect the reproductive system. The text encourages students to take an active role in health promotion, and includes health-oriented exercises and features, such as techniques for breast and testicular self-examination, reducing the risk of HIV infection, and ways of coping with menstrual discomfort.

BREADTH OF COVERAGE

We realized when setting out to write the first edition of this book that a contemporary human sexuality textbook must provide a comprehensive review of the latest scientific findings in the field. Authors of textbooks in a field as far reaching as human sexuality face a daunting task of keeping up with new scientific developments, especially in areas in which new information is reported at a dizzying pace, such as contraception and new reproductive technologies, and especially, sexually transmitted diseases. We hope you found that our first edition met this challenge and will hold us accountable in this and future editions to remain current and relevant. Toward this end, we have incorporated more than 500 new citations to scientific research reported in just the past two years.

Comprehensive in scope and theoretically balanced in coverage, *Human Sexuality in a World of Diversity* helps students acquire a broader view of human sexual experience by examining multiple perspectives on human sexuality—historical, biological, psychological, cultural, and sociological. The textbook contains comprehensive coverage of the core topics in the field of human sexuality, including research methods, sexual anatomy and physiology, sexual arousal and response, gender roles, attraction, love, intimate relationships, sexual communication, sexual techniques, sexual orientation, conception, contraception, abortion, prenatal development, childbirth, sexual behavior across the life span, sexual dysfunctions and sex therapy, sexually transmitted diseases, atypical variations in sexual behavior, sexual coercion, and commercial sex. *Human Sexuality in a World of Diversity* emphasizes pressing issues that are likely to confront or concern students today, such as sexual harassment, date rape, contraception, and the threat of AIDS. Students today are the first generation to come of age with the threat of a deadly disease, AIDS, hanging over every sexual decision. Consequently, we felt we could do no less than provide full-chapter coverage on the important topics of HIV infection and AIDS and incorporate the latest available

information about prevalence, diagnosis, treatment, and prevention. (The AIDS chapter (Chapter 17) received the most revisions in this edition, befitting the developments that have been reported since the first edition went to press).

Though we discuss the threats posed by HIV and AIDS with healthy respect, we do not approach the topic with irrational fear. We also provide a great deal of emphasis (see Chapter 16) on other sexually transmitted diseases, such as chlamydia and genital warts, that may be less deadly than AIDS but represent much wider threats, especially among the college population.

FEATURES

Human Sexuality in a World of Diversity contains various features designed to stimulate student interest and enhance understanding.

A WORLD OF DIVERSITY

A World of Diversity boxes in each chapter highlight the rich variety of human sexual customs and practices in our own society and around the world. Viewing human sexuality in a multicultural context helps students better understand how cultural beliefs, values, and attitudes can influence the expression of sexuality. Students may come to understand that their partners, who may not share the same ethnic or religious heritage as themselves, may feel differently than they do about sexual intimacy. Students will learn about cultural differences that relate to gender roles, sexual orientation, sexual jealousy, and premarital and extramarital sexual patterns.

A CLOSER LOOK

A Closer Look boxes include an in-depth examination of social issues that are in the public eye (e.g., "Should Schools Distribute Condoms?"), as well as illustrative case histories, self-scoring questionnaires (e.g., the STD Attitude Scale), and skill-building exercises (e.g., developing date-seeking skills, coping with loneliness).

WRITING STYLE

Human Sexuality in a World of Diversity conveys the excitement of the science of human sexuality in all of its dimensions. The text is written in a style intended to capture student interest in the material and at a level that students will find compelling and accessible, but not over-simplified or patronizing. The selective use of humor and personal asides builds interest and enlivens descriptions.

LEARNING AIDS

Perhaps more than anything else, a textbook is a teaching tool—a device for presenting material in a way that stimulates learning and critical thinking. *Human Sexuality in a World of Diversity* was designed to maximize this goal by means of such pedagogical aids as the following:

1. **Chapter Outlines.** Each chapter begins with an outline that organizes the subject matter for the student. Headings were created to be succinct and to promote student interest in the topics they address.
2. **"Truth or Fiction?"** and **"Truth or Fiction Revisited"** Sections. Appearing at the beginning of each chapter, the "Truth or Fiction" sections challenge common-sense assumptions, stereotypes, and folklore, while highlighting fascinating research findings. Posed as statements that allow students to test their prior knowledge, we have found these "Truth or Fiction" items to be effective ways of stimulating and challenging students. "Truth or Fiction Revisited" sections are interspersed throughout each chapter and provide feedback to students regarding the accuracy of their assumptions in the light of the evidence presented in the chapter. New to this edition, we repeat each "Truth or Fiction?" question when we revisit it within the chapter.
3. **Glossary.** Key terms are boldfaced in the text and defined in the margins where they appear, thus allowing students to maintain their concentration on the flow of the material at-hand. Word origins are also given for many of the key terms. Some words that to refer sexual anatomy (for example, *pudendum*) have interesting derivations that reflect upon ancient cultural beliefs and prejudices.
4. **Summing Up.** The concluding section of each chapter is a summary that reviews the material from the chapter in a way that promotes integration and understanding.
5. **Illustrations.** Full-color illustrations and figures are used throughout the text to highlight and emphasize material. The illustration program, like the text itself, is intended to reflect the cultural diversity of the society and the world in which we live.

CNN VIDEO PACKAGE

Allyn & Bacon is pleased to offer a package of integrated video segments drawn from the video library of Cable News Network (CNN). The video package consists of approximately 40 taped segments of news features produced by CNN that relate to key topics in human sexuality. Ranging in length from two to six minutes, the segments add depth and enrich understanding and help personalize the material presented in the text. Topics include: breast cancer, aphrodisiacs, gender equality, lesbian parents,

Russian abortions, elderly divorce, sexually transmitted diseases, AIDS and many others.

NEW TO THIS EDITION

While retaining the themes and organization of the first edition, this new edition has undergone a comprehensive updating to incorporate the many important new developments in the field, including the following:

• Coverage of the sex survey conducted by Samuel and Cynthia Janus—the Janus Report.
• New information on the dangers of smoking during pregnancy.
• New information on odor receptors in sperm and how fertile ova may attract sperm through a variation of the sense of smell.
• New data on the number of C-sections performed in the United States.
• New information on treatments of male infertility and the success rates of IVF clinics.
• New information on the dangers of light drinking during pregnancy.
• New data on rates of same-gender sexual activity drawn from surveys conducted in the United States, Britain, and France, with special emphasis on the controversial findings of the Battelle Institute survey.
• New studies on homophobia on college campuses.
• New findings on concordance rates for homosexuality in MZ and DZ twins.
• New evidence linking the X sex chromosome to a homosexual orientation in men.
• Latest evidence on effectiveness and safety of various methods of contraception.
• New evidence on breakage and slippage rates of condoms.
• Latest evidence on rates of teenage pregnancy.
• Latest government reports on the increased percentage of single-parent families and the rise in out-of-wedlock births.
• Cross-cultural data on women's emotional reactions to first intercourse.
• New evidence relating ethnicity to sexual values in college students.
• Latest data on safer sex practices among college students in the United States and Canada.
• Discussion of the controversy over Katie Roiphe's book, *The Morning After.*
• Discussion of the Antioch College sexual offense policy.
• New evidence on psychiatric problems faced by female survivors of rape.
• New evidence on effects of child sexual abuse on children from different racial/ethnic groups.
• New evidence on effectiveness of innovative, prison-based treatment programs for sex offenders in Vermont and California.
• New evidence on rates of sexual harassment in the

workplace and in the schools.

• Recent evidence reported on use of Prozac in treating voyeurism and fetishism.
• New evidence of gender differences in reasons cited for engaging in extramarital sex.
• New evidence reported on benefits of consuming yogurt with active bacterial cultures in reducing rate of recurrent vaginitis.
• New evidence on biological factors in erectile dysfunction.
• New recommendations from NIH concerning use of penile implants.
• New evidence on satisfaction with penile injections for erectile dysfunction.
• Report citing data that the marriage rate in the United States has hit a 25-year low.
• Latest reports on rates of cohabitation.
• Canadian study examining factors relating to attitudes toward cohabitation .
• Extensive, up-to-date, and comprehensive coverage of the latest scientific evidence on HIV/AIDS and other sexually transmitted diseases, including citations to more than 150 new studies since the first edition.

NEW FEATURE: WHAT DO YOU SAY NOW?

The second edition introduces a new feature, "What Do You Say Now?," which encourages students to examine their attitudes and ways of handling challenging social situations, including the following:

• Talking to Your Children about Sex (Chapter 13)
• Talking to Your Partner about STDs (Chapter 16)
• Talking Back to Sexual Pressure Lines (Chapter 19)

These are situations that relate to experiences that students may be presently experiencing or are likely to experience in the future. We encourage students to formulate their attitudes and think through alternative responses in handling these situations so that they will be better prepared to respond to them.

NEW SELF-SCORING QUESTIONNAIRE

We responded to adopters who wanted more hands-on questionnaires to help students examine their own attitudes and behaviors. In addition to the three questionnaires contained in the first edition (Sternberg's Triangular Love Scale, STD Attitude Scale, Reasoning About Abortion Scale), we have added another questionnaire, the "Love Attitudes Scale" (see Chapter 7), which helps students examine whether they are romantics or realists when it comes to matters of the heart.

NEW STUDENT-ORIENTED EXERCISES

We believe that a textbook should represent more than a compendium of information and knowledge about a discipline. It should also help students apply the knowledge they gain to their personal lives. Toward that end, we include the applied features we introduced in the first edition, including building date-seeking skills, handling menstrual discomfort, conducting breast self-examinations and testicular self-examination, rape prevention, and suggestions for responding to an exhibitionist. New to this edition are the following:

• Tracking Menstrual Complaints with the PMS Calendar (Chapter 3)
• What To Do If You Suspect You Have Contracted an STD (Chapter 16)

ACKNOWLEDGMENTS

The authors owe a great debt of gratitude to the many researchers and scholars whose contributions to the body of knowledge in the field of human sexuality is represented in these pages. Underscoring the interdisciplinary nature of the field, we have drawn upon the work of scholars in such fields as psychology, sociology, medicine, anthropology, theology, and philosophy, to name a few. We are also indebted to the many researchers who have generously allowed us to quote from their work and reprint tabular material representing their findings. We also wish to thank our professional colleagues who served as reviewers at various stages in the development of this text and who contributed immeasurably toward strengthening the final version of the text:

Willie A. Campbell, South Suburban College; Michael Gonzales, Ph.D., University Psychological Associates; Elaine Baker, Marshall University; Larry Bell, Northeastern Oklahoma University; Jean Byrne, Kent State University; David Johnson, University of Southern Alabama; Vicki Krenz, California State University Fresno; Robert Pollack, University of Georgia; Karen Huffman, Palomar College; R. Martin Lobdell, Pierce College; Gregory D. Murrow, Edinboro University of Pennsylvania; G. David Johnson, University of Southern Alabama; Paul Zelhart, East Texas State University; Kenneth R. Beausang, Black Hawk College; Tom Springer, Louisiana Tech University; Judith Baker, Texas Women's University; John T. Long, San Antonio College; Daphne Long Rankin, Virginia Commonwealth University; Richard J. Hardy, Central Michigan University; Linda DeVillers, Chaffey College; Barry R. Burkhart, Auburn University;Vera Dunwoody, Chaffey College; Mary Anne Watson, Metro State College of Denver; Mona Coates, Orange Coast College; Julio R. Garcia, Southwestern College; Basil Fiorito, California Polytechnic State University.

We would also like to thank the reviewers of the first edition of the text:

Richard Archer, Southwest Texas State University; Thomas Billimek, San Antonio College; Clive Davis, Syracuse University; Beverly Drinnin, Des Moines Area

Community College; Katherine Ellison, Montclair College; Ralph Hammond, University of Arkansas at Little Rock; Robert Holdsambeck, Allan Hancock College; Deborah McDonald, New Mexico State University; Gilbert Meyer, Illinois Valley Community College; Robert Pollack, University of Georgia; Jane Ellen Smith, University of New Mexico; Sherman Sowby, California State University-Fresno; Marlene Tufts, Clackamus Community College; Charles Weichert, San Antonio College.

We would also like to single out the contribution to the first and second editions of one extraordinary professional reviewer and editor, Beverly Drinnin. Professor Drinnin not only brought a wealth of knowledge concerning the field of human sexuality but was instrumental in helping us sharpen our writing style and approach. We are also grateful to Professor Drinnin for writing the Instructor's Manual, and annotations of both editions, that appear in the margins of the Annotated Instructor's Edition.

We are also thankful to the many professionals at Allyn & Bacon who encouraged and supported us and helped steer our course through the two editions of this text: Susan Badger, Vice President and Publisher, who brought the project (and us) to Allyn & Bacon and helped us find our bearing and chart an initial course; Laura Pearson, Executive Editor, who was editor for the first and second editions; Hannah Rubenstein, the developmental editor for the first edition and Cheryl Marconi, the developmental editor for the second edition; Deborah Brown, production editor who continues to direct the production process with nary a hitch and Eleanor Sabini, her assistant; Linda Knowles, who researched the cover art; Melinda Grosser, the book designer who was responsible for the two stunning interior designs for both editions; and the other fine professionals at Allyn & Bacon who were involved in many other aspects of design, development, and production.

We also wish to acknowledge the important contributions of our research assistant, John Moulton III, who helped to gather material and ensure that the text was as comprehensive and accurate as possible in its coverage of the most recent scientific findings. The first author also wishes to extend a special thanks to his wife, Judith Wolf-Nevid.

J.S.N.
New York, New York

L.F.-R.
Short Hills, New Jersey

S.A.R
Short Hills, New Jersey

ABOUT THE AUTHORS

Jeffrey S. Nevid is a Professor of Psychology at St. John's University in New York, where he also directs the Doctoral Program in Clinical Psychology. He received his Ph.D. in Clinical Psychology from SUNY Albany and holds a Diplomate in Clinical Psychology from the American Board of Professional Psychology. Dr. Nevid has been awarded several research grants to support his research on health interventions and has published numerous research articles in scientific journals on such topics as attitudes toward homosexuality, sexual attraction, assessment of sex offenders, and health psychology. He has authored the books *Adjustment and Growth* and *Behavior Therapy* with Spencer A. Rathus, *Abnormal Psychology in a Changing World* with Spencer A. Rathus and Beverly Greene, and *A Student's Guide to AIDS and Other Sexually Transmitted Diseases, 201 Things You Should Know About AIDS and Other Sexually Transmitted Diseases, and Choices.*

Lois Fichner-Rathus is an Associate Professor of Art at Trenton State College. She received her Ph.D. in History, Theory, and Criticism of Art from Massachusetts Institute of Technology. She has published numerous articles in professional journals and has authored several exhibition catalogues. She has received grants to curate several exhibitions of art by women artists and by artists of color; has served as Coordinator of the Women's Studies program at Trenton State College; and has worked to integrate gender, race, and social-class issues in the college curriculum. She is author of *Understanding Art* and coauthor, with Spencer A. Rathus, of *Making the Most of College.*

Spencer A. Rathus received his Ph.D. in psychology from SUNY Albany. A member of the psychology faculty of St. John's University, he has also engaged in clinical practice and published numerous articles in scientific journals on topics such as orgasm disorders in women and men, atypical variations in sexual behavior, and assessment of deviant behavior. Dr. Rathus is also the author of the Rathus Assertiveness Schedule and of several books, including *Psychology, Essentials of Psychology,* and *Understanding Child Development.* He has coauthored *AIDS—What Every Student Needs to Know* with Susan Boushn; coauthored *Making the Most of College* with Lois Fichner-Rathus; and coauthored *Behavior Therapy and Adjustment and Growth*, with Jeffrey S. Nevid and *Abnormal Psychology in a Changing World* with Jeffrey S. Nevid and Beverly Greene.

DEDICATED WITH LOVE TO OUR CHILDREN, MICHAEL ZEV NEVID AND TAYLOR LANE RATHUS, WHO WERE BORN DURING THE TIME THAT THE FIRST EDITION OF THIS BOOK WAS BEING WRITTEN.

Taylor Lane Rathus
November 3, 1990

Michael Zev Nevid
January 17, 1991

CHAPTER OUTLINE

_____ Ancient civilizations worshipped women's ability to bear children and perpetuate the species.

_____ In ancient Greece, a mature man would take a sexual interest in an adolescent boy, often with the blessings of the boy's parents.

_____ The production of illustrated sex manuals originated in modern times.

_____ Trobrianders consider their children old enough to engage in sexual intercourse when they are . . . old enough.

_____ In our dreams, airplanes, bullets, snakes, sticks, and similar objects symbolize the male genitals.

C H A P T E R 1

What Is Human Sexuality?

We are about to embark on an exploration of human sexuality. You might wonder, why do we even need to *study* human sexuality? After all, isn't sexuality a natural function? Don't we normally learn everything we need to know on the basis of personal experience or from information passed along to us by our parents, friends, peers, or teachers? Yes, we can learn how our bodies respond to sexual stimulation—what turns us on and what turns us off—through personal experience. Personal experience teaches us little, however, about the biological processes that bring about sexual response and orgasm. Nor does experience inform us about the variations in sexual behavior that exist around the world, or in the neighborhood. Experience does not prepare us to recognize the signs of sexually transmitted diseases or to evaluate the risks of pregnancy. Nor does experience help us deal with most sexual problems or dysfunctions. As for our parents, what many of us learned about sex from our parents can probably be summarized in a single word: "Don't." The information we received from our friends was probably riddled with fabrication, exaggeration, and folklore. Yes, many young people today do receive accurate information through sex education courses in the schools, which is all the more important now that the specter of AIDS hangs over every sexual decision. School-based sex-education courses, however, often focus more on the biological aspects of sexuality and the risks of unwanted pregnancies and sexually transmitted diseases than on our experience of our sexuality and how we can enhance that experience.

There is also something of a myth in our culture that love conquers all—that love is all we need to achieve and sustain satisfying and healthy relationships. Yet how likely are we to establish healthy and mutually satisfying relationships without some formal knowledge of our own and our partners' sexuality? Without some knowledge of the biology of how our bodies function? Without some awareness of the psychological aspects of our sexuality, or in a scientific vacuum?

Concerns about AIDS and unwanted teenage pregnancies have focused greater attention today on the importance of sex education. Many children receive some form of sex education as early as elementary school. Courses on human sexuality, rarely offered a generation ago, are now routine on college campuses across the United States and Canada. You may know more about human sexuality than your parents or grandparents did at your age, or do today, but how much do you really know? What, for example, happens inside your body when you are sexually stimulated? What causes erection or vaginal lubrication? Can people who are paralyzed from the neck down become erect or lubricated? What knowledge do we have of the factors that determine a person's sexual orientation—and what don't we know? What are the causes of sexual dysfunctions? How do our sexual responsiveness and interests change as we age? Why does the United States have the unfortunate distinction of possessing the highest incidence of rape in the industrialized world? Can you contract a sexually transmitted disease and not know that you have it until you wind up sterile? Can you infect others without having any symptoms yourself?

These are just a few of the issues we will explore in this book. Much of the information we present was discovered in recent years. It is almost as new to us as it may be to you. We also expect to debunk some common but erroneous ideas about sex that you may have picked up before you began this course. Before we proceed further, let us define our subject.

Activity: *How Much Do You Know About Sex?* The IM includes this 18-item questionnaire used by the Roper Organization and the Kinsey Institute in a nationwide survey of "sexual literacy." The results, published in 1990, are included in the IM.

WHAT IS HUMAN SEXUALITY?

What *is* human sexuality? This is not a trick question. Consider the meaning, or rather meanings, of the word *sex*. The word derives from Latin roots meaning "to cut or divide," signifying the division of organisms into male and female genders. One use of the term *sex,* then, refers to our **gender,** or state of being male or female. The word *sex* (or *sexual*) is also used to refer to anatomic structures, called sex (or sexual) organs, that play a role in reproduction or sexual pleasure. We may also speak of sex when referring to physical activities involving our sex organs for purposes of reproduction or pleasure: masturbation, hugging, kissing, **coitus,** and so on. Sex also relates to **erotic** feelings, experiences, or desires, such as sexual fantasies and thoughts, sexual urges, or feelings of sexual attraction to another person.

We usually make our usage of the term *sex* clear enough in our everyday speech. When we ask about the sex of a newborn, we are referring to anatomic sex. When we talk of "having sex" (a rather ugly phrase, since it implies that we engage in sexual activity as we "have" a ham sandwich), we generally mean the physical expression of erotic feelings.

The terms *sex organ* and *sexual organ* may be used in different ways. Sometimes the terms are used to refer to those organs required for, and involved directly in, reproduction, such as the penis and testes in men, and the vagina, uterus, and ovaries in women. The terms *sex organs* and *sexual organs* are also sometimes used to refer to organs or structures that are eroticized, even though they may play no direct role in reproduction (such as the clitoris or the breasts). Let us define sex (or sexual) organs as bodily structures that can be eroticized (such as the clitoris or the breasts), or that play a role in reproduction (such as the testes in the man and the uterus in the woman), or that both are eroticized and play a reproductive role (such as the penis in the man and the vagina in the woman). Let us also add that we will use the word *gender* in this text to refer to the state of being male or female, as in **gender identity** and **gender roles.**

The term *sexual behavior* refers to a wide range of physical activities that involve the body in the expression of erotic or affectionate feelings. This description of sexual behavior includes but is not limited to behavior involving reproduction. *Masturbation,* for example, is sexual behavior that is performed for pleasure, not reproduction. Kissing, hugging, manual manipulation of the genitals, and oral-genital contact are all sexual behaviors that can provide sensual stimulation, even though they do not directly lead to reproduction. They may also be used as forms of **foreplay,** which leads to coitus, which can lead to reproduction.

We can now define **human sexuality** as the ways in which we experience and express ourselves as sexual beings. Our awareness of ourselves as females or males is part of our sexuality, as is the capacity we have for erotic experiences and responses. Our sexuality is an essential part of ourselves, whether or not we ever engage in sexual intercourse or sexual fantasy, or even if we lose sensation in our genitals because of injury.

THE STUDY OF HUMAN SEXUALITY

The study of human sexuality is an interdisciplinary enterprise that draws upon the scientific expertise of anthropologists, biologists, medical researchers, sociologists, and psychologists, to name but a few of the many professional groups involved in the field. Perhaps no other area of study draws on so many disciplines. These disciplines all have contributions to make, since sexual behavior reflects our biological capabilities, our psychological characteristics, and the social and cultural influences to which we are exposed. Biologists inform us about the physiological mechanisms of sexual arousal and response. Medical science teaches us about sexually transmitted diseases and the biological bases of sexual dysfunctions. Psychologists examine how our sexual behavior and attitudes are shaped by perception, learning, thought, motivation and emotion, and personality. Sociologists consider the societal contexts of sexual behavior, examining, for example, relationships between sexual behavior and religion, race, and social class. Anthropologists focus on cross-cultural similarities and differences in sexual behavior. Scientists from many disciplines explore parallels between the sexual behavior of humans and other animals.

Learning Objective 1:
State the authors' definition of human sexuality.

Gender
The state of being male or female.

Coitus
Sexual intercourse.

Erotic
Arousing sexual feelings or desires. (From the Greek word for love, *eros*.)

Gender identity
One's concept of being male or female.

Gender roles
Complex clusters of ways in which males and females are expected to behave within a given culture.

Foreplay
Mutual sexual stimulation that precedes sexual intercourse.

Human sexuality
The ways in which we experience and express ourselves as sexual beings.

Learning Objective 2:
Discuss the reasons for studying human sexuality, including the possible applications of this study to daily living.

Scientific Study of Human Sexuality. Named after the pioneering sex researcher Alfred Kinsey, the Kinsey Institute at Indiana University is a major research center for the scientific study of human sexuality. Here, Kinsey Institute director June Reinisch announces the publication of a new Kinsey Institute report on sexuality.

Values
The qualities in life that are deemed important or unimportant, right or wrong, desirable or undesirable.

Science provides us with information, but it cannot make sexual decisions for us. Our **values** come into play in determining our sexual choices and behavior. The Declaration of Independence endorsed the fundamental values of "life, liberty, and the pursuit of happiness"—not a bad beginning. Our religious traditions also play a prominent role in shaping our values. Our study of human sexuality will thus consider how religious teachings shape sexual values.

WHY STUDY HUMAN SEXUALITY?

Why study human sexuality? Is this another trick question? After all, people have shown little trouble in reproducing themselves in ever growing numbers, without benefit of scientific inquiry about sexuality.

One reason to study sexuality is that it represents a primary source of motivation. Consider the amount of time people spend thinking about and planning for sex, let alone the time spent engaged in sexual behavior itself. As we shall see, some psychological theorists place a great deal of importance—some critics say too much importance—on the role of sexual motivation in determining human behavior. Most investigators agree that sexuality is an important aspect of the human experience, however, and that it influences our behavior to a significant degree. The knowledge acquired from the study of human sexuality can also be put to personal use in communicating more effectively with a partner and learning techniques that enhance sexual response and pleasure.

Another reason for studying human sexuality is that we may face various personal and social problems that involve sexuality, such as sexually transmitted diseases, unwanted pregnancies, sexual harassment, and rape. Sexual knowledge and personal values may provide the basis for making informed decisions about preventing and responding to these problems.

Notes: In a study designed to explore behavioral and attitudinal changes, students enrolled in a human sexuality class completed a questionnaire in the first and last class periods. "Sexual attitudes became more permissive during the period of the course" and there were "no significant changes in behavior as a group." However, no control group was used, and the students' backgrounds and previous experiences may have been determining factors in *individual* behavioral and attitudinal changes. (1992. *Journal of Sex Research, 29(1)*, pp. 43–59.)

Activity: *The Sexual Permissiveness Scale* The IM includes this six-item scale, which allows students to identify their values about premarital intercourse.

SEXUALITY AND VALUES

Our society is pluralistic. It embraces a wide range of sexual attitudes and values. Some readers may be liberal in their sexual views and behavior. Others may be more conservative or traditional. Some will be staunchly pro-choice on abortion, others adamantly pro-life. Some will approve of premarital sex for couples who are dating casually, whereas others will hold the line at emotional commitment, and still others will hold to the belief that people should wait until marriage.

Since we encourage you through the course of this text to explore your own values about the issues we discuss, let us reveal two of the principal values that guided *our* writing:

1. *Sexual knowledge and critical thinking skills are of value because they allow us to make informed sexual decisions.* We hope that readers will confirm our belief. Having agreed on this much, we admit that we hold different values about a number of the issues we discuss. Therefore, we do not try to persuade readers to adopt a particular

stance concerning specific issues raised in the textbook. We present opposing points of view on such controversial matters as abortion and the distribution of condoms in schools, without attempting to take sides or impose our personal views on our readers. In this way we hope that readers will think critically about their preconceptions and that the views that they form will be their own. We do not believe that textbooks on human sexuality should take a liberal or a conservative view on premarital sex, birth control, or any other value-laden issue. While we all have personal biases, our aim is to present information as evenhandedly as possible and with respect for differences of values and opinions that exist among students and in society at large. We hope that by doing so, we will encourage students to develop respect for people who hold differing views.

2. *Students should take an active role in enhancing their health.* In the course of this text, we will urge you, for example, to examine your bodies for possible abnormalities, to see your physician when you have questions about painful menstruation or other physical complaints, to become sensitive to the signs of sexually transmitted diseases, to get good prenatal care, and so forth.

People's sexual attitudes, experiences, and behaviors are shaped to a large extent by their cultural traditions and beliefs. Because our world consists of such diverse peoples and cultures, it may be best to consider the study of human sexuality as the study of human *sexualities.* In this book we highlight the diverse ways in which people of the world experience their sexuality. We preview some of the findings of our review of sexuality in this chapter's World of Diversity feature.

THINKING CRITICALLY ABOUT HUMAN SEXUALITY

Learning Objective 3: List the characteristics of critical thinking and discuss how critical thinking skills can be applied to the study of human sexuality.

We are inundated with so much information about sex that it is difficult to separate truth from fiction. Newspapers, television shows, and popular books and magazines contain one feature after another about sex. Many of them contradict one another, contain half-truths, or draw misleading or unsubstantiated conclusions. One of the purposes of a scientific approach to human sexuality is to encourage people to think critically about the claims and findings that are passed along as truthful.

Sad to say, most of us take certain "truths" for granted. We tend to assume that authority figures like doctors and government officials provide us with factual information and are qualified to make decisions that affect our lives. When two doctors disagree on the need for a hysterectomy, however, or two officials disagree as to whether condoms should be distributed in public schools, we wonder how both can be correct. Critical thinkers never say, "This is true because so-and-so says that it is true."

To help students evaluate claims, arguments, and widely held beliefs, most colleges encourage students to engage in *critical thinking.* Critical thinking has several meanings. One aspect of critical thinking is skepticism—not taking things for granted. It means being skeptical of things that are presented in print or uttered by authority figures or celebrities or passed along by friends. Another aspect of critical thinking is thoughtful analysis and probing of the claims and arguments of others. Critical thinking involves a willingness to challenge the conventional wisdom and common knowledge that many of us take for granted. It means scrutinizing definitions of terms, evaluating the premises or assumptions behind arguments, and then examining the logic of arguments. It also means finding *reasons* to support your beliefs, rather than relying on feelings or "gut impressions." When people think critically, they maintain open minds. They are willing to suspend their beliefs until they have obtained and evaluated evidence that either supports or refutes them.

Throughout the book we raise issues that demand critical thinking. These issues may stimulate you to analyze and evaluate your beliefs and attitudes about sex in the light of scientific evidence. For example, upon reading Chapter 10 you may wish to reconsider your beliefs on whether or not homosexuals *choose* their sexual orientation. Upon reading Chapter 4 you may reexamine folklore that suggests that sexual activity impairs a

Learning Objective 4: Describe some of the cross-cultural variations in sexual behaviors and attitudes.

A WORLD OF DIVERSITY

Around the World in Eighty Ways—A Preview

Like other aspects of human behavior, sexual beliefs and behaviors vary widely around the world. The United States alone is a nation of hundreds of different ethnic and religious groups, which vary in their sexual customs, attitudes, and beliefs. This diversity extends to the entire "global village" of the world's nearly 200 nations and to each nation's own distinctive subcultures.

The World of Diversity features that appear throughout this text explore the rich variety of sexual expression found worldwide. Seeing sexuality in contexts other than our own can be enlightening for many reasons. It helps us understand the role of a culture's beliefs, values, and attitudes on our own and others' expressions of sexuality. It may help us understand why our partners, who may not share the same ethnic or religious heritage, feel different from us about certain aspects of sexual intimacy. Exploring diversity can also help us understand differences related to gender, sexual orientation, sexual attraction, sexual jealousy, premarital sex, teenage pregnancy, and risks of sexually transmitted diseases, among other issues relating to human sexuality.

People in some societies believe, for instance, that a brother and sister who eat at the same table are engaging in a mildly erotic type of act. The practice is therefore forbidden (Davenport, 1977). In contemporary Islamic societies, female sexuality is often viewed as dangerous because women's behavior and attire, if not kept under strict control, can be "fatal attractions" for men (Kammeyer et al., 1990). What is sexually arousing, too, varies enormously among different cultures. Among the Abkhasians in the southern part of what used to be the Soviet Union, for instance, men regard the female armpit as highly arousing. A woman's armpits are, therefore, a sight for her husband alone (Kammeyer et al., 1990).

Of course, one glaring reason for today's heightened interest in understanding sexuality in a broader perspective is the worldwide AIDS epidemic. Any effort to end this scourge requires that we open our eyes to cultural attitudes and traditions that may increase the risk of transmission of the disease.

If we take a quick tour of the world of diversity within our own borders and beyond, we find that:

Kissing is practiced nearly universally as a form of petting in the United States, but it is unknown among some cultures in Africa and South America (see Chapter 9).

Some societies encourage sexual experimentation and even sexual intercourse among children and adolescents, while others punish any form of childhood sexual play (see Chapter 13).

Marital fidelity is a prominent value in Western culture, but among some people of the Arctic it is considered hos-pitable for a man to offer his wife to a visiting tribesman (see Chapter 14).

Cultural traditions that make it acceptable, even expected, for husbands to engage in extra-marital relationships appear to be contributing to the spread of AIDS in some societies, as men become infected during extramarital liaisons and then go on to infect their wives through sexual contact (see Chapter 17).

Although prostitution is illegal everywhere in the United States, except for certain counties in Nevada (see Chapter 20), no one tries to hide the fact that it exists. In the former Soviet Union, however, Communist officials completely denied the existence of one class of worker—the "working girl"

AIDS Awareness Postage Stamp. Issued December 1, 1993 to commemorate World AIDS Day.

man's athletic performance on the following day. The discussion of abortion in Chapter 12 will encourage you to consider exactly when we begin to be *human*. When you read Chapters 13 and 17, you will face the question of whether or not schools should provide students with contraceptives.

(prostitute). The system of communism, after all, was supposed to eradicate such social ills as poverty, homelessness, and prostitution. Not until glasnost—the new openness—in the 1980s was the shocking reality of the country's widespread prostitution revealed, including one highly publicized case of a trio in Moscow consisting of a woman, her mother, and her grandmother (Bohlen, 1987). Today in Russia, prostitution flourishes—a result of more liberal societal attitudes and disastrous economic conditions.

In the United States, there remains a tendency to blame the victims of crimes—especially rape victims—rather than the perpetrators (see Chapter 19). In the strongly patriarchal society of Islamic Pakistan, however, the so-called Hudood Ordinance has actually resulted in prison sentences for some women who have brought rape charges against men. Hudood, you see, grants more credibility to the testimony of men than to that of women. An accused man may claim that any sexual contact between himself and the woman making the accusations was consensual, and the court will be inclined to believe him. Women too are also frequently prevented from testifying in court. The result has been that some women who bring charges of rape are sometimes prosecuted for adultery and

Offerings Made at a Buddhist Temple in Japan by Women Who Have Had Abortions.

jailed if found guilty while their assailants go free (Schork, 1990).

Although U.S. government officials may occasionally voice public condemnation of premarital sexual relations, the majority of U.S. inhabitants engage in them without fear of government reprisal. In China, however, where the results of a recent national survey (see Chapter 2) showed that about half of the population engages in premarital relations, a male college student was expelled from a Beijing university in April 1990 when it became known that he had engaged in premarital sexual relations (Southerland, 1990). Other students reported that the

punishment was typical.

Perhaps in response to feelings of guilt or remorse, many Japanese women who have abortions place miniature stone statues known as mizuko-jizo in Buddhist temples in memory of their aborted fetuses. They sometimes decorate the statues with bibs or little hats and surround them with little stuffed animals, baby food, and pacifiers—all in the belief that it keeps the souls of their aborted fetuses warm and entertained (Bumiller, 1990).

We shall elaborate on these and other topics and issues concerning sexual diversity in subsequent chapters.

SOME FEATURES OF CRITICAL THINKING

Critical thinkers maintain a healthy skepticism. They examine definitions of terms, weigh premises, examine evidence, and consider whether or not arguments are valid and logical. The key features of critical thinking are represented in the following suggestions:

1. *Be skeptical.* Politicians, religious leaders, and other authority figures attempt to convince you of their points of view. Even researchers and authors may hold certain biases. Have the attitude that you will accept nothing as true—including the comments of the authors of this text—until you have personally examined the evidence.

2. *Examine definitions of terms.* Some statements are true when a term is defined in one way but not true when it is defined in another. Consider the statement, "Love is blind." If love is defined as head-over-heels infatuation, there may be substance to the statement. Infatuated people tend to idealize loved ones and overlook their faults. If love is defined as deep caring and commitment involving a more realistic (if still somewhat slanted) appraisal of the loved one, however, then love is not so much blind as a bit nearsighted.

3. *Examine the assumptions or premises of arguments.* Consider the statement, "Abortion is murder." The current edition of *Webster's New World Dictionary* defines murder as "the unlawful and malicious or premeditated killing of one human being by another." The statement can be true, according to this dictionary, only if the victim is held to be a human being (and if the act is unlawful and either malicious or premeditated). Pro-life advocates argue that embryos and fetuses are human beings, whereas pro-choice advocates claim that they are not, at least not until they are capable of surviving on their own. So the argument that abortion is murder would rest in part on the assumption that the embryo or fetus is a human being.

4. *Be cautious in drawing conclusions from evidence.* In Chapter 14 we shall discuss research findings that show that married people who cohabited before marriage are more likely to eventually get divorced than are those who didn't cohabit first. It may sound as if cohabitation in couples who later tie the knot is a *cause* of divorce, but married couples who cohabited before marriage may differ from those who did not in important ways other than cohabitation—which brings us to our next suggestion for critical thinking.

5. *Consider the kinds of evidence upon which conclusions are based.* Some conclusions, even seemingly "scientific" conclusions, are based on anecdotes and personal endorsements, rather than on scientifically sound research.

6. *Consider alternative interpretations of research evidence.* For example, cohabitors who later get married may be more likely to eventually get divorced because they are more liberal and less traditional than married couples who did not cohabit before marriage, not because of the effects of cohabitation.

7. *Do not oversimplify.* Consider the statement, "Homosexuality is inborn." There is some evidence that sexual orientation may involve "inborn" biological predispositions, such as genetic influences, but biology is not destiny in human sexuality. Homosexual—and heterosexual—sexual orientations appear to develop as the result of a complex interaction of biological and environmental factors.

8. *Do not overgeneralize.* Consider the belief that gay males are effeminate and lesbians are masculine. Certainly some gay males and lesbians fit these stereotypes, but many do not. It is doubtful that homosexuality in general is characterized by the assumption of behavior patterns traditionally associated with the opposite gender.

Teaching Tip: Clip a recent newspaper article on a sexuality issue. Distribute copies to students. Have the class examine and discuss the article, keeping in mind the features of critical thinking.

As educator Robert M. Hutchins noted, "The object of education is to prepare the young to educate themselves throughout their lives." One of the primary ways of educating yourself is through critical thinking.

PERSPECTIVES ON HUMAN SEXUALITY

Human sexuality is a complex topic, and no single theory or perspective can capture all its nuances. In this book we explore human sexuality from many perspectives. We cannot hope to render a full accounting of a topic as complex as human sexuality by adopting a narrow focus. Each perspective has something to offer our understanding, but none offers a total view. In this section we introduce a number of perspectives—historical, biological, cross-species, cross-cultural, psychological, and sociological. We shall draw on these approaches in subsequent chapters.

Learning Objective 5:
Identify the sexual attitudes
and practices characteristic
of the historical eras
described in this chapter.

The Venus of Willendorf.
Anthropologists believe that
the Venus is an ancient fertility symbol.

Phallic worship
Worship of the penis as a
symbol of generative power.

THE HISTORICAL PERSPECTIVE

History places our sexual behavior in context. It informs us as to whether our sexual behavior reflects trends that have been with us through the millennia or solely the customs of a particular culture and era.

Our reading of history shows little evidence of universal sexual trends. Attitudes and behaviors vary extensively from one time and place to another. Contemporary U.S. society may be permissive when compared to the Victorian and postwar eras, but it looks rather staid when compared to the sexual excesses of some ancient societies, most notably the Roman ruling class.

History also involves the study of religious traditions. Religions provide explanations for natural events based on a supreme being or beings or on supernatural forces and offer foundations for moral and ethical behavior. Religions have also been major influences on sexual values and behavior. Yet the traditions and religions of diverse cultures have cast sexual behavior in different lights.

The rise of science since the *Age of Enlightenment* in the eighteenth century has also profoundly affected contemporary views of human sexuality. Let us trace some historical changes in attitudes toward sexuality. We begin by turning the clock back some five thousand years, to the days before written records were kept—that is, to *pre*history.

PREHISTORIC SEXUALITY: FROM FEMALE IDOLS TO PHALLIC WORSHIP

Evidence of life among our Stone Age ancestors is drawn largely from cave drawings, stone artifacts, and the customs of modern-day preliterate peoples whose existence may have changed little over the millennia. From such sources, historians and anthropologists infer a prehistoric division of labor. Men by and large hunted for game. Women tended to remain close to home. They nurtured children and gathered edible plants and nuts, crabs, and other marine life that wandered along the shore or swam in shallow waters.

Art produced in the Stone Age, some 20,000 years ago, suggests the worship of women's ability to bear children and perpetuate the species (Fichner-Rathus, 1992). Primitive statues and cave drawings portray women with large, pendulous breasts, rounded hips, and prominent sex organs. Most theorists regard the figurines as fertility symbols.

Ancient civilizations worshipped women's ability to bear children and perpetuate the species. True. Stone Age art suggests that people did worship women's ability to bear children and perpetuate the species. Primitive statues and cave drawings portraying women are regarded as fertility symbols. •

Emphasis on the female reproductive role may also have signified ignorance of the male's contribution to reproduction (Rawson, 1973).

As the ice sheets of the last ice age retreated (about 11,000 B.C.), and the climate warmed, human societies turned agrarian, and hunters and gatherers became farmers and herders. Villages sprang up around fields. Men, who were longtime students of animals, tended the livestock. Women became farmers, supplementing their plant-gathering skills with expertise in cultivation. As people grew aware of the male role in reproduction, **phallic worship** sprang into being. Knowledge of paternity is believed to have developed around 9000 B.C., which is about the time that people shifted from being hunters and gatherers to being farmers and shepherds. Although the male's role in reproduction may seem obvious to us, it is not surprising that uninformed people might not have connected childbirth to a sexual act that predated the most visible signs of pregnancy by months. Knowledge of paternity may have been a side benefit of the herding of livestock:

> For the first time, [people were] watching the same individual animals every day, all the year around, and [they] could scarcely fail to note the relatively constant length of the interval that elapsed between a ram servicing a ewe and the ewe dropping her lambs.
>
> (Tannahill, 1980, p. 46)

Of course, prehistoric people did not keep records that might help us to confirm this explanation. Had they done so, they would not have been *pre*historic.

In any event, the penis was glorified in art as a plough, an axe, or a sword. **Phallic symbols** played roles in religious ceremonies in ancient Egypt. Ancient Greek art revered phalluses, rendering them sometimes as rings and sometimes as necklaces. Some phalluses were given wings, suggesting the power ascribed to them. In ancient Rome, a large phallus was carried like a float in a parade honoring Venus, the goddess of love.

Incest taboo
The prohibition against intercourse and reproduction among close blood relatives.

The **incest taboo** appears to have been the first human taboo (Tannahill, 1980). The origins of the incest taboo remain open to discussion, but all human societies apparently have some form of an incest taboo (Ember & Ember, 1990). Societies have varied in terms of the strictness of the taboo, however. Brother-sister marriages were permitted among the presumably divine rulers of ancient Egypt and among the royal families of the Incas and of Hawaii, though they were generally prohibited among commoners. Father-daughter marriages were even permitted among the aristocracy and royalty of ancient Egypt. Incestuous relationships in these royal blood lines may have assured that wealth and power, as well as self-perceived divinity, would be kept in the family. Many societies, even today, permit marriages between some blood relatives, such as first cousins (Thornhill & Thornhill, 1987).

Polygamy
The practice of having two or more spouses at the same time. (From the Greek roots meaning "many" [*poly-*] and "marriage" [*gamos*].)

Monogamy
The practice of having one spouse. (From the Greek *mono-*, meaning "single" or "alone.")

Notes: In 1953 Israel passed a law bringing all Jews under jurisdiction of the religious courts for all matters of personal status (marriage, adultery, divorce, birth, death, legitimacy, and the legality of abortion, battery and rape in marriage). Under Jewish law, only the husband can grant a divorce. If a wife leaves her husband without permission from the courts, she can be labeled a "rebellious wife." She will then lose custody of the children and all rights to financial support.

THE ANCIENT HEBREWS   The ancient Hebrews viewed sex, at least sex in marriage, as a fulfilling experience that was intended to fulfill the divine injunction to "be fruitful and multiply." Homosexuality was strongly condemned, as it was believed to represent a threat to the perpetuation of the family. Adultery, too, was condemned—at least for a woman. Although the Hebrew Bible (called the Old Testament in the Christian faith) permitted **polygamy,** it expressed a clear preference for **monogamy**—"one man, one wife" (Telushkin, 1991). As a contemporary Jewish writer, Rabbi Telushkin notes, "Indeed, the most obvious evidence of the Torah's [the first five books of the Bible] preference for monogamy is that the first human beings God created were Adam and Eve, not Adam, Eve, and Joan" (1991, p. 178). In any event, the vast majority of the Hebrews were monogamous.

The ancient Hebrews approved of sex within marriage not simply for procreation but also for mutual pleasure and fulfillment. They believed that the expression of sexual needs and desires helped strengthen marital bonds and so served to solidify the family. Jewish law even legislated the minimum frequency of marital relations, which varied according to the man's profession and the amount of time he spent at home:

> Every day for those who have no occupation, twice a week for laborers, once a week for ass-drivers; once every thirty days for camel drivers; and once every six months for sailors.
>
> (Mishna Ketubot 5:6; Ketubot 62b–62b; quoted in Telushkin, 1991, p. 616)

What of the feminine gender role among the ancient Hebrews? Women were to be good wives and mothers. What does it mean to be a "good wife"? According to the book of Proverbs, a good wife rises before dawn to tend to her family's needs, brings home the food, instructs the servants, tends the vineyards, makes the clothes, keeps the ledger, helps the needy, and works well into the night. For all this, among the ancient Hebrews, a wife was considered the property of her husband, and if she offended him, she could be divorced on a whim (although they almost never were). A wife could also be stoned to death for adultery. She might also have had to share him with his secondary wives and even concubines. Men who committed adultery by consorting with the wives of other men were considered to have violated the property rights of the other men, and though subject to harsh penalties (for violation of property rights), they would not be put to death.

THE ANCIENT GREEKS   The classical or Golden Age of ancient Greece lasted about 200 years, from about 500 B.C. to 300 B.C. Within this relatively short span lived the philosophers Socrates, Plato, and Aristotle; the playwrights Aristophanes, Aeschylus, and Sophocles; and the lawgiver Solon. Like the Hebrews, the Greeks valued family life, but they did not cement family ties by limiting sexual interests to marriage, at least not male sexual interests. The Greeks expressed sexual interests openly. They admired the well-developed body, male or female, and enjoyed nude wrestling among men in the arena. The female ideal was slender compared with the earth mother ideals of prehistory. She epitomized graceful sensuality, not reproduction. Erotic encounters and off-color jokes characterized the plays of Aristophanes and other playwrights. The Greeks held that the healthy mind must dwell in a healthy body. They cultivated muscle and movement along with mind.

The Greeks viewed their gods—Zeus, god of gods, Apollo, who inspired art and music, Aphrodite, the goddess of carnal love whose name is the basis of the word *aphrodisiac,* and others—as voracious seekers of sexual variety. Not only were they believed to have sexual adventures among themselves, they also were thought to have seduced mortals.

Three aspects of Greek sexuality are of particular interest to our study of sexual practices in the ancient world: **homosexuality,** pederasty, and prostitution. The Greeks viewed men and women as **bisexual.** One of their heroes was Heracles (Hercules). Heracles is said to have ravished 50 virgins in a night, but he also had affairs with men, including "sweet Hylas, he of the curling locks" (Tannahill, 1980, p. 85). Homosexual *sex* was deemed normal. However, only a few homosexual *relationships,* such as relationships between soldiers and between adolescents and older men, received the stamp of social approval. Homosexuality was tolerated so long as it did not threaten the institution of the family. Exclusive homosexuality, therefore, was discouraged since men were expected to marry and raise families (Bullough, 1976). Some Greeks idealized romantic love between men, of the sort that bound Achilles to Patroclus in Homer's *Iliad.* The warrior Achilles could not be moved to fight the Trojans by love of country or the pleas of his king. He sprang into action, however, when the enemy slew his lover Patroclus.

Pederasty means love of boys. Greek men in their thirties might take on an adolescent male as a lover and pupil. Sex between men and prepubescent boys was illegal, however. Families were generally pleased if their adolescent sons attracted socially prominent mentors. Pederasty did not impede the boy's future heterosexual functioning, since the pederast himself was usually married, and Greeks believed people equally capable of heterosexual and homosexual activity.

Homosexuality
The sexual orientation characterized by sexual attraction to and formation of romantic relationships with members of one's own gender. (From the Greek *homos,* meaning "same.")

Bisexual
Sexually responsive to either gender. (From the Latin *bi-,* meaning "two.")

Pederasty
Sexual love of boys. (From the Greek *paidos,* meaning "boy.")

The School of Athens, **an Engraving after Raphael.** In ancient Greece, people were seen as bisexual, and sexual relationships between adolescent boys and adult men (pederasty) were commonplace.

In ancient Greece, a mature man would take a sexual interest in an adolescent boy, often with the blessings of the boy's parents. It is true that mature men in ancient Greece took sexual interest in adolescent boys, and that the boys' parents frequently approved. The Greeks viewed people as naturally bisexual. •

Not all Greeks approved of pederasty, however. Aristotle, for one, considered it depraved.

Prostitution flourished at every level of society. Prostitutes ranged from refined **courtesans** to **concubines,** who were usually slaves. Courtesans were similar to the Geisha girls of Japan. They could play musical instruments, dance, engage in witty repartee, or discuss the latest political crisis. They were also skilled in the arts of love. There was no social stigma attached to visiting a courtesan. Their clients included philosophers, playwrights, politicians, generals, and the very affluent. At the lower rungs of society were streetwalkers and prostitutes who lived in tawdry brothels. They were not hard to find. A wooden or painted penis invariably stood by the door.

Women in general held a low social status in society. The women of Athens had no more legal or political rights than slaves. They were subject to the authority of their male next-of-kin before marriage and to their husbands afterwards. They received no formal education, and were consigned most of the time to women's quarters in their homes. They were chaperoned when they ventured out of doors. A husband could divorce his wife without cause and was obligated to do so if she committed adultery. A wife, however, could only divorce her husband under extreme circumstances, which did not include adultery or pederasty. The legal and social rights of women in ancient Athens were similar to those of their contemporaries in Babylonia and Egypt, and among the ancient Hebrews. All in all, the women of the ancient world were treated as *chattels*—property.

THE WORLD OF ANCIENT ROME Much is made of the sexual excesses of the Roman emperors and ruling families. Julius Caesar is reputed to have been bisexual—"a man to every woman and a woman to every man." Other emperors, like Caligula, sponsored orgies at which guests engaged in a wide variety of sexual practices, including in some cases **bestiality** and **sadism.** These sexual excesses were found more often among the upper classes of palace society than among average Romans, however. Unlike their counterparts in ancient Greece, Romans viewed homosexuality as a threat to the integrity of the Roman family and to the position of the Roman woman. Thus, it was not held in favor.

Western society traces the roots of many of its sexual terms to Roman culture, as indicated by their Latin roots. **Fellatio,** for example, derives from the Latin *fellare,* meaning "to suck." **Cunnilingus** derives from *cunnus,* meaning "vulva," and *lingere,* "to lick." **Fornicate** derives from *fornix,* an arch or vault. The term stems from Roman streetwalkers' practice of serving their customers in the shadows of archways near public buildings like stadiums and theaters.

The family was viewed as the source of strength of the Roman empire. Although Roman women were more likely than their Greek counterparts to share their husbands' social lives, they still were considered to be the property of their husbands.

THE EARLY CHRISTIANS Christianity emerged within the Roman Empire during the centuries following the death of Christ. According to the Christian Bible's New Testament, Jesus taught that love and tolerance are paramount in human relations, and that God is forgiving. Little is known about Jesus' views on sex, however. Early Christian views on sexuality were largely shaped by Saint Paul and the church fathers in the first century and by Saint Augustine in the latter part of the fourth century. Adultery and fornication were rampant among the upper classes of Rome during this era, and it was against this backdrop of sexual decadence that the early Christian fathers began to associate sexuality with sin (Branden, 1981).

Courtesan
A prostitute—especially the mistress of a noble or wealthy man. (From Italian roots meaning "court lady.")

Concubine
A secondary wife, usually of inferior legal and social status. (From Latin roots meaning "lying with.")

Bestiality
Sexual relations between a person and an animal.

Sadism
The practice of achieving sexual gratification through hurting or humiliating others.

Fellatio
A sexual activity involving oral contact with the penis.

Cunnilingus
A sexual activity involving oral contact with the female genitals.

Fornication
Sexual intercourse between people who are not married to one another. (If one of the partners is married, the act may be labeled *adultery.*)

In replacing the pagan values of Rome, the early Christians, like the Hebrews, sought to restrict sex to the marriage bed. They saw temptations of the flesh as distractions from spiritual devotion to God. Paul preached that celibacy was closer to the Christian ideal than marriage. He recognized that not everyone could achieve celibacy, however, so he said that it was "better to marry than to burn" (with passion, that is). Marriage was no sin, but it was spiritually inferior to celibacy.

Christians, like Jews before them, demanded virginity of brides. Masturbation and prostitution were condemned as sinful. The early Christians taught that men should love their wives with restraint, not passion. The goal of procreation should govern sexual behavior—the intellect should rule the flesh. Divorce was outlawed. Unhappiness with one's spouse might reflect sexual, thus sinful, restlessness. Dissolving a marriage might also jeopardize the tight social structure that supported the church.

Over subsequent centuries, Christian leaders took an even more negative view of sexuality. Particularly influential were the ideas of Saint Augustine (A.D. 353–430), who associated sexual lust with the original sin of Adam and Eve in the Garden of Eden. According to Augustine, lust had transformed the innocent procreative instinct, instilled in humanity by God, into sin. Following their fall from grace, Adam and Eve cloaked their nakedness with fig leaves; shame had entered the picture.

To Augustine, lust and shame were passed down from Adam and Eve through the generations, making any sexual expression, even intercourse in marriage, inherently evil and wicked. It was only through celibacy, according to Augustine, that men and women could attain a state of grace.

Nonprocreative sexual activity was deemed most sinful. Masturbation, homosexuality, oral-genital contact, anal intercourse—all were viewed as abominations in the eyes of God. To the Jews, sex was a natural and pleasurable function, so long as it was practiced within marriage. There was no sin attached to sexual pleasure. To the early Christians, however, sexual pleasure, even within marriage, was stained by the original sin of Adam and Eve. Marital sex was deemed somewhat less sinful when practiced for procreation and without passion.

SEXUALITY AND THE EASTERN RELIGIONS An appreciation of the religious traditions of the Middle East and Far East can broaden our perspective of the history of sexual customs and practices. Islam, the dominant religion in the Middle East, was founded by the Prophet Muhammad, who was born in Mecca, in what is now Saudi Arabia, in about A.D. 570 or 580. The Islamic tradition treasures marriage and sexual fulfillment in marriage. Premarital intercourse invites shame and social condemnation—and, in some fundamentalist Islamic states, it incurs the death penalty.

The family is the backbone of Islamic society, and celibacy is frowned upon (Ahmed, 1991). Muhammad decreed that marriage represents the only road to virtue (Minai, 1981). Islamic tradition permits a sexual double standard, however. Men may take up to four wives, but women are permitted only one husband. Public social interactions between men and women are more severely restricted in Islamic societies than in Western cultures. In traditional Islamic cultures, social dancing between the genders is shunned. Women in most traditional Islamic societies are expected to keep their heads and faces veiled in public and to avoid all contact, even a handshake, with men other than their husbands.

In the cultures of the Far East, sexuality was akin to spirituality. To the Taoist masters of China, who influenced Chinese culture for millennia, sex was anything but sinful. Rather, they taught that sex was a sacred duty, a form of worship that was believed to lead toward immortality. Sex was to be performed well and often if one was to achieve harmony with nature. The Chinese culture was the first to produce a detailed sex manual, which came into use about 200 years before the birth of Christ. The manual helped educate men and women in the art of lovemaking. The man was expected to extend intercourse as long as possible, thereby absorbing more of his wife's natural essence, or *yin*. Yin would enhance his own masculine essence, or *yang*. Moreover, he was expected to help bring his partner to orgasm so as to increase the flow of energy that he might absorb. The woman's pleasure was incidental or secondary.

Illustrations from the *Kama Sutra*. The *Kama Sutra,* an Indian sex manual believed to have been written sometime between the third and fifth centuries A.D., contained graphic illustrations of sexual techniques and practices.

Taoists believed that it was wasteful for a man to "spill his seed." Masturbation, acceptable for women, was ruled out for men. Such sexual practices as anal intercourse and oral-genital contact (fellatio and cunnilingus) were permissible, so long as the man did not squander *yang* through wasteful ejaculation. Another parallel to Western cultures was the role accorded women in traditional Chinese society. The "good wife," like her Western counterparts, was limited largely to the domestic roles of child care and house-keeping.

Perhaps no culture has cultivated sexual pleasure as a spiritual ideal to the extent of the ancient Hindus of India. Hindu sexual practices were codified in a sex manual, the *Kama Sutra.* The *Kama Sutra* contains descriptions and illustrations of sexual positions, some of which would challenge a contortionist. It holds recipes for alleged aphrodisiacs, descriptions of ways of kissing and embracing a lover, and so on. This manual remains the most influential sex manual ever produced. It is believed to have been written by the Hindu sage Vatsyayana sometime between the third and fifth centuries A.D., at about the time that Christianity was taking shape in the West as an organized religion.

TRUTH OR *FICTION?*

R E V I S I T E D

The production of illustrated sex manuals originated in modern times. *Not true. Actually, the most influential sex manual ever produced was written and illustrated—profusely!—in ancient India.* •

The *Kama Sutra,* in its graphic representations of sexual positions and practices, reflected the Hindu belief that sex was a religious duty, not a source of shame or guilt. In the Hindu doctrine of *karma* (the passage or transmigration of souls from one place to another), sexual fulfillment was regarded as one way to become reincarnated at a higher level of existence—though not as important a way as leading a virtuous life.

All in all, early Indian culture viewed sex as virtuous and natural. Indian society grew more restrictive toward sexuality after about A.D. 1000, however (Tannahill, 1980).

THE MIDDLE AGES   The Middle Ages, sometimes called medieval times, span the millennium of Western history from about A.D. 476 to A.D. 1450. They are sometimes alluded to as the Dark Ages because some historians have depicted them as an era of cultural and intellectual decay and stagnation. The Roman Catholic church continued to grow in influence. Its attitudes toward sexuality, largely unchanged since the time of Augustine, dominated medieval thought. Some cross-currents of change crept across medieval Europe, however, especially in the social standing of women. The Roman Catholic church had long regarded all women as being tainted by the sin of Eve, whom it blamed for humankind's downfall in the Garden of Eden. In the Eastern church of Constantinople, the cult of the Virgin Mary flourished. The ideal of womanhood was in the image of Mary: good, gracious, loving, and saintly.

Imported by the Crusaders and others who returned from the East, the cult of the Virgin Mary swept European Christendom and helped elevate the status of women. Hundreds of new abbeys were founded across Europe. Their monks were devoted to the Virgin. They erected chapels in their churches in her honor and wore white in tribute to her purity.

Two conflicting concepts of women thus dominated medieval thought: one, *woman as Eve,* the temptress; the other, *woman as Mary,* virtuous and pure. Contemporary Western images of women still show the schism between the good girl and the bad girl—the Madonna and the whore. Part of the fascination of the rock star Madonna is that she combines the name of the Virgin Mary and the crucifixes with an open display of undergarments and simulated lovemaking on the stage and in her videos. Note the Western double standard: an unmarried, sexually active woman runs the risk of being branded a "slut"; a single, sexually active man is likely to receive more accepting labels, such as "stud," "playboy," or "ladies' man." Feminists note that men have always been more accepting of their own sexuality, but have been unable to accept women's sexuality as a natural part of their being.

Among the upper classes of medieval times, a concept of courtly love also emerged, which was part chivalry and part romance novel. Troubadours of the twelfth and thirteenth centuries sang of pure and ennobling love that burned brightly but remained unconsummated. Their verses often depicted the chaste love between a married lady of the court and a handsome suitor of lower rank who sought her favor through heroic deeds.

Two Conflicting Concepts of Women. Two conflicting concepts of women dominated medieval thought. One was of woman as Eve, the temptress, as shown in the engraving on the right; the other, of woman as Mary, as shown in this painting on the left, virtuous and pure. Contemporary Western images of women still show the schism between the good girl and the bad girl—the Madonna and the whore.

THE PROTESTANT REFORMATION During the Reformation, Martin Luther (1483–1546) and other Christian reformers like John Calvin (1509–1564) split off from the Roman Catholic church and formed their own sects, which led to the development of the modern Protestant denominations of Western Europe (and later, the New World). Luther disputed many Roman Catholic doctrines on sexuality. He believed that priests should be allowed to marry and rear children. To Luther, marriage was as much a part of human nature as eating or drinking (Tannahill, 1980). Calvin rejected the Roman church's position that sex in marriage was permissible only for the purpose of procreation. To Calvin, sexual expression in marriage fulfilled other legitimate roles, such as strengthening the marriage bond and helping to relieve the stresses of everyday life. The Protestant Reformation encouraged a more accepting view of sexuality, although it maintained strict adherence to the belief that sex was permissible only in the context of marriage. Stern penalties were meted out for premarital and extramarital sex. The Puritans, one of the earliest Protestant sects to settle in America, subjected fornicators to flogging and sent parents to the pillory or the stocks if their children were born too soon after the wedding date. Adulterers, too, were flogged and sometimes branded. Remember the scarlet *A* that the adulteress Hester Prynne was compelled to wear in Nathaniel Hawthorne's novel *The Scarlet Letter.*

Learning Objective 6:
Recognize that the origins of sexual attitudes and behaviors can often be traced to earlier eras.

SHAPING THE PRESENT: FROM REPRESSION TO REVOLUTION TO REACTION
Early settlers brought to the New World the religious teachings that had dominated Western thought and culture for centuries. Whatever their differences, each religion stressed the ideal of family life and viewed sex outside of marriage as immoral or sinful. A woman's place, by and large, was in the home and in the fields. Not until the twentieth century did women gain the right to vote, and, in large numbers, begin attending universities and pursuing careers in the professions and the business world.

In this century, social change has swept through Western culture at a sometimes dizzying pace. Sexual behaviors and attitudes that would have been unthinkable a couple of generations ago—such as cohabitation ("living together")—have become commonplace. The social barriers that had restricted women's roles have largely broken down.

The middle and later parts of the nineteenth century are generally called the Victorian period, named after Queen Victoria of England, who assumed the throne in 1837 and ruled until her death in 1901. Her name has become virtually synonymous with sexual repression.

Victorian society in Europe and the United States, on the surface at least, was prim and proper. Sex was not discussed in polite society. Even the legs of pianos were draped with cloth for the sake of modesty. Many women viewed sex as a marital duty to be performed for procreation or to satisfy their husbands' cravings. Consider the following quotation:

> I am happy now that Charles calls on my bedchamber less frequently than of old. As it is, I now endure but two calls a week and when I hear his steps outside my door I lie down on my bed, close my eyes, open my legs and think of England.

> (Attributed to Alice, Lady Hillingdon, wife of the Second Baron Hillingdon)

Women were assumed not to experience sexual desires or pleasures. "I would say," observed Dr. William Acton (1814–1875), an influential English physician, in 1857, "that the majority of women (happily for society) are not much troubled with sexual feeling of any kind." Women, thought Acton, were born with a sort of *sexual anesthesia.*

It was widely believed among medical authorities in England and the United States that sex drains the man of his natural vitality. Physicians thus recommended that intercourse be practiced infrequently, perhaps once a month or so. The Reverend Sylvester Graham (1794–1851) preached that ejaculation deprived men of the "vital fluids" they need to maintain health and vitality. Graham believed that the loss of an ounce of semen was equal to the loss of several ounces of blood (Bullough, 1976). Each time a man ejaculated, in Graham's view, he risked his physical health. Graham preached against the dangers of "wasting the seed" by masturbation or even by frequent marital intercourse.

(How frequent was frequent? In Graham's view, intercourse more than once a month could dangerously deplete the man's vital energies.) Graham recommended that young men control their sexual appetites by adopting a diet consisting largely of simple foods based on whole-grain flours. To this day, his name is identified with a type of cracker he developed for this purpose in the 1830s, the graham cracker, derived from unbolted wheat (graham flour).

It appears, though, that the actual behavior of Victorians was not as repressed as advertised. Despite the belief in female sexual anesthesia, Victorian women, as women before and after them, certainly did experience sexual pleasure and orgasm. One piece of evidence was provided by an early sex survey conducted in 1892 by a female physician, Clelia Duel Mosher. Though her sample was small and nonrandom, 35 of the 44 women who responded admitted to desiring sexual intercourse, and 34 of the 44 reported experiencing orgasm. Women's diaries of the time also contained accounts of passionate and sexually fulfilling love affairs (Gay, 1984).

Prostitution also flourished during the Victorian era. Men apparently thought that they were doing their wives a favor by looking elsewhere. Accurate statistics are hard to come by, but there may have been as many as one prostitute for every twelve London men during the nineteenth century; in Vienna, perhaps one for every seven men (Tannahill, 1980).

Discussion Question: What modern beliefs, myths, or practices can you trace to the influences of earlier eras?

Sexologist
A person who engages in the scientific study of sexual behavior.

THE FOUNDATIONS OF THE SCIENTIFIC STUDY OF SEXUALITY It was against this backdrop of sexual repression that scientists and scholars first began to approach sexuality as an area of legitimate scientific investigation. An early important contributor to the science of human sexuality was the English physician Havelock Ellis (1859–1939). Ellis compiled a veritable encyclopedia of sexuality: a series of volumes published between 1897 and 1910 entitled *Studies in the Psychology of Sex*. Ellis drew information from various sources, including case histories, anthropological findings, and medical knowledge. He challenged the prevailing view by arguing that sexual desires in women were natural and healthy. He promoted the view that many sexual problems had psychological rather than physical causes. He also promoted acceptance of the view that homosexuality was a naturally occurring variation within the spectrum of normal sexuality, rather than an aberration. Presaging some contemporary views, Ellis treated homosexuality as an inborn disposition, not a vice or character flaw.

Another influential **sexologist,** the German psychiatrist Richard von Krafft-Ebing (1840–1902) described more than 200 case histories of individuals with various sexual deviations in his book *Psychopathia Sexualis*. His writings contain vivid descriptions of deviations ranging from sadomasochism (sexual gratification through inflicting or receiving pain) and bestiality (sex with animals) to yet more bizarre and frightening forms, such as necrophilia (intercourse with the dead). Krafft-Ebing viewed sexual deviations as mental diseases that could be studied and perhaps treated by medical science.

At about the same time, a Viennese physician, Sigmund Freud (1856–1939), was developing a theory of personality that has had an enormous influence on modern culture and science. Freud believed that sexual drives or impulses were our principal motivating forces.

Although these early scientists paved the way, it was Alfred Kinsey (1894–1956), an Indiana University zoologist, and his colleagues, who in the 1930s and 1940s conducted the first large-scale studies of sexual behavior. It was then that sex research became recognized as a field of scientific study in its own right. In 1938 Kinsey had been asked to teach a course at Indiana University on marriage. When researching the course, Kinsey discovered that little was known about sexual practices in American society. He soon embarked upon an ambitious research project. Detailed, personal interviews with nearly 12,000 people across the United States were conducted. The results of his surveys were published in two volumes, *Sexual Behavior in the Human Male* (1948) and *Sexual Behavior in the Human Female* (1953)—the first scientific attempts to provide a comprehensive picture of sexual behavior in the United States. Despite the fact that these books made for rather dry reading and were filled with statistical tables rather than racy pictures or vignettes, they became best-sellers. They exploded on a public that had not yet learned to discuss sex openly, and their publication (especially the book on female sexual behavior) unleashed a torrent of criticism. Kinsey's work had some methodological flaws, but much of the criticism branded it immoral and obscene. The *New York Times* refused to run advertisements for the 1948 volume on male sexuality, and many newspapers refused even to report the results of his survey on female sexuality. A congressional committee in the 1950s went so far as to claim that Kinsey's work undermined the moral fiber of the nation, rendering it more vulnerable to a Communist takeover (Gebhard, 1976b).

Kinsey died in 1956. His death may have been hastened by the emotional toll he suffered for his work (Gagnon, 1990). Even so, Kinsey and his colleagues made sex research a scientifically respectable field of study and helped lay the groundwork for greater openness in the larger society in discussing sexual behavior.

THE PATH TO THE PRESENT: SEXUALITY IN THE TWENTIETH CENTURY Victorian attitudes toward sexuality dominated society's view of sexuality well into the middle of the twentieth century. The belief that women did not desire sex was something of a self-fulfilling prophecy. That is, couples who held this belief may not have sought ways of enhancing the woman's sexual pleasure. Women were expected to remain virgins until marriage, although society gave tacit permission to men to sow their wild oats. Men were permitted to seek sex with prostitutes or "loose" women, or at least others looked the other way when they did (Gagnon, 1977).

Although steamy passages were found in early twentieth-century writings like D. H. Lawrence's *Lady Chatterley's Lover,* the most explicit sexual contact permitted in the films of the 1930s and 1940s was a discreet kiss (no open-mouth kissing allowed). No public forums featured sexual exotica or discussed sex openly. Nor was human sexuality widely taught in public schools, colleges, or even medical schools. By and large, sex remained shrouded in ignorance and secrecy.

The period of the mid-1960s to the mid-1970s is often referred to as the *sexual revolution,* since dramatic changes occurred in U.S. sexual attitudes and practices. When the folksinger Bob Dylan sang that "The Times They Are A-Changin'" in the early 1960s, our society was on the threshold of major social upheaval, not only in sexual behavior, but also in science, politics, fashion, music, art, and cinema. The so-called Woodstock generation, disheartened by commercialism and the Vietnam War, tuned in (to rock music on the radio), turned on (to drugs), and dropped out (of mainstream society). The

Are Today's Young People More or Less Liberal in the Expression of Their Sexuality than People in Earlier Generations? Today the threat of AIDS hangs over every sexual encounter. Although many young people today are selective in their choice of partners and take precautions to make sex safer, evidence also shows that more teenagers are engaging in sexual activity, and at younger ages, than in previous generations.

battle was on between the hippies and the hardhats. Long hair became commonplace on men, bell-bottomed jeans were in vogue, movies became sexually explicit (the pornography classic *Deep Throat* made headlines), and rock music carried the message of rebellion and revolution.

No single event marked the onset of the sexual revolution. There was no charge up a sexual Bunker Hill. Social movements often gain momentum from a timely interplay of scientific, social, political, and economic forces. The war (in Vietnam), the bomb (fear of the nuclear bomb), the pill (the introduction of the birth-control pill), and the tube (TV, that is) were four such forces. The pill effectively ended the risk of unwanted pregnancy for young people, permitting them to engage in recreational or casual sex, rather than procreative sex. Pop psychology movements, like the so-called Human Potential Movement of the 1960s and 1970s (the "Me Decade"), spread the message that people should focus on getting in touch with and expressing their genuine feelings, including their sexual feelings. "Doing your own thing" became one catchphrase. "If it feels right, go with it," became another. The sexual genie had popped out of the bottle.

The sexual revolution also seems to have been tied to increased permissiveness and political liberalism. Perhaps in part reflecting the times, in part acting as a catalyst, the media dealt more openly with sex. Popular books encouraged people to explore their sexuality. Sexually explicit film scenes became so commonplace that the movie rating system was introduced to alert parents. Protests against the Vietnam War and racial discrimination spilled over into broader protests against conventional morality and hypocrisy. Traditional prohibitions against drugs, casual sex, even group sex tumbled down suddenly, like the Berlin Wall in 1989.

Some of the alternative lifestyles that preoccupied the media in the 1960s and 1970s have fallen by the wayside. We no longer hear much about mate-swapping (also called *swinging*) or "open marriages." Casual sex (sex between partners who are not emotionally committed) may also be on the wane, in part because of increased fear of sexually transmitted diseases, especially AIDS. Many singles' bars, where the phrase "Your place or mine?" became popular, have closed or been turned into "health bars."

Yet if the pendulum has begun to swing partway back, the incidence of premarital sex among teenagers, especially younger teens, appears headed in the opposite direction. More teenagers are engaging in sexual relations today, and at younger ages (Barringer, 1990; Brooks-Gunn & Furstenberg, 1989; Sonnerstein et al., 1988; Zeman, 1990). In addition to premarital sex, two other features of the sexual revolution have become permanent parts of our social fabric: the liberation of female sexuality and a greater willingness to discuss sex openly.

SUMMING UP   What, then, does history tell us about sex? Is there a universal standard for defining sexual values, or are there many standards? All societies have some form of an incest taboo, and most societies have placed a value on procreative sex within the context of an enduring relationship. The societal value of an enduring social, economic, and intimate relationship—usually in the form of marriage—lies in the roles it serves in providing security for children, maintaining or increasing the population, and ensuring the orderly transfer of property from generation to generation.

Other sexual practices—masturbation, promiscuous sex, homosexuality, prostitution, polygamy, and so on—have been condemned in some societies, tolerated by others, and encouraged by still others. Some societies have looked with favor upon nonprocreative sex (at least within the context of marriage), whereas others have condemned it. Some historians argue that the pagan "degradations" of Rome led to its demise—that otherwise a "purer" Rome might still bestride the earth. They warn that the "excesses" of our own sexual revolution may also bring us down. Rome, however, suffered from the administrative difficulties of tending to a far-flung empire and was besieged by "barbarians" in the outposts and, eventually, at the city gates. In fact, the civilizations of ancient Greece and Rome maintained their prominence for hundreds of years. When we consider their contributions to Western art, philosophical thought, and the languages we speak, we may question whether they fell at all.

Orgasm
The climax of sexual excitement.

Spinal reflex
An automatic response to a stimulus that does not involve the brain.

THE BIOLOGICAL PERSPECTIVE

The biological perspective focuses on the role of biological processes, such as genetic, hormonal, vascular, and neural factors, in explaining human sexual behavior. Sex, after all, serves the biological function of reproduction. We are biologically endowed with anatomical structures and physiological capabilities that make sexual behavior possible—and pleasurable.

Studying the biology of sex informs us of the mechanisms of reproduction and the biological processes that give rise to sexual maturation. It also informs us of the physiological mechanisms of sexual arousal and response. By studying the biology of sex, we learn that erection occurs when the penis becomes engorged in blood. We also learn that, in women, a "sweating" action of the vaginal walls, also the result of engorgement, produces vaginal lubrication (vaginal "wetness"). We see that **orgasm** is a **spinal reflex** as well as a psychological event.

Biological researchers have made major strides in assisting infertile couples to conceive through laboratory-based methods of fertilization. "Test-tube babies" have been conceived in laboratory dishes and inserted in their mothers' uteruses, where they have developed to term. In some cases in which women fail to release ripened egg cells of their own, other women have served as egg donors, supplying the ovum that is fertilized by the father's sperm in a laboratory dish and then inserted in the intended mother's uterus.

The study of human sexuality from the biological perspective presents some unique difficulties. Sexual behavior in humans is most always conducted in private, which makes it extremely difficult for researchers to study the biological mechanisms of human sexual arousal and response directly. Not until William Masters and Virginia Johnson's pioneering research in the 1950s and 1960s did we learn of many of the bodily changes that occur during sexual stimulation. Masters, a physician, and Johnson, a researcher, believed that sexual responses should be studied through careful observation and measurement in the laboratory.

Knowledge of biology has furthered our understanding of sexuality and our ability to overcome sexual problems. To what extent does biology govern sexual behavior? Is sex controlled by biological instincts? Or are psychosocial factors, such as culture, experience, and decision-making ability more important? Although the sexual behavior of other species is largely governed by biological processes, culture and experience play vital roles—and in many cases, more important roles than biological factors—in the sexuality of humans. All in all, most students of sexuality recognize that *human* sexuality involves a complex interaction of biological and psychosocial factors. Biology indicates what is possible and, often, what is pleasurable or painful. Biology is not destiny, however. It does not imply what is proper and improper or determine the sexual decisions that we make. Religious tradition, cultural and personal values, and learning and experience guide these decisions.

Analogue
Something that is similar or comparable to something else.

Dorsal-ventral position
The rear-entry coital position. (From Latin roots meaning "back" [*dorsum*] and "belly" [*venter*].)

Copulation
Sexual intercourse. (From the Latin *copulare*, meaning "to unite" or "to couple.")

Ventral-ventral position
The face-to-face (or belly-to-belly) coital position.

THE CROSS-SPECIES PERSPECTIVE

The study of other animal species places human behavior in broader context. A surprising variety of sexual behaviors exists among nonhumans. There are animal examples, or **analogues,** of such human sexual behavior as homosexuality, oral-genital contact, and oral-oral behavior (i.e., kissing). Foreplay is also well known in the animal world. Turtles massage their mates' heads with their claws. Male mice nibble at their partners' necks. Most mammals use only a **dorsal-ventral** position for **copulation,** but some animals, such as apes, have been found to use a variety of coital positions. Nadler (1976) observed both dorsal-ventral and **ventral-ventral** positions among lowland gorillas in captivity. Still, the rear-entry position accounted for 80 percent of the copulations and 74 percent of the ejaculations in the gorillas.

We even find analogues of deviant forms of sexual behavior, like rape, in the animal world. We should be careful about drawing a connection between human rape and animal analogues, however. Human (perhaps we should say *in*human) rape is often motivated by

Evolution
The development of a species to its present state, which is believed to involve adaptations to its environment.

Natural selection
The evolutionary process by which adaptive traits enable members of a species to survive to reproductive age and transmit these traits to future generations.

Charles Darwin

Genes
The basic units of heredity, which consist of chromosomal segments of DNA.

Chromosomes
The rod-like structures that reside in the nuclei of every living cell and carry the genetic code in the form of genes.

DNA
Deoxyribonucleic acid—the chemical substance whose molecules make up genes and chromosomes.

Mutations
Random changes in the molecular structure of DNA.

Sociobiology
The theory that dispositions toward behavior patterns that enhance reproductive success may be genetically transmitted.

the desire to punish and humiliate the victim, a motive that may be entirely absent in the forced copulations in other animals that resemble rape in humans.

Cross-species research reveals an interesting pattern. Sexual behavior among "higher" mammals, such as primates, is less directly controlled by instinct than it is among the "lower" species, such as birds, fish, or lower mammals. Experience and learning play more important roles in sexuality as we travel up the evolutionary ladder.

Species vary not only in their physical characteristics but also in their social behavior, including their mating behavior. Scientists look to the process of **evolution** to help explain such variability. What is evolution? How might the sexual behavior of various species, including our own, be influenced by evolutionary forces?

The English naturalist Charles Darwin (1809–1882), the father of the theory of evolution, believed that animal and plant species were not created independently, but evolved over time from other life-forms. The mechanism by which species evolved was **natural selection,** or in the vernacular, "survival of the fittest." In each species, Darwin pointed out, some individuals are better adapted to their environments than others. The better adapted members are more likely to survive to reproduce, and therefore more likely to pass along their traits to succeeding generations. So over time, a greater proportion of the species population carries the traits of the fittest members. Fitness, in the evolutionary sense, does not mean strength or stamina. Rather, it means reproductive success, or the ability to produce surviving offspring. The fittest members of a species produce the greatest number of surviving offspring. They are not necessarily the strongest or fleetest of foot, although these traits may be adaptive in some environments and so enhance reproductive success.

Over time, natural selection favors traits that contribute to survival and reproduction. When environmental conditions change, natural selection favors those members of a species who possess traits that help them adapt. These forms of the species proliferate, eventually replacing forms that fail to survive and reproduce. Species that lack forms that possess adaptive traits will eventually become extinct and be replaced by species that are better suited to their environmental conditions.

Darwin was too early—he did not have enough information to be able to account for the mechanisms that could explain how traits were passed along from generation to generation. Nor could he explain how a species evolved from one form to another. Not until the discovery of the principles of genetic inheritance by the Austrian monk Gregor Mendel (1822–1884) did the pieces of the puzzle of evolution begin to fall into place. Mendel discovered that traits are transmitted from generation to generation by units of heredity that we now call **genes.** Traits are determined by the combinations of genes that offspring inherit from their parents.

We now understand that the units of heredity, or genes, that carry the genetic code are segments of **chromosomes,** which are composed of **DNA.** The chemical structure of genes provides genetic instructions. Each human cell normally contains a complement of 46 chromosomes, which are arranged in 23 pairs. Each human chromosome consists of more than 1,000 genes. A child normally inherits one member of each pair of chromosomes from each parent. So each offspring inherits 50 percent of his or her genes from each parent. The particular combinations of genes that one inherits from one's parents account for whether one has blue eyes or brown eyes, light or dark hair, and a wide range of other characteristics.

New variations in species are introduced through random genetic changes called **mutations.** Mutations occur randomly but are subject to natural selection. That is, some mutations are adaptive in that they enhance reproductive success. As a result, these adaptive mutations are more likely to be retained and to proliferate in a species. As more members of the species possess a variety of these adaptive traits, the species as a whole changes in form. Most mutations are not adaptive, however, and quickly disappear from the genetic pool.

In recent years, some theorists have suggested that there is a genetic basis to social behavior, including sexual behavior, among humans and other animals (Wilson, 1975). This theory, called **sociobiology,** proposes that dispositions toward *behavior patterns* that enhance reproductive success—as well as physical traits that do so—may be geneti-

Notes: Some shorebirds, such as the jacana and some species of sandpipers, practice polyandry. A female jacana has up to six mates simultaneously. These males build the nests, incubate the eggs, care for the young, and scream for the female if their territory needs defending.

cally transmitted. If so, we may carry traits that helped our prehistoric ancestors survive and reproduce successfully, even if these traits are no longer adaptive in modern culture. "Modern culture"—dating, say, from classical Greece—is but a moment in the lifetime of our species.

There is a tendency to think of adaptive traits as somehow more "worthy," "good," or "admirable" than less adaptive traits. Evolution is not a moralistic enterprise, however. A trait either does or does not enhance reproductive success; it is not in itself good or bad. It may be adaptive for the female of a species to eat the male after mating. "Dad" then literally nourishes his offspring during the period of gestation. In evolutionary terms, his personal sacrifice is adaptive if it increases the chances that the offspring will survive and carry his genes. In other species, it may be adaptive for fathers to "love them and leave them"—that is, to mate with as many females as possible and abruptly abandon them to "plant their seed" elsewhere.

Sociobiologists are interested in sexual behavior because it is so interwoven with reproductive success. They seek common sexual themes across cultures in the belief that common themes may represent traits that helped our ancestors survive and became part of the human genetic endowment. For example, there is considerable cross-cultural evidence that men are more promiscuous than women and have "spread their seed" widely.

Some sociobiologists argue that men are naturally more promiscuous because they are the genetic heirs of ancestors whose reproductive success increased in relation to the number of women they were able to impregnate (Symons, 1979). Women, by contrast, can produce only a few offspring in their lifetimes. Thus, the theory goes, they have to be more selective with respect to their mating partners. Women's reproductive success is enhanced by mating with the fittest males—not with any Tom, Dick, or Harry who happens by. From this perspective, the male's "roving eye" and the female's selectivity are embedded in their genes.

To some sociobiologists, human beings are like marionettes on strings being tugged by invisible puppet masters—their genes. Genes govern the biological processes of sexual maturation and the production of sex hormones. Hormones, in turn, are largely responsible for regulating the sexual behavior of other animal species. Extending the sociobiological model to human behavior sparks considerable controversy, however. Critics contend that human behavior largely reflects learning and personal choice, not heredity.

Critics also claim that sociobiology is largely conjectural. No one, for example, has yet discovered a gene for promiscuity. There is no direct evidence that either male promiscuity or female selectivity is genetically determined. Critics also point to examples of cultural diversity as evidence that culture and experience, not genetics, play the pivotal role in human behavior. Nor is cross-cultural similarity in sexual practices necessarily proof of a common genetic factor. Different cultures may adopt similar customs because such customs serve a similar function. For example, marriage exists in some form in every human society, perhaps because marriage serves similar functions in various cultures, such as in regulating the availability of sexual partners and providing an economic and social arrangement that will provide for the care of offspring. All in all, the evidence is far from clear (or compelling) for regarding human social and sexual behavior as direct products of our genes.

THE CROSS-CULTURAL PERSPECTIVE

Learning Objective 9: Discuss possible conclusions about the universality of human sexual behavior given the cross-cultural information presented.

The cross-cultural perspective, like the historical perspective, provides insight into the ways in which cultural beliefs affect sexual behavior and people's sense of morality. Unlike historians, who are limited in their sources to the eyewitness accounts of others and the shards of information that can be gleaned from fading relics, anthropologists can observe other cultures firsthand. Interest in the cross-cultural perspective on sexuality was spurred by work during the early twentieth century by the anthropologists Margaret Mead (1901–1978) and Bronislaw Malinowski (1884–1942).

In *Sex and Temperament in Three Primitive Societies* (1935), Mead laid the groundwork for recent psychological and sociological research challenging gender-role stereo-

Village Life. Anthropologists study sexual customs among preliterate societies to learn about the similarities and differences across cultures.

types. In most cultures characterized by a gender division of labor, men typically go to business or to the hunt, and—when necessary—to war. In such cultures, men are perceived as strong, active, independent, and logical. Women are viewed as passive, dependent, nurturant, and emotional. Mead concluded that these stereotypes are not inherent in our genetic heritage. Rather, they are acquired through cultural expectations and socialization. That is, men and women learn to behave in ways that are expected of them in their particular culture.

Malinowski lived on the Trobriand island of Boyawa in the South Pacific, during World War I. There he gathered data on two societies of the South Pacific, the Trobrianders and the Amphett islanders. The Amphett islanders maintained strict sexual prohibitions, whereas the Trobrianders enjoyed greater freedom. Trobrianders, for example, encouraged their children to masturbate. Boys and girls were expected to begin to engage in intercourse when they were biologically old enough. According to custom, they would pair off, exchange a coconut, a bit of betel nut, a few beads, or some fruit from the bush. Then they would go off together and engage in intercourse (Malinowski, 1929, p. 488). Adolescents were expected to have multiple sex partners until they married.

TRUTH OR *FICTION?*
R E V I S I T E D

Trobrianders consider their children old enough to engage in sexual intercourse when they are . . . old enough. *In traditional Trobriand society, children were encouraged by their elders to engage in sexual intercourse when they were biologically mature enough to do so.* •

Malinowski found the Trobrianders less anxiety-ridden than the Amphett islanders. He attributed the difference to their sexual freedom, thus making an early plea to relax prohibitions in Western societies. Even sexually permissive cultures like that of the Trobrianders, however, placed limits on sexual freedom. They frowned on extramarital relationships, for example. Other cultures, however, like that of the Toda of southern India, consider it immoral for a husband to restrict his wife's extramarital relations (Howard, 1989). Chukchee men of Arctic Siberia often exchange their wives with their friends.

CROSS-CULTURAL COMMONALITIES AND DIFFERENCES IN SEXUAL BEHAVIOR
In 1951, Clellan Ford, an anthropologist, and Frank Beach, a psychologist, reviewed sexual behavior in preliterate societies around the world, as well as in other animals. They found great variety in sexual customs and beliefs among the almost 200 societies they studied. They also found some common threads, although there were exceptions to each. Although Ford and Beach's work is almost half a century old, it remains a valuable source of information about cross-cultural and cross-species patterns in sexuality

(Frayser, 1985). Throughout the text, our discussion of cross-cultural patterns in sexuality is guided by their work and by more recent cross-cultural studies conducted by Gwen Broude and Sarah Greene (1976) and by Suzanne Frayser (1985), among others.

Ford and Beach reported that kissing was quite common across the cultures they studied, although not universal. The Thonga of Africa were one society that did not practice kissing. Upon witnessing two European visitors kissing each other, members of the tribe commented that they could not understand why Europeans "ate" each other's saliva and dirt. The frequency of sexual intercourse also varies from culture to culture, but intercourse is relatively more frequent among young people everywhere.

Societies differ in their attitudes toward childhood masturbation. Some societies, such as the Hopi Native Americans of the southwest United States, ignore it. Trobrianders encourage children to stimulate themselves. Other societies condemn it. The people of the Pacific island of East Bay discourage children from touching their genitals and may subject them to ridicule or scolding (Davenport, 1965).

Although all cultures place some prohibitions on incestuous relationships, intercourse between brother and sister has been viewed as natural and desirable in some cultures, such as that of the Dahomey of West Africa (Stephens, 1982). The acceptability of incestuous relations has also varied in some cultures according to social class. In some societies incestuous marriages were permitted among the ruling classes. Virtually all cultures have strict incest taboos, however. Ford and Beach reported that marriage was even taboo between people speaking the same dialect in one Australian tribe—a prohibition that did not enhance marital communication.

Eighty-four percent of Ford and Beach's (1951) preliterate cultures practiced polygamy. The researchers concluded that monogamy was relatively uncommon. More common is the form of polygamy called **polygyny,** in which men are permitted to have more than one wife. Similarly, Frayser (1985) found that polygyny was practiced by the great majority (82 percent) of societies in her cross-cultural sample. In many cultures, the number of wives a man has is an emblem of his wealth and status. The cultures studied in Ford and Beach's and Frayser's cross-cultural samples typically had few members, however; monogamy, which is the custom in the more populous, technologically advanced cultures, is thus more prevalent worldwide. Even in polygynous cultures, the numbers of people who are monogamously married are greater than those who are married polygamously. Few societies have the oversupply of women that universal polygyny would entail (Ember & Ember, 1990). Rarer still is **polyandry,** a practice that permits women to have more than one husband. Frayser (1985) found polyandry in only 2 percent of societies she studied. In fraternal polyandry, the most common form of polyandry, two or more brothers share a wife, and all live together in the same household. The wife "visits" each brother according to a schedule arranged by the men (Ember & Ember, 1990).

Polygyny has a long tradition in Western culture. King Solomon was reputed to have 700 wives. Polygyny was practiced in the nineteenth-century United States by an early leader of the Mormon church, Brigham Young, and by some of his followers. It has since been banned by the Mormon church as well as by state laws, although it is still practiced in some disenfranchised Mormon communities.

The cross-cultural perspective illustrates the importance of learning in human sexual behavior. Societies differ widely in their sexual attitudes, customs, and practices. The members of all human societies share the same anatomical structures and physiological capacities for sexual pleasure, however. The same hormones flow through their arteries. Yet their sexual practices, and the pleasure they reap or fail to attain, may set them apart. Were human sexuality completely or predominantly determined by biology, we would not find such diversity.

Although sexual practices vary widely across cultures, there are some universal patterns. For one, all societies regulate sexual behavior in some fashion. No society allows unbounded sexual freedom. There is usually some societal control over the acceptability of sexual and marital partners, and extramarital relations. All societies have some form of an incest taboo. Nevertheless, cross-cultural comparisons show evidence of great variety.

Polygyny
A form of marriage in which a man has two or more wives. (From the Greek *gyne,* meaning "woman.")

Polyandry
A form of marriage in which a woman has two or more husbands. (From the Greek *andros,* meaning "man" or "male.")

Notes: Brigham Young had nearly two dozen wives and 47 children.

Teaching Tip: Introduce the term *ethnocentrism,* which is a belief in the superiority of one's own cultural group and a tendency to view other groups in terms of one's own culture. Discuss how ethnocentrism can interfere with students' willingness to learn about and accept cultural differences.

Ethnocentric
Adjectival form of the noun *ethnocentrism,* meaning the tendency to view other groups or cultures according to the standards of one's own. (From the Greek *ethnos* meaning "race," "culture," or "people," and *kentric,* meaning "center.")

Psychoanalysis
The theory of personality originated by Sigmund Freud, which proposes that human behavior represents the outcome of clashing inner forces.

Sigmund Freud

Id
In Freud's theory, the mental structure that is present at birth, embodies physiological drives, and is fully unconscious.

Ego
In Freud's theory, the second mental structure to develop, which is characterized by self-awareness, planning, and delay of gratification.

TRUTH OR FICTION?

R E V I S I T E D

Superego
In Freud's theory, the third mental structure, which functions as a moral guardian and sets forth high standards for behavior.

What is considered natural, normal, or moral in one culture may be deemed unnatural, abnormal, or immoral in another.

Yet people often apply an **ethnocentric** standard when judging other cultures. That is, they tend to treat the standards of their own cultures as the norm by which to judge other peoples. Cross-cultural information helps us to appreciate the relativity of the concept of normalcy, and to recognize the cultural contexts of sexual behavior. When we consider the historical and cross-cultural perspectives, we come to appreciate that our behavior exists in the context both of our own culture and our own time.

PSYCHOLOGICAL PERSPECTIVES

Psychological perspectives focus on the many psychological influences—perception, learning, motivation, emotion, personality, and so on—that affect our sexual behavior and our experience of ourselves as female or male. Some psychological theorists, like Sigmund Freud, focused on the motivational role of sex in human personality. Others focus on how our experiences and mental representations of the world affect our sexual behavior.

SIGMUND FREUD AND PSYCHOANALYTIC THEORY   Sigmund Freud, a Viennese physician, formulated a grand theory of personality termed **psychoanalysis.** Freud believed that we are all born with biologically based sex drives. These drives must be channeled through socially approved outlets if family and social life are to carry on without undue conflict. He hypothesized that conflicts between sexuality and society become internalized in the form of an inner conflict between two opposing parts of the personality, the **id,** which is the repository of biologically based drives or "instincts" (like hunger, thirst, elimination, sex, and aggression), and the **ego,** which represents reason and good sense. The ego seeks socially appropriate outlets for satisfying the basic drives that arise from the id. Your id, for example, prompts you to feel sexual urges. Your ego attempts to find ways of satisfying those urges without incurring condemnation from others or from your own moral conscience, which Freud called the **superego.** How these internal conflicts are resolved, in Freud's view, largely determines our ability to love, work, and lead well-adjusted lives.

Freud proposed that the mind operates on conscious and unconscious levels. The conscious level corresponds to our state of present awareness. The **unconscious mind** refers to the darker reaches of the mind that lie outside our direct awareness. The ego shields the conscious mind from awareness of our baser sexual and aggressive urges by means of **defense mechanisms** such as **repression,** or motivated forgetting. Examples of defense mechanisms are shown in Table 1.1.

Although many sexual ideas and impulses are banished to the unconscious, they continue to seek expression. One avenue of expression is the dream, through which sexual impulses may be perceived in disguised, or symbolic, form. The therapists and scholars who follow in the Freudian tradition are quite interested in analyzing dreams, and the dream objects listed in Table 1.2 are often considered sexual symbols. Freud himself maintained a bit of skepticism about the import of dream symbols, however. He once remarked, "Sometimes a cigar is just a cigar."

In our dreams, airplanes, bullets, snakes, sticks, and similar objects symbolize the male genitals. To a psychoanalyst, dreams of airplanes, bullets, snakes, sticks, and similar objects may symbolize the male genitals. Even Freud had to admit, however, that "sometimes a cigar is just a cigar"! •

Freud introduced us to many new and often controversial ideas about ourselves as sexual beings. For example, he originated the concept of **erogenous zones**—the idea that many parts of the body, not just the genitals, are responsive to sexual stimulation.

One of Freud's most controversial beliefs was that children normally harbor erotic interests. He believed that the suckling of the infant in the oral stage was an erotic act. So too was anal bodily experimentation through which children learn to experience pleasure

Unconscious mind
Those parts or contents of the mind that lie outside of conscious awareness.

Defense mechanisms
In psychoanalytic theory, automatic processes that protect the ego from anxiety by disguising or ejecting unacceptable ideas and urges.

Repression
The automatic ejection of anxiety-evoking ideas from consciousness.

Erogenous zones
Parts of the body, including but not limited to the sex organs, that are responsive to sexual stimulation.

Psychosexual development
In psychoanalytic theory, the process by which sexual feelings shift from one erogenous zone to another.

Fixation
In psychoanalytic theory, arrested development. Attachment to objects of an earlier stage of psychosexual development.

in the control of their sphincter muscles and the processes of elimination. He theorized that it was normal for children to progress through stages of development in which the erotic interest shifts from one erogenous zone to another, as, for example, from the mouth or oral cavity to the anal cavity. According to his theory of **psychosexual development,** children undergo five stages of development: oral, anal, phallic, latency, and genital, which are named according to the predominant erogenous zones of each stage. As shown in Table 1.3, each stage gives rise to certain kinds of conflicts. Moreover, inadequate or excessive gratification in any stage can lead to **fixation** in that stage and the development of traits and sexual preferences characteristic of that stage. (Parents who seek to rear their children according to psychoanalytic theory have been frustrated in that Freud never specified the proper amount of gratification in any stage or how to provide it.)

Freud also believed that it was normal for children to develop erotic feelings toward the parent of the opposite gender during the phallic stage of psychosexual development. Such incestuous urges lead to conflict with the parent of the same gender. In later chap-

TABLE 1.1 Some defense mechanisms in psychoanalytic theory

Mechanism	Definition	Examples
Repression	Ejecting unacceptable impulses and memories from consciousness.	Repressing incestuous impulses toward one's parents (or one's children).
Denial	Not perceiving a threatening event.	A person is overwhelmed by sexual passion and engages in sexual relations with a stranger, thinking, "There's no chance I'll get AIDS."
Projection	Attributing one's own unacceptable impulses to others.	A sexually repressed person assumes that others are making sexual advances toward him or her.
Rationalization	Finding an apparently logical reason for unacceptable behavior.	The Victorian husband rationalizes a visit to a prostitute by telling himself that he is sparing his wife an odious chore. The prostitute rationalizes her behavior, in turn, by arguing that she would be out of business if wives were properly performing their duty. The rapist rationalizes his aggression by claiming that the victim should not have been wearing a miniskirt.
Reaction Formation	Expressing emotions and ideas that contradict one's genuine emotions and ideas as a way of keeping them repressed.	A sexually repressed individual goes on a campaign against revealing clothing or local news outlets that distribute the swimsuit edition of *Sports Illustrated.*
Intellectualization	Perceiving threatening events and emotional conflicts in emotionless, theoretical terms.	A physician examines an attractive person without regarding him or her as sexually stimulating.
Sublimation	Redirecting basic impulses from sexual objects or activities to socially approved cultural or creative activities.	Writing novels, building cities, drawing or painting nudes, advancing biological science.

TABLE 1.2 Dream symbols in psychoanalytic theory[1]

Symbols for the Male Genital Organs

airplanes	fish	neckties	tools	weapons
bullets	hands	poles	trains	
feet	hoses	snakes	trees	
fire	knives	sticks	umbrellas	

Symbols for the Female Genital Organs

bottles	caves	doors	ovens	ships
boxes	chests	hats	pockets	tunnels
cases	closets	jars	pots	

Symbols for Sexual Intercourse

climbing a ladder	flying in an airplane
climbing a staircase	riding a horse
crossing a bridge	riding a roller coaster
driving an automobile	riding an elevator
entering a room	walking into a tunnel or down a hall

Symbols for the Breasts

apples	peaches

[1]Freud theorized that the content of dreams symbolized urges, wishes, and objects of fantasy that we would censor in the waking state.

Source: Adapted from Rathus, S. A. (1990). *Psychology* (4th ed.). Ft. Worth, TX: Harcourt Brace Jovanovich.

Learning Objective 10: Explain the psychoanalytic theory and several learning theories of human sexual behavior.

Oedipus complex
In psychoanalytic theory, a conflict of the phallic stage in which the boy wishes to possess his mother sexually and perceives his father as a rival in love. (The analogous conflict for girls is sometimes referred to as the *Electra complex.*)

Behaviorists
Learning theorists who argue that a scientific approach to understanding behavior must refer only to variables (that is, behaviors) that are publicly observable and measurable.

ters we shall see that these developments, which Freud termed the **Oedipus complex,** have profound implications for the assumption of gender roles and sexual orientation.

LEARNING THEORIES   To what extent does sexual behavior reflect experience? Would you hold the same sexual attitudes and do the same things if you had been reared in another culture? We think not. Even within the same society, family and personal experiences can shape unique sexual attitudes and behaviors. Whereas psychoanalytic theory plumbs the depths of the unconscious, learning theorists focus on environmental factors that shape behavior.

Behaviorists like John B. Watson (1878–1958) and B. F. Skinner (1904–1990) emphasized the importance of rewards and punishments in the learning process. In psychology, events (such as rewards) that increase the frequency or likelihood of behavior are termed reinforcements. Children left to explore their bodies without parental condemnation will learn what feels good and tend to repeat it. The Trobriand child who is rewarded for masturbation and premarital coitus through parental praise and encouragement will be more likely to repeat these behaviors (at least openly!) than the child in a more sexually restrictive culture, who is punished for the same behavior. When sexual behavior (like masturbation) feels good, but parents connect it with feelings of guilt and shame, the child is placed in conflict and may vacillate between masturbating and swearing it off.

Of course parental punishment does not necessarily eliminate childhood masturbation. Nor has it stemmed the rising rate of teenage pregnancy in our society. Punishment tends to suppress behavior in circumstances in which it is expected to occur. People can

TABLE 1.3 Stages of psychosexual development, according to psychoanalytic theory

Stage	Ages (years)	Characteristic Conflicts	Traits and Behaviors Connected with Fixation
Oral	0–1	Weaning	Dependency, excessive optimism (or pessimism), alcoholism, interest in oral sex
Anal	1–2	Toilet training, other issues of self-control	Neatness (slovenliness), perfectionism, interest in anal sex, sexual sadism
Phallic	2–5 or 6	Masturbation, possessiveness toward parent of opposite gender, hostility toward parent of same gender	Narcissism, masturbation, homosexual orientation, assumption of inappropriate gender role
Latency	6–12	(A sexually inactive period during which children focus on schoolwork and consolidate gender roles)	
Genital	Puberty and above		Interest in achieving sexual gratification through intercourse with an adult of the opposite gender

Social-learning theory
A cognitively oriented learning theory in which observational learning, values, and expectations play major roles in determining behavior.

Modeling
Acquiring knowledge and skills by observing others.

Discussion Question: How would a Freudian psychologist explain why a five-year-old girl likes to play with dolls? A behaviorist? A social learning theorist?

learn to engage in prohibited behavior secretly, however. Still, if we as young children are severely punished for sexual exploration, we may come to associate sexual stimulation *in general* with feelings of guilt or anxiety. Such early learning experiences can set the stage for sexual dysfunctions in adulthood.

Social-learning theorists also use the concepts of reward and punishment, but they emphasize the importance of cognitive activity (anticipations, thoughts, plans, and so on) and learning by observation. Observational learning, or **modeling,** refers to acquiring knowledge and skills through observing others. Observational learning involves more than direct observation of other people. It includes seeing models in films or on television, hearing about them, and reading about them. According to social-learning theory, children acquire the gender roles deemed appropriate in a society through reinforcement of gender-appropriate behavior and through observing the gender-role behavior of their parents, their peers, and other models on television, in films, in books, and so on.

Psychological theories shed light on the ways in which sexuality is influenced by rewards, punishments, and mental processes such as fantasy, thoughts, attitudes, and expectations. Sigmund Freud helped bring sexuality within the province of scientific investigation. He also helped make it possible for people to recognize and talk about the importance of sexuality in their lives. Critics contend, however, that he may have placed too much emphasis on sexual motivation in determining behavior and on the role of unconscious processes.

The psychological perspective has much to offer to our understanding of human sexuality. Psychological factors affect every dimension of our sexuality. Those who harbor excessive guilt or anxiety over sexual activity may have difficulty enjoying sex or responding adequately to sexual stimulation. Even our basic gender identity is largely shaped by psychological factors, such as the experience in a given society of being reared as a girl or as a boy.

SOCIOLOGICAL PERSPECTIVES

Learning Objective 11: Describe the contributions that sociology makes to the study of human sexual behavior.

Although cultures have certain characteristics, individuals within a particular culture may vary greatly from one another in their sexual attitudes, beliefs, and behavior. This is especially true in a pluralistic society such as ours. Whereas anthropologists contribute to our understanding of cross-cultural variance in sexuality, sociologists focus on differences in sexuality among the subgroups of a society, as defined, for example, by differences in religion, race, country of origin, socioeconomic status, age, educational level, and gender.

The sociological perspective informs us of the relationship between one's sexuality and one's social group within a society. Sociologists view sexual behavior as a form of social behavior occurring within a particular social system. Sexual behavior is influenced by the family, religion, and other social institutions; by the values of a society as well as by social forces such as the distribution of power in society and gender roles. Sociologists are concerned with the ways in which the values, beliefs, and norms of a particular group influence the sexual behavior of members of the group. To a certain extent, we share attitudes and behavior patterns with people from similar backgrounds—for example, people with the same ethnic identity. Even so, not all Catholics, Jews, or Protestants, or all members of a given racial or ethnic group, act or think alike. We thus need to account for individual differences in human sexuality as well as the commonalities that exist among members of the same group.

POWER AND SEX Sociologists also examine the relationships between power—as defined in terms of strength, wealth, or social standing—and sex. Wealthy people may use their economic power to secure the services of prostitutes or mistresses. Rapists use physical power or threats to coerce victims into sexual activity. Some men (and women) use positions of power in the business world and in institutions of learning to sexually harass subordinates and students.

Power or social standing can also limit one's choices of sexual or marital partners. In societies where divisions of wealth and status are rigidly defined, persons of high status are generally discouraged from marrying "beneath" them. Commoners who marry into royalty stand to gain power and social status, but royalty stands to lose power. Witness the abdication of England's King Edward VIII, who stepped down in 1937 to marry U.S. commoner and divorcée Wallis Simpson. In our society, class boundaries are more permeable, but people still tend to marry at their level.

Notes: At the end of 1991, women held only 4.5 percent of all of the seats on boards of Fortune 500 companies.

GENDER ROLES Sociologists also study gender roles. In Western cultures, men have traditionally been expected to be the breadwinners, whereas women have been expected to remain in the home and rear the children. Traditional gender roles also define sexual relations. Men, by this standard, are expected to be assertive; women, compliant. Men are to initiate romantic overtures, whereas women are to perform a "gatekeeping" role and determine which advances they will accept. Today, many of these traditions are falling by the wayside. Most women today are members of the workforce, and many are pursuing careers in traditionally male domains like law, medicine, and engineering. Some women command naval vessels; others pilot military helicopters; yet even women who become presidents and vice presidents of corporations are still burdened with the bulk of household chores (Rogan, 1984). Sexual practices are also changing to a certain extent. More women today initiate dates and sexual interactions than was the case in past generations.

MULTIPLE PERSPECTIVES ON HUMAN SEXUALITY

Learning Objective 12: Discuss human sexuality from each of the perspectives presented in this chapter.

Given the complexity and range of human sexual behavior, we need to consider multiple perspectives to understand sexuality. Each perspective—historical, biological, cross-species, cross-cultural, psychological, and sociological—has something to offer to this enterprise. Let us venture a few conclusions based on our overview of these perspectives. First, human sexuality appears to reflect a combination of biological, social, cultural, sociological, and psychological factors that interact in complex ways, perhaps in combinations that are unique for each individual. Second, there are few universal patterns of sexual behavior, and views on what is right and wrong show great diversity. Third, although our own cultural values and beliefs may be deeply meaningful to us, they may not indicate what is normal, natural, or moral in terms of sexual behavior. The complexity of human sexuality—complexity that causes it to remain somewhat baffling to scientists—adds to the wonder and richness of our sexual experience.

SUMMING UP

WHAT IS HUMAN SEXUALITY?

The term *human sexuality* refers to matters of gender, sexual behavior, sexual feelings, and the biology of sex. Human sexuality concerns the ways in which we experience and express ourselves as sexual beings.

The Study of Human Sexuality
The study of human sexuality draws upon the expertise of anthropologists, biologists, med-

ical researchers, sociologists, psychologists, and other scientists.

Why Study Human Sexuality?
We study human sexuality for numerous reasons. Sex is a primary source of motivation. The study of human sexuality can be put to use in enhancing sexual response and pleasure. Sexual knowledge also provides the basis

for making informed decisions about preventing and responding to problems such as sexually transmitted diseases, unwanted pregnancies, sexual harassment, and rape.

Sexuality and Values Our pluralistic society embraces a wide range of sexual attitudes and values.

THINKING CRITICALLY ABOUT HUMAN SEXUALITY

The text encourages critical thinking to help students evaluate claims, arguments, and widely held beliefs. Critical thinking encourages thoughtful analysis and probing of arguments, willingness to challenge conventional

wisdom and common knowledge, and maintaining open minds.

Some Features of Critical Thinking The text enumerates several features of critical thinking. These include being skeptical, examining definitions of terms,

examining the assumptions or premises of arguments, being cautious in drawing conclusions from evidence, considering alternative interpretations of evidence, and avoiding oversimplification and overgeneralization.

PERSPECTIVES ON HUMAN SEXUALITY

Human sexuality is a complex field, and no single theory or perspective can capture all its nuances. The text offers diverse perspectives on sexuality.

The Historical Perspective
History places our sexual behavior in the context of time. History shows little evidence of universal sexual trends. There is prehistoric evidence of worship of generative power in women and men. Jews and Christians have emphasized the role of sex as a means of propagation and have generally restricted sex to the context of

family life. The ancient Greeks and Romans dwelled in male-oriented societies that viewed women as chattel. Some Eastern civilizations have equated sexual pleasure with religious experience and have developed sex manuals. Repressive Victorian sexual attitudes gave way to the sexual revolution of the 1960s and 1970s in the West.

The Biological Perspective
The biological perspective focuses on the role of biological processes, such as genetic, hormonal, vascular, and neural factors, in explaining

human sexual behavior. Knowledge of biology helps us understand how our bodies respond to sexual stimulation and enhances aspects of our sexual health.

The Cross-Species Perspective The study of other animal species reveals a surprising variety of sexual behaviors among nonhumans. There are, for example, animal analogues of homosexuality, oral sex, foreplay, and rape. Still, we must be cautious in generalizing from lower animals to humans. We find that experience and learning play more important roles in sexuality as we travel up the evolutionary ladder. Sociobiological theory proposes that dispositions toward behavior patterns that enhance reproductive success—as well as physical traits that do so—may be genetically transmitted.

The Cross-Cultural Perspective This perspective, like the historical perspective, provides insight into the ways in which cultural beliefs affect sexual behavior and people's sense of morality. Anthropologists observe other cultures firsthand when possible. Cross-cultural evidence challenges the notion of the universality of gender-role stereotypes. All cultures apparently place some limits on sexual freedom (and all cultures place some prohibitions on incestuous relationships), but some cultures are more sexually permissive than others.

Psychological Perspectives

Psychological perspectives focus on the psychological factors of perception, learning, motivation, emotion, personality, and so on that affect gender and sexual behavior in the individual. Sigmund Freud formulated the theory of psychoanalysis, which proposes that biologically based sex drives come into conflict with social codes. Erogenous zones shift through the process of psychosexual development, and defense mechanisms keep threatening ideas and impulses out of conscious awareness. Learning theorists focus on the roles of rewards, punishments, and modeling on sexual behavior.

Sociological Perspectives

Sociologists focus on differences in sexuality among the subgroups of a society, as defined, for example, by differences in religion, race, country of origin, socioeconomic status, age, educational level, and gender.

Multiple Perspectives on Human Sexuality Given the complexity and range of human sexual behavior, we need to consider multiple perspectives to understand human sexuality.

_____ You could study millions of U.S. inhabitants and still not obtain an accurate picture of the sexual behavior of the general U.S. population.

_____ Residents of Communist China are more likely than people in the United States to approve of extramarital affairs.

_____ Male chimpanzees have been observed greeting females by taking their hands and kissing them.

_____ Some sex researchers have engaged in "swinging" with their subjects.

_____ Masters and Johnson created a transparent artificial penis containing photographic equipment to study female sexual response.

_____ Regular churchgoers report higher levels of sexual satisfaction.

_____ Case studies have been carried out on subjects who are dead.

 HAPTER 2

Research Methods in Human Sexuality

Have you ever found yourself wondering about any of the following questions about human sexuality? Are my sexual interests and behavior patterns unique or shared by many others? Does alcohol stimulate or dampen sexual response? Why do people engage in homosexual behavior? How do people contract AIDS? Does pornography cause rape?

You may have had these questions, and you may have expressed opinions on them as well. Scientists insist that opinions about behavior, including sexual behavior, be supported by evidence, however. Evidence, in turn, must be based upon careful observations in the laboratory or in the field.

In this chapter we explore the methods that scientists use to study human sexuality. We then focus on ethical issues in research on sex. Researchers in all behavioral sciences confront ethical problems, but the problems are heightened in sex research. After all, the field of human sexuality touches on some of the most personal and intimate experiences of our lives.

A SCIENTIFIC APPROACH TO HUMAN SEXUALITY

Empirical
Derived from or based on observation and experimentation.

Scientists and researchers who study human sexuality take an **empirical** approach. They seek knowledge based on research evidence, rather than on intuition, faith, or superstition. Scientists' and other people's intuitions or religious beliefs may suggest topics to be studied scientifically. Yet once the topics are selected, answers are sought on the basis of the scientific method.

THE SCIENTIFIC METHOD

Learning Objective 1:
Explain the four essential elements of the research method.

Critical thinking and the scientific approach both share the hallmark of skepticism. As skeptics, scientists who explore human sexuality are open to questioning prevailing assumptions and theories about sexual behavior. They suspend judgment about matters that are widely accepted by the public at large. They are willing to dispute the assertions of authority figures such as political and religious leaders—even renowned scientists. Scientists also recognize that they cannot gain perfect knowledge and that one era's truths may become another era's ancient myths and fallacies. Scientists view themselves as involved in a continuous struggle to approach truth, but they do not see themselves as capable of experiencing instant revelations or defining final truths.

The *scientific method* is a systematic way of gathering scientific evidence and testing assumptions through empirical research. It has a number of elements:

1. *Formulating a research question.* Does alcohol inspire or impair sexual response? Scientists formulate research questions on the basis of their observations of, or theories about, events or behavior. They then seek answers to such questions by conducting empirical research.

Hypothesis
A precise prediction about behavior that is tested through research.

2. *Framing the research question in the form of a hypothesis.* Experiments are usually undertaken with a **hypothesis** in mind—a precise prediction about behavior that is often derived from theory. A hypothesis is tested through research. For instance, a scientist might theorize that alcohol enhances sexual responsiveness either by directly stimulating sexual response or by reducing feelings of guilt associated with sex. He or she might then hypothesize that an intervention (called, in experimental terms, a "treatment"), such as drinking alcohol in a laboratory setting, will lead to heightened sexual arousal in the presence of erotic stimuli (like sexually explicit films). Hypotheses, then, can be considered educated guesses that anticipate the results of an experiment in advance.

3. *Testing the hypothesis.* Scientists then test hypotheses through carefully controlled observation and experimentation. A specific hypothesis about alcohol and sexual arousal—that alcohol either increases or decreases sexual responsiveness—might be tested by administering a certain amount of alcohol to one group of subjects and then comparing their level of sexual arousal following specific types of sexual stimulation (such as exposure to sexually explicit films) to the level of sexual arousal of another group of subjects who were shown the films but not given any alcohol.

4. *Drawing conclusions.* Scientists then draw conclusions or inferences about the correctness of their hypotheses, based on their analyses of the results of their studies. If the results of well-designed research studies fail to bear out certain hypotheses, scientists can revise the theories that served as the frameworks for the hypotheses. Research findings often lead scientists to modify their theories, and in turn, generate new hypotheses that can be tested in further research.

Some investigators include the publication of results in professional journals as part and parcel of the scientific method. Publication shares scientific knowledge with the public at large and also exposes research methods to evaluation by the scientific community. In this way, results can be interpreted in terms of potential flaws in methodology.

GOALS AND METHODS OF THE SCIENCE OF HUMAN SEXUALITY

Learning Objective 2: List the four broad goals of the science of human sexuality.

The goals of the science of human sexuality are congruent with those of other sciences: to describe, explain, predict, and control the events (in this case, the sexual behaviors) that are of interest. Let us discuss some of the general goals of science and how they relate to the study of human sexuality as a science.

Description is a basic objective of science. To understand sexual behavior, for example, we must first be able to describe it. So description of behavior precedes understanding. Scientists attempt to be clear, unbiased, and precise in their descriptions of events and behavior. The scientific approach to human sexuality describes sexual behavior through techniques as varied as the field study, the survey, the individual case study, and the laboratory experiment.

To underscore the importance of the need for unbiased description, consider the name of a tropical fish that will be familiar to many readers: the kissing gourami. These small flat fish—particularly the males—approach each other frontally and press their open mouths against one another. Yet the term *kissing gourami* may well be something of a misnomer if the word "kissing" is meant to imply affection. Prolonged observations of the fish suggest that it is more likely that kissing in gouramis is a test of strength. More powerful "kissers" apparently achieve positions of social dominance that are connected with privileges in feeding and mating.

Inference
Conclusion or opinion.

Anthropomorphism
The attributing of human characteristics to an animal.

The error in describing the behavior of gouramis as "kissing" is confusion of **inference** with description. It is, in fact, an **anthropomorphic** inference, in that it involves applying human standards to explain animal behavior. One of the great challenges to scientists is the separation of description from inference.

Inference, like description, is crucial to science. Inference allows us to move from observations or descriptions of particular events or behavior to general principles that can be woven into models and theories that help explain them, such as the psychoanalytic and learning theories or models. Without a means for organizing our descriptions of events and behavior in terms of models and theories, we would be left with nothing more than a buzzing confusion of disconnected observations. Scientists need to distinguish between *description* and *inference*, however—to recognize when they jump from a description of events to an inference based on an interpretation of those events. For example, one does not *describe* a person's sexual behavior as "deviant." Rather, one *labels* or *classifies* it as deviant when one believes it to deviate from a certain norm. But what is deviant in one culture may be normal in another. Incestuous relationships between brothers and sisters are permitted among the Dahomey of West Africa (Stephens, 1982). The same behavior is considered deviant in our own culture and virtually all others. Even within the same larger culture, behavior may be deviant by the stan-

Teaching Tip: Have students *describe* a time they witnessed two people displaying affection in public. What *inferences* did they make about the partners? How would they *label or classify* the behaviors they observed?

Sadomasochistic
Descriptive of sexual practices in which sexual arousal is achieved through inflicting and receiving pain or humiliation.

Variables
Quantities or qualities that vary or may vary.

Demographic
Concerning the vital statistics (density, race, age, etc.) of human populations.

Teaching Tip: As examples of the goals of the science of human sexuality, use the research on HIV transmission. Research has identified and *described* the virus, it has *explained* the process by which the virus attacks the body's immune system, and it has attempted to *predict* the number of people who will be infected by the virus. Research findings have been used to *control* the spread of the virus through enforcement of CDC (Centers for Disease Control) guidelines established for medical settings.

Learning Objective 3:
Explain what operational definitions are and why they are necessary to the research process.

dards of some subcultures and not by others. Some in our own culture may consider it deviant to tie one's lover's hands to the bedpost when making love, yet such behavior is considered routine within the **sadomasochistic** subculture.

When researchers make a series of observations, they attempt to relate them to other factors (called **variables** in experimental terminology) that can help explain them. For example, researchers may attempt to explain variations in the frequency of coitus by relating coitus to **demographic** variables such as age or religious or social background, or to cultural expectations. The variables that are commonly used to explain sexual behavior include biological (age, health), psychological (anxieties, skills), and sociological (educational level, socioeconomic status, ethnicity) variables. Explanations of behavior can involve reference to many variables, even variables that cannot be measured directly, such as unconscious motivation. Relationships among variables may be tied together into theories of behavior. For example, psychoanalytic theory emphasizes the role of unconscious forces in determining behavior, whereas learning theories focus on how variables such as rewards, punishments, and expectations shape behavior.

Theories provide frameworks within which scientists can explain observed behavior and predict future behavior. It is not sufficient for theories to help us make sense of events that have already occurred. Theories must allow us to make predictions. So one test of psychoanalytic and learning theories is whether or not they allow us to predict behavior. Prediction requires discovering variables that anticipate events. Geologists seek clues in the forces that affect the earth to forecast events such as earthquakes and volcanic eruptions. Sex researchers study factors that may predict various types of sexual behavior. Some researchers, for example, have examined childhood interests and behavior patterns that may predict the development of a homosexual orientation. Others have explored factors, such as the age at which dating begins and the quality of the relationships between teens and their parents, that may predict the likelihood of premarital intercourse during adolescence.

The notion of controlling human behavior of any kind—especially sexual behavior—is highly controversial and much misunderstood. Behavioral scientists and health practitioners are generally committed to preserving the dignity of the individual. The idea of human dignity demands that people be free to make their own decisions. Within this context, *controlling behavior* does not mean coercing people to do the bidding of others, like puppets dangling on strings pulled by others. Rather, it means drawing upon scientific knowledge to help people create their own goals and marshal their resources to meet them. Reputable scientists are held to ethical and professional standards that ban the use of harmful techniques in research or practice and safeguard the rights of subjects in research.

The science of human sexuality does not tell people how they *ought* to behave. It does not attempt to limit or expand their variety of sexual activities. Rather, it furnishes information that people may use to help themselves or others make decisions about their own behavior. For instance, the science of human sexuality provides information that increases the chances that a couple who are having difficulty becoming pregnant will be able to conceive. At the same time, it develops and evaluates means of birth control that can be used to help couples regulate their reproductive choices. The science of human sexuality also seeks to develop techniques that can help people overcome sexual dysfunctions and enhance the gratification they find in sexual relations. "Control" also takes the form of curing sexually transmitted diseases, of enabling couples to give and receive more sexual pleasure, of enhancing fetal health, and of providing the means to curb population growth in crowded, famine-prone societies.

OPERATIONAL DEFINITIONS

How do we study such concepts as "sexual satisfaction" or an even broader concept, "marital satisfaction"? One of the requirements in sex research, as in other types of research, is specification of the definitions of the concepts, or "constructs," of interest.

Physiological Measures of Sexual Arousal

Scientific studies depend on the ability to measure the phenomena of interest. The phenomena of sexual arousal may be measured by different means, such as self-report and physiological measures. Self-report measures of sexual arousal are considered *subjective*. They ask subjects to give their impressions of the level of their sexual arousal at a given time, such as by circling their response on a ten-point scale that ranges from zero, "not at all aroused," to ten, "extremely aroused." Physiological devices measure the degree of vasocongestion that builds up in the genitals during sexual arousal. (Vasocongestion—that is, congestion with blood—leads to erection in men and vaginal lubrication in women.) In men, vasocongestion is frequently measured by a **penile strain gauge.** This device is worn under the man's clothing. It is fitted around the penis and measures his erectile response by recording changes in the circumference of the penis. The device is sensitive to small changes in circumference that

may not be noticed (and thus not reported) by the man.

Physiological measurement of sexual arousal in women is most often accomplished by means of a **vaginal photoplethysmograph.** The vaginal photoplethysmograph is a tampon-shaped probe with a light and a photocell in its tip. It is inserted in the vagina and indicates the level of blood congestion by means of measuring the amount of light reflected from the vaginal walls (Conte, 1986; Geer et al., 1974; Hoon et al., 1977). The more light that is absorbed by the vaginal walls, the less that is reflected. Less reflected light indicates greater vasocongestion.

Sex researchers sometimes measure sexual arousal in response to stimuli such as erotic films or audiotaped dramatizations of erotic scenes. What happens when physiological devices give a different impression of sexual arousal than those offered by self-report? There is some evidence that objectively (physiologically) measured sexual arousal does not agree very highly

with subjective measures of self-report, at least among women (Heiman, 1978; Kockott et al., 1980; Morokoff & Heiman, 1980). For example, a person may say that he or she is relatively unaroused while the physiological measures suggest otherwise. Which is the *truer* measure of arousal, the person's subjective reports or the levels shown on the objective instruments?

Discrepancies across measures raise the possibility that people may be sexually aroused (as measured by physiological indicators) but psychologically unprepared to recognize it or unwilling to admit it. Without further evidence, however, it is premature to conclude that one measure is more valid than another (Conte, 1986). The assessment of sexual arousal is perhaps best approached from multiple vantage points, such as self-reports and physiological measures. Multiple assessment may provide more useful information than one method alone (Conte, 1986).

The Penile Strain Gauge and the Vaginal Photoplethysmograph. These devices measure vasocongestion in the genitals of men and women and thereby indicate their level of sexual arousal.

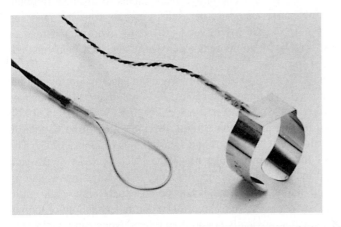
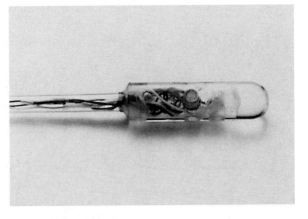

Penile Strain Gauge
A device for measuring sexual arousal in men in terms of changes in the circumference of the penis.

Vaginal photo-plethysmograph
A tampon-shaped probe that is inserted in the vagina and suggests the level of vasocongestion by measuring the light reflected from the vaginal walls.

Vasocongestion
Congestion from the flow of blood. (From the Latin *vas*, meaning "vessel.")

Operational definition
A definition of a construct or variable in terms of the methods used to measure it.

Survey
A detailed study of a sample obtained by means such as questionnaires.

Different investigators may define marital satisfaction or sexual satisfaction in different ways. They may be studying different events although they may use the same terms.

What, for example, is "sexual arousal"? Many studies seek to assess the effects of various stimuli (such as sexually explicit material) on sexual arousal, but sexual arousal can mean several things. It can mean the *subjective* "feeling" that one is sexually aroused. It can mean one's self-report of genital sensations. It may refer to direct physiological measures of blood congestion (**vasocongestion**) in the genitals. We further explore the measurement of sexual arousal in the nearby Closer Look section.

The **operational definition** of a construct links its meaning to the methods used to measure it. In some studies reported in this book, sexual arousal is operationally defined as vasocongestion. In others, it is operationally defined as self-report of sexual interest or genital sensations. In still others, a combination of measures is used. It is important to recognize that our ability to generalize the results of research is limited by the operational definitions of the variables (Bentler & Abramson, 1981). That is, we may only be able to generalize to instances that employ the same definitions of terms.

Let us now examine the various methods that scientists use to study human sexuality, including the survey, and observational, experimental, and case-study methods.

METHODS OF RESEARCH IN HUMAN SEXUALITY

There are many ways of gathering scientific evidence about human sexuality. Some focus on description, others on identifying relationships between variables, still others in identifying cause and effect. Let us consider a number of the methods in use, and evaluate their strengths and weaknesses and appropriateness to the questions posed.

THE SURVEY METHOD

Surveys typically gather information about behavior through interviews or questionnaires. In some cases researchers administer questionnaires or conduct interviews with thousands of subjects to learn about the sexual behavior and attitudes of particular population groups. Interviews such as those used by Kinsey and his colleagues (1948, 1953) have the advantages of face-to-face contact and of giving the interviewer the opportunity to *probe*—that is, to follow up on answers that seem to lead toward useful information. A skilled interviewer may be able to set a respondent at ease and establish a sense of trust or *rapport* that encourages self-disclosure. On the other hand, unskilled interviewing may cause respondents to conceal information.

Questionnaires are inexpensive when compared to interviews. The major expenses involved in using questionnaires are for printing and distribution. Questionnaires can be administered to groups of people at once and respondents can return them unsigned, so that they are anonymous. Anonymity may encourage respondents to disclose intimate information. Questionnaires, of course, can only be used by people who can read and record their responses. Interviews can be used even with people who cannot read or write. But interviewers must be trained, sometimes extensively, and then paid for their time.

Some of the major surveys described in this book were conducted by Kinsey and his colleagues (1948, 1953), the Playboy Foundation (Hunt, 1974), Bell and his colleagues (1978, 1981), Coles and Stokes (1985), Wyatt and her colleagues (Wyatt, 1985, 1989; Wyatt et al., 1988a, 1988b), researchers at the Battelle Memorial Institute of Seattle (Billy et al., 1993; Tanfer et al., 1993), and Janus and Janus (Janus & Janus, 1993). The book also discusses surveys conducted by popular magazines such as *Redbook*. By and large, these surveys have reported the incidence and frequency of sexual activities among men and women, married and single, heterosexual and homosexual, adolescent, adult, and elderly. Each of these surveys has something to offer to our understanding of human sexuality, but some are more methodologically sound than others. None can lay claim to represent the U.S. population at large, however. Most people consider their sexuality to be among the most intimate and *private* aspects of their lives. People who willingly agree

Learning Objective 4:
Describe and compare the
sampling methods used to
select a representative sample of subjects to participate
in a survey.

Sample
Part of a population.

Population
A complete group of organisms or events.

Generalize
To go from the particular
to the general.

Random sample
A sample in which every
member of a population
has an equal chance of
participating.

Probability sample
A sample in which the probability of inclusion in the
sample of any particular
member is known.

to be polled as to their political preferences may resist participation in surveys concerning their sexual behavior. As a result, it is difficult, if not impossible, for researchers to
recruit a truly representative sample of the population. Bear in mind, then, that the survey
results reported by Kinsey and other researchers provide, at best, an approximation of the
sexual attitudes, beliefs, and behaviors of the U.S. population.

Let us now consider some of the methods that survey researchers use to gather data.

SAMPLING METHODS   The individuals who participate in a survey are said to comprise a survey **sample.** A sample is a segment or part of a population of interest. A *representative sample* is a research sample of participants who accurately represent the population of interest, which is sometimes called the *target* population.

SAMPLES AND POPULATIONS   A **population** is a complete group of organisms.
For example, the population of interest in a study of dating practices at your college or
university might be the total student population. If you were to select your research sample from one dormitory or class, it would probably not be a representative sample (unless
the dormitory or class contained a true cross-section of the entire student body). If our
samples do not represent the target populations, we may not be able to generalize the
results of our surveys to the populations of interest.

If we wished to study the sexual behavior of inhabitants of the United States, our
population would consist of *all* U.S. inhabitants. If we wished to study cohabiting college students, our population would include *all* college students who cohabit. In a perfect
world, research into populations would include every member of the target populations.
Then we would know that our findings applied to these populations. Including all U.S.
inhabitants in a study of sexual behavior would be expensive, impractical, and, in fact,
impossible. We cannot even find all inhabitants of the United States when we conduct
the census each decade; sex research would undoubtedly cause many more people to
refuse to participate than does a simple counting of noses. Sampling a part of a target
population makes research practical and possible—if imperfect.

In order for us to **generalize** from a sample to a population with confidence, the
sample must represent the population. One way of acquiring a representative sample is
through random sampling. A **random sample** is one in which every member of the target population has an equal chance of participating. A random sample is a type of **probability sample.** Statisticians use the term *probability sample* to describe samples in which
the probability of any particular member's being included in the sample is known.

RANDOM AND STRATIFIED RANDOM SAMPLES   Now and then magazine editors
boast that they have surveyed samples of 20,000 or 30,000 readers, but size alone cannot
guarantee that a sample is representative. As an example, the *Literary Digest* magazine
polled thousands of voters by telephone to predict the outcome of the 1936 presidential
election. Based on the survey, the magazine predicted that Alfred Landon would defeat
Franklin D. Roosevelt, but Roosevelt won by a landslide of nearly 11 million votes. The
problem was that the election was held during the Great Depression, when only relatively affluent people could afford telephones. Those who could afford phones were also
more likely to be Republicans and to vote for the Republican candidate, Landon. Thus,
the *Digest* poll, although large, was biased. A sample of 30 million voters will not provide an accurate picture if it is biased.

TRUTH OR FICTION?

R E V I S I T E D

*You could study millions of U.S. inhabitants and still not obtain an accu-
rate picture of the sexual behavior of the general U.S. population.* Yes, a
sample of many millions might not represent the U.S. population. Sample size
alone does not guarantee that the sample's members have been selected in
an unbiased manner. •

Researchers attempt to overcome biased sampling by drawing *random* or *stratified
random* samples of populations. In a random sample, every member of a population has

Stratified random sample
A random sample in which known subgroups in a population are represented in proportion to their numbers in the population.

an equal chance of participating. In a **stratified random sample,** known subgroups of a population are represented in proportion to their numbers in the population. For instance, about 14 percent of the U.S population is African American. Researchers could therefore decide that 14 percent of their sample must be African American if they are to represent all U.S. inhabitants. The randomness of the sample would be preserved since the members of the subgroups would be selected randomly from their particular subgroups. In practical terms, however, a reasonably large *random* sample with no prior stratification will turn out to be reasonably well stratified in the end. Put it another way: If you blindfold yourself, shake up a jar of jelly beans, and take out a scoopful, the proportions of the different colors of beans in the scoop are likely to approximate the proportions of those colors in the entire jar.

Despite the recognized value of random sampling, random samples are hard to come by, especially when it comes to asking people about their sexual attitudes or behavior. For instance, the Playboy Foundation (Hunt, 1974) sampled people listed in telephone directories in various cities in the United States in the early 1970s. Most people at the time had phones, yet the sample could not have included the very poor who may not have been able to afford to keep a phone, those who had unlisted numbers, and groups like college students who may not have had private phones in their dormitories. Another problem is that sexual research is almost invariably conducted with people who volunteer to participate, and volunteers may differ in various ways from people who refuse to participate. For example, volunteers may be more open about their sexuality than the general population. They may even tend to exaggerate behaviors that others might consider deviant or abnormal.

Volunteer bias
A slanting of research data that is caused by the characteristics of subjects who volunteer to participate, such as willingness to discuss intimate behavior.

The problem of a **volunteer bias** is a thorny one for sex researchers, since the refusal of people who have been randomly selected to participate in the survey can ruin the representativeness of the sample. Since it would be unethical to coerce people to participate in a sex survey (or another type of survey), researchers must use samples of volunteers, rather than true random samples. A low response rate to a voluntary survey is an indication that the responses obtained may not be representative of the original sample (Biggar & Melbye, 1992). They may only be reflective of the type of people who made the effort to complete the questionnaire.

In some cases, samples obtained in sex research are samples of convenience. They consist of individuals who happen to be available to the researcher and who share some characteristics in common with the target population, perhaps religious background or sexual orientation. Still, they may not truly represent the target group. Convenience samples often consist of white, middle-class college students who volunteer for studies conducted at their schools. They may not be (and probably are not) representative of students in general or even of the general student population at their own school. Random samples of gay males or lesbians are perhaps the most difficult to come by, because the social stigmas attached to homosexuality may discourage homosexuals from disclosing their sexual orientation.

Learning Objective 5:
Describe and analyze the sampling techniques used in several large-scale surveys discussed in this chapter.

SAMPLING TECHNIQUES OF SELECTED STUDIES   Let us review the sampling techniques of some of the major studies of human sexuality. Throughout the book we shall reconsider the findings of these surveys, especially those that shed light on the changes that have occurred between Kinsey's surveys and the present. But for now let us focus on the methods used by Kinsey and others to survey sexual behavior patterns in the United States.

Alfred Kinsey. Kinsey and his colleagues conducted the first large-scale scientific study of sexual behavior in the United States.

THE KINSEY REPORTS   Kinsey and his colleagues (1948, 1953) interviewed 5,300 males and 5,940 females in the United States between 1938 and 1949. They asked a wide array of questions on various types of sexual experiences, including masturbation, oral sex, and coitus before, during, and outside of marriage. The survey was a reasonable method for obtaining these data, since Kinsey was interested in studying the frequencies of various sexual behaviors, rather than their underlying causes. For obvious reasons Kinsey could not use more direct observational methods, such as sending his researchers to peer through bedroom windows. Kinsey chose not to try to obtain a random sample

because he believed, plausibly enough, that a high refusal rate would wreck the chances of accurately representing the general population. Instead, he adopted a *group sampling* approach; that is, he recruited subjects from the organizations and community groups to which they belonged, such as college fraternities and sororities. He contacted representatives of groups in diverse communities and tried to persuade them to secure the cooperation of fellow group members. If he showed these individuals that they would not be subjected to embarrassment or discomfort, Kinsey hoped that they would persuade other members to participate. Kinsey understood that the groups he solicited were not necessarily representative of the general population. He believed, however, that his sampling approach was dictated by practical constraints. Even so, he made an attempt to sample as broadly as possible from the groups he solicited. In some cases he obtained 100 percent participation; in other cases he obtained a large enough proportion of the group membership to help ensure representativeness, at least of the group.

Still, Kinsey's samples must be considered unrepresentative of the general population. People of color, people living in rural areas, the elderly, the poor, and Catholics and Jews were all underrepresented in his samples. Statisticians who have reviewed Kinsey's methods have concluded that there were systematic biases in his sampling methods, but that it would have been impossible to obtain a true probability sample from the general population (see, e.g., Cochran et al., 1953). There is thus no way of knowing whether or not Kinsey's results accurately mirrored the U.S. population at the time. In Chapter 10 we shall see that his estimate that 37 percent of the male population had reached orgasm at least once through homosexual contact was probably too high. The *relationships* Kinsey uncovered, however, such as the positive link between level of education and participation in oral sex, may be more generalizable (see Chapter 9).

To his credit, Kinsey took several measures to instill candor in his subjects. For one, subjects were assured of the confidentiality of their records. For another, Kinsey's interviewers were trained to conduct the interviews in an objective and matter-of-fact style. To reduce the tendency to slant responses in a socially desirable direction, subjects were reassured that the interviewers were not passing judgment on them. Interviewers were trained not to show emotional reactions that subjects could interpret as signs of disapproval (to maintain a "calm and steady eye" and a constant tone of voice).

Kinsey also checked the **reliability** of his data by evaluating the consistency of the responses given by several hundred interviewees who were reexamined after at least 18 months. Their reports of the **incidence** of sexual activities (for example, whether or not they had ever engaged in premarital or extramarital coitus) were highly reliable. That is, subjects tended to give the same answers on both occasions. But reports of the **frequency** of sexual activities (such as the number of times one has masturbated to orgasm, or the frequency of coitus in marriage) were less consistent. People do tend to find it more difficult to compute the frequencies of their activities than to answer whether or not they have ever engaged in them.

Kinsey recognized that consistency of responses across time—or *retakes,* as he called them—did not guarantee their **validity.** That is, the retakes did not show whether the reported behaviors had some basis in fact. He could not validate self-reports directly, as one might validate reports that one is drug-free by means of a urine analysis. He could not send his investigators to peer through bedroom windows, so he had to use indirect means to validate the data. One indirect measure was comparison of the reports of husbands and wives, for example, with respect to the *incidence* of oral-genital sex or the *frequency* of intercourse. There was a remarkable consistency in the reports of 706 pairs of spouses; this lends support to the view that their self-reports were accurate. (It is possible, but highly unlikely, that spouses colluded to misrepresent their behavior.)

THE PLAYBOY FOUNDATION SURVEY   A survey of sexual practices in the 1970s was commissioned by the Playboy Foundation. The results were reported by Morton Hunt in his 1974 book, *Sexual Behavior in the 1970s*. The *Playboy survey,* or *Hunt survey,* as it is sometimes called, sought to examine the changes in sexual behavior in the United States between Kinsey's time and the early 1970s.

Reliability
The consistency or accuracy of a measure.

Incidence
A measure of the occurrence or the degree of occurrence of an event.

Frequency
The number of times an action is repeated within a given period.

Validity
With respect to tests, the degree to which a particular test measures the constructs or traits it purports to measure.

The *Playboy* sample was drawn randomly from phone book listings in 24 U.S. cities. Subjects were asked to participate in small group discussions focusing on trends in sexual practices in the United States. They were not told that they would also be completing a questionnaire, an approach that has raised ethical concerns. That is, the subjects were not fully informed about their role in the study when they agreed to participate. (Interestingly, though, none of 2,026 people who participated in the group meetings refused to complete the personal questionnaires when they were presented with them.) The phone sampling method was supplemented by an additional sample of young people, who were likely to have been underrepresented in telephone directories. But even with these additional people, rural people and inmates of prisons and mental hospitals remained underrepresented.

Because the Playboy Foundation did not sample rural people and selected only 24 urban centers, participants cannot be considered representative of the general U.S. population at the time. Hunt argues, with some justification, that the final sample of 2,026 is stratified properly as to the ages and races of urban residents across a diverse sample of U.S. cities. The major drawback to the method, however, is that 80 percent of the people contacted refused to participate. The final 2,026 were clearly willing to volunteer to participate in discussion groups and to then complete a sex questionnaire. We suspect that they were more open and frank about sexual issues than the population at large, but we cannot actually compare them to those who declined to participate.

We will focus in later chapters on specific comparisons between Kinsey's findings from the late 1930s and 1940s and those from the *Playboy* survey from the early 1970s. Suffice it to say that the *Playboy* survey found evidence of major changes in the incidence of premarital sex among women, oral-genital sex, and length of intercourse among married couples, among other changes.

THE JANUS REPORT   A recent nationwide survey of sexual behavior in the United States was conducted from 1988 to 1992 by a husband-and-wife team, Samuel and Cynthia Janus (Janus & Janus, 1993). The Janus Report was based on a survey of 2,765 people (1,347 men and 1,418 women), age 18 years or older, who anonymously completed written questionnaires assessing a wide range of sexual behaviors and attitudes. In-depth interviews were also conducted with a subset of the larger sample. The Janus sample, like the Kinsey sample before it, was not randomly selected from the general population. Rather, the Januses assembled a team of researchers from every region of the contiguous 48 states, who then went out and made contact with groups of potential respondents. In all, the survey team distributed 4,550 questionnaires in various sites across the country. Satisfactorily completed questionnaires (those with few missing responses) were returned from 2,765 respondents, representing a return rate of 61 percent, a fairly good rate of return for sex surveys. The surveyists attempted to construct a sample that represented a fairly typical cross-section of the U.S. population with respect to characteristics such as age, gender, income, and educational background. Although the findings may offer some insights into contemporary sexuality in American society, we can't say whether the sample was truly representative of the general population. Whereas the sample may have had a proportionate number of males and females, and of younger and older respondents, we have no way of knowing whether the people who participated are typical of American men or women in general. People who respond to sex surveys may not only be more open about discussing their sexuality than the general population, but may also hold more permissive or liberal views about sex.

Discussion Question: Have you ever completed and returned a sex questionnaire published in a magazine? Did you (or would you) answer the questions as honestly as possible? On what topics would you refuse to answer questions?

THE MAGAZINE SURVEYS   Major readership surveys have also been conducted by popular magazines, such as *Psychology Today* (Athanasiou et al., 1970), *Redbook* (Tavris & Sadd, 1977), the *Ladies Home Journal* (Schultz, 1980), *McCall's* (Gittelson, 1980), *Cosmopolitan* (Wolfe, 1981), and *Consumer Reports* (Brecher, 1984). Although these surveys all offer some useful information and may be commended for attaining large samples (ranging from 20,000 to 106,000!), their sampling techniques are inherently unscientific and biased. Each sample represents, at best, the readers of the magazine in which the questionnaire appeared. Moreover, we learn only about readers who volunteered to respond to these questionnaires. They likely differed in important ways from the majority of readers who failed to respond. Finally, readers of these magazines are more affluent than the public at large, and readers of *Cosmopolitan, Psychology Today,* and even *Redbook* tend to be more liberal. So the samples may represent only those readers who were willing to complete and mail in the surveys.

A lay researcher, Shere Hite, published several popular—perhaps we should say "notorious"—books on sexual behavior in men and women. Her samples for her 1976 book on female sexuality, *The Hite Report,* and her 1981 book on male sexuality, *The Hite Report on Male Sexuality,* were gleaned from people who completed questionnaires received in direct mailings, printed in sexually explicit magazines like *Penthouse,* and made available through other outlets, including some churches. Her final samples of some 3,000 women, in the 1976 report, and 7,000 men, in the 1981 book, may seem large. However, they actually represent small return rates of 3 and 6 percent, respectively. For these reasons, among others, the "Hite reports" cannot be considered scientific studies (Gould, 1981).

SURVEYS OF SPECIFIC POPULATIONS   The Kinsey, *Playboy,* and Janus surveys were broad based, in that they surveyed men and women from different localities, socioeconomic strata, and age groups. Magazine surveys tend to recruit subjects more narrowly, as defined by reader characteristics. In some cases, however, researchers have focused their efforts on particular populations, such as adolescents (Coles & Stokes, 1985; Kantner & Zelnik, 1972; Sonenstein et al., 1989, 1990; Sorensen, 1973; Zelnik & Kantner, 1980), older people (George & Weiler, 1981; Starr & Weiner, 1981, 1982), African Americans (Wyatt, 1985, 1989; Wyatt et al., 1988a, 1988b), couples (Blumstein & Schwartz, 1983), and gay men and lesbians (Bell & Weinberg, 1978; Bell et al., 1981).

In recent years a number of large-scale studies in the United States and other countries have been conducted to acquire information concerning sexual practices that might prove useful in the fight against AIDS (Adler, 1993). In the United States, for example, researchers from the Battelle Memorial Institute of Seattle interviewed a nationally representative sample of 3,321 men between the ages of 20 and 39 in order to determine the prevalences of unsafe sexual practices among young adult men (Billy et al., 1993; Grady et al., 1993; Tanfer et al., 1993).

In later chapters we shall discuss some of the findings from these various surveys. In this chapter's first World of Diversity feature, we consider some survey findings concerning the sexuality of Native Americans. Other features will consider the approaches taken to study two other populations: African Americans and people in China.

THE KINSEY INSTITUTE REPORTS ON HOMOSEXUALITY: 1978 AND 1981
These reports by the Indiana University Institute for Sex Research, also called the Kinsey Institute, were based on a sample of 979 homosexuals from the San Francisco area and a reference group of 477 heterosexuals matched for age, race, and educational and occupational achievements (Bell & Weinberg, 1978; Bell et al., 1981). In their 1978 book, *Homosexualities,* researchers Alan Bell and Martin Weinberg recognized that their findings could not necessarily be extended to homosexuals who lived in other cities or sections of the country. Indeed, they acknowledged that their sample might not even represent San Francisco homosexuals. It consisted of people who had "come out of the closet" to join gay rights organizations, who attended gay bars and baths, and so forth. Nevertheless, these reports have provided wide-ranging information on parent-child relationships and sexual orientation and on the diversity of homosexual lifestyles (see Chapter 10).

Learning Objective 6:
Identify the problems associated with using self-report measures and give examples of each.

LIMITATIONS OF THE SURVEY METHOD   The Kinsey studies may be criticized because the interviewers were all men. Women respondents might have felt more free to open up to female interviewers. Gender of the interviewer can have an impact on a

A Survey of the Reproductive Behavior of Native-American Women

The research literature has been virtually silent on the reproductive behavior of Native Americans. Kinsey did not survey Native Americans. Nor did Hunt, Wyatt, or other leading researchers. The 1982 government survey known as the National Survey of Family Growth (NSFG), which surveyed the reproductive behavior of more than 7,500 women nationwide, included only 83 Native-American women in the sample, far too few to be a meaningful indicator of general patterns (Warren et al., 1990).

In one of the first efforts to survey the reproductive and health behavior of Native Americans, the Billings (Montana) Indian Health Service office surveyed 232 Native-American women in the Billings area, ages 15 to 49. Half of the women lived on the Blackfeet Reservation, and the other half lived off the reservation in nearby Great Falls (Warren et al., 1990). Surveys were conducted in 1987, and the results were compared to data on white and African-American women obtained from the 1982 NSFG survey. Because nearly 40 percent of the Native-American households did not have telephones, a face-to-face interview format was adopted. Virtually all of the women interviewed on the Blackfeet Reservation were Blackfeet, but a variety of tribes were represented among interviewees living in Great Falls, including Chippewa-Cree, Little Shell, Assiniboine, and Chippewa, as well as Blackfeet.

Slightly more than half of the Native-American women and African-American women reported having engaged in sexual intercourse by the age of 17, as compared to 28 percent of the white women. Native-American women bore an average of 3.4 to 4.0 children, which was higher than the average among whites (2.7 children) but similar to the average among African Americans (3.4). The percentage of last pregnancies that were unplanned was similar for off-reservation Native-American women (63.6%) and African-American women (60.7%) but was higher than that for white women (44.6%). Native-American women living on the reservation showed an intermediate level (51.2%) of unplanned last pregnancies. Reservation women were more likely than white women to use contraception (79 versus 69%). The percentage of off-reservation Native-American women who used contraception was lower, 58 percent—a figure that was similar to the level of contraceptive use among African-American women (60%). Although female sterilization was the most commonly used contraceptive method among all three groups, its incidence was higher among Native Americans (more than 30%) than among whites (16%) or African Americans (21%).

Overall, the survey underscores the similarities in repro-

---

respondent's willingness to disclose sensitive material. A recent investigation in the Asian country of Nepal, for example, showed that male interviewers generally elicited an underreporting of some sensitive aspects of sexual activity (Axinn, 1991). Problems in obtaining reliable estimates may also occur when interviewers and respondents are of different racial or socioeconomic backgrounds.

Yet another limitation of all surveys is that they require self-report of respondents' behaviors. But self-reports are subject to inaccuracies or biases because of such factors as faulty memories of sexual behavior; tendencies to distort or conceal information because of embarrassment, shame, or guilt; or attempts to present a socially favorable image of oneself. Survey data may also be drawn from haphazard or nonrepresentative samples and thus not represent the target population. Let us consider several weaknesses of the survey method.

Discussion Question: How many of you would volunteer to complete a lengthy questionnaire about your sexual behaviors and attitudes? Why or why not? What differences in attitudes might there be between those of you who would volunteer and those who would not?

VOLUNTEER BIAS Many people simply refuse to participate in surveys. Samples are thus biased by large numbers of volunteers. Volunteers are in general willing to take the time to participate. In the case of sex surveys, they also tend to be more sexually permis-

ductive patterns between Native-American women living off the reservation and African-American women in the larger community. Both groups tended to initiate intercourse at an early age, have a high number of unplanned pregnancies, and make only moderate use of contraception.

Members of these groups tend to face hard economic conditions and a lack of opportunity. The reproductive patterns they shared in common may reflect more broadly upon the plight of economically disadvantaged groups in the United States. Although the researchers looked only at relationships in reproductive patterns among the ethnic groups they studied, it would be interesting to see whether similarities and differences relate more to socioeconomic status than to ethnicity. Native-American women living on the reservation showed reproductive patterns different from those of African Americans and white Americans, and even from those of the urbanized, off-reservation Native-

American sample. We can only speculate that their reproductive behavior may adhere more closely to traditional cultural norms than does that of Native-American women living off the reservation who may be attempting to assimilate into the larger community. Health officials from the Indian Health Service plan to explore the reproductive behavior patterns of other Native-American groups.

Native American Women. Research compares the reproductive behavior of women who live on reservations with those living in urban areas.

sive and liberal-minded than nonvolunteers (Morokoff, 1986). The results of a survey based on a volunteer sample thus may not accurately reflect the population at large.

FAULTY ESTIMATION   Respondents may recall their behavior inaccurately or purposefully misrepresent it. People may not recall the age at which they first engaged in petting or masturbated to orgasm. People may have difficulty recalling or calculating the frequencies of certain behaviors, such as the weekly frequency of marital intercourse ("Well, let's see, this week I think it was four times, but last week only two times, and I can't remember the week before that"). Kinsey and Hunt speculated that people who desire more frequent sex tend to underestimate the frequency of marital coitus, whereas people who want less frequent sex tend to overestimate it.

Social desirability
A response bias to a questionnaire or interview in which the subject provides a socially acceptable response.

SOCIAL-DESIRABILITY RESPONSE BIAS   Even people who consent to participate in surveys of sexual behavior may feel pressured to answer questions in the direction of **social desirability.** Some respondents, that is, try to ingratiate themselves with their interviewers by offering what they believe to be socially desirable answers. Although

A WORLD OF DIVERSITY

The Wyatt Survey on African-American and White Women in Los Angeles

Alfred Kinsey and his colleagues (1948, 1953) obtained some data on the sexual behavior of African Americans. They did not report it in their surveys, however, because African Americans were clearly underrepresented in their samples.

In more recent years some researchers have set out to provide portraits of the sexual behavior of African-Americans. In the 1980s, for example, UCLA researcher Gail Wyatt and her colleagues, (Wyatt, 1985, 1989; Wyatt et al., 1988a, 1988b) examined the sexual behavior of a sample of 122 white and 126 African-American women in the Los Angeles County, ranging form 18 to 36 years of age.[1] The subjects were sampled randomly form telephone listings. Subjects who agreed to participate were selected to balance the sample with respect to demographic characteristics such as age, education, number of children, and marital status. One in three prospective subjects refused to cooperate. The participants were interviewed in Kinsey-style, face-to-face interviews that lasted 3 to 8 hours each. Past and present sexual behavior were covered, along with reports of sexual abuse in childhood.

Because Wyatt and Kinsey used similar means to obtain data, direct comparisons can be made between their studies. Wyatt used statistical adjustments to control for differences in the sociodemographic characteristics (age, education, social class) between her samples and Kinsey's to enable comparisons between the two.

Wyatt's work is important for several reasons. It addresses changes in sexual behavior that have taken place in U.S. society since Kinsey's day. It focuses on social issues that have become prominent, such as sexual abuse in childhood. It also is one of the few detailed studies of sexual behavior among African-American women.

One of the striking differences between Kinsey's data and Wyatt's was that women in her 1980s sample—African-American and white—engaged in intercourse for the first time at earlier ages than was the case in Kinsey's sample, interviewed 40 years or so earlier. Kinsey reported that by the age of 20, about one in five women had engaged in premarital coitus (Kinsey et al., 1953). By contrast, Wyatt reported that 98 percent of her subjects (African-American and white) had experienced premarital intercourse by that age (Wyatt, 1989). When social class differences were taken into consideration, the ages of first intercourse for African-American and white women in Wyatt's sample were quite similar.

Wyatt's research, of course, was limited to Los Angeles and may not represent the general U.S. population. Kinsey's sample was also geographically skewed; he overrepresented the northeastern United States, although he did include respondents from many regions of the country.

Let us also note the refusal rate in Wyatt's study. Wyatt was more successful in obtaining cooperation than the *Playboy* survey (67% of the people contacted agreed to participate, versus 20% for *Playboy*). Nonetheless, Wyatt's 33 percent refusal rate may have compromised representativeness. Also, to control for demographic differences between white and African-American women, Wyatt limited the pool of cooperating subjects to demographically comparable women. Her sample of African-American women matched the demographic characteristics of the larger population of African-American women in Los Angeles County, but her white sample did not match the population characteristics for white women in the county. It contained a greater proportion of white women from lower income families than does Los Angeles county as a whole. These are the kinds of trade-offs that can occur when researchers attempt to control for demographic differences.

[1]Wyatt used the terms *Afro-American* and *black* interchangeably to refer to women of African descent. We shall use *African American* in discussing Wyatt's results and throughout the textbook.

Activity: *The Social-Desirability Scale* The IM includes this 33-item questionnaire, which allows students to determine if they would tend to answer truthfully or to construct socially desirable answers to survey questions.

some respondents may readily divulge information concerning the frequency of marital coitus, they may deny experiences involving prohibited activities like child molestation, voyeurism, or coerced sexual activity. (People who engage in these proscribed activities may also be more likely to decline to participate in sex surveys.)

Some people may not divulge sensitive information for fear of disapproval by the interviewer. Others may fear criminal prosecution. Even though interviewers may insist that they are nonjudgmental and that subjects will remain anonymous, respondents may fear that their identities may be uncovered some day.

This book's first author, with a graduate student, Francis McGovern (McGovern & Nevid, 1986), conducted a study on the effects of social-desirability on self-report psychological inventories among inmates at a correctional facility for sex offenders (mostly rapists and child abusers). We found that the willingness of sex offenders to disclose deviant and symptomatic responses on psychological inventories was related to the social-desirability cues or hints we gave them prior to administering the tests. Some subjects were encouraged to associate psychological health with self-disclosure; for example, they were told that "one cannot control one's impulses unless one is first willing to admit them." Other subjects were given cues that fostered nondisclosure; for example, they were told that "to control deviant behavior you must first control your deviant thoughts and feelings." Still others received no cues from the researchers. Subjects encouraged to associate psychological health with self-disclosure reported more deviant and symptomatic responses, and were less psychologically guarded in their responses, than subjects receiving nondisclosure cues or no cues. Since the responses of subjects who received nondisclosure cues did not differ from those of the subjects receiving no cues, inmates apparently do not need to be prompted to cover up deviant thoughts and feelings. They seem to do so already. But willingness to disclose sensitive information may be enhanced by suggesting that self-disclosure is connected with psychological health or adjustment.

EXAGGERATION For some respondents, the "socially desirable" response is one of exaggeration. In our culture men may tend to exaggerate their sexual exploits, and women may tend to play them down (Havemann & Lehtinen, 1990). Males and "liberated" females may fear that the interviewer will think less of them for reporting only infrequent sexual contacts, or for sounding too "straight." Some respondents, for reasons best known to themselves, falsify their attitudes and exaggerate the bizarreness of their behavior, perhaps to draw attention to themselves, perhaps to foul up the results.

DENIAL Another source of bias in sex survey research is denial. People may deny, even to themselves, sexual feelings or experiences that might elicit anxiety if they were acknowledged, such as homosexual fantasies or feelings.

Activity: *Thinking About the Limitations of Sex Surveys* The IM includes directions and possible answers for this activity, which asks students to apply their general knowledge about the limitations of sex surveys to their possible responses to survey questions.

DIFFERENCES IN MEANINGS OF TERMS Survey respondents can only respond to the questions posed by interviewers or questionnaires. A word or phrase may mean different things to different people, however. One person asked whether he or she has engaged in French kissing may think of deep, open-mouth tongue kissing (the generally accepted meaning of the term). To another, the term may denote a prolonged but gentle kiss on the lips. To some people, the term "sexual satisfaction" may denote an intense orgasm. To others, it signifies the pleasure of sharing physical intimacy with a loved one. To the extent that people interpret the same terms on sex surveys differently, they may differ in their responses because of differences in semantics, not because of differences in behavior.

You might think that with all these problems the survey method would be fairly useless as a means of gathering data about human sexuality. Actually, carefully conceived and executed surveys can offer many insights into sexual attitudes and practices. They are especially useful when looking at changes in sexual practices over the years, as we shall see in later chapters. All in all, sex surveys remain the most practical means of obtaining information about sexual behavior. In many cases they are the only available means. Before Kinsey we had little information about the sexual practices of people in

The Liu Report: Sexual Behavior in the Chinese Male and Female

China has never been a particularly prudish country. China's tradition of concubines and prostitution predates the birth of Jesus. Nevertheless, after the Communists came into power in 1949, China became transformed into one of the world's more puritanical societies.

Yet according to a survey by Shanghai-based sociologist Liu Dalin, since China's opening to the outside world in the 1970s, the times have been a-changin'. A little.

As reported by Southerland (1990), Liu's volunteers interviewed 23,000 Chinese over a period of 18 months. This was the first nationwide sex survey ever conducted in China, and it is referred to as China's "Kinsey Report." It polled twice as many subjects as Kinsey and his colleagues did. Subjects ranged from students and professionals to peasants and convicted sex offenders, who were questioned in three major cities and 12 provinces. The researchers encountered problems in the form of lack of funds, illiterate subjects, and reluctance to reveal intimate sexual information.

Here are some of Liu's findings:

Chinese youth today are reaching sexual maturity about a year earlier than their grandparents did, partly because of improved nutrition.

About 50 percent of the young people in cities and on farms reported that they engaged in premarital intercourse.

About 14 percent of the women living in large cities said they engaged in extramarital sex, and overall 69 percent of the respondents approved of such affairs. This is a larger approval rate than is found in the United States, where the majority of respondents to surveys disapprove of affairs (e.g., Blumstein & Schwartz, 1990; Hunt, 1974).

TRUTH OR FICTION?
REVISITED

Residents of Communist China are more likely than people in the United States to approve of extramarital affairs. It does appear from the results of the Liu survey that the Chinese are more likely to approve of extramarital affairs than are people in the United States. •

Many Chinese couples use very little foreplay; 44 percent of urban wives and 37 percent of rural wives reported at least some pain during intercourse due to insufficient vaginal lubrication.

Women are more likely than men to initiate divorces. Three out of five divorces are sought by women.

Although about 50 percent of China's young people engage in premarital intercourse, the government maintains a strict policy of condemning sexual activity outside of marriage. As a result, a male student was expelled from a Beijing university as recently as April 1990, when it became known that he was engaging in premarital sexual relations. Other students said that the punishment was typical.

A Sex Survey in Contemporary China. In a recent survey of 23,000 people in China, about 50 percent of the young people in cities and on farms reported engaging in premarital intercourse.

our society. Kinsey and the surveyors who followed have helped us become better aware of the frequencies of such sexual practices as masturbation, premarital sex, extramarital sex, homosexual activity, and so on. Yet because of the problems of nonrepresentative sampling and response bias, we still lack precise knowledge of sexual behavior patterns in the general population.

OBSERVATIONAL METHODS

Learning Objective 7:
Describe the four observational methods and suggest situations in which each might be used.

Ethnography
The branch of anthropology that deals descriptively with specific cultures, especially preliterate societies.

Naturalistic observation
A method in which organisms are observed in their natural environments.

A psychologist once noted that if you want to find out something about people, ask them. They may just tell you. But although surveys are convenient and direct, questions remain as to how accurate a picture they paint. Researchers thus also employ other means of gathering data that avoid some of the problems of surveys.

Observational methods, for example, employ the investigator as a direct observer of sexual behavior. Such observations may take place in field settings or laboratories. Some methods, such as observations of animals in the wild, avoid the problems of self-reports altogether. In other cases, such as in **ethnographic** studies of people in preliterate societies, direct observation can be supplemented by interviews. Thus, a combination of observational and self-report methods is used. Yet observational methods also have their limitations, as we shall see. Let us consider several observational methods for the study of sexual behavior.

THE NATURALISTIC-OBSERVATION METHOD   In **naturalistic observation,** also called the *field study,* scientists directly observe the behavior of animals and humans where it happens. Anthropologists, for example, have lived among preliterate societies and reported on their social and sexual customs. Other disciplines, too, have adopted methods of naturalistic observation in their research on human sexuality. Sociologists have observed the street life of prostitutes. Psychologists have observed patterns of non-verbal communication and body language among couples in dating situations.

Scientists take precautions to keep their naturalistic observations *unobtrusive,* so as not to influence the behavior of their subjects. Over the years, naturalistic observers have been placed in ethical dilemmas. They have allowed sick or injured animals to die, rather than intervene, when medical assistance could have saved them. They have allowed substance abuse and illicit sexual behavior to go unreported to authorities. The ethical trade-off is that unobtrusive observation may yield data that will benefit large numbers of people—the greatest good for the greatest number.

NATURALISTIC OBSERVATION OF ANIMALS   The famed naturalist Jane Goodall (Goodall, 1963; van Lawick-Goodall, 1971) lived for many years among groups of chimpanzees in Africa, observing them in their natural environment to learn about their sexual

FIGURE 2.1 **Naturalistic Observation.** In naturalistic observation—also called the *field study*—scientists directly observe the behavior of animals and humans where it happens. Scientists take precautions to keep their naturalistic observations *unobtrusive,* so as not to influence the behavior of their subjects. Jane Goodall, shown here, lived for many years among groups of chimpanzees in Africa, observing them in their natural environment to learn about their sexual behaviors and other facets of chimp life.

behaviors and other facets of chimp life (Figure 2.1). Among her many observations was that kissing is used by primates other than humans—namely, chimps. Goodall concluded that chimp kissing, like some human kissing, was a form of social greeting. Given the extent of her observations and the broad understanding she developed of the ways of chimps, Goodall's interpretation may well be correct. As noted earlier, however, behavioral scientists sometimes err by interpreting animal behavior in human terms, rather than describing it in more neutral terms.

TRUTH OR *FICTION?*

R E V I S I T E D

Male chimpanzees have been observed greeting females by taking their hands and kissing them. Yes, the naturalist Jane Goodall made such observations. But we must be cautious in distinguishing between observations and possible anthropomorphic interpretations. •

ETHNOGRAPHIC OBSERVATION   Anthropologists have lived among societies of people in the four corners of the earth in order to observe and study human diversity. Margaret Mead (1935) reported on the social and sexual customs of various peoples of New Guinea. Bronislaw Malinowski (1929) studied the Trobriand islanders, among other peoples. Ford and Beach's (1951) account of sexual practices around the world and in nonhuman species remains to this date a classic study of cross-cultural and cross-species comparisons. Ethnographic research has provided us with data concerning sexual behaviors and customs that occur widely across cultures and those that are limited to one or few cultures. Ethnographers are trained to be keen observers, but direct observation has its limits in the study of sexual behavior. Sexual activities are most commonly performed away from the watchful eyes of others, especially from those of visitors from other cultures. Ethnographers may thus have to rely on such methods as personal interviewing to learn more about sexual customs.

Participant observation
A method in which observers interact with their subjects as they collect data.

Swinging
Mate swapping.

THE PARTICIPANT-OBSERVATION METHOD   In **participant observation,** the investigators learn about people's behavior by directly interacting with them. Participant observation has been used in studies of homosexuality and mate-swapping. In effect, participation has been the "price of admission" for observation.

Investigators of mate-swapping, or **swinging,** have contacted swinging couples through newsletter ads and other sources and presented themselves as "baby swingers" (novices) seeking sexual relations (Bartell, 1970; Palson & Palson, 1972). Thus, some investigators may have deceived their subjects. In some cases, however, as in Bartell's study, subjects were informed that the investigator was conducting research after he was admitted to the party. In some cases, researchers have engaged in coitus with their subjects during "swinging parties," which raises questions about how far one should go "for the sake of science."

TRUTH OR *FICTION?*

R E V I S I T E D

Some sex researchers have engaged in "swinging" with their subjects. Researchers have in fact "swung" with their subjects. But this is a rare occurrence, and the ethics of this research method have been questioned. •

Sampling biases are another concern. There is no way of knowing whether the swingers who were contacted by newspaper ads were typical of swingers in general. The sampling methods also limited the investigations to active swingers and excluded people who had once "swung" but no longer did so.

Discussion Question:
Would you agree to participate in a direct laboratory observation study similar to Masters and Johnson's study? Under what circumstances? Why or why not?

THE LABORATORY-OBSERVATION METHOD   In *Human Sexual Response* (1966), William Masters and Virginia Johnson were among the first to report direct laboratory observations of individuals and couples engaged in sexual acts. In all, 694 people (312 men and 382 women) participated in the research. The women ranged from 18 to 78 in age; the men, from 21 to 80. There were 276 married couples, 106 single women, and 36 single men. The married couples engaged in intercourse and other forms of mutual stimula-

William Masters and Virginia Johnson.

tion, such as manual and oral stimulation of the genitals. The unmarried subjects participated in studies that did not require intercourse, such as measurement of female sexual arousal to insertion of a penis-shaped probe and male ejaculation during masturbation. Masters and Johnson performed similar laboratory observations of sexual response among homosexual subjects for their 1979 book, *Homosexuality in Perspective.*

Direct laboratory observation of biological processes was not invented by Masters and Johnson, but they were confronting a society that was still unprepared to speak openly of sex, let alone to observe people engaged in sexual activity in the laboratory. Masters and Johnson were accused by some people of immorality, voyeurism, and an assortment of other evils. Nevertheless, their methods offered the first reliable set of data on what happens inside the body during sexual response. Their instruments permitted them to directly measure vasocongestion (blood flow to the genitals), myotonia (muscle tension), and a host of other physiological responses. Perhaps their most controversial device was a "coition machine"—a transparent artificial penis that contained photographic equipment. This apparatus enabled them to record changes in women's internal sexual organs as they became sexually aroused. From these studies, Masters and Johnson observed that it is useful to divide sexual response into four stages (their "sexual response cycle"), and that the sexual response of both genders, heterosexual and homosexual, is more similar than had been thought.

Researchers have since developed more sophisticated physiological methods of measuring sexual arousal and response. Masters and Johnson's laboratory method is now used, with some variations but with less controversy, in research centers across the country (Rosen & Beck, 1988).

Observer effect
A distortion of subjects' behavior caused by the act of observation.

Learning Objective 8:
Discuss several weaknesses of the various observational methods.

LIMITATIONS OF OBSERVATIONAL RESEARCH One of the basic problems with naturalistic observation is the possibility that the behavior under study may be *reactive* to the measurement itself. This source of bias is referred to as the **observer effect.**

The ethnographer who studies a particular culture or subgroup within a culture may unwittingly alter the behavior of the members of the group by focusing attention on some facets of their behavior. Falling prey to social desirability, some subjects may "straighten out their act" while the ethnographer is present. Other subjects may try to impress the ethnographer by acting in ways that are more aggressive or sexually provocative than usual. In either case, subjects supply distorted or biased information about their own behavior or the customs or behavior of their group. Ethnographers must corroborate self-reported information by using multiple sources. They must also be sensitive to the possibility that their own behavior is more obtrusive than they think.

Observer bias can distort researchers' perceptions of the behaviors they observe. Observers who hold rigid sexual attitudes may be relatively unwilling to examine subject activities that they consider offensive or objectionable. They may unwittingly slant interviews in a way that presents a "sanitized" view of their subjects' behavior. Or they may unwittingly (or intentionally) exaggerate or "sensationalize" certain sexual practices to conform to their preconceptions of the sexual behavior of their subjects.

The method of laboratory observation used by Masters and Johnson may be even more subject to distortion. Unlike animals, which naturalists may observe unobtrusively from afar, subjects who participate in laboratory observation know that they are being observed and that their responses are being measured. The problem of volunteer bias, troublesome for sex surveys, is even thornier in laboratory observation. How many of us would assent to performing sexual activities in the laboratory while we were connected to physiological monitoring equipment and in full view of researchers? Some of the women observed by Masters and Johnson were patients of Dr. Masters who felt indebted to him and agreed to participate. Many were able to persuade their husbands to participate as well. Some were medical students and graduate students from the local academic community, who were undoubtedly motivated by the desire to earn some extra money (subjects were paid for their time), and perhaps by scientific curiosity as well.

Another methodological concern of the Masters and Johnson approach is that observing people engaged in sexual activities may in itself alter their responses. People may not respond publicly in the same way that they would in private. Perhaps sexual response in the laboratory bears little relationship to sexual response in the bedroom. The physiological monitoring equipment may also alter their natural responses. (With these constraints in mind, it is perhaps remarkable that Masters and Johnson's subjects were able to become sexually aroused to the point of orgasm.) Finally, although naturalistic observation provides a good deal of information as to how people behave, it does not necessarily disclose *why* they behave as they do. Questions of cause and effect are best approached by means of experiments.

THE EXPERIMENTAL METHOD

Most scientists would agree that the best (if not always feasible) method for studying *cause-and-effect* relationships is the **experiment.** Experiments permit scientists to draw conclusions about cause-and-effect relationships because the experimenter is able to control or manipulate the factors or variables of interest directly and observe their effects.

In an experiment on the effects of alcohol on sexual arousal, for example, a group of subjects would receive an intervention, called a **treatment,** such as a dose of alcohol. (In other experiments, the intervention or treatment might involve the administration of a drug, exposure to violent pornography, a program of sex education, etc.) They would then be carefully observed to learn whether this treatment made a difference in their behavior—in this case, their sexual arousal.

INDEPENDENT AND DEPENDENT VARIABLES In an experiment, the variables (treatments) that are hypothesized to have a causal effect are manipulated or controlled by the researcher. Consider an experiment designed to determine whether or not alcohol stimulates sexual arousal. The design might involve giving one group of subjects a certain dosage of alcohol, and then measuring the effects of the drug. In such an experimental arrangement, the dosage of alcohol is considered an **independent variable,** whose presence and quantity is manipulated by the researchers. The measured results are called **dependent variables,** since changes in their values are believed to depend on the independent variable or variables. In this experiment measures of sexual arousal would be the dependent variables. Dependent variables are outcomes; they are observed and measured by the researchers, but not manipulated. Sexual arousal might be measured by such means as physiological measurement (gauging the degree of penile erection in the male, for example) or self-report (asking subjects to rate their sexual arousal on a rating scale).

In a study of the effects of sex education on teenage pregnancy, sex education would be the independent variable, and the incidence of teenage pregnancy, the dependent variable. Researchers would administer the experimental treatment (sex education) and track the participants for a period of time to determine their pregnancy rates. But how would experimenters know whether or not the treatment had made a difference in the pregnancy rate? One way would be to compare the pregnancy rate among experimental subjects to rates found in public records. It could be argued, however, that the experimental subjects may have differed in other ways (besides having received sex education) from the people whose records were kept in the public documents, that the records were made at a different time, and so forth. So experimenters would prefer to compare the pregnancy rates of experimental subjects with those of control subjects who did not receive the experimental treatment.

EXPERIMENTAL AND CONTROL GROUPS Well-designed experiments randomly assign subjects to experimental and control groups. **Experimental subjects** receive the

Experiment
A scientific method that seeks to confirm cause-and-effect relationships by manipulating independent variables and observing their effects on dependent variables.

Treatment
In experiments, an intervention administered to subjects (e.g., a test, a drug, a sex-education program, or instructions to perform a certain act) so that its effects may be observed.

Independent variable
A condition in a scientific study that is manipulated so that its effects may be observed.

Dependent variables
The measured results of an experiment, which are believed to be a function of the independent variables.

Experimental subjects
Subjects who receive a treatment in an experiment.

Control subjects
Experimental participants who do not receive the experimental treatment but for whom all other conditions are comparable to those of experimental subjects.

Selection factor
A bias that may operate in research when subjects are allowed to determine whether or not they will receive a treatment.

treatment, whereas **control subjects** do not. Every effort is made to hold all other conditions constant for both groups. By using random assignment and holding other conditions constant, researchers can be reasonably confident that the independent variable (treatment), and not extraneous factors such as the temperature of the room in which the treatment was administered or differences between the types of subjects in the experimental and control groups, brought about the results.

WHY IS RANDOM ASSIGNMENT IMPORTANT?   Why do experimenters assign subjects to experimental and control groups at random, whenever possible? Consider a study conducted to determine the effects of alcohol on sexual arousal in response to sexually explicit material, like X-rated films. If we permitted subjects to elect whether or not they would be members of the group given alcohol, we might not know if it was the alcohol itself that accounted for the results or some other factor, called a **selection factor,** that might discriminate between people who would or would not elect to receive alcohol. One difference might be that subjects who chose to participate in the alcohol group might also have more permissive attitudes toward sexually explicit material than the others, which in turn could affect their sexual responsiveness to these stimuli. If this were the case, experimental outcomes might reflect the effects of this underlying selection factor, rather than of the alcohol itself.

Teaching Tip: To help students better understand the experimental method, plan a "real" study (ex: testing a new treatment for AIDS). Discuss the ethical considerations involved, how you would choose the subjects to participate, assignment to the control and experimental groups and the variables.

EXPERIMENTATION WITH ANIMALS   Researchers frequently undertake studies with other animal species that would be impractical or unethical with humans. For example, it may be hypothesized that prenatal sexual hormones "feminize" or "masculinize" the brain, giving rise to gender-typed behaviors and perhaps predisposing the individual to a heterosexual or homosexual orientation (see Chapters 6 and 10). The ideal method for examining these hypotheses would be to alter the balance of sex hormones systematically at various stages of fetal development and then monitor subjects' behavior in subsequent years. However, neither parents nor researchers would be willing to risk the well-being of children through such an experiment. Therefore, studies of this kind have been conducted on animals in the hope that they would shed some light on similar processes in humans.

To the extent that we share physiological processes with lower animals, experiments with other species may inform us about ourselves. Because of their physiological similarities to people, rats and monkeys, particularly rhesus monkeys, are commonly used in laboratory experiments. Unfortunately—or fortunately?—these animals are more similar biologically to humans than psychologically. Thus, we may make some generalizations from them to people concerning the effects of drugs and other biochemical treatments. We cannot, however, assume that their responses provide much of a clue to higher cognitive processes, such as thinking and reasoning. Nor can we claim that *pair bonding* between animals is equivalent to human marriage, or that (apparently) affectionate displays between animals are the equivalent of romantic love among humans.

Learning Objective 10:
Cite the limitations of the experimental method and give examples of situations in which it could not be used.

LIMITATIONS OF THE EXPERIMENTAL METHOD   Although scientists agree that the experimental method provides the strongest evidence of cause-and-effect relationships, experimenters cannot manipulate many variables of interest directly. We may suspect that sexual trauma in the form of rape or sexual assault is a causal factor in the development of psychological or emotional problems in the immediate aftermath of the attack or years later (see Chapter 19). However, we would not expose subjects to sexual trauma to observe its effects. In the absence of a direct manipulation of the presumed causal factor (rape), we cannot be sure that adjustment problems in rape victims are directly attributable to rape itself, especially when they occur years later. Other factors may be involved, such as insensitive treatment of rape victims by their families or by representatives of the criminal justice system.

Nor can we conduct experiments to determine the effects of cohabitation on college students. We cannot assign an experimental group to cohabitation and a control group to separate living quarters. We can only compare groups of students who have chosen to cohabit to groups of noncohabitors. Our research may thus inform us that cohabitors have certain problems (for example, jealousy), but it cannot show that these problems (like jealousy) are caused by cohabiting (see Chapter 14). Cohabitors and noncohabitors may differ on other factors, besides cohabiting, which give rise to these differences in adjustment.

Similarly, we cannot conduct experiments to determine the effects of pornography on children and adolescents. Societal prohibitions and ethical standards preclude experimenters from exposing children or adolescents to erotic materials.

Experimenters must use other approaches to research, such as the correlational method, to study variables that cannot be manipulated. Correlational studies are also undertaken to suggest possible causal relationships that can be followed up with (often more costly) experimental studies.

THE CORRELATIONAL METHOD

Correlation
A statistical measure of the relationship between two variables.

Correlation coefficient
A statistic that expresses the strength and direction (positive or negative) of the relationship between two variables.

Learning Objective 11:
List the terms associated with the correlational method and explain why correlations do not indicate a cause-and-effect relationship.

A **correlation** is a statistical measure of the relationship between two variables. In correlational studies two or more variables are related, or linked to, one another by statistical means. The experimenter does not directly manipulate the variables of interest, but rather measures the degree to which they are related to one another. The strength and direction (positive or negative) of the relationship between any two variables is expressed with a statistic called a **correlation coefficient.**

Research has shown relationships (correlations) between marital satisfaction and a host of variables such as communication skills, shared values, flexibility, frequency of social interactions with friends, and churchgoing, to name a few. Although such research may give us an idea of the factors associated with marital satisfaction, the experimenters have not manipulated the variables of interest. For this reason we cannot say which, if any, of the factors is causally related to marital happiness. Consider the relationship between churchgoing and marital happiness. Couples who attend church more frequently have been found to report higher rates of marital satisfaction (Wilson & Filsinger, 1986). It is possible that churchgoing may have a causal influence on stabilizing marriages, but it is also possible that people who attend church regularly are more stable and committed to marriage in the first place.

Regular churchgoers report higher levels of sexual satisfaction. *Regular churchgoers do in fact report higher levels of sexual satisfaction. We cannot say, however, that churchgoing is causally related to marital satisfaction.* •

Correlations may be *positive* or *negative*. Two variables are positively correlated if one increases as the other increases. Frequency of intercourse, for example, has been found to be positively correlated with sexual satisfaction (Blumstein & Schwartz, 1983). It is not surprising that married couples who engage more frequently in coitus tend to report higher levels of satisfaction. After all, we usually repeat behavior that is rewarding. Then again, since the experimenters did not manipulate the variables, we cannot say that sexual satisfaction has a causal effect on coital frequency. The reverse may be true. Perhaps people who practice coitus more frequently may come to experience greater satisfaction. It is also possible that there is no causal relationship between the variables, just as height and weight tend to be correlated with each other but one is not the cause of the other.

LIMITATIONS OF THE CORRELATIONAL METHOD   Throughout this text you should bear in mind that correlation is not causation. Variables may be correlated but not causally related to one another. Although correlational research does not show cause and effect, it can be used to predict behavior. When variables are correlated, we can predict one on the basis of the other. For example, we can predict that people who were sexually traumatized as children are more likely to encounter psychological problems and to find it difficult to establish intimate relationships in adulthood, even though we cannot demonstrate that sexual trauma directly causes these problems. Although the correlation does not provide causal knowledge, it may permit us to anticipate the needs of victims of sexual assault for treatment services. Knowledge of the variables that predict psychological problems may also help us direct prevention efforts to avert the development of these problems in high-risk groups. Knowledge of correlational relationships may also lead to controlled experiments that more directly address questions of cause and effect.

THE CASE-STUDY METHOD

Case study
A carefully drawn, in-depth biography of an individual or a small group of individuals that may be obtained through interviews, questionnaires, and psychological tests.

A **case study** is a carefully sketched, in-depth biography of an individual or a small group of individuals. The focus is on understanding an individual or several individuals as fully as possible by unraveling the interplay of various factors in their backgrounds. In most case studies the researcher comes to know the individual or group of individuals through interviews or other contacts conducted over a prolonged period of time. The interviewing pattern tends to build upon itself with a good deal of freedom, as opposed to the one-shot, standardized set of questions used in survey questionnaires.

Researchers may also conduct case studies by interviewing people who have known the subjects or even by drawing upon public records. Sigmund Freud, for example, drew upon historical records in his case study of the Renaissance inventor and painter Leonardo da Vinci. Freud concluded that Leonardo's artistic productions represented the sublimating, or channeling, of homosexual impulses—an assertion whose validity can never be tested.

TRUTH OR *FICTION?*

R E V I S I T E D

Case studies have been carried out on subjects who are dead. *Yes, case studies have in fact been carried out on subjects who are dead. They rely on historical records rather than interviews with subjects themselves or their contemporaries.* •

Reports of innovative treatments for sexual dysfunctions usually appear as well-described case studies. A clinician typically reports the background of the client in depth, describes the treatment fully, reports the apparent outcomes, and suggests factors that might have contributed to the treatment's success or failure. In writing a treatment case study, the therapist attempts to provide information that may be of help to other therapists treating clients with similar problems. Case studies or "multiple case studies" (reports concerning a few individuals) that hold promise may also be subjected to controlled investigation—ideally, experimental studies involving treatment and control groups.

LIMITATIONS OF THE CASE-STUDY METHOD   Despite the richness of material that may be derived from the case-study approach, a case study is not as rigorous a form of research design as an experiment. Subjects often have gaps in memory, especially concerning events that they experienced in childhood. The potential for observer biases is also a prominent concern. Interviewers may unintentionally encourage subjects to slant their personal histories in ways that lend support to the interviewers' theoretical perspectives. Clinicians and interviewers run the risk of indirectly guiding subjects into saying what they expect to hear. Then, too, researchers may inadvertently color subjects' reports when they jot them down—subtly shaping them in ways that are more congruent with their own views.

Remember that clinicians who test a treatment method with a single client (or with a few clients) through a course of therapy are manipulating an independent variable (the treatment) with one or more people who are unlikely to represent the general population. For one thing, the clients have sought (or been placed in) professional treatment. Case studies also lack control groups. In the absence of a control group, we cannot be certain whether treatment outcomes are due to the following factors:

Nonspecific treatment factors
Factors other than the treatment method itself that may be the actual cause of the treatment outcome—for example, a more hopeful attitude that grows out of being in therapy.

1. Specific treatment methods.
2. **Nonspecific treatment factors,** such as giving clients hope or having them talk out their problems with a sympathetic therapist.

3. Improvement that comes about naturally as a result of time ("spontaneous remission").
4. External factors, such as counsel from loved ones, financial gains, and so forth.

Recognize, too, that therapists, like many of us, sometimes engage in self-serving explanations. They may take credit for treatment successes but pin the blame for treatment failures on other factors, such as a lack of motivation on the client's part.

ETHICS IN SEX RESEARCH

Learning Objective 13: Discuss the major ethical issues researchers encounter when conducting sex research.

Volumes have been written about moral and ethical issues concerning sex. This section, however, refers to the ethics followed by researchers who study sexuality. In a nutshell, sex researchers are required to protect the people being studied (Bentler & Abramson, 1981). The concept of protection implies that people will not be subjected to physical or psychological harm and will participate of their own free will. Yet there are some experiments that have exposed subjects to some degree of pain and stress.

In virtually all institutional or organized settings, such as colleges, universities, hospitals, and research institutions, ethics review committees help researchers weigh the potential harm of administering the independent variables to subjects and review proposed studies in light of ethical guidelines. Ethics review committees are obliged to pass judgment on the acceptability of a proposed study before it may begin. If the committee finds fault with a proposal, it may advise the researcher how to modify the research design to comply with ethical standards and will withhold approval until the proposal has been so modified.

PAIN AND STRESS

Subjects may be harmed if they are exposed to pain or placed in stressful situations. For this reason many potentially informative or useful studies have not been done. Researchers have not exposed children to erotic materials in order to determine the effects. Researchers have not exposed human fetuses to male or female sex hormones to learn whether they create fundamental predispositions toward tomboyishness, homosexuality, career choices, and other variables of interest.

Sex researchers *have* studied children born to mothers who were given certain sex hormones to help maintain their pregnancies (see Chapter 6). But these treatments were standard medical procedures that were undertaken to help the women and their fetuses. The availability of these cases has made it possible for scientists to examine the effects on later gender-role behavior and sexual behavior of prenatal exposure to these hormones. But the investigators did not administer these treatments to the pregnant women for purposes of research.

In some studies, subjects have been exposed to a moderate degree of pain or stress. Chapter 20 discusses the results of complex experiments in which male subjects have been shown violent pornography and been misled into believing that they were delivering electric shocks to women by pressing switches on a fearsome-looking console. Receiving even a mild electric shock may be painful and the belief that one is shocking another person can also be stressful.

Notes: Studies examining the effects of AZT and other AIDS treatments on HIV-positive pregnant women and their fetuses force researchers to weigh both the potential benefits and the possible harm in conducting these studies. Although AZT now appears to reduce the incidence of HIV infection in infants born to HIV-positive mothers, the long-term effects of AIDS treatments on fetuses may not be known for as long as ten or twenty years after their births.

When considering the ethical acceptability of a study that poses a risk of harm to subjects, ethics review committees weigh the potential harm in light of the potential benefits to the subjects themselves, to science, and to society in general. Ethical standards require that research may be conducted only when the expected benefits of the research outweigh the anticipated risks to subjects, when the experimenter attempts to minimize any expected harm or risks, and when the experimenter ensures that the pain and stress experienced by subjects is neither excessive nor lasting. Moreover, subjects are given general information about the stressful or painful conditions to which they will be exposed prior to the study. Thus, they can decide whether or not they wish to participate and can better prepare themselves.

CONFIDENTIALITY

Sex researchers must keep the identities and responses of their subjects confidential to protect them from the harm or embarrassment that might result if their responses were divulged. Some information that subjects confide to researchers might be legally incriminating, such as reports of illegal sexual activities. Some people might suffer harm or embarrassment even if it were known that they had participated in sex research.

Researchers can do many things to assure the confidentiality of their subjects. They can make questionnaires anonymous. Interviewers may not be given the identities of interviewees. In reports of research, enough information about subjects' backgrounds can be given to make the studies useful (size of city of origin, region of country, religion, age group, race, educational level, and so on) without divulging the identities of participants. Information that might reveal the person's identity (place of employment, date of marriage) can be withheld or disguised. Once the need for follow-up has passed and the results have been fully analyzed, the names and addresses of subjects and their research records can be destroyed. If the names and addresses of subjects are maintained, researchers can code them, keep them under lock and key, and spread the keys among several people, so that no one person has enough information to link any subject to a sexual history or sexual activity.

INFORMED CONSENT

Informed consent
The term used by researchers to indicate that subjects have agreed to participate in research after receiving information about the purposes of the study, the nature of the treatments, and the risks and benefits they might incur.

The principle of **informed consent** requires that subjects freely agree to participate after being given enough information about the general procedures and purposes of the research, and the risks and benefits they might incur, to permit them to make an informed decision about whether or not to participate. The information must be presented to them in a manner that they can understand. Prospective subjects may not be coerced to participate, and once they have begun the study they must be free to withdraw at any time without penalty. In some cases subjects may be told that certain information about the experimental conditions will be withheld from them until the conclusion of the study. This is especially true when deception is involved.

THE USE OF DECEPTION

Ethical conflicts may emerge when experiments require that subjects not be fully informed about their purposes and methods. For example, in experiments that involve the effects of violent pornography on aggression against women, subjects may be misled into believing that they are administering electric shocks to female subjects (who are actually confederates of the experimenter), even though no shocks are actually delivered. The experimenter seeks to determine subjects' willingness to hurt women following exposure to aggressive erotic films. Such studies could not be carried out if subjects knew in advance that no shocks would actually be delivered. In studies that involve deception, researchers must demonstrate that the effects of the treatment the subjects receive are not seriously harmful or prolonged and that the benefits of the information obtained outweigh the risks.

DEBRIEFING

Debriefing
Information about a just completed procedure that is provided to subjects to avert potential harm.

Professional organizations like the American Psychological Association require that subjects who are deceived receive a **debriefing** after their participation in research, to reduce potential harm. For example, subjects who are led to believe they have shocked other people in experiments on aggression following exposure to violent pornography are informed that they did not actually administer shocks, and that their "victims" were in league with the experimenter. They are informed that deception was necessary to carry out the experiment, and that their behavior was understandable under the circumstances. Researchers are also responsible for easing any lingering distress in subjects by providing additional support or counseling as needed.

Note that only a relatively few scientific studies of human sexuality have required the administration of painful or stress-inducing stimuli or the use of deception. The vast majority of studies pose no forseeable harm to subjects, are perfectly straightforward in their purposes, and are generally limited to completion of questionnaires.

Research is the backbone of human sexuality as a science. Discussions throughout this textbook will focus on the many scientific findings on sexual behavior that have emerged from Kinsey's time to our own. These findings illuminate our understanding of human sexuality and provide information that can help enhance our sexual experience, prevent and treat sexually transmitted diseases, build more rewarding relationships, and help us learn about ourselves as sexual beings.

SUMMING UP

A SCIENTIFIC APPROACH TO HUMAN SEXUALITY

Scientists insist that assumptions about sexual behavior be supported by evidence. Evidence is based on careful observations in the laboratory or in the field.

The Scientific Method The scientific method is a systematic way of gathering scientific evidence and testing assumptions through empirical research. It entails formulating a research question, framing a hypothesis, testing the hypothesis, and drawing conclusions about the hypothesis.

Goals and Methods of the Science of Human Sexuality The goals of the science of human sexuality are to describe, explain, predict, and control sexual behaviors. People often confuse description with inference. Inferences are woven into theories, when possible.

Operational Definitions The operational definition of a construct is linked to the methods used to measure it, enabling diverse researchers to understand what is being measured.

METHODS OF RESEARCH IN HUMAN SEXUALITY

The Survey Method Surveys typically gather information about behavior through interviews or questionnaires administered to large samples of people. Research samples should accurately represent the population of interest. Representative samples are usually obtained through random sampling. Use of volunteers and the tendency of respondents to offer socially desirable responses are sources of bias in surveys.

Observational Methods In naturalistic observation, scientists directly observe the behavior of animals and humans where it happens—in the "field." In participant observation, investigators learn about people's behavior by interacting with them. In the laboratory-observation method, subjects engage in the behavior under study in the laboratory setting. When methods of observation influence the behavior under study, that behavior may be distorted.

The Experimental Method Experiments allow scientists to draw conclusions about cause-and-effect relationships because they directly control or manipulate the variables of interest and observe their effects. Well-designed experiments randomly assign subjects to experimental and control groups.

The Correlational Method Correlational studies reveal the relationships between variables but not cause and effect.

The Case-Study Method Case studies are carefully drawn biographies of individuals or small groups that focus on unraveling the interplay of various factors in subjects' backgrounds.

ETHICS IN SEX RESEARCH

Ethics concerns the ways in which researchers protect their subjects from harm.

Pain and Stress Ethical standards require that research may be conducted only when the expected benefits of the research outweigh the anticipated risks to subjects, when the experimenter attempts to minimize expected risks, and when the experimenter ensures that the pain and stress experienced by subjects is neither excessive nor lasting.

Confidentiality Sex researchers keep the identities and responses of their subjects confidential to protect them from embarrassment and other potential sources of harm.

Informed Consent The principle of informed consent requires that subjects agree to participate in research only after being given enough information about the purposes, procedures, risks, and benefits to make informed decisions.

The Use of Deception Some research cannot be conducted without deceiving subjects as to its purposes and procedures. In such cases the potential harm and benefits of the proposed research are weighed especially carefully.

Debriefing When subjects are deceived in research studies, they are debriefed afterwards to minimize the risk of harm.

_____ One name for the external female genitals is derived from Latin roots that mean "something to be ashamed of."

_____ Women, but not men, have a sexual organ whose only known function is the reception and transmission of sexual pleasure.

_____ One may determine whether or not a woman is a virgin by examination of the hymen.

_____ Women with larger breasts produce more milk while nursing.

_____ In some cultures, menstruating women have been consigned to special menstrual huts.

_____ At menopause, women suffer debilitating hot flashes.

_____ Menopause signals an end to women's sexual appetite.

_____ Women's college grades slump during menstruation.

C H A P T E R   *3*

Female Sexual Anatomy and Physiology

Pudendum
The external female genitals.

The French have a saying, *Vive la différence!* ("Long live the difference!"), which celebrates the differences between men and women. The differences between the genders, at least their anatomical differences, have often been met with prejudice and misunderstanding, however. History recounts that men have often exalted their own genitals, whereas the less visible genitals of women have been deemed inferior. The derivation of the word **pudendum**, which refers to the external female genitals, speaks volumes about sexism in the ancient Mediterranean world. *Pudendum* derives from the Latin *pudendus,* literally meaning "something to be ashamed of."

One name for the external female genitals is derived from Latin roots that mean "something to be ashamed of." True, this is the derivation of one of the terms we use to refer to women's external genitals •

Learning Objective 1: Recognize the lingering effects of the negative bias that has been present historically in attitudes toward female sexuality and female sexual organs.

Even today, this cultural heritage may lead women to develop negative attitudes toward their genitals and to view them as inferior to men's. Children of both genders are sometimes reared to regard their genitals with a sense of shame or disgust and may be reprimanded for expressing normal curiosity about their genital structures and functions. They may be reared with a "hands-off" attitude and encouraged to keep their "private parts" private, even to themselves. Touching them may be discouraged except as necessary for the purposes of toileting or bathing. Witness the childhood recollections of one woman:

> When I was six years old I climbed up on the bathroom sink and looked at myself naked in the mirror. All of a sudden I realized I had three different holes. I was very excited about my discovery and ran down to the dinner table and announced it to everyone. "I have three holes!" Silence. "What are they for?" I asked. Silence even heavier than before. I sensed how uncomfortable everyone was and answered for myself. "I guess one is for pee-pee, the other for doo-doo and the third for ca-ca." A sigh of relief; no one had to answer my question. But I got the message—I wasn't supposed to ask "such" questions, though I didn't fully realize what "such" was about at that time.
>
> (*Our Bodies, Ourselves,* 1979, p. 40)

Ova
Egg cells. (Singular: ovum.)

In this chapter we conduct a tour of women's external and internal sexual organs. Even generally sophisticated students may fill in some gaps in their knowledge. Most of us know what a vagina is, but how many of us realize that only the female gender has an organ that is exclusively dedicated to pleasure? Or that a woman's passing of urine does not involve the vagina? How many of us know that a newborn girl already has all the **ova** she will ever produce?

As women readers encounter the features of their sexual anatomy in their reading, they may wish to examine their own genitals with a mirror. By following the text and the illustrations, even students who are familiar with the appearance and feel of their own genitals may discover some new anatomical features, or marvel at how their genitals can resemble those in the illustrations yet also be unique.

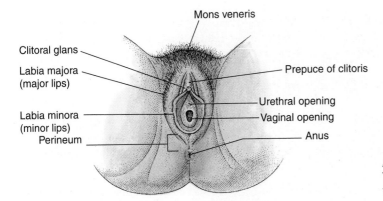

Mons veneris

Clitoral glans

Labia majora
(major lips)

Prepuce of clitoris

Urethral opening

Labia minora
(minor lips)

Vaginal opening

Perineum

Anus

FIGURE 3.1 **External female sexual organs.**
This figure shows the vulva with the labia opened
to reveal the urethral and vaginal openings.

EXTERNAL SEXUAL ORGANS

Vulva
The external sexual structures of the female.

Learning Objective 2:
Name and describe the female external sexual organs.

Taken collectively, the external sexual structures of the female are termed the pudendum or the **vulva.** Pudendum, because of its derivation, may be a less desirable term than *vulva.* Vulva is a Latin word that means "wrapper" or "covering." The vulva consists of the *mons veneris,* the *labia majora* and *minora* (major and minor lips), the *clitoris,* and the vaginal opening (see Figure 3.1). Figure 3.2 shows variations in the appearance of women's genitals (see page 66).

THE MONS VENERIS

Mons veneris
A mound of fatty tissue that covers the joint of the pubic bones in front of the body, below the abdomen and above the clitoris. (The name is a Latin phrase meaning "hill" or "mount of Venus," the Roman goddess of love. Also known as the *mons pubis,* or simply *mons.*)

The **mons veneris** consists of fatty tissue that covers the joint of the pubic bones in front of the body, below the abdomen and above the clitoris. At puberty the mons becomes covered with pubic hair that is often thick and curly, but varies from woman to woman in waviness, texture, and color. The pubic hair captures the chemical secretions that exude from the vagina during sexual arousal. Despite the preoccupation in this country with chemical preparations that promise to kill odors, these secretions produce a scent that lovers may find sexually alluring.

The mons cushions a woman's body during sexual intercourse, protecting her and her partner from the pressure against the pubic bone that stems from thrusting motions. There is an ample supply of nerve endings in the mons, so that caresses of the area can produce pleasurable sexual sensations.

THE LABIA MAJORA

Labia majora
Large folds of skin that run downward from the mons along the sides of the vulva. (Latin for "large lips" or "major lips.")

The **labia majora** are large folds of skin that run downward from the mons along the sides of the vulva. The labia majora of some women are thick and bulging. In other women, they are thinner, flatter, and less noticeable. When close together, they hide the labia minora and the urethral and vaginal openings.

The outer surfaces of the labia majora, by the thighs, are covered with pubic hair and darker skin than that found on the thighs or labia minora. The inner surfaces of the labia majora are hairless and lighter in color. They are amply supplied with nerve endings that respond to stimulation and can produce sensations of sexual pleasure. The labia majora also shield the inner portion of the female genitals.

THE LABIA MINORA

Labia minora
Hairless, light-colored membranes, located between the labia majora. (Latin for "small lips" or "minor lips.")

The **labia minora** are two hairless, light-colored membranes, located between the major lips. They surround the urethral and vaginal openings. The outer surfaces of the labia minora merge with the major lips. At the top they join at the prepuce (hood) of the clitoris.

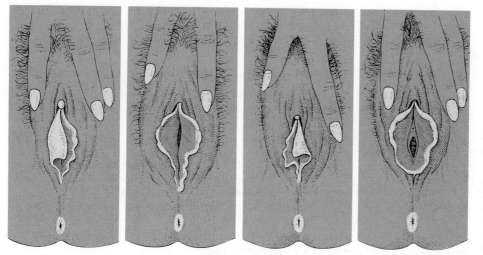

FIGURE 3.2 **Normal variations in the vulva.** The features of the vulva show a great deal of variation. A woman's attitude toward her genitals is likely to reflect her general self-concept and early childhood messages rather than the appearance of her vulva per se.

Discussion Question: At what age did you become aware of the word *clitoris* and the sexual organ to which it refers? Why are girls not taught this term at the age boys are taught the term *penis*? What cultural or religious factors influence this?

Learning Objective 3: Recognize that the clitoris is the only sexual organ whose only known function is pleasure.

Clitoris
A female sex organ consisting of a shaft and glans located above the urethral opening. It is extremely sensitive to sexual sensations.

Corpora cavernosa
Masses of spongy tissue in the clitoral shaft that become engorged with blood and stiffen in response to sexual stimulation. (Latin for "cavernous bodies.")

Prepuce
The fold of skin covering the glans of the clitoris (or penis). (From Latin roots meaning "before a swelling.")

The labia minora differ markedly in appearance from woman to woman. The labia minora of some women form protruding flower shapes that are valued greatly in some cultures, such as that of the Hottentots of Africa. In fact, Hottentot women purposefully elongate their labia minora by tugging at them.

Rich in blood vessels and nerve endings, the labia minora are highly sensitive to sexual stimulation. When stimulated they darken and swell, indicating engorgement with blood.

THE CLITORIS

What's the matter, papa? please don't stall.
Don't you know I love it and want it all?
I'm wild about that thing. Just give my bell a ring.
You pressed my button. I'm wild about that thing.

("I'm Wild about That Thing," recorded by Bessie Smith, 1929)

Worldwide, the clitoris is known by many names, from *bijou* (French for "jewel") to *pokhotnik* (Russian for "lust"). The Tuamotuan people of Polynesia have ten words for it, emblematic of their cultivated interest in female sexuality. By any name, however, the clitoris is the only sex organ whose only known function is the reception and transmission of pleasure.

Clitoris (Figure 3.1) derives from the Greek word *kleitoris,* meaning "hill" or "slope." The clitoris receives its name from the manner in which it slopes upward in the shaft and forms a mound of spongy tissue at the glans. The body of the clitoris, termed the clitoral shaft, is about 1 inch long and 1 quarter-inch wide. The clitoral shaft consists of erectile tissue that contains the spongy masses called **corpora cavernosa** ("cavernous bodies") that fill with blood (become engorged) and become erect in response to sexual stimulation. The stiffening of the clitoris is less apparent than the erection of the penis, because the clitoris does not swing free from the body as the penis does. The **prepuce** (meaning "before a swelling"), or hood, covers the clitoral shaft. It is a sheath of skin formed by the upper part of the labia minora. The clitoral glans is a smooth, round knob or lump of tissue. It resembles a button and is situated above the urethral opening. The clitoral glans may be covered by the clitoral hood but is readily revealed by gently separating the labia minora and retracting the hood. It is highly sensitive to touch because of the rich supply of nerve endings.

The clitoris is the female sexual organ that is most sensitive to sexual sensation. The size of the clitoris varies from woman to woman, just as the size of the penis varies among men. There is no known connection between the size of the clitoris and sensitivity to sexual stimulation. The clitoral glans is highly sensitive to touch, so women usually prefer to be stroked or stimulated on the mons, or on the clitoral hood, rather than directly on the glans.

In some respects, the clitoris is the female counterpart of the penis. Both organs develop from the same embryonic tissue, which makes them similar in structure, or **homologous.** They are not fully similar in function, or **analogous,** however. Both organs receive and transmit sexual sensations, but the penis is directly involved in reproduction and excretion by serving as a conduit for sperm and urine, respectively. The clitoris, however, seems to be a unique sexual organ; it serves no known purpose other than sexual pleasure. It is ironic that many cultures—including Victorian culture—have viewed women as unresponsive to sexual stimulation. It is ironic because women, not men, possess a sexual organ that is apparently solely devoted to pleasurable sensations. The clitoris is the woman's most erotically charged organ, which is borne out by the fact that women most often masturbate through clitoral stimulation, not vaginal insertion.

TRUTH OR *FICTION?*
R E V I S I T E D

Women, but not men, have a sexual organ whose only known function is the reception and transmission of sexual pleasure. Yes, only women have such an organ—the clitoris. •

Surgical removal of the clitoral hood, a form of female circumcision, is a common practice among Moslems in the Near East and Africa. This form of female circumcision may have been rooted in ancient efforts to ensure hygiene. Circumcision, for example, helps control the collection of **smegma.** Smegma has a cheeselike appearance and a foul odor. It is a collection of local secretions without known sexual or reproductive functions, decaying skin cells, and microscopic organisms that form lumps beneath the clitoral hood and can make sexual activity painful. Smegma can be removed by retracting the clitoral hood while bathing and washing the area. There is no hygienic reason for female circumcision today. As we see in the World of Diversity feature, female circumcision in one form or another continues to be a widespread practice in some parts of the world and represents a form of genital torture or mutilation that has as its aim the control of female sexuality.

THE VESTIBULE

The word *vestibule,* which means "entranceway," refers to the area within the labia minora that contains the openings to the vagina and the urethra. The vestibule is richly supplied with nerve endings and is very sensitive to tactile or other sexual stimulation.

THE URETHRAL OPENING

Urine passes from the female's body through the **urethral opening** (Figure 3.1), which is connected by a short tube called the urethra to the bladder (see Figure 3.3, page 70), where urine collects. The urethral opening lies below the clitoral glans and above the vaginal opening. The urethral opening, urethra, and bladder are unrelated to the reproductive system. Many males (and even some females), however, believe erroneously that for women urination and coitus occur through the same bodily opening. The confusion may arise from the fact that urine and semen both pass through the penis of the male, or that the urethral opening lies near the vaginal opening.

The proximity of the urethral opening to the external sexual organs may pose some hygienic problems for sexually active women. The urinary tract, which includes the urethra, bladder, and kidneys, may become infected from bacteria that are transmitted from the vagina or rectum. Infectious microscopic organisms may also pass from the male's sexual organs to the female's urethral opening during sexual intercourse. Manual stimulation of the vulva with dirty hands may also transmit bacteria through the urethral opening to the bladder. If anal intercourse is followed by vaginal intercourse microscopic organisms

A WORLD OF DIVERSITY

Female Circumcision

Cultures in some parts of Africa and the Middle East routinely practice a form of female circumcision on young girls that involves the ritual mutilation or removal of the entire clitoris, not just the clitoral hood. The removal of the clitoris, or **clitoridectomy,** is considered a rite of initiation into womanhood in many of these predominantly Islamic cultures and is often performed as a puberty ritual in late childhood or early adolescence (not at birth, like male circumcision) (Simons, 1993; Tempest, 1993). The clitoris is the organ in the woman that gives rise to feelings of sexual pleasure, and its removal or mutilation represents an attempt to ensure the girl's chastity, since it is assumed that uncircumcised girls are consumed with sexual desires they are unable to control (Ahmed, 1991; Rosenthal, 1992). Some groups in rural Egypt and in the northern Sudan, however, perform clitoridectomies primarily because it is a social custom that has been passed down through the generations from ancient times or because they perceive it as part of their faith in Islam, although neither Islam nor any other religion requires it (Ahmed, 1991; Rosenthal, 1993).

Clitoridectomies are performed under unsanitary conditions without the benefit of anesthesia as the girl is held down (Rosenthal, 1993). Medical complications are common, including infections, bleeding, tissue scarring, painful menstruation, and obstructed labor (Ahmed, 1991). The procedure can also be psychologically traumatizing. An even more radical form of clitoridectomy, called *infibulation* or Pharaonic circumcision, is practiced widely in the Sudan (Ahmed, 1991; Lightfoot-Klein, 1989). Researcher Hanny Lightfoot-Klein (1989) found that more than 90 percent of the 300 Sudanese women she interviewed had received Pharaonic circumcisions, generally between the ages of 4 and 8. Pharaonic circumcision entails complete removal of the clitoris along with the labia minora and the inner layers of the labia majora. After removal of the skin tissue, the raw edges of the labia majora are sewn together and only a tiny opening is left to allow passage of urine and menstrual discharge. The sewing together of the vulva may be intended to ensure the girls' chastity until marriage. Medical complications are common, including menstrual and urinary problems and even death (Lightfoot-Klein, 1989). After marriage, the opening is enlarged to permit intercourse to occur. Enlargement is a gradual process that is often made difficult by scar tissue from the circumcision, and hemorrhaging and tearing of surrounding tissues often occur. It may take three months or longer before the opening is large enough to allow penile penetration. Mutilation of the labia is now illegal in the Sudan, although the law continues to allow removal of the clitoris. Some African countries have outlawed clitoridectomies, although such laws are rarely enforced (Rosenthal, 1992).

Clitoridectomy
The surgical removal of the clitoris.

Cystitis
An inflammation of the urinary bladder. (From the Greek *kystis,* meaning "sac.")

may transfer from the rectum to the bladder and cause infection. For similar reasons women should first wipe the vulva, then the anus, when using the bathroom, in order to prevent organisms that normally dwell in the rectum or intestines from infecting the urinary or reproductive tracts.

Cystitis is a bladder inflammation that may stem from any of these sources. Its primary symptoms are burning and frequent urination (also called *urinary urgency*). Pus or a bloody discharge are common, and there may be an intermittent or persistent ache just above the pubic bone. These symptoms may disappear after several days, but consultation with a **gynecologist** is recommended, because untreated cystitis can lead to serious kidney infections.

A shockingly high number of women in Africa and the Middle East—85 to 114 million by some estimates (Kaplan, 1993)—have undergone some form of genital mutilation involving removal of the clitoris and the labia minora. Clitoridectomies remain common or even universal in nearly 20 countries in Africa, in many countries in the Middle East, and in parts of Malaysia, Yemen, Oman, Indonesia, and the India-Pakistan subcontinent (Rosen-thal, 1992; Simons, 1993). In addition, thousands of African immigrant girls living in Euro-pean countries are also believed to be at risk of having their genitals mutilated by their parents (Tempest, 1993). Even in the United States, some girls have been subjected to these ritual mutilations (Rosenthal, 1993).

Do not confuse male circumcision with the maiming or genital torture inflicted on girls in the name of circumcision. Representative Patricia Schroeder of Colorado depicts the male equivalent of female genital mutilation

as involving the amputation or cutting off of the penis and its surrounding tissue (Rosenthal, 1993). *New York Times* columnist A. M. Rosenthal (1993) calls female genital mutilation the most widespread existing violation of human rights in the world. The Pulitzer prize–winning novelist Alice Walker has drawn attention to the practice of female genital mutilation in her best-selling novel *Possessing the Secret of Joy* and has called for the abolition of the practice in her recent book and televised movie, *Warrior Marks*. Rosenthal (1992) argues that pressure should be placed on nations that fail to take meaningful action to stop this ritual mutilation of women. He suggests that Western nations could tie economic aid to efforts to eliminate clitoridectomies in developing countries. The United Nations as well could treat clitoridectomies as a permanent priority. France has recently taken action to stem clitoridectomies among African immigrants by bringing to trial family members

from more than 30 families on criminal charges of having mutilated their daughters (Simons, 1993). Yet calls from Westerners to ban female circumcision in parts of Africa and the Middle East has sparked controversy on grounds of "cultural condescension"—the attempt by people in one culture to dictate the cultural traditions of people in another. A leader of an influential women's rights organization in Kenya put the issue thus: "Let indigenous people fight it [female circumcision] according to their own traditions . . . It will die faster than if others tell us what to do." Yet for Alice Walker, "torture is not culture." As the debate continues, the reality is that two million African girls continue to undergo ritual genital mutilations each year.

Clitoridectomies were also occasionally recommended to "cure" female masturbators and women with "loose" moral virtues in the nineteenth- and early twentieth-century United States. Fortunately, it was practiced only rarely.

Gynecologist

A physician who treats women's diseases, especially of the reproductive tract. (From the Greek *gyne*, meaning "woman.")

So-called honeymoon cystitis is caused by the tugging on the bladder and urethral wall that occurs during vaginal intercourse. It may occur upon beginning coital activity (though not necessarily on one's honeymoon) or upon resuming coital activity after lengthy abstinence. Figure 3.3 shows the close proximity of the urethra and vagina.

A few precautions may help women prevent serious inflammation of the bladder:

Drinking two quarts of water a day to flush the bladder.

Drinking orange or cranberry juice to maintain an acid environment that discourages growth of infectious organisms.

Decreasing use of alcohol and caffeine (from coffee, tea, or cola drinks) that may irritate the bladder.

EXTERNAL SEXUAL ORGANS

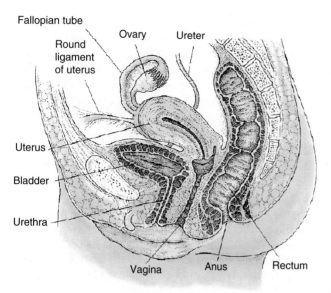

Fallopian tube
Ovary
Ureter
Round ligament of uterus
Uterus
Bladder
Urethra
Vagina
Anus
Rectum

FIGURE 3.3 **The Female Reproductive System.** This cross-section locates many of the internal sexual organs that compose the female reproductive system. Note that the uterus is normally tipped forward.

Notes: In October 1990, twenty-two-year-old Aminata Ciop fled Mali and requested political asylum in France. When she refused to be circumcised before her arranged marriage, as her family and fiancé insisted, her father had beaten her.

Learning Objective 5:
Explain why the condition of the hymen cannot be used to prove or disprove virginity.

Introitus
The vaginal opening. (From the Latin for "entrance.")

Hymen
A fold of tissue across the vaginal opening that is usually present at birth and remains at least partly intact until a woman engages in coitus. (Greek for "membrane.")

TRUTH OR *FICTION?*
R E V I S I T E D

Washing one's hands prior to masturbation or self-examination.
Washing one's partner's and one's own genitals before and after intercourse.
Preventing objects that have touched the anus (fingers, penis, toilet tissue) from subsequently coming into contact with the vulva.
Urinating immediately following intercourse to help wash away bacteria.

None of these measures carries a guarantee of protection against transmission of infectious organisms, but they may help.

THE VAGINAL OPENING

When I was five or six, my mother told me about sex. I remember that I was confused about what my mother said, because somehow I couldn't conceptualize what the female vagina looked like. I was curious to see an actual vagina and not just how it looked diagrammed in a book.

(Morrison et al., 1980, p. 35)

One does not see an entire vagina, but rather the vaginal opening, or **introitus,** when one parts the labia minora, or minor lips. The introitus lies below and is larger than the urethral opening. Its shape resembles that of the **hymen.**

The hymen is a fold of tissue across the vaginal opening that is usually present at birth and may remain at least partly intact until a woman engages in coitus. For this reason the hymen has been called the "maidenhead." Its presence has been taken as proof of virginity, and its absence as evidence of coitus. However, some women are born with incomplete hymens, and other women's hymens are torn accidentally, such as during horseback riding, strenuous exercise, or gymnastics—or even when bicycle riding. A punctured hymen is therefore poor evidence of coital experience. A flexible hymen may also withstand many coital experiences, so its presence does not guarantee virginity. Some people believe incorrectly that virgins cannot insert tampons or fingers into their vaginas, but most hymens will accommodate these intrusions without great difficulty. Some hymens, however, are torn accidentally when inserting tampons.

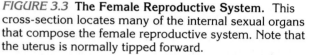

One may determine whether or not a woman is a virgin by examination of the hymen. *Contrary to myth, examination of the hymen may yield false information as to whether or not a woman is a virgin.* •

Notes: In 1989, formal charges were filed against a U.S. physician for what he termed "love surgeries" (or "reconstructive" surgery on the genitals of women). Some Western doctors performed clitoridectomies as a "cure" for masturbation as late as the 1940s.

Discussion Question: What messages did peers give you about the hymen and virginity? What terms were used? What were you told to expect when you had intercourse for the first time?

Defloration
Destruction of the hymen (especially as a cultural ritual).

Perineum
The skin and underlying tissue that lies between the vaginal opening and the anus. (From Greek roots meaning "around" and "to empty out.")

Episiotomy
A surgical incision in the perineum that may be made during childbirth to protect the vagina from tearing. (From the Greek roots *epision,* meaning "pubic region," and *tome,* meaning "cutting.")

Figure 3.4 illustrates various vaginal openings. The first three show common shapes of hymens among women who have not had coitus. The fifth drawing shows a *parous* ("passed through") vaginal opening, typical of a woman who has delivered a baby. Now and then the hymen consists of tough fibrous tissue and is closed, or *imperforate,* as in the fourth drawing. An imperforate hymen may not be discovered until after puberty, when menstrual discharges begin to accumulate in the vagina. In these rare cases, a simple surgical incision will perforate the hymen. A woman may also have a physician surgically perforate her hymen if she would rather forgo the tearing and discomfort that may accompany her initial coital experiences. This procedure is unnecessary, however, for the great majority of women. They experience little pain or distress during initial coitus despite old horror stories. A woman may also stretch the vaginal opening in preparation for intercourse by inserting a finger—preferably lubricated with saliva or K-Y jelly—and gently pressing downward toward the anus. After several repetitions, she may insert two fingers and repeat the process, spreading the fingers slightly after insertion. This procedure is sometimes followed over several days or weeks.

The hymen is found only in female horses and humans. It is not present in animal species closest to humans on the evolutionary scale, such as chimps and gorillas. The hymen remains something of a biological mystery, since it serves no apparent biological function.

DEFLORATION The hymen has been of great cultural significance because of the (erroneous) association between it and virginity. In some societies its destruction, or **defloration,** is ritualized. For example, in some ancient religious rites, young girls were deflowered by sculpted phalluses in ceremonies conducted on the temple steps. During the Middle Ages, the lord of the manor held the *droit du seigneur* (French for "right of the lord") to deflower (by means of intercourse) a maiden on her wedding night, after which she became her husband's sexual property. Among the Yungar of Australia, elderly women deflowered maidens prior to marriage. Girls who were found to have ruptured hymens might be tortured or killed. Since some girls are born with minimal hymens, many have probably been unjustly punished for purported sexual indiscretions.

Defloration usually leads to at least minor bleeding, and in cultures as diverse as the traditional Arabian and the European, bloody bed sheets have been paraded around villages on the wedding night. Woe to the virgin who, through no fault of her own, failed to bleed! In rural villages in seventeenth- and eighteenth-century Europe and Latin America, the well-prepared bride would have a handy supply of pigeon or dove blood to smear upon her sheets, just in case hymenal blood failed to flow.

THE PERINEUM

The **perineum** incorporates the skin and underlying tissue between the vaginal opening and the anus. The perineum is rich in nerve endings, and stimulation of this area may heighten sexual arousal. Many physicians make a routine perineal incision during labor, called an **episiotomy,** to facilitate childbirth.

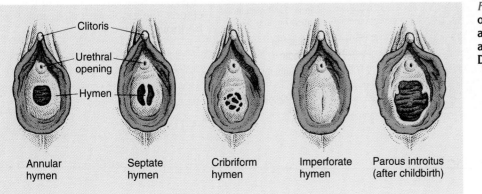

Clitoris

Urethral opening

Hymen

| Annular hymen | Septate hymen | Cribriform hymen | Imperforate hymen | Parous introitus (after childbirth) |

FIGURE 3.4 Appearance of Various Types of Hymens and the Introitus (at Right) as It Appears Following Delivery of a Baby.

STRUCTURES THAT UNDERLIE THE EXTERNAL SEXUAL ORGANS

Sphincters
Ring-shaped muscles that surround body openings and open or close them by expanding or contracting. (From the Greek for "that which draws close.")

Crura
Anatomical structures resembling legs that attach the clitoris to the pubic bone. (Singular: crus. A Latin word meaning "leg" or "shank.")

Vestibular bulbs
Cavernous structures that extend downward along the sides of the introitus and swell during sexual arousal.

Bartholin's glands
Glands that lie just inside the minor lips and secrete fluid just before orgasm.

Pubococcygeus muscle
The muscle that encircles the entrance to the vagina.

Figure 3.5 shows what lies beneath the skin of the vulva. The vestibular bulbs and Bartholin's glands are active during sexual arousal and are found on both sides (shown on the right of Figure 3.5). Muscular rings (**sphincters**) that constrict bodily openings, such as the vaginal and anal openings, are also found on both sides.

The clitoral **crura** are wing-shaped, leglike structures that attach the clitoris to the pubic bone beneath. The crura contain corpora cavernosa, which engorge with blood and stiffen during sexual arousal.

The **vestibular bulbs** are attached to the clitoris at the top and extend downward along the sides of the vaginal opening. Blood congests them during sexual arousal, swelling the vulva and lengthening the vagina. This swelling contributes to coital sensations for both partners.

Bartholin's glands lie just inside the minor lips on each side of the vaginal opening. They secrete a couple of drops of lubrication just before orgasm. This lubrication is not essential for coitus. In fact, the fluid produced by the Bartholin's glands has no known purpose. If the glands become infected and clogged, however, a woman may notice swelling and local irritation. It is wise to consult a gynecologist if these symptoms do not fade within a few days.

It was once believed that the source of the vaginal lubrication or "wetness" that women experience during sexual arousal was produced by the Bartholin's glands. It is now known that engorgement of vaginal tissues during sexual excitement results in a form of "sweating" by the lining of the vaginal wall. During sexual arousal the pressure from this engorgement causes moisture from the many small blood vessels that lie in the vaginal wall to be forced out and to pass through the vaginal lining, forming the basis of the lubrication. In less time than it takes to read this sentence (generally within 10 to 30 seconds), beads of vaginal lubrication or "sweat" appear along the interior lining of the vagina in response to sexual stimulation, in much the same way that rising temperatures cause water to pass through the skin as perspiration.

Pelvic floor muscles permit women to constrict the vaginal and anal openings. They contract automatically, or involuntarily, during orgasm, and their tone may contribute to coital sensations. Gynecologist Arnold Kegel (1952) developed a set of exercises to help build pelvic muscle tone in women who had problems controlling urination after childbirth. The stress of childbirth on the pelvic muscles sometimes reduces muscle tone, leading to an involuntary loss of urine when a woman sneezes or coughs. Kegel also observed that women with thin or weak **pubococcygeus (P-C) muscles** reported they

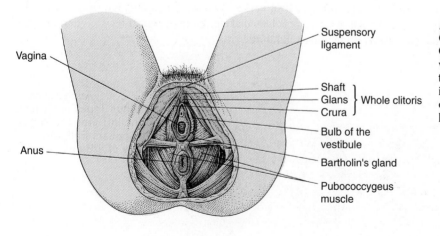

THE PELVIC FLOOR

FIGURE 3.5 Structures That Underlie the Female External Sexual Organs. If we could see beneath the vulva, we would find muscle fibers that constrict the various body openings, plus the crura ("legs") of the clitoris, the vestibular bulbs, and Bartholin's glands.

Kegels

Kegel exercises are now commonly used in programs designed to help women heighten their awareness of vaginal sensations. They may also have a psychological benefit, because women who perform Kegel exercises assume a more active role in enhancing their genital sensations. Sex therapist Lonnie Barbach (1975) offers the following instructions for Kegel exercises:

1. Locate the P-C muscle by purposefully stopping the flow of urine. The muscle you squeeze to stop the urine flow is the P-C muscle. (The P-C muscle acts as a sphincter for both the urethral and vaginal openings.)

2. In order to learn to focus consciously on contracting the P-C muscle, insert a finger into the vaginal opening and contract the muscle so that it can be felt to squeeze or contain the finger. (The P-C muscle can contract to contain objects as narrow as a finger. Thus men need not fear that a large penis is required in order to induce stimulating vaginal sensations in a woman.)

3. Remove your finger and squeeze the P-C muscle for three seconds, then relax. Repeat several times. This part of the exercise may be performed while seated at a classroom or business desk. No one (except the woman herself) will be the wiser. Many women practice a series of Kegel exercises consisting of ten contractions three times a day.

4. The P-C muscle may also be tensed and relaxed in rapid sequence. Since this exercise may be more fatiguing than the above, women may choose to practice it perhaps 10 to 25 times, once a day.

had little or no vaginal sensations during coitus or experienced unpleasant vaginal sensations. Some women with weak P-C muscles complained, "I just don't feel anything" (during coitus), or "I don't like the feeling" (Kegel, 1952, p. 522). Kegel found that women who practiced his exercises improved their urinary control along with their genital sensations during coitus. Kegel believed that many women could enhance vaginal sensations during coitus by exercising their P-C muscles through exercises that have since become known as "Kegels."

INTERNAL SEXUAL ORGANS

Learning Objective 6:
Name, describe, and discuss the functions of the female internal sexual organs.

The internal sexual organs of the female include the innermost parts of the vagina, the cervix, the uterus, and two ovaries, each connected to the uterus by a Fallopian tube (Figure 3.3 and Figure 3.6). Taken as a unit, these structures are referred to as the female reproductive system.

THE VAGINA

Vagina
The tubular female sex organ which contains the penis during sexual intercourse and through which a baby is born. (Latin for "sheath.")

The **vagina** extends back and upward from the vaginal opening (Figure 3.3). It is usually 3 to 5 inches long at rest. Menstrual flow and babies pass from the uterus to the outer world through the vagina. During coitus, the penis is contained within the woman's vagina.

The vagina is commonly pictured as a canal or barrel, but when at rest, it is like a collapsed muscular tube. Its walls touch each other like the fingers of an empty glove or a deflated balloon. The vagina expands in length and width during sexual arousal. The vagina can also expand to allow insertion of a tampon, as well as the passage of a baby's head and shoulders during childbirth.

The vaginal walls have three layers. The inner lining, or *vaginal mucosa,* is made visible by opening the labia minora. It is a mucous membrane similar to the skin that

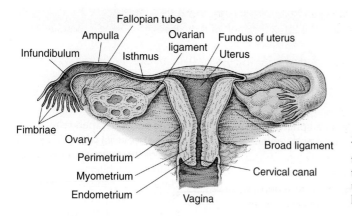

FIGURE 3.6 **Internal Female Reproductive Organs.** This drawing highlights the relationship of the uterus to the Fallopian tubes and ovaries. Note the layers of the uterus, the ligaments that attach the ovaries to the uterus, and the relationship of the ovaries to the fimbriae of the Fallopian tubes.

Labels: Fallopian tube, Ampulla, Ovarian ligament, Fundus of uterus, Infundibulum, Isthmus, Uterus, Fimbriae, Ovary, Perimetrium, Myometrium, Endometrium, Vagina, Broad ligament, Cervical canal

lines the inside of the mouth. It feels fleshy, soft, and corrugated. It may vary from very dry (especially if the female is anxious about something like examinations) to very wet, in which case fingers slide against it readily. The middle layer of the vaginal wall is muscular. The outer or deeper layer is a fibrous covering that connects the vagina to other pelvic structures.

The vaginal walls are rich with blood vessels but poorly supplied with nerve endings. Unlike the sensitive outer third of the vaginal barrel, the inner two thirds are so insensitive to touch that minor surgery may sometimes be performed on those portions without anesthesia. The entire vaginal barrel is sensitive to pressure, however, which can be experienced as sexually pleasurable.

The vaginal walls secrete substances that help maintain the vagina's normal acidity (pH 4.0 to 5.0). Normally the secretions taste salty. The odor and taste of these secretions may vary during the menstrual cycle. Although the evidence is not clear, the secretions are thought to contain substances that may act as sexual attractants. Women who frequently **douche** or use feminine deodorant sprays may remove or mask substances that their sexual partners *may* find arousing. Douching or spraying may also alter the natural chemical balance of the vagina, which can increase the risk of vaginal infections. Feminine deodorant sprays can also irritate the vagina and evoke allergic reactions. The normal, healthy vagina cleanses itself through regular chemical secretions that are evidenced by a mild white or yellowish discharge.

Vaginitis refers to any vaginal inflammation, whether it is caused by an infection, an allergic reaction, or chemical irritation. Vaginitis may also stem from the use of birth-control pills or antibiotics that alter the natural body chemistry, or from other factors, such as lowered resistance (from fatigue or poor diet). Changes in the natural body chemistry or lowered resistance permit microscopic organisms normally found in the vagina to multiply to infectious levels. Vaginitis may be recognized by abnormal discharge, itching, burning of the vulva, and, sometimes, urinary urgency. The causes and treatments of vaginitis are elaborated in Chapter 16. Women with vaginitis are advised to seek medical attention, but let us note some suggestions that may help prevent vaginitis (Boston Women's Health Book Collective, 1984, p. 518):

1. Wash your vulva and anus regularly with mild soap. Pat dry (taking care not to touch the vulva after dabbing the anus).
2. Wear cotton panties; nylon underwear retains heat and moisture that cause harmful bacteria to flourish.
3. Avoid pants that are tight in the crotch.
4. Be certain that sexual partners are well-washed. Condoms may also reduce spread of infections from one's sexual partner.
5. Use a sterile, water-soluble jelly like K-Y jelly if artificial lubrication is needed for intercourse. Do *not* use Vaseline. Birth-control jellies can also be used for lubrication.

Douche
Application of a jet of liquid to the vagina as a rinse. (From the Italian *doccia,* meaning "shower bath.")

Vaginitis
Vaginal inflammation.

6. Avoid intercourse that is painful or abrasive to the vagina.
7. Avoid diets high in sugar and refined carbohydrates since they alter the normal acidity of the vagina.
8. Women who are prone to vaginal infections may find it helpful to douche occasionally with plain water, a solution of 1 or 2 tablespoons of vinegar in a quart of warm water, or a solution of baking soda and water. Douches consisting of unpasteurized plain (unflavored) yogurt may help replenish the "good" bacteria that is normally found in the vagina and that may be destroyed by use of antibiotics. Be careful when douching, and do not douche when pregnant or when you suspect you may be pregnant. Consult your physician before deciding to douche or to apply any preparations to the vagina.
9. Remember to take care of your general health. Eating poorly or getting insufficient rest will reduce your resistance to infection.

THE CERVIX

When someone first said to me two years ago, "You can feel the end of your own cervix with your finger," I was interested but flustered. I had hardly ever put my finger in my vagina at all, and felt squeamish about touching myself there, in that place "reserved" for lovers and doctors. It took me two months to get up nerve to try it, and then one afternoon, pretty nervously, I squatted down in the bathroom and put my finger in deep, back into my vagina. There it was, feeling slippery and rounded, with an indentation at the center through which, I realized, my menstrual flow came. It was both very exciting and beautifully ordinary at the same time. Last week I bought a plastic speculum so I can look at my cervix. Will it take as long this time?

(*Our Bodies, Ourselves,* 1984, p. 203)

Cervix
The lower end of the uterus. (Latin for "neck.")

Os
The opening in the middle of the cervix. (Latin for "mouth.")

Pap smear
A sample of cervical cells that is examined to screen for cervical cancer and other abnormalities. (Named after the originator of the technique, Dr. Papanicolaou.)

Radiotherapy
Treatment of a disease by X-rays or by emissions from a radioactive substance.

Uterus
The hollow, muscular, pear-shaped organ in which a fertilized ovum implants and develops until birth.

The **cervix** is the lower end of the uterus. Its walls, like those of the vagina, produce secretions that contribute to the chemical balance of the vagina. The opening in the middle of the cervix, or **os,** is normally about the width of a straw, although it expands to permit passage of a baby from the uterus to the vagina during childbirth. Sperm pass from the vagina to the uterus through the cervical canal.

A **Pap smear** is a sample of cervical cells that are "smeared" on a slide and examined to screen for cervical cancer and other abnormalities. Cervical cancer is one of the most common forms of cancer in women. An estimated 13,000 new cases of cervical cancer are reported annually (American Cancer Society, 1991). Cervical cancer is more common among women who have had many sex partners, who became sexually active at a relatively early age, who come from lower socioeconomic status, and who smoke. All women are at risk, however. Most cases can be successfully treated by surgery and **radiotherapy** if they are detected early. The five-year survival rate for cervical cancer is 88 percent if the cancer is localized, 51 percent if it has spread to adjoining regions, and 26 percent if it has spread to distant sites in the body (American Cancer Society, 1991).

THE UTERUS

The **uterus** or womb (Figures 3.3, 3.6) is the pear-shaped organ in which a fertilized ovum implants and develops until birth. The uterus usually slants forward (is *antroverted*), although about 10 percent of women have uteruses that tip backward (are *retroverted*). In most instances a retroverted uterus causes no problems, but some women with retroverted uteruses find coitus in certain positions painful. (They quickly learn more comfortable positions by trial and error.) A retroverted uterus normally tips forward during pregnancy. This condition probably does not interfere with conception, although at one time it was thought that it might do so. The uterus is suspended in the pelvis by flexible ligaments. In a woman who has not given birth, it is about three inches long, three inches wide, and an inch thick near the top. The uterus expands to accommodate a fetus during pregnancy and shrinks after pregnancy, though not to its original size.

Fundus

The uppermost part of the uterus. (*Fundus* is a Latin word meaning "base.")

Endometrium

The innermost layer of the uterus. (From Latin and Greek roots meaning "within the uterus.")

Endometriosis

A condition caused by the growth of endometrial tissue in the abdominal cavity or elsewhere outside the uterus, and characterized by menstrual pain.

Myometrium

The middle, well-muscled layer of the uterus. (*Myo-* stems from the Greek *mys*, meaning "muscle.")

Perimetrium

The outer layer of the uterus. (From roots meaning "around the uterus.")

Hysterectomy

Surgical removal of the uterus.

Complete hysterectomy

The surgical removal of the ovaries, Fallopian tubes, cervix, and uterus.

Fallopian tubes

Tubes that extend from the upper uterus toward the ovaries and conduct ova to the uterus. (After the Italian anatomist Gabriel Fallopio, who is credited with their discovery.)

Isthmus

The segment of a Fallopian tube closest to the uterus. (A Latin word meaning "narrow passage.")

Ampulla

The wide segment of a Fallopian tube near the ovary. (A Latin word meaning "bottle.")

Infundibulum

The outer, funnel-shaped part of a Fallopian tube. (A Latin word meaning "funnel.")

The uppermost part of the uterus is called the **fundus** (see Figure 3.6). The uterus is shaped like an inverted pear. If a ceramic model of a uterus were placed on a table, it would balance on the fundus. The central region of the uterus is called the body. The narrow lower region is the cervix, which leads downward to the vagina.

Like the vagina, the uterus has three layers (also shown in Figure 3.6). The innermost layer, or **endometrium,** is richly supplied with blood vessels and glands. Its structure varies according to a woman's age and phase of the menstrual cycle. Endometrial tissue is discharged through the cervix and vagina at menstruation. For reasons not entirely understood, in some women endometrial tissue may also grow in the abdominal cavity or elsewhere in the reproductive system. This condition is called **endometriosis,** and the most common symptom is menstrual pain. If left untreated, endometriosis may lead to infertility.

Cancer of the endometrial lining, called endometrial cancer, occurs more commonly in obese women, diabetic women, women with arteriosclerosis, and women with unusual vaginal bleeding (Levy et al., 1987). Like cervical cancer, the majority of endometrial cancers can be treated successfully if they are discovered early before they have spread.

The second layer of the uterus, the **myometrium,** is well muscled. It endows the uterus with flexibility and strength and creates the powerful contractions that propel a fetus outward during labor. The third or outermost layer, the **perimetrium,** provides an external cover.

One woman in three in the United States has a **hysterectomy** by the age of 60. Most hysterectomy patients are between the ages of 35 and 45 (Brody, 1991a). The hysterectomy is now the second most commonly performed operation on women in this country. (Caesarean sections are the most common.) A hysterectomy may be performed when women develop cancer of the uterus, ovaries, or cervix, or other diseases that cause pain or excessive bleeding from the uterus. A hysterectomy may be partial or complete. A **complete hysterectomy** is the surgical removal of the ovaries, Fallopian tubes, cervix, and uterus. It is usually performed to reduce the risk of cancer spreading throughout the reproductive system. A partial hysterectomy removes the uterus but spares the ovaries and Fallopian tubes. Sparing the ovaries allows the woman to continue to ovulate and produce adequate quantities of female sex hormones.

The hysterectomy has become steeped in controversy. In many cases it is possible that less radical medical interventions might successfully treat whatever problem the woman is experiencing (Kaspar, 1985). Based on a sample of more than 5,000 hysterectomies performed in seven health maintenance organizations (HMOs) across the country, a panel of experts in gynecology and obstetrics reported that 28 percent of these operations in younger women, and 16 percent in women overall, were inappropriate (Bernstein et al., 1993). As with any recommendations for major surgery, women whose physicians advise a hysterectomy are advised to seek a second opinion before proceeding.

THE FALLOPIAN TUBES

Two uterine tubes, also called **Fallopian tubes,** are about 4 inches in length and extend from the upper end of the uterus toward the ovaries (Figure 3.6). The part of each tube nearest the uterus is the **isthmus,** which broadens into the **ampulla** as it approaches the ovary. The outer part, or **infundibulum,** has fringelike projections called **fimbriae** that extend toward, but are not attached to, the ovary.

Ova pass through the Fallopian tubes on their way to the uterus. The Fallopian tubes are not inert passageways. They help nourish and conduct ova (Gordon & Snyder, 1989). These tubes are lined with tiny hairlike projections termed cilia ("lashes") that help move ova through the tube. The exact mechanisms by which ova are guided are unknown, however. It is tempting to say that ova move at a snail's pace, but a snail would leave them far behind. They journey toward the uterus at about an inch per day. Since ova must be fertilized within a day or two after they are released from the ovaries, fertilization usually occurs in the infundibulum within a couple of inches of the ovaries. The

Fimbriae

Projections from a Fallopian tube that extend toward an ovary. (Singular: fimbria. Latin for "fiber" or "fringe.")

Ectopic pregnancy

A pregnancy in which the fertilized ovum implants outside the uterus, usually in the Fallopian tube. (*Ectopic* derives from Greek roots meaning "out of place.")

Ovaries

Almond-shaped organs that produce ova and the hormones estrogen and progesterone.

Estrogen

A generic term for female sex hormones (including estradiol, estriol, estrone, and others) or synthetic compounds that promote the development of female sex characteristics and regulate the menstrual cycle. (From the roots meaning "generating" (*-gen*) and "estrus.")

form of sterilization called tubal ligation ties off the Fallopian tubes, so that ova cannot pass through them or become fertilized.

In an **ectopic pregnancy,** the fertilized ovum implants outside the uterus, most often in the Fallopian tube where fertilization occurred. Ectopic pregnancies can eventually burst Fallopian tubes, causing hemorrhaging and death. Ectopic pregnancies are thus removed surgically (aborted) before the tube ruptures. They are not easily recognized, however, because their symptoms—missed menstrual period, abdominal pain, irregular bleeding—are suggestive of many conditions. These symptoms are an excellent reason for consulting a gynecologist. Women who have had pelvic inflammatory disease (PID), undergone tubal surgery, or used intrauterine devices (IUDs) are at increased risk of developing ectopic pregnancies (Marchbanks, 1988).

THE OVARIES

The two **ovaries** are almond-shaped organs that are each about 1¹/₂ inches long. They lie on either side of the uterus, to which they are attached by ovarian ligaments. The ovaries produce ova (egg cells) and the female sex hormones **estrogen** and **progesterone.**

Estrogen is a generic term for several hormones (including estradiol, estriol, estrone, and others) that promote the changes of puberty and regulate the menstrual cycle. Progesterone also has multiple functions, including regulating the menstrual cycle and preparing the uterus for pregnancy by stimulating the development of the endometrium (uterine lining). Estrogen and progesterone levels vary with the phases of the menstrual cycle.

The human female is born with all the ova she will ever have (about 400,000), but they are immature in form. Each is contained in the ovary within a thin capsule, called a **follicle.** During a woman's reproductive years, from puberty to menopause, only 400 or so ripened ova, typically one per month, will be released by their rupturing follicles for possible fertilization. How these ova are selected is among the mysteries of nature.

About one woman in 70 will develop ovarian cancer in her lifetime (Brody, 1993f). The American Cancer Society estimates that each year some 22,000 women in the United States are diagnosed with the disease and 13,300 die from it. It most often strikes women between the ages of 40 and 70 and ranks as the fourth leading cancer killer of women, behind lung cancer, breast cancer, and colon cancer (Brody, 1993f). Women most at risk are those with blood relatives who had the disease, especially a first-degree

A Magnified Human Ovum (Egg Cell).

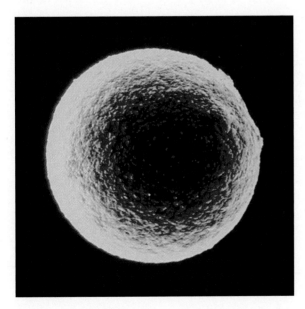

Progesterone

A steroid hormone secreted by the corpus luteum or prepared synthetically that stimulates proliferation of the endometrium and is involved in regulation of the menstrual cycle. (From the root *pro-*, meaning "promoting," and the words "gestation," "steroid," and "one.")

Follicle

A capsule within an ovary that contains an ovum. (From a Latin word meaning "small bag.")

Learning Objective 7: Describe the pelvic exam procedure and explain the importance of routine pelvic exams.

relative (mother, sister, or daughter). Having a first-degree relative with the disease raises one's personal risk fivefold, to a lifetime risk of 7 percent (Brody, 1993f). But other risk factors are also important, since about nine women in ten who develop ovarian cancer do not have any family history of the disease. Researchers have identified several risk factors that increase the chances of developing the disease, including never having given birth, having used talcum powder in the area between the anus and the vagina for many years, being infertile, having a history of breast cancer, and having a diet rich in meat and animal fats (Brody, 1993f).

Early detection is the key to fighting ovarian cancer. When it is detected before spreading beyond the ovary, 90 percent of victims survive. If not, survival plummets to 10 percent (Brody, 1993f). Though every woman should have an annual pelvic examination, unfortunately these exams are not sensitive enough to detect small tumors in the ovaries. The use of ultrasound technology, which involves the use of sound waves to generate an image of the woman's reproductive organs on a monitor screen, can detect growths on the ovary but cannot distinguish between a cancerous tumor and a harmless cyst. More refined (and expensive) ultrasound technologies have been developed that can detect early tumors and distinguish them from benign growths, but these tests are not yet widely available. A blood test is also available, but is not very reliable. Recognizing that no one technique is ideal, physicians may rely on a combination of techniques for early screening purposes, especially in women in high-risk groups.

THE PELVIC EXAMINATION

Women are advised to have an internal (pelvic) examination at least once a year by the time they reach their late teens, or earlier if they become sexually active, and twice yearly if they are over age 35 or use birth-control pills. The physician (usually a gynecologist) first examines her externally for irritations, swellings, abnormal vaginal discharges, and clitoral adhesions. The physician normally inserts a speculum to help inspect the cervix and vaginal walls for discharges (which can be signs of infection), discoloration, lesions, or growths. This examination is typically followed by a Pap smear to detect cervical cancer. A sample of vaginal discharge may also be taken to test for the sexually transmitted disease gonorrhea.

To take a Pap smear, the physician will hold open the vaginal walls with a plastic or (hopefully prewarmed!) metal speculum so that a sample of cells (a "smear") may be scraped from the cervix with a wooden spatula (Figure 3.7). Women should not douche prior to Pap smears or schedule them during menstruation, since douches and blood con-

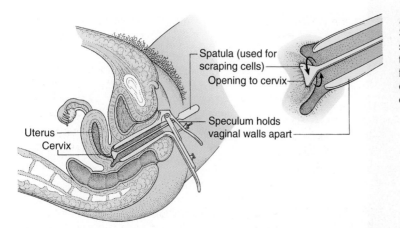

Uterus
Cervix

Spatula (used for scraping cells)
Opening to cervix

Speculum holds vaginal walls apart

FIGURE 3.7 **Use of the Speculum and Spatula During a Pelvic Examination.** The speculum holds the vaginal walls apart while the spatula is used to gently scrape cells from the cervix. The so-called Pap smear is examined to screen for cervical cancer and other abnormalities.

Teaching Tip: Reduce fears about pelvic exams by showing students a speculum and a spatula used during a Pap smear. Emphasize the need to choose a different physician if the physician does not explain the procedure, is not sensitive to the woman's possible embarrassment, or is not receptive to questions. Urge students to encourage all the women they know and love to get regular pelvic exams.

found analysis of the smear. A woman may also examine her own cervix with a speculum and mirror. Some groups of women have formed so-called self-help or "self-health" groups to encourage frequent self-examination. These groups have aroused some controversy since observation skills vary, and some members visit their physicians less often than they might if they weren't in the groups. Self-examination is no substitute for regular medical checkups.

The speculum exam is normally followed by a bimanual vaginal exam in which the index and middle fingers of one hand are inserted into the vagina while the lower part of the abdomen is palpated (touched) by the other hand from the outside. The physician uses this technique to examine the location, shape, size, and movability of the internal sexual organs, searching for abnormal growths and symptoms of other problems. Palpation may be somewhat uncomfortable, but severe pain is a sign that something is wrong. A woman should not try to be "brave" and hide such discomfort from the examiner. She may only be masking a symptom (that is, depriving the physician of useful information). Physical discomfort is usually mild, however, and psychological discomfort may often be relieved by discussing it frankly with the examiner.

Finally, the physician should do a recto-vaginal examination in which one finger is inserted into the rectum while the other is inserted into the vagina. This procedure provides additional information about the ligaments of the uterus, the ovaries, and the Fallopian tubes. The procedure also helps the physician evaluate the health of the rectum.

Although it may be somewhat uncomfortable, the pelvic examination is not ordinarily painful. It is normal for a woman who has not had one, or who is visiting a new doctor, to be anxious about the exam. The doctor should be reassuring if the woman expresses concern. If the doctor is not, the woman should feel free to consult another doctor. She should not forgo the pelvic examination itself, however. It is essential for early detection of problems.

THE BREASTS

Learning Objective 8: Describe normal breast appearance and function and explain the importance of breast self-examination, mammograms, and regular medical checkups.

The degree of attention which breasts receive, combined with the confusion about what the breast fetishists actually want, makes women unduly anxious about them. They can never be just right; they must always be too small, too big, the wrong shape, too flabby. The characteristics of the mammary stereotype are impossible to emulate because they are falsely simulated, but they must be faked somehow or another. Reality is either gross or scrawny.

(Germaine Greer, *The Female Eunuch*)

Some college women recall:

I was very excited about my breast development. It was a big competition to see who was wearing a bra in elementary school. When I began wearing one, I also liked wearing see-through blouses so everyone would know....

My breasts were very late in developing. This brought me a lot of grief from my male peers. I just dreaded situations like going to the beach or showering in the locker room....

All through junior high and high school I felt unhappy about being "overendowed." I felt just too uncomfortable in sweaters—there was so much to reveal and I was always sure that the only reason boys liked me was because of my bustline....

By the time I was eleven I needed a bra....The girls in my gym class in sixth grade laughed at me because my breasts were pretty big and I still didn't have a bra. I tried to cover myself up when I dressed and undressed. On my eleventh birthday my mom gave me a sailor blouse and inside was my first bra....[It] was the best present I could have received. The bra made me feel a lot better about myself, but I was still unsure of my femininity for a long time....

(Morrison et al., 1980, pp. 66–70)

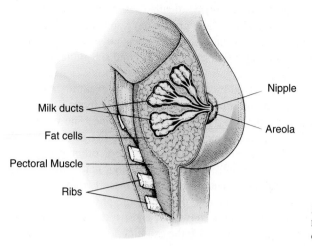

Milk ducts

Fat cells

Pectoral Muscle

Ribs

Nipple

Areola

FIGURE 3.8 A Breast of An Adult Woman. This drawing reveals the structures underlying the breast, including milk ducts and fat cells.

Secondary sex characteristics
Traits that distinguish women from men but are not directly involved in reproduction.

Mammary glands
Milk-secreting glands. (From the Latin *mamma*, which means both "breast" and "mother.")

In some cultures the breasts are viewed merely as biological instruments for feeding infants. In our culture, however, breasts have achieved such erotic significance that a woman's self-esteem may become linked to her perception of the attractiveness of her bustline.

The breasts are **secondary sex characteristics.** That is, like the rounding of the hips, they distinguish women from men, but they are not directly involved in reproduction. Each breast contains 15 to 20 clusters of milk-producing **mammary glands** (Figure 3.8). Each gland opens at the nipple through its own duct. The mammary glands are separated by soft, fatty tissue. It is the amount of this fatty tissue, not the amount of glandular tissue, that largely determines the size of the breasts. Women vary little in their amount of glandular tissue, so breast size does not determine the quantity of milk that can be produced.

TRUTH OR FICTION?

R E V I S I T E D

Women with larger breasts produce more milk while nursing. *Not true. It is the amount of fatty tissue, not the amount of glandular milk-producing tissue, that largely determines the size of the breasts.* •

Areola The dark ring on the breast that encircles the nipple.

The nipple, which lies in the center of the **areola,** contains smooth muscle fibers that make the nipple become erect when they contract. Milk ducts conduct milk from the mammary glands through the nipples. Nipples are richly endowed with nerve endings, so

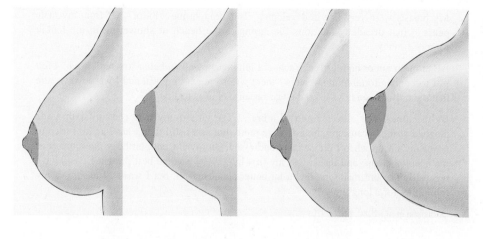

FIGURE 3.9 Normal Variations in the Size and Shape of the Breasts of Adult Women. The size and shape of the breasts have little bearing on ability to produce milk or on sensitivity to sexual stimulation. Breasts have become highly eroticized in our culture.

that stimulation of the nipples heightens sexual arousal for many women. Male nipples are similar in sensitivity. Gay males often find nipple stimulation pleasurable, whereas male heterosexuals generally do not—largely because heterosexual men have learned to associate breast stimulation with the female sexual role, not because their nipples are less sensitive. The areola, or area surrounding the nipple, darkens during pregnancy and remains darker after delivery. Oil-producing glands in the areola help lubricate the nipples during breast-feeding.

Figure 3.9 shows normal variations in the size and shape of the breasts of adult women. The sensitivity of the breasts to sexual stimulation is unrelated to their size. Small breasts may have as many nerve endings as large breasts, but they will be more densely packed.

Women can prompt their partners to provide breast stimulation by informing them that their breasts are sensitive to stimulation. They can also guide their partners' hands in ways that provide the type of stimulation they desire. The breasts vary in sensitivity with the phases of the menstrual cycle, and some women appear less responsive to breast stimulation than others. However, some less sensitive women may learn to enjoy breast stimulation by focusing on breast sensations during lovemaking in a relaxed atmosphere.

BREAST CANCER

Learning Objective 9:
Discuss the incidence of breast cancer in women, the major treatments available, survival rates and the support needed by women following breast removal.

Mammography
A specialized type of X-ray test that detects cancerous lumps in the breast.

Breast cancer strikes about 175,000 women and takes some 44,500 lives annually. It is the second leading cause of cancer deaths among women, after lung cancer (American Cancer Society, 1991). (An estimated 300 men also die of breast cancer annually.) The National Cancer Institute estimates that one woman in eight in the United States will develop breast cancer during her lifetime ("Chance of breast cancer is figured at 1 in 8," 1993). The disease takes the lives of nearly three of ten women who develop it. It is not the cancer in the breast itself that causes death, but rather the spreading of the cancer to vital body parts, such as the brain, the bones, the lungs, or the liver, that kills (Wallis, 1991b).

Despite the popular impression to the contrary, rates of breast cancer in the United States are not on the increase (Kolata, 1993d). Rather, more early cases of breast cancer are being detected because of an increased use of **mammography,** a specialized form of X-ray used to detect cancerous lumps in the breast. The National Cancer Society reports that underlying rates of breast cancer in the population has actually remained almost constant for decades (Kolata, 1993d). Advances in early detection and treatment have led to increased rates of recovery. The five-year survival rate for women whose breast cancers

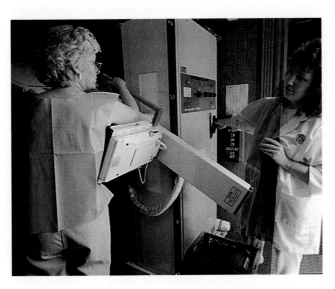

Mammography. Mammography, a specialized X-ray test, can detect cancerous lumps in the breast before they can be felt by touch. Mammography can detect small tumors before they have spread to other parts of the body.

A CLOSER LOOK

Breast Self-Examination

Regular breast self-examination, combined with regular visits to a physician, is the best protection against breast cancer, since it may lead to early detection and treatment. One study estimated that regular breast self-examination may reduce breast cancer mortality by nearly 20 percent (Carlile, 1981). A woman may wish to undertake an initial breast self-examination with a physician in order to determine the degree of "lumpiness" that seems normal for her. Then she should conduct a breast self-examination at least once a month, preferably about a week after her period ends (when the breasts are least influenced by hormones), so that any changes can be reported promptly to a physician (see Figure 3.10).

The following instructions for breast self-examination are based on American Cancer Society guidelines. Additional material on breast self-examination may be obtained from the American Cancer Society by calling this toll-free number: (800) ACS-2345.

1. In the shower. Examine your breasts during bath or shower; hands glide more easily over wet skin. Keep your fingers flat and move gently over every part of each breast. Use the right hand to examine the left breast and the left hand for the right breast. Check for any lump, hard knot, or thickening.

2. Before a mirror. Inspect your breasts with your arms at your sides. Next, raise your arms high overhead. Look for any changes in the contour of each breast, a swelling, dimpling of skin, or changes in the nipple. Then rest your palms on your hips and press down firmly to flex your chest muscles. Your left and right breasts will not exactly match—few women's breasts do. Regular inspection shows what is normal for you and will give you confidence in your examination.

3. Lying down. To examine your right breast, put a pillow or folded towel under your right shoulder. Place your right arm behind your head—this distributes breast tissue more evenly on the chest. With your left hand, fingers flat, press gently with the finger pads (the top thirds of the fingers) of the three middle fingers in small circular motions around an imaginary clock face. Begin at the outermost top of your right breast for 12 o'clock, then move to 1 o'clock, and so on around the circle back to 12.

Metastasize
To spread to other parts of the body, as by means of the bloodstream or lymphatics.

Discussion Question: How do you think you would react if you received a diagnosis of breast cancer? If your mother received this diagnosis? If your girlfriend or wife did? What could you do to support a woman going through this crisis?

 Breast Cancer

have not **metastasized**—that is, spread beyond the breast—is 91 percent, up from 78 percent in the 1940s (American Cancer Society, 1991). The five-year survival rate drops to 69 percent if the cancer has spread to the surrounding region and to 18 percent if it has spread to distant sites in the body.

Breast cancer is rare in women under age 25. The risk increases sharply with age, with about four of five cases developing in women over the age of 50 ("Chance of breast cancer is figured at 1 in 8," 1993). The National Cancer Institute (NCI) estimates that from birth to age 40, 1 in 217 women develop breast cancer. From birth to age 50 the risk rises to 1 in 50; by age 60, 1 in 24; and by age 70, 1 in 14 (Ochs, 1993a). The risk is also higher among women with a family history of the disease (Slattery & Kerber, 1993). A large-scale study of more than 100,000 women nurses showed that those with mothers or sisters who had breast cancer had nearly twice the chance of developing the disease themselves than did other women (Colditz et al., 1993). Women who had both a mother and a sister with the disease had between two and three times greater risk than other women. Still, the great majority of women with breast cancer have no family history of the disease. Only about 6 percent of the women with breast cancer in the nurses' study had either a mother or sister with the disease (Johnson & Williams, 1993).

Other risk factors include early onset of menstruation (before age 12), late menopause (after age 50), delayed childbearing (after age 30), never giving birth, and obesity (American Cancer Society, 1991; Wallis, 1991a). It is not yet fully known why these factors create greater risk, but it is suspected that exposure to estrogen is responsi-

FIGURE 3.10 **Woman Examining Her Breast for Lumps.**

A ridge of firm tissue in the lower curve of each breast is normal. Then move in an inch, toward the nipple. Keep circling to examine every part of your breast, including the nipple. This requires at least three more circles. Now slowly repeat the procedure on your left breast. Place the pillow beneath your left shoulder, your left arm behind your head, and use the finger pads on your right hand.

After you examine your left breast fully, squeeze the nipple of each breast gently between your thumb and index finger. Any discharge, clear or bloody, should be reported to your doctor immediately.

Cysts
Sac-like structures filled with fluid or diseased material.

Benign
Doing little or no harm.

Fibroadenoma
A benign, fibrous tumor.

Malignant
Causing or likely to cause death.

ble for much of the risk. Estrogen stimulates breast development in young women. Earlier onset of menstruation, later menopause, and delayed childbearing are all connected to longer, uninterrupted exposure to high levels of estrogen (Wallis, 1991a). Estrogen levels have also been linked to obesity and to the level of fat in the diet.

DETECTION Women with breast cancer will have lumps in the breast, *but most lumps in the breasts are not cancerous.* Most are either **cysts** or **benign** tumors called **fibroadenomas.** Breast cancer involves lumps in the breast that are **malignant.**

There is no clear-cut way to prevent breast cancer, but early detection and treatment reduce the risk of mortality. The sooner cancer is detected, the less likely it is to have metastasized to critical organs.

Breast cancer may be detected in a number of ways, including breast self-examination, medical examination, and mammography. Through mammography, tiny, highly curable cancers can be detected—and treated—before they can be felt by touch (Brody, 1990a). By the time a malignant lump is large enough to be felt by touch, it already contains millions of cells, some of which may already have splintered off to form colonies elsewhere in the body (Wallis, 1991a). A mammography can detect minuscule tumors before they have metastasized. A recent study found that 82 percent of women whose breast cancers were detected early by mammography survived for at least five years following surgery, as compared to 60 percent of those whose cancers were discovered later (Wallis, 1991a). Early detection may also offer another benefit: smaller cancerous lumps

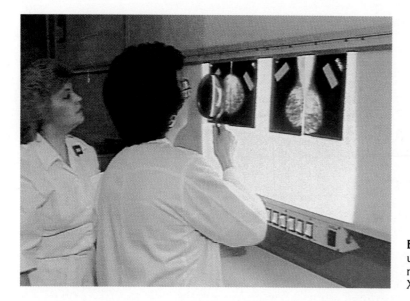

Examining a Mammogram. A physician uses a magnifying glass to examine a mammogram, the photographic display of a breast X-ray, or mammography.

Lumpectomy
Surgical removal of a lump from the breast.

Mastectomy
Surgical removal of the entire breast.

Teaching Tip: Discuss the 1992 Food and Drug Administration (FDA) hearings on the cancer risk posed by polyurethane-covered silicone breast implants. Explore with students whether women should have the right to choose a treatment of doubtful safety to boost their self-esteem if that self-esteem is based on rigid social standards of female beauty.

 Breast Implant Settlement

can often be removed by **lumpectomy,** which spares the breast. More advanced cancers are likely to be treated by **mastectomy** (Wallis, 1991a).

The American Cancer Society recommends that women should have a clinical breast exam every three years when they are between 20 and 40 years of age and then annually thereafter ("Breast fears fade," 1993). They also recommend that women between 35 and 39 years of age receive a baseline mammogram for comparison with later tests. Women of ages 40 to 49 are encouraged to have mammograms every year or two, and then once a year from age 50. The mortality rate from breast cancer may be cut by 30 percent or more if women follow these guidelines (Brody, 1990a). Mammography is not foolproof, however. One study, for example, showed that mammography failed to detect existing breast cancers in about one in five cases (Edeiken, 1987). So the chances of early detection are optimized through a combination of monthly breast self-examinations (see the Closer Look section on pp. 82–83), annual breast examinations by a physician, and regular mammographies.

However, questions were raised about the recommendation that women in their forties obtain regular mammograms, when the results of a 1992 Canadian study were published that showed that women in their forties who had received mammograms had the same death rates from breast cancer as women who did not (Kolata, 1993d). A further analysis of data from around the world confirmed the Canadian results by failing to show that mammograms saved lives of women in their forties (Kolata, 1993b, 1993d). Mammograms clearly do save lives of women age 50 and over, reducing the death rate from breast cancer by as much as 25 to 30 percent (Kolata, 1993a, 1993b). Why the difference? One possibility is that since younger women have denser breasts, mammograms in younger women are more difficult for doctors to read and so may be less reliable indicators of early cancers.

These negative findings for younger women call into question the benefits of regular mammography for women in their forties, as the American Cancer Society and many cancer experts and radiologists recommend. The National Cancer Institute (NCI) broke ranks with the American Cancer Society in 1993 by deciding to stop recommending regular mammograms for women in their forties. The NCI recommended that the decision should rest with the woman and her doctor, after the woman is presented with all the available scientific information regarding the potential benefits and risks (Kolata, 1993a; 1993d, 1993e). One of the drawbacks of mammography is that unnecessary surgery may be undertaken to treat microscopic lesions detected on mammograms that would never have developed into life-threatening cancers if left alone (Brody, 1993b; Kolata, 1993d, 1993e). Yet the debate over the value of mammograms for women in their forties is far

Women Who Lose Breasts Define Their Own Femininity[1]

Twenty to 30 years ago, women with breast cancer worried that even if they survived the disease, the loss of a breast would somehow diminish their femininity and sexual attractiveness. Many women hid their mastectomies, disguising their single-breasted figures with cumbersome prostheses even around family members.

Today, women are less likely to perceive breast cancer as an attack on their feminine nature. For one thing, more and more women are having surgery that removes the malignancy but spares the breast. When a mastectomy is necessary, many women have reconstructive surgery using an implant or their own fatty tissue (see Figure 3.11, page 86).

And although breasts are still viewed in many societies and cultures as a symbol of womanhood, nurturing, and sexuality, many men no longer consider the loss of a woman's breast as having lessened her physical attributes or sexual desirability.

"We Are What We Are"

"When it comes to self-image, you can't let cancer dictate who and what you are," said Jean Ettesvold, a 60-year-old retired social worker from Grand Rapids, Michigan, who had a mastectomy. "We are what we are, in spite of the trauma we have suffered."

In a recent study of the effects of breast cancer on sexuality, body image, and intimate relationships, Leslie R. Schover, a staff psychologist at the Center for Sexual Function at the Cleveland Clinic Foundation in Ohio, concluded, "The majority of women cope well with the stress of cancer surgery and the loss of a breast. The options of breast conservation and reconstruction give

women a new sense of control over their treatment and are quite successful in helping women feel comfortable with their bodies again."

In more than a dozen recent interviews, women who had lost a breast to cancer, ranging in age from their thirties to their sixties, said they did not feel less attractive than women with natural breasts. Most chose reconstructive surgery, though some used prostheses.

Breast cancer survivors like Audre Lorde, a poet who had a mastectomy, reject any kind of camouflage after mastectomy. They say cosmetic remedies undermine efforts to focus attention on thousands of women suffering and dying from the disease.

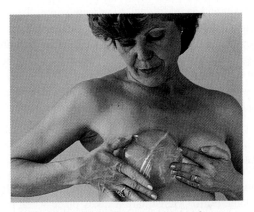

Alternatives after Mastectomy. After removal of a breast, some women prefer not to camouflage a missing breast. Others are comfortable using external prostheses. Still others decide on a surgical approach, such as breast implants (shown here) or breast reconstruction using tissue from elsewhere in the body. Serious concerns have been raised about the safety of silicone breast implants, however, and their use is presently under review. An alternative, the saline-filled implant, has also raised safety concerns.

"When other one-breasted women hide behind the mask of prosthesis or reconstruction, I find little support in the broader female environment for my rejection of what feels like a cosmetic sham," said Ms. Lorde who chose not to wear a prosthesis for philosophical and political reasons. "The social and economic discrimination practiced against women who have breast cancer is not diminished by pretending that mastectomies do not exist . . . . I would lie if I did not also speak of loss. Any amputation is a physical and psychic reality that must be integrated into a new sense of self. The absence of my breast is a recurrent sadness, but certainly not one that dominates my life."

Most of the married women said their mastectomies had not harmed their marriages or their sex lives. The single women said their surgery had not impaired their relationships with men or dating. Some said they found men to be even more supportive after their mastectomies than before. Others said men seemed emotionally moved by their stories, often calling them courageous or survivors.

Other Traumas

Ann Marcou, the founder of Y-Me, a national support network for women with cancer, said: "I think [mastectomy] doesn't have quite the stigma it did. . . . People used to hide in the closet. Individual women still tussle with their body because it's so valued in society. Every woman who goes through this will wonder about her femininity and sexuality. But it comes down to this: 'Your femininity is not determined by whether or not you have breasts.'"

[1]Adapted from Williams, L. (1991, December 25). Women who lose their breasts define their own femininity. *The New York Times,* p. 39.

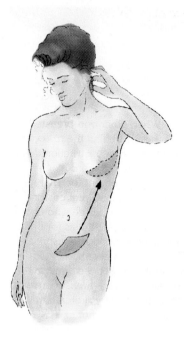

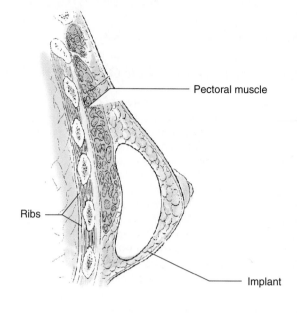

Pectoral muscle

Ribs

Implant

from over, with many specialists believing that evidence favoring the use of early mammography will emerge in time (Brody, 1993b).

The number of women who have had mammographies has risen dramatically in recent years. By 1990, three of four women over the age of 40 had at least one mammogram, up from 54 percent just three years earlier ("Mammograms on rise, federal study finds," 1992). Of those who had mammograms, 60 percent had received one within the past year and an additional 20 percent within the past two years. Nearly half (45%) of the women over 40 who had never had a mammogram explained that their doctors had never recommended it. Some women forgo mammograms for fear of finding out that something is wrong (Brody, 1990a). They may be encouraged to learn that more than 95 percent of women who receive a mammogram are given a clean bill of health. Most of the remaining 5 percent, moreover, show no evidence of cancer on follow-up tests. Even if cancer is present, it is best discovered and treated early.

THE MENSTRUAL CYCLE

Menstruation is the cyclical bleeding that stems from the shedding of the uterine lining (endometrium). Menstruation takes place when a reproductive cycle has not led to the fertilization of an ovum. The word *menstruation* derives from the Latin *mensis,* meaning "month," because the human menstrual cycle averages about 28 days in length.

The menstrual cycle is regulated by the hormones estrogen and progesterone, and can be divided into four phases. During the first phase of the cycle, the *proliferative phase,* which follows menstruation, estrogen levels increase, causing the ripening of perhaps 10 to 20 ova (egg cells) within their follicles and the proliferation of endometrial tissue in the uterus. During the second phase of the cycle, estrogen reaches peak blood levels and **ovulation** occurs. Normally only one ovum reaches maturity and is released by an ovary during ovulation. Then the third phase—the *secretory,* or *luteal,* phase—of the cycle begins. The luteal phase begins right after ovulation and continues through the beginning of the next cycle.

The term *luteal phase* is derived from **corpus luteum,** the name given the follicle that releases an ovum. The corpus luteum functions as an **endocrine gland** and produces copious amounts of progesterone and estrogen. Progesterone causes the endometrium to

Notes: Following the FDA decision in 1992, Dow Corning Wright, the largest producer of silicone gel-filled breast implants, decided to quit producing them.

Menstruation
The cyclical bleeding that stems from the shedding of the uterine lining (endometrium).

Ovulation
The release of an ovum from an ovary.

Learning Objective 10:
Identify the four phases of the menstrual cycle and discuss the hormonal and physical changes associated with each.

Corpus luteum
The follicle that has released an ovum and then produces copious amounts of progesterone and estrogen during the luteal phase of a woman's cycle. (From Latin roots meaning "yellow body.")

Endocrine gland
A ductless gland that releases its secretions directly into the bloodstream.

Menarche
The first menstrual period.

Estrous cycle
The female reproductive cycle of most mammals (other than primates), which is under hormonal control and includes a period of heat, followed by ovulation.

Estrus
The periodic sexual excitement when female mammals (other than primates) are most receptive to the sexual advances of males.

Hypothalamus
A bundle of neural cell bodies near the center of the brain that are involved in regulating body temperature, motivation, and emotion.

Pituitary gland
The gland that secretes growth hormone, prolactin, oxytocin, and others.

Hormone
A substance secreted by an endocrine gland that regulates various body functions. (From the Greek *horman,* meaning "to stimulate" or "to excite.")

Testes
The male gonads.

Testosterone
The male sex hormone that fosters the development of male sex characteristics and is connected with the sex drive.

thicken, so that it would be able to support an embryo if fertilization were to occur. If the ovum goes unfertilized, however, estrogen and progesterone levels plummet. These falloffs provide the trigger for the fourth phase, the *menstrual phase,* which leads to the beginning of a new cycle.

Ovulation may not occur in every menstrual cycle. Anovulatory ("without ovulation") cycles are most common in the years just after **menarche.** They may become frequent again in the years prior to menopause, but they may also occur irregularly among women in their twenties and thirties.

Although the menstrual cycle averages about 28 days, variations among women, and in the same woman from month to month, are quite common. Girls' cycles are often irregular for a few years after menarche, but later assume reasonably regular patterns. Variations from cycle to cycle tend to occur during the proliferative phase that precedes ovulation. That is, menstruation tends to reliably follow ovulation by about 14 days. Variations of more than two days in the postovulation period are rare.

Although hormones regulate the menstrual cycle, psychological factors can influence the secretion of hormones. Stress can delay or halt menstruation. Anxiety that she may be pregnant and thus miss her period may also cause a woman to be late. Many women in otherwise good health stopped menstruating during imprisonment in German concentration camps during World War II.

MENSTRUATION VERSUS ESTRUS

The menstrual cycle is found only in women, female apes, and female monkeys. It differs from an ovarian, or **estrous cycle,** which occurs in "lower" mammals like rodents, cats, and dogs. **Estrus** is the periodic sexual excitement (otherwise referred to as being "in heat") when the female is most receptive to the advances of the male. Estrus occurs when the animal is ovulating, and hence most likely to conceive offspring. Women (and other female primates), however, ovulate about halfway through the cycle and may be interested in sexual activity at any time during their cycles. Estrous cycles, moreover, may be characterized by little bleeding ("spotting") or no bleeding. Menstruation typically involves a heavier flow of blood.

REGULATION OF THE MENSTRUAL CYCLE

The menstrual cycle involves finely tuned relationships between structures in the brain—the **hypothalamus** and the **pituitary gland**—and the ovaries and uterus. All these structures are parts of the endocrine system, which means that they secrete chemicals directly into the bloodstream (see Figure 3.12). The ovaries and uterus are also reproductive organs. The chemicals secreted by endocrine glands are called **hormones.** (Other bodily secretions, such as milk, saliva, sweat, and tears, arrive at their destinations by passing through narrow, tubular structures called ducts.)

Behavioral and social scientists are especially interested in hormones because of their behavioral effects. Hormones regulate such bodily processes as the metabolic rate, growth of bones and muscle, production of milk, metabolism of sugar, and storage of fats, among others. Several hormones play important roles in sexual and reproductive functions.

The gonads—the **testes** (or testicles) in the male and the ovaries in the female—secrete sex hormones directly into the bloodstream. The female gonads, the ovaries, produce the sex hormones estrogen and progesterone. The male gonads, the testes, produce the male sex hormone **testosterone.** Males and females also produce sex hormones of the *opposite* gender, but in relatively small amounts.

The hypothalamus is a tiny structure in the front part of the brain. It weighs about 4 to 5 grams and lies above the pituitary gland and below the thalamus (hence the prefix *hypo-,* for "under"). Despite its small size, it is involved in regulating many states of motivation, including hunger, thirst, aggression, and sex. For example, when the rear part of a male rat's hypothalamus is stimulated by an electric probe, the rat runs through its courting and mating sequence. It nibbles at a female's ears and at the back of her neck.

THE MENSTRUAL CYCLE

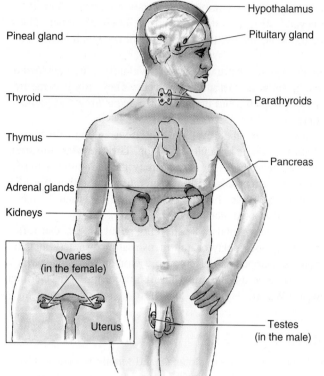

Hypothalamus
Pituitary gland
Pineal gland
Thyroid
Parathyroids
Thymus
Pancreas
Adrenal glands
Kidneys
Ovaries
(in the female)
Uterus
Testes
(in the male)

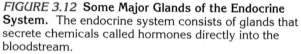

FIGURE 3.12 **Some Major Glands of the Endocrine System.** The endocrine system consists of glands that secrete chemicals called hormones directly into the bloodstream.

Prolactin

A pituitary hormone that stimulates production of milk.

Oxytocin

A pituitary hormone that stimulates uterine contractions in labor and the ejection of milk during nursing.

Gonadotropins

Pituitary hormones that stimulate the gonads. (Literally, "that which 'feeds' the gonads.")

Follicle-stimulating hormone (FSH)

A gonadotropin that stimulates development of follicles in the ovaries.

Luteinizing hormone (LH)

A gonadotropin that helps regulate the menstrual cycle by triggering ovulation.

When she responds, they copulate. Human sexuality is not so stereotyped or mechanical—although in the cases of some people who are highly routinized in their behavior, it may appear so.

The pituitary gland, which is about the size of a pea, lies below the hypothalamus at the base of the brain. Because many pituitary secretions regulate other endocrine glands, the pituitary has also been called the *master gland.* Pituitary hormones regulate bone and muscle growth and urine production. Two pituitary hormones are active during pregnancy and motherhood: **prolactin,** which stimulates production of milk; and **oxytocin,** which stimulates uterine contractions in labor and the ejection of milk during nursing. The pituitary gland also produces **gonadotropins** (literally, "that which 'feeds' the gonads") that stimulate the ovaries: **follicle-stimulating hormone (FSH)** and **luteinizing hormone (LH).** These hormones play central roles in regulating the menstrual cycle.

The hypothalamus receives information about bodily events through the nervous and circulatory systems. It monitors the blood levels of various hormones, including estrogen and progesterone, and releases a hormone called **gonadotropin releasing hormone (Gn-RH),** which stimulates the pituitary to release gonadotropins. Gonadotropins, in turn, regulate the activity of the gonads. It was once thought that the pituitary gland ran the show, but it is now known that the pituitary gland is regulated by the hypothalamus. Even the "master gland" must serve another.

PHASES OF THE MENSTRUAL CYCLE

We noted that the menstrual cycle has four stages or phases: proliferative, ovulatory, secretory, and menstrual (Figure 3.13). It might seem logical that a new cycle begins with the first day of the menstrual flow, since this is the most clearly identifiable event of the cycle. Many women also count the days of the menstrual cycle beginning with the onset of menstruation. Biologically speaking, however, menstruation is really the culmination of the cycle. In fact, the cycle begins with the end of menstruation and the initia-

Gonadotropin releasing hormone (Gn-RH)

A hormone secreted by the hypothalamus that stimulates the pituitary to release gonadotropins.

Proliferative phase

The first phase of the menstrual cycle, which begins with the end of menstruation and lasts about nine or ten days. During this phase, the endometrium proliferates.

Ovulatory phase

The second stage of the menstrual cycle, during which a follicle ruptures and releases a mature ovum.

Zygote

A fertilized ovum (egg cell).

Clomiphene

A synthetic hormone that is chemically similar to LH and induces ovulation.

tion of a series of biological events that lead to the maturation of an immature ovum in preparation for ovulation and possible fertilization.

THE PROLIFERATIVE PHASE   The first phase, or **proliferative phase,** begins with the end of menstruation and lasts about 9 or 10 days in an average 28-day cycle (see Figures 3.13 and 3.14). During this phase the endometrium develops, or "proliferates." This phase is also known as the *preovulatory* or *follicular* phase, because certain ovarian follicles mature and the ovaries prepare for ovulation.

Low levels of estrogen and progesterone are circulating in the blood as menstruation draws to an end. When the hypothalamus senses a low level of estrogen in the blood, it increases its secretion of Gn-RH, which in turn triggers the pituitary gland to release FSH. When FSH reaches the ovaries, it stimulates some follicles (perhaps 10 to 20) to begin to mature. As the follicles ripen, they begin to produce estrogen. Normally, however, only one of them—called the *graafian follicle*—will reach full maturity in the days just preceding ovulation. As the graafian follicle matures, it moves toward the surface of the ovary, where it will eventually rupture and release a mature egg (see Figures 3.14 and 3.15).

Estrogen causes the endometrium in the uterus to thicken to about one eighth of an inch. Glands develop that would eventually nourish an embryo. Estrogen also stimulates the appearance of a thin cervical mucus. This mucus is alkaline and provides a hospitable, nutritious medium for sperm. The chances are thus increased that sperm that enter the female reproductive system at the time of ovulation will remain viable.

THE OVULATORY PHASE   During ovulation, or the **ovulatory phase,** the graafian follicle ruptures and releases a mature ovum *near* a Fallopian tube—not actually *into* a Fallopian tube (Figure 3.15). The other ripening follicles degenerate and are harmlessly reabsorbed by the body. If two ova mature and are released during ovulation, which happens occasionally, and both are fertilized, fraternal (nonidentical) twins will develop. Identical twins develop when one fertilized ovum divides into two separate **zygotes.**

Ovulation is set into motion when estrogen production reaches a critical level. The high level of estrogen is detected by the hypothalamus, which triggers the pituitary to release copious amounts of FSH and LH (see Figure 3.14). The surge of LH triggers ovulation, which usually begins 12 to 24 hours after the level of LH in the body has reached its peak.

The synthetic hormone **clomiphene** is chemically similar to LH and has been used by women who ovulate irregularly to induce reliable ovulation. The induction and accurate prediction of the timing of ovulation increase the chances of conceiving.

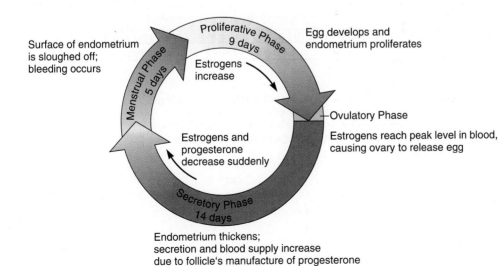

Surface of endometrium is sloughed off; bleeding occurs

Menstrual Phase 5 days

Proliferative Phase 9 days

Estrogens increase

Egg develops and endometrium proliferates

Ovulatory Phase

Estrogens reach peak level in blood, causing ovary to release egg

Estrogens and progesterone decrease suddenly

Secretory Phase 14 days

Endometrium thickens; secretion and blood supply increase due to follicle's manufacture of progesterone

FIGURE 3.13 **The Four Phases of the Menstrual Cycle.** The menstrual cycle has proliferative, ovulatory, secretory (luteal), and menstrual phases.

THE MENSTRUAL CYCLE

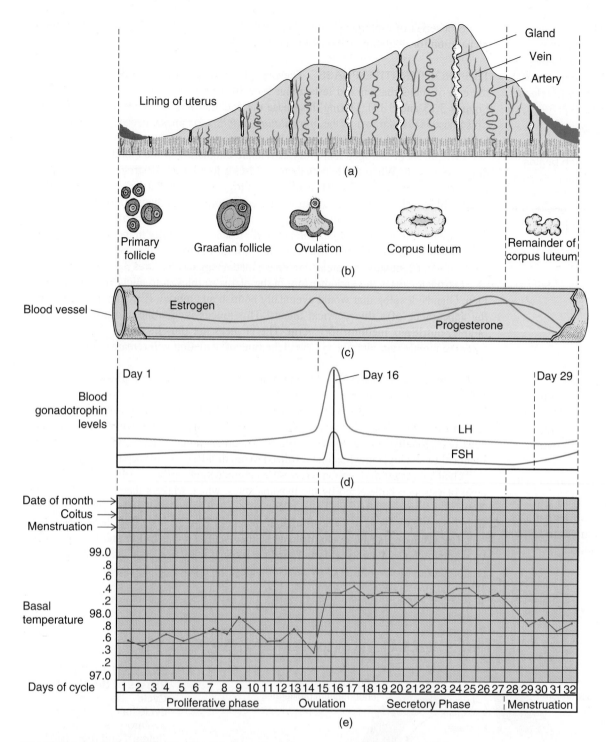

FIGURE 3.14 **Some of the Bodily Changes That Occur During the Menstrual Cycle.** This figure shows five categories of biological change: (a) changes in the development of the uterine lining (endometrium), (b) follicular changes, (c) changes in blood levels of ovarian hormones, (d) changes in blood levels of pituitary hormones, and (e) changes in basal temperature. Note the dip in temperature that is connected with ovulation.

Mittelschmerz

Pain that occurs during ovulation. (German for "middle pain," reflecting the fact that the pain occurs midway between menstrual periods).

A woman's *basal body temperature,* taken by oral or rectal thermometer, dips slightly at ovulation (Figure 3.14) and rises by about 1 degree Fahrenheit on the day following ovulation. Many women use this information to help them conceive or avoid conceiving. Note, however, that Figure 3.14 is idealized. Many women show greater fluctuations in daily temperature or gradual rises in temperature for about two days after ovulation.

Some women have discomfort or cramping during ovulation, termed *mittelschmerz.* **Mittelschmerz** is sometimes confused with appendicitis. Mittelschmerz, however, may occur on either side of the abdomen, depending on which ovary is releasing an ovum. A ruptured appendix always causes pain on the right side.

Secretory phase

The third phase of the menstrual cycle, which follows ovulation. Also referred to as the *luteal phase,* after the *corpus luteum,* which begins to secrete large amounts of progesterone and estrogen following ovulation.

THE SECRETORY PHASE   The phase following ovulation is called the postovulatory or **secretory phase.** Some people refer to it as the *luteal phase,* which reflects the name given the ruptured (graafian) follicle—the *corpus luteum.* Figures 3.14 and 3.15 show the transformation of the graafian follicle into the corpus luteum.

Under the influence of LH, the corpus luteum, which has remained in the ovary, begins to produce large amounts of progesterone and estrogen. Levels of these hormones peak at around the twentieth or twenty-first day of an average cycle (see Figure 3.14). These hormones cause the glands in the endometrium to secrete nutrients to sustain a fertilized ovum that becomes implanted in the uterine wall.

If implantation does not occur, the hypothalamus responds to the peak levels of progesterone in the blood by signaling the pituitary to stop producing LH and FSH. Although certainly more complex, this feedback process is similar to that of a thermostat in a house reacting to rising temperatures by shutting down the furnace. The levels of LH and FSH decline rapidly, leading the corpus luteum to decompose. After its decomposition, levels of estrogen and progesterone fall precipitously. In this sense, the corpus luteum sows the seeds of its own destruction: Its hormones signal the brain to shut down secretion of substances that maintain it.

Menstrual phase

The fourth phase of the menstrual cycle, during which the endometrium is sloughed off in the menstrual flow.

THE MENSTRUAL PHASE: AN END AND A BEGINNING   The **menstrual phase** is the sloughing off of the uterine lining (the endometrium) in the menstrual flow. Menstruation occurs when estrogen and progesterone levels decline to the point where they can no longer sustain the uterine lining. The lining then disintegrates and is discharged from the body along with the menstrual flow. Menstruation itself is the passing of the lining through the cervix and vagina.

The low estrogen levels of the menstrual phase signal the hypothalamus to release Gn-RH, which in turn stimulates the pituitary to secrete FSH. FSH, in turn, prompts ovarian secretion of estrogen and the onset of another proliferative phase. Thus a new cycle begins. The menstrual phase is a beginning as well as an end.

Menstrual flow contains blood from the endometrium (uterine lining), endometrial tissue, and cervical and vaginal mucus. Although the flow can appear persistent and last for 5 days or more, most women lose only a total of 2 or 3 ounces of blood (4 to 6 table-

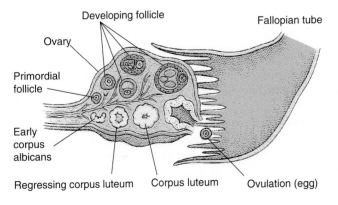

Developing follicle

Fallopian tube

Ovary

Primordial follicle

Early corpus albicans

Regressing corpus luteum   Corpus luteum   Ovulation (egg)

FIGURE 3.15 **Maturation and Eventual Decomposition of an Ovarian Follicle.** Many follicles develop and produce estrogen during the proliferative phase of the menstrual cycle. Usually only one, the graafian follicle, ruptures and releases an ovum. The graafian follicle then develops into the corpus luteum, which produces copious quantities of estrogen and progesterone. When fertilization does not occur, the corpus luteum decomposes.

Historical and Cross-Cultural Perspectives on Menstruation

In Peru, they speak of a "visit from Uncle Pepe," whereas in Samoa, menstruation is referred to as "the boogie man" (Logan, 1978). One of the more common epithets given menstruation through the course of history is "the curse." The Fulani of Upper Volta in Africa use a term for it that translates "to see dirt" (Riesman, 1977). Nationalism also rises to the call, with some nations blaming "the curse" on their historical enemies. In earlier times the French referred to menstruation as "the English" and to its onset as, "the English are coming" (Logan, 1978).

It is a common folk belief that menstruating women are contaminated. Men thus avoid contact with menstruating women for fear of their lives. To prevent their contaminating others, menstruating women in tribal societies may be dispatched to special huts on the fringe of the village. In the traditional Navajo Indian culture, for instance, menstruating women would be consigned to huts that were set apart from other living quarters (Paige, 1977). In many Islamic societies, a menstruating woman is considered polluted and is not permitted either to pray or to enter a mosque (Weideger, 1977). Similarly, the Könkämä Lapps of Sweden do not permit women to attend important religious rituals; they believe that their presence would pollute the sanctified area (Frayser, 1985).

TRUTH OR FICTION?
REVISITED

In some cultures, menstruating women have been consigned to special menstrual huts. True. *This is just one historical example of the harmful effects of ignorance about the significance of menstruation.* •

Women in industrialized nations are not consigned to special huts, but throughout the history of Western culture, menstruation has been seen as unclean, contaminating, and even magical. In A.D. 77, the Roman historian Pliny summed up Roman misbeliefs about menstrual blood:

> Contact with it turns new wine sour, crops touched by it become barren, grafts die, seeds in gardens are dried up, the fruit of trees falls off. . . [The] edge of steel and the gleam of ivory are dulled, hives of bees die, even bronze and iron are at once seized by rust, and a horrible smell fills the air; to taste it drives dogs mad and infects their bites with an incurable poison.

The Old Testament (Leviticus 15:19) warns against any physical contact with a menstruating woman, including, of course, coitus:

> And if a woman have an issue, and her issue in her flesh be blood, she shall be put apart seven days; and whosoever toucheth her shall be unclean.

Orthodox Jews still abstain from coitus during menstruation and the week afterward. Prior to resuming sexual relations, the woman must attend a *mikvah*— a ritual cleansing in which the genitals are washed and all foreign substances are removed. Such practices are grounded in religious tradition, not science. The attitudes of people in ancient and present-day preliterate societies toward menstruation should be understood in terms of their limited understanding of bodily processes. Because they lack knowledge that menstruation is

---

Tampon
A cylindrical plug of cotton that is inserted into the vagina and left in place to absorb menstrual fluid. (A French word, meaning a gun barrel "plug.")

spoonfuls). A typical blood donor, by contrast, donates 16 ounces of blood at a sitting. A woman's blood loss through menstruation is thus usually harmless. Extremely heavy or prolonged (over a week) menstrual bleeding may reflect health problems and should be discussed with a health provider.

Prior to 1933, women generally used external sanitary napkins or pads to absorb the menstrual flow. In that year, however, **tampons** were introduced and altered the habits of millions of women. Women who use tampons can swim without concern while menstruating, wear more revealing or comfortable apparel, and feel generally less burdened.

Tampons are inserted into the vagina and left in place to absorb menstrual fluid. When tampons first became available, some public moralists equated their use with mas-

a part of the woman's natural menstrual cycle, they may regard the flow of blood from a woman's loins as a sign of filth or contamination and believe that it is healthier for others to temporarily avoid physical contact with her. Science teaches that there is no medical basis to these fears, and that there are no dangers in menstrual coitus—despite the persistence of superstition.

Fears of contamination by menstruating women are nearly universal across cultures (Fisher, 1980) and remain quite current in some circles. As late as the 1950s, women were not allowed in some European breweries for fear that the beer would turn sour (Ruble & Brooks-Gunn, 1979). Some Indian castes still teach that a man who touches a woman during menses becomes contaminated and must be purified by a priest (Ullrich, 1977).

We might laugh off these misconceptions as folly and ignorance, if it were not for their profound effect on women. Women who believe the myths about menstruation may see themselves as sources of pollution and endure anxiety, depression, and lowered self-esteem. There is also some evidence that negative cultural beliefs concerning menstruation can also contribute to menstrual distress.

There is also evidence that traditional cultural beliefs about menstruation may be changing. In a survey of 575 men and women, Paige (1978) found that 71 percent of respondents age 55 and above had not engaged in coitus during menstruation. Among people 35 and younger, however, only 28 percent had abstained during menses. Perhaps even fewer members of future generations will misperceive menstruation as a source of pollution.

The Menstrual Hut. Cultural beliefs linking menstruation with impurity and uncleanliness are common in both preliterate and technological societies. This engraving shows a traditional Navajo village, where, as in many preliterate societies, women were consigned to special huts during menstruation to prevent others from becoming contaminated by menstrual blood.

turbation or defloration (Delany et al., 1976), but these notions seem to have fallen by the wayside. In recent years, however, questions have arisen about whether or not tampons cause or exacerbate infections, so women may wish to discuss the use of tampons with their gynecologists or health providers.

For example, tampon use has been linked to toxic shock syndrome (TSS), an infection that is sometimes fatal. Signs of TSS include fever (102 degrees Fahrenheit or greater), headache, sore throat, vomiting, diarrhea, muscle aches, rash, and dizziness. Peeling skin, disorientation, and a plunge in blood pressure may follow (Price, 1981).

TSS is linked to the *Staphylococcus aureus* bacterium. In 1980, the peak year for cases of TSS, there were 344 recorded cases of TSS and 28 fatalities. Proctor and

Gamble removed its "extra-absorbent" tampon, Rely, from the market when it was discovered that 71 percent of these TSS victims had used the product. The "staph" bacteria may be brought into the vagina when the tampon is inserted. The plugging of the vagina by a highly absorbent tampon that remains in place for 6 hours or more may create an ideal breeding ground for staph. The number of TSS cases has declined dramatically since 1980, most likely due to the removal of some highly absorbent tampons from the market (Petitti & Reingold, 1988; Reingold et al., 1982). Not all cases of TSS are transmitted menstrually. Although TSS can strike women (and men) of any age, the greatest risk is borne by women ages 15 to 25 who regularly use tampons.

Some researchers believe that the panic concerning TSS has been unjustified. Nevertheless, many women now use regular rather than super-absorbent tampons, to reduce the chance of creating a breeding ground for staph bacteria. Some women alternate tampons with sanitary napkins during each day of menstruation. Some change their tampons three or four times a day. These alternatives may also present problems, however. If more tampons are used, the increased number of insertions may increase the chances of transferring staph from the fingers or vaginal opening into the vagina. Other women have returned to external sanitary napkins. Still others use natural sponges. Women are encouraged to seek the advice of their gynecologists or health providers regarding the risk of TSS.

COITUS DURING MENSTRUATION

Many couples continue to engage in coitus during menstruation, but others abstain. One study found that men and women are less likely to initiate sexual activity during menstruation than during any other phase of the woman's cycle (Harvey, 1987). Some people abstain because of religious prohibitions. Others express concern about the "fuss" or the "mess" of the menstrual flow. Despite traditional attitudes that associate menstruation with uncleanliness, there is no evidence that coitus during menstruation is physically harmful to either partner. Ironically, menstrual coitus may be helpful to the woman. The uterine contractions that occur during orgasm may help relieve cramping by dispelling blood congestion. Orgasm achieved through masturbation may have the same effect.

Women may be sexually aroused at any time during the menstrual cycle. Evidence is mixed, however, as to whether or not couples are more likely to engage in coitus during any given phase. Some researchers have reported that people are somewhat more likely to engage in coitus near the time of the woman's ovulation (Gold & Adams, 1978; Harvey, 1987; James, 1971), whereas others find no such relationship (Bancroft et al., 1983). The preponderance of the research evidence, however, points to a peak in sexual desire in women around the time of ovulation (Kresin, 1993).

Human coital patterns during the phases of the menstrual cycle apparently reflect personal decisions, not hormone fluctuations. Some couples may decide to increase their frequency of coitus at ovulation in order to optimize the chances of conceiving, or to abstain during menstruation because of religious beliefs or beliefs linking menses with uncleanliness. Some may also increase their coital activity preceding menstruation to compensate for anticipated abstinence during menses, or increase coital activity afterwards to make up for deprivation (Gold & Adams, 1981). In contrast, females of other species that are bound by the estrous cycle respond sexually only during estrus, except in relatively rare cases in which the female submits to sexual advances to fend off attacks from an aggressive male.

MENOPAUSE

Menopause
The cessation of menstruation.

Climacteric
A long-term process, including menopause, that involves the gradual decline in the reproductive capacity of the ovaries.

Menopause, or the "change of life," is the cessation of menstruation. Menopause is a process that most commonly occurs between the ages of 46 and 50 and lasts for about two years. However, it may begin any time between the ages of 35 and 60. There is at least one case of a woman who became pregnant at 61.

Menopause is a specific event in a long-term process known as the **climacteric** ("critical period"), which refers to the gradual decline in the reproductive capacity of the ovaries. The climacteric generally lasts for about 15 years, from ages 45 to 60 or so. After about the age of 35, the menstrual cycles of many women shorten, from an average of 28 days to 25 days at age 40 and to 23 days by the mid-forties. By the end of her forties, a woman's cycles often become erratic, with some periods close together and others missed.

In menopause, the pituitary gland continues to pour normal levels of FSH and LH into the bloodstream, but for reasons that are not well understood, the ovaries gradually lose their capacity to respond. The ovaries no longer ripen egg cells or produce the sex hormones estrogen and progesterone.

The deficit in estrogen may lead to a number of unpleasant physical sensations, such as night sweats and hot flashes (suddenly feeling hot) and hot flushes (suddenly looking reddened). Hot flashes and flushes may alternate with cold sweats, in which a woman feels suddenly cold and clammy. Anyone who has experienced "cold feet" or hands from anxiety or fear will understand how dramatic the shifting patterns of blood flow can be. Hot flashes and flushes stem largely from "waves" of dilation of blood vessels across the face and upper body. All of these sensations reflect "vasomotor instability." That is, there are disruptions in the body mechanisms that dilate or constrict the blood vessels to maintain an even body temperature. Additional signs of estrogen deficiency include dizziness, headaches, pains in the joints, sensations of tingling in the hands or feet, burning or itchy skin, and heart palpitations. The skin usually becomes drier. There is some loss of breast tissue and decreased vaginal lubrication during sexual arousal. Women may also encounter sleep problems, such as awakening more frequently at night and having difficulty falling back to sleep.

Osteoporosis
A condition caused by estrogen deficiency and characterized by a decline in bone density, such that bones become porous and brittle. (From the Greek *osteon,* meaning "bone," and the Latin *porus,* meaning "pore.")

Hormone-replacement therapy (HRT)
Replacement of naturally occurring estrogen or estrogen and progesterone with synthetic equivalents following menopause.

Long-term estrogen deficiency has been linked to brittleness and porosity of the bones (**osteoporosis**). In this condition, bones break more readily and some women develop so-called dowager's hump. Osteoporosis is potentially severely handicapping, even life-threatening. The increased brittleness of the bones increases the risk of serious fractures, especially of the hip, and many elderly women never recover from these fractures.

Some women who experience severe physical symptoms have been helped by **hormone-replacement therapy (HRT),** which typically consists of synthetic estrogen and progesterone. These synthetic hormones are used to offset the losses of their naturally occurring counterparts. HRT may help reduce the hot flashes and other symptoms brought about by hormonal deficiencies during menopause and is especially helpful in protecting the woman against the development of osteoporosis (Ettinger, 1988).

Estrogen replacement has become quite controversial. Although HRT has certainly been helpful to many menopausal women, some studies link prolonged and continuous use of high doses of estrogen to a slightly increased risk of breast and uterine cancer (Goldman & Tosteson, 1991). On the other hand, estrogen replacement dramatically lowers the woman's risk of cardiovascular disorders (heart and artery disease) as well as osteoporosis. HRT may reduce the risk of cardiovascular disease by lowering the levels of cholesterol in the bloodstream (Henderson et al., 1988). A follow-up study of 49,000 postmenopausal nurses found that HRT was connected with 44 percent fewer heart attacks and a reduced risk of death from heart disease of 39 percent (Stampfer et al., 1991). Use of progestin along with estrogen for about 10 days of the 30-day cycle appears to virtually eliminate any additional risk of uterine cancer (Bachmann & Gill, 1988). The progestin causes a sloughing of the uterine wall in a monthly flow, which appears to reduce the risk that cancer may develop in the uterine wall from constant estrogen stimulation. It is not yet known whether adding progestin provides any protection against breast cancer, however (Brody, 1993c).

Hormone-replacement therapy is not recommended for women whose medical conditions or family histories make it inadvisable for them (Brody, 1992a). It is usually not recommended, for example, for women with a family history of breast cancer. A *New England Journal of Medicine* editorial suggests that the health benefits of HRT may outweigh the risks for women who do not fall into identifiable risk categories. The editorial notes that 31 percent of women who die between the ages of 50 and 94 die of heart disease and only 2.8 percent die from breast cancer (Goldman & Tosteson, 1991).

Overall, fewer than one in five postmenopausal women receive hormone-replacement therapy (Brody, 1992a). For those who do not receive replacement hormones, other drugs are available, when they are needed, to help them deal with menopausal complaints, such as hot flashes.

Menopause and Sexuality. Menopause does not mark the end of a woman's sexual life. Many women, in fact, feel more sexually liberated by the severing of ties between sexual activity and reproduction.

Learning Objective 12: Distinguish the myths from the facts regarding the effects of menopause on women.

Notes: In a study of Japanese women's experience of menopause, only 20 percent reported that they had ever had a hot flash (as compared to 65% of Canadian women). Japanese women are more likely to report headaches, shoulder stiffness, ringing in the ears, and dizziness. (Lock, M. 1991. Contested meanings of the menopause. *The Lancet, 337,* 1270–1272.)

MYTHS ABOUT MENOPAUSE   Menopause is certainly a major life change for most women. Yet exactly what types of changes do we find? Many of us harbor misleading ideas about menopause—ideas that can be harmful to women. Consider the following myths and the realities. To which myths have you fallen prey?

Myth 1.   *Menopause is abnormal.* The fact is that menopause is a normal development in women's lives.

Myth 2.   *The medical establishment considers menopause a disease.* No longer. Menopause is described as a "deficiency syndrome" today, referring to the decline in secretion of estrogen and progesterone. Unfortunately, the term *deficiency* also has negative meanings.

Myth 3.   *After menopause, women need complete replacement of estrogen.* Not necessarily. Some estrogen continues to be produced by the adrenal glands, fatty tissue, and the brain.

Myth 4.   *Menopause is accompanied by depression and anxiety.* Not necessarily. Karen Matthews and her colleagues (1990) followed 541 healthy women through menopause and found that menopause was not significantly connected to depression, anxiety, stress, anger, or job dissatisfaction. (Outcomes may differ for women who have had psychological problems prior to menopause.) Another group of researchers reported finding no overall relationship between mental health symptoms and menopausal status in a sample of 522 African-American women (Jackson, Taylor, & Pyngolil, 1991).

   Much of a woman's response to menopause reflects its meaning to her, not physical changes. Women who adopt the commonly held belief that menopause signals the beginning of the end of life may develop a sense of hopelessness about the future, which in turn can set the stage for depression. Women whose entire lives have centered around childbearing and child rearing are more likely to suffer a strong sense of loss. Moreover, there is a cultural bias to explain depression and other complaints of middle-aged women in terms of menopause, rather than to explore psychosocial factors.

Myth 5.   *At menopause, women suffer debilitating hot flashes.* Many women do not have hot flashes at all. Among those who do, the flashes are often relatively mild.

TRUTH OR *FICTION?*
R E V I S I T E D   ***At menopause, women suffer debilitating hot flashes.*** *Women at menopause do not necessarily have debilitating hot flashes. Many women have none at all. For most of those who do, hot flashes are mild.* •

Myth 6.   *A woman who has had a hysterectomy will not undergo menopause afterward.* It depends on whether or not the ovaries (the major producers of estrogen) were also removed. If they were not, menopause should proceed normally.

Myth 7.   *Menopause signals an end to a woman's sexual appetite.* Not at all. Many women feel liberated by the severing of the ties between sex and reproduction.

Myth 8.   *Menopause ends a woman's childbearing years.* Not necessarily! Postmenopausal women do not produce ova. However, ova from donors have been fertilized in laboratory dishes, and the developing embryos have been implanted in the uteruses of postmenopausal women and carried to term (Sauer et al., 1990).

Myth 9.   *A woman's general level of activity is lower after menopause.* Many postmenopausal women actually become peppier and more assertive.

Myth 10.   *Men are not affected by their wives' experience of menopause.* Many men are, of course. Men could become still more understanding if they learned about menopause and if their wives felt freer to talk to them about it.

MENSTRUAL PROBLEMS

Learning Objective 13: Summarize the research regarding the cultural, social, psychological, and biological correlates of dysmenorrhea.

Although menstruation is a natural biological process, the majority of women experience some discomfort prior to or during menstruation. Table 3.1 (see p. 98) contains a list of commonly reported symptoms of menstrual problems. The problems we explore in this section include dysmenorrhea, mastalgia, menstrual migraine headaches, amenorrhea, and premenstrual syndrome (PMS).

DYSMENORRHEA

Dysmenorrhea
Pain or discomfort during menstruation.

Primary dysmenorrhea
Menstrual pain or discomfort that occurs in the absence of known organic problems.

Secondary dysmenorrhea
Menstrual pain or discomfort that is caused by identified organic problems.

Pain or discomfort during menstruation, or **dysmenorrhea,** is the most common type of menstrual problem. Most women at some time have at least mild menstrual pain or discomfort. Pelvic cramps are the most common manifestation of dysmenorrhea. They may be accompanied by headache, backache, nausea, or bloated feelings. Women who develop severe cases usually do so within a few years of menarche. So-called **primary dysmenorrhea** refers to menstrual pain or discomfort in the absence of known organic pathology. Women with **secondary dysmenorrhea** do have identified organic problems that are believed to cause their menstrual problems. That is, their pain or discomfort is caused by, or secondary to, these problems. Endometriosis, pelvic inflammatory disease, and ovarian cysts are just a few of the organic disorders that can give rise to secondary dysmenorrhea. Yet evidence is accumulating that supposed primary dysmenorrhea is often *secondary* to hormonal changes, although the precise causes have not been delineated. For example, menstrual cramps sometimes decrease dramatically after childbirth, as a result of the massive hormonal changes that occur with pregnancy.

Painful menstruation was reported by nearly 75 percent of the participants in a sample of college women (Wildman & White, 1986). The symptoms varied not only from person to person but also according to whether or not the women had been pregnant. Women who had been pregnant reported a lower incidence of menstrual pain but a higher incidence of premenstrual symptoms and menstrual discomfort.

Prostaglandins
Hormones that cause muscle fibers in the uterine wall to contract, as during labor.

BIOLOGICAL ASPECTS OF DYSMENORRHEA   Menstrual cramps appear to result from uterine spasms which may be brought about by copious secretion of hormones called **prostaglandins.** Prostaglandins apparently cause muscle fibers in the uterine wall to contract, as during labor. Most contractions go unnoticed, but powerful, persistent contractions are discomfiting in themselves and may temporarily deprive the uterus of oxygen, another source of distress (American College of Obstetricians and Gynecologists,

TABLE 3.1 Common symptoms of menstrual problems	
Physical Symptoms	**Psychological Symptoms**
Swelling of the breasts	Depressed mood, sudden tearfulness
Tenderness in the breasts	Loss of interest in usual social or recreational activities
Bloating	Anxiety, tension (feeling "on edge," or "keyed up")
Weight gain	Anger
Food cravings	Irritability
Abdominal discomfort	Changes in body image
Cramping	Concern over skipping routine activities, school, or work
Lack of energy	A sense of loss of control
Sleep disturbance, fatigue	A sense of loss of ability to cope
Migraine headache	
Pains in muscles and joints	
Aggravation of chronic disorders like asthma and allergies	

Mastalgia
A swelling of the breasts that sometimes causes premenstrual discomfort.

1985). Women with more intense menstrual discomfort apparently produce higher quantities of prostaglandins. Prostaglandin-inhibiting drugs, such as ibuprofen, indomethacin, and aspirin are thus often of help. Menstrual pain may also be secondary to endometriosis.

Pelvic pressure and bloating may be traced to pelvic edema (Greek for "swelling")—the congestion of fluid in the pelvic region. Fluid retention can lead to a gain of several pounds, sensations of heaviness, and **mastalgia**—a swelling of the breasts that sometimes causes premenstrual discomfort. Masters and Johnson (1966) noted that orgasm (through coitus or masturbation) can help relieve menstrual discomfort by reducing the pelvic congestion that spawns bloating and pressure. Orgasm may also increase the menstrual flow and shorten this phase of the cycle.

Headaches frequently accompany menstrual discomfort. Most headaches (in both sexes) stem from simple muscle tension, notably in the shoulders, back of the neck, and the scalp. Pelvic discomfort may cause muscle contractions, thus contributing to the tension that produces headaches. Women who are tense about their menstrual flow are thus candidates for muscle tension headaches. Migraine headaches may arise from changes in the blood flow in the brain, however. Migraines are typically limited to one side of the head and are often accompanied by visual difficulties.

Amenorrhea
The absence of menstruation.

Primary amenorrhea
Lack of menstruation in a woman who has never menstruated.

Secondary amenorrhea
Lack of menstruation in a woman who has previously menstruated.

Anorexia nervosa
A psychological disorder of eating characterized by intense fear of putting on weight and refusal to eat enough to maintain normal body weight.

AMENORRHEA

Amenorrhea is the absence of menstruation and is a primary sign of infertility. **Primary amenorrhea** describes the absence of menstruation in a woman who has not menstruated at all by about the age of 16 or 17 (Kunz & Finkel, 1987). **Secondary amenorrhea** describes delayed or absent menstrual periods in women who have had regular periods in the past. Amenorrhea has various causes, including abnormalities in the structures of the reproductive system, hormonal abnormalities, growths such as cysts and tumors, and psychological problems, such as stress. Amenorrhea is normal during pregnancy and following menopause. Amenorrhea is also a symptom of **anorexia nervosa,** an eating disorder characterized by an intense fear of putting on weight and a refusal to eat enough to maintain a normal body weight, which often results in extreme (and sometimes life-threatening) weight losses. Hormonal changes that accompany emaciation are believed responsible for the cessation of menstruation (Falk et al., 1983). Amenorrhea may also occur in women who exercise strenuously, such as competitive long-distance runners. It is unclear whether the cessation of menstruation in female athletes is due to the effects of

The "Raging Hormones" Theory

Women have long suffered from the stereotype that they are incapable of managing responsibility because cyclical hormone fluctuations render their moods and behavior unstable. There is some evidence linking mood to hormonal fluctuation, but does this make women helpless victims of chemicals that course through their bodies? Karen Paige (1973) recounts the traditional prejudice against women:

> Women, the old argument goes, are eternally subject to the whims and wherefores of their biological clocks. Their raging hormonal cycles make them emotionally unstable and intellectually unreliable. If women have second-class status, we are told, it is because they cannot control the implacable demands of that bounding estrogen (p. 41).

In recent years the so-called PMS defense has even been used in some highly publicized cases in which it was argued that a woman accused of a violent crime was not responsible for her actions because she was impaired by PMS.

Research suggests that only about 10 percent of women report menstrual symptoms severe enough to impair their social, academic, or occupational functioning (Brody, 1989a). Even among women who report premenstrual syndrome, the symptoms of most fall in a mild range (Brooks et al., 1977). Environmental sources of stress—like exams—are linked to greater mood changes in women than are the phases of the menstrual cycle (Wilcoxon et al., 1976). Men's mood fluctuations, in fact, appear to vary as much as women's (Dan, 1976; Wilcoxon et al., 1976).

All in all, the majority of young women report some menstrual problems. However, fewer than 1 percent of the employed women in a survey by Gruber and Wildman (1987) reported *ever* missing work because of menstrual problems. Fewer still commit violent crimes or wind up in mental wards. Most studies concur that cyclical changes in mood and behavior are generally minor.

TRUTH OR *FICTION?*

R E V I S I T E D

Women's college grades slump during menstruation. *The great majority of menstruating women do not experience any fall off in occupational, academic, or social functioning during menstruation.* •

Woman Executive. Do the cyclical hormone fluctuations that women experience during their menstrual cycles make them too emotionally unstable to hold leadership or executive positions? What do you think?

---

strenuous exercise itself, to related physical factors such as low body fat, to the stress of intensive training, or to a combination of factors (Loucks & Horvath, 1985).

PREMENSTRUAL SYNDROME (PMS)

Learning Objective 14: Identify the common symptoms of PMS, cite the number of women who experience symptoms, and list the possible causes of PMS and its proposed treatments.

In late 1980, in a town about 50 miles from London, a 37-year-old woman, Christiana English, rammed her car into her boyfriend and killed him. She was subsequently convicted of manslaughter but released on probation. Her attorney persuaded the court that English was not fully responsible for her violent behavior, because it was induced by **premenstrual syndrome (PMS)** (Parlee, 1982). This case and similar ones received widespread attention in the press and provoked a storm of controversy. The sensationalism that attended the English case has died down, but the belief that premenstrual women

Premenstrual syndrome (PMS)

A combination of physical and psychological symptoms (e.g., anxiety, depression, irritability, weight gain from fluid retention, and abdominal discomfort) that regularly afflicts many women during the four- to six-day interval that precedes their menses each month.

Notes: In a large double-blind study, the results of which were published on July 18, 1990 in the *Journal of the American Medical Association*, researchers again found no significant difference in relief of PMS symptoms (as measured by 20 variables) between progesterone and a placebo. These findings replicate several earlier, smaller studies. (Freeman, Rickels, Sondheimer and Polensky. Ineffectiveness of progesterone suppository treatment for premenstrual syndrome.)

are prone to otherwise uncharacteristic emotional turbulence and violence remains widespread. It has even been argued by some that the tumult associated with PMS makes women incapable of assuming positions of responsibility in government and industry.

What is PMS? How are women affected by it? Let us see if we can separate truth from fiction.

The term *PMS* describes the combination of bodily and psychological symptoms that may afflict women during the 4- to 6-day interval that precedes their menses each month. The constellation of symptoms includes some combination of anxiety, depression, irritability, weight gain from fluid retention, and abdominal discomfort. PMS also appears to be linked with increased appetite. In one study, women who suffered from PMS and non-sufferers alike showed increased appetite during the luteal phase, but the increases were greater for women with PMS (Both-Orthman et al., 1988). For many women, premenstrual symptoms continue right through menstruation (Woods et al., 1987).

It is estimated that nearly three women in four in our society experience some form of PMS (Brody, 1989a). The great majority of cases involve mild to moderate levels of discomfort. Yet between 10 and 20 percent of women endure more severe, problematic symptoms (Woods et al., 1987). PMS is not unique to our culture. Researchers find premenstrual symptoms to be equally prevalent among women studied in the United States, Italy, and in the Islamic nation of Bahrain (Brody, 1992e).

The causes of PMS are unclear, but evidence is accumulating showing a biological basis to premenstrual symptoms, although the precise mechanisms remain undetermined (Asso & Magos, 1992). Researchers are looking to possible relationships between menstrual problems, including PMS, and hormone fluctuations. Researchers have yet to find differences in either the levels of estrogen or progesterone between women with severe PMS and those with mild symptoms or no symptoms (Brody, 1990b; Trunnel et al., 1988). It is conceivable that it is not hormone levels themselves but rather the sensitivity of brain centers to these hormones that predisposes some women to PMS.

Treatments for PMS range from exercise and dietary control (for example, limiting salt and sugar), to the use of vitamin supplements, to hormone treatments (usually progesterone). The scientific jury on the effectiveness of these treatments is still out.

HOW TO HANDLE MENSTRUAL DISCOMFORT

Most women suffer from some degree of menstrual discomfort. Women with persistent menstrual distress may profit from the suggestions listed below (adapted from Rathus & Nevid, 1991). Researchers are just beginning to explore the effectiveness of these techniques in controlled studies. For now, you might consider running a personal experiment. Adopt the techniques that sound right for you—all of them, if you wish. Try them out for a few months to see if you reap any benefits. Such personal experiments are uncontrolled, and it is scientifically difficult to pin down the reasons for results. (You may feel better simply because you *expect* to do so, or because of overall improvements in health.) Still, the methods may enhance your comfort, your health, and your outlook on menstruation not bad outcomes at all!

1. Don't blame yourself! Menstrual problems were once erroneously attributed to women's "hysterical" nature. This is nonsense. Menstrual problems appear, in large part, to reflect hormonal variations or chemical fluctuations in the brain during the menstrual cycle. Researchers have not yet fully identified all the causal elements and patterns, but their lack of knowledge does not render women who suffer from menstrual complaints "hysterical."
2. Keep a menstrual calendar, so that you can track your menstrual symptoms systematically and identify patterns.
3. Develop strategies for dealing with days that you experience the greatest distress—strategies that will help enhance your pleasure and minimize the stress affecting you on those days. Activities that distract you from your menstrual discomfort may be helpful. Go see a movie or get into that novel you've been meaning to read.
4. Ask yourself whether you harbor any self-defeating attitudes toward menstruation that might be compounding distress. Do close relatives or friends see menstruation

Tracking Your Premenstrual Complaints with a PMS Calendar

Do you have PMS? Clinicians often determine whether PMS is present by asking the woman to track her physical and emotional complaints over at least two cycles. PMS is suspected if the same complaints appear during the week preceding menstruation and then disappear within a few days of the start of her period on two successive cycles.

Researchers at the University of California at San Diego have developed a PMS calendar that flags the 22 most common premenstrual complaints (Podolsky, 1991). Using the calendar, the researchers correctly identified 35 of 36 women who had previously been diagnosed with PMS; none of a comparison group of non-PMS sufferers was selected. The calendar is not a substitute for a medical evaluation but may provide helpful information that the woman can bring to her physician's attention. Using the PMS calendar involves these steps (Podolsky, 1991):

1. Using graph paper, set up a chart like Figure 3.16, numbering the columns across the page to 28 or to the number of days that correspond to the length of your own menstrual cycle. Day 1 corresponds to the first day of your period.
2. For each day, rate the severity of any noticeable symptoms using a three-point scale, where 1= noticeable, 2 = moderate, and 3 = intolerable.
3. Shade the boxes in the row marked *Bleeding* for days of menstrual bleeding. Use an X to mark days in which there is spotting.
4. Start a new calendar for your next cycle.
5. When you have completed a calendar for two successive cycles, add up the scores for each of the cycles for the week preceding your period (Day 1). You should consider seeking a medical consultation if *all of the following criteria are met:*

a. The scores for both weeks are 30 or greater.
b. You marked five or more of the first ten listed symptoms each cycle.
c. The symptoms decline within four days after active bleeding starts.
d. These symptoms do not return for at least a week.
e. You find that your symptoms interfere with either your personal or professional life.

Whatever your score or pattern of symptoms, bring any troubling symptom or complaint to the attention of your physician. Check it out.

PMS Calendar

Jane Doe

CYCLE DAY	1	2	3	4	5		24	25	26	27	28
Bleeding	X				X						
Date March	3	4	5	6	7		26	27	28	29	30
Weight (Before Breakfast)	126	126	126	124	126		128	129	130	130	130

SYMPTOMS

Symptom	1	2	3	4	5		24	25	26	27	28
*Depression	2	1	1				2	2	2	1	2
*Anger, violent tendencies							2	2	1	2	3
*Irritability	1							2	2	2	2
*Anxiety, tension, nervousness	1						2	2	2	2	2
*Confusion, difficulty concentrating											
*Desire to be left alone											
*Tender breasts	1						2	2	3	3	3
*General bloated feeling							2	2	2	3	3
*Headaches	2	1					2	2	3	3	3
*Swelling of hands, ankles or breasts	1						2	2	2	3	3
Acne	2	1	1				1	1	1	1	1
Dizziness											
Fatigue	2	2	1	1			2	2	2	2	2
Hot flashes											
Nausea, diarrhea, constipation										1	1
Racing or pounding heart											
Crying easily	2						2	2	1	2	3
Food cravings (sweet, salty)							1	1	1	1	1
Forgetfulness											
Increased appetite									1	1	1
Mood swings	1						1	2	2	2	2
Overly sensitive	1						2	2	2	3	3

a. None											
b.											

MEDICATIONS

a. None											
b.											

*Especially significant PMS symptoms.

FIGURE 3.16 **The PMS Calendar.** Keeping a PMS calendar may provide helpful information regarding the pattern of PMS symptoms that women may experience. Symptoms should be tracked for at least two cycles to reveal the pattern of complaints.

Source: Mortola, J.F., et al. (1990). Diagnosis of premenstrual syndrome by a simple, prospective, and reliable instrument: the calendar of premenstrual experiences, *Obstetrics and Gynecology, 76;* 302. Reprinted with permission from the University of California, San Diego.

as an illness, a time of "pollution," a "dirty thing"? Have you adopted any of these attitudes—if not verbally, then in ways that affect your behavior, such as by restricting your social activities during your period?

5. See a doctor about your concerns, especially if you suffer severe symptoms. Severe menstrual symptoms are often secondary to medical disorders like endometriosis and pelvic inflammatory disease (PID). Check it out.

6. Develop nutritious eating habits—and continue them throughout the entire cycle (that means always). Consider limiting intake of alcohol, caffeine, fats, salt, and sweets, especially during the days preceding menstruation.

7. Some women find that vigorous exercise—jogging, swimming, bicycling, fast walking, dancing, skating, even jumping rope—helps relieve premenstrual and menstrual discomfort. Evidence is pointing to the benefits of exercise in helping to relieve and possibly even prevent menstrual discomfort (Choi, 1992). By the way, develop regular exercise habits—don't seek to become solely a premenstrual athlete.

8. Check with your doctor about vitamin and mineral supplements (such as calcium and magnesium). Vitamin B6 appears to help some women.

9. Ibuprofen (brand names Medipren, Advil, Motrin, etc.) and other medicines available over the counter may be helpful for cramping. Ask your doctor for a recommendation.

10. Remind yourself that menstrual problems are time-limited. Don't worry about getting through life or a career. Just get through the next couple of days.

In this chapter we have explored female sexual anatomy and physiology. In the following chapter, we turn our attention to the male.

SUMMING UP

EXTERNAL SEXUAL ORGANS

The female external sexual structures are collectively known as the vulva and consist of the mons veneris, labia majora and minora, the clitoris, the vestibule, and the vaginal opening.

The Mons Veneris The mons veneris consists of fatty tissue that covers the joint of the pubic bones in front of the body.

The Labia Majora The labia majora are large folds of skin that run downward from the mons along the sides of the vulva.

The Labia Minora The labia minora are hairless, light-colored membranes that surround the urethral and vaginal openings.

The Clitoris The clitoris is the female sexual organ that is most sensitive to sexual sensation, but it is not directly involved in reproduction.

The Vestibule The vestibule contains the openings to the vagina and the urethra.

The Urethral Opening Urine passes from the female's body through the urethral opening.

The Vaginal Opening The vaginal opening, or introitus, lies below the urethral opening.

The Perineum The perineum is the area that lies between the vaginal opening and the anus.

Structures That Underlie the External Sexual Organs These structures include the vestibular bulbs, Bartholin's glands, the sphincters, the clitoral crura, and the pubococcygeus (P-C) muscle.

INTERNAL SEXUAL ORGANS

The internal female sexual organs— or female reproductive system— include the innermost parts of the vagina, the cervix, the uterus, the ovaries, and the Fallopian tubes.

The Vagina Menstrual flow and babies pass from the uterus to the outer world through the vagina. During coitus, the vagina contains the penis.

The Cervix The cervix is the lower end of the uterus.

The Uterus The uterus or womb is the pear-shaped organ in which a fertilized ovum implants and develops until birth.

The Fallopian Tubes Two Fallopian tubes extend from

the upper end of the uterus toward the ovaries. Ova pass through the Fallopian tubes on their way to the uterus and are normally fertilized within these tubes.

The Ovaries The ovaries lie on either side of the uterus and produce ova and the sex hormones estrogen and progesterone.

The Pelvic Examination
Regular pelvic examinations are essential for early detection of problems involving the reproductive tract.

THE BREASTS

In some cultures the breasts are viewed merely as biological instruments for feeding infants. In our culture, however, they have achieved erotic significance. The breasts are secondary sex characteristics that contain mammary glands.

Breast Cancer Breast cancer is the second leading cancer killer in women, after lung cancer. Women with breast cancer will have lumps in the breast, but most lumps in the breasts are benign. Breast cancer may be detected in a number

of ways, including breast self-examination, medical examinations, and mammography. Early detection yields the greatest chance of survival.

THE MENSTRUAL CYCLE

Menstruation is the cyclical bleeding that stems from the shedding of the endometrium when a reproductive cycle has not led to the fertilization of an ovum. The menstrual cycle is regulated by estrogen and progesterone.

Regulation of the Menstrual Cycle The menstrual cycle involves finely tuned relationships between the hypothalamus, the pituitary gland, and the ovaries and uterus. Hormones produced by the hypothalamus regulate the pituitary, which in turn secretes hormones that regulate the secretions of the ovaries and uterus.

Phases of the Menstrual Cycle The menstrual cycle has four stages or phases: proliferative, ovulatory, secretory, and

menstrual. During the first phase of the cycle, which follows menstruation, ova ripen within their follicles and endometrial tissue proliferates. During the second phase, ovulation occurs. During the third phase, the corpus luteum produces copious amounts of progesterone and estrogen that cause the endometrium to thicken. If the ovum goes unfertilized, a plunge in estrogen and progesterone levels triggers the fourth, or menstrual, phase, which leads to the beginning of a new cycle.

Coitus During Menstruation
Couples are apparently less likely to initiate sexual activity during menstruation than during any other phase of the woman's cycle.

Menopause Menopause is the

cessation of menstruation, which most commonly occurs between the ages of 46 and 50. Estrogen deficiency in menopause may give rise to night sweats, hot flashes, hot flushes, cold sweats, dry skin, loss of breast tissue, and decreased vaginal lubrication. Long-term estrogen deficiency has been linked to osteoporosis. Hormone-replacement therapy can offset losses of estrogen and progesterone but has been linked to a slightly increased risk of breast and endometrial cancers, but also to a marked reduction in risk of cardiovascular disease and osteoporosis. For most women, menopausal problems are mild. Psychological problems can reflect the meaning of menopause to the individual.

MENSTRUAL PROBLEMS

Most women experience some discomfort prior to or during menstruation. Common menstrual problems include dysmenorrhea, amenorrhea, and premenstrual syndrome (PMS).

Dysmenorrhea Dysmenorrhea is the most common menstrual problem, and pelvic cramps are the most common symptom. Dysmenorrhea can be caused by problems such as endometriosis, pelvic inflammatory disease, and ovarian cysts.

Amenorrhea Amenorrhea can be caused by problems such as abnormalities in the structures of the reproductive system, hormonal abnormalities, cysts, tumors, and stress.

Premenstrual Syndrome (PMS) As many as three women in four have some form of PMS. The causes of PMS are unclear, but most researchers look to potential links between menstrual prob-

lems and hormone levels. Women have long suffered from the stereotype that they are incapable of managing responsibility because of cyclical hormone fluctuations, but evidence contradicts the stereotype.

How to Handle Menstrual Discomfort Women with persistent menstrual problems may benefit from a number of active coping strategies for handling menstrual distress.

_____ The penis consists of bone and muscle tissue.

_____ Uncircumcised men are more sensitive than circumcised men to sexual stimulation.

_____ The father determines the baby's gender.

_____ Morning erections reflect the need to urinate.

_____ Men can will themselves to have erections.

_____ The penis has a mind of its own.

_____ Many men paralyzed below the waist can attain erection, engage in sexual intercourse, and ejaculate.

_____ Men can have orgasms without ejaculating.

C H A P T E R 4

Male Sexual Anatomy and Physiology

The first great Western civilization was Sumer, in what is now Iraq. Although the language of Sumer has been extinct for nearly 4,000 years, scholars continue to puzzle over an enigmatic phrase. Despite their attempts to decipher it otherwise, the phrase stubbornly insists on being translated as, "He put a hot fish in her navel" (Tannahill, 1980, p. 58).

Phallic symbols
Images of the penis that are usually suggestive of generative power.

The woman's navel, throughout history, has held wonderful jewelry and erotic objects. Wherefore a hot fish, however? Tannahill suggests that the term might have been Sumerian slang for the male sexual organ. The ancient Greeks carried oversized images of fish as **phallic symbols** in their Dionysian processions, which celebrated the wilder and more frenzied aspects of human sexuality. In the murky predawn light of Western civilization, humankind showed its reverence for the penis in the form of phallic worship. Phallic symbols played roles in religious worship and became glorified in art in the form of ploughs, axes, and swords.

Notes: Phalluses sculpted from stone can be seen at the ancient Maya ruins of Uxmal and Chichen Itza in Mexico.

The tradition of phallic worship became raised to progressively higher aesthetic levels. The ancient Greeks adorned themselves with phallic rings and necklaces. In ancient Rome, celebrations were held to honor Venus, the goddess of love. The Romans outfitted a float in the shape of a large phallus and paraded it through the streets. There were no tributes to the female pudendum. Even though Venus was being honored, no artisans devoted themselves to the creation of floats bearing the likeness of the vulva or the clitoris.

Testes
The male sex glands, suspended in the scrotum, that produce sperm cells and male sex hormones. Singular: testis.

Testicles
Testes.

From the earliest foundations of Western civilization, male-dominated societies elevated the status of men and exalted male genitalia. Men held their own genitals in such high esteem that it was common courtroom practice for them to swear to tell the truth with their hands on their genitals—as we swear to tell the truth in the name of God or by placing our hands on the Bible. The words **testes** and **testicles** derive from the same Latin word as "testify." The Latin *testis* means "a witness." This ancient custom suggests the pride that men have historically taken in their sexual organs.

Notes: In the fifteenth and sixteenth centuries, some men wearing hose or tight-fitting pants would also wear a decorated cover over their crotch. Often the decorations on the covers were ornate and matched their costumes.

Even today, we see evidence of pride—indeed veneration!—of the male genitalia. Men with large genitals are accorded respect from their male peers and sometimes adoration from female admirers. In *The Sun Also Rises*, Ernest Hemingway describes how matadors stuffed the front of their trousers with fabric. With their "manhood" fully packed, they plunged the sword into the poor animal's head before their adoring public. U.S. slang describes men with large genitals as "well-hung" or "hung like a bull" (or stallion).

Given these cultural attitudes, it is not surprising that young men (and some not-so-young men) belittle themselves if they feel, as many do, that they are little—that is, that their penises do not measure up to some ideal. Boys who mature late are often ridiculed by their peers for their small genitals. Their feelings of inadequacy may persist into adulthood. Adult men, too, may harbor doubts that their penises are large enough to satisfy their lovers, or they may fear that their partners' earlier lovers had larger genitals.

Flaccid
Soft, limp. (From the Latin *flaccus*, meaning "flabby.")

In this chapter we examine male sexual anatomy and physiology, and we attempt to sort out truth from fiction. We see, for example, that despite his lingering doubts, a man's capabilities as a lover do not depend on the size of his penis (at least within very broad limits). Moreover, the size of the penis in the resting, or **flaccid**, state bears little relationship to the size of the erect penis. For a man to judge his sexual prowess on the basis of locker-room comparisons makes about as much sense as choosing a balloon by measuring it when it is deflated.

In our exploration of male sexual anatomy and physiology, as in our exploration of female sexual physiology and anatomy, we begin with the external genitalia and then move inward. Once inside, we focus on the route of sperm through the male reproductive system.

EXTERNAL SEXUAL ORGANS

The male external sexual organs include the penis and the scrotum (Figures 4.1 and 4.2).

THE PENIS

Learning Objective 1:
Describe the penis and the internal structures that make erection possible.

The penis mightier than the sword.

(Mark Twain)

Is that a gun in your pocket, or are you just glad to see me?

(Mae West)

Penis
The male organ of sexual intercourse. (From the Latin for "tail.")

At first glance the **penis** may seem rather simple and obvious in its structures, particularly when compared to women's organs. This apparent simplicity may have contributed to cultural stereotypes that men are straightforward and aggressive, whereas women tend to be complicated and, perhaps, mysterious. Yet, as Figure 4.1 shows, the apparent simplicity of the penis is misleading. Much goes on below the surface. Gender stereotypes regarding anatomy are as misleading as those regarding personality (see Chapter 6).

The penis, like the vagina, is the sexual organ used in sexual intercourse. Unlike the vagina, however, urine also passes through the penis. Semen and urine pass out of the penis through the urethral opening. The opening is called the urethral *meatus* (pronounced mee-ATE-us), meaning "passage."

Cloaca
The cavity in birds, reptiles, and many fish into which the genitourinary and intestinal tracts empty. (From the Latin *cluere,* meaning "to cleanse.")

The penis appears to have arrived on the evolutionary scene about 100 million years ago. It was found then in creatures that belonged to the reptile family—including the ancestors of our present-day crocodiles and lizards, and the behemoth dinosaurs. Earlier in the evolutionary process, male and female animals each had a genital opening called a **cloaca,** which functioned as both an excretory and a sexual organ. It took some fancy bodywork for twosomes to position themselves to make contact between their respective cloacae, so that the male's sperm could find their way into the female's cloacal cavity. At the risk of sounding chauvinistic, the penis seems like a more effective shape—a shaft—for funneling sperm deep inside the female. It gives them a head start on their journey toward the ovum.

FIGURE 4.1 **The Penis.** During sexual arousal the corpora cavernosa and corpus spongiosum become congested with blood, causing the penis to enlarge and stiffen.

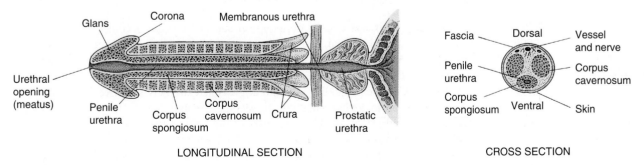

LONGITUDINAL SECTION

CROSS SECTION

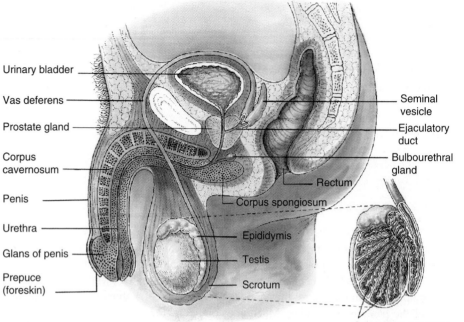

Urinary bladder

Vas deferens

Prostate gland

Corpus cavernosum

Penis

Urethra

Glans of penis

Prepuce (foreskin)

Seminal vesicle

Ejaculatory duct

Bulbourethral gland

Rectum

Corpus spongiosum

Epididymis

Testis

Scrotum

Seminiferous tubules

Figure 4.2 **The Male Reproductive System.** The external male sex organs include the penis and the scrotum.

Many mammals, including dogs, have penile bones that stiffen the penis to facilitate copulation. Despite the slang term "boner," the human penis contains no bones. Nor, despite another slang term, "muscle," does the penis contain muscle tissue. However, muscles at the base of the penis, like the muscles surrounding the vaginal and urethral openings in women, are involved in controlling urination and ejaculation.

The penis consists of bone and muscle tissue. *Despite the slang terms, the penis contains neither bone nor muscle.* •

Corpora cavernosa
Cylinders of spongy tissue in the penis that become congested with blood and stiffen during sexual arousal.

Corpus spongiosum
The spongy body that runs along the bottom of the penis, contains the penile urethra, and enlarges at the tip of the penis to form the glans.

Corona
The ridge that separates the glans from the body of the penis. (From the Latin for "crown.")

Rather than bones or muscles, the penis contains three cylinders of spongy material that run its length. The larger two of these cylinders, the **corpora cavernosa** (Figure 4.1), lie side by side and function like the cavernous bodies in the clitoris. These cylinders fill up with blood and stiffen during sexual arousal. In addition, a **corpus spongiosum** (spongy body) runs along the bottom, or ventral, surface of the penis. It contains the penile urethra that conducts urine through the penis to the urinary opening (urethral meatus) at the tip. At the tip of the penis, the spongy body enlarges to become the glans or head of the penis.

All three cylinders consist of spongy tissue that swells (becomes engorged) with blood during sexual arousal, resulting in erection. The urethra is connected to the bladder, which is unrelated to reproduction, and to those parts of the reproductive system that transport semen.

The glans of the penis, like the clitoral glans, is extremely sensitive to sexual stimulation. Direct, prolonged stimulation can become irritating, even painful. Men generally prefer to masturbate by stroking the shaft of the penis rather than the glans, although some prefer the latter. The **corona,** or coronal ridge separates the glans from the body of the penis. It is also quite sensitive to sexual stimulation. After the glans, the parts of the penis that men tend to find most sensitive are the corona and an area on the underside of

Frenulum

The sensitive strip of tissue that connects the underside of the penile glans to the shaft. (From the Latin *frenum,* meaning "bridle.")

Root

The base of the penis, which extends into the pelvis.

Shaft

The body of the penis, which expands as a result of vasocongestion.

Foreskin

The loose skin that covers the penile glans. Also referred to as the *prepuce.*

Circumcision

Surgical removal of the foreskin of the penis. (From the Latin *circumcidere,* meaning "to cut around.")

Learning Objective 2: Cite the reasons people give for having male babies circumcized and the research evidence on this topic.

Phimosis

An abnormal condition in which the foreskin is so tight that it cannot be withdrawn from the glans. (From the Greek *phimos,* meaning "muzzle.")

the penis called the **frenulum.** The frenulum is a thin strip of tissue that connects the underside of the glans to the shaft. Most men find the top part of the penis to be the least sensitive part.

The base of the penis, called the **root,** extends into the pelvis. It is attached to pelvic bones by leglike structures, called crura, that are like those that anchor the female's clitoris. The body of the penis is called the penile **shaft.** The penile shaft, unlike the clitoral shaft, is free-swinging. Thus, when sexual excitement engorges the penis with blood, the result—erection—is obvious. The expression "getting shafted," which means being taken advantage of, presumably refers to the penile shaft. Another phrase, "getting screwed," refers more directly to sexual intercourse.

The skin of the penis is hairless and loose, allowing expansion during erection. It is fixed to the penile shaft just behind the glans. Some of it, however, like the labia minora in the female, folds over to partially cover the glans. This covering is the prepuce, or **foreskin.** It covers part or all of the penile glans just as the clitoral prepuce (hood) covers the clitoral shaft. The prepuce consists of loose skin that freely moves over the glans. However, in the male, as in the female, smegma may accumulate below the prepuce, causing the foreskin to adhere to the glans.

CIRCUMCISION **Circumcision** is the surgical removal of the prepuce. Advocates of circumcision believe that it has hygienic benefits because it eliminates a site where smegma might accumulate and bacteria might grow. Opponents of circumcision believe that it is unnecessary because regular cleaning is sufficient to reduce the risk of these problems.

Male circumcision has a long history as a religious rite. Jews traditionally carry out male circumcision shortly after a baby is born. Circumcision is performed as a sign of the covenant between God and the people of Abraham—and for purposes of hygiene (Figure 4.3). Moslems also have ritual circumcisions for religious reasons. Circumcision is common among Christians for hygienic reasons alone, however.

Evidence concerning the health benefits of circumcision seems mixed and inconclusive. For example, Jewish women, whose husbands are universally circumcised, were found in some early research to have a somewhat lower incidence of cervical cancer than Christian women (Weiner et al., 1951). The wives of Lebanese Moslems, however, who also practiced circumcision, were no less prone to cervical cancer than were the wives of Lebanese Christians, who did not (Abou-David, 1967). There is also some evidence that penile cancer, a rare form of cancer, is slightly more common among uncircumcised men (Hand, 1970; Harahap & Siregar, 1988; Warner & Strashin, 1981). Physicians continue to debate the health benefits of circumcision. They do agree, however, that circumcision is the treatment of choice for **phimosis,** a condition in which it is difficult to retract the foreskin from the glans.

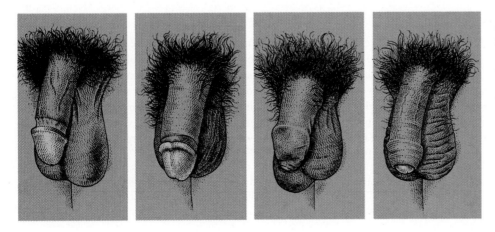

FIGURE 4.3 **Circumcision.** Circumcision is the surgical removal of the foreskin, or prepuce, of the penis. Circumcision has a long history as a religious rite among Jews. Many Christians also practice circumcision for hygienic reasons.

In 1971 the American Academy of Pediatrics announced that it did not recommend routine circumcision as a means of enhancing health. This position has not changed. Perhaps as a result, the incidence of circumcision has declined dramatically in the United States from 90 percent of newborn males in 1970 to 59 percent by the mid-1980s (Lindsey, 1988).

Recent research suggests, however, that urinary tract infections are more common among uncircumcised male infants than among circumcised infants (Herzog, 1989; Wiswell et al., 1987). Still, it has been argued that the risks associated with urinary tract infections in infancy are too low to justify routine circumcision (King, 1988; Lohr, 1989). There is also emerging evidence that suggests that uncircumcised men may be at greater risk than circumcised men of becoming infected by the AIDS virus (Holmes, 1988; Simonsen et al., 1988). It is suspected that certain cells in the foreskin may be especially susceptible to the AIDS virus (Touchette, 1991).

Questions have also been raised about the *sexual* effects of circumcision. One argument is that circumcised males may have more difficulty controlling ejaculation since the penile glans is directly exposed to sexual stimulation. As a result, the argument goes, such men would be more likely to suffer from **premature ejaculation.** Common sense—or should we say, common nonsense?—has actually had it both ways: that circumcised men are more *and* less sensitive to sexual stimulation than the uncircumcised. The first belief rests shakily on the assumption that circumcised are more "exposed," thus *more* sensitive and less capable of controlling ejaculation. The latter argument is based on the fact that circumcised men have lost some sexually sensitive skin. Thus they should be *less* sensitive to erotic stimulation. Perhaps the debate has continued this long because of the virtual absence of well-controlled scientific research comparing the sexual sensitivity of circumcised and uncircumcised men. The only clinical study ever reported found no significant differences in sensitivity to various forms of tactile stimulation between circumcised and uncircumcised men (Masters & Johnson, 1966). Moreover, the foreskin retracts during sexual arousal in uncircumcised men, directly exposing the clitoral glans to stimulation. It is thus unlikely that there are significant differences in coital sensitivity between circumcised and uncircumcised men that might lead to premature ejaculation.

TRUTH OR *FICTION?*
R E V I S I T E D

Uncircumcised men are more sensitive than circumcised men to sexual stimulation. *Actually, there is no reliable empirical evidence that uncircumcised men are more sensitive to sexual stimulation.* •

Teaching Tip: Set up two columns on the chalkboard—one labeled "Arguments for Circumcision" and the other labeled "Arguments against Circumcision." Have students suggest items for each column. Then have students identify which items would influence their decision about circumcizing a baby boy. Does social pressure or research evidence exert greater influence on their decisions?

Premature ejaculation A sexual dysfunction in which the male persistently ejaculates too early to afford the couple adequate sexual gratification.

Learning Objective 3: Distinguish between myths and facts derived from research on the effects of penis size on sexual performance and a partner's sexual satisfaction.

PENIS SIZE

IRAS: Am I not an inch of fortune better than she?

CHARMIAN: Well, if you were but an inch of fortune better than I, where would you choose it?

IRAS: Not in my husband's nose.

(From Shakespeare's *Antony and Cleopatra*)

In our culture the size of the penis is sometimes seen as a measure of a man's masculinity and his ability to please his sex partner (see the Closer Look feature, page 111). Shakespeare and other writers inform us that men have looked down at themselves for centuries, sometimes in delight but more often in chagrin. Men who are heralded for their sexual or reproductive feats are presumed to have more prominent "testaments" to their manhood. When the Dionne quintuplets were born in 1935, stories began to circulate that the father, Oliva Dionne, must have an exceptionally large penis. Such beliefs fostered jokes about Papa Dionne, such as:

While visiting a fair, Papa Dionne asked to see a prized bull which was very well endowed. "Listen," he was told, "it's no problem. The prized bull just asked to see you."

(Cited in Milsten, 1979, pp. 118–119)

A CLOSER LOOK

On Penis Size and Sexual Performance

Perhaps most men have had concerns about the size of their penises. As sex therapist Bernard Zilbergeld put it in his book *Male Sexuality,* "Women, we are given to believe, crave nothing so much as a penis that might be mistaken for a telephone pole" (1978, p. 27). Think critically about the belief that men with bigger penises make more effective lovers. What assumptions is it based upon? Is there supportive evidence?

The belief that the size of the man's penis determines his sexual prowess is based upon the assumption that men with bigger penises are better equipped to satisfy a woman sexually. Zilbergeld and others point out, however, that women rarely mention penis size as an important element in their sexual satisfaction. Quite regularly they *do* mention ability to communicate with partners, the emotional atmosphere of the relationship, and sensitivity to employing sexual techniques that enhance their partner's pleasure.

Does your knowledge of female sexual physiology support or challenge the assumption that bigger is necessarily better? From your reading of Chapter 3, what do you know about how the vagina accommodates the penis? What is the role of the P-C muscle? Which part of the vagina is most sensitive to tactile stimulation? What, if any, might be the relationships between the clitoris—the woman's most erotically sensitive organ—and the size of the penis?

Which seems more crucial: sexual technique and the quality of the relationship or penis size? Why?

The diameter of the penis, rather than its length, may actually have a greater bearing on a partner's sexual sensations, since thicker penises may provide more clitoral stimulation during coital thrusting (Milsten, 1979). Nonetheless, even though the inner vagina is relatively insensitive to touch, some women find the *pressure* of deeper penetration sexually pleasurable. Others, however, find deeper penetration to be uncomfortable or painful, especially if thrusting is too vigorous.

It may be of some comfort to note that even the smallest normal human penis is between three and four times the length of the phallus of the burly gorilla. Even so, the human penis does not merit comparison with the phallus of the blue whale. This ocean-dwelling mammal, the largest animal on earth, is about 100 feet from end to end, and possesses a penis about seven feet in length. When not in use, the penis is cached in the male's abdomen, which is a fortunate thing. If it were to trail down permanently, it might act as a rudder and muddle the animal's internal navigational system.

Masters and Johnson (1966) reported that the penises of the 312 male subjects they studied generally ranged in length from 3½ inches to a little more than 4 inches when flaccid. The average erect penis ranges from 5 to 7 inches long (Reinisch, 1990). Erect penises differ less in size than flaccid penises do (Jamison & Gebhard, 1988). Penises that are small when flaccid tend to gain more size when they become erect. Larger flaccid penises gain relatively less. Size differences in flaccid penises may thus be largely canceled out by erection. Nor is there a relationship between penis size and body weight, height, or build (Money et al., 1984).

Even when flaccid, the same penis can vary in size (Carrera, 1981). Such factors as cold air or water or emotions of fear or anxiety can cause the penis (along with the scrotum and testicles) to draw closer to the body, reducing its size. The flaccid penis may also grow in size in warm water or when the man is relaxed.

Learning Objective 4: Describe the scrotum and its role in maintaining optimum temperature for sperm production.

Scrotum
The pouch of loose skin that contains the testes. (From the same linguistic root as the word *shred,* meaning, "a long, narrow strip" and probably referring to the long furrows on the scrotal sac.)

THE SCROTUM

The **scrotum** is a pouch of loose skin that becomes covered lightly with hair at puberty. The scrotum consists of two compartments that hold the testes. Each testicle is held in

Spermatic cord
The cord that suspends a testicle within the scrotum and contains a vas deferens, blood vessels, nerves, and the cremaster muscle.

Vas deferens
A tube that conducts sperm from the testicle to the ejaculatory duct of the penis. (From Latin roots meaning "a vessel" that "carries down.")

Cremaster muscle
The muscle that raises and lowers the testicle in response to temperature changes and sexual stimulation.

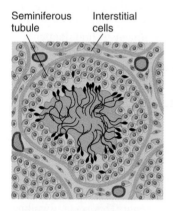

Seminiferous tubule   Interstitial cells

FIGURE 4.4 **Interstitial Cells.** Testosterone is produced by the interstitial cells, which lie between the seminiferous tubules in each testis.

Dartos muscle
The muscle in the middle layer of the scrotum that contracts and relaxes in response to temperature changes.

Germ cell
A cell from which a new organism develops. (From the Latin germen, meaning "bud" or "sprout.")

Sperm
The male germ cell. (From a Greek root meaning "seed.")

place by a **spermatic cord,** a structure that contains the **vas deferens,** blood vessels and nerves, and the cremaster muscle. The **cremaster muscle** raises and lowers the testicle within the scrotum in response to temperature changes and sexual stimulation (the testes are drawn closer to the body during sexual arousal).

Sperm production is optimal at a temperature that is slightly cooler than the 98.6 degrees Fahrenheit that is desirable for most of the body. Typical scrotal temperature is about 93 degrees Fahrenheit, or 5.6 degrees lower than body temperature (Tessler & Krahn, 1966). The loose-hanging scrotum is a flexible organ that permits the testes and nearby structures to escape the higher body heat, especially in warm weather, and thus remain at a stable temperature. In the middle layer of the scrotum is the **dartos muscle,** which (like the cremaster) contracts and relaxes reflexively in response to temperature changes. In cold weather, or when a man jumps into a body of cold water, it contracts to bring the testes closer to the body. In warm weather, it relaxes, allowing the testes to dangle farther from the body. The dartos muscle also increases or decreases the surface area of the scrotum in response to temperature changes. Smoothing allows greater dissipation of heat in hot weather. Tightening or constricting the skin surface helps retain heat and gives the scrotum a wrinkled appearance in the cold.

The scrotum is developed from the same embryonic tissue that becomes the labia majora of the female. Thus, like the labia majora, it is quite sensitive to sexual stimulation. It is somewhat more sensitive than the top side of the penis but less so than other areas of the penis.

INTERNAL SEXUAL ORGANS

The internal sexual organs of the male consist of the testes, the organs that manufacture sperm and the male sex hormone testosterone; the system of tubes and ducts that conduct sperm through the male reproductive system; and the organs that help nourish and activate sperm and neutralize some of the acidity that sperm encounter in the vagina.

THE TESTES

The testes are the male gonads (*gonad* derives from the Greek *gone,* meaning "seed"). In slang the testes are frequently referred to as "balls" or "nuts." These terms are considered somewhat vulgar, but they are reasonably descriptive. They also make it easier for many people to refer to the testes in informal conversation.

The testes serve two functions analogous to those of the ovaries. They secrete sex hormones and produce mature **germ cells.** In the case of the testes, the germ cells are **sperm** and the sex hormones are **androgens.** The most important androgen is **testosterone.**

TESTOSTERONE   Testosterone is secreted by **interstitial cells,** which are also referred to as **Leydig's cells.** Interstitial cells lie between the seminiferous tubules and release testosterone directly into the bloodstream (see Figure 4.4). Testosterone stimulates prenatal differentiation of male sexual organs, sperm production, and development of **secondary sex characteristics,** such as the beard, deep voice, and growth of the muscle mass.

In men, several endocrine glands—the hypothalamus, pituitary gland, and testes (Figure 4.5)—keep blood testosterone levels at a more or less constant level. This is in sharp contrast to the peaks and valleys in the levels of female sex hormones that occur during the phases of the menstrual cycle in women. Testosterone levels do vary slightly with stress, time of day or month, and other factors, but a feedback loop among the endocrine glands keeps them at a relatively stable level.

The same pituitary hormones, FSH and LH, that regulate the activity of the female gonads, or ovaries, also regulate the activity of the male gonads, or testes. In men FSH regulates the production of sperm by the testes, whereas LH stimulates secretion of

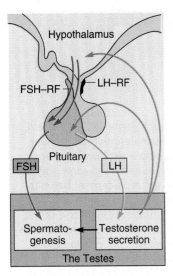

FIGURE 4.5 **Hormonal Control of the Testes.** Several endocrine glands—the hypothalamus, the pituitary gland, and the testes—keep blood testosterone levels at a more or less constant level. Low testosterone levels signal the hypothalamus to secrete LH-releasing hormone (LH-RH). Like dominoes falling in line, LH-RH causes the pituitary gland to secrete LH, which in turn stimulates the testes to release testosterone into the blood system. Follicle-stimulating hormone releasing hormone (FSH-RH) from the hypothalamus causes the pituitary gland to secrete FSH, which in turn causes the testes to produce sperm cells.

Androgens

Male sex hormones. (From the Greek *andros,* meaning "man" or "males," and *-gene,* meaning "born.")

Testosterone

A male steroid sex hormone.

Interstitial cells

Cells that lie between the seminiferous tubules and secrete testosterone. (*Interstitial* means "set between.")

Leydig's cells

Another term for *interstitial cells.*

Secondary sex characteristics

Traits that distinguish the genders but are not directly involved in reproduction.

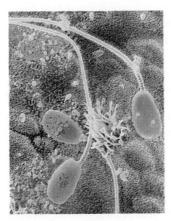

A Human Sperm Cell Magnified Many Times.

testosterone by the interstitial cells. Low testosterone levels signal the hypothalamus to secrete a hormone, called LH-releasing hormone (LH-RH). Like dominoes falling in line, LH-RH causes the pituitary gland to secrete LH, which in turn stimulates the testes to release testosterone into the blood system. LH is also referred to as *interstitial-cell-stimulating-hormone,* or ICSH.[1]

When the level of testosterone in the blood system reaches a certain peak, the hypothalamus triggers the pituitary gland *not* to secrete LH. This system for circling information around these three endocrine glands is called a *feedback loop.* This feedback loop is *negative.* That is, increases in hormone levels in one part of the system trigger another part to shut down, and vice versa.

The testes usually range between 1 and 1.75 inches in length, and are about half as wide and deep. The left testicle usually hangs lower, because the left spermatic cord tends to be somewhat longer.

SPERM Each testicle is divided into many lobes. The lobes are filled with winding **seminiferous tubules** (Figure 4.2). Although packed into a tiny space, these tubules, placed end to end, would span the length of several football fields. Through a process called **spermatogenesis,** these threadlike structures produce and store hundreds of billions of sperm through the course of a lifetime.

Sperm cells develop through several stages. It takes about 72 days for the testes to manufacture a mature sperm cell (Leary, 1990). In an early stage, sperm cells are called **spermatocytes.** Each one contains 46 chromosomes, including one X and one Y sex chromosome. Each spermatocyte divides into two **spermatids,** each of which has 23 chromosomes. Half the spermatids have X sex chromosomes, and the other half have Y sex chromosomes. Looking something like tadpoles when examined under a microscope, mature sperm cells, called **spermatozoa,** each have a head, a cone-shaped midpiece, and a tail. The head is about 5 microns (1/50,000 of an inch) long and contains the cell nucleus that houses the 23 chromosomes. The midpiece contains structures that provide the energy that the tail needs to lash back and forth in a swimming motion. Each sperm cell is about 50 microns, or 1/5,000 of an inch long, one of the smallest cells in the body (Thompson, 1993).

During fertilization, the 23 chromosomes from the father's sperm cell combine with the 23 chromosomes from the mother's ovum, furnishing the standard ensemble of 46

---

[1]We do not throw all these terms at you willy-nilly, or to complicate matters. In future years, you will be reading and hearing about the biology of sex in the popular media, and since it is unlikely that all commentators will agree on the terminology that is to be used, we want you to be able to recognize the meanings of various terms.

Is There a Manopause?

Men cannot undergo menopause; they have never menstruated. Yet one now and then hears of a so-called male menopause, occasionally referred to as "manopause." Some men during their later years are loosely referred to as menopausal. Sadly, this description is usually meant to convey the negative, harmful stereotype of the aging person as crotchety and irritable. Such stereotypes of menopause are unfortunate reminders of sexism and ageism, and are not necessarily consistent with the biology or psychology of aging.

The scientific jury is still out on the existence of the male menopause. Women encounter relatively sudden age-related declines in sex hormones and fertility during menopause. Men experience a gradual decline in testosterone levels as they age, but nothing like the sharp plunge in estrogen levels that women experience during menopause (Angier, 1992). Still, men may experience as much as a 30 to 40 percent reduction in testosterone levels between the ages of 48 and 70.

The drop in testosterone levels that occurs as men age may be connected to a variety of age-related symptoms, including reduced muscle mass and strength, accumulation of body fat, reduced energy levels, lowered fertility, and reduced erectile ability. However, despite a decline in testosterone levels, most men remain potent throughout their lives. Little is known about the critical levels of testosterone that are needed to maintain erectile ability. Certain age-related changes, such as reduced muscle mass and strength and increased body fat, may be due to other factors associated with aging rather than to declining testosterone production, such as a gradual loss of *human growth hormone,* a hormone that helps maintain muscle strength and that may prevent fat buildup.

Although some experts believe that testosterone replacement may help avert bone loss and frailty, in much the same way that estrogen replacement benefits postmenopausal women, others worry that excessive use of the hormone may increase the risks of prostate cancer and cardiovascular disease (Angier, 1992).

Although men do experience a gradual decline in the number and motility of sperm as they age, which reduces their fertility, some viable sperm continue to be produced even into late adulthood. So it is not surprising to find a man in his seventies or older fathering a child.

Men can remain sexually active and father children at advanced ages. For both genders, attitudes toward the physical changes of aging—along with general life satisfaction—apparently influence sexual behavior as profoundly as the physical changes themselves.

Seminiferous tubules
Tiny, winding, sperm-producing tubes that are located within the lobes of the testes. (From Latin roots meaning "seed bearing.")

chromosomes in the offspring. Among the 23 chromosomes borne by sperm cells is one sex chromosome—an X sex chromosome or a Y sex chromosome. Ova contain X sex chromosomes only. The union of an X sex chromosome and a Y sex chromosome leads to the development of male offspring. Two X sex chromosomes combine to yield female offspring. So the presence of an X or Y sex chromosome from the father determines the baby's gender.

TRUTH OR *FICTION?*

R E V I S I T E D

The father determines the baby's gender. *Yes, in a manner of speaking. The presence of an X or Y sex chromosome from the father determines the baby's gender. If the fertilizing sperm has an X sex chromosome, the child will be a girl. If it has a Y sex chromosome, the child will be a boy.* •

Spermatogenesis
The process by which sperm cells are produced and developed.

The testes are veritable dynamos of manufacturing power, churning out about 1,000 sperm per second or about 30 billion—yes, *billion*—per year (Elmer-Dewitt, 1991). Mathematically speaking, 10 to 20 ejaculations hold enough sperm to populate the earth. (Men are always so taken with themselves, notes the second author.)

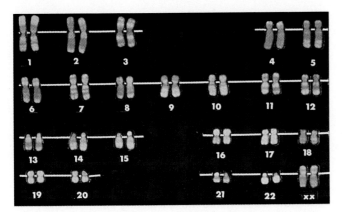

The Normal Human Cell Contains 46 Chromosomes Which Are Arranged in Pairs. When a sperm cell and ovum unite, 23 chromosomes from the father's sperm cell combine with 23 chromosomes from the mother's ovum, to form the normal complement of 46 chromosomes in the offspring. The presence of an X or Y sex chromosome from the father determines the baby's gender.

Spermatocyte

An early stage in the development of sperm cells, in which each parent cell has 46 chromosomes, including one X and one Y sex chromosome.

Spermatids

Cells formed by the division of spermatocytes. Each spermatid has 23 chromosomes.

Spermatozoa

Mature sperm cells.

Epididymis

A tube that lies against the back wall of each testicle and serves as a storage facility for sperm. (From Greek roots meaning "upon testicles.")

Vasectomy

A sterilization procedure in which the vas deferens is severed, preventing sperm from reaching the ejaculatory duct.

Seminal vesicles

Small glands that lie behind the bladder and secrete fluids that combine with sperm in the ejaculatory ducts.

Ejaculatory duct

A duct formed by the convergence of a vas deferens with a seminal vesicle through which sperm pass through the prostate gland and into the urethra.

Belgian researchers have discovered that sperm cells possess the same kind of receptors that the nose uses to sense odors (Angier, 1992). This discovery suggests that sperm may find their way to an egg cell by detecting its scent. Researchers at the Texas Southwestern Medical Center in Dallas had earlier discovered that fertile egg cells emit a compound that attracts the interest of sperm cells. Scientists speculate that these odor receptors may be the mechanism by which sperm recognize these attractants. Yet more research is needed to determine whether the receptors identified on the sperm cell do in fact function in this way. If this turns out to be the case, it could potentially lead to new contraceptives that might prevent fertilization by blocking these receptors.

Following their manufacture in the seminiferous tubules, sperm proceed through an intricate maze of ducts that converge in a single tube called the **epididymis.** The epididymis lies against the back wall of the testicle and serves as a storage facility for sperm. The epididymis, which is some 2 inches in length, consists of twisted passages that would be 10 to 20 feet in length if stretched end to end. Sperm are inactive when they enter the epididymis. They continue to mature as they slowly make their way through the epididymis for another two to four weeks.

THE VAS DEFERENS

Each epididymis empties into a vas deferens (also called *ductus deferens*), a thin, cylindrical tube about 16 inches long that serves as a conduit for mature sperm. In the scrotum, the vas deferens lies near the skin surface within the spermatic cord. Therefore, a **vasectomy,** an operation in which the right and left vas deferens are severed, is a convenient means of sterilization. The tube leaves the scrotum, follows a circuitous path up into the abdominal cavity, then loops back along the rear surface of the bladder (Figure 4.5).

THE SEMINAL VESICLES

The two **seminal vesicles** are small glands, each about two inches long. They lie behind the bladder and open into the **ejaculatory ducts** where the fluids they secrete combine with sperm (see Figure 4.6). A vesicle is a small cavity or sac; the seminal vesicles were so named because they were mistakenly believed to be reservoirs for semen, rather than glands.

The fluid produced by the seminal vesicles is rich in **fructose,** a form of sugar, which nourishes sperm and helps them become active, or motile. Sperm motility is a major factor in male fertility. Before reaching the ejaculatory ducts, sperm are propelled along their journey by contractions of the epididymis and vas deferens and by **cilia** that line the walls of the vas deferens. Once they become motile, they propel themselves by whipping their tails.

At the base of the bladder, each vas deferens joins a seminal vesicle to form a short ejaculatory duct that runs through the middle of the prostate gland (Figure 4.6). In the

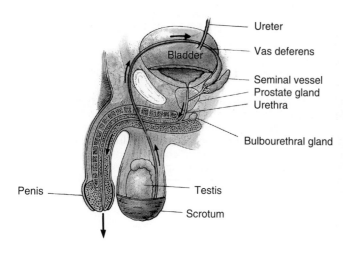

Ureter
Vas deferens
Bladder
Seminal vessel
Prostate gland
Urethra
Bulbourethral gland
Penis
Testis
Scrotum

Learning Objective 6: Trace the route of the sperm as they leave the testes and combine with the several glandular fluids that form semen.

FIGURE 4.6 **Passage of Spermatozoa.** Each testicle is divided into lobes that contain seminiferous tubules. Through spermatogenesis, these threadlike tubules produce and store hundreds of billions of sperm through the course of a lifetime. During ejaculation, sperm cells travel through the vas deferens, up and over the bladder, into the ejaculatory duct, and then through the urethra. Secretions from the seminal vesicles and the bulbourethral glands join with sperm to compose semen.

Fructose
A form of sugar found in seminal fluid; its purpose is to nourish the sperm. Fructose is also present in sweet fruits and honey.

Cilia
Hairlike projections from cells that beat rhythmically to produce locomotion or currents.

Ejaculatory duct
A duct formed by the convergence of a vas deferens with a seminal vesicle through which sperm pass through the prostate gland and into the urethra.

Prostate gland
The gland that lies beneath the bladder and secretes prostatic fluid, which gives semen its characteristic odor and texture.

Cowper's glands
Structures that lie below the prostate and empty their secretions into the urethra during sexual arousal.

Bulbourethral glands
Another term for *Cowper's glands.*

Semen
The whitish fluid that constitutes the ejaculate, consisting of sperm and secretions from the seminal vesicles, prostate, and Cowper's glands.

prostate the ejaculatory duct opens into the urethra, which leads to the tip of the penis. The urethra carries sperm and urine out through the penis, but normally not at the same time.

THE PROSTATE GLAND

The **prostate gland** lies beneath the bladder and approximates a chestnut in shape and size (about ³/4 inch in diameter). Note the spelling of the name of the gland—pros*tate,* not pros*trate.* (*Prostrate* means lying with one's face on the ground, as in some forms of prayer.) The prostate gland contains muscle fibers and glandular tissue that secrete prostatic fluid. Prostatic fluid is milky and alkaline. It provides the characteristic texture and odor of the seminal fluid. The alkalinity neutralizes some of the acidity of the vaginal tract, prolonging the life span of sperm as seminal fluid spreads through the female reproductive system. The prostate is continually active in mature males, but sexual arousal further stimulates secretions. Secretions are conveyed into the urethra by a sievelike duct system. There the secretions combine with sperm and fluid from the seminal vesicles.

A vasectomy prevents sperm from reaching the urethra but does not cut off fluids from the seminal vesicles or prostate gland. A man who has had a vasectomy thus emits an ejaculate that appears normal but contains no sperm.

COWPER'S GLANDS

The **Cowper's glands** are also known as the **bulbourethral glands,** in recognition of their shape and location. These two structures lie below the prostate and empty their secretions into the urethra. During sexual arousal they secrete a drop or so of clear, slippery fluid that appears at the urethral opening. The functions of this fluid are not entirely understood. It may help buffer the acidity of the male's urethra and lubricate the urethral passageway to ease the passage of seminal fluid. The fluid is not produced in sufficient amounts to play a significant role in lubricating the vagina during intercourse.

Fluid from the Cowper's glands precedes the ejaculate and often contains viable sperm. Thus, coitus may lead to pregnancy even if the penis is withdrawn prior to ejaculation. This is one reason why people who practice the "withdrawal method" of birth control are frequently called "parents."

SEMEN

Sperm and the fluids contributed by the seminal vesicles, the prostate gland, and the Cowper's glands make up **semen,** or whitish seminal fluid, which is expelled through the tip of the penis during ejaculation. The seminal vesicles secrete about 70 percent of the fluid that constitutes the ejaculate (Eliasson & Lindholmer, 1976; Spring-Mills & Hafez, 1980). The remaining 30 percent of seminal fluid consists of sperm and fluids produced by the prostate gland and the Cowper's glands. Sperm themselves account for only about 1 percent of the volume of semen. This is why men with vasectomies continue to ejaculate about as much semen as before, although their ejaculates are devoid of sperm.

Semen is the medium that carries sperm through much of the male's reproductive system and the reproductive tract of the female. Semen contains water, mucus, sugar (fructose), acids, and bases. It activates and nourishes sperm and the bases help shield sperm from vaginal acidity. The typical ejaculate contains between 200 and 400 million sperm and ranges between 3 and 5 milliliters in volume. (Five milliliters is equal to about one tablespoon.) The quantity of semen decreases with age and frequency of ejaculation.

DISEASES OF THE UROGENITAL SYSTEM

Because the organs that comprise the urinary and reproductive systems are near each other and share some "piping," they are referred to as the urinogenital or urogenital system. A number of diseases affect the urogenital system. The type of physician who specializes in their diagnosis and treatment is a **urologist**.

URETHRITIS

Men, like women, are subject to bladder and urethral inflammations, which are generally referred to as **urethritis.** The symptoms include frequent urination (urinary frequency), a strong need to urinate (urinary urgency), burning during urination, and a penile discharge. People with symptoms of urinary frequency and urinary urgency feel the pressing need to urinate repeatedly, even though they may have just done so and may have but another drop or two to expel. The discharge may dry on the urethral opening, in which case it may have to be peeled off or wiped away before it is possible to urinate. The urethra also may become constricted when it is inflamed, slowing or halting urination. It is a frightening sensation for a male to feel the urine rush from his bladder and then suddenly stop at the urethral opening!

Preventive measures for urethritis parallel those suggested for cystitis (bladder infection): drinking more water, drinking cranberry juice (four ounces, two or three times a day), and lowering intake of alcohol and caffeine. Cranberry juice is highly acidic, and acid tends to eliminate many of the bacteria that can give rise to urethritis.

CANCER OF THE TESTES

Cancer of the testicles remains a relatively rare form of cancer, accounting for about 6,000 new cases annually, or about 1 percent of all new cancers in men (American Cancer Society, 1991). It is the most common form of solid tumor cancer to strike men between the ages of 20 and 34, however (Vazi et al., 1989). It accounts for nearly 10 percent of all deaths from cancer among men in that age group.

There is no evidence that testicular cancer results from sexual overactivity or masturbation. Men who had **cryptorchidism** as children (a condition in which one or two testicles fails to descend from the abdomen into the scrotum) stand about a 40 times greater chance of contracting testicular cancer. Undescended testicles appear to occur more commonly in boys born to mothers who used the hormone diethylstilbestrol (DES) during pregnancy (Gill et al., 1977). In the 1940s and 1950s, pregnant women were often prescribed DES to help prevent miscarriages.

Although testicular cancer was generally fatal in earlier years, the prognosis today is quite favorable, especially for cases that are detected early. Treatments include surgical removal of the diseased testis, radiation, and chemotherapy. The survival rate among cases that are detected early, before the cancer has spread beyond the testis, is 96 percent

Discussion Question:
What is the link between the Cowper's glands and the possible failure of the withdrawal method as a means of birth control? (Many young people choose withdrawal as a means of birth control because they believe that this method will be effective if they are careful to withdraw the penis before ejaculation.)

Urologist
A physician who specializes in the diagnosis and treatment of diseases of the urogenital system.

Urethritis
An inflammation of the bladder or urethra.

Learning Objective 7:
Discuss the incidence, symptoms, treatments, and survival rates associated with testicular cancer.

Cryptorchidism
An abnormal condition in which one of two testicles fails to descend from the abdomen into the scrotum.

A CLOSER LOOK

Testicular Self-Examination

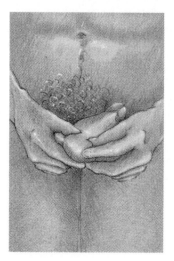

FIGURE 4.7 **Testicular Self-Examination.**

Self-examination (Figure 4.7) is best performed shortly after a warm shower or bath, when the skin of the scrotum is most relaxed. The man should examine the scrotum for evidence of pea-sized lumps. Each testicle can be rolled gently between the thumb and the fingers. Lumps are generally found on the side or front of the testicle. The presence of a lump is not necessarily a sign of cancer, but it should be promptly reported to a physician for further evaluation. The American Cancer Society (1990) lists these warning signals:

1. A slight enlargement of one of the testicles.

2. A change in the consistency of a testicle.
3. A dull ache in the lower abdomen or groin. (Pain may be absent in cancer of the testes, however.)
4. Sensation of dragging and heaviness in a testicle.

Learning Objective 8: Describe the testicular self-examination procedure and the importance of self-exams and regular medical checkups for early detection of testicular and prostate cancer.

Discussion Question: How would you react if you received a diagnosis of testicular cancer? If your brother, boyfriend, or husband received this diagnosis? How could you be supportive to a man who has had a testicle removed? (Remember that testicular cancer is the most common solid-tumor cancer in men ages 20 to 34.)

(American Cancer Society, 1991). Delayed treatment markedly reduces the chances of survival, however, because survival is connected with the extent to which the cancer has spread.

The surgical removal of a testicle may have profound psychological implications. Some men who have lost a testicle feel less "manly." Fears related to sexual performance can engender sexual dysfunctions. From a physiological standpoint, sexual functioning should remain unimpaired, as adequate quantities of testosterone are produced by the remaining testis.

The early stages of testicular cancer usually produce no symptoms, other than the mass itself. Because early detection is crucial to survival, men are advised to examine themselves each month once they undergo puberty (Reinisch, 1990) and to go for regular medical checkups. Self-examination may also reveal evidence of sexually transmitted diseases and other problems. Unfortunately, fewer than 10 percent of the male college students sampled in one study reported regularly examining their genitals (Goldenring & Purtell, 1984).

DISORDERS OF THE PROSTATE

Learning Objective 9: Identify the disorders of the prostate and their symptoms and treatments.

The prostate gland is tiny at birth and grows rapidly at puberty. It may shrink during adulthood, but generally becomes enlarged in almost all men past the age of 50. Hormonal changes associated with aging have been implicated in enlargement of the prostate, but there may also be other causes, such as inflammation resulting from sexually transmitted diseases.

ENLARGEMENT OF THE PROSTATE The prostate surrounds the upper part of the urethra (see Figure 4.2). As the prostate enlarges, it constricts the urethra, causing such

118   *CHAPTER 4   MALE SEXUAL ANATOMY AND PHYSIOLOGY*

symptoms as urinary frequency (including increased frequency of nocturnal urination), urinary urgency, and difficulty starting the flow of urine. Surgical removal of a part of the prostate can help relieve the pressure on the urethra, and is considered more or less routine. Many nonsurgical treatments are also under development, including chemotherapy and use of microwave radiation.

CANCER OF THE PROSTATE   A more serious and life-threatening problem is prostate cancer. The American Cancer Society estimates that about one man in eight in the United States will develop prostate cancer (Ochs, 1993b). Prostate cancer is the second most common form of cancer among men, after skin cancer, and the second leading cause of cancer deaths in men, after lung cancer. According to the National Cancer Institute, 165,000 men in the United States are diagnosed with prostate cancer each year, and 35,000 die from the disease (Kolata, 1993g). Deaths due to prostate cancer in the United States have increased 17 percent over the past three decades (Brody, 1993g).

Prostate Test. A blood test is now available that assists in the early detection of prostate cancer.

 Prostrate Support Group

African-American men are more likely than white men to develop the disease. The lifetime probability of developing prostate cancer is estimated to be 9.6 percent for African-American men in the United States, as compared to 5.2 percent for white men (American Cancer Society, 1987). African-American men may also have less access to routine medical evaluations than white men and so may be diagnosed at a later stage in the disease. Researchers have identified intake of animal fat as a potential risk factor. Men whose diets are rich in animal fats, especially fats from red meat, have a substantially higher chance of developing advanced prostate cancer than do men with a low intake of animal fat (Brody, 1993g).

Prostate cancer involves the growth of malignant prostate tumors that can metastasize to bones and lymph nodes if not detected and treated early. If prostate cancer is detected early, before it has metastasized, the five-year survival rate is 85 percent (American Cancer Society, 1991). The five-year survival rate drops to 29 percent, however, if the cancer has metastasized to distant sites in the body. The disease rarely strikes men under 40, but the risk of prostate cancer increases progressively after that age. Eighty percent of all cases occur in men over the age of 65 (American Cancer Society, 1991).

Treatment usually consists of surgical removal of the prostate gland. Years ago there was a notable risk of surgical complications from prostate removal, usually because of damage to the surrounding nerves. Problems in controlling the flow of urine or achieving erection or ejaculation often resulted. Surgical techniques that have been introduced in the past 15 years tend to spare the surrounding nerves and reduce, though not eliminate, the risk of complications.

The early symptoms of cancer of the prostate may mimic those of benign prostate enlargement, such as urinary frequency and difficulty urinating. Most cases, however, occur without noticeable symptoms in the early stages. Thus cancer is usually first suspected on the basis of a rectal examination, in which the physician inserts a finger into the rectum and feels for abnormalities in the prostate gland. The procedure may be uncomfortable, but it is brief and not particularly painful. When a cancerous growth is suspected, further tests can confirm the diagnosis.

Discussion Question: Were you as aware of the disorders of the male reproductive organs as you were of the disorders of the female reproductive organs? How do you account for the difference in your awareness? What role might male and female stereotypes play? Are men as likely as women to do self-exams and get regular medical exams of their reproductive organs?

A blood test has also been developed that can detect evidence of prostate cancer even among men whose prostates feel normal upon physical examination. A study of more than 10,000 men found that the blood test was about twice as successful in detecting early prostate cancer than were physical examinations (Catalona et al., 1993). The blood test measures prostate-specific antigen, or PSA, which is a type of protein that seeps out of the prostate gland when it is cancerous or enlarged ("Blood test's value in early prostate cases," 1993). Although early detection increases the chances of a cure, the blood test is not completely reliable. Many medical authorities thus recommend that men receive annual rectal examinations beginning at about age 40. Unfortunately, many men are reluctant to undergo a rectal examination, even though it is only mildly uncomfortable and may save their lives. Some are embarrassed or reluctant to discuss urinary problems with their physicians. Some may even resist the rectal examination because they associate rectal insertion with homosexual sex. Still others are fearful that they may indeed have cancer and choose to remain ignorant. Avoidance of, or ignorance of the need for, annual rectal exams among men is a major contributor to the death rate from prostate cancer.

PROSTATITIS   Many infectious agents can inflame the prostate, causing **prostatitis.** The chief symptoms are an ache or pain between the scrotum and anal opening and painful ejaculation. Prostatitis is usually treated with antibiotics. Although aspirin and ibuprofen may relieve the pain, men with these symptoms should consult a physician. Painful ejaculation may discourage masturbation or coitus, which is ironic, since regular flushing of the prostate through ejaculation may be helpful in the treatment of prostatitis.

MALE SEXUAL FUNCTIONS

At this point in the text, we have reviewed the external and internal sexual organs that comprise the male reproductive system. We have seen that sperm, the male germ cells that carry the father's inheritance, are manufactured and reach maturation in the testes.

This section describes the male sexual functions of erection and ejaculation—the means by which sperm travel from the male's reproductive tract to the female's. There, if luck and circumstances will have it, a sperm cell and an ovum will unite, and a new human being will be conceived. Of course the natural endowment of this process with sensations of pleasure helps ensure that it will take place whether or not any of these biological facts are known.

ERECTION

Erection

The enlargement and stiffening of the penis as a consequence of engorgement with blood.

Learning Objective 10: Describe the conditions under which erections can occur and explain why the process of erection is a spinal reflex.

Erection is the process by which the penis becomes engorged with blood, increases in size, and stiffens. When erect, the penis is an efficient conduit, or funnel, for depositing sperm deep within the vagina. In mechanical terms, the process of erection is a hydraulic event. The spongy, cavernous masses of the penis are equipped to hold blood. Filling these masses with blood causes them to enlarge, much like a kitchen sponge swells as it absorbs water. This simple description belies the fact that erection is a remarkable feat of biological engineering that involves the cooperation of the vascular (blood) system and the nervous system.

In a few moments—as quickly as 10 or 15 seconds—the penis can double in length, become firm, and shift from a funnel for passing urine to one that expels semen. Moreover, the bladder is closed off when the male becomes sexually aroused, decreasing the likelihood that semen and urine will mix.

Blood that fills the penis during sexual arousal causes erectile tissue to expand, but what accounts for the firmness of an erection? A sponge that fills with water expands but does not grow hard. It turns out that the two corpora cavernosa are surrounded by a tough, fibrous covering called the *tunica albuginea*. As the rubber of a balloon resists the pressure of pumped-in air, this housing resists expansion, causing the penis to rigidify (Gordon & Snyder, 1989). The corpus spongiosum, which contains the penile urethra, also engorges with blood during erection. It does not become hard, however, since it lacks the fibrous casing. The penile glans, which is formed by the crowning of the spongiosum at the tip of the penis, turns a dark purplish hue as it becomes engorged, but it too does not stiffen.

Despite the advanced state of biological knowledge, some mechanics of erection are not completely understood. It is not entirely clear, for example, whether penile cavities become engorged because the veins that carry blood away from the penis do not keep pace with the rapid flow of blood entering the penis, or whether the returning blood flow is reduced by compression of the veins at the base of the penis (as stepping lightly on a hose slows the movement of water).

We do know that erection is reversed when more blood flows out of the erectile tissue than flows in, restoring the pre-erectile circulatory balance and shrinking the erectile tissue or spongy masses. The erectile tissue thus exerts less pressure against the fibrous covering, resulting in a loss of rigidity. Loss of erection occurs when sexual stimulation

Performance anxiety
Feelings of dread and foreboding experienced in connection with sexual activity (or any other activity that might be judged by another person).

ceases, or when the body returns to a (sexual) resting state following orgasm. Loss of erection can also occur in response to anxiety or perceived threats. Loss of erection in response to threat can be abrupt, as when a man in the "throes of passion" suddenly hears a suspicious noise in the adjoining room, suggestive of an intruder. Yet the "threats" that induce loss of erection are more likely to be psychological than physical. In our culture, men often measure their manhood by their sexual performance. A man who fears that he will be unable to perform successfully may experience **performance anxiety** that can prevent him from achieving erection or lead to a sudden loss of erection at the moment of penetration or shortly afterwards.

The male capacity for erection quite literally spans the life cycle. Erections are common in babies, even within minutes after birth. Evidence from ultrasound studies shows that male fetuses may even have erections months prior to birth (Calderone, 1983; Masters, 1980). Men who are well into their eighties and nineties continue to experience erections and engage in coitus.

Nor are erections limited to the conscious state. Men have nocturnal erections every 90 minutes or so as they sleep, generally during a stage of sleep called REM (rapid eye movement) sleep. REM sleep is associated with dreaming (Karacan, 1970). REM sleep is so named because the sleeper's eyes dart about rapidly under the closed eyelids during this stage. Erections tend to occur in about 80 to 90 percent of REM periods (Dement, 1965; Fisher et al., 1965). When awakened during REM sleep, a person usually reports that he or she has been dreaming, even though the details of the dream may be lost to memory.

The mechanism of nocturnal erection appears to be physiologically based. Erections, that is, occur along with dreams that may or may not have erotic content. Morning erections are actually nocturnal erections. They occur when the man is awakened during REM sleep, as by an alarm clock. Men sometimes erroneously believe that a morning erection is caused by the need to urinate. When the man awakens with both an erection and the need to urinate, he may mistakenly assume that the erection was caused by the pressure of his bladder.

Morning erections reflect the need to urinate. *False. Morning erections are actually a form of nocturnal erection.* •

SPINAL REFLEXES AND SEXUAL RESPONSE

Men may become sexually aroused by a range of stimulation, including tactile stimulation provided by their partners, visual stimulation (such as from scanning photos of nude models in men's magazines), or even mental stimulation from engaging in sexual fantasies. Regardless of the source of stimulation, the man's sexual responses, erection and ejaculation, occur by **reflex.**

Reflex
A simple, unlearned response to a stimulus that is mediated by the spine rather than the brain.

Erection and ejaculation are reflexes: automatic, unlearned responses to sexual stimulation. So too are vaginal lubrication and orgasm in women. We do not control sexual reflexes voluntarily, as we might control the lifting of a finger or an arm. We can set the stage for them to occur by ensuring the proper stimulation. Once the stage is set, the reflexes are governed by automatic processes, not by conscious effort. Efforts to control sexual responses consciously by "force of will" can backfire and make it more difficult to become aroused (for example, to attain erection or vaginal lubrication). We need not "try" to become aroused. We need only expose ourselves to effective sexual stimulation and allow our reflexes to do the job for us.

Men can will themselves to have erections. *No, men* cannot *will erections. They can only set the stage for them by providing physical or cognitive sexual stimulation.* •

The reflexes governing erection and ejaculation are controlled at the level of the spinal cord. Thus, they are considered spinal reflexes. How does erection occur?

Erections may occur in response to different types of stimulation. Some erections occur from direct stimulation of the genitals, as from stroking, licking, or fondling the penis or scrotum. Erectile responses to such direct stimulation involve a simple spinal reflex that does not require the direct participation of the brain.

Erections can also be initiated by the brain, without the genitals being touched or fondled at all. Such erections may occur when a man has sexual fantasies, when he views erotic materials, or when he catches a glimpse of a woman in a bikini walking by on a beach. In the case of the "no-hands" type of erections, stimulation from the brain travels to the spinal cord, where the erectile reflex is triggered. To better understand how this reflex works, we need to first explain the concept of the reflex arc.

THE REFLEX ARC   When you withdraw your hand from a hot stove or blink in response to a puff of air, you do so before you have any time to think about it. These responses, like erection, are reflexes that involve sensory neurons and effector neurons (Figure 4.8). In response to a stimulus like a touch or a change in temperature, sensory neurons or receptors in the skin "fire" and thereby send messages to the spinal cord. The message is then transmitted to effector neurons that begin in the spinal cord and cause muscles to contract or glands to secrete chemical substances. So if you accidentally touched a hot stove, sensory neurons in your fingers or hand would propagate a message to the spinal cord, which would trigger effector neurons to contract muscles that pull your hand away from the stove. Notice that the brain does not control this spinal reflex arc. That is not to say that the brain fails to "get the message" shortly afterwards. Sensory messages usually rise from the spinal cord to the brain to make us aware of stimulation. (Awareness "dwells" within the nerve cells, or gray matter, of the brain.) The experience of pain occurs when a message travels from the site of the injury to the spinal cord, and then to receiving stations in the brain that "interpret" the message to produce the sensation of pain. The withdrawal of your hand from a harmful object begins before your brain even gets the message.

THE ROLE OF THE SPINAL CORD   Let us look more closely at the spinal reflex that produces erection in response to tactile stimulation (touch). Tactile stimulation of the penis or nearby areas (lower abdomen, scrotum, inner thighs) causes sensory neurons to

FIGURE 4.8 **Reflexes.** Reflexes involve sensory neurons, effector neurons, and, sometimes, interneurons that connect the two in the spinal cord. Reflexes need not involve the brain, although messages to the brain may make us aware when reflexes are occurring. Reflexes are the product of "local government" in the spine.

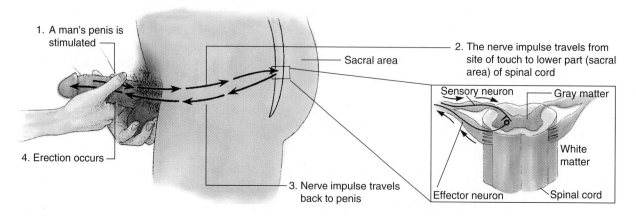

1. A man's penis is stimulated
2. The nerve impulse travels from site of touch to lower part (sacral area) of spinal cord
— Sacral area
Sensory neuron — Gray matter
4. Erection occurs
White matter
3. Nerve impulse travels back to penis
Effector neuron — Spinal cord

Source: From *Human Sexuality* by S. A. Rathus. Copyright © 1983 by Holt, Rinehart and Winston, Inc., reprinted by permission of the publisher.

Sacral
Of the sacrum—the thick, triangular bone located near the bottom of the spinal column.

Learning Objective 11:
Explain the effects of spinal cord injuries on erection and ejaculation.

Learning Objective 12:
Discuss the role of the brain and the autonomic nervous system in erection.

Notes: Although an inability to have an erection may result from psychological causes, men who persistently cannot get erections should be checked by a physician for biological causes. This is especially true for older men who have health problems or are taking medications.

transmit nerve messages (signals) to an erection center in the lower back, in an area of the spinal cord called the **sacrum.** The sacral erection center controls reflexive erections—that is, erections occurring in response to direct stimulation of the penis and nearby areas (Spark, 1991). When direct penile stimulation occurs, messages in the form of nerve impulses are received by this erection center, which in turn sends impulses to the genitalia via nerves that service the penis. These impulses cause arteries carrying blood to the corpora cavernosa and corpus spongiosum to dilate, so that more blood flows into these tissues, and as these tissues expand, the penis becomes erect.

The existence of the sacral erection center makes it possible for men whose spinal cords have been injured or severed above the center to achieve erections (and ejaculate) in response to direct tactile stimulation of the penis. Erection occurs even though their injuries prevent nerve signals from reaching their brains. Because of the lack of communication between the genital organs and the brain, there are no sensations, no physical pleasure. Many spinal-injured men report that sex remains psychologically pleasurable and fulfilling nonetheless. They can observe the responses of their partners, and perhaps the brain fills in some sensations from memory or imagination.

THE ROLE OF THE BRAIN   If direct penile stimulation triggers erection at the spinal level, what is the role of the brain? Although it may seem that the penis sometimes has a mind of its own, the brain plays an important role in regulating sexual responses.

Tactile (touch) stimulation of the penis may trigger the erection reflex through a simple reflex arc in the spinal cord. Penile sensations are then normally relayed to the brain, which generally results in sensations of pleasure and perhaps in a decision to focus on erotic stimulation. The sight of one's partner, erotic fantasies, memories, and so forth can result in messages being sent by the brain through the spinal cord to the arteries servicing the penis, helping to maintain the erection.

The brain can also originate messages that trigger the erectile reflex. The "no-hands" type of erection can occur while recalling sexual memories, entertaining sexual fantasies, viewing erotic stimuli, or even while asleep. In such cases the brain plays a more direct role in the erectile response by transmitting nerve impulses to a second and higher erection center located in the upper back in the lumbar region of the spinal cord. This higher spinal erection center serves as a "switchboard" between the brain and the penis, allowing perceptual, cognitive, and emotional responses to make their contributions. When the nerve pathways between the brain and the upper spinal cord are blocked or severed, men cannot achieve "psychogenic erections"—that is, erections in response to mental stimulation alone.

The brain can also stifle sexual response. A man who is highly anxious about his sexual abilities may be unable to achieve an erection even with the most direct and intense penile stimulation. Or a man who believes that sexual pleasure is sinful or dirty may be filled with anxiety and guilt and be unable to achieve erection when he is sexually stimulated by his partner.

In some males, especially adolescents, the erectile reflex is so easily tripped that incidental rubbing of the genitals against his own undergarments, the sight of an attractive passerby, or a fleeting sexual fantasy produces erection. Spontaneous erections may occur under embarrassing circumstances, such as before classes change in junior or senior high school, or when walking on a public beach. In an effort to distract himself from erotic fantasies, and to allow an erection to subside, many a male adolescent in the classroom has desperately renewed his interest in his algebra or foreign language textbook before the bell has rung. (A well-placed towel may serve in a pinch on a public beach.)

As men mature they require more penile stimulation to achieve full erection. Partners of men in their thirties and forties need not feel that their attractiveness has waned if their lovers no longer have instant "no-hands" erections (Comfort, 1974) when they disrobe. It takes men longer to achieve erection as they age, and direct penile stimulation becomes a more critical source of arousal.

THE ROLE OF THE AUTONOMIC NERVOUS SYSTEM   Although stimulation that brings about an erection can originate in the brain, this does not mean that erection is a voluntary response, like raising your arm. Whatever the original or dominant source of stimulation—direct penile stimulation or sexual fantasy—erection remains an unlearned, automatic reflex.

Automatic responses, such as erection, involve the division of the nervous system called the **autonomic nervous system** (ANS). *Autonomic* means "automatic." The ANS controls automatic bodily processes such as heartbeat, pupil dilation, respiration, and digestion. In contrast, voluntary movement (like raising an arm) is under the control of the *somatic* division of the nervous system.

The ANS has two branches, the **sympathetic** and the **parasympathetic.** These branches have largely opposing effects; when they are activated at the same time, their effects become balanced out to some degree. In general, the sympathetic branch is in command during processes that involve a release of bodily energy from stored reserves, such as during running, performing some other athletic task, or being gripped by fear or anxiety. The sympathetic branch also governs the general mobilization of the body, such as by increasing the heart rate and respiration rate in response to threat.

The parasympathetic branch is most active during processes that restore reserves of energy, such as digestion. When we experience fear or anxiety, the sympathetic branch of the ANS quickens the heart rate. When we relax, the parasympathetic branch curbs the heart rate. The parasympathetic branch activates digestive processes, but the sympathetic branch inhibits digestive activity. Since the sympathetic branch is in command when we feel fear or anxiety, fear or anxiety can inhibit the activity of the parasympathetic system, thereby slowing down digestive process and possibly causing indigestion.

The divisions of the autonomic nervous system play different roles in sexual arousal and response. The nerves that cause penile arteries to dilate during erection belong to the parasympathetic branch of the autonomic nervous system. It is thus the parasympathetic system that largely governs erection. The nerves governing ejaculation belong to the sympathetic branch, however. One implication of this division of neural responsibility is that intense fear or anxiety, which involves sympathetic nervous system activity, may inhibit erection by counteracting the activity of the parasympathetic nervous system. Since sympathetic arousal is involved in triggering the ejaculatory reflex, anxiety or fear may also accelerate ejaculation, causing premature ejaculation. Intense emotions like fear and anxiety can thus lead to problems in achieving or maintaining erection as well as causing hasty ejaculation.

The connection between the emotions, sympathetic activity, and ejaculation can set up a vicious cycle. Anxiety in a sexual encounter may trigger premature ejaculation. During a subsequent sexual encounter, the man might fear a recurrence of premature ejaculation. This fear may engender the reality. He may thus face further sexual encounters with yet greater fear, possibly further hastening ejaculation—and possibly inhibiting erection itself. Methods for helping men with erectile dysfunction and premature ejaculation aim at reducing their levels of anxiety and thereby lessening sympathetic activity.

Because erections seem spontaneous at times, and often occur when the man would rather not have them, it may seem to men that the penis has a mind of its own. Despite this common folk belief, however, the penis possesses no guiding intelligence. It consists of spongy masses of erectile tissue, not the lovely dense gray matter that renders your thought processes so incisive.

TRUTH OR *FICTION?*

R E V I S I T E D

The penis has a mind of its own. *False. Although it may seem that the penis follows its own mind at times, it is governed by the autonomic (automatic) nervous system.* •

ERECTILE ABNORMALITIES   Some men find that their erect penises are slightly curved or bent. Some degree of curvature is perfectly normal, but men with **Peyronie's**

disease have excessive curvature that can make erections painful or make it difficult to enjoy coitus (Carrera, 1981). The condition is caused by buildup of fibrous tissue in the penile shaft. Although some cases of Peyronie's disease appear to clear up on their own, most require medical attention.

Some men experience erections that persist for hours or days. This condition is called *priapism,* after Priapus of Greek myth, the son of Dionysus and Aphrodite who personified male procreative power. Priapism is often caused by leukemia, sickle cell anemia, or diseases of the spinal cord, although in some cases the cause remains unknown (Carrera, 1981). Priapism occurs when the mechanisms that drain the blood that erects the penis are damaged and so cannot return the blood to the circulatory system. The name of the disorder is truly a misnomer, because Priapus had a voracious sexual appetite. Men with priapism, instead, suffer from a painful condition that should receive medical attention. Priapism may become a medical emergency since prolonged erection beyond six hours can starve penile tissues of oxygen, leading to tissue deterioration. Immediate medical intervention in the form of drugs or even surgery may be required to reverse the condition and allow blood to drain from the penis (Spark, 1991).

EJACULATION

Ejaculation, like erection, is a spinal reflex. It is triggered when sexual stimulation reaches a critical point or threshold. Ejaculation generally occurs together with **orgasm,** the sudden muscle contractions that occur at the peak of sexual excitement and result in the abrupt release of sexual tension that had built up during sexual arousal. Orgasm is accompanied by subjective sensations that are generally intensely pleasurable. Ejaculation, however, refers only to the expulsion of semen from the tip of the penis. Orgasm and ejaculation are *not* synonymous, however; nor do they always occur simultaneously. For example, **paraplegics** can ejaculate if the area of the lower spinal cord that controls ejaculation is intact. They do not experience the subjective aspects of orgasm, however, since the sensations of orgasm do not reach the brain.

Many men paralyzed below the waist can attain erection, engage in sexual intercourse, and ejaculate. Yes, men who are paralyzed below the waist can indeed attain erections, engage in sexual intercourse, and ejaculate, if the spinal centers controlling erection and ejaculation remain intact. •

Conversely, prepubertal boys may experience orgasms even though they emit no ejaculate. Orgasms without ejaculate are termed "dry orgasms." Boys do not begin to produce seminal fluid (and sperm) until puberty. Mature men, too, can experience dry orgasms. They can take the form of "little orgasms" preceding a larger orgasm, or they can follow "wet orgasms" when sexual stimulation is continued but seminal fluids have not been replenished. These dry orgasms are perfectly normal. Dry orgasms can also be a result of retrograde ejaculation, however, as we shall see below.

Men can have orgasms without ejaculating. Yes, such orgasms are termed dry orgasms. •

Ejaculation occurs in two stages. The first phase, often called the **emission phase,** involves contractions of the prostate, seminal vesicles, and the upper part of the vas deferens (the **ampulla**). The force of these contractions propels seminal fluid into the prostatic part of the urethral tract—a small tube called the **urethral bulb**—which balloons out as muscles close at either end, trapping the semen. It is at this point that the man perceives that orgasm is inevitable. Masters and Johnson term this feeling a sense of "ejaculatory inevitability" (Masters & Johnson, 1966). Men might colloquially describe the

Urethral bulb
The small tube that makes up the prostatic part of the urethral tract and that balloons out as muscles close at either end, trapping semen prior to ejaculation.

Expulsion stage
The second stage of ejaculation, during which muscles at the base of the penis and elsewhere contract rhythmically, forcibly expelling semen and providing pleasurable sensations.

feeling as being about to "come." The man feels that a point of no return has been passed, that nothing can prevent ejaculation, perhaps not even a "lightning bolt shepherded by angels."

The second stage, which is often referred to as the **expulsion stage,** involves the propulsion of the seminal fluid through the urethra and out of the urethral opening at the tip of the penis. In this stage, muscles at the base of the penis and elsewhere contract rhythmically, forcefully expelling semen. The second stage is generally accompanied by the highly pleasurable sensations of orgasm.

In ejaculation, the seminal fluid is released from the urethral bulb and expelled by forceful contractions of the pelvic muscles that surround the urethral channel and the crura of the penis. The first few contractions are most intense and occur at 0.8-second intervals. Subsequent contractions lessen in intensity and the interval between them gradually increases. Seminal fluid is expelled in spurts during the first few contractions. The contractions are so powerful that seminal fluid may be propelled to distances of 12 to 24 inches, according to observations made by Masters and Johnson. Some men, however, report that semen travels but a few inches or just oozes from the penile opening. The force of the expulsion varies with the condition of the man's prostate, his general health, and his age. There is some correspondence between the force of the expulsion and the pleasure of orgasm. That is, more intense orgasms, psychologically speaking, often accompany more forceful ejaculations.

Like erection, ejaculation is regulated by two centers in the spinal cord, one in the sacral region and one in the higher lumbar region. When sexual arousal rises to a critical level—the point of ejaculatory inevitability—the lumbar ejaculatory center triggers the first stage of ejaculation, seminal emission. The lower, or sacral, ejaculatory center triggers the second stage of orgasm: the rhythmic muscle contractions that expel the ejaculate from the body.

Although ejaculation occurs by reflex, a man can delay ejaculation by maintaining the level of sexual stimulation below the critical threshold, or "point of no return." Men who suffer from premature ejaculation have been successfully treated in programs that train them to learn to recognize their "point of no return" and maintain sexual stimulation below it. (Issues concerning the definition and treatment of premature ejaculation are explored in Chapter 15 on sexual dysfunction.) Recognizing the point of no return and keeping stimulation beneath the critical level can also prolong coitus and enhance sexual pleasure for couples even when the man does not experience premature ejaculation.

Retrograde ejaculation
Ejaculation in which the ejaculate empties into the bladder. (From the Latin *retrogradi,* meaning "to go backward.")

RETROGRADE EJACULATION   Some men experience **retrograde ejaculation,** in which the ejaculate empties into the bladder rather than being expelled from the body. During normal ejaculation an external sphincter opens, allowing seminal fluid to pass out of the body. Another sphincter, this one internal, closes off the opening to the bladder, preventing the seminal fluid from backing up into the bladder. In retrograde ejaculation, the actions of these sphincters are reversed. The external sphincter remains closed, preventing the expulsion of the seminal fluid, while the internal sphincter opens, allowing the ejaculate to empty into the bladder. The result is a dry orgasm. No ejaculate is apparent because semen has backed up into the bladder. Retrograde ejaculation condition may be caused by prostate surgery (much less so now than in former years), drugs such as tranquilizers, certain illnesses, and accidents. Retrograde ejaculation is usually harmless in itself, since the seminal fluid is later discharged with urine. Infertility can result, however, and there may be some changes in the sensations associated with orgasm. Persistent dry orgasms should be medically evaluated, since their underlying cause may be more of a threat to health.

Male sexual functions, like female sexual functions, are incredibly complex. They involve the cooperation of the nervous system, the endocrine system, the cardiovascular system, and the musculoskeletal system. In Chapter 5 we learn more about how the female and male sexual organs respond to sexual stimulation. In Chapter 6 we examine the similarities and differences between the genders with respect to sexual differentiation, behavior, and personality.

SUMMING UP

EXTERNAL SEXUAL ORGANS

The male external sexual organs include the penis and the scrotum.

The Penis Semen and urine pass out of the penis through the urethral opening. The penis contains cylinders that fill with blood and stiffen during sexual arousal. Circumcision—surgical removal of the prepuce—has been carried out for religious and hygienic reasons.

The Scrotum The scrotum is the pouch of loose skin that contains the testes. Each testicle is held in place by a spermatic cord, which contains the vas deferens and the cremaster muscle.

INTERNAL SEXUAL ORGANS

The male internal sexual organs consist of the testes, a system of tubes and ducts that conduct sperm, and organs that nourish and activate sperm.

The Testes The testes serve two functions analogous to those of the ovaries. They secrete male sex hormones (androgens) and produce germ cells (sperm). The hypothalamus, pituitary gland, and testes keep blood testosterone levels at a more or less constant level through a hormonal negative feedback loop. Testosterone is produced by interstitial cells. Sperm are produced by seminiferous tubules. Sperm are stored and mature in the epididymis.

The Vas Deferens Each epididymis empties into a vas deferens that conducts sperm over the bladder.

The Seminal Vesicles The seminal vesicles are glands that open into the ejaculatory ducts where the fluids they secrete combine with and nourish sperm.

The Prostate Gland The prostate gland secretes fluid that provides the characteristic texture and odor of semen.

Cowper's Glands During sexual arousal, the Cowper's glands secrete a drop or so of clear, slippery fluid that appears at the urethral opening.

Semen Sperm and the fluids contributed by the seminal vesicles, prostate gland, and Cowper's glands make up semen, the whitish fluid that is expelled through the tip of the penis during ejaculation.

DISEASES OF THE UROGENITAL SYSTEM

Urethritis Men, like women, are subject to bladder and urethral inflammations, generally referred to as urethritis.

Cancer of the Testes This common form of solid tumor cancer strikes men between the ages of 20 and 34.

Disorders of the Prostate The prostate gland generally becomes enlarged past the age of 50. Prostate cancer involves the growth of malignant prostate tumors that can metastasize to bones and lymph nodes. The chief symptoms of prostatitis are an ache or pain between the scrotum and anal opening and painful ejaculation.

MALE SEXUAL FUNCTIONS

Erection Erection is the process by which the penis becomes engorged with blood, increases in size, and stiffens in response to sexual stimulation often during REM sleep.

Spinal Reflexes and Sexual Response Erection and ejaculation occur by reflex. Reflexes involve sensory neurons and effector neurons, which meet in the spinal cord. There are two erection centers in the spinal cord. Although erection is a reflex, penile sensations are relayed to the brain, where they generally result in pleasure. Erection and ejaculation also involve the autonomic nervous system (ANS). The parasympathetic branch of the ANS largely governs erection, whereas the sympathetic branch largely controls ejaculation.

Ejaculation Ejaculation is a reflex, triggered when sexual stimulation reaches a critical threshold. Ejaculation usually but not always occurs with orgasm, but the terms are not synonymous. The emission phase of ejaculation involves contractions of the prostate, seminal vesicles, and the upper part of the vas deferens. In the expulsion stage, semen is propelled through the urethra and out of the penis. In this stage, muscles at the base of the penis and elsewhere contract rhythmically, forcibly expelling semen. There are two ejaculation centers in the spinal cord. In retrograde ejaculation, the ejaculate empties into the bladder rather than being expelled from the body.

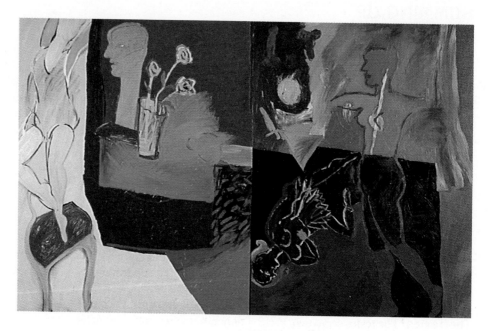

_____ The menstrual cycles of women who live together tend to become synchronized.

_____ The primary erogenous zone is the brain.

_____ "Spanish fly" will not turn your date on, but may cure his or her warts.

_____ Alcohol is a sexual stimulant.

_____ Electrical stimulation of certain areas in the human brain can yield sensations similar to those of sexual pleasure and gratification.

_____ Normal men produce estrogen, and normal women produce androgens.

_____ Written descriptions of men's and women's experiences during orgasm cannot be told apart.

_____ Orgasms attained through masturbation are more intense than those attained through coitus.

C H A P T E R   5

Sexual Arousal and Response

What turns you on? What springs your heart into your mouth, tightens your throat, and opens the floodgates into your genitals? The sight of your lover undressing, a photo of Mel Gibson or Julia Roberts, a sniff of some velvety perfume, a sip of wine?

Many factors contribute to sexual arousal. Some people are aroused by magazines with photographs of nude or seminude models that have been airbrushed to perfection. Some need only to imagine Hollywood's latest sex symbol. Others become aroused by remembrances of past lovers. Others are stimulated by sexual fantasies of flings with strangers.

People vary greatly in the cues that excite them sexually and in the frequency with which they experience sexual thoughts and feelings. Some young people seem perpetually aroused or arousable. For example, college students who are asked to press a wrist counter whenever they have a sexual thought, fantasy, or feeling may tally upwards of 300 a day (Goleman, 1988). Yet other people rarely or never entertain sexual thoughts or fantasies.

In this chapter we look at factors that contribute to sexual arousal and the processes that relate to sexual response. The word *look* is appropriate in this context, since visual cues are important determinants of sexual arousal. We consider the roles played by the other senses as well, especially the senses of touch and smell. We explore the ways in which alcohol and other drugs affect sexual response, and whether or not there is such a thing as a *true* aphrodisiac. We discuss the role of the brain and the nervous system in governing sexual response and describe how our bodies respond when we are sexually stimulated. You'll find that there is remarkable similarity between men and women in the bodily changes that signal sexual arousal. (Yes, there are some differences, too.)

Since our experience of the world is initiated by our senses, we begin the chapter by focusing on the role of the senses in sexual arousal.

MAKING SENSE OF SEX: THE ROLE OF THE SENSES IN SEXUAL AROUSAL

We come to apprehend the world around us through our senses—vision, hearing, smell, taste, and the skin senses, which include that all-important sense of touch. Each of the senses plays a role in our sexual experience, but some senses play larger roles than others.

VISION: THE BETTER TO SEE YOU WITH

Learning Objective 1: Describe the role of vision in sexual arousal.

It was the face of Helen of Troy, not her scent or her melodic voice, that "launched a thousand ships." Men's and women's magazines are filled with pictures of comely members of the opposite sex, not with "scratch and sniff" residues of their scents (but wait, a new marketing idea is dawning!).

In matters of sexual attraction, we humans appear to have more in common with birds than with fellow mammals such as dogs and cats. Birds identify prospective mates within their species on the basis of their plumage and other visual markings. People also tend to be visually oriented when it comes to sexual attraction. By contrast, dogs and cats are more attracted to each other on the basis of scents that signal sexual receptivity.

Visual Cues Can Be Sexual Turn-ons or Turn-offs. Despite cross-cultural differences in standards of physical attractiveness, a clear complexion is universally appealing.

Visual cues can be sexual turn-ons. We may be turned on by the sight of our lovers in the nude, disrobing, or dressed in evening wear. Lingerie companies hope to convince customers that they will enhance their sex appeal by wearing strategically concealing and revealing nightwear. Some couples find it arousing to observe themselves making love in an overhead mirror or on videotape. Some people find it arousing to view sexually explicit movies, whereas others are bored or offended by them. Though both genders can be sexually aroused by visually mediated erotica (a technical term for porn films) (Heiman, 1975; Rubinsky et al., 1987), men seem generally more interested in them (Symons, 1979).

SMELL: DOES THE NOSE KNOW BEST?

Although the sense of smell plays a lesser role in governing sexual arousal in humans than in lower mammals, odors can be sexual turn-ons or turn-offs. Perfume companies, for example, bottle fragrances purported to be sexually arousing.

Most Westerners prefer their lovers to be clean and fresh-smelling. Inclinations to find underarm or genital odors offensive may reflect cultural conditioning and not our biological predispositions. In some societies, genital secretions are considered to have potent **aphrodisiac** effects. By contrast, people in our society learn to neutralize or disguise such odors by the use of soaps, deodorants, and so on. There is some evidence, however, that natural body odors may have **subliminal,** instinctively arousing effects. This brings us to the topic of pheromones.

PHEROMONES: HAS SCIENCE FOUND A MAGIC POTION? Many organisms, from insects to reptiles to mammals, are sexually aroused by naturally produced chemicals called **pheromones** (Cobb & Jallon, 1990; Eggert & Muller, 1989; Goodwin et al., 1979; Mason et al., 1989). Animals may signal their sexual receptivity by secreting pheromones that are detected by other members of their species through the senses of smell or taste. Pheromones are commonly contained in vaginal secretions and in urine. Female dogs, for example, deposit drops of urine on the ground that serve as scent markings to signal sexual receptivity.

The sense of smell, which is considered a more primitive brain function, is more directly involved in controlling mating among the "lower" mammals such as mice, rats, dogs, and cats than among primates such as monkeys, chimps, and, most notably, humans. Among lower mammals, such as mice, exposure to male urine, which contains male pheromones, can induce estrus in the female (i.e., put her "in heat"). In many species of mammals, males will sniff or taste the female's genital secretions before

Learning Objective 2:
Describe the role of smell in sexual arousal and discuss the research on the influence of pheromones on human and other animal behavior.

Aphrodisiac
Any drug or other agent that is sexually arousing or increases sexual desire. (From *Aphrodite,* the Greek goddess of love and beauty.)

Subliminal
Below the threshold of conscious awareness.

Pheromones
Chemical substances secreted externally by certain animals, which convey information to, or produce specific responses in, other members of the same species. (From the Greek *pherien,* meaning "to bear [a message]" and *hormone.*)

mounting. We can induce male mice to attempt to mate with other males by placing urine from females, which contains pheromones, on the backs of the males (Connor, 1972). Male mice also show less sexual arousal when their sense of smell is blocked (Cooper, 1978). Vaginal secretions also arouse male monkeys (Michael et al., 1971), but monkeys seek to engage in coitus even when nose drops have blocked their sense of smell (Goldfoot et al., 1978).

What, then, of the effects of pheromones on humans? We do not know the extent to which these body chemicals may influence sexual attraction and behavior in humans. An early study showed that a chemical extract from human female vaginal secretions had sexually arousing effects on male monkeys (yes, male monkeys) (Michael et al., 1974). The production of these vaginal secretions tends to peak around the time of ovulation, when women are capable of conceiving. The effects of these vaginal secretions on men remain unclear, however.

A musky substance, *exaltolide,* is relatively highly concentrated in the urine of men. Its odor is more detectable by and more appealing to adult women than to children or other men (Hassett, 1978). Moreover, women are most sensitive to exaltolide around the time of ovulation. Morris and Udry (1978) ran an intriguing experiment with married couples in which women smeared various perfumes on their breasts at bedtime. One perfume contained substances thought to be human pheromones. The couples tracked their sexual behavior. One couple in five showed significantly more frequent sexual activity under the influence of the pheromone-laced perfume, though they were not informed as to when the substance was mixed in with the perfume the woman used. Pheromone-sensitive couples also engaged in coitus more frequently at the time of ovulation.

In other studies (Durden-Smith, 1980), subjects rated photos of men and women more attractive when a suspected pheromone was in the air. People also dallied significantly longer in pheromone-sprayed telephone booths. Although they could not consciously detect a suspected male pheromone, women subjects were more likely than men to sit on a waiting room chair that had been sprayed with the substance. Women were also more likely than men to sit in theater seats that had been sprayed with the substance. This particular substance, *alpha androstenol,* is extracted from men's sweat. You can find it on the shelves of certain sex shops (or on men's bodies in locker rooms).

MENSTRUAL SYNCHRONY   Research by several investigators suggests that exposure to other women's sweat can modify the menstrual cycle. In one study, women exposed to underarm secretions from other women, which may contain some as yet unidentified

Discussion Question: Would you agree to participate in Morris and Udry's (1978) study on "perfume"? In what way might knowing you were recording your sexual activity influence the frequency of your sexual activity? Would you record it accurately?

Discussion Question: How many of the female students have experienced the menstrual synchrony phenomenon? How long did the women live together before menstrual synchrony occurred? Did the amount of time they spent together seem to influence the synchrony?

Female Dorm. Researchers have observed that the menstrual cycles of women living together in dormitories often become synchronized. An unidentified pheromone contained in female body sweat may be responsible.

Eau de B.O.: The Ultimate Cologne?

Human sweat attracts mosquitoes, but does it also attract lovers? Fragrance manufacturers have marketed several products that are represented as having the powers of animal attraction. Some contain musky scents. One fragrance, Andron, was advertised to be "capable of triggering an intense magnetic reaction" in both men and women. It contained a synthetic compound that is chemically similar to a substance found in human perspiration. Another, simply called Pheromone, claimed to contain a similar extract.

The links between such substances and human sexuality remain uncertain. Though whiffs of passing joggers hardly arouse fulminating lust in most people, the effects of these natural odors on sexual behavior remain undetermined. Anecdotal evidence is hard to come by, since most people in our culture regularly wash such natural scents away. Moreover, since we are taught that body odors are offensive, we may learn to respond negatively to stimuli that might otherwise be arousing.

Our culture is not alone in washing away or disguising body odors. The ancient Egyptians invented the practice of scented bathing to rid themselves of offensive odors (Ramirez, 1990). The ancient Romans had such a passion for perfume that they would bathe in fragrances and even dab their horses and household pets (Ackerman, 1990).

Much remains to be learned about the role of smell in sexual attraction in humans. Perhaps the key factor in the effort to market perfumes as sexual attractants is this: what sells is sex, or at least the perception of sex appeal.

---

pheromones, showed converging shifts in their menstrual cycles (Preti et al., 1986). Similar synchronization of menstrual cycles has also been observed among women who share dormitory rooms (McClintock, 1971). In another study, 80 percent of the women who dabbed their upper lips with an extract of perspiration from other women began to menstruate in sync with the cycles of the donors after about three menstrual cycles (Cutler & Preti, 1986). A control group, who dabbed their lips with alcohol, showed no changes in their menstrual cycles. In yet another study from this research group, the length of the cycles of subjects with unusually short or long cycles began to normalize when they were exposed to an extract of *male* underarm perspiration (Preti et al., 1986).

In another study—one that stretches the limits of scientific decorum—bathroom stalls in men's and women's rest rooms were treated with a suspected pheromone, a musky-smelling substance found in the urine of both sexes but in greater concentrations in male urine (Gustavson et al., 1987). Half of the stalls were treated with the substance and the other half were treated with a control odor. The results showed that men avoided the stalls treated with the suspected pheromone; the control odor had no effect on men's stall selections. Neither odor affected the women's selection of stalls. Researchers suggest that the suspected pheromone may signal other males to keep a distance, much as the scent markings left by males of many other mammalian species discourage competing males from invading their personal space. Then again, research on the role of smell in human sexual behavior is still in its infancy and does not permit definite conclusions about the possible role of pheromones in regulating behavior or sexual attraction among humans. As you can see in the Closer Look feature above, the perfume industry has not ignored the prospects of pheromones.

The menstrual cycles of women who live together tend to become synchronized. *The menstrual cycles of women who live together do tend to become synchronized, probably in response to pheromones.* •

THE SKIN SENSES: SEX AS A TOUCHING EXPERIENCE

We have three major skin senses; they enable us to sense pain, changes in temperature, and pressure (or touch). Whatever the roles of vision and smell in sexual attraction and arousal, the sense of touch has the most direct effects on sexual arousal and response. Any region of that sensitive layer we refer to as skin can become eroticized. The touch of your lover's hand upon your cheek, or your lover's gentle massage of your shoulders or back, can be sexually stimulating. Certain parts of the body have special sexual significance because of their response to erotic stimulation. These areas are termed erogenous zones.

EROGENOUS ZONES **Erogenous zones** are parts of the body that are especially sensitive to tactile sexual stimulation—to strokes and other caresses. **Primary erogenous zones** are erotically sensitive because they are richly endowed with nerve endings. **Secondary erogenous zones** are parts of the body that become erotically sensitized through experience.

Primary erogenous zones include the genitals; the inner thighs, perineum, buttocks, and anus; the breasts (especially the nipples); the ears (particularly the earlobes); the mouth, lips, and tongue; the neck; the navel; and, yes, the armpits. Preferences vary somewhat from person to person, reflecting possible biological, attitudinal, and experiential differences. Areas that are exquisitely sensitive for some people may produce virtually no reaction, or even discomfort, in others. Many women, for example, report little sensation when their breasts are stroked or kissed, and many men are uncomfortable when their nipples are caressed. On the other hand (or foot), many people find the areas between their toes sensitive to erotic stimulation and enjoy keeping a toehold on their partners during coitus.

Secondary erogenous zones become eroticized through association with sexual stimulation, as by being touched regularly when one has sexual fantasies or engages in sexual relations. For example, a woman might become sexually aroused when her lover gently caresses her shoulders, because such caresses have been incorporated as a regular feature of the couple's lovemaking. A few of the women observed by Masters and Johnson (1966) reached orgasm when the smalls of their backs were rubbed.

People are also highly responsive to images and fantasies—which is why the brain is sometimes referred to as the primary sexual organ or an erogenous zone. Some women report reaching orgasm through fantasy alone (Heiman, 1975; Kinsey et al., 1953). Men regularly experience erection and nocturnal emissions ("wet dreams") without direct stimulation of the genitals.

Ironically, the brain is not an erogenous zone. It is not stimulated directly by touch. (The brain processes tactile information from the skin, but does not have sensory neurons to directly gather this information itself.) However, etymology or word origins of the term *erogenous* clearly apply to the brain; it *can* give birth to erotic sensations through production of fantasy, erotic memories, and other thoughts.

Erogenous zones
Parts of the body that are especially sensitive to tactile sexual stimulation. (*Erogenous* is derived from roots meaning "giving birth to erotic sensations.")

Primary erogenous zones
Erogenous zones that are particularly sensitive because they are richly endowed with nerve endings.

Secondary erogenous zones
Parts of the body that become erotically sensitized through experience.

Learning Objective 3:
Define erogenous zones and identify their locations.

TRUTH OR FICTION?

R E V I S I T E D

The primary erogenous zone is the brain. No, the brain is not an erogenous zone in the strict sense of the term. Erogenous zones are directly sensitive to touch. The brain, however, processes information received through erogenous zones and can have such an impact on sexual arousal that it has been dubbed an erogenous zone in recognition of its importance. •

Teaching Tip: Remind students that STDs can be transmitted during oral-genital contact. Unless both partners are HIV-negative, free of other STDs, and monogamous, they should use condoms during fellatio and dental dams during cunnilingus. (Condoms now come in a variety of flavors.)

TASTE: ON SAVORY SEX

Taste appears to play a minor role in sexual arousal and response, unless we digress into puns and note that taste in the form of a zesty meal or a delicate wine may make its contribution to arousal. In any event, some people report that they are sexually aroused by the taste of genital secretions, such as vaginal secretions or seminal fluid. We do not know, however, whether these secretions are laced with chemicals that have biologically arousing effects, or whether arousal reflects the meaning that these secretions have to the individual. That is, we may learn to become aroused by, or to seek out, flavors or odors that have been associated with sexual pleasure.

Animals and their mating songs

HEARING: THE BETTER TO HEAR YOU WITH

Learning Objective 4:
Describe the roles of taste and hearing in sexual arousal.

Given the mushrooming of the telephone sex industry (see Chapter 20), it should come as no surprise that the sense of hearing provides an important medium for sexual arousal and response. Like visual and olfactory cues, sounds can be turn-ons or turn-offs. The sounds one's lover makes, whether whispers, soft indications of pleasure, or more animated sounds that may attend orgasm, may be arousing during the heat of passion. For some people, key words or vocal intonations may become as arousing as direct stimulation of an erogenous zone. Many people are aroused when their lovers "talk dirty" to them. To them, spoken vulgarities can unlock sexual arousal. Others find vulgar language offensive.

Words of love and "dirty talk" may be arousing, but it is the meaning of the words and not the sounds themselves that inspire a sexual response. The same words, uttered by the same voice but in an unfamiliar language, would be unlikely to elicit a sexual response.

Yet sounds themselves can be eroticized. The sultry voices of screen sirens Lauren Bacall and Kathleen Turner have aroused the ardor of many a moviegoer. Teenagers may shriek at the music of groups like Aerosmith or Pearl Jam, just as their parents (and grandparents) did when they heard the Beatles, Frank Sinatra, Johnny Mathis, or the King himself (Elvis, that is). Of course, the sex appeal of these performers goes beyond the sounds that they produce. The music itself can contribute to sexual arousal, perhaps because it relaxes us and helps put us "in the mood," and perhaps because of associations ("They're playing our song!"). Ravel's *Bolero* may stir us both through its pulsing, insistent rhythms and through its association with a sex scene in the movie *10*. Many couples find background music "atmospheric"—a vital accoutrement of lovemaking. Sounds can also be sexual turn-offs. Most of us would find funeral music a damper on sexual arousal. We may also be inhibited by scratchy, unnerving voices. Heavy metal rock might be a sexual turn-off to many (are your authors showing their age?), but it could help set the right tone for others.

APHRODISIACS: OF SPANISH FLIES AND RHINO HORNS

Learning Objective 5:
Summarize the research on substances that have aphrodisiac or anaphrodisiac properties.

The only known aphrodisiac is variety.

(Marc Connolly)

An aphrodisiac is a substance that is sexually arousing or capable of increasing one's capacity for sexual pleasure or response. You may have heard of "Spanish fly," an alleged aphrodisiac once extracted from a Spanish beetle. (The beetle from which it was taken, *Lytta vesicatoria,* is near extinction.) A few drops in a date's drink was believed to make you irresistible. Spanish fly is but one of many purported aphrodisiacs. Spanish fly is toxic, however, not sexually arousing (Kaplan, 1974; Leavitt, 1974). Spanish fly is now synthesized—but not as an aphrodisiac. The active ingredient, *cantharidin,* is a skin irritant that can burn off warts (Diamond, 1981). If it can burn off warts, consider the damage it can do when taken internally. It irritates the urinary tract and can cause severe tissue damage or death. It inflames the urethra, producing a burning sensation in the penis, which is sometimes misinterpreted as sexual feelings.

We should also be concerned about an expectancy or placebo effect when evaluating the effectiveness of a purported aphrodisiac (Brody, 1993a). The belief that a substance has sexually stimulating effects may itself inspire sexual excitement. If a person tries a supposed aphrodisiac and feels sexually aroused, the person may well attribute the turn-on to the effects of the substance, even if the substance had no direct effect on sexual drive.

TRUTH OR *FICTION?*

R E V I S I T E D

"Spanish fly" will not turn your date on, but may cure his or her warts.
Spanish fly contains cantharidin, a skin irritant that can in fact burn off warts. Cantharidin is not an aphrodisiac, but it can inflame the urethra, producing a burning sensation that could be misinterpreted as sexual feelings. •

Foods that in some way resemble male genitals have now and then been considered aphrodisiacs. They include oysters, clams, bull's testicles ("prairie oysters"), tomatoes, and "phallic" items like celery stalks, bananas, and even ground-up rhinoceros, reindeer, and elephant horns (which is one derivation of the slang term "horny").

Even potatoes have been held to be aphrodisiacs. Yes, potatoes. McCary (1971) notes that when potatoes were first introduced to Europe, they were regarded as sexual stimulants. Shakespeare echoed this belief when he wrote, "Let the sky rain potatoes . . . ; let a tempest of provocation come." None of these foods or substances has been shown to be sexually stimulating, however, not even deep-fried potato skins with cheddar cheese and bacon. Sadly, myths about the sexually arousing properties of substances drawn from rhinoceri or elephants may be contributing to the rapidly diminishing numbers of these animals.

Other drugs and psychoactive substances may have certain effects on sexual arousal and response. The drug *yohimbine,* an extract from the African yohimbe tree, does stimulate blood flow to the genitals (Brody, 1993a). Although it appears to increase sexual arousal and performance in male rats (Davidson et al., 1984), researchers have failed to show similar aphrodisiac effects of the drug on men (Buffum, 1985). Yohimbine also has serious toxic side effects (Brody, 1993a).

Amyl nitrate (in the form of "snappers" or "poppers") has been used mostly by gay men (and by some heterosexuals) in the belief that it heightens sensations of arousal and orgasm (Everett, 1975). Poppers dilate blood vessels in the brain and genitals, producing sensations of warmth in the pelvis and possibly facilitating erection and prolonging orgasm. Amyl nitrate does have some legitimate medical uses, such as helping reduce heart pain (angina) among cardiac patients. Amyl nitrate is inhaled from ampules that "pop" open for rapid use when heart pain occurs. Poppers can cause dizziness, fainting, and migraine-type headaches, however, and should only be taken under a doctor's care for a legitimate medical need, not to intensify sexual sensations.

Certain drugs appear to have aphrodisiac effects by acting on the brain mechanisms controlling sexual drive. For example, drugs that affect brain receptors for the neuro-transmitter dopamine, such as the antidepressant drug *bupropion* (trade name Wellbutrin) and the drug L-dopa used in the treatment of Parkinson's disease, can increase sexual drive (Brody, 1993a).

The most potent chemical aphrodisiac may be a naturally occurring substance in the body, the male sex hormone testosterone. Evidence indicates that it is the basic fuel of sexual desire in both genders (Brody, 1993a). We shall have more to say about the role of testosterone in sexual arousal later in the chapter. Yet the safest and perhaps most effective method for increasing sexual drive is not a drug or substance, but a program of regular exercise. Researchers find that regular exercise, in addition to having health enhancing effects, boosts energy and increases sexual drive in both men and women (Brody, 1993a). Perhaps the most potent aphrodisiac of all is novelty, the invention of ever new ways of sexually discovering one another, which can involve making love in novel places, experimenting with different techniques, wearing sexually provocative clothing, sharing or enacting fantasies, or whatever the imaginations of lovers can inspire.

Some substances like potassium nitrate (saltpeter) have been considered inhibitors of sexual response, or **anaphrodisiacs.** Saltpeter, however, only indirectly dampens sexual arousal. As a diuretic that can increase the need for urination, it may make the thought of sex unappealing. It does not directly dampen sexual response, however.

Other chemicals do dampen sexual arousal and response. Tranquilizers and central nervous system depressants, such as barbiturates, can lessen sexual desire and impair sexual performance. These drugs may paradoxically enhance sexual arousal in some people, however, by lessening sexual inhibitions or fear of possible repercussions from sexual activity. Antihypertensive drugs, which are used in the treatment of high blood pressure, may produce erectile and ejaculatory difficulties in men, and reduction of sexual desire in both genders. Certain antidepressant drugs, such as fluoxetine (brand name Prozac), amitriptyline (brand name Elavil), and imipramine (brand name Tofranil) appear to dampen sexual drive (Brody, 1993a; Meston & Gorzalka, 1992). Antidepressants may also impair erectile response and delay ejaculation in men and orgasmic responsiveness in women (Meston & Gorzalka, 1992). Nicotine, the active drug in tobacco smoke, constricts the blood vessels. Thus it can impede sexual arousal by reducing the capacity of the genitals to become engorged with blood. Chronic cigarette smoking can also reduce the blood levels of testosterone in men, which can in turn lessen sexual drive or motivation.

Antiandrogen drugs may have anaphrodisiac effects; they will be discussed in Chapters 18 and 19. Their effectiveness in modifying deviant behavior patterns such as sexual violence and sexual interest in children is questionable. Their use in "treating" rapists and child molesters also raises ethical and legal questions.

PSYCHOACTIVE DRUGS

Psychoactive drugs, such as alcohol and cocaine, are widely believed to have aphrodisiac effects. Yet, as we see in the following sections, their effects may reflect our expecta-

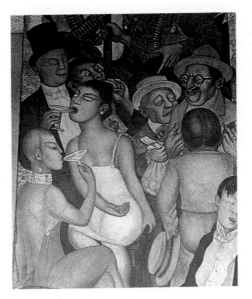

Is Alcohol a Sexual Stimulant? Despite folklore to the effect that alcohol provokes the sexual appetite, the biochemical effects of alcohol dampen sexual response. However, alcohol may stimulate sexual behavior because of the social expectations that people hold about alcohol use and because alcohol may impair one's ability to weigh the consequences of one's behavior.

tions of them, or their effects on sexual inhibitions, rather than direct stimulation of sexual response.

ALCOHOL: THE "GREAT PROVOKER OF THREE THINGS"

In Shakespeare's *Macbeth,* the following exchange takes place between Macduff and a porter:

> PORTER: Drink, sir, is a great provoker of three things.
>
> MACDUFF: What three things does drink especially provoke?
>
> PORTER: Marry,[1] sir, nose painting,[2] sleep, and urine. Lechery,[3] sir, it provokes and unprovokes; it provokes the desire, but takes away the performance.

The fact that alcohol curbs sexual response is not surprising since it is a depressant—a drug that reduces central nervous system activity. So it is logical that alcohol biochemically dampens sexual arousal. Ingestion of larger amounts of alcohol can severely impair sexual performance in both men and women.

Although alcohol may biochemically dampen sexual arousal and sexual response, people who drink moderate amounts of alcohol may feel more sexually aroused because of their expectations about alcohol, not because of its chemical properties. That is, people who expect alcohol to enhance sexual responsiveness may act the part. Expectations that alcohol serves as an aphrodisiac may lead men with problems achieving erection to turn to alcohol as a cure (Roehrich & Kinder, 1991). The fact is that alcohol is a depressant and can reduce sexual potency rather than restore it.

Alcohol may also lower sexual inhibitions, because it allows us to ascribe our behavior to the effects of the alcohol rather than to ourselves (Crowe & George, 1989; Lang, 1985). Alcohol is connected with a liberated social role and thus provides an external excuse for dubious behavior. "It was the alcohol," people can say, "not me." People may thus more readily express their sexual desires and perhaps do things when drinking that they would not do when sober. For example, a person who feels guilty about sex may become sexually active when drinking because he or she can later blame the alcohol.

Consider a survey of 1,100 undergraduates taken at the University of Virginia (Grossman, 1991). Forty-three percent of the respondents were classified as "heavy drinkers" on the basis of their statements that they had had at least five alcoholic beverages in a row on one occasion within the two weeks preceding the survey. *More than half* of the heavy drinkers reported that under the influence of alcohol, they had engaged in sexual activity with someone they would not ordinarily have become involved with. All in all, between 20 and 25 percent of the total sample had engaged in sexual activity they deemed unwise when "under the influence" of alcohol!

In laboratory studies, men who were misled into believing that they had drunk alcohol spent more time lingering over pornographic pictures as researchers looked on than did men who thought they had not. Did subjects believe that they would evade the (possible) censure of the onlookers because they could attribute their prurience to the alcohol? If so, perhaps alcohol provides an excuse for socially deviant behavior. The amount of time the subjects lingered over the pornographic material was unaffected by whether or not they had actually drunk alcohol (Lang et al., 1980; Lansky & Wilson, 1981).

Teaching Tip: Point out that the studies cited in the text address the issue of regretted or unwise, yet voluntary, sexual behavior. By reducing inhibitions and impairing the ability to weigh information and forsee consequences, alcohol consumption can lead to pressuring others or being pressured to engage in sexual behaviors.

TRUTH OR *FICTION?*

R E V I S I T E D

Alcohol is a sexual stimulant. *Chemically, alcohol actually depresses sexual response. Yet people may be more readily aroused after a drink or two because they* believe *that alcohol is arousing and because their inhibitions are lowered.* •

---

[1] Contraction of the expression "By the Virgin Mary"; used by Elizabethans like Shakespeare to speak emphatically yet avoid disrespect to the Virgin Mary.

[2] The reddening of the nose that occurs in many chronic alcoholics as a result of the bursting of small blood vessels.

[3] Excessive indulgence of sexual desire. (Related to the German *lecken,* meaning "to lick.")

Notes: "Candy is dandy, but liquor is quicker" is a line from the poem "Reflections on Ice-breaking" by Ogden Nash. Consider the messages it conveys about alcohol and sex.

Though alcohol is not sexually arousing, it can induce general feelings of euphoria, which may also help wash away qualms about expressing sexual desires. Alcohol also appears to impair the ability to weigh information ("information processing") that might otherwise inhibit sexual impulses (Hull et al., 1983; Steel & Southwick, 1985). When people drink, they may be less able to foresee the consequences of misconduct and are less likely to ponder their standards of conduct.

In sum, alcohol is viewed in our society as a stimulant of socializing, sexual activity, and aggression. People often live up to these expectations—even if the drug they have taken has chemically opposing effects.

HALLUCINOGENICS There is no evidence that marijuana and other hallucinogenic drugs directly stimulate sexual response. However, fairly to strongly intoxicated marijuana users claim to have more empathy with others, to be more aware of bodily sensations, and to experience time as passing more slowly when they are "high" (Tart, 1971). These sensations could heighten subjective feelings of sexual response. Some marijuana users report that the drug inhibits their sexual responsiveness, however (Wolman, 1985). The effects of the drug on sexual response may depend upon the individual's prior experiences with the drug, attitudes toward the drug, and the amount taken.

Other hallucinogenics, like LSD and mescaline, have also been reported by some users to enhance sexual response. Again, these effects may reflect dosage level, as well as expectations, user experiences, attitudes toward the drugs, and altered perceptions.

STIMULANTS Stimulants like amphetamines ("speed," "uppers," "bennies," "dexies") have been reputed to heighten arousal and sensations of orgasm. High doses can give rise to irritability, restlessness, hallucinations, paranoid delusions, insomnia, and loss of appetite. These drugs generally activate the central nervous system, but are not known to have specific sexual effects. However, they can elevate the mood, and perhaps sexual pleasure is heightened by general elation.

Cocaine is a natural stimulant that is extracted from the leaves of the coca plant—the plant from which the soft drink Coca-Cola obtained its name. In fact, Coke—Coca-Cola—contained cocaine as part of its original formula. (Cocaine was removed from the secret formula in 1906, but Coca-Cola is still flavored with an extract from the coca plant, one that does not have psychoactive effects.) Cocaine is ingested in various forms, snorted as a powder, smoked in hardened rock form ("crack" cocaine) or in a free-base form, or injected directly in liquid form. Cocaine produces a euphoric rush, which tends to ebb quickly. Physically, cocaine constricts blood vessels, reducing the oxygen supply to the heart, elevates the blood pressure, and accelerates the heart rate (Altman, 1988). There are scattered reports of respiratory and cardiovascular collapse resulting from cocaine use, as with the highly publicized deaths of athletes Len Bias, Dave Croudip, and Don Rogers.

Despite the popular belief that cocaine is an aphrodisiac, frequent use can lead to sexual dysfunctions, such as erectile disorder and failure to ejaculate among males, decreased vaginal lubrication in females, and decreased sexual interest in men and women (Weiss & Mirin, 1987). Some people do report initial increased sexual pleasure with cocaine use, however, an increase that may reflect cocaine's loosening of inhibitions. Over time, though, regular users may become dependent on cocaine for sexual arousal or lose the ability to enjoy sex for long periods of time (Weiss & Mirin, 1987).

Teaching Tip: A model of the brain that can be disassembled is helpful when explaining the locations of various parts of the cerebral cortex and the limbic system that are involved in sexual functioning.

SEXUAL RESPONSE AND THE BRAIN

The brain may not be an erogenous zone, but it plays a central role in sexual functioning. Direct genital stimulation may trigger spinal reflexes that produce erection in the male and vaginal lubrication in the female without the direct involvement of the brain. The same reflexes may also be triggered by sexual stimulation that originates in the brain in the form of erotic memories, fantasies, visual images, and thoughts, however. The brain may

Medulla

An oblong area of the hindbrain involved in regulation of heartbeat and respiration.

Pons

A structure of the hindbrain that regulates respiration, attention, sleep, and dreaming.

Cerebellum

A part of the hindbrain that governs muscle coordination and balance.

Reticular activating system

A part of the brain active during attention, sleep, and arousal.

Thalamus

An area near the center of the brain involved in the relay of sensory information to the cortex and in the functions of sleep and attention.

Hypothalamus

A brain structure below the thalamus that regulates body temperature, motivation, and emotion.

also inhibit sexual responsiveness, as when we experience guilt or anxiety in a sexual situation, or when we suddenly realize in the midst of a sexual encounter that we have left the car lights turned on. Let us explore the brain mechanisms involved in sexual functioning.

THE GEOGRAPHY OF THE BRAIN

The brain consists of three major parts, the hindbrain, the midbrain, and the forebrain (see Figure 5.1). The lower part of the brain, called the hindbrain, consists of the **medulla,** the **pons,** and the **cerebellum.** The medulla plays a role in regulating such vital functions as heart rate, respiration, and blood pressure. The pons relays information about body movement and plays a role in such states or functions as attention, sleep, and respiration. The cerebellum, which lies behind the pons, is involved in the regulation of balance and motor (muscle) behavior. Rising from the hindbrain is the **reticular activating system** or RAS, which plays a vital role in processes relating to attention, arousal, and sleep. The RAS passes through the midbrain into the forebrain.

Five important parts of the forebrain, or frontal part of the brain, are the **thalamus, hypothalamus, limbic system, basal ganglia,** and **cerebrum.** The thalamus, which lies in the center of the brain, plays a role in regulating sleep and attention, as well as relaying sensory information to the cerebral cortex. Sensory information from the eyes, for example, is relayed by the thalamus to the visual areas of the cerebral cortex where the information is processed. The tiny hypothalamus lies between the thalamus and the pituitary gland and plays important roles in motivation and emotion, as well as in vital body functions such as control of body temperature, concentration of fluids, storage of nutrients, and regulation of the menstrual cycle. The basal ganglia lie under the cortex and in front of the thalamus. They help regulate posture and coordination.

The limbic system consists of parts of the hypothalamus and contains other structures such as the amygdala, the cingulate gyrus, the fornix, the hippocampus, and the septum (see Figure 5.2). The limbic system is active in processes of memory and in regulating hunger, aggressive behavior, and sexual behavior.

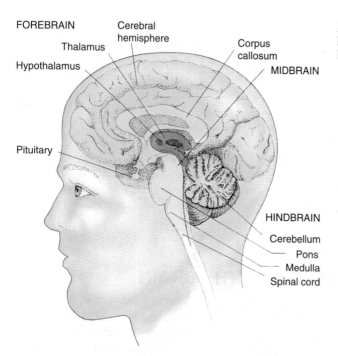

FOREBRAIN
Cerebral hemisphere
Thalamus
Hypothalamus
Corpus callosum
MIDBRAIN
Pituitary
HINDBRAIN
Cerebellum
Pons
Medulla
Spinal cord

FIGURE 5.1 **The Geography of the Brain.** A view of the brain, split from top to bottom, with some key structures labeled.

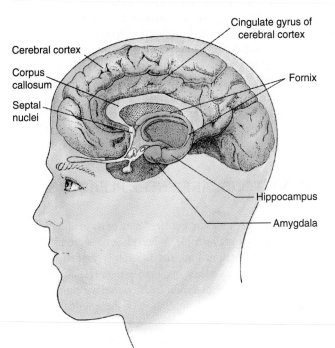

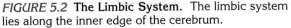

Cerebral cortex

Corpus callosum

Septal nuclei

Cingulate gyrus of cerebral cortex

Fornix

Hippocampus

Amygdala

FIGURE 5.2 **The Limbic System.** The limbic system lies along the inner edge of the cerebrum.

Limbic system
A group of structures active in memory, motivation, and emotion; the structures that are part of this system form a fringe along the inner edge of the cerebrum.

Basal ganglia
Clusters of cell bodies located between the thalamus and cerebrum that are involved in motor coordination.

Cerebrum
The large mass of the forebrain, which consists of two hemispheres.

Cerebral cortex
The wrinkled surface area (gray matter) of the cerebrum.

Corpus callosum
A thick bundle of nerve fibers that connects the hemispheres of the cortex.

Your cerebrum is your crowning glory, however. The large mushroom-shaped outer surface of the cerebrum, convoluted with ridges and valleys, is called the **cerebral cortex,** which consists of a right and left hemisphere connected by a thick fiber bundle called the **corpus callosum.** Thinking, language, memory, and fantasy are mental functions that are controlled by the cerebral cortex, which is sometimes called the *gray matter*.

BRAIN MECHANISMS IN SEXUAL FUNCTIONING

Various parts of the brain, in particular the cerebral cortex and the limbic system, play important roles in sexual functioning. Cells in the cerebral cortex fire (transmit messages) when we experience sexual thoughts, images, wishes, fantasies, and the like. Cells in the cerebral cortex interpret sensory information as sexual turn-ons or turn-offs. The sight of your lover disrobing, the anticipation of a romantic kiss, a passing sexual fantasy, or the viewing of an erotic movie can trigger the firing of cortical cells. These cells, in turn, transmit messages through the spinal cord that send blood rushing to the genitals, causing erection or vaginal lubrication. It is also by means of the cortex that we deem sexual behavior to be proper or improper, moral or immoral, relaxing or anxiety- or guilt-provoking.

Researchers have found that areas of the brain that lie below the cortex (*subcortical regions*), especially the limbic system, also play roles in regulating sexual processes (Carlson, 1988; Everitt, 1990). Numerous experiments have demonstrated the importance of subcortical regions of the brain in sexual response in animals (Chateau & Aron, 1988; Hart, 1986; Kondo et al., 1990). When the rear part of a male rat's hypothalamus is stimulated by an electrical probe, the animal mechanically runs through its courting and mounting routine. It nibbles at the ears and the back of the neck of a female rat and mounts her when she responds. People, of course, are influenced by learning, fantasy, and values as well as simple brain (or spinal) stimulation.

The importance of the limbic system in regulating sexual behavior in animals was demonstrated in early experiments by Heinrich Klüver and Paul Bucy of the University of Chicago in 1939. Klüver and Bucy reported that destruction of certain areas of the limbic system tamed wild monkeys, making them gentle, but also triggered incessant sexual behaviors that included masturbation and heterosexual and homosexual mounting attempts. The monkeys even tried to mount the experimenters. For obvious ethical reasons, researchers have not injured or destroyed parts of people's brains to observe the effects on humans.

Electrical stimulation of the hippocampus and septum of the limbic system has also been found to produce erections in laboratory monkeys (MacLean et al., 1976). Electrical stimulation of a pathway in the thalamus, moreover, produced a seminal discharge in these monkeys—without erection. Other reports suggest that stimulation of certain areas in the thalamus and hypothalamus may induce ejaculation (e.g., Herberg, 1963; Robinson & Mishkin, 1966). Still, the precise relationships among brain structures that regulate erection and ejaculation in animals or humans have not been fully mapped out.

Learning Objective 7: Identify the parts of the cerebral cortex and the limbic system that play roles in sexual arousal and sexual behavior.

ON PUSHING THE RIGHT BUTTONS: ARE THERE PLEASURE CENTERS IN THE BRAIN?

Research with electrical probes suggests that "pleasure centers" may exist in and near the hypothalamus in other animals and perhaps even in people. When electrodes are implanted in certain parts of the limbic system, investigators find that laboratory animals such as rats (Olds, 1956; Olds & Milner, 1954)—and in at least one case, a man (Heath, 1972)—will repeatedly press controls to receive bursts of electricity. Of course we cannot know what the rats experience, but the man reported that stimulation of these so-called pleasure centers led to feelings of sexual arousal and gratification.

Heath (1972) found that electrical stimulation of the septal region of the limbic system resulted in orgasmlike sensations in two people. Delgado (1969) reported that two female epileptic patients who received limbic stimulation as part of a diagnostic evaluation became sexually aroused by the stimulation:

> [One] reported a pleasant tingling sensation in the left side of her body "from my face down to the bottom of my legs." She started giggling and. . . [stated] that she enjoyed the sensation "very much." Repetition of these stimulations made the patient more communicative and flirtatious, and she ended by openly expressing her desire to marry the therapist. [The other patient reported] a pleasant sensation of relaxation and considerably increased her verbal output, which took on a more intimate character. [She] expressed her fondness for the therapist [whom she had just met], kissed his hands, and talked about her immense gratitude (p. 145).

TRUTH OR *FICTION?*

R E V I S I T E D

Electrical stimulation of certain areas in the human brain can yield sensations similar to those of sexual pleasure and gratification. Electrical stimulation of certain parts of the limbic system yielded sensations similar to those of sexual gratification—at least in the relatively small number of human subjects who have been studied. •

We cannot say whether specific "pleasure centers" in the brain are responsible for sexual pleasure. It may be that feelings of sexual pleasure involve a complex interplay of cortical and subcortical centers. We might wonder, however, whether we would even bother to develop sexual relationships if there were such "pleasure centers" that could be accessed through direct stimulation. Before you run to the store for electrodes, you should note that this avenue of research has not been actively pursued by researchers in recent years. The first phase of research seems to have climaxed in the 1970s and waned in intensity during the last couple of decades. Ultimately it may be no more than a footnote to the expansion of the science of human sexuality, although the advent of computer mapping of the brain may provide a second wave of enthusiasm. Still, very few researchers are suggesting that we may someday replace our lovers with battery-powered kits.

SEX HORMONES

In one episode of the television situation comedy *Growing Pains*, a male adolescent was described as a "hormone with feet." Ask parents why teenagers act the way they do and

Are Adolescents "Hormones with Feet"? Research shows that levels of androgens are connected with sexual interest in male and female adolescents. Hormone levels are more likely to predict sexual behavior in males, however, perhaps because society places greater restraints on adolescent female sexuality.

you are likely to hear a one-word answer: hormones! Hormones are chemical substances that are secreted by the ductless glands of the endocrine system and discharged directly into the bloodstream. Hormones regulate various bodily functions, from growth to stress resistance to sexual functions.

Both men and women produce small amounts of the sex hormones of the opposite gender in their bodies. Testosterone, the major form of androgen, or male sex hormone, is secreted in small amounts by the adrenal glands (located above the kidneys) in both genders, but in much larger amounts by the testes. The ovaries produce small amounts of androgens but much larger amounts of the female sex hormones, estrogen and progesterone. The testes similarly produce small amounts of estrogen and progesterone.

Normal men produce estrogen, and normal women produce androgens. *True. However, men do not produce as much estrogen as women do, and women do not produce as much of the male sex hormones as men do.* •

Secondary sex characteristics
Physical traits that differentiate males from females but are not directly involved in reproduction.

The hypothalamus and pituitary gland regulate gonadal secretion of sex hormones, specifically testosterone in males and estrogen and progesterone in females. At puberty a surge of sex hormones causes the blossoming of reproductive maturation: the sperm-producing ability of the testes in males and the maturation of ova and ovulation in females (see Chapter 13). Sex hormones released at puberty also cause the flowering of **secondary sex characteristics.** In males, these include the lengthening of the vocal cords (and consequent lowering of the voice) and the growth of facial and pubic hair. In females, the breasts and hips round with fatty tissue and pubic hair grows.

SEX HORMONES AND SEXUAL BEHAVIOR: ORGANIZING AND ACTIVATING INFLUENCES Sex hormones have organizing and activating effects on behavior. That is, they exert an influence on the type of behavior that is expressed (an *organizing* effect)

Learning Objective 8:
Summarize the research
on the role of sex hormones
in sexual orientation and
interest in male and female
humans and other animals.

and the frequency or intensity of the drive that motivates the behavior and the ability to perform the behavior (*activating* effects). For example, sex hormones predispose lower animals and possibly people toward stereotypical masculine or feminine mating behaviors (an organizing effect). They also facilitate sexual response and influence sexual desire (activating effects).

Though sex hormones clearly determine the sexual "orientations" and drives of many lower animals, their roles in human sexual behavior may be relatively more subtle and are not as well understood. Much of our knowledge of the organizing and activating effects of sex hormones comes from research with other species in which hormone levels were manipulated by castration or injection. Ethical standards prohibit such research with human infants, for obvious reasons.

The activating effects of testosterone can be clearly observed among male rats. For example, males who are castrated in adulthood and thus deprived of testosterone discontinue sexual behavior. If they are given injections of testosterone, however, they resume stereotypical male sexual behaviors, such as attempting to mount receptive females.

In rats, testosterone organizes or differentiates the brain in the masculine direction. As a result, adult male rats display stereotypical masculine behaviors upon activation by testosterone. Male fetuses and newborns normally have sufficient amounts of testosterone in the blood systems to organize their brains in the masculine direction. Female fetuses and newborns normally have lesser amounts of testosterone, so their brains become organized in a feminine direction. In some studies, however, female rats were prenatally exposed to large doses of testosterone, either naturally because of sharing the mother's uterus with many brothers, or experimentally by means of injection. Their sexual organs became somewhat masculinized, and they were predisposed toward masculine mating behaviors in adulthood. When they received testosterone as adults, they attempted to mount other females about as often as males normally do (Goy & Goldfoot, 1976).

In rats and other rodents, sexual differentiation of the brain is not complete at birth. Female rodents who are given testosterone injections shortly before or shortly following birth (depending on the species) will show typical masculine sexual patterns in adulthood, attempting to mount other females and resisting mounting by males (Ellis & Ames, 1987).

Transsexuals
People who have a gender-identity disorder in which they feel trapped in a body of the wrong gender.

Questions remain about the organizing effects of sex hormones on human sexual behavior. Prenatal sex hormones are known to play a role in the sexual differentiation of the genitalia and of the brain structures, such as the hypothalamus (see Chapter 6). Their role in patterning sexual behavior in adulthood remains unknown, however. Researchers have speculated that the brains of **transsexuals** may have been prenatally sexually differentiated in one direction, while their genitals were being differentiated in the opposite direction (Money, 1987). It has been speculated that prenatal sexual differentiation of the brain may also be connected with sexual orientation (see Chapter 10).

What of the activating effects of sex hormones on human sexual drive and behavior? Though the countless attempts to extract or synthesize aphrodisiacs have failed to produce the real thing, men and women normally produce one genuine aphrodisiac (Goleman, 1988). That aphrodisiac is testosterone. Whatever the early organizing effects of sex hormones in humans, evidence has accumulated that testosterone has activating effects on the sexual drives of both men and women.

Notes: Historically, in China and the Middle East, some male children were chosen to be castrated and serve as guards of women's quarters. This practice ceased in the twentieth century. In sixteenth- and seventeenth-century Europe, boys with beautiful voices were sometimes castrated so they could continue to sing in church choirs after puberty. This was done because of the Roman Catholic ban on female singers in church choirs.

SEX HORMONES AND MALE SEXUAL BEHAVIOR Some evidence of the role of hormones on sexual drive is found among men who suffer a marked decline in testosterone levels as the result of castration. Castration (removal of the testes) is sometimes performed as a medical treatment for cancer of the prostate or other diseases of the male reproductive tract, such as genital tuberculosis. In Europe, however, some men who have been convicted of sexual offenses have voluntarily undergone castration as a condition of release back into society (Heim, 1981).

Regardless of the reason for castration, men who are surgically or chemically castrated usually exhibit a gradual loss of sexual desire. They also gradually tend to lose the capacities to attain erection and to ejaculate—an indication that testosterone is important in maintaining sexual functioning as well as drive, at least in males. Castrated men show great variation in their sexual interest and functioning, however. Some continue to experience sexual desires and are able to function sexually for years, even decades (Leshner, 1978). Learning appears to play a large role in determining continued sexual response following castration. Males who were sexually experienced before castration show a more gradual decline in sexual activity. Those who were sexually inexperienced at the time show relatively little or no interest in sex (Leshner, 1978). Male sexual motivation and functioning thus involve an interplay of hormonal influences and such factors as learning and experience.

Hypogonadism
An abnormal condition marked by abnormally low levels of testosterone production.

Further evidence of the relationship between hormonal levels and male sexuality is found in studies of men with **hypogonadism,** a condition marked by abnormally low levels of testosterone production. Hypogonadal men generally suffer loss of sexual desire and a decline in sexual activity (Carani et al., 1990). Here again, hormones do not tell the whole story. Research has shown hypogonadal men to be capable of erection, at least for a while, even though sexual interest may wane (Bancroft, 1984). The role of testosterone as an activator of sexual drives in men is further supported by evidence of the effects of testosterone replacement in hypogonadal men. When these men are given testosterone injections, their sexual drives, fantasies, and activity are often restored to former levels (Cunningham et al., 1989; Goleman, 1988).

Though minimal levels of androgens are critical to male sexuality, there is no one-to-one correspondence between hormone levels and the sex drive or sexual performance in adult men (Byrne, 1982). In men who have ample supplies of testosterone, sexual interest and functioning depends more on learning, fantasies, attitudes, memories, and other psychosocial factors than on hormone levels. At puberty, however, hormonal variations may play a more direct role in stimulating sexual interest and activity in males. Udry and his colleagues (Udry et al., 1985; Udry et al., 1986; Udry & Billy, 1987) found, for example, that testosterone levels predicted sexual interest, masturbation rates, and the likelihood of engaging in sexual intercourse among teenage boys. A positive relationship also has been found between testosterone levels in adult men and frequency of sexual intercourse (Dabbs & Morris, 1990; Knussman et al., 1986). Moreover, drugs that reduce the levels of androgen in the blood system, called *antiandrogens,* lead to reductions in sexual drive and related fantasies and urges (Berlin, 1983; Money, 1987) (see Chapters 18 and 19).

SEX HORMONES AND FEMALE SEXUAL BEHAVIOR   The female sex hormones estrogen and progesterone play prominent roles in promoting the changes that occur during puberty and in regulating the menstrual cycle. Female sex hormones do not appear to play a direct role in determining sexual motivation or response in human females, however.

In most mammals, females are sexually receptive only during estrus. Estrus is a brief period of fertility that corresponds to time of ovulation, and during estrus, females are said to be "in heat." Estrus occurs once a year in some species; in others, it occurs periodically during the year in so-called sexual or mating seasons. Estrogen peaks at time of ovulation, so there is close relationship between fertility and sexual receptivity in most female mammals. Women's sexuality is not clearly linked to hormonal fluctuations, however. Unlike females of most other species of mammals, the human female is sexually responsive during all phases of the reproductive (menstrual) cycle—even during menstruation, when ovarian hormone levels are low—and after menopause.

There is some evidence, however, that sexual responsiveness in women is influenced by the presence of circulating androgens, or male sex hormones, in their bodies. The adrenal glands of women produce small amounts of androgens, just as they do in males. The fact that women normally produce smaller amounts of androgens than men does not mean that they necessarily have weaker sex drives. Rather, women appear to be more sensitive to smaller amounts of androgens (Bancroft, 1984). For women, it seems that less is more.

Ovariectomy
Surgical removal of the ovaries.

Women who receive **ovariectomies,** sometimes carried out when a hysterectomy is performed, continue to experience sexual drives and interest as before, even though they no longer produce female sex hormones. Loss of the ovarian hormone estradiol may cause vaginal dryness and make coitus painful, but it does not reduce sexual desire. (The dryness can be alleviated by a lubricating jelly or by estrogen replacement therapy.) However, women whose adrenal glands *and* ovaries have been removed (so that they no longer produce androgens) gradually lose sexual desire. An active and enjoyable sexual history seems to ward off this loss, however, providing further evidence of the impact of cognitive and experiential factors on human sexual response.

Research provides further evidence on the links between androgens and women's sex drives. Levels of testosterone in the bloodstream have been associated with increased sexual interest in women (Persky et al., 1982; Sherwin et al., 1985). The frequency of masturbation in women appears to be associated with changes in androgen levels (Bancroft et al., 1983)—another indication of the activating role of androgens in female sexuality. In the studies by Udry and his colleagues mentioned earlier, androgen levels were also found to predict sexual interest among teenage girls. In contrast to boys, however, girls' androgen levels were unrelated to the likelihood of coital experience. Androgens apparently affect sexual desire in both genders, but sexual interest may be more likely to be directly translated into sexual activity in men than women (Bancroft, 1990). This gender difference may be explained by society's placement of greater restraints on adolescent female sexuality.

Other researchers report that women's sexual activity increases at points in the menstrual cycle when levels of androgens in the bloodstream are high (Morris et al., 1987). Another study was conducted with women whose ovaries had been surgically removed ("surgical menopause") as a way of treating disease. The ovaries supply major quantities of estrogen. Following surgery, the women in this study were treated either with estrogen-replacement therapy (ERT), with ERT *plus* androgens, or with a placebo (an inert substance made to resemble an active drug) (Sherwin et al., 1985). This was a double-blind study; neither the women nor their prescribing physicians knew which drug the subjects were receiving. The results showed that the combination of androgens and ERT heightened sexual desire and sexual fantasies more than ERT alone or the placebo.

The available evidence thus suggests that androgens play a more prominent role than ovarian hormones in activating and maintaining women's sex drives. As with men, however, women's sexuality is too complex to be explained fully by hormone levels. For example, an active and enjoyable sexual history seems to ward off the loss of sexual interest that generally follows the surgical removal of the adrenal glands and ovaries.

THE SEXUAL RESPONSE CYCLE

Although we may be culturally attuned to focus on gender differences rather than similarities, Masters and Johnson (1966) found that the physiological responses of men and women to sexual stimulation (whether from coitus, masturbation, or other sources) are quite alike. The sequence of changes in the body that takes place as men and women become progressively more aroused is referred to as the **sexual response cycle.** Masters and Johnson divided the cycle into four phases: *excitement, plateau, orgasm,* and *resolution.* Figure 5.3 suggests the levels of sexual arousal associated with each phase.

Both males and females experience **vasocongestion** and **myotonia** early in the response cycle. Vasocongestion is the swelling of the genital tissues with blood, which causes erection of the penis and engorgement of the area surrounding the vaginal opening. The testes, nipples, and even earlobes become engorged as blood vessels in these areas dilate. Vasocongestion has been observed in men and women in response to both direct genital stimulation (Masters & Johnson, 1966) and exposure to sexual stimuli, such as sexually explicit films (Rubinsky et al., 1987).

Myotonia refers to muscle tension. Myotonia causes voluntary and involuntary muscle contractions, which produce facial grimaces, spasms in the hands and feet, and eventually, the spasms of orgasm. Let us follow these and other changes that take place in the body in response to sexual stimulation as we discuss the phases of the sexual response cycle.

Learning Objective 9: Name the four phases and describe the changes associated with each phase of the sexual response cycle proposed by Masters and Johnson.

Sexual response cycle
Masters and Johnson's model of sexual response, which consists of four phases.

Vasocongestion
The swelling of the genital tissues with blood, which causes erection of the penis and engorgement of the area surrounding the vaginal opening.

Myotonia
Muscle tension.

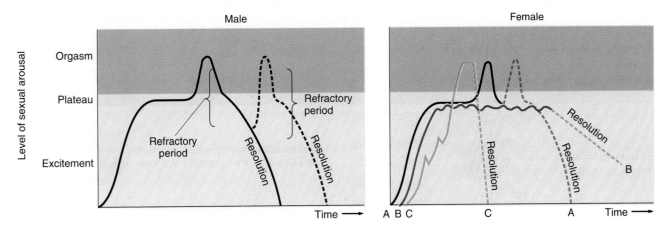

FIGURE 5.3 **Levels of Sexual Arousal During the Phases of the Sexual Response Cycle.**
Masters and Johnson have divided the sexual response cycle into the four phases shown in
these graphs: excitement, plateau, orgasm, and resolution. During the resolution phase the level
of sexual arousal returns to the prearoused state. For men there is a refractory period following
orgasm. As shown by the broken line, however, men can become rearoused to orgasm once
the refractory period is past and their levels of sexual arousal have returned to pre-plateau levels.
Pattern A for women shows a typical response cycle, with the broken line suggesting multiple
orgasms. Pattern B shows the cycle of a woman who reaches the plateau phase but for whom
arousal is "resolved" without reaching the orgasmic phase. Pattern C shows the possibility of
orgasm in a highly aroused woman who passes quickly through the plateau phase.

EXCITEMENT PHASE

Excitement phase
The first phase of the sexual
response cycle, which is
characterized by erection in
the male, vaginal lubrication
in the female, and muscle
tension and increases in
heart rate in both males and
females.

In younger men, vasocongestion during the **excitement phase** produces penile erection
as early as 3 to 8 seconds after stimulation begins. Erection may occur more slowly in
older men, but the responses are essentially the same. Erection may subside and return as
stimulation varies. The scrotal skin thickens, losing its baggy appearance. The testes
increase in size. The testes and scrotum become elevated.

In the female, vaginal lubrication may start 10 to 30 seconds after stimulation
begins. Vasocongestion swells the clitoris, flattens the labia majora and spreads them
apart, and increases the size of the labia minora. The inner two thirds of the vagina
expand. The vaginal walls thicken, and because of the inflow of blood, turn from their
normal pink to a deeper hue. The uterus becomes engorged and elevated. The breasts
enlarge, and blood vessels near the surface become more prominent.

Sex flush
A reddish rash that appears
on the chest or breasts late
in the excitement phase of
the sexual response cycle.

The skin may take on a rosy **sex flush** late in this phase. It varies with intensity of
arousal and is more pronounced in women. The nipples may become erect in both genders, especially in response to direct stimulation. Men and women show some increase in
myotonia, heart rate, and blood pressure.

PLATEAU PHASE

Plateau phase
The second phase of the
sexual response cycle,
which is characterized by
increases in vasocongestion,
muscle tension, heart rate,
and blood pressure in
preparation for orgasm.

A plateau is a level region, and the level of arousal remains somewhat constant during
the **plateau phase** of sexual response. Nevertheless, the plateau phase is an advanced
state of arousal that precedes orgasm. Men in this phase show a slight increase in the circumference of the coronal ridge of the penis. The penile glans turns a purplish hue, a
sign of vasocongestion. The testes are elevated further into position for ejaculation and
may reach one and a half times their unaroused size. The Cowper's glands that are found
at the tip of the penis secrete a few droplets of fluid (see Figure 5.4 on page 148).

In women, vasocongestion swells the tissues of the outer third of the vagina, contracting
the vaginal opening (thus preparing it to "grasp" the penis) and building the **orgasmic
platform** (Figure 5.5, page 150). The inner part of the vagina expands fully. The uterus

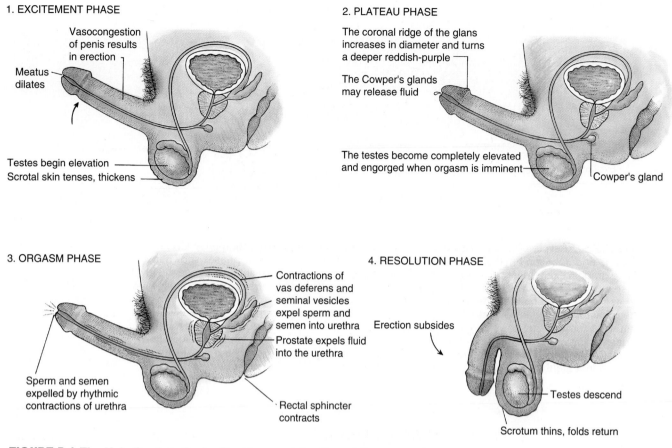

1. EXCITEMENT PHASE

Vasocongestion of penis results in erection

Meatus dilates

Testes begin elevation
Scrotal skin tenses, thickens

2. PLATEAU PHASE

The coronal ridge of the glans increases in diameter and turns a deeper reddish-purple

The Cowper's glands may release fluid

The testes become completely elevated and engorged when orgasm is imminent

Cowper's gland

3. ORGASM PHASE

Contractions of vas deferens and seminal vesicles expel sperm and semen into urethra

Prostate expels fluid into the urethra

Sperm and semen expelled by rhythmic contractions of urethra

Rectal sphincter contracts

4. RESOLUTION PHASE

Erection subsides

Testes descend

Scrotum thins, folds return

FIGURE 5.4 **The Male Genitals During the Phases of the Sexual Response Cycle.**

Orgasmic platform
The thickening of the walls of the outer third of the vagina, due to vasocongestion, that occurs during the plateau phase of the sexual response cycle.

Sex skin
Reddening of the labia minora that occurs during the plateau phase.

Orgasmic phase
The third phase of the sexual response cycle, characterized by orgasmic contractions of the pelvic musculature. Orgasm in the male occurs in two stage of muscular contractions. Orgasm in the female is manifested by contractions of the pelvic muscles that surround the vaginal barrel.

becomes fully elevated. The clitoris withdraws beneath the clitoral hood and shortens. Thus a woman (or her partner) may feel that the clitoris has become "lost." This may be mistaken as a sign that the woman's sexual arousal is waning, whereas it is actually increasing.

Coloration of the labia minora appears, which is referred to as the **sex skin.** The labia minora become a deep wine color in women who have borne children, and bright red in women who have not. Further engorgement of the areolas of the breasts may make it seem that the nipples have lost part of their erection (see Figure 5.6 on page 152). The Bartholin's glands secrete a fluid that resembles mucus.

About one man in four, and about three women in four, show a sex flush, which often does not appear until the plateau phase. Myotonia may cause spasmodic contractions in the hands and feet and facial grimaces. Breathing becomes rapid, like panting, and the heart rate may increase to 100 to 160 beats a minutes. Blood pressure continues to rise. The increase in heart rate is usually less dramatic with masturbation than during coitus.

ORGASMIC PHASE

The orgasmic phase in the male consists of two stages of muscular contractions. In the first stage, contractions of the vas deferens, the seminal vesicles, the ejaculatory duct, and the prostate gland cause seminal fluid to collect in the urethral bulb at the base of the penis (see Figure 5.4). The bulb expands to accommodate the fluid. The internal sphincter of the urinary bladder contracts, preventing seminal fluid from entering the bladder in a backward, retrograde ejaculation. The normal closing off of the bladder also serves to prevent urine from mixing with semen. The collection of semen in the urethral bulb produces feelings of ejaculatory inevitability—the sensation that nothing will stop the ejaculate from "coming." This sensation lasts about 2 to 3 seconds.

In the second stage, the external sphincter of the bladder relaxes, allowing passage of semen. Contractions of muscles surrounding the urethra and urethral bulb and the base of the penis propel the ejaculate through the urethra and out of the body. Sensations of pleasure tend to be related to the strength of the contractions and the amount of seminal fluid. The first three to four contractions are generally most intense and occur at 0.8-second intervals (five contractions every four seconds). Another two to four contractions occur at a somewhat slower pace (Masters & Johnson, 1966). Other researchers (e.g., Bohlen et al., 1980) report a slightly faster pace (e.g., every 0.6 second). Researchers agree that rates and patterns vary somewhat from man to man.

Orgasm in the female is manifested by three to fifteen contractions of the pelvic muscles that surround the vaginal barrel. The contractions first occur at 0.8-second intervals, producing, as in the male, a release of sexual tension. Another three to six weaker and slower contractions follow. The spacing of these contractions is generally more variable in women than in men. The uterus and the anal sphincter also contract rhythmically. Uterine contractions occur in waves from the top to the cervix. In both genders, muscles go into spasm throughout the body. Blood pressure and heart rate reach a peak, with the heart beating up to 180 times a minute. Respiration may increase to 40 breaths a minute.

Activity: *Is the Orgasm Male or Female?* The IM contains a self-scoring questionnaire that students can use to test whether they are able to distinguish written descriptions of orgasm taken from a sample of male and female students.

SUBJECTIVE EXPERIENCE OF ORGASM   The sensations of orgasm have challenged the descriptive powers of poets. Words like "rush," "warmth," "explosion," and "release" do not adequately capture them. We may assume (rightly or wrongly) that others of our gender experience pretty much what we do, but can we understand the sensations of the opposite gender?

A number of studies (Proctor et al., 1974; Vance & Wagner, 1976; Wiest, 1977) suggest that the orgasms of both genders may feel quite similar. In one study (Proctor et al., 1974), 48 men and women provided written descriptions of orgasms. The researchers modified the language (e.g., changing "penis" to "genitals") so that the authors' genders would not be apparent. They then asked 70 "experts" (psychologists, gynecologists, and so on) to indicate the gender of each author. The ratings were no more reliable than guesswork.

TRUTH OR *FICTION?*

R E V I S I T E D

Written descriptions of men's and women's experiences during orgasm cannot be told apart. *Men's and women's written descriptions of experiences during orgasm may not be clearly different when they are altered to exclude language that gives away exactly which anatomic features are involved. So this Truth-or-Fiction item is only qualifiedly "true." (Listen: life is complex. Be tolerant.)* •

RESOLUTION PHASE

Resolution phase
The fourth phase of the sexual response cycle, during which the body gradually returns to its prearoused state.

The period following orgasm, in which the body returns to its prearoused state, is called the **resolution phase.** Following ejaculation the man loses his erection in two stages. The first occurs in about a minute. Half the volume of the erection is lost as blood from the corpora cavernosa empties into the other parts of the body. The second stage occurs over a period of several minutes: the remaining tumescence subsides as the corpus spongiosum empties. The testes and scrotum return to normal size, and the scrotum regains its wrinkled appearance.

In women orgasm also triggers release of blood from engorged areas. In the absence of continued stimulation, swelling of the areolas decreases; then the nipples return to normal size. The sex flush lightens rapidly. In about 5 to 10 seconds the clitoris descends to its normal position. The clitoris, vaginal barrel, uterus, and labia gradually shrink to their prearoused sizes. The labia minora turn lighter (the "sex skin" disappears) in about 10 to 15 seconds.

1. EXCITEMENT PHASE

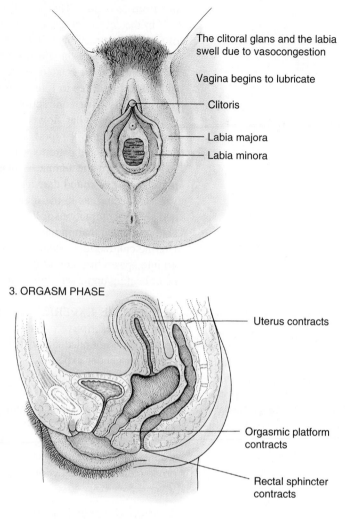

The clitoral glans and the labia swell due to vasocongestion

Vagina begins to lubricate

Clitoris

Labia majora

Labia minora

3. ORGASM PHASE

Uterus contracts

Orgasmic platform contracts

Rectal sphincter contracts

FIGURE 5.5 **The Female Genitals During the Phases of the Sexual Response Cycle.**

Refractory period
A period of time following a response (e.g., orgasm) during which an individual is no longer responsive to stimulation (e.g., sexual stimulation).

Most muscle tension (myotonia) tends to dissipate within 5 minutes after orgasm in both men and women. Blood pressure, heart rate, and respiration may return to their prearousal levels within a few minutes. About 30 to 40 percent of men and women find their palms, the soles of their feet, or their entire bodies covered with a sheen of perspiration. Both men and women may feel relaxed and satiated. However , . . .

Although the processes by which the body returns to its prearousal state are similar in men and women, there is an important gender difference during the resolution phase. Unlike women, men enter a **refractory period** during which they are physiologically incapable of experiencing another orgasm or ejaculation (in much the same way that the flash attachment to a camera cannot be set off again immediately after it is used—it has to be recharged). The refractory period of adolescent males may last only minutes, while that of men age 50 and above may last from several minutes (yes, "it could happen") to a day. Women do not undergo a refractory period and so can become quickly rearoused to the point of repeated (multiple) orgasm if they desire and receive continued sexual stimulation (see Figure 5.3).

Myotonia and vasocongestion may take an hour or more to dissipate in people who are aroused but who do not reach orgasm. Persistent pelvic vasocongestion may cause "blue balls" in males—the slang term for a throbbing ache. Some men insist that their dates should consent to coitus, since it is unfair to stimulate them to the point where they

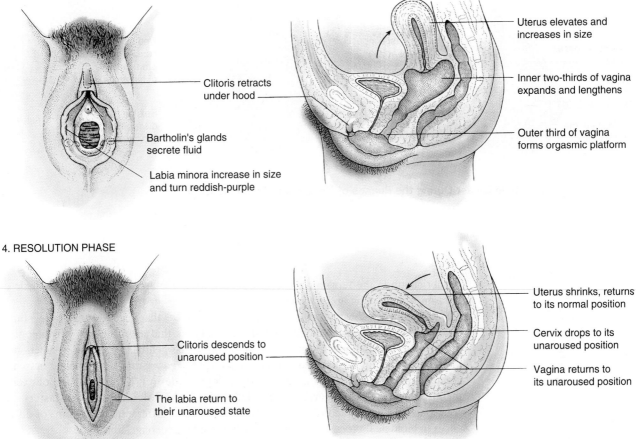

2. PLATEAU PHASE

Clitoris retracts under hood

Bartholin's glands secrete fluid

Labia minora increase in size and turn reddish-purple

Uterus elevates and increases in size

Inner two-thirds of vagina expands and lengthens

Outer third of vagina forms orgasmic platform

4. RESOLUTION PHASE

Clitoris descends to unaroused position

The labia return to their unaroused state

Uterus shrinks, returns to its normal position

Cervix drops to its unaroused position

Vagina returns to its unaroused position

have this condition. This condition can be relieved through masturbation as well as coitus, however—or allowed to dissipate naturally. Although it may be uncomfortable, it is not dangerous and should not be an excuse to pressure or coerce another person into any sexual activity. "Blue" sensations are not limited to men. Women, too, may experience unpleasant pelvic throbbing if they have become highly aroused and do not find release (Barbach, 1975). Women, too, can find relief from the discomfort of pelvic throbbing through masturbation.

KAPLAN'S THREE STAGES OF SEXUAL RESPONSE: AN ALTERNATE MODEL

Learning Objective 10: Compare Kaplan's three-stage model of sexual arousal with Masters and Johnson's four-phase model.

Helen Singer Kaplan is a prominent sex therapist and author of several leading books (1974, 1979, 1987) for professionals on conducting sex therapy. Whereas Masters and Johnson had proposed a four-stage model of sexual response, Kaplan developed a three-stage model consisting of (1) desire, (2) excitement, and (3) orgasm. Kaplan's model is an outgrowth of her clinical experience in working with people with sexual dysfunctions. She believes that their problems can best be classified according to these three phases. Kaplan's model makes it convenient for clinicians to classify sexual dysfunctions involving desire (low or absent desire), excitement (such as problems with erection in the male

THE SEXUAL RESPONSE CYCLE

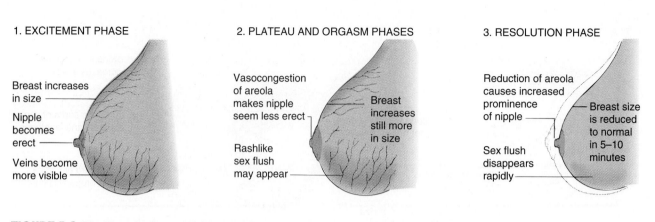

1. EXCITEMENT PHASE

Breast increases in size

Nipple becomes erect

Veins become more visible

2. PLATEAU AND ORGASM PHASES

Vasocongestion of areola makes nipple seem less erect

Breast increases still more in size

Rashlike sex flush may appear

3. RESOLUTION PHASE

Reduction of areola causes increased prominence of nipple

Breast size is reduced to normal in 5–10 minutes

Sex flush disappears rapidly

FIGURE 5.6 The Female Breast During the Phases of the Sexual Response Cycle.

or lubrication in the female), and orgasm (such as premature ejaculation in the male or orgasmic dysfunction in the female).

Masters and Johnson focus on physiological changes that occur during sexual stimulation, whereas Kaplan's model includes two phases that are primarily physiological (*excitement,* consisting of initial vasocongestion of the genitals, resulting in erection in the male and vaginal lubrication in the female, and *orgasm,* marked by pelvic muscular contractions) and one that is primarily psychological (desire). Kaplan's stages of excitement and orgasm are clearly differentiated along physiological lines. (Masters and Johnson's excitement and plateau stages are less clearly differentiated in terms of differences in biological processes. Both primarily involve vasocongestion.)

Masters and Johnson view sexual response as composed of *successive* stages; the order is crucial and invariant. Kaplan treats her phases as relatively independent components of sexual response whose sequence is somewhat variable. For example, a person may experience sexual excitement and even orgasm, though sexual desire remains low. Excitement may also precede desire in some situations. For example, people with low sexual desire may find their sexual appetites sparked as their bodies respond to their partners' sexual stimulation. A person who lacks desire may not be motivated to seek sexual stimulation or be able to respond adequately to sexual stimuli, however.

Kaplan's model is noteworthy for designating desire as a separate phase of sexual response. Problems in lack of sexual interest or desire are among the most common brought to the attention of sex therapists (see Chapter 15).

CONTROVERSIES ABOUT ORGASM

Learning Objective 11:
Summarize the research on the female and male capacity for multiple orgasms.

Multiple orgasms
One or more additional orgasms following the first, which occur within a short period of time and before the body has returned to a pre-plateau level of arousal.

Are women capable of experiencing multiple orgasms? Are men? Physiologically speaking, is there but one type of orgasm? Or are there different types of orgasms depending on the site of stimulation? Do women ejaculate during orgasm? If so, what fluid do they emit?

Few other topics in human sexuality have aroused more controversies over the years than orgasm. We do not have all the answers, but some intriguing research findings have shed light on some of these continuing controversies.

MULTIPLE ORGASMS: WHEN YOU'RE HAVING MORE THAN ONE

Kinsey's report (Kinsey et al., 1953) that 14 percent of his female respondents regularly had **multiple orgasms** sent shock waves through the general community and even surprised his fellow scientists. Many people were aghast that women could have more than one orgasm at a time. There were comments (mostly by men, of course!) that the women in the Kinsey surveys must be "nymphomaniacs" who were incapable of being satisfied with the "normal" complement of one orgasm per occasion. However, only 13 years later, Masters and Johnson (1966) reported that most, if not all, women are capable of multiple orgasms. Though all women may have a biological capability for multiple orgasm, not all women report having multiple orgasms. A recent survey of 720 nurses showed that only 43 percent reported experiencing multiple orgasms (Darling et al., 1991).

It is difficult to offer a precise definition of multiple orgasm. In Masters and Johnson's view, however, multiple orgasm involves the occurrence of one or more *additional* orgasms following the first, within a short period of time and before the body has returned to a pre-plateau level of arousal. By this definition, a person would not have experienced a multiple orgasm if he or she had two or more successive orgasms that were separated by a return to a prearoused state or a pre-plateau (excitement stage) level of arousal. (Note that the pattern shown by the broken line for the male in Figure 5.3 does *not* constitute a multiple orgasm, even if it occurs reasonably rapidly after the first orgasm, because he *does* return to a pre-plateau level of sexual arousal between orgasms.) The lines of demarcation between the excitement and plateau stages of arousal are not too obvious, however, and a person may experience two or more successive orgasms within a short time but not know whether these are, technically speaking, "multiple orgasms." Whether or not the orgasm meets these definitional requirements does not diminish the experience, but it does raise the question of whether both men and women are capable of multiple orgasm.

By Masters and Johnson's definition, men are not capable of achieving multiple orgasms, because they enter a refractory period following ejaculation during which they are physiologically incapable of achieving another orgasm or ejaculation for a time. Put more simply, men who want more than one orgasm during one session may have to relax for a while and allow their sexual arousal to subside. Yet women can maintain a high level of arousal between multiple orgasms and have them in rapid succession.

Women do not enter a refractory period; they can continue to have orgasms if they continue to receive effective stimulation (and, of course, are interested in continuing).

Reproduced by special permission of Playboy Magazine, ©1984

"Front desk? Look, I hate to sound like a prude, but the folks in room 614 seem to be having an excessive number of orgasms."

Some men thus refrain from reaching orgasm until their partners have had the desired number. The differential capacity for multiple orgasms is one of the major gender differences in sexual response.

Researchers have reported that some men appear to be capable of multiple orgasms consisting of two or more *nonejaculatory* orgasms preceding a final ejaculatory orgasm (Hartman & Fithian, 1984; Robbins & Jensen, 1978). These men may not have entered a refractory period following their initial nonejaculatory orgasms, and therefore may have been capable of maintaining their level of stimulation at near peak levels. Researchers have also interviewed men who report having multiple orgasms in which nonejaculatory, or so-called dry, orgasms follow an ejaculatory orgasm, with little or no **detumescence** between orgasms (Dunn & Trost, 1989). Some men report more varied patterns, with ejaculatory orgasms and "dry" orgasms preceding or following each other in different sequences.

Men who report multiple orgasms indicate that if they are highly aroused following an initial orgasm, and if sexual stimulation continues, they can achieve one or more subsequent orgasms before losing their erections (Dunn & Trost, 1989). Still, the evidence for multiple orgasm in men is largely ancedotal and limited to a relatively few case examples. Nor is it known whether such "multiple" orgasms meet the technical definition given by Masters and Johnson of two or more orgasms in rapid succession without a return to a *pre-plateau* stage of arousal in between. Nor do we know what percentage of men might be multiply orgasmic (Dunn & Trost, 1989).

Masters and Johnson found that some women experienced 20 orgasms or more by masturbating. Still, few women have multiple orgasms during most of their sexual encounters, and many are satisfied with just one orgasm per occasion. Some women who have read or heard about female orgasmic capacity wonder what is "wrong" with them if they are content with just one. Nothing is wrong with them, of course: A biological capacity does not create a behavioral requirement.

HOW MANY KINDS OF ORGASMS DO WOMEN HAVE? ONE, TWO, OR THREE?

Until Masters and Johnson (1966) published their laboratory findings, many people believed that there were two types of female orgasms, as proposed by the psychoanalyst Sigmund Freud: the *clitoral orgasm* and the *vaginal orgasm*. Clitoral orgasms were achieved through direct clitoral stimulation, such as by masturbation. Clitoral orgasms were seen by psychoanalysts (mostly male psychoanalysts, naturally) as emblematic of a childhood fixation—a throwback to an erogenous pattern acquired during childhood masturbation.

The term *vaginal orgasm* referred to an orgasm achieved through deep penile thrusting during coitus and was theorized to be a sign of mature sexuality. Freud argued that women achieve sexual maturity when they forsake clitoral stimulation for vaginal stimulation. This view would be little more than an academic footnote but for the fact that some adult women who continue to require direct clitoral stimulation to reach orgasm, even during coitus, have been led by traditional (generally male) psychoanalysts to believe that they are sexually "fixated" at an immature stage, or are, at least, sexually inadequate.

Despite Freudian theory, Masters and Johnson (1966) were able to find only one kind of orgasm, physiologically speaking, regardless of the source of stimulation (manual-clitoral or penile-vaginal). By monitoring physiological responses to sexual stimulation, they found that the female orgasm involves the same biological events whether it is reached through masturbation, petting, coitus, or just breast stimulation. All orgasms involve spasmodic contractions of the pelvic muscles surrounding the vaginal barrel, leading to a release of sexual tension. A poet wrote, ". . . A rose is a rose is a rose." Biologically speaking, the same principle can be applied to orgasm: ". . . a n orgasm is an orgasm is an orgasm." In men, it also matters not how orgasm is achieved—through masturbation, petting, oral sex, coitus, or by fantasizing about a fellow student in chem

Detumescence
Loss of erection.

Learning Objective 12:
Evaluate the research concerning the types of orgasms women experience.

lab. Orgasm still involves the same physiological processes: involuntary contractions of the pelvic muscles at the base of the penis expel semen and release sexual tension. A woman or a man might prefer one source of orgasm to another—she or he might prefer achieving orgasm with a lover rather than by masturbation, but the biological events that define orgasm remain the same.

Though orgasms attained through coitus or masturbation may be physiologically alike, there are certainly key psychological or subjective differences. (Were it not so, there would be fewer sexual relationships.) The coital experience, for example, is often accompanied by feelings of attachment, love, and connectedness toward one's partner. Masturbation, by contrast, is more likely to be experienced solely as a sexual release.

Orgasms experienced through different means may also vary in physiological and subjective intensity. Masters and Johnson (1966) found that orgasms experienced during masturbation were generally more physiologically intense than those experienced during intercourse, perhaps because masturbation allows one to focus only on one's own pleasure and on ensuring that one receives effective stimulation to climax. This does not mean that orgasms during masturbation are more enjoyable or gratifying than those experienced through coitus, however. Given the emotional connectedness we may feel toward our lovers, we are unlikely to break off our relationships in favor of masturbation. So "physiological intensity," as measured by laboratory instruments, does not translate directly into subjective pleasure or fulfillment.

Orgasms attained through masturbation are more intense than those attained through coitus. *Orgasms attained through masturbation were indeed found by Masters and Johnson to be physiologically more intense than those attained through coitus. (That does not mean that they are more enjoyable.)* •

The purported distinction between clitoral and vaginal orgasms also rests on an assumption that the clitoris is not stimulated during coitus. Masters and Johnson showed this to be a *false* assumption. Penile coital thrusting actually does stimulate the clitoris, although indirectly. Thrusting draws the clitoral hood back and forth against the clitoris. This kind of clitoral stimulation may actually trigger women's orgasms in intercourse as well as in masturbation.

One might think that Masters and Johnson's research settled the question of whether or not there are different types of female orgasms. Other investigators, however, have proposed that there are distinct forms of female orgasms, yet not those suggested by psychoanalytic theory. For example, Singer and Singer (1972) suggested that there are three types of female orgasms: *vulval, uterine,* and *blended.* According to the Singers, the vulval orgasm represents the type of orgasm described by Masters and Johnson (1966) that involves *vulval* contractions; that is, contractions of the vaginal barrel. Consistent with the findings of Masters and Johnson (1966), they note that the vulval orgasm remains the same regardless of the source of stimulation, clitoral or vaginal.

According to the Singers, the uterine orgasm does not involve vulval contractions. It occurs only in response to deep penile thrusting against the cervix. This thrusting slightly displaces the uterus and stimulates the tissues that cover the abdominal organs. The uterine orgasm is accompanied by a certain pattern of breathing: gasping or gulping of air is followed by an involuntary holding of the breath as orgasm approaches. When orgasm is reached, the breath is explosively exhaled. The uterine orgasm is accompanied by deep feelings of relaxation and sexual satisfaction.

The third type, or blended orgasm, is described as combining features of the vulval and uterine orgasms. It involves both an involuntary breath-holding response and contractions of the pelvic muscles. The Singers note that the type of orgasm a woman experiences—vulval, uterine, or blended—depends on such factors as the parts of the body that are stimulated and the length of stimulation. Each produces its own kind of satisfaction, and no one type is necessarily better or preferable to any other.

The Singers' hypothesis of three distinct forms of female orgasms remains controversial. Researchers initially scoffed at the idea that orgasms could arise from vaginal stimulation alone. The vagina, after all, especially the inner two thirds of the vaginal cavity, is relatively insensitive to stimulation (erotic or otherwise). Proponents of the Singers' model counter that the type of uterine orgasm described by the Singers is induced more by pressure resulting from deep pelvic thrusting than by touch.

THE GRAFENBERG SPOT

Grafenberg spot
A part of the anterior wall of the vagina, whose prolonged stimulation is theorized to cause particularly intense orgasms and a female ejaculation. Abbreviated *G-spot.*

Learning Objective 13:
Evaluate the evidence concerning the existence of the Grafenberg spot in women.

Recent research findings suggest that a particular part of the vagina, notably a bean-shaped area within the anterior wall of the vagina, may have special erotic significance. This area is believed to lie about 1 to 2 inches from the vaginal entrance and to consist of a soft mass of tissue that swells from the size of a dime to a half dollar when stimulated (Davidson et al., 1989). It has been called the **Grafenberg spot**—the "G-spot" for short (see Figure 5.7). The spot is most directly stimulated by the woman's or her partner's fingers or by penile thrusting in the rear entry or the female-superior positions of coitus. Some researchers suggest that stimulation of the spot produces intense erotic sensations and that with prolonged stimulation, a distinct form of orgasm occurs. This orgasm is characterized by intense pleasure and, in some cases, by a biological event earlier thought to be exclusively male in nature: ejaculation (Addiego et al., 1981; Belzer, 1981; Perry & Whipple, 1981; Whipple & Komisaruk, 1988). These claims, as with other claims of distinct forms of female orgasms, have been steeped in controversy.

The G-spot was named after a gynecologist, Ernest Grafenberg, who first suggested the erotic importance of this area. Grafenberg (1950) observed that orgasm in women could be induced by stimulating this area, and that such orgasms may be accompanied by the discharge of a milky fluid or "ejaculate" from the urethra. In a laboratory experiment, Zaviacic and his colleagues (1988) found evidence of an ejaculate in this area in 10 of 27 women studied. Some researchers believe that this fluid is urine that some women release involuntarily from the bladder during orgasm (Alzate, 1985; Goldberg et al., 1983). Other researchers consider it to be chemically distinct from urine (Addiego et al., 1981; Belzer et al., 1984; Zaviacic et al., 1988; Zaviacic & Whipple, 1993). The nature of this fluid and its source remain a source of controversy, but Zaviacic and Whipple (1993) suggest that it may represent a fluid that is released during sex by a "female prostate," a system of ducts and glands called *Skene's glands,* in much the same way that semen is released by the prostate gland in men. Zaviacic and Whipple suggest that "many women who felt that they may be urinating during sex . . . [may be helped by] the knowledge that the fluid they expel may be different from urine and a normal phenomenon that occurs during sexual response" (1993, p. 149). (Some women, however, may expel urine during sex, perhaps because of urinary stress incontinence—Zaviacic & Whipple, 1993.) Zaviacic and Whipple also note that stimulation of the G-spot and ejaculation may be related in some women but not in others.

Even proponents of the existence of the G-spot recognize that it is difficult to locate since it not apparent to the eye (Ladas et al., 1982). Perry and Whipple (1981) suggest that women may try to locate the spot either by self-exploration or with the assistance of a partner. In either case, two fingers should be used to press deeply but gently into the front, or anterior, wall of the vagina to locate the spot, which may feel like a small lump within the anterior wall (see Figure 5.7). When the spot is stimulated by stroking, the woman may initially experience an urge to urinate, perhaps because the sensitive area lies close to the bladder and urethra. A few minutes of continued stimulation leads to strong sensations of sexual pleasure in some women, which is accompanied by vasocongestion that swells the area. More prolonged stimulation may lead to an intense orgasm; however, fear of loss of urinary control leads some women to avoid such prolonged stimulation (Ladas et al., 1982).

Perry and Whipple (1981) relate the G-spot to the Singers' model of three kinds of orgasms. They suggest that sustained stimulation of the G-spot can produce a uterine orgasm that is characterized by deeper sensations than those that occur during the vulval

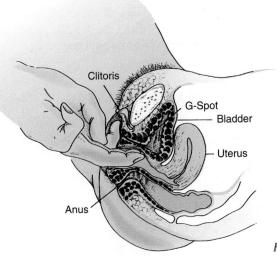

FIGURE 5.7 **The Grafenberg Spot.**

orgasm that is produced by clitoral stimulation. The connection between the G-spot and the Singers' model is controversial.

The very existence of the G-spot remains debatable. Ladas, Whipple, and Perry (1982) reported locating the G-spot in every one of more than 400 women they examined. Zaviacic and his colleagues (1988) reported finding the spot in each of 27 women they examined. Other researchers have been unable to find an area of heightened sensitivity corresponding to the G-spot, however (Alzate & Londono, 1984; Masters et al., 1989). Some researchers (e.g., Alzate & Dippsy, 1984; Hock, 1983) deny the existence of the G-spot as a distinct anatomical structure. They argue that the entire anterior wall of the vagina, and not any one spot or area, is richly supplied with nerve endings and sensitive to erotic stimulation.

Although the existence of the G-spot continues to be debated among researchers, a recent survey of 1,289 professional women in the health and counseling professions revealed that a majority believe that the G-spot exists and that they have experienced sexual pleasure when it has been stimulated directly (Davidson et al., 1989). Still, there was considerable confusion among these women as to the precise location of this sensitive area. About three of four women reported experiencing an orgasm from stimulation of this area, most frequently from manual stimulation.

More research is needed to determine the scientific basis of the claims for different kinds of orgasms in women and whether there are specific sites in the vagina, such as the G-spot, that may be especially sensitive to erotic stimulation.

SUMMING UP

This chapter considers factors that contribute to sexual arousal and the processes that relate to sexual response.

MAKING SENSE OF SEX: THE ROLE OF THE SENSES IN SEXUAL AROUSAL

Each sense plays a role in sexual experience, but some play more of a role than others.

Vision: The Better to See You With Visual information plays a major role in human sexual attraction. Visual cues can be sexual turn-ons or turn-offs.

Smell: Does the Nose Know Best? Although the sense of smell plays a lesser role in governing sexual arousal in humans than in lower mammals, particular odors can be sexual turn-ons or turn-offs. Many organisms are sexually aroused by naturally produced chemicals called pheromones, but their role in human sexual behavior remains unclear.

The Skin Senses: Sex as a Touching Experience The sense of touch has the most direct effects on sexual arousal and response. Erogenous zones are especially sensitive to tactile sexual stimulation.

Taste: On Savory Sex Taste appears to play only a minor role in sexual arousal and response.

Hearing: The Better to Hear You With Like visual and olfactory cues, sounds can be turn-ons or turn-offs.

APHRODISIACS: OF SPANISH FLIES AND RHINO HORNS

Alleged aphrodisiacs such as Spanish fly and foods that in some way resemble the genitals have not been shown to contribute to sexual arousal or response.

Psychoactive Drugs The alleged aphrodisiac effects of psychoactive drugs, such as alcohol and cocaine, may reflect our expectations of them or their effects on sexual inhibitions, rather than direct stimulation of sexual response. Alcohol is also connected with a liberated social role and thus provides an external excuse for dubious behavior. Some people report initial increased sexual pleasure with cocaine use, but frequent use can lead to sexual dysfunctions.

SEXUAL RESPONSE AND THE BRAIN

The brain plays a central role in sexual functioning.

The Geography of the Brain The brain consists of three major parts: the hindbrain, the midbrain, and the forebrain.

Brain Mechanisms in Sexual Functioning The cerebral cortex interprets sensory information as sexual turn-ons or turn-offs. The cortex transmits messages through the spinal cord that cause vasocongestion. Direct stimulation of parts of the limbic system may cause erection and ejaculation in male animals.

On Pushing the Right Buttons: Are There Pleasure Centers in the Brain? Electrical stimulation of certain parts of the limbic system apparently yields sensations similar to those of sexual gratification.

Sex Hormones Sex hormones have organizing and activating effects on behavior. Men and women normally produce one genuine aphrodisiac: testosterone. Female sex hormones do not appear to play a direct role in determining sexual motivation or response in human females. Yet levels of testosterone in the bloodstream have been associated with sexual interest in women.

THE SEXUAL RESPONSE CYCLE

Masters and Johnson found that the physiological responses of men and women to sexual stimulation are quite alike. Both —experience vasocongestion and myotonia early in the response cycle.

Excitement Phase Sexual excitement is characterized by erection in the male and vaginal lubrication in the female.

Plateau Phase The plateau phase is an advanced state of arousal that precedes orgasm.

Orgasmic Phase Orgasm in the male occurs in two stages of muscular contractions. Orgasm in the female is manifested by contractions of the pelvic muscles that surround the vaginal barrel.

Resolution Phase During the resolution phase, which follows orgasm, the body returns to its prearoused state.

Kaplan's Three Stages of Sexual Response: An Alternate Model Kaplan developed a three-stage model of sexual response consisting of desire, excitement, and orgasm. Kaplan's model makes it more convenient for clinicians to classify and treat sexual dysfunctions.

CONTROVERSIES ABOUT ORGASM

Multiple Orgasms: When You're Having More Than One Multiple orgasm is the occurrence of one or more additional orgasms following the first, within a short period of time and before the body has returned to a pre-plateau level of arousal. Most women, but not most men, are capable of multiple orgasms.

How Many Kinds of Orgasms Do Women Have? One, Two, or Three? Freud theorized the existence of two types of orgasms in women: clitoral and vaginal. Masters and Johnson found only one kind of orgasm among women. Singer and Singer suggested that there are three types of female orgasms: vulval, uterine, and blended orgasm.

The Grafenberg Spot The G-spot—an allegedly distinct area of the vagina within the anterior wall—may have special erotic significance. Some researchers suggest that prolonged stimulation of the spot produces an orgasm that is characterized by intense pleasure and, in some women, by a type of ejaculation. The nature of this ejaculate remains in doubt.

_____ If male sex hormones were not present during critical stages of prenatal development, we would all develop female sexual organs.

_____ The gender of a baby crocodile is determined by the temperature at which the egg develops.

_____ Thousands of people have changed their genders through gender-reassignment surgery.

_____ Men act more aggressively than women do.

_____ A 2¹/₂-year-old child may know that he is a boy but think that he can grow up to be a mommy.

_____ Adolescent girls who show a number of masculine traits are more popular than are girls who thoroughly adopt the traditional feminine gender role.

C **H** A *P* *T* E **R**   **6**

Gender Identity and Gender Roles

Whatever women do they must do twice as well as men to be thought half as good. Luckily, this is not difficult.

(Charlotte Whitton, on her inauguration as the mayor of Ottawa)

I like men to behave like men—strong and childish.

(French author Françoise Sagan)

As witty as these remarks from war correspondents in the battle of the genders may be, they signify key issues in the study of gender, including gender roles, the actual differences between the genders, and the enduring problem of sexism. This chapter addresses the biological, psychological, and sociological aspects of gender. First we focus on sexual differentiation—the process by which males and females develop distinct reproductive anatomy. Sexual differentiation differs from gender identity, or one's sense of being male or female. In nearly all cases, gender identity is consistent with anatomic gender. In transsexualism, however, gender identity and biological gender are at odds.

We then turn to gender roles—the complex behavior patterns that are deemed "masculine" or "feminine" in a particular culture. Each culture expects men and women to behave in ways that are gender appropriate. What is considered appropriate in one society may not be so in another, however. The discussion of sexism reveals that the costs of stereotyping have historically been borne disproportionately by women. The chapter examines empirical findings on actual gender differences, which may challenge some of the preconceptions that many of us hold regarding the differences between men and women. We next consider gender typing—the processes by which boys come to behave in line with what is expected of men (most of the time) and girls with what is expected of women (most of the time). We shall also explore the concept of psychological androgyny, which applies to people who display characteristics associated with both genders.

Learning Objective 1:
Trace the influences of sex chromosomes and hormones on sexual differentiation during the embryonic and fetal stages.

Sexual differentiation
The process by which males and females develop distinct reproductive anatomy.

Chromosome
One of the rodlike structures found in the nucleus of every living cell that carry the genetic code in the form of genes.

Zygote
A fertilized ovum (egg cell).

PRENATAL SEXUAL DIFFERENTIATION

Over the years many ideas have been proposed to account for **sexual differentiation,** such as the belief that sperm from the right testicle make females whereas sperm from the left testicle make males (Angier, 1990). If this were so, males would indeed be sinister, because *sinister* means "left-hand" or "unlucky side" in Latin.

According to the Old Testament, as you may recall, Adam was created first and Eve issued forth from one of his ribs. From the standpoint of modern biological knowledge, however, it would be more accurate to say that "Adams" (that is, males) develop from "Eves" (females). Let us trace the development of sexual differentiation from the point of conception.

When a sperm cell fertilizes an ovum, 23 **chromosomes** from the male parent normally combine with 23 chromosomes from the female parent. The **zygote,** the beginning of a new human being, is only $1/175$ of an inch long. Yet, on this tiny stage, one's stamp as a unique individual has already been assured—whether one will have black or blond hair, grow bald or develop a widow's peak, or become male or female.

The chromosomes from each parent combine to form 23 pairs. The twenty-third pair are the sex chromosomes. An ovum carries an X sex chromosome, but a sperm carries either an X or a Y sex chromosome. If a sperm with an X sex chromosome fertilizes the ovum, the newly conceived person will normally develop as a female, with an XX sex chromosomal structure. If the sperm carries a Y sex chromosome, the child will normally develop as a male (XY).

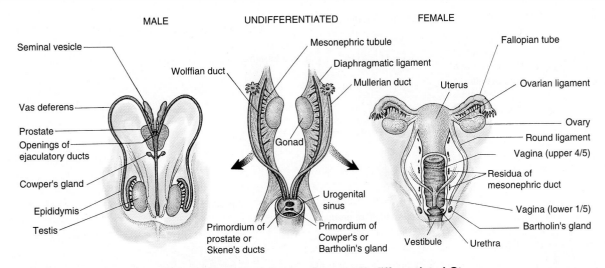

MALE **UNDIFFERENTIATED** **FEMALE**

Seminal vesicle

Wolffian duct

Mesonephric tubule

Diaphragmatic ligament

Mullerian duct

Fallopian tube

Uterus

Ovarian ligament

Vas deferens

Gonad

Ovary

Prostate

Round ligament

Openings of ejaculatory ducts

Vagina (upper 4/5)

Residua of mesonephric duct

Cowper's gland

Urogenital sinus

Vagina (lower 1/5)

Epididymis

Bartholin's gland

Testis

Primordium of prostate or Skene's ducts

Primordium of Cowper's or Bartholin's gland

Vestibule

Urethra

FIGURE 6.1 **Development of the Internal Sexual Organs from an Undifferentiated Stage at About 5 or 6 Weeks Following Conception.**

Embryo

The stage of prenatal development that begins with implantation of a fertilized ovum in the uterus and concludes with development of the major organ systems at about two months after conception.

After fertilization, the zygote divides repeatedly. After a few short weeks one cell has become billions. At about 3 weeks a primitive heart begins to drive blood through the embryonic bloodstream. At about 5 to 6 weeks, when the **embryo** is only 1/4 to 1/2 inch long, primitive gonads, ducts, and external genitals whose gender cannot be distinguished visually have formed (Figures 6.1 and 6.2). Each embryo possesses primitive external genitals, a pair of sexually undifferentiated gonads, and two sets of primitive duct structures, the Müllerian (female) ducts and the Wolffian (male) ducts.

During the first 6 weeks or so of prenatal development, embryonic structures of both genders develop along similar lines and resemble primitive female structures. At about the seventh week after conception, the genetic code (XX or XY) begins to assert itself, causing changes in the gonads, genital ducts, and external genitals. The Y sex chromosome causes the testes to begin to differentiate. Ovaries begin to differentiate if the Y chromosome is absent. Some rare individuals who have only one X sex chromosome instead of the typical XY or XX arrangement also become females, since they too lack the Y chromosome (Angier, 1990).

Thus, the basic blueprint of the human embryo is female. The genetic instructions in the Y sex chromosome cause the embryo to deviate from the female developmental course. In a manner of speaking, "Adams" develop from embryos that otherwise would continue along the path toward becoming "Eves."

By about the seventh week of prenatal development, the Y sex chromosome stimulates the production of *H-Y antigen*, a protein that fosters the development of testes. Strands of tissue begin to organize into seminiferous tubules. Female gonads begin to develop somewhat later than male gonads. The forerunners of follicles that will bear ova are not found until the fetal stage of development, about 10 weeks after conception. Ovaries begin to form at 11 or 12 weeks.

THE ROLE OF SEX HORMONES IN SEXUAL DIFFERENTIATION

Androgens

Male sex hormones.

Testosterone

The male sex hormone that fosters the development of male sex characteristics and is connected with the sex drive.

Once the testes develop in the embryo, they begin to produce male sex hormones, or **androgens.** The most important androgen, **testosterone,** spurs differentiation of the male (Wolffian) duct system (Figure 6.1). Each Wolffian duct develops into an epididymis, vas deferens, and seminal vesicle. The external genitals, including the penis, begin to take shape at about the eighth week of development under the influence of another androgen, *dihydrotestosterone* (DHT). Yet another testicular hormone, one secreted during the fetal stage, prevents the Müllerian ducts from developing into the female duct system. It is appropriately termed Müllerian inhibiting substance (MIS).

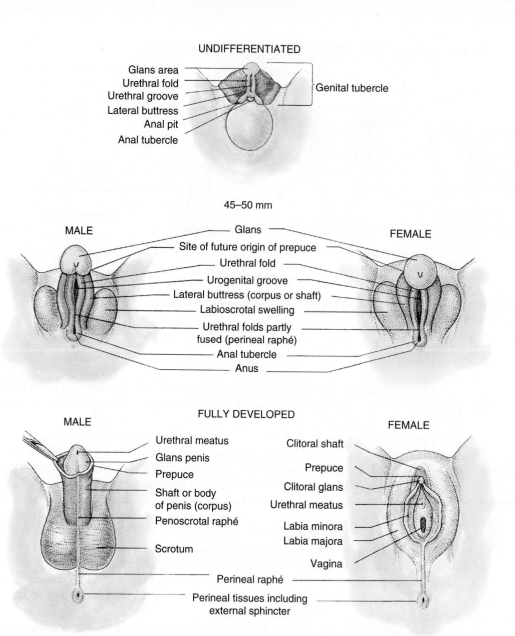

UNDIFFERENTIATED

Glans area
Urethral fold
Urethral groove
Lateral buttress
Anal pit
Anal tubercle

Genital tubercle

45–50 mm

MALE   Glans   FEMALE
Site of future origin of prepuce
Urethral fold
Urogenital groove
Lateral buttress (corpus or shaft)
Labioscrotal swelling
Urethral folds partly
fused (perineal raphé)
Anal tubercle
Anus

FULLY DEVELOPED

MALE   FEMALE

Urethral meatus
Glans penis
Prepuce
Shaft or body
of penis (corpus)
Penoscrotal raphé
Scrotum

Clitoral shaft
Prepuce
Clitoral glans
Urethral meatus
Labia minora
Labia majora
Vagina

Perineal raphé
Perineal tissues including
external sphincter

FIGURE 6.2 **Development of the External Sexual Organs from an Undifferentiated Stage at About 5 or 6 Weeks Following Conception.**

Small amounts of androgens are produced in female fetuses, but they are not normally sufficient to cause male sexual differentiation. In female fetuses, the relative absence of androgens causes degeneration of the Wolffian ducts and prompts development of female sexual organs. The Müllerian ducts evolve into Fallopian tubes, the uterus, and the upper two thirds of the vagina. These developments occur even in the absence of female sex hormones. Although female sex hormones are crucial in puberty, they are not involved in fetal sexual differentiation. If a fetus with an XY sex chromosomal structure failed to produce testosterone, it would develop female sexual organs.

TRUTH OR *FICTION?*

R E V I S I T E D

If male sex hormones were not present during critical stages of prenatal development, we would all develop female sexual organs. *Yes, embryos will develop female sexual organs in the absence of male sex hormones. The basic "blueprint" for development is female.* •

DESCENT OF THE TESTES AND THE OVARIES

Inguinal canal
A fetal canal that connects the scrotum and the testes, allowing their descent. (From the Latin *inguinus,* meaning "near the groin.")

Cryptorchidism
The condition defined by undescended testes. (From roots meaning "hidden testes.")

The testes and ovaries develop from slender structures high in the abdominal cavity. By about 10 weeks after conception they have descended so that they are almost even with the upper edge of the pelvis. The ovaries remain there for the rest of the prenatal period. Later they rotate and descend farther to their adult position in the pelvis. About 4 months after conception the testes normally descend into the scrotal sac through the **inguinal canal.** After their descent, this passageway is closed.

In 1 to 2 percent of males, one or both testes remain undescended. They are still in the abdomen at birth (Campbell, 1970). The condition is termed **cryptorchidism.** In most cases of cryptorchidism, the testes migrate to the scrotum during infancy. In still other cases the testes descend by puberty. Men with undescended testes are usually treated through surgery or hormonal therapy, since they are at higher risk for cancer of the testes. Sperm production is also impaired because the undescended testes are subjected to higher-than-optimal body temperature, causing sterility.

SEX CHROMOSOMAL ABNORMALITIES

Klinefelter's syndrome
A sex-chromosomal disorder caused by an extra X sex chromosome.

Abnormalities of the sex chromosomes can have profound effects on sexual characteristics, physical health, and psychological development. **Klinefelter's syndrome,** a condition that affects about one in 500 males, is caused by an extra X sex chromosome, so the man has an XXY rather than an XY pattern. Men with this pattern fail to develop appropriate secondary sex characteristics. They have enlarged breasts, poor muscular development, and, because they fail to produce sperm, they are infertile. They also tend to be mildly retarded.

Turner's syndrome, found only in women, occurs in about one in 2,500 female births. It is caused by the presence of one X sex chromosome rather than the normal two. These women develop typical external genital organs, but their ovaries do not develop or function normally. Yet they appear to be indistinguishable from other females in terms of their interests and behavior (Money & Ehrhardt, 1972). On the other hand, they are shorter than average and infertile. They also show evidence of mild retardation, especially in skills connected with math and science.

PRENATAL SEXUAL DIFFERENTIATION OF THE BRAIN

The brain, like the genital organs, undergoes prenatal sexual differentiation. Scientists have focused on gender-specific changes that seem to occur in the hypothalamus during prenatal development. Testosterone in the blood causes cells in the hypothalamus of male fetuses to become insensitive to the female sex hormone estrogen. In the absence of testosterone, as in female fetuses, the hypothalamus does develop sensitivity to estrogen.

Sensitivity to estrogen is important in the regulation of the menstrual cycle of women after puberty. The hypothalamus detects low levels of estrogen in the blood at the end of each cycle and initiates a new cycle by stimulating the pituitary gland to secrete FSH. FSH, in turn, stimulates estrogen production by the ovaries and the ripening of an immature follicle in an ovary. Scientists believe that sexual differentiation of the hypothalamus most likely occurs during the second trimester of fetal development (Pillard & Weinrich, 1986).

GENDER IDENTITY

Gender identity
The psychological sense of being male or female.

Gender assignment
The labeling of a newborn as a male or female.

For all of us, our awareness of being male or being female—our **gender identity**—is one of the most obvious and important aspects of our self-concepts. Our gender identity is not an automatic extension of our anatomical gender. Gender identity is a psychological construct, a sense of being male or being female. **Gender assignment** reflects the child's anatomic gender and usually occurs at birth. Gender identity is so important to parents that they may want to know "Is it a boy or a girl?" before they begin to count fingers and toes.

Children generally begin to acquire an awareness of their anatomic gender by about the age of 18 months. By 36 months most children have acquired a rather firm sense of gender identity (Marcus & Corsini, 1978; McConaghy, 1979; Money, 1977).

NATURE AND NURTURE IN GENDER IDENTITY

Learning Objective 2:
Discuss the research relevant to the nature-nurture debate about determination of gender identity.

What determines gender identity? Are our brains biologically programmed along masculine or feminine lines by prenatal sex hormones? Does the environment, in the form of postnatal learning experiences, shape our self-concepts as males or females? Or does gender identity reflect an intermingling of biological and environmental influences?

Gender identity is almost always consistent with chromosomal gender. Such consistency does not certify that gender identity is biologically determined, however. We also tend to be reared as males or females, according to our anatomic genders. How, then, might we sort out the roles of nature and nurture, of biology and the environment?

Clues may be found in the experiences of rare individuals, **pseudohermaphrodites,** who possess the gonads of one gender but external genitalia that are ambiguous or typical of the opposite gender. Pseudohermaphrodites are sometimes reared as members of the gender that is opposite to their chromosomal gender. So researchers wondered, would the gender identity of these children reflect their chromosomal and gonadal gender or the gender in which they were reared? Before going further with this, let us distinguish between true hermaphroditism and pseudohermaphroditism.

Pseudohermaphrodites
People who possess the gonads of one gender but external genitalia that are ambiguous or typical of the opposite gender.

HERMAPHRODITISM

Hermaphrodites
People who possess both ovarian and testicular tissue. (From the names of the male and female Greek gods *Hermes* and *Aphrodite*.)

Hormonal errors during prenatal development produce various congenital defects. Some individuals are born with both ovarian and testicular tissue. They are called **hermaphrodites,** after the Greek myth of the son of Hermes and Aphrodite, whose body became united with that of a nymph while he was bathing. True hermaphrodites may have one gonad of each gender (a testicle and an ovary), or gonads that combine testicular and ovarian tissue.

Regardless of their genetic gender, hermaphrodites usually assume the gender identity and gender role of the gender assigned at birth. Figure 6.3 shows a genetic female (XX) with a right testicle and left ovary. This person married and became a stepfather

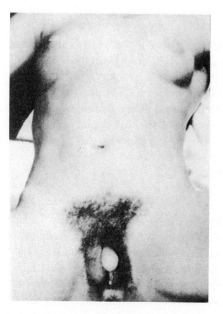

FIGURE 6.3 **A True Hermaphrodite.** This genetic female (XX) has one testicle and one ovary and the gender identity of a male.

with a firm male identity (Money, 1968). The roles of biology and environment remain tangled, however, since true hermaphrodites have gonadal tissue of both genders.

True hermaphroditism is extremely rare. More common is pseudohermaphroditism, which occurs in perhaps one infant in 1,000 (Green & Green, 1965). The occurrence of pseudohermaphroditism has given scientists an opportunity to examine the roles of nature (biology) and nurture (environmental influences) in the shaping of gender identity.

PSEUDOHERMAPHRODITISM *Pseudohermaphrodites* ("false" hermaphrodites) have testes or ovaries, but not both. Unlike true hermaphrodites, their gonads (testes or ovaries) match their chromosomal gender. Because of prenatal hormonal errors, however, their external genitals and sometimes their internal reproductive anatomy are ambiguous or resemble those of the opposite gender.

The most common form of female pseudohermaphroditism is **androgenital syndrome,** in which a genetic female (XX) has female internal sexual structures (ovaries), but masculinized external genitals (Figure 6.4, page 168). The clitoris is so enlarged that it may resemble a small penis. The syndrome occurs as a result of excessive levels of androgens. In some cases the fetus's own adrenal glands produce excess androgen (the adrenal glands usually produce low levels of androgen). In other cases mothers may have received synthetic androgens during their pregnancies. In the 1950s and 1960s, before these side effects were known, synthetic androgens were sometimes prescribed to help prevent miscarriages in women with histories of spontaneous abortions.

Another type of pseudohermaphroditism, **androgen-insensitivity syndrome,** describes genetic males (XY) who had lower-than-normal prenatal sensitivity to androgens. As a result their genitals did not become normally masculinized. At birth their external genitals are feminized, including a small vagina, and their testes are undescended. Because of insensitivity to androgens, the male duct system (epididymis, vas deferens, seminal vesicles, and ejaculatory ducts) fails to develop. Nevertheless, the fetal testes produce Müllerian inhibiting substance, preventing the development of a uterus or Fallopian tubes.

A third type of pseudohermaphroditism is named **Dominican Republic syndrome,** because it was first documented in a group of 18 affected boys in two rural villages in that nation (Imperato-McGinley et al., 1974). Dominican Republic syndrome is a genetic enzyme disorder that prevents testosterone from masculinizing the external genitalia. The boys were born with normal testes and internal male reproductive organs, but their external genitals were malformed. Their penises were stunted and resembled clitorises. Their scrotums were incompletely formed and resembled female labia. They also had partially formed vaginas.

PSEUDOHERMAPHRODITISM AND GENDER IDENTITY The experiences of pseudohermaphrodites have provided insights into the origins of gender identity. The genitals of girls who have androgenital syndrome are usually surgically feminized in infancy, and the girls receive hormone treatments to correct excessive adrenal output of androgens. As a result, they usually acquire a feminine gender identity and develop physically as normal females. What if the syndrome is not identified early in life, however? Consider the cases of two children who were treated at Johns Hopkins University Hospital. The children both suffered from androgenital syndrome, but their treatments and the outcomes were very different. Each child was genetically female (XX). Each had female internal sex organs. Because of prenatal exposure to synthetic male sex hormones, however, each developed masculinized external sex organs (Money & Ehrhardt, 1972).

The problem was identified in one child (let's call her Abby) in infancy. Her masculinized sex organs were removed surgically when she was 2. Like many other girls, Abby was tomboyish during childhood, but she was always feminine in appearance and had a female gender identity. She began to develop breasts by the age of 12, but did not begin to menstruate until age 20. She dated boys, and her fantasy life centered around marriage to a man.

Androgenital syndrome
A form of pseudohermaphroditism in which a genetic female has internal female sexual structures but masculinized external genitals.

Androgen-insensitivity syndrome
A form of pseudohermaphroditism in which a genetic male is prenatally insensitive to androgens. As a result his genitals do not become normally masculinized.

Dominican Republic syndrome
A form of pseudohermaphroditism in which a genetic enzyme disorder prevents testosterone from masculinizing the external genitalia.

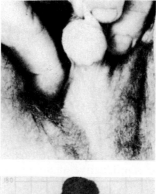

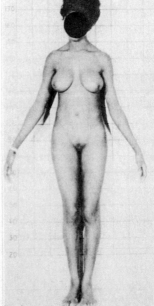

FIGURE 6.4
Pseudohermaphroditism.
In androgenital syndrome (top photo) a genetic female (XX) has female internal sexual structures (ovaries), but masculinized external genitals. The bottom photo shows a genetic male (XY) with androgen-insensitivity syndrome. The external genitals were clearly feminized, and she has always lived as a female.

Activity: *Thinking About Gender and Reality* The IM includes this activity, which asks students to write about what they think really determines whether a person is male or female.

The other child (let's call him James) was initially mistaken for a genetic male with stunted external sex organs. The error was discovered at the age of 3½. By then he had a firm male gender identity, so instead of removing his external sex organs, surgeons further masculinized them. At puberty, hormone treatments stoked the development of body hair, male musculature, and other male secondary sex characteristics.

As an adolescent, James did poorly in school. Possibly in an effort to compensate for his poor grades, he joined a gang of semidelinquents. He became one of the boys. In contrast to Abby, James was sexually attracted to women.

Both children were pseudohermaphrodites. Both had internal female sexual organs and masculinized external organs, but they were treated and reared differently. In Abby's case, the newborn was designated female, surgically altered to remove the masculinized genitals, and reared as a girl. In James's case, the infant was labeled and reared as a boy. Each child acquired the gender identity of the assigned gender. Environmental influences appeared to play the critical role in shaping the gender identity of these children.

Further evidence for the import of psychosocial influences on gender identity is found in studies of genetic males (XY) with androgen-insensitivity syndrome. They possess testes but are born with feminine appearing genitals and are typically reared as girls. They develop a female gender identity and stereotypical feminine interests. They show as much interest in dolls, dresses, and future roles as mothers and housewives as do genetic girls (XX) of the same ages and social class (Brooks-Gunn & Matthews, 1979; Money et al., 1968; Money & Ehrhardt, 1972).

The boys with Dominican Republic syndrome also resembled girls at birth and were reared as females. At puberty, however, their testes swung into normal testosterone production, causing startling changes: their testes descended, their voices deepened, their musculature filled out, and their "clitorises" expanded into penises. Of the 18 boys who were reared as girls, 17 shifted to a male gender identity. Sixteen of the 18 assumed a stereotypical masculine gender role. Of the remaining two, one adopted a male gender identity but continued to maintain a feminine gender role, including wearing dresses. The other maintained a female gender identity and later sought a sex-change operation to "correct" the pubertal masculinization.

The Dominican transformations show how malleable gender identity can be. What of the roles of nature and nurture in the formation of gender identity, however? If environmental forces (nurture) were predominant, gender identity would be based on the gender in which the person is reared, regardless of biological abnormalities. With the Dominicans, however, pubertal biological changes led to changes in both gender identity and gender roles. Is nature (biology) then the primary determinant of gender identity? Unfortunately, the Dominican study does not allow clear separation of the effects of nature and nurture. One intriguing hypothesis is that the pubertal surges of testosterone may have activated brain structures that were masculinized during prenatal development. Prenatal testosterone levels in these boys were presumably normal and could have affected the sexual differentiation of brain tissue, even though the genetic defect prevented the hormone from masculinizing the external genitalia.

Consider some other possibilities: Did the children, seeing themselves transforming into men, begin to change their self-concepts to be consistent with their anatomical changes? Did the children choose to assume male gender identities because the masculine gender role was positively valued in their culture? Either possibility permits an explanation of gender identity in psychological or cultural terms rather than in terms of the dictates of biology.

What, then, can we conclude from studies of pseudohermaphrodites? For one thing, gender identity and the assumption of gender roles are strongly influenced by psychosocial factors. Pseudohermaphrodites can acquire the gender identity of the opposite chromosomal gender when they are reared as members of that gender. The genetic females (XX)—Abby and James—were reared as members of different genders and acquired the gender identity in which they were reared. Yet both were treated with sex hormones appropriate to their assigned gender. Thus, we cannot be certain that sex hormones did not influence their subsequent gender identity. The Dominican study also suggests that gender identity may not be fixed by early learning influences, but may be subject to subsequent biological and/or psychosocial influences.

We should also recognize that the experiences of people affected by these hormonal errors may not generalize to others. It remains unclear how prenatal hormonal errors affect the sexual differentiation of the brain. Perhaps the brains of these children had not been clearly gender typed prenatally and were thus capable of an unusual degree of postnatal flexibility in the assumption of gender identity. Perhaps in normal people the brain is more clearly differentiated prenatally, so that gender identity is not so readily influenced by experience.

Most scientists today conclude that the acquisition of gender identity is influenced by complex interactions between biological and psychosocial factors. Some place relatively greater emphasis on psychosocial factors (Money, 1987b; Money & Ehrhardt, 1972; Money & Wiedeking, 1980); others emphasize the role of biological factors (Diamond, 1977, 1982). The debate over the relative contributions of nature and nurture is likely to continue.

In case you have had enough discussion of the complex issues surrounding the origins of gender in human beings, consider the crocodile. Crocodile eggs do not carry sex chromosomes. The baby's gender is determined, instead, by the temperature at which the eggs develop (Ackerman, 1991). Some (males) like it hot (at least in the mid-90s Fahrenheit), and some (females) like it not cold perhaps, but under the mid-80s Fahrenheit.

The gender of a baby crocodile is determined by the temperature at which the egg develops. *Yes, the gender of baby crocodiles is determined by the temperature at which the eggs develop.* •

TRANSSEXUALISM

Transsexuals
People who have a gender-identity disorder in which they feel trapped in the body of the wrong gender.

In 1953 an ex-GI who journeyed to Denmark for a "sex-change operation" made headlines. She became known as Christine (formerly George) Jorgensen. Since then, thousands of **transsexuals** have undergone gender-reassignment surgery. Among the better known is the tennis player Dr. Renée Richards, formerly Dr. Richard Raskin.

Gender-reassignment surgery cannot implant the internal reproductive organs of the opposite gender. Instead, it generates the likeness of external genitals typical of the opposite gender. This can be done more precisely with male-to-female than female-to-male transsexuals. After such operations, people can participate in sexual activity and even attain orgasm, but they cannot conceive or bear children.

Thousands of people have changed their genders through gender-reassignment surgery. *Whether or not you believe that people have changed their genders through sex-reassignment surgery depends on your interpretation of the concept of* gender. *If "real gender," to you, depends on sex chromosomal structure (XX or XY), then no one can ever change gender. If you believe that gender rests more squarely on gender identity and gender typing, the issue becomes debatable.* •

Transsexuals harbor a deep sense of discomfort about their anatomic gender. They wish to be rid of their own primary sex characteristics (their external genitals and internal sex organs) and to live fully as members of the opposite gender. A male transsexual perceives himself to be a female who, through some quirk of fate, was born with the wrong genital equipment. A female transsexual perceives herself as a man trapped in a woman's body. Although the prevalence of transsexualism remains unknown, it is thought to be rare. One investigator estimated the prevalence at one in 100,000 males and one in 130,000 females (Pauly, 1974). Experts estimate the number of transsexuals in the United States to be about 25,000, with about 6,000 to perhaps 11,000 having undergone gender-reassignment surgery (Selvin, 1993).

Renée Richards (née Richard Raskin). Physician Richard Raskin (left) underwent gender reassignment to become Renée Richards (right). Richards played professional tennis on the women's circuit for a number of years.

Patterns of sexual attraction do not appear to be central in importance. Some transsexuals are "asexual" (American Psychiatric Association, 1987). They report never having had strong sexual feelings. Others are attracted to members of their own (anatomic) gender. They are unlikely to regard themselves as homosexuals, however. From their perspective, their lovers are members of the opposite gender. Still others are attracted to members of the opposite anatomic gender. Nonetheless, they all want to be rid of their own sex organs and to live as members of the opposite gender.

Transsexualism is not to be confused with homosexuality (Selvin, 1993). Homosexuals—gay males and lesbians—are erotically attracted to members of their own gender. A gay man may desire another man as a lover; a lesbian may sexually desire another woman. Gay men and lesbians perceive their gender identities to be consistent with their anatomic gender, however. They would no more want to be rid of their own genitals than would heterosexuals. As one gay man put it, "Just because I'm turned on by other men doesn't make me feel less like a man."

Transsexuals usually show cross-gender preferences in play and dress in early childhood. Many report that they felt they belonged to the opposite gender for as long as they can remember. Only a few were unaware of their transsexual feelings until adolescence. Male transsexuals generally recall that as children, they preferred playing with dolls, enjoyed wearing frilly dresses, and disliked rough-and-tumble play. They were often perceived by their peers as "sissy boys." Female transsexuals usually report that as children they disliked dresses and preferred to dress like boys and acted much like "tomboys." They also preferred playing "boys' games," and doing so with boys. Female transsexuals appear to have an easier time adjusting than male transsexuals (Selvin, 1993). "Tomboys" generally find it easier to be accepted by their peers than "sissy boys." Even in adulthood, it may be easier for a female transsexual to don men's clothes and "pass" as a slightly built man than it is for a brawnier man to pass for a tall woman.

The transition to adolescence is particularly difficult for transsexuals. They find their bodies changing in ways that evoke their disgust. Female transsexuals abhor the onset of menstruation and the development of breasts. They may seek to disguise their budding breasts by binding them or wearing loose clothing. Some have mastectomies at the age of consent to remove the obvious reminder of what they perceive as "nature's mistake."

THEORETICAL PERSPECTIVES No clear understanding of the nature or causes of transsexualism has emerged (Lothstein, 1984). Views on its origins somewhat parallel

Learning Objective 3: Define transsexualism, discuss the theoretical perspectives on transsexualism, and describe the techniques and limitations of gender-reassignment surgery.

Identification

In psychoanalytic theory, the process of incorporating within ourselves our perceptions of the behaviors, thoughts, and feelings of others.

Notes: Billy Tipton, a talented pianist and saxophonist, died January 21, 1989. After Billy's death, his three adopted sons were told by the funeral home director that their "father" was a woman. About fifty years earlier Billy had begun playing in bands as a man, possibly to increase her chances of employment as a jazz musician. She was accepted as a man by fellow musicians, her sons, and all who knew her. Was Billy a transsexual? We do not know whether Billy possessed a male or female gender identity. The woman with whom Billy lived for almost 20 years and to whom he claimed to be married will not talk about their lives, so the answer may never be clear. (Chin, Paula. 1989. Death discloses Billy Tipton's strange secret: He was a she. *People Weekly,* 31, 95–96.)

Discussion Question: How would you react if one of your classmates told you he or she had had gender-reassignment surgery? If a friend told you? If your date told you? What questions would you want to ask him or her?

those on the origins of homosexuality, which is surprising given the fundamental differences that exist between the two.

Psychoanalytic theorists have focused on early parent-child relationships. Male transsexuals, in this view, may have had "close-binding mothers" (extremely close mother-son relationships) and "detached-hostile fathers" (fathers who were absent or disinterested) (Stoller, 1969). Such family circumstances may have fostered intense **identification** with the mother, to the point of an inversion of typical gender roles and identity. Girls with weak, ineffectual mothers and strong, masculine fathers may identify with their fathers, rejecting their own female identities.

There is some evidence that male transsexuals tend to have had unusually close relationships with their mothers during childhood, whereas female transsexuals tend to have identified more with their fathers and to have perceived their mothers as cold and rejecting (Pauly, 1974). Yet one problem with the psychoanalytic view is that the roles of cause and effect may be reversed. It could be that in childhood, transsexuals gravitate toward the parent of the opposite gender and reject the efforts of the parent of the same gender to reach out to them and engage them in gender-typed activities. These views also do not account for the many transsexuals whose family backgrounds fail to match these patterns. Moreover, these views lack predictive power; most children—in fact, the vast majority!—with such family backgrounds do *not* become transsexuals.

The early onset of transsexual feelings suggests that critical early learning experiences, if they exist, might occur in the preschool years. Transsexuals may also be influenced by prenatal hormonal imbalances. The brain is in some ways "masculinized" or "feminized" by sex hormones during prenatal development. The brain could be influenced in one direction, even as the genitals are being differentiated in the other direction (Money, 1987b). Still, no direct evidence with humans connects the effects of prenatal sex hormones on the brain to transsexualism. Scholars of transsexualism admit that they are less than satisfied with their own hypotheses.

GENDER REASSIGNMENT   Gender-reassignment surgery for transsexuals has been controversial since its inception. Yet psychotherapy is not considered a reasonable alternative, because it has been generally unsuccessful in helping transsexuals accept their anatomic genders (Roberto, 1983; Tollison & Adams, 1979).

Surgery is one element of a broader process of gender reassignment. Since the surgery is irreversible, health professionals conduct careful evaluations to determine that people seeking reassignment are competent to make such decisions and have thought through the consequences. They usually require that the transsexual live openly as a member of the opposite gender for a trial period of at least a year before surgery. Health professionals refuse the request for surgery if they think that patients are seeking a change without having carefully thought through the consequences or because of a psychological disorder.

Once the decision is reached, a lifetime of hormone treatments is begun. Male-to-female transsexuals receive estrogen, which fosters the development of female secondary sex characteristics. It causes fatty deposits to develop in the breasts and hips, softens the skin, and inhibits growth of the beard. Female-to-male transsexuals receive androgens, which promote male secondary sex characteristics. The voice deepens, hair becomes distributed according to the male pattern, muscles enlarge, and the fatty deposits in the breasts and hips are lost. The clitoris may also become more prominent.

Gender-reassignment surgery is largely cosmetic. Medical science cannot construct internal genital organs or gonads. Male-to-female surgery is generally more successful. The penis and testicles are first removed. Tissue from the penis is placed in an artificial vagina so that sensitive nerve endings will provide sexual sensations. A penis-shaped form of plastic or balsa wood is used to keep the vagina distended during healing.

In female-to-male transsexuals, the internal sex organs (ovaries, Fallopian tubes, uterus) are removed along with the remaining fatty tissue in the breasts. The nipples are moved an inch or so to keep them at the proper height on the torso. The urethra is rerouted through the enlarged clitoris, or an artificial penis and scrotum are constructed from tissue from the abdomen, the labia, and the perineum through a series of operations. In either case, the patient can urinate while standing, which appears to provide psychologi-

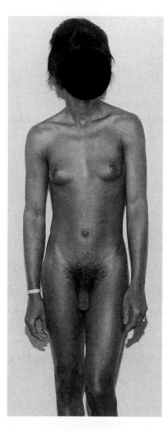

Gender Reassignment.
Gender reassignment involves hormone treatments and surgery to make the genitals appear as similar as possible to the opposite gender. On these pages we see a male to female transsexual during two stages of gender reassignment. The photo above shows the feminizing effects on breast development of female hormone treatment. The photo opposite shows the patient after removal of the penis and the construction of an artificial vagina from other tissue.

Stereotype
A fixed, conventional idea about a group of people.

Gender roles
Complex clusters of ways in which males and females are expected to behave.

cal gratification. Although the artificial penis does not stiffen and become erect naturally, a variety of methods, including implants, can be used to allow the artificial penis to approximate erection.

Some transsexuals hesitate to undertake sex-change operations because they are repulsed by the prospect of such extreme medical intervention. Others forgo surgery so as not to jeopardize high-status careers or marital and family relationships (Kockott & Fahrner, 1987). Such people continue to think of themselves as members of the opposite gender, however, even without surgery.

OUTCOMES OF GENDER-REASSIGNMENT SURGERY   Following the introduction of gender-reassignment surgery in the United States in the 1960s, most reports of postoperative adjustment were positive (Pauly, 1986). An influential study in the 1970s conducted at the Gender Identity Clinic at Johns Hopkins University was quite negative, however (Meyer & Reter, 1979). The study included a control group of transsexuals who did not receive gender-reassignment surgery. Psychological adjustment was more positive among the control subjects than among those transsexuals who had undergone surgery.

More recent reviews have reported more positive outcomes for gender-reassignment surgery (Kockott & Fahrner, 1987; Lundstrom et al., 1984; Pauly & Edgerton, 1986), especially when it is restricted to the most "qualified" candidates (Lothstein, 1982). One study of 42 postoperative male-to-female transsexuals found that all but one would repeat the surgery. Moreover, the great majority found sexual activity more pleasurable as a "woman" (Bentler, 1976).

Reviewers of the international literature reported in 1984 that about 90 percent of transsexuals who undergo gender-reassignment surgery experience positive results (Lundstrom et al., 1984). In Canada, a follow-up study of 116 transsexuals (female-to-male and male-to-female) at least one year after surgery found that most of them were content with the results and were reasonably well-adjusted (Blanchard et al., 1985). Positive results for surgery were also reported in a study of 141 Dutch transsexuals (Kuiper & Cohen-Kettenis, 1988). Nearly nine of ten male-to-female and female-to-male transsexuals in a recent study of 23 transsexuals reported they were very pleased with the results of their gender-reassignment surgery (Lief & Hubschman, 1993). Still another study (Abramowitz, 1986) reported that about two out of three cases showed at least some postoperative improvement in psychological adjustment. These favorable results do not mean that postoperative transsexuals were ecstatic about their lives; in many cases it meant that they were less unhappy. Most transsexuals are socially maladjusted prior to gender reassignment, and many remain lonely and isolated afterward. Moreover, about half incur postoperative medical complications (Lindermalm et al., 1986).

Male-to-female transsexuals whose surgery permitted them to "pass" as members of the opposite gender showed better adjustment than those whose surgery left telltale signs (such as breast scarring and leftover erectile tissue) that they were not "real" women (Ross & Need, 1989). Social and family support also contributed to postsurgical adjustment (Ross & Need, 1989).

Male-to-female transsexuals outnumber female-to-males, but postoperative adjustment is apparently more favorable for female-to-males. Nearly 10 percent of male-to-female cases, as compared to 4 to 5 percent of female-to-males, have had disturbing outcomes, such as severe psychological disorders, hospitalization, requests for reversal surgery, even suicide (Abramowitz, 1986). One reason for the relatively better postoperative adjustment of the female-to-male transsexuals may be society's more accepting attitudes toward women who desire to become men (Abramowitz, 1986). Female-to-male transsexuals tend to be better adjusted socially before surgery as well (Kockott & Fahrner, 1988; Pauly, 1974), so their superior postoperative adjustment may be nothing more than a selection factor.

A growing number of programs across the country have been established to help transsexuals come to terms with themselves and adjust to living in a society in which they rarely feel welcome (Selvin, 1993). One example is the Gender Identity Project in New York City's Greenwich Village, which sponsors meetings where transsexuals get

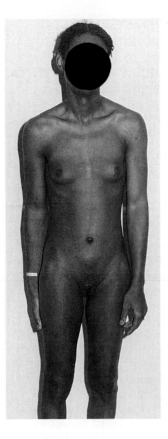

together and share common concerns. Such programs help create a sense of community for a group of people who feel alienated from the larger society.

GENDER ROLES AND STEREOTYPES

"Why can't a woman be more like a man?" You may recall this lyric from the song that Professor Henry Higgins sings in the musical *My Fair Lady*. In the song the professor laments that women are emotional and fickle, whereas men are logical and dependable. The "emotional woman" is a **stereotype**—a fixed, oversimplified, and often severely distorted idea about a group of people. The "logical man" is also a stereotype—albeit more generous. Gender roles are stereotypes in that they evoke fixed conventional expectations of men and women.

Our gender identities—our personal identification of ourselves according to our concepts of masculinity and femininity—do not determine the roles or behaviors that are deemed masculine or feminine in our culture. Cultures have broad expectations of men and women that are termed **gender roles.**

In our culture the stereotypical female has such traits as gentleness, dependency, kindness, helpfulness, patience, and submissiveness (Cartwright et al., 1983). The masculine gender-role stereotype is one of toughness, gentlemanliness, and protectiveness (Myers & Gonda, 1982). Females are generally seen as warm and emotional; males as independent, assertive, and competitive. The times are a-changing, somewhat. Women, as well as men, now bring home the bacon, but women are still more often expected to fry it in the pan and bear the primary responsibility for child rearing (Deaux & Lewis, 1983). In some cultures, however, women are reared to be the hunters and food gatherers while men stay close to home and tend the children.

Sexism
The prejudgment that because of gender, a person will possess negative traits.

SEXISM

We have all encountered the effects of **sexism**—the prejudgment that because of gender, a person will possess negative traits. These negative traits are assumed to disqualify the

A Woman's Place—Fighting Fires? Contemporary men and women are entering occupations that had been traditionally associated with the opposite gender. Women fight fires and pilot aircraft; men pursue careers in nursing and primary education.

A WORLD OF DIVERSITY

Machismo/Marianismo Stereotypes and Hispanic Culture[1]

People who are unfamiliar with the diversity that exists among the Spanish-speaking peoples of Latin America tend to perceive all Latinos as part of a single culture. The term *Hispanic* or *Latino*, is generally used to describe Spanish-speaking peoples of Latin America whose cultures were influenced by a mixture of Spanish, African, and Native-American (Indian) cultures. Although Hispanic peoples do share some common cultural traditions, most notably the Spanish language and devotion to Christianity, each Spanish-speaking nation in Latin America has its own cultural tradition, as well as distinct subcultures. The differences among the peoples of Latin America can be seen in their dress styles, their use of language, and their music and literary traditions. Argentinians,

for example, tend to be more Europeanized in their style of dress and tastes in music. In the Dominican Republic and Puerto Rico, the influence of African and native Carib Indian cultures blossoms forth in the colorful style of dress and in the use of percussion instruments in music.

The *machismo* tradition should be evaluated in this light. Machismo is a cultural stereotype that defines masculinity in terms of an idealized view of manliness. To be *macho* is to be strong, virile, and dominant. Each Hispanic culture puts its own particular cultural stamp on the meaning of machismo, however. In the Spanish-speaking cultures of the Caribbean and Central America, the macho code encourages men to restrain their feelings and maintain an emotional distance. In my travels

in Argentina and some other Latin American countries, however, I have observed that men who are sensitive and emotionally expressive are not perceived as compromising their macho code. More research is needed into differences in cultural conceptions of machismo and other gender roles among various Hispanic groups.

Marianismo
In counterpoint to the macho ideal among Hispanic peoples is the cultural idealization of femininity embodied in the concept of *marianismo*. The marianismo stereotype, which derives its name from the Virgin Mary, refers to the ideal of the virtuous woman as one who "suffers in silence," submerging her needs and desires to those of her husband and children. With the mar-

[1]This "World of Diversity" feature was written by Rafael Art. Javier, Ph.D. Dr. Javier is Associate Clinical Professor of Psychology and Director of the Center for Psychological Services and Clinical Studies at St. John's University in Jamaica, New York. Dr. Javier was born in the Dominican Republic and educated in philosophy in the Dominican Republic, Puerto Rico, and Venezuela, and in psychology and psychoanalysis at New York University. Dr. Javier is a practicing psychoanalyst and maintains a research interest in psycholinguistics and psychotherapy with ethnic minorities. All rights are reserved by Dr. Javier.

Learning Objective 4:
Define sexism, give examples, and discuss its effects on women and men.

 Gender Equality

person for certain vocations or prevent him or her from performing adequately in these jobs or in some social situations.

Sexism may even lead us to interpret the same behavior in prejudicial ways when performed by women or by men. We may see the man as "self-assertive," but the woman as "pushy." We may look upon *him* as flexible, but brand *her* fickle and indecisive. *He* may be rational, whereas *she* is cold. *He* is tough when necessary, but *she* is bitchy. When the businesswoman engages in stereotypical masculine behaviors, the sexist reacts negatively by branding her abnormal or unhealthy.

Sexism may make it difficult for men to act in ways that are stereotyped as feminine. A "sensitive" woman is simply sensitive, but a sensitive man may be seen as a "sissy." A woman may be perceived as polite, whereas a man showing the same behavior seems passive or weak. Only recently have men begun to enter occupational domains previously restricted largely to women, such as secretarial work, nursing, and teaching in the pri-

ianismo stereotype the image of a woman's role as a martyr is raised to the level of a cultural ideal. According to this cultural stereotype, a woman is expected to demonstrate her love for her husband by waiting patiently at home and having dinner prepared for him at any time of day or night he happens to come home, to have his slippers ready for him, and so on. The feminine ideal is one of suffering in silence and being the provider of joy, even in the face of pain. Strongly influenced by the patriarchal Spanish tradition, the marianismo stereotype has historically been used to maintain women in a subordinate position in relation to men.

Acculturation: When Traditional Stereotypes Meet the Financial Realities of Life in the United States

Acculturation—the merging of cultures that occurs when immigrant groups become assimilated into the mainstream culture—has challenged this traditional machismo/marianismo division of marital roles among Hispanic couples in the United States. I have seen in my own work in treating Hispanic-American couples in therapy that marriages are under increasing strain from the conflict between traditional and modern expectations about marital roles. Hispanic-American women have been entering the workforce in increasing numbers, usually in domestic or child-care positions, but they are still expected to assume responsibility for tending their own children, keeping the house, and serving their husbands' needs when they return home. In many cases, a reversal of traditional roles occurs in which the wife works and supports the family, while the husband remains at home because he is unable to find or maintain employment.

It is often the Hispanic-American husband who has the greater difficulty accepting a more flexible distribution of roles within the marriage and giving up a rigid set of expectations tied to traditional machismo/marianismo gender expectations. Although some couples manage to reshape their expectations and marital roles in the face of changing conditions, many relationships buckle under the strain and are terminated in divorce. While I do not expect either the machismo or marianismo stereotype to disappear entirely, I would not be surprised to find a greater flexibility in gender role expectations as a product of continued acculturation.

Rafael Art. Javier

---

mary grades. Only recently have the floodgates opened for women into traditionally masculine professions such as engineering, law, and medicine.

Although children of both genders have about the same general learning ability, stereotypes limit their horizons. Children tend to show preferences for gender-typed activities and toys by as early as 2 or 3 years of age. If they should stray from them, their peers are sure to remind them of the "errors of their ways." How many little girls are discouraged from considering professions like architecture and engineering because they are handed dolls, not blocks and fire trucks? How many little boys are discouraged from pursuing child-care and nursing professions because of the "funny" looks they get from others when they reach for dolls?

Children not only develop stereotyped attitudes about play activities; they also develop stereotypes about the differences between "man's work" and "woman's work." Women have been historically excluded from "male occupations," and stereotypical expectations concerning "men's work" and "women's work" filter down to the primary grades. For example, according to traditional stereotypes, women are *not expected* to excel in math. Exposure to such negative expectations may discourage women from careers in science and technology.

GENDER DIFFERENCES: *VIVE LA DIFFÉRENCE* OR *VIVE LA SIMILARITÉ?*

If the genders were not anatomically different, this book would never have been written. How do the genders differ in cognitive abilities and personality, however?

DIFFERENCES IN COGNITIVE ABILITIES

A classic review by Eleanor Maccoby and Carol Nagy Jacklin (1974) found persistent evidence that females are somewhat superior to males in verbal ability. But a more recent review of the accumulated evidence found no overall gender differences in verbal abilities, with the exception that boys are more often slower to develop language skills (Hyde & Linn, 1988). There is also evidence that males have somewhat superior visual-spatial abilities (Maccoby & Jacklin, 1974; Halpern, 1986). Visual-spatial skills include the ability to follow a map when traveling to an unfamiliar location, to construct a puzzle or assemble a piece of equipment, and to perceive relationships among figures in space (as in Figure 6.5). These differences appear to have narrowed in recent years (Feingold, 1988), adding further evidence to the body of research showing remarkable convergence in abilities between the genders.

Despite the stereotype of male superiority in math, reviews of the literature suggest that girls actually show greater computational ability than boys in elementary school (Hyde et al., 1990). Males, however, begin to show relatively greater problem-solving ability in high school, and this difference persists in college.

In our culture, then, girls are somewhat advanced in their development of verbal abilities. Boys apparently show greater mathematical problem-solving ability, beginning in adolescence. Three factors should caution us not to attach too much importance to these gender differences, however:

1. Most of these gender differences are small (Deaux, 1984; Hyde, 1981; Hyde et al., 1990; Maccoby, 1990). For example, in one study of 440,000 high school students, boys did outperform girls on tests of mathematical ability (Fox et al., 1979), but only by an average of 0.6 of an item.

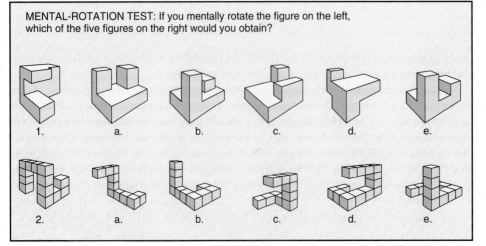

MENTAL-ROTATION TEST: If you mentally rotate the figure on the left, which of the five figures on the right would you obtain?

1. a. b. c. d. e.
2. a. b. c. d. e.

FIGURE 6.5 **Rotating Geometric Figures in Space.** Visual-spatial skills—for example, the ability to rotate geometric figures in space—have been considered part of the male gender-role stereotype. Gender differences in visual-spatial skills are small, however, and can be modified by training.

Source: From Rathus, S. A., et al. (1990). *Psychology.* (4th ed.). Copyright © 1990 by Holt, Rinehart and Winston, Inc. Reprinted by permission of the publisher.

Girls' Education. According to traditional stereotypes, girls are not expected to excel in math or science or have aptitude for computers. How might gender biases of teachers affect the expectations of female students concerning their potential in these areas?

2. These gender differences are *group* differences. Variation in ability on tests of verbal or math skills is larger *within,* than between, the genders (Maccoby, 1990). Despite differences between groups of boys and girls, millions of boys exceed the "average" girl in writing and spelling skills. Likewise, millions of girls outperform the "average" boy in problem-solving and spatial tasks. The male gender has produced its Shakespeares and the female gender its Madame Curies.

3. The small differences that may exist may largely reflect environmental influences and cultural expectations (Tobias, 1982). Spatial and math skills are stereotyped in our culture as masculine, whereas reading skills are stereotyped as feminine. In one study, however, female introductory psychology students who were given but three hours of training in performing such visual-spatial skills as rotating geometric figures performed these tasks as well as men (Stericker & LeVesconte, 1982).

DIFFERENCES IN PERSONALITY

DIFFERENCES IN PLAY Stereotypical gender preferences for toys and play activities are in evidence at an early age Before their first birthdays boys are already showing evidence of more explorative and independent play; girls appear relatively quieter, more dependent and restrained (Goldberg & Lewis, 1969). From 18 to 36 months, we are more likely to find girls playing with dolls or dancing, whereas boys are more likely to play with blocks and other hard objects and with transportation toys like trucks and cars (Fagot, 1974). Preexisting stereotypes may influence children's play patterns, however. If little girls are given dolls to play with and little boys are given trucks, should we be surprised to see them develop gender-typed preferences?

Discussion Question: Do your experiences confirm the research finding that boys often dominate classroom discussions and discussions in mixed-gender groups? Do your experiences confirm that men interrupt others more? What effects do these patterns have on conversations? On intimate relationships?

DIFFERENCES IN COMMUNICATION STYLES: "HE'S JUST AN OLD CHATTERBOX" We have been inundated with cartoons of suburban housewives gossiping across the fence or pouring endless cups of coffee when the "girls" drop by for a chat. Research has shown, however, that in many situations men spend more time talking than women do. Men are also more likely to introduce new topics and interrupt others (Brooks, 1982; Deaux, 1985; Hall, 1984). Girls tend to be more talkative during early childhood than boys (Haas, 1979). By the time they enter school, however, boys dominate classroom discussions (Sadker & Sadker, 1985). As girls mature, it appears that they learn to "take a back seat" to boys and let the boys do most of the talking when they are in mixed-gender groups (Hall, 1984).

Women are more willing than men to disclose their feelings and personal experiences, however (Cozby, 1973). The stereotype of the "strong and silent" male may not discourage men from hogging the conversation, but it may inhibit them from expressing their personal feelings.

DIFFERENCES IN AGGRESSIVENESS In almost all cultures (Ford & Beach, 1951; Mead, 1935), it is the males who march off to war and who battle for fame, glory, and shaving-cream-commercial contracts in stadiums and arenas. In most psychological studies on aggression, males have been found to behave more aggressively than females, whether the subjects are children or adults (Maccoby & Jacklin, 1980; White, 1983).

TRUTH OR FICTION?

R E V I S I T E D

Men act more aggressively than women do. *Men certainly do act more aggressively, on the whole, than women do. The question remains,* why*? •*

There are other gender differences. Most societies, for example, differentiate between males and females in terms of *appearance,* as the World of Diversity feature reveals (page 178).

A WORLD OF DIVERSITY

Multicultural Perspectives on Telling "Where the Boys (and the Girls) Are"

Each society marks a person's public identity as male or female on the basis of appearance. Men and women can often be distinguished by their manner of dress or by the amount and style of jewelry they wear (Ember & Ember, 1990; Frayser, 1985). In modern Western society, however, traditional gender differences in styles of clothing and hair have somewhat blurred with the advent of *androgynous* styles.

Among preindustrial societies, the areas of the body that are covered are sometimes more important gender markings than the style of clothing. Among the Ganda people of Uganda, every part of a man's body from his neck to his ankles must be covered. It is much less shocking for a woman to go naked than for a man. Even minimal coverings

may be enough to bestow modesty. Among the Native-American Comanches of the southern plains, for example, men wear a braided "G-string" to cover their genitals—barely. The use of the G-string may be sufficient for people to consider the body to be clothed, however, even though it may appear immodest to outsiders. People in such cultures may be taught to refrain from looking at a person's exposed body parts. In many African societies, women cover their genitals but leave their breasts exposed. Men in such societies are not sexually aroused by the breasts as many men in our society are.

Many societies use tattooing, a form of body mutilation, as a means of distinguishing men from women. The Maria Gond women of southwest India tattoo

the faces and foreheads of girls as young as 8 or 9 years old. Men in the Marshall Islands in the Pacific confirm their masculine identity by heavily tattooing their chests, shoulders, arms, backs, buttocks, and thighs.

Body scarification and deformation are sometimes used to distinguish men from women. The women of the Pacific island of Fiji deliberately cut their skin to make ornamental scars, for example, and burn wartlike spots into their arms and backs. The Otoro men of Africa mark their passage to manhood by cutting their skin to make scar tissue. The Tupinamba men of Brazil pierce their lips and cheeks and insert pieces of wood or stone through them. Tupinamba women stretch their earlobes, sometimes to their shoulders or breasts, by inserting large shell

---

ON BECOMING A MAN OR A WOMAN: GENDER TYPING

Gender typing
The process by which children acquire behavior that is deemed appropriate to their gender.

We have chronicled the biological process of sexual differentiation, and we have explored some gender differences in cognitive abilities and behavior. In this section we consider various explanations of **gender typing.**

BIOLOGICAL PERSPECTIVES

Learning Objective 6:
Summarize the biological and sociobiological perspectives on gender typing.

Biological views on gender typing tend to focus on the roles of genetics and prenatal influences in predisposing men and women to gender-linked behavior patterns. Biological perspectives have also focused on the possible role of hormones in sculpting the brain during prenatal development.

SOCIOBIOLOGY: IT'S ONLY NATURAL To the sociobiologist, the story of the survival of our ancient ancestors is etched in our genes. Sociobiologists propose that those genes that bestow attributes that increase an organism's chances of surviving to produce viable offspring are most likely to be transmitted to future generations. We thus possess the genetic remnants of traits that helped our ancestors survive and reproduce. This her-

Culture and Appearance.
Styles of dress and physical appearance vary with cultural traditions and customs. In traditional Islamic societies, women are veiled and cloaked from head to foot. In other cultures, people may adorn or mutilate their bodies, such as by tattooing, to distinguish their gender. Among some preindustrialized societies, men receive full-body tatoos, like those worn by the man pictured on the right.

cylinders in them. Suku women of the southwest Congo elongate their breasts by tying them down. Piercing the ears is a popular means of body deformation that cuts across preindustrial and technologically advanced societies.

Men and women are also often differentiated by their hairstyles. Traditionally, Comanche men braided their hair, wrapped it in beaver fur, and adorned it with ornaments made of silver, beads, and feathers. Among modern Kurds, a man without a

mustache is considered "not quite a man." Despite the emphasis in Western culture on women removing "unwanted" body hair, men in preindustrial societies are more likely to be the ones who pluck out facial and body hair to differentiate themselves from women.

Body decoration does not simply mark gender identity. It may also convey one's social status or rank, or indicate one's ethnic, religious, or local identity. Body decoration also holds erotic

significance. Women may seek to enhance their erotic appeal by the use of body or facial paint or lipstick, or by wearing decorative jewelry. Men may grow beards or apply tattoos to enhance their masculine appeal. Clothing may be worn not only for warmth and comfort, but also to adorn the body to enhance one's sex appeal. Some societies emphasize body adornment for men; others emphasize the adornment of women. The reasons for these differences remain unclear.

Notes: Body scarification and piercing are not limited to non-Western cultures. A guest on a radio show in Los Angeles, a professional "piercer," described her 33 piercings: 10 in her right ear, 6 in her left ear, 5 in her tongue, 4 in her genitals, and piercings of her right eyebrow, nasal septum, lower lip, the webs of her hands, her naval, and her nipples. (*Glendale News-Press,* October 22, 1991.)

itage, according to sociobiologists, influences our social and sexual behavior as well as our anatomic features.

According to sociobiologists, men's traditional roles as hunters and warriors, and women's roles as caregivers and gatherers of fruits and vegetables, are bequeathed to us in our genes. Men are better suited to war and the hunt because of physical attributes passed along since ancestral times. Upper-body strength, for example, would have enabled them to throw spears and overpower adversaries. Men also possess perceptual-cognitive advantages, such as superior visual-motor skills, that favor aggression. Visual-motor skills would have enabled men to aim spears or bows and arrows.

Women, it is argued, are genetically predisposed to be empathic and nurturant because these traits enabled ancestral women to respond to children's needs and enhance the likelihood that their children would flourish and eventually reproduce, thereby transmitting their own genetic legacy to future generations. Prehistoric women thus tended to stay close to home, care for the children, and gather edible plants, whereas men ventured from home to hunt and raid their neighbors' storehouses.

Sociobiology is steeped in controversy. Although scientists do not dispute the importance of evolution in determining physical attributes, many are reluctant to attribute complex social behaviors, such as aggression and gender roles, to heredity. The sociobiological argument implies that stereotypical gender roles—men as breadwinners

Gender Typing and Socialization. At an early age boys and girls are given toys deemed appropriate for their gender, such as cars, trucks, and construction sets for boys, and dolls and play houses for girls. What other socialization influences contribute to gender typing?

and women as homemakers, for example—reflect the natural order of things. Critics contend that biology is not destiny, that our behavior is not dictated by our genes.

PRENATAL BRAIN ORGANIZATION   Researchers have sought the origins of gender-typed behavior in the organization of the brain. Is it possible that the cornerstone of gender-typed behavior is laid in the brain before the first breath is taken?

Evidence has accumulated that the hemispheres of the brain are specialized to carry out certain functions (Levy, 1985). In most people, the right hemisphere ("right brain") appears to be specialized to perform visual-spatial tasks. The "left brain" appears to be more essential to verbal functions, such as speech, in most people.

We know that sex hormones are responsible for prenatal sexual differentiation of the genitals and for the gender-related structural differences in the hypothalamus of the developing prenatal brain. Sexual differentiation of the brain may also partly explain men's (slight!) superiority at spatial-relations tasks, such as interpreting road maps and visualizing objects in space. Testosterone in the brains of male fetuses spurs greater growth of the right hemisphere, and slows the rate of growth of the left hemisphere (Geshwind, 1972). This difference may be connected with the ability to accomplish spatial-relations tasks.

Might boys' inclinations toward aggression and rough-and-tumble play also be prenatally imprinted in the brain? Some theorists argue that prenatal sex hormones masculinize or feminize the brain by creating predispositions that are consistent with gender-role stereotypes (Diamond, 1977; Money, 1977, 1987b). Diamond takes an extreme view. She suggests that prenatal brain masculinization causes tomboyishness and assertiveness—even preferences for trousers over skirts and for transportation toys. Money allows a role for prenatal dispositions, but argues that social learning plays a stronger role in gender typing. He claims that social learning is even potent enough to counteract prenatal predispositions.

CROSS-CULTURAL PERSPECTIVES

Sociobiology cannot account for differences in gender roles that exist across cultures, especially neighboring cultures. The anthropologist Margaret Mead (1935) lived among several tribes on the South Pacific island of New Guinea and found that gender roles in these tribes differed not only from those of Western culture, but also from each other.

Among the Mundugumor, a tribe of headhunters and cannibals, both men and women were warlike and aggressive. The women disdained bearing and rearing children, because it interrupted participation in warring parties against neighboring villages. The men and women of the Arapesh tribe were gentle and peaceful, by contrast. Both genders

Learning Objective 7: Summarize the cross-cultural evidence on gender typing.

Notes: So they would not be accused of a second "offense," the 47 Saudi women who drove from a supermarket parking lot in Riyadh to the center of town were very careful to veil their faces. Among the women were eleven with doctoral degrees and ten university professors. Saudi Arabia is currently the only Arab country that prohibits women from driving.

nurtured the children. The Tchambuli were even more unusual in terms of what we consider stereotypical behavior in our society. The men spent most of their time caring for children, gossiping, bickering, primping and applying makeup, and haggling over prices. Fish was the staple diet of the Tchambuli, and women brought home the daily catch. Women kept their heads shaven, disdained ornaments, and were more highly sexed and aggressive than men.

Whatever the influence of biology on behavior, biological factors alone do not make men aggressive or independent, or women passive or submissive (Havemann & Lehtinen, 1990). Cultural expectations and learning play a large role.

GENDER ROLES AS A CULTURAL ADAPTATION   The Mundugumor, Arapesh, and Tchambuli peoples of New Guinea—and members of modern industrialized societies—all share the same biological makeup. Within each gender, the same sex hormones pulse through the arteries of the peoples of New Guinea as through the arteries of stockbrokers on Wall Street. (Yes, even stockbrokers are warm-blooded.) Yet despite this common biological makeup, wide cultural variations exist with respect to gender roles.

Anthropologists believe that cultural differences in gender roles can be explained in terms of the adaptations that cultures make to their social and natural environments (Werner & Cohen, 1990). Consider differences in gender roles between the Sambian people of New Guinea and the !Kung people of Africa. The Sambians have rigidly defined gender roles. Boys are socialized to become warriors whereas women tend the children and keep a discreet distance from men (Herdt, 1987). Among the !Kung people, however, women play a more active role in tribal affairs and are permitted more autonomy (Draper, 1975).

How might such differences arise? The Sambians, until recently, were subject to repeated attacks from enemies and could only survive by rearing their sons as warriors (Werner & Cohen, 1990). Sambians' rigid gender roles may be seen as an adaptation to these onslaughts. The !Kung live in small scattered groups and forage for their food. Both genders make substantial contributions to the food supply. In this egalitarian society, gender roles are more flexible. Both men and women enjoy considerable autonomy and influence.

PSYCHOLOGICAL PERSPECTIVES

Children acquire awareness of gender-role stereotypes by the tender ages of 2$\frac{1}{2}$ to 3$\frac{1}{2}$ (Kuhn et al., 1978). Both boys and girls generally agree, when asked to describe the differences between the genders, that boys build things, play with transportation toys such as cars and fire trucks, enjoy helping their fathers, and hit other children. Both boys and girls also agree that girls enjoy playing with dolls and helping their mothers cook and clean, and are talkative, dependent on others for help, and nonviolent. They perceive the label "cruel" to be a masculine trait, whereas "cries a lot" is perceived as a feminine trait. By the time they are 3, most children have acquired an awareness of the differences in stereotypical ways men and women dress and the types of occupations that are considered appropriate for each gender (Ruble & Ruble, 1982). Psychologists have attempted to explain how children acquire such knowledge and adopt stereotypical behavior patterns in terms of psychodynamic, social-learning, and cognitive theories.

Oedipus complex
A conflict of the phallic stage in which the boy wishes to possess his mother sexually and perceives his father as a rival in love.

PSYCHOANALYTIC THEORY   Sigmund Freud explained gender typing in terms of identification. Appropriate gender typing, in Freud's view, requires that boys come to identify with their fathers and girls with their mothers. Identification is completed, in Freud's view, as children resolve the **Oedipus complex** (sometimes called the Electra complex in girls).

According to Freud, the Oedipus complex occurs during the phallic period of psychosexual development, at about the ages of 3 to 5. During this period the child develops incestuous wishes for the parent of the opposite gender and comes to perceive the parent of the same gender as a rival for the affections of the other parent.

The complex is resolved by the child forsaking incestuous wishes for the parent of the opposite gender and identifying with the parent of the same gender. Through identification with the same-gender parent, the child comes to develop gender-typed behaviors that are typically associated with that gender. Children display stereotypical gender-typed behaviors earlier than Freud would have predicted, however. Even during the first year, boys are more independent than girls. Girls are more quiet and restrained. Girls show preferences for dolls and soft toys, and boys for hard transportation toys, by the ages of $1\frac{1}{2}$ to 3.

SOCIAL-LEARNING THEORY   Social-learning theorists explain the development of gender-typed behavior in terms of such processes as observational learning, identification, and socialization. Children can learn what is deemed masculine or feminine by observational learning, as suggested by the results of an experiment by Perry and Bussey (1979). Eight- and 9-year-old boys and girls in this study watched adult role models indicate their preferences for each of 16 pairs of items—pairs such as toy cows versus toy horses and oranges versus apples. What the children didn't know was that the expressed preferences were made arbitrarily. The children then were asked to indicate their own preferences for the items represented in the pairs. The boys' choices agreed with the adult men's an average of 14 out of 16 times. Girls chose the pair item selected by the men, on the average, only 3 out of 16 times.

In social-learning theory, identification is viewed as a continuing and broadly based learning process in which rewards and punishments influence children to imitate adult models of the same gender—especially the parent of the same gender (Storms, 1979). Identification is more than imitation, however. In identification, the child not only imitates the behavior of the model, but tries to become like the model in broad terms.

Socialization also plays a role in gender typing. Almost from the moment a baby comes into the world, it is treated according to its gender. Parents tend to talk more to baby girls, and fathers especially (Jacklin et al., 1984) engage in more roughhousing with boys. When children are old enough to speak, parents and other adults—even other children—begin to instruct children as to how they are expected to behave. Parents may reward children for behavior they consider gender appropriate and punish (or fail to reinforce) them for behavior they consider inappropriate for their gender. Girls are encouraged to practice caretaking behaviors, which are intended to prepare them for traditional feminine adult roles. Boys are handed erector sets or doctor sets to help prepare them for traditional masculine adult roles.

Mothers in our culture usually bear the major responsibility for the day-to-day nurturance of children (Belsky, 1984; Feldman et al., 1983). Mothers usually play a pivotal role in providing the supportive and empathic functions—the "emotional glue"—that holds the family together and keeps it integrated as a social unit (Johnson & McGillicudy-Delari, 1983). Yet fathers are more likely to communicate gender-role expectations (Lamb, 1981; Power, 1985). Mothers share fathers' cultural expectations concerning gender-appropriate behavior, but are usually less demanding that children show gender-typed behavior (McHale & Huston, 1984). Fathers generally encourage their sons to develop assertive, instrumental behavior (that is, behavior that gets things done or accomplishes something) and their daughters to develop nurturant, cooperative behavior. Fathers are likely to cuddle their daughters gently. They are likely to carry their sons like footballs or toss them into the air. Fathers also tend to use heartier and harsher language with their sons, such as "How're yuh doin', Tiger?" and "Hey you, get your keester over here" (Jacklin et al., 1984; Power & Parke, 1982). Being a nontraditionalist, your third author made sure to toss his young daughters into the air, which raised immediate objections from the relatives who chastised him for being too rough. This, of course, led him to modify his behavior. He learned to toss his daughters into the air when the relatives were not around.

Generally speaking, from an early age boys are more likely to receive toy cars and guns and athletic equipment and to be encouraged to compete aggressively. Even rela-

Socialization
The process of guiding people into socially acceptable behavior patterns by means of information, rewards, and punishments.

Notes: The Barbie doll has been marketed for three decades and its sales are climbing. It is available in many racial and ethnic versions and is sold in 67 countries outside the United States. Barbie's measurements, were she real, would be 36–18–33. The "Happy To Be Me" doll has "real-life" measurements of 36–27–38, certainly more realistic. (*Utne Reader,* March/April 1992, 46–47.)

tively sophisticated college students are likely to select traditionally masculine toys as gifts for boys and traditionally feminine toys for girls (Fisher-Thompson, 1990). Girls are spoken to more often, whereas boys are handled more frequently and more roughly. Whatever the biological determinants of gender differences in aggressiveness and verbal skills, early socialization experiences clearly contribute to gender typing.

Parental roles in gender typing are apparently changing. With more mothers working outside the home, daughters today are exposed to more women who represent career-minded role models than was the case in earlier generations (Levy et al., 1987). More parents today are encouraging their daughters to become career-minded and engage in strenuous physical activities, such as organized sports. Many boys today are exposed to fathers who take a larger role than men used to in child care and household responsibilities.

Schools are also important socialization influences. According to Judith Meece (1987), schools have been slow to adapt to recent changes in gender roles. Schools may be exposing children to masculine and feminine images that are even more rigid and polarized than those currently held in society at large. Therefore, schools may be reinforcing rigid gender distinctions while neglecting children's needs to develop greater flexibility in gender-role conceptions. Teachers often expect girls to perform better than boys in reading and language arts and have higher expectations of boys in math and science. These expectations may be conveyed to children, patterning their choices of careers.

CNN Girls' Education

A 1992 report by the American Association of University Women Education Foundation concluded that sexism in America's schools is widespread (Chira, 1992). The report concluded that some tests remain biased against girls, which reduces their chances of obtaining scholarships and gaining admission to more competitive colleges. The report also cited evidence that many science teachers and some math teachers tend to ignore girls in favor of boys. Such biases may discourage young women with aptitude in math and science from pursuing careers in these areas. Yet the report highlighted some promising developments. The traditional gender gap in math scores is narrowing as girls have made significant gains in catching up to boys. Moreover, specialized programs in math and science for girls held after school and in the summer have helped bolster the girls' confidence and interest in these subjects.

The popular media—books, magazines, radio, film, and especially television—also convey gender stereotypes (Remafedi, 1990). The media by and large portray men and women in traditional roles (Signorielli, 1990). Men more often play doctors, attorneys, and police officers; women more often play nurses, secretaries, paralegals, and teachers. Even when women portray attorneys or police officers, they are more likely than men to handle family disputes. The male police officer is more likely to be shown in action roles, the male attorney as holding the court spellbound with a probing cross-examination. Working women are also more likely than men to be portrayed as undergoing role conflict—being pulled in opposite directions by job and family. A 1990 study funded by the Ford and Tides foundations reported that despite current awareness of sexism, "Women are often still depicted on television as half-clad and half-witted, and needing to be rescued by quick-thinking, fully clothed men" (Adelson, 1990). Ageism buttresses sexism in that female characters age 40 and above are only rarely depicted in roles other than mothers and grandmothers.

Social-learning theorists believe that aggression is largely influenced by learning. Boys are permitted, even encouraged, to engage in more aggressive behavior than girls. Nonetheless, females are likely to act aggressively under certain conditions. Ann Frodi and her colleagues (1977) reviewed 72 studies that examined gender differences in aggression. All in all, females acted as aggressively as men when they were given the physical means to do so and believed that aggression was justified. In an influential review article, Maccoby and Jacklin commented on the socialization influences that discourage aggression in girls:

> Aggression in general is less acceptable for girls, and is more actively discouraged in them, by either direct punishment, withdrawal of affection, or simply cognitive training that "that isn't the way girls act." Girls then build up greater anxieties about aggression, and greater inhibitions against displaying it (1974, p. 234).

Discussion Question: Can you think of examples of boys and girls "teasing" their playmates into making more "gender appropriate" choices of activities and toys? In what ways might this pressure affect children?

Social-learning theorists have made important contributions to our understanding of how rewards, punishments, and modeling influences foster gender-typed behavior patterns. How do children integrate gender-role expectations within their self-concepts? And how do their concepts concerning gender influence their development of gender-typed behavior? Let us consider two cognitive approaches to gender typing that shed light on these matters: cognitive-developmental theory and gender-schema theory.

Schema
Concept; way of interpreting experience or processing information.

COGNITIVE-DEVELOPMENTAL THEORY   Psychologist Lawrence Kohlberg (1966) proposed a cognitive-developmental view of gender typing. From this perspective, gender typing is not the product of environmental influences that mechanically "stamp in" gender-appropriate behavior. Rather, children themselves play an active role. They form concepts or **schemas** about gender and then conform their behavior to their gender concepts. These developments occur in stages and are entwined with general cognitive development.

Gender stability
The concept that people retain their genders for a lifetime.

According to Kohlberg, gender typing entails the emergence of three concepts: *gender identity, gender stability,* and *gender constancy.* Gender identity is usually acquired by the age of 3. By the age of 4 or 5, most children develop a concept of **gender stability**—the recognition that people retain their genders for a lifetime. Prior to this age, boys may think that they will become mommies when they grow up, and girls, daddies.

TRUTH OR _FICTION?_

R E V I S I T E D

A 2¹/₂-year-old child may know that he is a boy but think that he can grow up to be a mommy. Yes, 2¹/₂-year-old boys may think that they will become mommies when they grow up. They have not yet developed gender stability. •

Gender constancy
The concept that people's genders do not change, even if they alter their dress or behavior.

The more sophisticated concept of **gender constancy** develops in most children by the age of 7 or 8. They recognize that gender does not change, even if people alter their dress or behavior. So gender remains constant even when appearances change. A woman who wears her hair short (or shaves it off) remains a woman. A man who dons an apron and cooks dinner remains a man.

According to cognitive-developmental theory, children are motivated to behave in gender-appropriate ways once they have established the concepts of gender stability and gender constancy. They then make an active effort to obtain information as to which behavior patterns are considered "masculine" and which "feminine" (Perry & Bussey, 1979). Once they obtain this information, they imitate the "gender-appropriate" pattern. So boys and girls who come to recognize that their genders will remain a fixed part of their identity will show preferences for "masculine" and "feminine" activities, respectively. Researchers find, for instance, that boys who had achieved gender constancy played with an uninteresting gender-typed toy for a longer period of time than did boys who hadn't yet achieved gender constancy (Frey & Ruble, 1992). Both groups of boys played with an interesting gender-typed toy for about an equal length of time.

Cross-cultural studies of the United States, Samoa, Nepal, Belize, and Kenya find that the concepts of gender identity, gender stability, and gender constancy emerge in the order predicted by Kohlberg (Munroe et al., 1984; Slaby & Frey, 1975). However, gender-typed play often emerges at an earlier age than would be predicted by the cognitive-developmental theory. Many children make gender-typed choices of toys by the age of 2 (Huston, 1983). Children as young as 18 months are likely to have developed a sense of gender identity, but gender stability and constancy are some years off (Fagot, 1985b). Gender identity alone thus seems sufficient to prompt children to assume gender-typed behavior patterns. Psychologist Sandra Bem (1983) also notes that Kohlberg's theory does not explain why the concept of gender plays such a prominent role in children's classification of people and behavior. Another cognitive view, gender-schema theory, attempts to address these concerns.

Gender schema
A cluster of mental representations about male and female physical qualities, behaviors, and personality traits.

GENDER-SCHEMA THEORY: AN INFORMATION-PROCESSING APPROACH
Gender-schema theory proposes that children develop a **gender schema** as a means of organizing their perceptions of the world (Bem, 1981, 1985; Martin & Halverson, 1981).

A gender schema is a cluster of mental representations about male and female physical qualities, behaviors, and personality traits. Gender gains prominence as a schema for organizing experience because of society's emphasis on it. Because of social emphasis, even young children start to mentally group people of the same gender according to the traits that represent that gender.

Children's gender schemas determine how important gender-typed traits are to them. Consider the dimension of *strength-weakness*. Children may learn that strength is connected with maleness and weakness with femaleness. (Other dimensions, like *light-dark*, are not gender-typed and thus may fall outside children's gender schemas.) Children also gather that some dimensions, like strong-weak, are more important to one gender (in this case, male) than the other.

Once children acquire a gender schema, they begin to judge themselves according to traits considered relevant to their genders. In doing so, they blend their developing self-concepts with the prominent gender schema of their culture. The gender schema furnishes standards for comparison. Children with self-concepts that are consistent with the prominent gender schema of their culture are likely to develop higher self-esteem than children whose self-concepts are inconsistent. Jack learns that muscle strength is a characteristic associated with "manliness." He is likely to think more highly of himself if he perceives himself as embodying this attribute than if he does not. Barbara is likely to discover that the dimension of kindness-cruelty is more crucial than strength-weakness to the way in which women are perceived in society.

According to gender-schema theory, gender identity itself is sufficient to inspire gender-appropriate behavior. Once children develop a concept of gender identity, they begin to seek information concerning gender-typed traits and strive to live up to them. Jack will retaliate when provoked, because boys are expected to do so. Barbara will be "sugary and sweet" if such is expected of little girls. Thus, gender-typed behavior is believed to emerge earlier than would be proposed by cognitive-developmental theory. Jack and Barbara's self-esteem depends in part on how they measure up to the gender schema.

Research suggests that children do process information according to a gender schema (Cann & Newbern, 1984; Carter & Levy, 1988; Levy & Carter, 1989; List et al., 1983; Stangor & Ruble, 1989). Objects and activities pertinent to children's own gender are better retained in memory. Boys, for example, do a better job of remembering transportation toys they have been shown previously, whereas girls are better at recalling dolls and other "feminine" objects (Bradbard & Endsley, 1984). In another study, Martin and Halverson (1983) showed elementary school children pictures of children involved in "gender-consistent" or "gender-inconsistent" activities. Gender-consistent pictures showed boys doing things like sawing wood and playing with trains. Girls were shown doing things like cooking and cleaning. Gender-inconsistent pictures showed models of the opposite gender involved in gender-typed endeavors. A week later, the children were asked whether boys or girls had engaged in each activity. Boys and girls both made errors recalling the genders of the models shown engaging in "gender-inconsistent" behavior.

Once established, gender schemas resist change, even when broad social changes occur. For this reason, many parents cannot accept their sons' wearing ("feminine") earrings. A generation earlier parents had similar difficulty accepting daughters in jeans or sons in long hair.

GENDER ROLES AND SEXUAL BEHAVIOR

Learning Objective 9: Examine the influence of stereotypical gender roles on sexual behavior and relationships.

Gender roles have had a profound influence on dating practices and sexual behavior. Children learn at an early age that men usually make dates and initiate sexual interactions, whereas women usually serve as the "gatekeepers" in romantic relationships. In their traditional role as gatekeepers, women are expected to wait to be asked out and to screen suitors. Men are expected to make the first (sexual) move and women to determine how far advances will proceed. Regrettably, some men refuse to take no for an answer. They feel that they have the right to force their dates into sexual relations.

MEN AS SEXUALLY AGGRESSIVE, WOMEN AS SEXUALLY PASSIVE

The cultural expectation that men are initiators and women are gatekeepers is embedded within the larger stereotype that men are sexually aggressive and women are sexually passive. Men not only initiate sexual encounters; they are expected to dictate all the "moves" thereafter, just as they are expected to take the lead on the dance floor. According to the stereotype, women are to let men determine the choice, timing, and sequence of sexual positions and techniques. Unfortunately, the stereotype favors men's sexual preferences, denying women the opportunity to give and receive their preferred kinds of stimulation.

Female-superior position
A coital position in which the woman is on top.

Male-superior position
A coital position in which the man is on top.

Activity: Thinking About Sleeping Beauty and Other Fairy Tales This handout in the IM helps students think critically about the gender-role messages in fairy tales.

A woman may more easily reach orgasm in the **female-superior position,** but her partner may prefer the **male-superior position.** If the man is calling the shots, she may not have the opportunity to reach orgasm. Even the expression of her preferences may be deemed "unladylike."

The stereotypical masculine role also imposes constraints on men. Men are expected to take the lead in bringing their partners to orgasm, but they should not ask their partners what they like because they are expected to be natural experts. ("Real men" not only don't eat quiche; they also need not ask women how to make love.)

Fortunately, more flexible attitudes are emerging. Women are becoming more sexually assertive and men are becoming more receptive to expressing tenderness and gentleness. Still, the roots of traditional gender roles run deep. A recent survey of students in human sexuality classes in colleges in the New York/New Jersey area showed that males reported more instances of women initiating sex than women reported initiating (Anderson & Aymami, 1993). Who's got it right? Are women who initiate sex less willing to admit they do so, perhaps even to themselves, because they hold to the stereotypical expectation that "nice girls don't"? Are men so taken with themselves that they believe that women can't help pursuing them for sexual relations? Perhaps a combination of factors is involved in explaining this discrepancy. What do you think?

MEN AS OVERAROUSED, WOMEN AS UNDERAROUSED

According to another stereotype, men become sexually aroused at puberty and remain at the ready throughout adulthood. Women, however, do not share men's natural interests in sex, and a woman discovers her own sexuality only when a man ignites her sexual flame. Men must continue to stoke women's sexual embers, lest they burn out. The stereotype denies that "normal" women have spontaneous sexual desires or are readily aroused.

It was widely believed in the Victorian period (even by so-called sex experts!) that women are naturally asexual and "unbothered" by sexual desires. The contemporary residues of this stereotype hold that women do not enjoy sex as much as men do and that women who openly express their sexual desires are "whores" or "sluts." The stereotype that women are undersexed also supports the traditional double standard that it is natural for men to sow their wild oats, but that women who are sexually active outside of committed relationships are sluts or *nymphomaniacs.*

Despite the stereotype, women are no less arousable than men. Nor do they wait upon the attentions of a man to discover their sexuality. Children of both genders routinely discover that touching their genitals produces pleasurable sensations long before they have intimate relationships.

Learning Objective 10:
Define psychological androgyny and examine its influence on self-esteem, adjustment, and sexual behavior.

PSYCHOLOGICAL ANDROGYNY: THE MORE TRAITS THE MERRIER?

Most of us consider masculinity and femininity to be opposite ends of one continuum (Storms, 1980). That is, we assume that the more masculine a person is, the less feminine he or she must be, and vice versa. So a man who exhibits stereotypical feminine traits of

Psychological androgyny
Possession of stereotypical masculine traits, such as assertiveness and instrumental skills, along with stereotypical feminine traits, such as nurturance and willingness to cooperate.

Activity: *The ANDRO Scale: Assessing Your Masculinity and Femininity* The IM includes this 56-item questionnaire, which allows students to assess how masculine, feminine, or androgynous they are.

nurturance, tenderness, and emotionality is often considered less masculine than other men are. Women who compete with men in business are perceived not only as more masculine but also as less feminine than other women are.

Some behavioral scientists have argued that masculinity and femininity actually comprise two independent personality dimensions, however (Bem, 1975; Helmreich et al., 1979; Spence et al., 1975). Thus, a person who is highly masculine, whether male or female, may also possess feminine traits—and vice versa. People who exhibit "masculine" assertiveness and instrumental skills (skills in the sciences and business, e.g.) along with "feminine" nurturance and cooperation fit both the masculine and feminine gender-role stereotypes. They are said to show **psychological androgyny** (see Figure 6.6). People high in assertiveness and instrumental skills fit only the masculine stereotype. People high in traits such as nurturance and cooperation fit only the feminine stereotype. People low in the stereotypical masculine and feminine patterns are considered "undifferentiated" according to gender-role stereotypes.

People who are psychologically androgynous may be capable of summoning a wider range of masculine and feminine traits to meet the demands of various situations and to express their desires and talents. Researchers, for example, have found psychologically androgynous persons of both genders to show "masculine" independence under group pressures to conform and "feminine" nurturance in interactions with a kitten or baby (Bem, 1975; Bem et al., 1976). Androgynous men and women are more apt to share leadership responsibilities in mixed-gender groups (Porter et al., 1985). By contrast, "masculine" men and women tend to dominate such groups, whereas "feminine" men and women are likely to take a back seat.

Many people who oppose the constraints of traditional gender roles may perceive psychological androgyny as a desirable goal. Some feminist writers, however, criticize psychological androgyny on grounds that the concept is defined in terms of, and thereby perpetuates, belief in the existence of masculine and feminine gender roles (Lott, 1981, 1985).

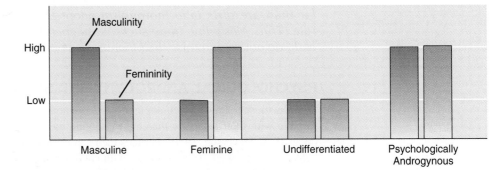

FIGURE 6.6 **A Model of Psychological Androgyny** Some behavioral scientists argue that masculinity and femininity are independent personality dimensions. People who exhibit "masculine" assertiveness and instrumental skills along with "feminine" nurturance and cooperation are said to be psychologically androgynous. People high in assertiveness and instrumental skills fit only the masculine stereotype. People high in traits such as nurturance and cooperation fit only the feminine stereotype. People low in the stereotypical masculine and feminine patterns are considered "undifferentiated."

Source: From Rathus, S.A. and Nevid, J. S. (1989). *Psychology and the challenges: Adjustment and growth* (4th ed.). Copyright © 1989 by Holt, Rinehart & Winston, Inc. Reprinted by permission of the publisher.

PSYCHOLOGICAL ANDROGYNY, PSYCHOLOGICAL WELL-BEING, AND PERSONAL DEVELOPMENT

Masculine and androgynous people of both genders tend to have higher self-esteem and to be generally better adjusted psychologically than people who are feminine or undifferentiated. Yet it appears that these benefits are more strongly related to the presence of masculine traits than to the combination of masculine and feminine traits (Bassoff & Glass, 1982; Whitley, 1983). That is, masculine traits like assertiveness and independence may be related to psychological well-being, whether or not they are combined with feminine traits such as warmth, nurturance, and cooperation. The presence of masculine personality features in one sample of college students was more strongly associated with adaptability and versatility than was androgyny (Lee & Scheurer, 1983). On the other hand, there is some evidence that shows that androgynous college students are more likely than feminine, undifferentiated, and masculine students to have a sense of personal identity and intimacy (Schiedel & Marcia, 1985). That is, they are more likely to have developed a firm sense of who they are and what they believe in (identity), and they have a greater capacity to establish and maintain intimate, sharing relationships.

There is also evidence that feminine traits, such as nurturance and sensitivity, appear to predict success in intimate relationships—in *men* as well as in women. Marital happiness as rated by husbands is positively related to femininity in the wives (Antill, 1983). More interestingly, perhaps, ratings of marital happiness from the wives were also positively correlated with their husbands' femininity. Androgynous men are more likely to express tender feelings of love toward their partners and to be more accepting of their partners' faults than are masculine-typed ("macho") men (Coleman & Ganong, 1985). It seems that both genders appreciate spouses who are sympathetic, able to express warmth and tenderness, and nurturant toward children.

Masculine and androgynous adolescents of both genders tend to be more popular and to have higher self-esteem than other adolescents do (Lamke, 1982b). We might not be surprised, given the prevalence of sexism, that adolescent boys fare better if they possess stereotypical masculine traits. What is more surprising is that adolescent girls also fare better when they exhibit stereotypical masculine traits, such as assertiveness and independence. It seems that young women do not risk having others question their femininity if they exhibit masculine traits, providing more evidence that the constellations of traits we call masculinity and femininity are independent clusters.

TRUTH OR *FICTION?*

R E V I S I T E D

Adolescent girls who show a number of masculine traits are more popular than are girls who thoroughly adopt the traditional feminine gender role. True. Masculine traits such as independence and assertiveness apparently do not compromise their friends' perceptions of their femininity. •

PSYCHOLOGICAL ANDROGYNY AND SEXUAL BEHAVIOR

Some evidence shows psychologically androgynous men and women to be more comfortable with their sexuality than are masculine men and feminine women, respectively (Walfish & Mayerson, 1980). Perhaps they can draw upon a broader repertoire of sexual behaviors. They may be comfortable with cuddling and tender holding, and also with initiating and directing sexual interactions. Researchers also find that androgynous women experience orgasm more frequently (Radlove, 1983) and express greater sexual satisfaction (Kimlicka et al., 1983) than do feminine women.

WHO IS ANDROGYNOUS?

In the 1970s Sandra Bem (1974) reported that about 50 percent of her college student samples adhered to their own gender-role stereotypes. About 15 percent were cross-typed (described by traits stereotypical of the opposite gender), and 35 percent were androgynous. In more recent research, other researchers found a somewhat lower incidence of androgyny, about 25 percent, based upon samples of high school students (e.g., Lamke, 1982a).

A recent sample of African-American and white women showed that relatively more African-American women could be classified as psychologically androgynous, whereas relatively more white women were categorized as undifferentiated (Binion, 1990). Although the African-American women were more psychologically androgynous in terms of their personality traits, they held predominantly traditional beliefs about the woman's role in the family.

In this chapter we have focused on the biology and psychology of gender. Our gender, both anatomically and psychologically, is a primary aspect of our sexuality. In the next chapter we begin to explore how we express our sexuality through intimate relationships with others.

SUMMING UP

This chapter discusses the biological, psychological, and sociocultural aspects of gender.

PRENATAL SEXUAL DIFFERENTIATION

During the first six weeks or so of prenatal development, embryonic structures of both genders develop along similar lines and resemble primitive female structures. At about the seventh week after conception, the genetic code (XX or XY) begins to assert itself, causing changes in the gonads, genital ducts, and external genitals.

The Role of Sex Hormones in Sexual Differentiation Testosterone spurs differentiation of the male (Wolffian) duct system. In the absence of testosterone, the Wolffian ducts degenerate and female sex organs develop.

Descent of the Testes and the Ovaries The testes and ovaries develop in the abdominal cavity. About four months after conception the testes normally descend into the scrotal sac.

Sex Chromosomal Abnormalities Abnormalities of the sex chromosomes can have profound effects on sexual characteristics, physical health, and psychological development. Examples include Klinefelter's syndrome and Turner's syndrome.

Prenatal Sexual Differentiation of the Brain Gender-specific changes occur in the hypothalamus during prenatal development. Testosterone causes cells in the hypothalamus of male fetuses to become insensitive to estrogen.

GENDER IDENTITY

Gender identity is a psychological construct, a sense of being male or being female.

Nature and Nurture in Gender Identity Gender identity is almost always consistent with anatomic gender.

Hermaphroditism Some individuals—hermaphrodites—are born with both ovarian and testicular tissue. Hermaphrodites usually assume the gender identity and gender role of the gender assigned at birth. Pseudoherm-aphrodites can acquire the gender identity of the opposite chromosomal gender when they are reared as members of that gender.

Transsexualism Transsexuals harbor a deep sense of discomfort about their anatomic gender. Hormone treatments and gender-reassignment surgery provide transsexuals with many of the characteristics of the opposite gender.

GENDER ROLES AND STEREOTYPES

Cultures have broad expectations of men and women that are termed gender roles. In our culture the stereotypical female is seen as gentle, dependent, kind, helpful, patient, and submissive. The stereotypical male is tough, competitive, gentlemanly, and protective.

SEXISM

Sexism is the prejudgment that because of gender, a person will possess negative traits that disqualify him or her for certain vocations or prevent him or her from performing adequately in these jobs or in some social situations. Women have been historically excluded from "male occupations," and stereotypical expectations concerning "men's work" and "women's work" filter down to the primary grades.

GENDER DIFFERENCES: *VIVE LA DIFFÉRENCE* OR *VIVE LA SIMILARITÉ?*

Differences in Cognitive Abilities Boys have historically been seen as excelling in math and spatial-relations skills, whereas girls have been viewed as excelling in language skills. Gender differences in these areas are small, however, and cultural expectations play a role in them.

Differences in Personality Stereotypical gender preferences for toys and play activities are in evidence at an early age. Males are more aggressive than females, but the question is *why*.

ON BECOMING A MAN OR A WOMAN: GENDER TYPING

Biological Perspectives
Biological views on gender typing focus on the roles of genetics and prenatal influences in predisposing men and women to gender-linked behavior patterns. Testosterone in the brains of male fetuses spurs greater growth of the right hemisphere, which may be connected with the ability to manage spatial-relations tasks.

Cross-Cultural Perspectives
Anthropologists have found that differences in gender roles exist among preliterate cultures, and even between neighboring cultures.

Psychological Perspectives
Psychologists have attempted to explain gender typing in terms of psychodynamic, social-learning, and cognitive theories. Sigmund Freud explained gender typing in terms of identification with the parent of the same gender as a result of resolution of the Oedipus complex.

Social-learning theorists explain the development of gender-typed behavior in terms of such processes as observational learning, identification, and socialization.

According to the cognitive-developmental view, children form concepts about gender and then conform their behavior to their gender concepts. According to Kohlberg, gender typing entails the emergence of three concepts: gender identity, gender stability, and gender constancy.

Gender-schema theory proposes that children develop a gender schema as a means of organizing their perceptions of the world. Once children acquire a gender schema, they begin to judge themselves according to traits considered relevant to their genders. In doing so they blend their developing self-concepts with the prominent gender schema of their culture.

GENDER ROLES AND SEXUAL BEHAVIOR

Stereotypical gender-role expectations affect dating practices and sexual behavior.

Men as Sexually Aggressive, Women as Sexually Passive
According to the stereotype, men are sexual initiators and women are sexual gatekeepers. Men not only initiate sexual encounters; they are expected to initiate all the "moves."

Men as Overaroused, Women as Underaroused According to another stereotype, women do not share men's interests in sex and discover their own sexuality only when a man ignites their sexual flame.

PSYCHOLOGICAL ANDROGYNY: THE MORE TRAITS THE MERRIER?

Masculinity and femininity may comprise two independent personality dimensions. People who combine stereotypical masculine and feminine behavior patterns are psychologically androgynous.

Psychological Androgyny, Psychological Well-Being, and Personal Development
Masculine and androgynous people of both genders tend to be better psychologically adjusted than people who are feminine or undifferentiated.

CHAPTER OUTLINE

Truth or Fiction?

Attraction

Physical Attractiveness:
How Important Is Looking
Good?

A WORLD OF DIVERSITY:
Gender Differences in
Preferences in Mates Across
37 Cultures

Attraction and Attitudinal
Similarity: Do Opposites
Attract?

Reciprocity: If You Like Me,
You Must Have Excellent
Judgment

Love

The Greek Heritage

Romantic Love in
Contemporary Western
Culture

Contemporary Models of
Love: Dare Science Intrude?

Summing Up

_____ Beauty is in the eye of the beholder.

_____ College men would like women to be thinner than the women want to be.

_____ People are regarded as more attractive when they are smiling.

_____ Physical appeal is the most important trait we seek in partners for long-term relationships.

_____ "Opposites attract." We are more apt, that is, to be attracted to people who disagree with our views and tastes than to people who share them.

_____ It is possible to be in love with someone who is not also a friend.

C H A P T E R   7

Attraction and Love

Candy and Stretch. A new technique for controlling weight gain? No, these are the names of a couple who have just met at a camera club that doubles as a meeting place for singles.

Candy and Stretch stand above the crowd—literally. She is almost 6 feet tall, an attractive woman in her early thirties. He is more plain looking, but "wholesome," in his late thirties and 6 feet 5 inches tall. Stretch has been in the group for some time. Candy is a new member. Let us follow them as they meet during a coffee break. As you will see, there are some differences between what they say and what they think.

THEY SAY	**THEY THINK**
STRETCH: Well, you're certainly a welcome addition to our group.	(Can't I ever say something clever?)
CANDY: Thank you. It certainly is friendly and interesting.	(He's cute.)
STRETCH: My friends call me Stretch. It's left over from my basketball days. Silly, but I'm used to it.	(It's safer than saying my name is David Stein.)
CANDY: My name is Candy.	(At least my nickname is. He doesn't have to hear Hortense O'Brien.)
STRETCH: What kind of camera is that?	(Why couldn't a girl named Candy be Jewish? It's only a nickname, isn't it?)
CANDY: Just this old German one of my uncle's. I borrowed it from the office.	(He could be Irish. And that camera looks expensive.)
STRETCH: May I? (He takes her camera, brushing her hand and then tingling with the touch.) Fine lens. You work for your uncle?	(Now I've done it. Brought up work.)
CANDY: Ever since college.	(Okay, so what if I only went for a year?)
It's more than being just a secretary. I get into sales, too.	(If he asks what I sell, I'll tell him anything except underwear.)
STRETCH: Sales? That's funny. I'm in sales, too, but mainly as an executive. I run our department.	(Is there a nice way to say used cars? I'd better change the subject.)
I started using cameras on trips. Last time I was in the Bahamas, I took—	(Great legs! And the way her hips move—)

CANDY:	Oh! Do you go to the Bahamas, too? I love those islands.	(So I went just once, and it was for the brassiere manufacturers' convention. At least we're off the subject of jobs.)
STRETCH:	I did a little underwater work there last summer. Fantastic colors. So rich in life.	(She's probably been around. Well, at least we're off the subject of jobs.)
		(And lonelier than hell.)
CANDY:	I wish I'd had time when I was there. I love the water.	(Look at that build. He must swim like a fish. I should learn.)
		(Well, I do. At the beach, anyway, where I can wade in and not go too deep.)

So begins a relationship, as reported by Bach and Deutsch (1970). Candy and Stretch have a drink and talk, talk, talk—sharing their likes and dislikes. Amazingly, they seem to agree on everything, from clothing to cars to politics. The attraction they feel is very strong, and neither of them is willing to turn the other off by disagreeing.

They spend the weekend in Stretch's apartment and feel that they have fallen very much in love. They still agree on everything, even though there is one topic they avoid scrupulously: religion. Their different backgrounds became apparent once they exchanged last names. That doesn't mean they have to talk about it, however.

They delay introducing one another to their parents. The O'Briens and the Steins are narrow-minded about religion. If the truth be known, so are Candy and Stretch. Candy errs by telling Stretch, "You're not like other Jews I know" (p. 87). Stretch also allows his feelings to be voiced now and then. After Candy has nursed him through a cold, he remarks, "You know, you're very Jewish" (p. 87). Candy and Stretch manage to continue playing the games required to maintain the relationship. They tell themselves that their remarks were mistakes, and, after all, anyone can make mistakes. They were meant as compliments, weren't they? Yet each is becoming isolated from family and friends. In order to avoid creating tension between themselves, they are narrowing the range of other relationships.

One of the topics they ignore is birth control. As a Catholic, Candy does not take oral contraceptives, although Stretch later claimed that he had assumed she did. Candy becomes pregnant and they choose to get married. Only through professional help do they learn each other's genuine feelings. And on several occasions the union comes close to dissolving.

How do we explain the goings-on in this tangled web of deception? Candy and Stretch felt strongly attracted to one another. What determines who is attractive? Why did Candy and Stretch pretend to agree on everything? Why didn't they bring each other home to meet their parents?

Two possible consequences of attraction are friendship and love. Candy and Stretch "fell in love." What *is* love? When the third author was a teenager, the answer was, "Five feet of heaven in a ponytail"—but this answer may lack scientific merit. In this chapter we explore the definition, or, rather, definitions of love. We see that there are different forms of love and that our concepts of love are not universally shared by other cultures.

Beauty and Culture. Can you find Mr. or Ms. Right among these people? Are your judgments of physical beauty based on universal standards or on your cultural experiences?

ATTRACTION

Learning Objective 1: Summarize the research on the role of physical attractiveness in attraction.

Let us explore some of the factors that determine interpersonal attraction.

PHYSICAL ATTRACTIVENESS: HOW IMPORTANT IS LOOKING GOOD?

We might like to think of ourselves as so sophisticated that physical attractiveness has a low priority among the traits we value in others—that we find sensitivity, warmth, and intelligence more important. Some of us may find such traits to be crucial, but we may also never learn about another's personality traits if she or he does not meet our minimal standards for physical attractiveness. Research has shown that physical attractiveness is a major determinant of interpersonal and sexual attraction (Hatfield & Sprecher, 1986; Hensley, 1992). In studies of experimenter-arranged and computer-arranged dates, physical attractiveness has been shown to be the key factor in consideration of partners for future dates, sex, and marriage (Green et al., 1984; Hatfield & Sprecher, 1986).

IS BEAUTY IN THE EYE OF THE BEHOLDER?   What determines physical attractiveness? Are our standards fully subjective, or is there broad agreement on what is attractive? Cross-cultural studies show that people universally want physically appealing partners (Ford & Beach, 1951), but what is appealing in one culture may be repulsive in others.

In certain African tribes, long necks and round, disklike lips are signs of feminine beauty. Women thus stretch their necks and lips to make themselves more appealing. Women of the Nama tribe persistently tug at their labia majora to make them "beautiful"— that is, prominent and elongated (Ford & Beach, 1951).

TRUTH OR FICTION?
———————————
R E V I S I T E D

Beauty is in the eye of the beholder. *Beauty may not be completely in the eye of the beholder. Though personal tastes may vary within and across cultures, there are cultural standards for physical attractiveness.* •

In our culture, tallness is a plus among men, although college women fancy men who are medium in height (Graziano et al., 1978). Undergraduate women prefer their dates to be about six inches taller than they are. Undergraduate men, on the average, prefer women who are about four and a half inches shorter (Gillis & Avis, 1980). Tall women are not viewed so positively. Shortness, though, is perceived to be a liability for both men and women in our culture (Jackson & Ervin, 1992).

Some women of Candy's stature find that shorter men are discouraged from asking them out. Some walk with a hunch, as if to minimize their height.

Female plumpness is valued in many and perhaps most societies (Anderson et al., 1992; Frayser, 1985). Wide hips and a broad pelvis are widely recognized as sexually appealing. In our culture, however, slenderness is in style. Some young women even suffer from an eating disorder called **anorexia nervosa,** in which they literally starve themselves to conform to the contemporary ideal (Boskind-White & White, 1986). Both genders find slenderness (though not anorexic thinness) attractive, especially for females (Fallon & Rozin, 1985; Franzoi & Herzog, 1987; Rozin & Fallon, 1988). Women generally prefer men with a V taper, but not an exaggerated "muscleman" physique (Horvath, 1981; Lavrakas, 1975).

Anorexia nervosa
A potentially life-threatening eating disorder characterized by refusal to maintain a healthful body weight, intense fear of being overweight, a distorted body image, and, in females, lack of menstruation (amenorrhea.)

Men prefer women with medium-sized—not enormous—busts (Kleinke & Staneski, 1980). Women's beliefs about men's breast preferences may be somewhat exaggerated. The belief that men want women to have busting bust lines leads many women to seek breast implants in the attempt to live up to an ideal that men themselves don't generally hold (Rosenthal, 1992). Researchers in one study showed young men and women (ages 17 to 25 years) a continuum of male and female figures that differed only in the size of the bust for the female figures and of the pectorals for the male figures (Thompson & Tantleff, 1992. The participants were asked to indicate the ideal size for their own gender and the size they believed the average man and woman would prefer. The results showed some support for the "big is better" stereotype—for both men and women. Women's conception of ideal bust size was greater than their actual average size. Men preferred women with still larger busts, but not nearly as large as the busts women *believed* that men prefer. Men believed that their male peers preferred women with much bustier figures than their peers themselves said they preferred. Likewise, when rating men's bodies, women preferred a more heavily muscled torso than men rated themselves as having. Yet, like the women, but by a somewhat smaller margin, men overestimated the size preferred by the opposite gender. This seems to mean that ample breast or chest sizes may be preferred by the opposite gender, but people seem to have an exaggerated idea of the sizes the opposite gender actually prefers.

Slim Is In. Pressures to conform to an idealized slender image play a key role in the development of eating disorders among young women.

Both genders find obese people unattractive (Harris et al., 1982), but there are gender differences in impressions of the most pleasing body shape. On the average, college men think that their present physiques are close to ideal and appealing to women (Fallon & Rozin, 1985). College women generally see themselves as much heavier than the figure that is most alluring to men, and heavier still than the figure they perceive as the ideal feminine form. Both genders are wrong about the preferences of the opposite gender, however. Men actually prefer women to be somewhat heavier than the women imagine they would. Women prefer their men to be a bit leaner than the men would have expected.

TRUTH OR *FICTION?*

R E V I S I T E D

College men would like women to be thinner than the women want to be. *College men actually prefer women who are heavier, though still slender, than the women expect. On the other hand, college women prefer men who are thinner than the men imagine.* •

HOW TRAITS AND NAMES AFFECT PERCEPTIONS OF PHYSICAL ATTRACTIVENESS: ON THE IMPORTANCE OF *NOT* BEING EARNEST Both genders rate the attractiveness of faces higher when they are shown smiling in photographs than when they are shown in a nonsmiling pose (Mueser et al., 1984). (Photographers are not ignorant of this fact.) So there is reason to "put on a happy face" when you meet people socially or ask someone out on a date. Context is important, however. It may be more appropriate in a business context to maintain a more serious countenance. The effects of a smile may also be a greater determinant of attractiveness in women than in men (Deutsch et al., 1987).

TRUTH OR *FICTION?*

R E V I S I T E D

People are regarded as more attractive when they are smiling. *Yes, people are considered more attractive when they are smiling, so it may make sense when meeting people socially to "put on a happy face."* •

Discussion Question:
What do women do to make themselves more physically attractive? What do women do to "dress up"? (Discuss make-up, hair styling, jewelry, high heels, clothing, nylons, etc.) Do we have similar "guidelines" men can or must follow to be more physically attractive? Discuss particularly the procedures and often discomfort women must go through to make themselves more attractive.

Stereotypical gender-role expectations may affect perceptions of attractiveness. Women who viewed videos of prospective dates found men who acted outgoing and self-expressive more appealing. Yet men who viewed videos were put off by the same behavior in women (Riggio & Woll, 1984). In another study, women rated videos of dominant college men (defined in this study as social control over a troublesome interaction with an instructor) as more appealing than submissive men. Again, male viewers were put off by similarly dominant women (Sadalla et al., 1987). Despite recent changes in traditional gender-role stereotypes, men in the United States apparently still prefer demure women. This is not to suggest that dominant, self-expressive women should stifle themselves to attract traditional men; the relationships would probably rub them both the wrong way.

Names also may affect perceptions of physical appeal. In one study, women who were randomly assigned names like Kathy, Jennifer, and Christine were rated more attractive than women assigned the names Harriet, Gertrude, and Ethel (Garwood et al., 1980). Seems silly, does it not? After all, our parents name us, and there need be no relationship between our names and our physical appeal. On the other hand, we may choose to keep our names or to use nicknames. So if you are unhappy with your name, why not assume a more popular nickname? Beginning college or a new job is an ideal time for doing so. Men, too, can doff their Sylvesters and Ernests, if they prefer. If you have an unusual name and are content with it, be yourself, however.

WHAT DO YOU LOOK FOR IN A LONG-TERM, MEANINGFUL RELATIONSHIP?
Your first author conducted a survey of college men and women in the early 1980s and found that psychological characteristics such as warmth, fidelity, honesty, and sensitivity were rated higher in importance than physical attractiveness as desirable qualities in a prospective partner for a meaningful, long-term relationship (Nevid, 1984) (see Table 7.1). Physical attractiveness won out when subjects were asked to consider the qualities that are most important in a partner for a sexual relationship. Overall, however, men placed greater emphasis on the physical characteristics of their partners for both types of

TABLE 7.1 Ratings of characteristics of prospective partners for sexual and meaningful relationships

Rated Highest by Males		Rated Lowest by Males	
Sexual Relationship	*Mean*	*Sexual Relationship*	*Mean*
Build/figure	4.53	Virtue	2.60
Sexuality	4.36	Achievement striving	2.52
Attractiveness	4.31	Strength	2.40
Facial features	4.25	Ethnic background	2.33
Buttocks	4.09	Ears	2.08
Weight	4.07	Ankles	1.89
Legs	4.02	Religion	1.74
Breath	3.94	Money	1.70
Skin	3.92	Knees	1.60
Chest/breasts	3.79	Political views	1.49
Meaningful Relationship		*Meaningful Relationship*	
Honesty	4.68	Religion	2.74
Personality	4.65	Height	2.71
Fidelity	4.60	Strength	2.65
Sensitivity	4.51	Nose	2.63
Warmth	4.49	Neck	2.56
Kindness	4.47	Hands	2.35
Character	4.41	Money	2.04
Tenderness	4.36	Ears	2.00
Patience	4.34	Political views	1.97
Gentleness	4.31	Knees	1.75

Rated Highest by Females		Rated Lowest by Females	
Sexual Relationship	*Mean*	*Sexual Relationship*	*Mean*
Attractiveness	4.51	Hands	2.70
Sexuality	4.46	Ethnic background	2.55
Warmth	4.42	Money	2.41
Personality	4.41	Nose	2.40
Tenderness	4.39	Neck	2.30
Gentleness	4.36	Religion	2.00
Sensitivity	4.24	Ears	1.84
Kindness	4.23	Political views	1.78
Build/figure	4.22	Knees	1.31
Character	4.20	Ankles	1.28
Meaningful Relationship		*Meaningful Relationship*	
Honesty	4.89	Waistline	2.62
Fidelity	4.83	Chest/breasts	2.48
Personality	4.82	Legs	2.46
Warmth	4.80	Hands	2.35
Kindness	4.79	Political views	2.33
Tenderness	4.77	Nose	2.09
Sensitivity	4.75	Neck	1.97
Gentleness	4.73	Ears	1.73
Character	4.70	Knees	1.28
Patience	4.56	Ankles	1.25

Note: Ratings are based on a five-point scale of judged importance.

Source: Nevid, J. S. (1984). Sex differences in factors of romantic attraction. *Sex Roles, 11*, 401–411. Reprinted by permission of Plenum Publishing Corporation.

Gender Differences in Preferences in Mates Across 37 Cultures

What do men in Nigeria, Japan, Brazil, Canada, and the United States have in common? For one thing, men in these countries report that they prefer mates who are younger than themselves. Buss (1989) reviewed survey evidence on the preferred age difference between oneself and one's mate in 37 cultures (representing 33 countries) in Europe, Africa, Asia, Australia, and New Zealand, and North and South America. In every culture men preferred younger mates (the range was from 0.38 years among Finnish men to 6.45 years among Nigerian men). Women, however, preferred older mates (the range was from 1.82 years among French Canadian women to 5.1 years among Iranian women; see Table 7.2).

Gender differences in the preferred age of mates paralleled actual differences in age of men and women at the time of marriage. Men were between two and five years older on the average than their brides at the time of marriage. The smallest age differences at marriage, 2.10 years, was found in Poland. The largest difference, 4.92 years, was found

in Greece. Men in the mainland United States are 2.71 years older than women at the time of marriage. In Canada, men are 2.51 years older than their mates on the average.

Buss finds that in all 37 cultures, men placed greater value on a prospective partner's "good looks" than did women.[1] On the other hand, women in 36 of 37 cultures placed greater value on "good earning capacity" of prospective mates. The lone exception was the sample from Spain, in which differences between the genders were in the same direction but were not statistically significant.

The sampling techniques in these surveys varied widely, and the samples may not be truly representative of the larger cultures in these countries. The consistency of findings nevertheless lends credence to the general notion that there are gender differences in preferences with respect to age, physical characteristics, and financial status of prospective mates. Generally speaking, men across cultures place greater value on the physical attractiveness and relative

youth of prospective mates, whereas women place relatively greater value on the earning capacity of prospective mates. Buss interprets women's preferences for relatively older mates as additional evidence that women appraise future mates on the basis of their ability to provide for a wife and family, since age and income tend to be linked among men.

Despite these gender differences in preferences for mates, Buss finds that both men and women placed greater weight on personal qualities than on looks or income potential of prospective mates. In *all* 37 cultures, the characteristics "kind-understanding" and "intelligent" were rated higher than earning power or physical attractiveness. Let us also note an interesting parallel between Buss's cross-cultural evidence and Nevid's findings with a sample of U.S. college students. Nevid reported that his college sample also rated personal characteristics more highly than physical characteristics in potential partners for meaningful relationships.

[1]Gender differences were statistically significant in 34 of the 37 countries. In the three countries in which the differences were not significant (India, Poland, Sweden) significant differences were found for ratings of a variable labeled "physically attractive," with men again placing greater value on this attribute.

---

relationships than did women. Women placed more value on qualities such as warmth, assertiveness, wit, and an achievement orientation. The single most highly desired quality students wanted in long-term partners was honesty. Honestly.

TRUTH OR FICTION?
REVISITED

Physical appeal is the most important trait we seek in partners for long-term relationships. *Not so, according to the results of a study that showed that physical appeal was not the most important trait that students said they sought in partners for long-term relationships. Honesty was reported to be more vital.* •

TABLE 7.2 Preferred age differences between self and spouse and actual age differences at marriage in 37 cultures

Sample	Males (mean)	Females (mean)	Actual Age Difference
Africa			
Nigeria	-6.45	4.90	—
S. Africa (whites)	-2.30	3.50	3.13
S. Africa (Zulu)	-3.33	3.76	2.38
Zambia	-7.38	4.14	—
Asia			
China	-2.05	3.45	—
India	-3.06	3.29	—
Indonesia	-2.72	4.69	—
Iran	-4.02	5.10	—
Israel (Jewish)	-2.88	3.95	3.57
Israel (Palestinian)	-3.75	3.71	3.57
Japan	-2.37	3.05	2.92
Taiwan	-3.13	3.78	3.50
Eastern Europe			
Bulgaria	-3.13	4.18	3.54
Estonia	-2.19	2.85	2.49
Poland	-2.85	3.38	2.10
Yugoslavia	-2.47	3.61	3.55
Western Europe			
Belgium	-2.53	2.46	2.37
France	-1.94	4.00	2.28
Finland	-0.38	2.83	2.30
Germany	-2.52	3.70	3.19
Great Britain	-1.92	2.26	2.61
Greece	-3.36	4.54	4.92
Ireland	-2.07	2.78	2.17
Italy	-2.76	3.24	3.68
Netherlands	-1.01	2.72	2.58
Norway	-1.91	3.12	2.87
Spain	-1.46	2.60	2.45
Sweden	-2.34	2.91	2.97
North America			
Canada (English)	-1.53	2.72	2.51
Canada (French)	-1.22	1.82	2.51
USA (mainland)	-1.65	2.54	2.71
USA (Hawaii)	-1.92	3.30	—
Australia and New Zealand			
Australia	-1.77	2.86	2.73
New Zealand	-1.59	2.91	2.78
South America			
Brazil	-2.94	3.94	3.52
Colombia	-4.45	4.51	4.53
Venezuela	-2.99	3.62	3.47
Overall Means	-2.66	3.42	2.99

Note: Negative values signify preference for a *younger* mate; positive values signify preference for an *older* mate.

Source: Buss, D. M. (1989). Sex differences in human mate preferences: Evolutionary hypotheses tested in 37 cultures. *Behavioral and Brain Sciences, 12,* 1–49. Reprinted by permission of Cambridge University Press.

Although personal qualities may assume more prominent roles in determining partner preferences in long-term relationships, physical appeal probably plays a "filtering" role. Unless a prospective date meets minimal physical standards, we might not look beneath the surface for "more meaningful" traits.

Nevid's results have been replicated in studies on initial attraction and on choice of mates. Women place relatively greater emphasis than men on traits like vocational status, earning potential, expressiveness, kindness, consideration, dependability, and fondness for children. Men give relatively more consideration to physical attractiveness, cooking ability (can't they switch on the microwave by themselves?), and frugality (Buss & Barnes, 1986; Howard et al., 1987; Sprecher, 1989a). European researchers also find that when it comes to mate selection, females in a sample composed of students from Germany and the Netherlands emphasized the financial prospects and status of a potential mate, whereas males emphasized the importance of physical attractiveness (de Raad & Doddema-Winsemius, 1992).

Learning Objective 3:
Discuss the sociobiological view of the different characteristics men and women desire in their mates.

ARE ATTRACTIVENESS PREFERENCES INHERITED? On the surface, gender differences in perceptions of attractiveness seem unbearably sexist—and perhaps they are. Yet some sociobiologists believe that evolutionary forces favor the continuation of gender differences in preferences for mates because certain preferred traits provide reproductive advantages. Some physical features, like cleanliness, good complexion, clear eyes, good teeth, good hair, firm muscle tone, and a steady gait are found to be universally appealing to both genders (Ford & Beach, 1951). Perhaps they have value as markers of better reproductive potential in prospective mates (Symons, 1979). Age and health may be relatively more important to a woman's appeal, since these characteristics tend to be associated with her reproductive capacity (Williams, 1975): the "biological clock" limits her reproductive potential. Physical characteristics associated with a woman's youthfulness, such as smooth skin, firm muscle tone and lustrous hair, may thus have become more closely linked to a woman's appeal (Buss, 1989). A man's reproductive value, however, may depend more on how well he can provide for his family than on his age or physical appeal. The value of men as reproducers, therefore, is more intertwined with factors that contribute to a stable environment for child rearing—such as economic status and reliability. Sociobiologists argue that these gender differences in mate preferences may have been passed down through the generations as part of our genetic heritage (Buss, 1989; Symons, 1979).

Men's interest in younger women is apparently universal. It occurs in both preliterate and industrialized societies (Buss, 1989; Symons, 1979). Female jealousy of younger women is another thread that spans cultures. Sexual competition, according to Margaret Mead, generally involves

> the struggle between stronger older men and weaker younger men or between more attractive younger women and more entrenched older ones.
>
> (Mead, 1967, p. 198)

Discussion Question: How do we perceive couples in which the woman is significantly older—maybe ten years or more older? How do we perceive couples in which the man is significantly older? Why do our perceptions differ?

Sociobiological views of gender differences in mate preferences are largely speculative and not fully consistent with the evidence. Despite gender differences both men and women report that they place greater weight on personal characteristics than on physical features in judging prospective partners for meaningful relationships (Nevid, 1984) and marriage (Buss, 1989). Many women, like men, are nevertheless attracted to physically appealing partners (Bixler, 1989), and women tend to marry men similar to themselves in physical attractiveness as well as socioeconomic standing. Note also that older men are more likely than younger men to die from natural causes. From the standpoint of reproductive advantages, women would thus achieve greater success by marrying fit, younger males who are likely to survive during the child-rearing years than by marrying older, higher-status males. Moreover, similar cultural influences, rather than inherited dispositions, may explain commonalities across cultures in gender differences in mate preferences. For example, in societies in which women are economically dependent on men, a man's appeal may depend more on his financial resources than on his physical appeal. Even sociobiologists allow that despite notions of innate predispositions, many men maintain sexual interest in older women. Human behavior is flexible at the very least (Symons, 1979).

Matching hypothesis
The concept that people tend to develop romantic relationships with people who are similar to themselves in attractiveness.

Learning Objective 4:
Analyze how the "matching hypothesis" accounts for partner choice.

THE MATCHING HYPOTHESIS: WHO IS "RIGHT" FOR YOU? Do not despair if you are less than exquisite in appearance, along with most of us mere mortals. You may be saved from permanently blending in with the wallpaper by the effects of the **matching hypothesis**—the concept that people tend to develop romantic relationships with people who are similar to themselves in physical attractiveness (Folkes, 1982), rather than the local Tom Cruise or Julia Roberts look-alike.

Researchers have found that people who are dating steadily, engaged, or married tend to be matched in physical attractiveness (Kalick, 1988). Young married couples even tend to be matched in weight (Schafer & Keith, 1990). Engaged and married couples even tend to resemble each other in facial characteristics (Hinsz, 1989). Couples in more committed and close relationships also tend to be better matched in physical attractiveness than couples in more casual relationships (McKillip & Riedel, 1983). This finding suggests that mismatched couples may not last, a belief that finds support in a study showing that mismatched couples were more likely to terminate their relationships than were others who were better matched in physical attractiveness (White, 1980).

Love in the 90s

Who Is Right for You? Research shows that people tend to pair off with others who are similar in physical characteristics and personality traits. (The type of eye glasses one wears may not be crucial, however.)

The central motive for seeking "matches" seems to be fear of rejection by more appealing people (Bernstein et al., 1983). Shanteau and Nagy (1979) found that college women who were asked to choose between two prospective dates were influenced both by the man's appearance (in a photograph) and the probability of his accepting the request (as suggested by statements attached to the photos varying from "sure thing" to "no chance"). A moderately attractive male who was depicted as "highly likely" to accept a date was chosen most often. In a second phase of the experiment, women were asked to select a date from a photograph alone. Most women chose moderately attractive males. Perhaps they assumed that the most attractive males would be least likely to accept their requests. Fear of rejection thus appears to have been the major motive for avoiding a mismatch.

There are some exceptions to the matching hypothesis. Now and then we find a beautiful woman married to a plain or ugly man (or vice versa). How do we explain it? What, after all, would *she* see in *him*? According to one study (Bar-Tal & Saxe, 1976), people judging "mismatched" pairs may tend to ascribe wealth, intelligence, or success to the man. We seek an unseen factor that will balance the physical attractiveness of one partner. For some mismatched couples, similarities in attitudes and personalities may balance out differences in physical attractiveness.

The matching hypothesis not only applies to physical appeal. It also describes the fact that we are also more apt to marry people who are akin to us in their attitudes, personality traits (Buss, 1984; Lesnik-Oberstein & Cohen, 1984), and psychological needs (Meyer & Pepper, 1977).

ATTRACTION AND ATTITUDINAL SIMILARITY: DO OPPOSITES ATTRACT?

Learning Objective 5:
Describe the influence of attitudinal similarity on attraction and on relationships.

It has been observed over the centuries that people tend to take a liking to people who agree with them (Jellison & Oliver, 1983). The more intolerant we are, the more apt we are to rebuff people who do not share our views (Palmer & Kalin, 1985). Similarity in attitudes and tastes is a robust contributor to initial attraction, friendships, and love relationships (Cappella & Palmer, 1990; Griffin & Sparks, 1990; Grover & Brockner, 1989; Lydon et al., 1988; Neimeyer & Mitchell, 1988; Park & Flink, 1989). People also prefer to work with others who hold similar attitudes to their own (Griffeth et al., 1989). Let us also note another gender difference. Evidence shows that women place greater weight on attitudinal similarity as a determinant of attraction to a stranger of the opposite sex than do men, whereas men place more value on physical attractiveness (Feingold, 1991).

We also tend to *assume* that people we find attractive share our attitudes (Dawes, 1989; Marks et al., 1981). The strong physical attraction Candy and Stretch felt for one another motivated them to pretend that their preferences, tastes, and opinions coincided. They entered into a nonspoken agreement not to discuss their religious differences. When sexual attraction is strong, perhaps we want to think that the kinks in the relationship will be small or that we can iron them out. Let us also note that though similarity may be important in determining initial attraction, compatibility appears to be an even stronger determinant of maintaining an enduring intimate relationship (Vinacke et al., 1988).

TRUTH OR *FICTION?*

R E V I S I T E D

"Opposites attract." We are more apt, that is, to be attracted to people who disagree with our views and tastes than to people who share them. Actually, "opposites" usually repel one another, both in terms of attitudes and in terms of tastes. •

RECIPROCITY: IF YOU LIKE ME, YOU MUST HAVE EXCELLENT JUDGMENT

Has anyone told you that you are good-looking, brilliant, and emotionally mature to boot? That your taste is elegant? Ah, what superb judgment!

Reciprocity
Mutual exchange.

Learning Objective 6: Define *reciprocity* and describe its effect on attraction and on maintaining relationships.

When we feel admired and complimented, we tend to return these feelings and behaviors. This is **reciprocity.** Reciprocity is an extremely potent determinant of attraction (Condon & Crano, 1988). We tend to be much more warm, helpful, and candid when we are with strangers whom we believe like us (Clark et al., 1989; Curtis & Miller, 1986). We even tend to welcome positive comments from others when we know them to be inaccurate (Swann et al., 1987).

Perhaps the power of reciprocity has enabled many couples to become happy with one another and reasonably well adjusted. By reciprocating positive words and actions, a person can perhaps stoke neutral or mild feelings into robust, affirmative feelings of attraction.

Attraction can lead to feelings of love. Let us now turn to that most fascinating topic.

Activity: *Thinking About. . . Does Love Make the World Go 'Round?* This activity in the IM asks students to examine the possible meaning of the phrase "love makes the world go 'round."

Teaching Tip: Have students generate a list of expressions about love or the way we talk about love (falling in love, moonstruck, struck by Cupid's arrow, swept off my feet, bewitched, smitten, lost my heart to, fell for, lovesick, etc.). Write these on the board. Examine them for evidence of the underlying assumption that we have little or no control over whom we love.

LOVE

For thousands of years, poets have sought to capture love in words. A seventeenth-century poet wrote that his love was like "a red, red rose." In Sinclair Lewis's novel *Elmer Gantry,* love is "the morning and the evening star." Love is beautiful and elusive. It shines brilliantly and heavenly. Passion and romantic love are also earthy and sexy, brimming with sexual desire.

Romantic love is hardly unique to our culture. Researchers report finding evidence of romantic love in 147 of the 166 different cultures they studied in a recent cross-cultural comparison (Jankowiak & Fischer, 1992). Romantic love occurs even in most preliterate societies. The absence of romantic love in the remaining 19 cultures, the investigators suspect, was most probably due to the limitations of their study methods (Gelman, 1993).

In our culture we are brought up to idealize the concept of romantic love. Thus we readily identify with the plight of the "star-crossed" lovers in *Romeo and Juliet* and *West Side Story,* who sacrificed for love. We learn that "love makes the world go round" and that "love is everything." Virtually all of the participants in the Janus and Janus nationwide survey (96% of the men and 98% of the women) reported that love is important to them (Janus & Janus, 1993). Like other aspects of sexual and social behavior among humans, the concept of love must be understood within a cultural context. Luckily (or miserably), we have such a context in Western culture . . . .

THE GREEK HERITAGE

The concept of love can be traced back at least as far as the classical age of Greece. The Greeks had four concepts related to the modern meanings of love: *storge, agape, philia,* and *eros.*

Storge can be translated as loving attachment, deep friendship, or nonsexual affection, the type of emotion that binds friends and parents and children. Some contemporary scholars believe that even romantic love is a form of attachment that is similar to the types of attachments infants have to their mothers (Hazan & Shaver, 1987). In a cross-cultural comparison, researchers found that a group of U.S. college students obtained higher scores on storge than did a group of French college students (Murstein et al., 1991). The researchers speculate that friendship patterns may evolve more naturally among American youngsters, because their society permits greater opportunities for shared schooling and socialization between boys and girls than does French society, where separation in schools by gender is more commonplace.

Storge

(STORE-gay) Loving attachment and nonsexual affection; the type of emotion that binds parents to children.

Agape is similar to generosity and charity. It implies the wish to share one's bounty, and is epitomized by anonymous donations. In relationships, it is characterized by selfless giving (Lee, 1988). Agape, according to Lee's research, is the kind of love least frequently found between adults in committed relationships.

Agape

(AH-gah-pay) Selfless love; a kind of loving that is similar to generosity and charity.

Philia is closest in meaning to friendship. It is based on liking and respect, rather than sexual desire. It involves the desire to do and enjoy things with the other person, and to see him or her when one is lonely or bored.

Philia

(FEEL-yuh) Friendship love, which is based on liking and respect rather than sexual desire.

Eros is closest in meaning to our concept of passion. Eros was a character in Greek mythology (transformed in Roman mythology into Cupido; now called Cupid) who would shoot unsuspecting people with his love arrows, causing them to fall madly in love with the person who was nearest to them at the time. Erotic love embraces sudden passionate desire: "love at first sight" and "falling head over heels in love." Passion can be so gripping that one is convinced that life has been changed forever. This feeling of sudden transformation was captured by the Italian poet Dante Alighieri (1265–1321), who exclaimed upon first beholding his beloved Beatrice, *"Incipit vita nuova,"* which can be translated as "My life begins anew." Romantic love can also be earthy and sexy, involving a solid dose of sexual desire. In fact, sexual arousal and desire may be the strongest component of passionate or romantic love (Berscheid, 1988). Romantic love begins with a powerful physical attraction or feelings of passion, and is associated with strong physiological arousal (Hatfield, 1988; Lee, 1988).

Eros

The kind of love that is closest in meaning to the modern-day concept of passion.

Unlike the Greeks, we tend to use the word "love" to describe everything from feelings of affection toward another to romantic ardor to sexual intercourse ("making love"). Still, there are different types or styles of love that are recognized in our own culture, as we shall see. Our focus will be on romantic love, because it is the type of love that is associated with sexual desire and arousal.

ROMANTIC LOVE IN CONTEMPORARY WESTERN CULTURE

The experience of *romantic love,* as opposed to loving attachment or sexual arousal per se, occurs within a cultural context in which the concept is idealized. Western culture has a long tradition of idealizing the concept of romantic love, as represented, for instance, by romantic fairy tales that have been passed down through the generations. In fact, our exposure to the concept of romantic love may begin with hearing the fairy tales of Sleeping Beauty, Cinderella, and Snow White—along with their princes charming. Later perhaps, the concept of romantic love blossoms with exposure to romantic novels, television and film scripts, and the heady tales of friends and relatives.

During adolescence, strong sexual arousal along with an idealized image of the object of our desires leads us to label our feelings as love. We may learn to speak of "love" rather than "lust," because sexual desire in the absence of a committed relationship might be viewed as primitive or animalistic. Being "in love" enables attraction and sexual arousal, not only to society but also to oneself. Unlike lust, love can even be discussed even at the dinner table. If others think we are too young to experience "the real

Are You a Romantic or a Realist? The Love Attitudes Scale

David Knox (1988) of East Carolina University contrasts romantic love with *realistic love*—the kind of love that is maintained across the years. Partners who share a realistic love have the blinders off. They accept and cherish each other, warts and all.

Knox (1983) developed the Love Attitudes Scale to evaluate the degree to which people hold a romantic or realistic view of love. How about you? Are you a realist or a romantic when it comes to matters of the heart? To find out, complete the scale and then turn to the scoring key in the Appendix.

Directions: Circle the number that best represents your opinion on each item according to the following code. Add up your scores to arrive at a total score.

1 = Strongly agree (SA)

2 = Mildly agree (MA)

3 = Undecided (U)

4 = Mildly disagree (MD)

5 = Strongly disagree(SD)

1. Love doesn't make sense. It just is.　　1 2 3 4 5

2. When you fall "head over heels" in love, it's sure to be the real thing.　　1 2 3 4 5

3. To be in love with someone you would like to marry but can't is a tragedy.　　1 2 3 4 5

4. When love hits, you know it.　　1 2 3 4 5

5. Common interests are really unimportant; as long as each of you is truly in love, you will adjust.　　1 2 3 4 5

6. It doesn't matter if you marry after you have known your partner for only a short time as long as you know you are in love.　　1 2 3 4 5

7. If you are going to love a person, you will "know" after a short time.　　1 2 3 4 5

8. As long as two people love each other, the educational differences they have really do not matter.　　1 2 3 4 5

9. You can love someone even though you do not like any of that person's friends.　　1 2 3 4 5

10. When you are in love, you are usually in a daze.　　1 2 3 4 5

11. Love "at first sight" is often the deepest an most enduring type of love.　　1 2 3 4 5

12. When you are in love, it really does not matter what your partner does because you will love him or her anyway.　　1 2 3 4 5

13. As long as you really love a person, you will be able to solve the problems you have with that person.　　1 2 3 4 5

thing"—which presumably includes knowledge of and respect for the other person's personality traits—our feelings may be called "puppy love" or a "crush."

Western society maintains much of the double standard toward sexuality. Thus, women are more often expected to justify sexual experiences as involving someone they love. Young men usually need not attribute sexual urges to love. So men are more apt to deem love a "mushy" concept. The vast majority of people in the United States nonetheless believe romantic love is a prerequisite for marriage. Romantic love is rated by young people as the single most important reason for marriage (Roper, 1985). Over 80 percent of college men and women now subscribe to the belief that "being in love" is a precondition for marriage (Berscheid, 1988; Simpson et al., 1986). More than half also believe that falling out of love is an adequate reason for divorce.

Which is the more romantic gender? While the question may well incite an argument in mixed company, the Janus and Janus (1993) nationwide survey of adult Americans found that a slightly greater percentage of the single men (82%) perceived themselves as being romantic than did single women (77%). Yet among married people, the figures were reversed, with 79 percent of the women describing themselves as romantic as compared to 72 percent of the men. Perhaps there is some truth to the stereotype that men are more romantic during the courtship stage of relationships than the mar-

14. Usually you can really love and be happy with only one or two people in the world.   1 2 3 4 5

15. Regardless of other factors, if you truly love another person, that is a good enough reason to marry that person.   1 2 3 4 5

16. It is necessary to be in love with the one you marry to be happy.   1 2 3 4 5

17. Love is more of a feeling than a relationship.   1 2 3 4 5

18. People should not get married unless they are in love.   1 2 3 4 5

19. Most people truly love only once during their lives.   1 2 3 4 5

20. Somewhere there is an ideal mate for most people.   1 2 3 4 5

21. In most cases, you will "know it" when you meet the right partners.   1 2 3 4 5

22. Jealousy usually varies directly with love; that is, the more you are in love, the greater your tendency to become jealous will be.   1 2 3 4 5

23. When you are in love, you are motivated by what you feel rather than by what you think.   1 2 3 4 5

24. Love is best described as an exciting rather than a calm thing.   1 2 3 4 5

25. Most divorces probably result from falling out of love rather than failing to adjust.   1 2 3 4 5

26. When you are in love, your judgment is usually not too clear.   1 2 3 4 5

27. Love often comes only once in a lifetime.   1 2 3 4 5

28. Love is often a violent and uncontrollable emotion.   1 2 3 4 5

29. When selecting a marriage partner, differences in social class and religion are of small importance compared with love.   1 2 3 4 5

30. No matter what anyone says, love cannot be understood.   1 2 3 4 5

Total Score for the Love Attitudes Scale: _____

Source: From Knox, D. (1983). The love attitudes inventory (rev. ed.). Saluda, NC: Family Life Publications. Reprinted with permission.

riage stage. Then again, maybe self-perceptions of being romantic don't quite jibe with the reality. In any event, you can explore self-perceptions of being a romantic or a realist when it comes to love by completing the Love Attitudes Scale.

When reciprocated, romantic love is usually a source of deep fulfillment and ecstasy (Hatfield, 1988, 1989). How wonderful when love meets its match. When love is unrequited, however, it can lead to emptiness, anxiety, or despair. Romantic love can thus teeter between states of ecstasy and misery (Hatfield, 1988, 1989). Perhaps no other feature of our lives can lift us up as high or plunge us as low as romantic love.

INFATUATION VERSUS "TRUE LOVE": WILL TIME TELL?   Perhaps you first noticed each other when your eyes met across a crowded room, like the star-crossed lovers in West Side Story. Or perhaps you met when you were both assigned to the same bunsen burner in chemistry lab—less romantic, but closer to the flame. However it happened, the meeting triggered such an electric charge through your body that you could not get him (or her) out of your mind. Were you truly in love, however, or was it merely a passing fancy? Was it infatuation or the "real thing"—a "true," lasting, and mutual love? How do you tell them apart?

Infatuation

A state of intense absorption in or focus on another person, which is usually accompanied by sexual desire, elation, and general physiological arousal or excitement; passion.

Teaching Tip: Instead of thinking of "Sleeping Beauty," "Cinderella," and "Snow White" as tales of romantic love, have students think about them as tales of men's and women's sexual roles. In "Sleeping Beauty" the woman is passive—she's "asleep" forever. She needs only the kiss of a prince to "awaken" her. In "Cinderella" a woman with a horrible family, great beauty, and small feet is "rescued" by her prince. Snow White is envied and poisoned because of her beauty and also "awakened" from the sleep of death by a prince. One message of these tales is that women have no sexuality of their own and need men to "awaken" them. The high value our society places on physical beauty should also be obvious from these tales.

Romantic love

A kind of love characterized by feelings of passion and intimacy.

Learning Objective 9: Discuss three contemporary models of love and the associated explanations of the origins of love.

Perhaps you don't, at least not at first. **Infatuation** may be defined as a state of intense absorption in or focusing on another person, which is usually accompanied by sexual desire, elation, and general physiological arousal or excitement. Some refer to passion as infatuation. Others dub it a "crush." Both monikers suggest that it is a passing fancy. In infatuation, your heart may pound whenever the other person draws near or enters your fantasies.

For the first month or two, infatuation and the more enduring forms of romantic love are essentially indistinguishable (Gordon & Snyder, 1989). At first, both may be characterized by intense focusing or absorption. Infatuated people may become so absorbed that they cannot sleep, work, or carry out routine chores. Logic and reason are swept aside. Infatuated people hold idealized images of their love objects and overlook their faults. Caution may be cast to the winds. In some cases, couples in the throes of infatuation rush to get married, only to find a few weeks or months later that they are not well suited.

As time goes on, signs that distinguish infatuation from a lasting romantic love begin to emerge. The partners begin to view each other more realistically and determine whether or not the relationship should continue.

Infatuation has been likened to a state of passionate love (Sternberg, 1986) that is based on intense feelings of passion but not on the deeper feelings of attachment and caring that typify a more lasting mutual love. Although infatuation may be a passing fancy, it can be supplanted by the deeper feelings of attachment and caring that characterize more lasting love relationships.

Note, too, that infatuation is not a necessary first step on the path to a lasting mutual love. Some couples develop deep feelings of love without ever experiencing the fireworks of infatuation (Sternberg, 1986). Or sometimes one partner is infatuated while the other manages to keep his or her head below the clouds.

CONTEMPORARY MODELS OF LOVE: DARE SCIENCE INTRUDE?

Despite the importance of love, scientists have historically paid little attention to it. Some people believe that love cannot be analyzed scientifically. Love, they maintain, should be left to the poets, philosophers, and theologians. Yet researchers are now applying the scientific method to the study of love. They recognize that love is a complex concept, involving many areas of experience—emotional, cognitive, and motivational (Sternberg & Grajek, 1984). They have reinforced the Greek view that there are different kinds and styles of love. Let us consider some of the views of love that have emerged from modern theorists and researchers.

LOVE AS APPRAISAL OF AROUSAL Social psychologists Ellen Berscheid and Elaine Hatfield (Berscheid & Walster, 1978; Walster & Walster, 1978) define **romantic love** in terms of a state of intense physiological arousal and the cognitive appraisal of that arousal as love. The physiological arousal may be experienced as a pounding heart, sweaty palms, and butterflies in the stomach when one is in the presence of or thinking about one's love interest. Cognitive appraisal of the arousal means attributing it to some cause, such as fear or love. The perception that one has fallen in love is thus derived from several simultaneous events: (1) a state of intense physiological arousal that is connected with an appropriate love object (that is, a person, not an event like a rock concert); (2) a cultural setting that idealizes romantic love; and (3) the attribution of the arousal to feelings of love toward the person.

STYLES OF LOVE Some psychologists speak in terms of *styles* of love. Clyde and Susan Hendrick (1986) developed a love-attitude scale that suggests the existence of six styles of love among college students. Following is a list of the styles, with each style exemplified by statements similar to those on the original scale. As you can see, the styles owe a debt to the Greeks:

1. *Romantic love (eros)*: "My lover fits my ideal." "My lover and I were attracted to one another immediately."
2. *Game-playing love*: "I keep my lover up in the air about my commitment." "I get over love affairs pretty easily."
3. *Friendship (storge, philia)*: "The best love grows out of an enduring friendship."
4. *Logical love:* "I consider a lover's potential in life before committing myself." "I consider whether my lover will be a good parent."
5. *Possessive, excited love*: "I get so excited about my love that I cannot sleep." "When my lover ignores me I get sick all over."
6. *Selfless love (agape)*: "I would do anything I can to help my lover." "My lover's needs and wishes are more important than my own."

Most people who are "in love" experience a number of these styles, but the Hendricks (1986) found some interesting gender differences in styles of love. College men are significantly more likely to develop game-playing and romantic love styles, whereas college women are more apt to develop friendly, logical, and possessive love styles. (There were no gender differences in selfless love.) The Hendricks and their colleagues (1988) have also found that romantically involved couples tend to experience the same kinds of love styles. They also showed that couples with romantic and selfless styles of love are more likely to remain together. A game-playing love style leads to unhappiness, however, and is one reason that relationships come to an end.

STERNBERG'S TRIANGULAR THEORY OF LOVE   Psychologist Robert Sternberg (1986, 1987, 1988) offers a triangular theory of love. In his view there are three distinct components of love:

1. *Intimacy*: the experience of warmth toward another person that arises from feelings of closeness, bondedness, and connectedness to the other. Intimacy also involves the desire to give and receive emotional support and to share one's innermost thoughts with the other.
2. *Passion*: an intense romantic or sexual desire for another person, which is accompanied by physiological arousal.
3. *Decision/Commitment*: a component of love that involves both short-term and long-term issues. In the short term there is the issue of deciding that one loves the other person. In the long term there is the issue of one's willingness to make a *commitment* to maintain the relationship through good times and bad. Decision and commitment need not go hand in hand. Although decision generally precedes commitment, some people become committed to a relationship before they even decide whether they love the other person. Others, however, never make a lasting commitment or openly acknowledge loving the other person.

According to Sternberg's model, love can be conceptualized in terms of a triangle in which each vertex represents one of these basic elements of love (see Figure 7.1). The way the components are balanced can be represented by the shape of the triangle. For example, a love in which all three components were equally balanced would be represented by an equilateral triangle, as in Figure 7.1.

Sternberg believes that couples are well-matched if they possess corresponding levels of passion, intimacy, and commitment. Compatibility can be represented visually in terms of the congruence of the love triangles. Figure 7.2(a) shows a perfect match in which the triangles are congruent. Figure 7.2(b) depicts a good match; the partners are similar in the three dimensions. Figure 7.2(c) shows a mismatch; major differences exist between the partners on all three components. Relationships may run aground when partners are mismatched. A relationship may fizzle, rather than sizzle, when one partner experiences more passion than the other, or when one wants a long-term commitment when the other's idea of commitment is to stay the night.

According to the Sternberg model, various combinations of the three elements of love characterize different types of love relationships (Sternberg, 1986, 1988) (see Figure

Intimacy

Passion   Decision/
               Commitment

FIGURE 7.1 **The Triangular Model of Love.** According to psychologist Robert Sternberg, love consists of three components, as shown by the vertices of this triangle. Various kinds of love consist of different combinations of these components. Romantic love, for example, consists of passion and intimacy. Consummate love—a state devoutly to be desired—consists of all three.

QUESTIONNAIRE

Sternberg's Triangular Love Scale

Which are the strongest components of your love relationship? Intimacy? Passion? Decision/commitment? All three components? Two of them?

    To complete the following scale, fill in the blank spaces with the name of one person you love or care about deeply. Then rate your agreement with each of the items by using a nine-point scale in which 1 = "not at all," 5 = "moderately," and 9 = "extremely." Use points in between to indicate intermediate levels of agreement between these values. Then consult the scoring key in the Appendix.

Intimacy Component

_____ 1. I am actively supportive of _____ 's well-being.

_____ 2. I have a warm relationship with _____.

_____ 3. I am able to count on _____ in times of need.

_____ 4. _____ is able to count on me in times of need.

_____ 5. I am willing to share myself and my possessions with _____.

_____ 6. I receive considerable emotional support from _____.

_____ 7. I give considerable emotional support to _____.

_____ 8. I communicate well with _____.

_____ 9. I value _____ greatly in my life.

___10. I feel close to _____.

___11. I have a comfortable relationship with _____.

___12. I feel that I really understand _____.

___13. I feel that _____ really understands me.

___14. I feel that I can really trust _____.

___15. I share deeply personal information about myself with _____.

Passion Component

___16. Just seeing _____ excites me.

___17. I find myself thinking about _____ frequently during the day.

___18. My relationship with _____ is very romantic.

___19. I find _____ to be very personally attractive.

___20. I idealize _____.

___21. I cannot imagine another person making me as happy as _____ does.

Activity: *Thinking About Whether or Not All You Need Is Love* This IM activity encourages students to examine whether passion is all that is needed for an enduring, successful relationship.

7.2 and Table 7.3). For example, infatuation (*passionate love*) is typified by strong sexual desire, but not by intimacy and commitment. The partners may each feel passionate love for the other, or, as in the case of Tom, such feelings may go unrequited:

Tom sat behind Lisa in physics class. Tom hated physics, but he could not say the same for Lisa. One look at her was enough to change his life. He had fallen madly in love with her. Instead of listening to the teacher or looking at the blackboard, he would gaze at Lisa throughout the class. Lisa was aware of this and was not happy about it. She did not much care for Tom, and when he tried to start a conversation with her, she moved on as quickly as possible. Tom's staring and his awkwardness in talking to her made her feel uncomfortable. Tom, on the other hand, could think of little else besides Lisa, and his grades began to suffer as he spent the time he should have been devoting to his homework thinking about her. He was a man obsessed. The obsession might have gone on for quite some time had not both Tom and Lisa graduated that June and gone to different colleges. Tom never saw Lisa again, and after several unanswered love letters, he finally gave up on her.

(Sternberg, 1988, p. 123)

___22. I would rather be with _____ than anyone else.

___23. There is nothing more important to me than my relationship with _____.

___24. I especially like physical contact with _____.

___25. There is something almost "magical" about my relationship with _____.

___26. I adore _____.

___27. I cannot imagine life without _____.

___28. My relationship with _____ is passionate.

___29. When I see romantic movies and read romantic books I think of _____.

___30. I fantasize about _____.

Decision/Commitment Component

___31. I know that I care about _____.

___32. I am committed to maintaining my relationship with _____.

___33. Because of my commitment to _____, I wouldn't let other people come between us.

___34. I have confidence in the stability of my relationship with _____.

___35. I could not let anything get in the way of my commitment to _____.

___36. I expect my love for _____ to last for the rest of my life.

___37. I will always feel a strong responsibility for _____.

___38. I view my commitment to _____ as a solid one.

___39. I cannot imagine ending my relationship with _____.

___40. I am certain of my love for _____.

___41. I view my relationship with _____ as permanent.

___42. I view my relationship with _____ as a good decision.

___43. I feel a sense of responsibility toward _____.

___44. I plan to continue my relationship with _____.

___45. Even when _____ is hard to deal with, I remain committed to our relationship.

Source: Sternberg, R. (1988). Reprinted by permission of Basic Books, Inc., Publishers, New York.

Liking is very much like friendship. It consists of feelings of closeness and emotional warmth without passion or decision/commitment. This form of love is not felt toward passing acquaintances but is reserved for people to whom one feels close enough to share one's innermost feelings and thoughts. We sometimes develop these intimate relationships without making the commitment to maintaining a long-term relationship that typifies other types of love, however. Liking may develop into a passionate love, however, or into a more committed form of friendship (called *companionate love* in Sternberg's model).

Should lovers also be friends, or are lovers and friends part of the twain that never meet? Candy and Stretch's relationship lacked the quality most often associated with true friendship, the willingness to share confidences. Despite their physical intimacy, their relationship remained so superficial that they couldn't even share information about their religious backgrounds.

TRUTH OR FICTION?

R E V I S I T E D

It is possible to be in love with someone who is not also a friend. True. *Being in love can refer to states of passion or infatuation, whereas friendship is usually based on shared interests, liking, and respect.* •

Consummate Love. According to Sternberg, romantic love may develop into a more complete love, called *consummate love*, in which desire is accompanied by deep intimacy and commitment. Consummate love is the special ideal toward which many Westerners strive.

The example of Candy and Stretch underscores the fact that couples can be "in love" even when they are not close friends. Friendship and passionate love do not necessarily overlap. There is nothing that prevents people in love from becoming good friends, however, perhaps even the best of friends. Sternberg's model recognizes that the intimacy we find in true friendships and the passion we find in love are blended in two forms of love—romantic love and consummate love. These love types differ along the dimension of decision/commitment, however.

Romantic love has both passion and intimacy but lacks commitment. Romantic love may burn brightly and then flicker out. Or it may develop into a more complete love, called *consummate love,* in which all three components flower. Desire is accompanied by a deeper intimacy and commitment. The flames of passion can be stoked across the years, even if they do not burn quite as brightly as once they did. Consummate love is most special, and certainly an ideal toward which many Westerners strive. In *empty love,* by contrast, there is nought but commitment. There is neither the warm emotional embrace of intimacy nor the flame of passion. With empty love one's lover is a person whom one tolerates and remains with because of a sense of duty.

Sometimes a love relationship has both passion and commitment but lacks intimacy. Sternberg calls this *fatuous (foolish) love.* Fatuous love is associated with whirlwind courtships that burn brightly but briefly as the partners come to the realization that they are not well matched. Intimacy can develop in such relationships, but couples who rush into marriage often find that the realities of marriage give the lie to their expectations:

> They expect a marriage made in heaven, but do not realize what they must do truly to maintain such a marriage. They base the relationship on passion and are disappointed when the passion starts to fade. They feel shortchanged—they have gotten much less than they bargained for. The problem, of course, is that they bargained for too much of one thing [passion] and not enough of another [intimacy].

(Sternberg, 1988, p. 128)

Learning Objective 10:
Identify the characteristics of love relationships that last.

In *companionate love,* finally, intimacy and commitment are strong, but passion is lacking. This form of love typifies long-term (so-called platonic) friendships and marriages in which passion has ebbed but a deep and abiding friendship remains. Berscheid and Walster defined companionate love as "the affection we feel for those with whom our lives are deeply entwined" (1978, p. 9).

Although romantic love may become transformed into companionate love, the process by which this transformation takes place remains vague (Shaver et al., 1988). Companionate love need not be sexless or lacking in romance, however. Although passion may have ebbed, the giving and receiving of sexual pleasure can help strengthen

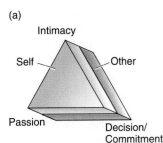

(a)

Intimacy

Self — Other

Passion — Decision/Commitment

Perfectly matched involvements

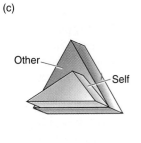

(b)

Self — Other

Closely matched involvements

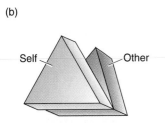

(c)

Other — Self

Severely mismatched involvements

FIGURE 7.2 **Compatibility and Incompatibility, According to the Triangular Model of Love.** Compatibility in terms of Sternberg's types of love can be represented as triangles. Part a shows a perfect match in which triangles are congruent. Part b depicts a good match; the partners are similar according to the three dimensions. Part c shows a mismatch; major differences exist between the partners on all three components.

bonds. Partners in companionate love relationships may feel that their sex lives have even become more deeply satisfying as they seek to please each other by practicing what they have learned about each other's sexual needs and wants. If companionate love blooms, the relationship can survive the fading of extremes of passion. At this point a couple can work together to meet each other's sexual as well as companionate needs. Skills can substitute for the excitement of novelty.

The balance among Sternberg's three aspects of love is likely to shift through the course of a relationship. A healthful dose of all three components—found in consummate love—typifies, for many of us, an ideal marriage. At the outset of marriage, passions may be strong but intimacy weak. Couples may only first be getting to know each other's innermost thoughts and feelings. Time alone does not cause intimacy and commitment to grow, however. Some couples are able to peer into each other's deeper selves and form meaningful commitments at relatively early stages in their relationships. Yet some long-married couples may remain distant and aloof from each other or waver in their commitment. Some couples experience only a faint flickering of passion early in the relationship. Then it becomes quickly extinguished. For some the flames of passion burn ever brightly. Yet many married couples find that passion tends to fade while intimacy and commitment grow stronger.

Knowing about these components of love may help couples avoid pitfalls. Couples who recognize that passion exerts a strong pull early in a relationship may be less likely

TABLE 7.3 Types of love according to Sternberg's triangular model

1. Nonlove	A relationship in which all three components of love are absent. Most of our personal relationships are of this type—casual interactions or acquaintanceships that do not involve any elements of love.
2. Liking	A loving experience with another person or an intimate friendship in which intimacy is present but passion and commitment are lacking.
3. Infatuation	A kind of "love at first sight" in which one experiences passionate desires for another person in the absence of both intimacy and decision/commitment components of love.
4. Empty love	A kind of love characterized by the decision (to love) and the commitment (to maintain the relationship) in the absence of either passion or intimacy. Stagnant relationships that no longer involve the emotional intimacy or physical attraction that once characterized them are of this type.
5. Romantic love	A loving experience characterized by the combination of passion and intimacy, but without decision/commitment components of love.
6. Companionate love	A kind of love that derives from the combination of intimacy and decision/commitment components of love. This kind of love often occurs in marriages in which passionate attraction between the partners has died down and has been replaced by a kind of committed friendship.
7. Fatuous love	The type of love associated with whirlwind romances and "quicky marriages" in which the passion and decision/commitment components of love are present, but intimacy is not.
8. Consummate love	The full or complete measure of love involving the combination of passion, intimacy, and decision/commitment. Many of us strive to attain this type of complete love in our romantic relationships. Maintaining it is often harder than achieving it.

Source: Adapted from Sternberg, 1988.

to let passion rush them into marriage. Couples who recognize that it is normal for passions to fade may avoid assuming that their love is at an end when it may, in fact, be changing into a deeper, more intimate and committed form of love. This knowledge may also encourage couples to focus on finding ways of rekindling the embers of romance, rather than looking to escape at the first signs that the embers have cooled.

Researchers have begun to test some facets of the triangular model. One recent study reported mixed results. As the model would predict, married adults reported higher levels of commitment to their relationships than did unmarried adults (Acker & Davis, 1992). Yet the expected decline in passion over time was found only for women. Critics contend that Sternberg's model does not account for all the nuances and complexities of love (Murstein, 1988). The model tells us little, for example, about the *goals* of love or the *sources* of love. In fairness, Sternberg's model is a major contribution to the scientific study of love, which is only now beginning. Poets, philosophers, and theologians, by comparison, have been writing about love for millennia.

In this chapter we have discussed interpersonal attraction—the force that initiates social contact. In the next chapter we follow the development of social contacts into intimate relationships.

SUMMING UP

ATTRACTION

A number of factors determine interpersonal attraction.

Physical Attractiveness: How Important Is Looking Good? Physical attractiveness is a major determinant of sexual attraction. In our culture, slenderness is in style. Both genders consider smiling faces more attractive. Socially dominant men, but not dominant women, are usually found attractive. Women place relatively greater emphasis on traits like vocational status and earning potential, whereas men give relatively more consideration to physical attractiveness. Some sociobiologists believe that evolutionary forces favor the continuation of such gender differences in preferred traits because certain preferred traits provide reproductive advantages. According to the matching hypothesis, people tend to develop romantic relationships with people who are similar to themselves in attractiveness.

Attraction and Attitudinal Similarity: Do Opposites Attract? Similarity in attitudes and tastes is a strong contributor to attraction, friendships, and love relationships.

Reciprocity: If You Like Me, You Must Have Excellent Judgment Through the reciprocation of positive words and actions, neutral or mild feelings may be stoked into feelings of attraction.

_____ Small talk is an insincere method of initiating a relationship.

_____ Swift self-disclosure of intimate information is the best way to deepen a new relationship.

_____ Many people remain lonely because they fear being rejected by others.

_____ People can have intimate relationships without being sexually intimate.

_____ When partners truly love one another, they instinctively know how to satisfy each other sexually.

_____ If you are criticized, the best course is to retaliate.

_____ Relationships come to an end when the partners cannot resolve their differences.

C H A P T E R   *8*

Relationships, Intimacy, and Communication

Will you, won't you, will you, won't you, will you join the dance?
(From Lewis *Carroll's Alice in Wonderland*)

No man is an island, entire of itself.
(John Donne)

"One, two. One, two." A great opening line? In the film *Play It Again, Sam,* Woody Allen plays the role of Allan Felix, a social klutz who has just been divorced. Diane Keaton plays his platonic friend Linda. At a bar one evening with Linda and her husband, Allan Felix spots a young woman on the dance floor who is so attractive that he wishes *he* could have *her* children.

The thing to do, Linda prompts him, is to begin dancing, then dance over to her and "say something." With a bit more prodding, Linda convinces Allan to dance. It's so simple, she tells him. He need only keep time—"One, two, one, two."

"One, two," repeats Allan. Linda shoves him off to his dream woman.

Hesitantly, Allan dances up to her. Working up courage, he says, "One, two. One, two, one, two." He is ignored and finds his way back to Linda.

"Allan, try something more meaningful," Linda implores.

Once more, Allan dances nervously back toward the woman of his dreams. He stammers, "Three, four, three, four."

"*Speak* to her, Allan," Linda insists.

He dances up to her again and tries, "You interested in dancing at all?"

"Get lost, creep," she replies.

Allan dances rapidly back toward Linda. "What'd she say?" Linda asks.

"She'd rather not," he shrugs.

So much for "One, two, one, two," and, for that matter, for "Three, four, three, four." Striking up a relationship requires some social skills, and the first few conversational steps can be big ones.

In this chapter we first define the stages that lead to intimacy in relationships. We define intimacy and see that not all relationships achieve this level of interrelatedness, even some supposedly deep and permanent relationships such as marriage. Moreover, we do not all have partners with whom we can develop intimate relationships; some of us remain alone, and, perhaps, lonely. There are steps we can take to overcome loneliness, however, as we illustrate in the pages ahead. Finally, we discuss the ways that communication contributes to relationships and sexual satisfaction, and we enumerate ways of enhancing communication skills.

Learning Objective 1: Cite the five stages of development characteristic of romantic relationships.

ABCDE model
Levinger's view, which approaches romantic relationships in terms of five stages: attraction, building, continuation, deterioration, and ending.

STAGES IN ROMANTIC RELATIONSHIPS

According to George Levinger (1980), romantic relationships, like people, undergo stages of development. Levinger proposes an **ABCDE model** to describe the stages of romantic relationships: (1) *A*ttraction, (2) *B*uilding, (3) *C*ontinuation, (4) *D*eterioration, and (5) *E*nding. During each stage positive factors sway partners toward maintaining and enhancing their relationship. Negative factors incline them toward not building the relationship or toward letting it deteriorate and draw to an end.

Discussion Question: How do you meet people to date? Through mutual acquaintances? At parties? Through work? Through leisure activities? Have you ever used a dating service? Did you consider it successful?

Need for affiliation
The need to feel associated or connected with other people.

Learning Objective 2:
Describe the process of building a relationship from initial conversation through mutual and increasing self-disclosure.

Surface contact
A probing phase of building a relationship in which people seek common ground and check out feelings of attraction.

Small talk
A superficial kind of conversation that allows exchange of information, but stresses breadth of topic coverage rather than in-depth discussion.

TRUTH O R *FICTION?*

R E V I S I T E D

Discussion Question:
Some people think they must have "cute" opening lines. What are some of the best, the worst, and the strangest ones you've heard?

ATTRACTION

Attraction occurs when two people become aware of each other and find one another appealing or enticing. Attraction may be initiated when we spot an enchanting person "across a crowded room," in a nearby office, or in a new class. We also may meet others through blind dates, introductions by mutual friends, computer match-ups, or by "accident."

The major promoter of attraction is propinquity, or coincidental nearness. In addition to propinquity, positive factors at this stage that serve to bring partners together include positive feelings toward the other, such as liking, and personality traits, such as a **need for affiliation.** Negative factors include lack of propinquity, negative feelings, and a low need for affiliation. Our impressions at this stage are largely visual, though we may also form initial impressions by overhearing people speak or hearing others talk about them.

BUILDING

The stage of building a relationship follows initial attraction. Factors that motivate us to try to build relationships include similarity in the level of physical attractiveness, similarity in attitudes, and mutual liking and positive evaluations. Factors that may deter us from trying to build relationships include marked differences in physical appeal, dissimilarity in attitudes, and negative mutual evaluations.

NOT-SO-SMALL TALK: AN AUDITION FOR BUILDING A RELATIONSHIP   In the early stages of building a relationship, we tend to probe one another with **surface contact:** We typically look for common ground in the form of overlapping attitudes and interests, and we check out our feelings of attraction. At this point the determination of whether to strive to develop the relationship is often made, at least in part, on the basis of **small talk.** Small talk allows an exchange of information but stresses breadth of topic coverage rather than in-depth discussion. Engaging in small talk may seem "phony," but premature self-disclosure of intimate information may repel the other person, as we shall see.

Small talk may serve as an "audition for friendship" (Knapp, 1978, p. 112). Successful small talk encourages a couple to venture beneath the surface. At a cocktail party, people may flit about from person to person exchanging small talk, but now and then a couple finds common ground and pairs off.

Small talk is an insincere method of initiating a relationship. Actually, small talk is a realistic way to begin a relationship. It allows couples to search for common ground and test feelings of attraction. •

THE "OPENING LINE": HOW DO YOU GET THINGS STARTED?   One kind of small talk is the greeting, or opening line. We usually precede verbal greetings with eye contact and decide to begin talking if eye contact is reciprocated. Avoidance of eye contact may mean that the person is shy, but it could be a sign of lack of interest. If you would like to progress from initial attraction to surface contact, try a smile and direct eye contact. If the eye contact is reciprocated, choose an opening line, or greeting. Since your opening line can be important, you may prefer to say something more meaningful than "One, two, one, two."

Knapp (1978, pp. 108–109) lists various greetings, or opening lines:

Verbal salutes, such as "Good morning."
Personal inquiries, such as "How are you doing?"
Compliments, such as "I like your outfit."
References to your mutual surroundings, such as "What do you think of that painting?" or "This is a nice apartment house, isn't it?"
References to people or events outside the immediate setting, such as "How do you like this weather we've been having?"
References to the other person's behavior, such as "I couldn't help noticing you

By permission of Johnny Hart and Creators Syndicate Inc.

were sitting alone," or "I see you out on this track every Saturday morning." *References to your own behavior, or to yourself,* such as "Hi, my name is Allan Felix" (feel free to use your own name, if you prefer).

The simple "Hi" or "Hello" is very useful. A friendly glance followed by a cheerful hello ought to give you some idea of whether the attraction you feel is reciprocated. If the hello is returned with a friendly smile and inviting eye contact, follow it up with another greeting, such as a reference to your surroundings, the other person's behavior, or your name.

EXCHANGING "NAME, RANK, AND SERIAL NUMBER"   Early exchanges are likely to include name, occupation, marital status, and hometown (Berger & Calabrese, 1975). This has been likened to exchanging "name, rank, and serial number" with the other person. Each person seeks a sociological profile of the other to discover common ground that may provide a basis for pursuing the conversation. An unspoken rule seems to be at work: "If I provide you with some information about myself, you will reciprocate by giving me an equal amount of information about yourself." Or... "I'll tell you my hometown if you tell me yours" (Knapp, 1978, p. 114). If the other person is unresponsive, she or he may not be attracted to you, and you may wish to try someone else. But you may also be awkward in your approach or perhaps turn the other person off by disclosing too much about yourself at once. The Closer Look section on page 221 offers suggestions for improving conversational date-seeking skills.

Self-disclosure
The revelation of personal, perhaps intimate, information.

SELF-DISCLOSURE: YOU TELL ME AND I'LL TELL YOU...CAREFULLY   Opening up, or **self-disclosure,** is central to building intimate relationships. But just what sort of information is safe to disclose upon first meeting someone? If you refuse to go beyond name, rank, and serial number, you may look uninterested or as if you are trying to keep things under wraps. If, on the other hand, you spill out the fact that you have a terrible rash on your thigh, it's likely that you have disclosed too much too soon.

If the surface contact provided by small talk and initial self-disclosure has been mutually rewarding, partners in a relationship may develop deeper feelings of liking for each other. Self-disclosure may continue to build gradually through the course of a relationship as partners come to trust one another enough to share confidences and more intimate feelings.

Mutuality
A phase in building a relationship in which a couple come to regard themselves as "we," no longer two "I's" who happen to be in the same place at the same time.

MUTUALITY: WHEN THE "WE," NOT THE "I'S," HAVE IT   When feelings of attraction and the establishment of common ground lead a couple to regard themselves as "we"—not just two "I's" who happen to be in the same place at the same time—they have attained what Levinger (1980) terms a state of **mutuality.** The development of mutuality favors the continuation and further deepening of the relationship.

CONTINUATION

Once a relationship has been established, the couple embarks upon the stage of continuation. Factors that encourage continuation include seeking ways to introduce variety and maintain interest (such as trying out new sexual practices and social activities), showing evidence of caring and positive evaluation (such as sending birthday or Valentine's Day cards), showing lack of jealousy, perceiving fairness in the relationship, and experiencing mutual feelings of general satisfaction.

Learning Objective 3:
Identify the factors that generally lead to continuation of a relationship.

A CLOSER LOOK

How to Improve Date-Seeking Skills

All right, now you know that Mr. or Ms. Right exists. So what do you do? How do you go about making a date?

Psychologists have learned that we can enhance our social skills, including our date-seeking skills, through the technique of *successive approximations*. That means that we can practice a series of tasks that are graded in difficulty. We can hone our social skills and gain self-confidence at each step. We can try out some of our skills on friends. Friends can role-play the prospective date and give honest feedback about our behavior.

Here is an example of a series of graduated tasks that may help you sharpen your own date-seeking skills:[1]

Easy Practice Level Select a person with whom you are friendly, but one whom you have no desire to date. Practice making small talk about the weather, about new films that have come into town, television shows, concerts, museum shows, political events, and personal hobbies.

Select a person you might have some interest in dating. Smile when you pass this person at work, school, or elsewhere, and say "Hi." Engage in this activity with other people of both sexes to increase your skills at greeting others.

Speak into your mirror, using behavior rehearsal and role playing. Pretend you are in the process of sitting next to the person you would like to date, say, at lunch or in the laundry room. Say "Hello" with a broad smile and introduce yourself. Work on the smile until it looks inviting and genuine. Make some comment about the food or the setting—the cafeteria, the office, whatever. Use a family member

or confidant to obtain feedback about the effectiveness of the smile, your tone of voice, posture, and choice of words.

Medium Practice Level Sit down next to the person you want to date and engage him or her in small talk. If you are in a classroom, talk about a homework assignment, the seating arrangement, or the instructor (be kind). If you are at work, talk about the building or some recent interesting event in the neighborhood. Ask your intended date how he or she feels about the situation. If you are at some group such as Parents Without Partners, tell the other person that you are there for the first time and ask for advice on how to relate to the group.

Engage in small talk about the weather and local events. Channel the conversation into an exchange of personal information. Give your "name, rank, and serial number"—who you are, your major field or your occupation, where you're from, why or how you came to the school or company. The other person is likely to reciprocate and provide equivalent information. Ask how he or she feels about the class, place of business, city, hometown, etc.

Rehearse asking the person out before your mirror, a family member, or a confidant. You may wish to ask the person out for "a cup of coffee" or to a film. It is somewhat less threatening to ask someone out to a gathering at which "some of us will be getting together." Or you may rehearse asking the person to accompany you to a cultural event, such as an exhibition at a museum or a concert—it's "sort of" a date, but also less anxiety inducing.

Target Behavior Level Ask the person out on a date in a man-

ner consistent with your behavior rehearsal. If the person says he or she has a previous engagement or can't make it, you may wish to say something like, "That's too bad," or "I'm sorry you can't make it," and add something like, "Perhaps another time." You should be able to get a feeling for whether the person you asked out was just seeking an excuse or has a genuine interest in you and, as claimed, could not in fact accept the specific invitation.

Before asking the date out again, pay attention to his or her apparent comfort level when you return to small talk on a couple of occasions. If there is still a chance, the person should smile and return your eye contact. The other person may also offer you an invitation. In any event, if you are turned down twice, do not ask a third time. And don't make a catastrophe out of the refusal. Look up. Note that the roof hasn't fallen in. The birds are still chirping in the trees. You are still paying taxes. Then give someone else a chance to appreciate your fine qualities.

Discussion Question: If men and women use the same date-seeking skills, will they be perceived differently? Give examples.

---

[1]Adapted from Rathus & Nevid, 1977, pp. 114–115.

Self-Disclosure: East May Be East and West May Be West, But Here, Perhaps, the Twain Do (Almost) Meet

Research suggests that we should refrain from disclosing certain types of information too rapidly if we want to make a good impression. In one study, confederates of the experimenters (Wortman et al., 1976) engaged in 10-minute conversations with subjects. Some confederates were "early disclosers," who shared intimate information early. Others, "late disclosers," shared intimate information toward the end of the conversation only. In either case, the information was identical. Subjects then rated the disclosers. Early disclosers were rated less mature, secure, well-adjusted, and genuine than the late disclosers. Subjects also preferred to continue relationships with the late disclosers. We may say we value "openness" and "honesty" in our relationships, but it may be a social mistake to open up too soon.

TRUTH OR FICTION?

R E V I S I T E D

Swift self-disclosure of intimate information is the best way to deepen a new relationship. Actually, swift or premature self-disclosure of intimate information can *make one seem emotionally distraught or socially awkward and turn people off.* •

A recent study in Japan showed similar results. Japanese college students rated actors in a mock conversation more favorably when they disclosed less about themselves (Nakanishi, 1986). Other researchers find that Chinese subjects also responded negatively to people who are prone to early self-disclosure (Wolfson & Pearce, 1983).

Despite such cross-cultural similarities, self-disclosure in general may be viewed less favorably in Eastern cultures. In Japanese society, for example, self-disclosure is often seen as inappropriate in social relationships (Nakanishi, 1986). Not surprisingly, researchers find that people in the United States tend to disclose much more about themselves in social interactions than do the Japanese (Barlund, 1975; Gudykunst & Nishida, 1984).

Do You Dare Let It All Hang Out? Despite the common belief that one should be honest and open, research suggests that people who self-disclose too much too soon are seen as socially inept. Researchers find that people in Japan tend to disclose less personal information in social interactions than people in the United States do.

Factors in this stage that can throw the relationship into a downward spiral include boredom (e.g., falling into a rut in leisure activities, sexual practices, and so on), displaying evidence of negative evaluation (such as bickering, forgetting anniversaries and other important dates or pretending that they do not exist), perceiving a lack of fairness in the relationship (such as one partner's always deciding how the couple will spend their free time), or experiencing feelings of jealousy and general dissatisfaction.

JEALOUSY

Learning Objective 4:
Explain the effects of jealousy in a relationship and identify characteristics of a jealous person.

O! beware, my lord, of jealousy;
It is the green-ey'd monster...

(From Shakespeare's *Othello*)

Thus was Othello, the Moor of Venice, warned of jealousy in the Shakespearean play that bears his name. Yet Othello could not control his feelings and slew his beloved Desdemona. The English poet John Dryden labeled jealousy a "tyrant of the mind." Anthropologists find evidence of jealousy in all cultures, although it may vary in amount and intensity across and within cultures (Gordon & Snyder, 1989). It appears to be more common and intense among cultures with a stronger *machismo* tradition in which men are expected to display their virility (Stephens, 1963).

Sexual jealousy is aroused when we suspect that an intimate relationship is threatened by a rival. Lovers can become jealous when others show sexual interest in their partners or when their partners show an interest (even a casual or nonsexual interest) in another. Jealousy can impair a relationship and produce feelings of mistrust of one's partner or toward potential rivals.

Sexual jealousy may be associated with a range of negative emotions, including fear of losing the loved one and anger toward the rival, the loved one, or both. Feelings of possessiveness, which are related to jealousy, can also stress a relationship (Pinto & Hollandsworth, 1984). In extreme cases jealousy can cause depression or give rise to spouse abuse, suicide, or, as with Othello, murder (Knox, 1988). But milder forms of jealousy are not necessarily destructive of a relationship and may sometimes even serve the positive function of revealing how much one cares for one's partner (Knox, 1988).

Discussion Question:
Describe some of your experiences with jealous partners. What were the effects on the relationship? Under what circumstances do you get jealous?

How common is sexual jealousy? Common. In a survey of 103 women at various stages of involvement in an intimate relationship, three out of four reported feelings of jealousy (Pines & Aronson, 1983). Fifty-four percent described themselves as jealous. Women who were in nonmonogamous relationships or were dissatisfied with their relationships were more likely to describe themselves as jealous. A typical situation that prompted jealousy was a party at which the woman's partner spent time talking to, or dancing or flirting with other women.

What causes jealousy? In some cases, people become mistrustful of their current partners because their former partners had cheated (Knox, 1988). Jealousy may also derive from low self-esteem or a lack of self-confidence (White, 1981). People with low self-esteem may experience sexual jealousy because they become overly dependent on their partners. They may also fear that they will not be able to find another partner if their present lover leaves (Hansen, 1983). Yet feelings of jealousy tend to make the relationship less rewarding and to lower the individual's self-esteem (Mathes et al., 1985). White (1981) has concluded from his research on jealousy that feelings of inadequacy lead to jealousy in women; in men, the reverse seems to be the case. For men, that is, feelings of jealousy tend to give rise to feelings of inadequacy, as if jealousy leads them to question whether they are worthy of their partners' affections. For both men and women, however, feelings of jealousy can lead to perceiving virtually anyone as a potential rival, which can make them feel continually mistrustful.

Many lovers, unfortunately—including many college students—play jealousy games. They let their partners know that they are attracted to other people. They flirt openly and even manufacture tales to make their partners pay more attention to them, to test the relationship, to inflict pain, or to take revenge for a partner's disloyalty (White, 1980).

DETERIORATION

Deterioration is the fourth stage of a relationship—but not necessarily one that we seek, and certainly not an inevitability. Positive factors that can deter or slow deterioration include putting time and energy into the relationship, striving to cultivate the relationship, and showing patience—for example, giving the relationship a reasonable opportunity to improve. Negative factors that foster deterioration include failure to invest time

Does Disagreement Threaten a Relationship? Social scientists maintain that it is irrational for people to believe that couples who care for one another never argue. Communication skills can help us resolve disagreements productively, but recurring hostile confrontations may cause couples to question whether the relationship should continue.

and energy in the relationship, deciding to put an end to it, or simply permitting deterioration to proceed unchecked. According to Levinger (1980), a relationship is set on the path to deterioration when one or both partners deem the relationship to be less enticing or rewarding than it had been. Couples who work toward maintaining and enhancing their relationships, however, may find that they become stronger and more meaningful.

Learning Objective 5: Examine passive and active responses that will determine whether a deteriorating relationship ends or is renewed.

ACTIVE AND PASSIVE RESPONSES TO DETERIORATION   When a couple perceives their relationship to be deteriorating, they can respond in active or passive ways (Rusbult et al., 1986; Rusbult & Zembrodt, 1983). Active means of response include doing something that may enhance the relationship (such as working on improving communication skills, negotiating differences, or seeking professional help) or making a decision to end the relationship. Passive methods of responding are basically characterized by waiting for something to happen, by just doing nothing. People can sit back passively and wait for the relationship to improve on its own (once in a great while, it does), or for the relationship to deteriorate to the point where it ends.

It is irrational (and damaging to a relationship) to assume that suitable relationships require no investment of time and effort. No two of us—with the possible exceptions of your second and third authors—are matched perfectly. Unless one member of a couple does double duty as a doormat, inevitable frictions will surface. When problems arise, it is better to work to resolve them than to act as if they don't exist and hope that they will disappear on their own accord.

ENDING

Discussion Question: Why don't people end relationships that have deteriorated beyond repair? (Fear of loneliness? Fear of not being part of a couple? Fear of not finding another partner? Not wanting to be the one to take responsibility for ending the relationship?)

Ending is the final, or fifth, stage of a relationship. Although it may be the ultimate stage of development, like deterioration, it need not be inevitable or desirable. Various factors can prevent a deteriorating relationship from ending. For example, people who continue to find some sources of satisfaction, who are committed to maintaining the relationship, or who believe that they will eventually be able to overcome their problems are more likely to invest what they must to prevent the collapse.

Relationships are likely to draw to a close when negative forces are in sway—when the partners find little satisfaction in the affiliation, when alternate partners are available, when couples are not committed to preserving them and expect them to falter. We tend to live up to our pessimistic as well as our optimistic expectations.

But the swan song of a relationship is not always a bad thing. When people are definitely incompatible and when genuine attempts to preserve the relationship have faltered, ending the relationship can offer each partner a chance for happiness with someone else.

LONELINESS

Many people start relationships because of **loneliness.** Loneliness and being alone are not synonymous. Loneliness is a state of painful isolation, of feeling cut off from others. Being alone, a state of solitude, can be quite desirable since it allows us to work, study, or reflect on the world around us. Solitude is usually a matter of choice; loneliness is not.

Lonely people tend to spend a lot of time by themselves, eat dinner alone, spend weekends alone, and participate in few social activities. They are unlikely to date (Russell, 1982; Russell et al., 1980). Some lonely people report having many friends, but a closer look suggests that these "friendships" are shallow, or lacking in intimacy. Lonely people are unlikely to share confidences. Sometimes their "friends" are astonished to learn that lonely people even look upon them as friends (Williams & Solano, 1983). Loneliness tends to peak during adolescence. This is when most young people begin to supplant family ties with peer relationships. Loneliness is often connected with feelings of depression and with feelings of being "sick at heart."

Significant levels of loneliness are even reported among some married people. In one study (Sadava & Matejcic, 1987), lonely wives tended to feel less liking and love for their partners and expressed less marital satisfaction. Lonely husbands reported less liking for their wives and less intimacy in their relationships.

CAUSES OF LONELINESS

The causes of loneliness are many and complex. Lonely people tend to have several of the following characteristics:

1. Lack of social skills. Lonely people often lack the interpersonal skills needed to make friends or to cope with disagreements (Rubin, 1982).
2. Lack of interest in other people (Cutrona, 1982).
3. Lack of empathy (Lear, 1987).
4. Fear of being rejected by others, which is often connected with self-criticism of social skills and expectations of failure in relating to others (Jones et al., 1981; Lear, 1987; Schultz & Moore, 1984).
5. Failure to disclose information about themselves to potential friends (Berg & Peplau, 1982; Solano et al., 1982).
6. Cynicism about human nature (for example, seeing people as only out for themselves).
7. Demanding too much too soon, as characterized by misperception of other people as cold and unfriendly in the early stages of developing a relationship (Lear, 1987).
8. Pessimism about life in general. When we expect the worst, we often get . . . you guessed it.
9. An external locus of control (Jones, 1982). That is, they do not see themselves as being capable of taking their lives into their own hands and achieving their goals through their own efforts.

TRUTH OR *FICTION?*
—————————————
R E V I S I T E D

Many people remain lonely because they fear being rejected by others.
Yes, many people remain lonely because of fears of social rejection. •

COPING WITH LONELINESS

Psychologists have helped people cope with loneliness by fostering more adaptive ways of thinking and behaving. Lonely people often have distorted views of other people. They may have one or two unfortunate experiences and jump to the conclusion that people are generally selfish and not worth the effort of getting involved. Let's face it: Some people *are* basically out for themselves, but the expectation that everyone is can perpetuate loneliness by motivating avoidance of social activities.

What can you do to deal with loneliness in your own life? We are all different, and the methods that might help one person may not aid another. But here is a list of suggestions compiled by Rathus and Fichner-Rathus (1991):

1. *Challenge your feelings of pessimism.* Adopt the attitude that things happen when you make them happen.
2. *Challenge your cynicism about human nature.* Yes, lots of people are selfish and not worth knowing, but if you assume that all people are like that, you can doom yourself to a lifetime of loneliness. Your task is to find people who possess the qualities that you value.
3. *Challenge the idea that failure in social relationships is awful and is thus a valid reason for giving up on them.* Sure, social rejection can be painful, but unless you happen to be Kevin Costner or Michelle Pfeiffer, you may not appeal to everyone. We must all learn to live with some rejection. But keep looking for the people who possess the qualities you value and who will find things of equal value in you.
4. *Follow the suggestions for improving your date-seeking skills spelled out in the Closer Look feature.* Sit down at a table with people in the cafeteria, not off in a corner by yourself. Smile and say hi to people who interest you. Practice opening lines for different occasions—and a few follow-up lines. Try them out in the mirror.
5. *Make numerous social contacts.* Join committees for student activities. Try intramural sports. Join social-action groups like environmental groups and community betterment groups. Join clubs like the photography club or the ski club. Get on the school yearbook or newspaper staff.
6. *Be assertive.* Express your genuine opinions.
7. *Become a good listener.* Ask people how they're doing. Ask them for their opinions about classes, politics, the campus events of the day. Then actually *listen* to what they have to say. Tolerate diverse opinions; remember that no two of us are identical in our outlooks (not even your "perfectly" matched second and third authors.) Maintain eye contact. Keep your face friendly. (No, you don't have to remain neutral and friendly if someone becomes insulting toward a religious or ethnic group).
8. *Give people the chance to know you.* Exchange opinions and talk about your interests. Yes, you'll turn some people off—who doesn't?—but how else will you learn whether you and another person share common ground?
9. *Fight fair.* Friends will inevitably disappoint you, and you'll want to tell them about it. Do so, but fairly. You can start by asking if it's okay to be open about something. Then say, "I feel upset because you . . ." You can ask your friend if he or she realized that his or her behavior upset you. Try to work together to find a way to avoid recurrences. Finish by thanking your friend for helping you resolve the problem.
10. *Remember that you're worthy of friends.* It's true—warts and all. None of us is perfect. We're all unique, but you may connect with more people than you imagine. Give people a chance.
11. *Use your college counseling center.* Many thousands of students are lonely but don't know what to do about it. Others just cannot find the courage to approach others. College counseling centers are very familiar with the problem of loneliness, and you should consider them a valuable resource. You might even ask if there's a group at the center for students seeking to improve their dating or social skills.

Intimacy
A state of relatedness between two people that is marked by feelings of emotional closeness and connectedness and the sharing of inmost thoughts and feelings.

INTIMACY

Intimacy involves feelings of emotional closeness and connectedness with another person and the desire to share each other's inmost thoughts and feelings. Intimate relationships are also characterized by attitudes of mutual trust, caring, and acceptance.

Sternberg's (1986) triangular theory of love (see Chapter 7) regards intimacy as a basic component of romantic love. But people can be intimate and not in love, at least not in romantic love. Close friends and family members become emotionally intimate

Building Intimacy. Intimate couples share each other's inmost thoughts and feelings. Intimacy also involves mutual trust, caring, and acceptance.

Learning Objective 7: Identify the characteristics of intimate relationships and the skills necessary to building and maintaining an intimate relationship.

when they care deeply for each other and share their private feelings and experiences. It is not necessary for people to be *sexually* intimate to have an emotionally intimate relationship. Nor does sexual intimacy automatically produce emotional intimacy. People who are sexually involved may still fail to touch one another's lives in emotionally intimate ways. Even couples who fall in love may not be able to forge an intimate relationship because of unwillingness or inability to exchange inmost thoughts and feelings. Sometimes husbands or wives share greater emotional intimacy with friends than with their spouses.

TRUTH OR *FICTION?*

R E V I S I T E D

People can have intimate relationships without being sexually intimate. *Yes, people can have intimate relationships without being sexually intimate. Close friends and relatives can have nonsexual but intimate relationships.* •

Let us now consider some of the factors that are involved in building and maintaining intimate relationships.

KNOWING AND LIKING YOURSELF

Some social scientists suggest that an initial step toward intimacy with others is getting to know and like yourself. By coming to know and value yourself, you identify your inmost feelings and needs and develop the security to share them.

Try a Little Tenderness? Tenderness is expressed physically and verbally—by kissing, hugging, cuddling, or holding hands, and by words of caring and appreciation.

Trust
The feeling that one will not be harmed or hurt by another person.

Caring
Genuine concern for another person's well-being.

Tenderness
The gentle expression of caring through words or physical affection.

Activity: Conducting a Personal Experiment: Should You Be Completely Open With Your Partner? The IM provides guidelines on ways to practice total openness with a partner for a short time and then evaluate the outcome.

Discussion Question: Think about the intimate relationships you've had in which you cared deeply about another person and you felt comfortable sharing your inmost feelings. How many of these were with friends of the same sex? How many were with friends of the opposite sex? With how many were you also romantically intimate? Do the men and women in class have different responses?

TRUSTING AND CARING

Two of the most important ingredients of an intimate relationship are trust and caring. When **trust** exists in a relationship, partners feel secure that disclosing intimate feelings will not lead to ridicule, rejection, or other kinds of harm. Trust usually builds gradually, as partners learn whether or not it is safe to share confidences. **Caring** is an emotional bond that allows intimacy to develop. In caring relationships, partners seek to gratify each other's needs and interests.

Tenderness is expressed by putting one's arm around a partner's shoulder to offer support, or by verbalizations of love, caring, and appreciation. In romantic relationships, tenderness also takes the form of kissing, hugging, cuddling, and holding hands.

BEING HONEST

Since intimacy involves the sharing of one's inmost thoughts and feelings, honesty is a core feature of intimacy. Without honesty, partners see only one another's facades. A person need not be an "open book" to develop and maintain intimacy, however. Some aspects of experience are kept even from one's most intimate partners, for they may be too embarrassing or threatening to reveal (Kammeyer et al., 1990). For example, we would not expect partners to disclose every passing sexual fantasy.

Intimate relationships thus usually involve balances in which some things are revealed and others are not (Kammeyer et al., 1990). Total honesty could devastate a relationship. It would not be reasonable, for example, to expect intimate partners to divulge the details of past sexual experiences (Gordon & Snyder, 1989). The recipient may wonder, "Why is Kimball telling me this?" "Am I as good a lover as _____?" "Is Kimball still in love with _____?" "What else did Kimball do with _____?" Discretion thus also buttresses intimate relationships. As Gordon and Snyder (1989) put it, "honesty means *saying what you mean,* not revealing every detail" (p. 24). Nor is intimacy established by frank but brutal criticism, even if it is honest.

GENDER DIFFERENCES IN SELF-DISCLOSURE   A woman complains to a friend: "He never opens up to me. It's like living with a stone wall." Women commonly declare that men are loath to express their feelings (Hawkins et al., 1980; Tannen, 1990). Researchers find that men tend to be less willing to disclose their feelings, perhaps in adherence to the traditional "strong and silent" male stereotype (see Chapter 6).

Yet gender differences in self-disclosure tend to be small. Overall, researchers find that women are only slightly more revealing about themselves than men (Dindia & Allen, 1992). We should thus be careful not to rush to the conclusion that men are always more "tight-lipped." The belief that there are large gender differences in self-disclosure appears to be something of a myth.

Stereotypes are also a-changing—somewhat. We now see depictions in the media of the "new" man as someone who is able to express feelings without compromising his masculinity. We shall have to wait to see whether this "new" sensitive image replaces the rugged, reticent stereotype, or is a passing fancy.

MAKING A COMMITMENT

Have you ever noticed that people may open up to strangers on airplanes or trains, yet find it hard to talk openly with people to whom they are closest? An intimate relationship involves more than the isolated act of baring one's soul to a stranger. Truly intimate relationships are marked by commitment or resolve to maintain the relationship through thick and thin. When we open up to strangers on a plane, we know it is unlikely that we will have to face them again.

This does not mean that intimate relationships require indefinite or lifelong commitments. A commitment, however, carries an obligation that the couple will work to overcome problems in the relationship rather than run for the exit at the first sign of trouble.

MAINTAINING INDIVIDUALITY WHEN THE *I* BECOMES *WE*

In committed relationships, a delicate balance exists between individuality and mutuality. In healthy unions, a strong sense of togetherness does not eradicate individuality. Partners in such relationships remain free to be themselves. Neither seeks to dominate or submerge himself or herself into the personality of the other. Each partner maintains individual interests, likes and dislikes, needs and goals.

COMMUNICATING

Learning Objective 8:
Explain the importance of good communication, both verbal and nonverbal, in an intimate relationship.

Notes: Proxemics is the study of the way people use the space around them, which is another way people communicate nonverbally. Generally, in the United States people's speaking distance with strangers is about the length of their arms. If people move closer than that, we often react negatively: The expression "Get out of my face!" is one such reaction. E.T. Hall, often considered the father of proxemics, specified four zones. The "intimate" distance, 0"–18" is usually reserved for parents, children, lovers, and those we wish to comfort or protect.

Good communication is another hallmark of an intimate relationship. Partners are able to share their most personal thoughts and feelings clearly and honestly. Communication is a two-way street. It embraces sending and receiving messages. The good communicator is thus a skilled listener as well as a clear speaker (Tannen, 1990). We generally associate communication with *talk,* which involves the use of verbal messages to convey a thought or a feeling. Through talk, the speaker *encodes* a thought or a feeling into words. The listener *decodes* the words to extract the meaning of the message. Problems in verbal communication can arise at several levels:

1. *The speaker may use words differently than the listener, leading to misunderstandings or miscommunication.* For example, the speaker might say, "You look really cute tonight." The listener might object, saying, "You think I look *cute*? What's wrong with the way I look?" The speaker protests, "No, I didn't mean it that way. I meant you look good. Yes, good."
2. *The speaker's words may not match his or her tone of voice, facial expression, or body gestures.* For example, the speaker says, "Darling, I really *don't mind* if we visit your mother this weekend." But the speaker did not say, "I really *want* to visit your mother," so the words "don't mind" come across as a kind of snarl. In such cases, the listener is likely to place greater weight on *how* something is said rather than on *what* is said.
3. *The speaker may not be able to put into words what he or she truly means or feels.* Sometimes we grasp for words to express our feelings, but they do not come or those that do come miss the mark.

NONVERBAL COMMUNICATION: THE BODY SPEAKS   Though the spoken word is a primary form of communication, we often express our feelings through nonverbal channels as well, such as by tone of voice, gestures, body posture, and facial expressions (Tannen, 1990). People may place more weight on how words are said than on their

Nonverbal Communication. Nonverbal cues such as posture, eye contact, and physical distance convey information about a person's underlying feelings toward another. What might you infer about the listener's attitudes toward the speaker in the photograph on the basis of the listener's nonverbal behavior?

A CLOSER LOOK

Who Are the Ideal Men for the 1990s?

We thank readers for assuming that the first and third authors are referring to themselves in the title of this piece. (The second author is considering abandoning this project.) However, the title refers to a recent poll by *Psychology Today* magazine (Keen & Zur, 1989). *Psychology Today* readers are wealthier (41% had a household income of $60,000 a year or more) and better educated (66% had earned at least a baccalaureate degree) than the public at large, but they are reasonably similar to readers of this textbook in their educational and socioeconomic backgrounds.

The study found that hard-driving businessmen and John Wayne types are on the "outs" for the 1990s. The compassionate, communicative man is definitely "in." Table 8.1 shows the percentages of women respondents who endorsed certain traits ascribed to the masculine ideal. Social receptivity, a powerful presence, and health were viewed as desirable. Macho, urbane, and Type A men needn't apply.

It appears that many men are living up to the new ideal, at least in the opinion of women who know them well. The *Psychology Today* article reported that 37 percent of the women respondents rated the men to whom they felt closest (fathers, brothers, friends, lovers, or husbands) as "ideal." Another 52 percent considered the man to whom they were closest as "good." And that may be good enough; the categories of ideal and good add up to 89 percent.

Do you want some examples of ideal men? Female respondents most often wrote in the names Jesus, Gandhi, Alan Alda, Tom Selleck, Abraham Lincoln, Paul Newman, Martin Luther King, Jr., Bill Cosby, John F. Kennedy, and George Bush. Why are these men ideal? The traits most frequently ascribed to them included caring/loving (65%), intelligent (34%), moral/honest (29%), sensitive (29%), and "family man" (20%).

Perhaps male readers need to unstiffen their upper lips and start listening and sharing their feelings—if they want to approximate the ideal for the 1990s (Tannen, 1990).

TABLE 8.1 Qualities ascribed to the ideal man by *Psychology Today* readers

Trait	Percent Who Endorse Trait
Is receptive, responsive to the initiatives of others	89%
Has strong intellectual, moral, or physical presence	87
Attends to diet, exercise, health	87
Expresses feelings of sadness	86
Stops often to wonder, to appreciate, perchance to dream	82
Follows inner authority	77
Is even-tempered, moderate	77
Is easy to be with	75
Is nonjudgmental	74
Accepts help willingly	70
Takes charge, is a doer	68
. . .	
Is urbane, suave	22
Has Type A personality	20
Is always found where the action is	20
Is introverted	16
Is critical	14
Has mood swings	10
Never shows pain	6
Basically ignores his body	2

Source: Reprinted with permission from *Psychology Today* magazine. Copyright 1989 (Sussex Publishers, Inc.).

denotative meaning. People also accentuate the meaning of their words through gestures, raising or lowering their voices, or using a sterner or softer tone of voice.

Nonverbal communication is used not only to accentuate the spoken word, but also to directly express feelings. We sometimes are better able to convey our feelings through body language than by the use of words. A touch or a gaze into someone's eyes may express more about our feelings than words can. Parents express feelings of tenderness and caring toward infants by hugging, holding, and caressing them, and by speaking in a gentle and soothing tone of voice, even though the meanings of the words cannot yet be grasped.

Let us examine some aspects of nonverbal communication.

ON "BEING UPTIGHT" AND "HANGING LOOSE"   The ways that people carry themselves offer cues about their feelings and potential actions. People who are emotionally "uptight" often stand or sit rigidly and straight-backed. People who feel relaxed more literally "hang loose."

People who face us and lean toward us are in effect saying that they like us or care about what we are saying. If we overhear a conversation between a couple and see that the woman is leaning toward the man, but he is leaning back and playing with his hair, we tend to infer that he is not accepting what she is saying or has lost interest (Clore et al., 1975; DePaulo et al., 1978).

Teaching Tip: Touch is interpreted in many ways. Consider the following examples: 1) A person has just told a friend that his grandparent has died. The friend puts an arm around his shoulders and asks if the person wants to talk. 2) A person tells a classmate that she has just qualified for a scholarship, and the classmate puts an arm around her shoulders and congratulates her. 3) A person is standing alone at a bus stop when a stranger comes up and puts an arm around his shoulders and asks if he wants a ride. Examine how the gender of those involved, their prior relationship, the situation, and the accompanying verbal message affect how we interpret touching. How would our interpretations be different if the gender of those involved were different.

TOUCHING   Touching is a powerful form of communication. Women are more apt than men to touch the people with whom they interact (Stier & Hall, 1984). In one experiment, women who were about to have surgical operations reported less anxiety and displayed lower blood pressure when nurses touched them on the arm as they explained the procedures (Whitcher & Fisher, 1979). Men treated in this manner, however, were more anxious and displayed elevated blood pressure. How do we explain this gender difference? Perhaps the women interpreted touching as a sign of warmth, and perhaps the men viewed touching as a threatening sign of the nurse assuming control of them. Or perhaps the men interpreted the touching as an unwanted sexual overture.

Touching may also establish a type of "property right" over one's partner. People may touch their partners in public or hold their hands, not as a sign of affection, but as a signal to others that their partners are taken and that others should keep a respectful distance. Similarly, the wearing of an engagement or wedding ring signals unavailability.

GAZING AND STARING: THE LOOK OF LOVE?   We also gather information about the motives, feelings, and attitudes of others through eye contact. In our culture, people who look others "squarely in the eye" are apt to appear self-assertive, direct, and candid. When people look away, they may be perceived as shy, deceitful, or depressed (Knapp, 1978). In a laboratory study, couples who had just met were instructed to gaze into one another's eyes for two minutes. Afterwards, many reported experiencing feelings of passion (Kellerman et al., 1989). Is this what is meant by "the look of love"?

All in all, there are many ways in which we communicate with others through verbal and nonverbal channels. Let us now look at ways in which partners can learn to communicate better with each other, especially about sex. Many couples, even couples who are able to share deepest thoughts and feelings, may flounder at communicating their sexual needs and preferences. Couples who have lived together for decades may know each other's tastes in food, music, and movies about as well as they know their own but still be hesitant to share their sexual likes and dislikes (Havemann & Lehtinen, 1990). They may also be reluctant, for fear of opening wounds in the relationship, to exchange their feelings about other aspects of their relationship, including each other's habits, appearance, and gender-stereotypical attitudes.

COMMUNICATION SKILLS FOR ENHANCING RELATIONSHIPS AND SEXUAL RELATIONS

Many marital counselors and sex therapists might be as busy as the proverbial Maytag repairman if more couples communicated with each other about their sexual feelings. Unfortunately, when it comes to sex, "talk" may be the most overlooked four-letter word.

Many couples suffer for years because one or both partners are unwilling to speak up (Levy et al., 1987). Or problems arise when one partner misinterprets the other. One partner might interpret the other's groans or grimaces of pleasure as signs of pain and pull back during sex, leaving the other frustrated (Levy et al., 1987). Improved communication may be no panacea, but it helps. Clear communication can take the guesswork out of relationships, avert misunderstandings, relieve resentments and frustrations, and increase both sexual and general satisfaction with the relationship (Gordon & Snyder, 1989; Knox, 1988).

COMMON DIFFICULTIES IN SEXUAL COMMUNICATION

Why is it so difficult for couples to communicate about sex? Here are some possibilities.

ON "MAKING WHOOPIE": IS SEX TALK VULGAR?   Vulgarity, like beauty, is to some degree in the eye of the beholder. One couple's vulgarity may be another couple's love talk. Some people may maintain a Victorian belief that any talk about sex is not fit for mixed company, even between intimate partners. Sex, that is, is something you may do, but not something to be talked about. Other couples may be willing in principle to talk about sex, but find the reality difficult because of the lack of an agreeable, common language.

How, for example, are they to refer to their genitals or to sexual activities? One partner may prefer to use coarse four-letter (or five-letter) words to refer to them, whereas the other might prefer more clinical terms. A partner who prefers slang terms for the sexual organs might be regarded by the other as vulgar or demeaning. (But as the forbidden fruit is often the sweetest, some people feel sexually aroused when they or their partners "talk dirty.") One who uses clinical terms, such as fellatio or coitus, might be regarded as, well, clinical. Some couples try to find a common verbal ground, one that is not vulgar at one extreme, or clinical at the other. They might speak, for example, of "doing it" rather than "engaging in sexual intercourse." (The title of the Eddie Cantor musical of the 1930s suggests that some people once spoke of "making whoopie.") Or they might speak of "kissing me down there" rather than engaging in fellatio or cunnilingus.

In some cases of a gross mismatch between the partners in their choices for the language of love, the differences actually run deeper than mere choice of words.

Learning Objective 9: Examine the irrational beliefs and fears about sexual communication that can cause difficulties in intimate relationships.

ON IRRATIONAL BELIEFS   Many couples also harbor irrational beliefs about relationships and sex, such as the notion that people should somehow *know* what their partners want, without having to ask. The common misconception that people should know what pleases their partners undercuts communication. Men, in particular, seem burdened with the stereotype that they should have a natural expertise at sex. Women may feel it is "unladylike" to talk openly about their sexual needs and feelings. Both partners may hold the idealized romantic notion that "love is all you need" to achieve sexual happiness. But such knowledge does not arise from instinct nor love. It is learned—or it remains unknown.

A related irrational belief is that "my partner will read my mind." We may erroneously assume that if our partners truly loved us, they would somehow "read our minds" and know what types of sexual stimulation we desire. Unfortunately, or fortunately, others cannot read our minds. We must assume the responsibility for communicating our preferences.

TRUTH OR *FICTION?*
R E V I S I T E D

When partners truly love one another, they instinctively know how to satisfy each other sexually. *Nonsense. It is irrational to believe that partners who truly love one another will instinctively know each other's sexual preferences. Communication is required.* •

Some people communicate more effectively than others, perhaps because they are more sensitive to others' needs or because their parents served as good models as communicators. But communication skills can be acquired at any time. Learning takes time and work, but the following guidelines should prove helpful if you want to enhance your communication skills (Cormier & Cormier, 1985; Gottman, et al., 1976; Havemann & Lehtinen, 1990; McKay et al., 1983; Rathus & Fichner-Rathus, 1991). The skills discussed can also be used to improve communication in areas of intimate relationships other than the sexual.

GETTING STARTED

How do you broach tough topics? Here are some ideas.

TALKING ABOUT TALKING   You can start by talking about talking. You can inform your partner that it is difficult for you to talk about problems and conflicts: "You know, I've always found it awkward to find a way of bringing things up," or, "You know, I think other people have an easier time than I do when it comes to talking about some things." You can allude to troublesome things that happened in the past when you attempted to resolve conflicts. This approach encourages your partner to invite you to proceed.

Broaching the topic of sex is perhaps the most difficult step in communicating with your partner. Couples who gab endlessly about their finances, their children, their work, and so on, suddenly clam up when sex comes up. So it may be helpful for you and your partner to first agree to talk about talking about sex. You can begin by admitting that it is hard or embarrassing for you to talk about sex. You can say that your sexual relationship is important to you and that you want to do everything you can to enhance it. Gently probe your partner's willingness to set aside time to talk about sex, preferably when you can dim the lights and not be interrupted.

The "right time" may be when you are both relaxed, rested, and unpressed for time. The "right place" can be any place where you can enjoy privacy and go undisturbed. Sex talk need not be limited to the bedroom. Couples may feel more comfortable talking about sex over dinner, when cuddling on the sofa, or when just relaxing together.

REQUESTING PERMISSION TO BRING UP A TOPIC   Another possibility is to request permission to raise an issue. You can say something like, "There's something on my mind. Do you have a few minutes? Is now a good time to tell you about it?" Or you can say, "There's something that we need to talk about, but I'm not sure how to bring it up. Can you help me with it?"

GIVING YOUR PARTNER PERMISSION TO SAY SOMETHING THAT MIGHT BE UPSETTING TO YOU   You can tell your partner that it is okay to point out ways in which you can become a more effective lover. For example, you can say, "I know that you don't want to hurt my feelings, but I wonder if I'm doing anything that you'd rather I didn't do?" Or, "I'd really like to know how I can please you better when we make love."

LISTENING TO THE OTHER SIDE

Skilled listening involves such skills as active listening, paraphrasing, the use of reinforcement, and valuing your partner even when the two of you disagree.

LISTENING ACTIVELY   To listen actively rather than passively, first adopt the attitude that you may actually learn something—or perceive things from another vantage point—by listening. Second, recognize that even though the other person is doing the talking, you need not sit back passively. In other words, it is not helpful to stare off into space while your partner is talking, or to offer a begrudging "mm-hmm" now and then, to be "polite." Instead, you can listen actively by maintaining eye contact and modifying your facial expression to show that you understand his or her feelings and ideas. For example, nod your head when appropriate.

Listening actively also involves asking helpful questions, such as, "Would you please give me an example?" or, "Can you tell me how it felt when I touched you?"

An active listener does not simply hear what the other person is saying, but focuses attentively on the speaker's words and gestures to grasp meaning. Nonverbal cues may reveal more about the speaker's inner feelings than the spoken word. Good listeners do not interrupt, change the conversation, or walk away when their partners are speaking.

PARAPHRASING   Paraphrasing shows that you understand what your partner is trying to say. In paraphrasing, you recast or restate the speaker's words to confirm your comprehension. For example, your partner says, "You hardly ever say anything when we're making love. I don't want you to scream or make obligatory grunts, or do something silly, but sometimes I wonder if I'm trying to make love to a brick wall." You can paraphrase it by saying something like this: "So it's sort of hard to know if I'm really enjoying it."

REINFORCING THE OTHER PERSON FOR COMMUNICATING   Even when you disagree with what your partner is saying, you can maintain good relations and keep channels of communication open by saying something like, "I really appreciate your taking the time to try to work this out with me," or, "I hope you'll think it's okay if I don't see things entirely in the same way, but I'm glad that we had a chance to talk about it."

SHOWING THAT YOU VALUE YOUR PARTNER, EVEN WHEN THE TWO OF YOU DISAGREE   When you disagree with your partner, do so in a way that shows that you still value your partner as a person. In other words, say something like, "I love you very much, but it annoys me when you ..." rather than, "you're really contemptible for doing ..." By so doing, you encourage your partner to disclose sensitive material without fear of personal attack or the risk of losing your love or support.

LEARNING ABOUT YOUR PARTNER'S NEEDS

Learning Objective 11: Identify the skills associated with giving and receiving information and requests in an intimate sexual relationship.

Listening is basic to learning about another person's needs, but sometimes it helps to go a few steps further.

ASKING QUESTIONS TO DRAW THE OTHER PERSON OUT   You can ask open-ended questions that allow for a broader exploration of issues, such as these:

"What do you like best about the way we make love?"
"What would you like to change about the way we make love?"
"Do you think that I do things to bug you?"
"Does it bother you that I go to bed later than you do?"
"Does anything disappoint you about our sexual relationship?"
"Do you think that I do things that are inconsiderate when you're studying for a test?"

Closed-ended questions that call for a limited range of responses would be most useful when you're looking for a simple "yes-or-no" type of response, such as, "Would you rather make love with the stereo off?"

If your partner finds open-ended questions too general, you can provide examples. Open-ended questions can yield information that you could not have anticipated. So if the other person has trouble with the broadness of the question, you can follow up by narrowing it a bit, but try not to make it so specific that you forgo the chance of learning anything important.

USING SELF-DISCLOSURE   Self-disclosure is essential to developing intimacy. You can also use self-disclosure to learn more about your partner's needs, because communicating your own feelings and ideas invites reciprocation. For example, you might say, "There are times when I feel that I disappoint you when we make love. I wonder what things I might do differently to please you?"

GRANTING PERMISSION FOR THE OTHER PERSON TO SAY SOMETHING THAT MIGHT UPSET YOU   You can ask your partner to level with you about an irksome issue. You can say that you recognize that it might be awkward to discuss it, but that you will try your best to listen conscientiously and not get too disturbed. You can also limit communication to one such difficult issue per conversation. If the entire emotional dam were to burst, the job of mopping up could be overwhelming.

PROVIDING INFORMATION

There are many skillful ways of communicating information, including "accentuating the positive," and using verbal and nonverbal cues. When you want to get something across, remember that it is irrational to expect that your partner can read your mind. He or she can tell when you're wearing a grumpy face, but your expression does not provide much information about your specific feelings. When your partner asks, "What would you like me to do?" responding "Well, I think you can figure out what I want," or, "Just do whatever you think is best," is not very helpful. Only you know what pleases you. Your partner is not a mind reader.

ACCENTUATING THE POSITIVE   Let your partner know when he or she is doing something right! Speak up or find another way to express your appreciation. Accentuating the positive is rewarding and also informs your partner about what pleases you. In other words, don't just wait around until your partner does something wrong and then seize the opportunity to complain!

USING VERBAL CUES   Sexual activity provides an excellent opportunity for direct communication. You can say something like, "Oh, that's great," or "Don't stop." Or you can ask for feedback, as in "How does that feel?"

Feedback provides direct guidance about what is pleasing. Partners can also verbalize specific requests ("Please caress my nipples"), acknowledgments ("Yes, that's it. Just continue doing that"), and suggestions ("Try stroking it from underneath"). Preferences can also be communicated nonverbally.

USING NONVERBAL CUES

> There's no art
> To find the mind's construction in the face.
>
> (From Shakespeare's *Macbeth*)

Effective sexual communication also occurs without words. As suggested by Shakespeare, our faces often reveal our feelings. Couples learn to interpret each other's facial expressions as signs of pleasure, boredom, even disgust. Our body language also communicates our likes and dislikes. Our partners may lean toward us or away from us when we touch them, or relax or tense up; in any case, they speak volumes in silence.

The following exercises may help couples use nonverbal cues to communicate their sexual likes and dislikes. Similar exercises are used by sex therapists to help couples with sexual dysfunctions.

1. *Taking turns petting.* Taking turns petting can help partners learn what turns one another on. Each partner takes turns caressing the other, stopping frequently enough to receive feedback by asking questions like, "How does that feel?" The recipient is responsible for giving feedback, which can be expressed either verbally ("Yes, that's it; yes, just like that," or "No, stroke a little lighter than that") or nonverbally, by making appreciative or disapproving sounds. Verbal feedback is usually more direct and less prone to misinterpretation. The knowledge gained through this exercise can be incorporated into the couple's regular pattern of lovemaking.
2. *Directing your partner's hand.* Gently guiding your partner's hand during sex—to show your partner where and how you like to be touched—is a most direct way of communicating sexual likes. While taking turns petting, and during other acts of

lovemaking, one partner can gently guide the other's fingers and hands through the most satisfying strokes and caresses. Women might show partners how to caress the breasts or clitoral shaft in this manner. Men might cup their partners' hands to show them how to stroke the penile shaft or caress the testes.

3. *Signaling.* Couples can use agreed-upon nonverbal cues to signal sexual pleasure. For example, one partner may rub the other in a certain way, or tap the other, to signal that something is being done right. The recipient of the signal takes mental notes and incorporates the pleasurable stimulation into the couple's lovemaking. This is a sort of "hit or miss" technique, but even near misses can be rewarding.

MAKING REQUESTS

A basic part of improving relationships or lovemaking is asking partners to change their behavior—to do something differently, or to stop doing something that hurts or is ungratifying. The skill of making requests now comes to the fore.

BEING SPECIFIC Be specific in requesting changes. Telling your partner something like, "I'd like you to be nicer to me," may accomplish little. Your partner may not know that his or her behavior is *not* nice and may not understand how to be "nicer." It is better to say something like, "I would appreciate it if you would get coffee for yourself, or at least ask me in a more pleasant way." Or, "I really have a hard time with the way you talk to me in front of your friends. It's as if you're trying to show them that you have control over me or something. For instance, when Cameron was leaving, you said, 'Honey, get the umbrella.' I'm not into taking orders." Similarly, it may be less effective to say, "I'd like you to be more loving," than to say, "When we make love, I'd like you to kiss me more and tell me how you care about me."

Of course, you can precede your specific requests with openers such as, "There's something on my mind. Is this a good time for me to bring it up with you?"

USING "*I*-TALK" Using the word *I* is an excellent way of expressing your feelings. Psychologists who help people become more assertive often encourage them to use the words *I, me,* and *my* in their speech, not just to express their feelings, but to buttress their sense of self-worth.

You are more likely to achieve desired results by framing requests in *I*-talk than by heaping criticisms on your partner. For example, "I would like it if we spent some time cuddling after sex" is superior to "You don't seem to care enough about me to want to stay in bed after we make love." Saying "I find it very painful when you use a harsh

voice with me" is probably more effective than "Sometimes people's feelings get hurt when their boyfriends [girlfriends] speak to them harshly in front of their friends or families."

You may find it helpful to try out *I*-talk in front of a mirror or with a confidant before using it with your partner. In this way, you can see whether your facial expression and tone of voice are consistent with what you are saying. Friends may also provide pointers on the content of what you are saying.

DELIVERING CRITICISM

Learning Objective 12: Explain the skills involved in giving and receiving criticism.

Delivering criticism effectively is a skill. It requires focusing partners' attention on the problem without inducing resentment or defensiveness, or reducing them to trembling masses of guilt or fear.

EVALUATING YOUR MOTIVES   First, weigh your goals forthrightly. Is your primary intention to punish your partner, or are you more interested in gaining cooperation? If your goal is punishment, you may as well be coarse and disparaging, but expect to invite reprisals. If your goal is to improve the relationship, however, a tactful approach may be in order.

Activity: *What Do You Say Now? Delivering Criticism* This activity in the IM gives student suggestions for delivering criticism in appropriate ways.

PICKING THE RIGHT TIME AND PLACE   Deliver criticism privately—not in front of friends or family members. Your partner has a right to be upset when you make criticism public. Making private matters public induces indignation and cuts off communication.

BEING SPECIFIC   Being specific may be even more important when delivering criticism than when making requests. By being specific about the *behavior* that disturbs you, you bypass the trap of disparaging your partner's personality or motives. For example, you may be more effective saying to your partner, "I could lose this job because you didn't write down the message," than, "You're completely irresponsible," or, "You're a flake." Similarly, you may achieve better results by saying, "The bathroom looks and smells dirty when you throw your underwear on the floor," rather than, "You're a filthy pig." It is more to the point (and less intimidating) to complain about specific, modifiable behavior than to try to overhaul another person's personality.

EXPRESSING DISPLEASURE IN TERMS OF YOUR OWN FEELINGS   Your partner is likely to feel less threatened if you express displeasure in terms of your own feelings than by directly attacking his or her personality. Attacks often arouse defensive behavior and, sometimes, retaliation, rather than enhance relationships. When confronting your partner for failing to be sensitive to your sexual needs when making love, it may be more effective to say, "You know, it really *upsets* me that you don't seem to care about my sexual satisfaction when we make love," than, "You're so wrapped up in yourself that you never think about anyone else."

KEEPING CRITICISM AND COMPLAINTS TO THE PRESENT   How many times have you been in an argument and heard things like, "You never appreciated me!" or "Last summer you did the same thing!" Bringing up the past during conflicts muddles current issues and heightens resentments. When your partner forgets to jot down the details of the telephone message, it is more useful to note that, "This was a vital phone call," than, "Three weeks ago you didn't tell me about the phone call from Chris and as a result I missed out on seeing *Home Alone: The College Years.*" It's better to leave who did what to whom last year (or even last week) alone. Focus on the present.

EXPRESSING CRITICISM CONSTRUCTIVELY   Be sensitive to your partner's needs by avoiding blunt criticisms or personal attacks and by suggesting constructive alternatives. Avoid saying things like, "You're really a lousy lover." Say instead, "When we make love, I'd prefer if you let me guide your hand to where I'd like it." As a general rule of thumb, unless you can criticize your partner constructively, it may be best not to criticize at all. Consider how you would wnt your partner to express a similar criticism of you.

EXPRESSING CRITICISM POSITIVELY   Whenever possible, express criticism positively and combine it with a concrete request. When commenting upon the lack of affection your partner displays during lovemaking, say, "I love it when you kiss me. Please kiss me more often while we're making love," rather than, "You never kiss me when we're in bed and I'm sick of it."

RECEIVING CRITICISM

> Honest criticism is hard to take, particularly from a relative, a friend, an acquaintance, or a stranger.
> (Franklin P. Jones)

Delivering criticism can be tricky, especially when you want to inspire cooperation. But receiving criticism can be even trickier. Nevertheless, the following suggestions offer some help.

Activity: *What Do You Say Now? Receiving Criticism* This activity in the IM gives students suggestions for responding appropriately to criticism.

CLARIFYING YOUR GOALS   When you hear "It's time you did something about . . . ," it would be understandable if the hair on the backs of your arms did a headstand; after all, it's a rather blunt challenge. And when we are confronted harshly, we are likely to become defensive and think of retaliating. But if your objective is to enhance the relationship, take a few moments to stop and think. To resolve conflicts, we need to learn about the other person's concerns, keep lines of communication open, and find ways of changing problem behavior.

So when your partner says, "It's about time you did something about the bathroom," stop and think before you summon up your most menacing voice and say, "Just what the hell is that supposed to mean?" Ask yourself what you want to find out.

ASKING CLARIFYING QUESTIONS   Just as it's important to be specific when delivering criticism, it helps if you encourage the other person to be specific when you are on the receiving end of criticism. In the example of the complaint about the bathroom, you can help your partner be specific and, perhaps, avert the worst, by asking clarifying questions such as, "Can you tell me exactly what you mean?" or, "The bathroom?"

Consider a situation in which a lover says something like, "You know, you're one of the most irritating people I know." Rather than retaliating and perhaps hurting the relationship further, you can say something like, "How about forgoing the character assassination and telling me what I did that's bothering you?" This response assertively requests an end to insults and requests that your partner be specific.

ACKNOWLEDGING THE CRITICISM   Even when you disagree with a criticism, you can keep lines of communication open and show some respect for your partner's feelings by acknowledging and paraphrasing the criticism.

On the other hand, if you are at fault, you can acknowledge that forthrightly. For example, you can say, "You're right. It was my day to clean the bathroom and it totally slipped my mind," or "I was so busy, I just couldn't get to it." Now the two of you should look for a way to work out the problem. When you acknowledge criticism, you cue your partner to back off a bit and look for ways to improve the situation. But what if your partner then becomes abusive and says something like, "So you admit you blew it?" You might then try a little education in conflict resolution. You could say, "I admitted that I was at fault. If you're willing to work with me to find a way to handle it, great; but I'm not going to let you pound me into the ground over it."

REJECTING THE CRITICISM   Now, if you think that you were not at fault, express your feelings. Use *I*-talk and be specific. Don't seize the opportunity to angrily point out your partner's shortcomings. By doing so, you may shut down lines of communication.

NEGOTIATING DIFFERENCES   Negotiate your differences if you feel that there is merit on both sides of the argument. You may want to say something like, "Would it help if I . . . ?" And if there's something about your obligation to clean the bathroom that seems totally out of place, perhaps you and your partner can work out an exchange—that is, you get relieved of cleaning the bathroom in exchange for tackling a chore that your partner finds equally odious.

If none of these approaches helps resolve the conflict, consider the possibility that your partner is using the comment about the bathroom as a way of expressing anger over other issues. You may find out by saying something like, "I've been trying to find a way to resolve this thing, but nothing I say seems to be helping. Is this really about the bathroom, or are there other things on your mind?"

And notice that we haven't suggested that you seize the opportunity to strike back by saying, "Who're you to complain about the bathroom? What about your breath and that pigsty you call your closet?" Retaliation is tempting, and may make you feel good in the short run, but it can do a relationship more harm than good in the long run.

If you are criticized, the best course is to retaliate. Retaliation is an inferior way to handle criticism—that is, if your goal is to resolve conflict. •

WHEN COMMUNICATION IS NOT ENOUGH: HANDLING IMPASSES

Communication helps build and maintain relationships, but sometimes partners have profound, substantial disagreements. Even when their communication skills are superbly tuned, now and then they reach an impasse.

Opening the lines of communication may also elicit hidden frustrations. These frustrations can lead partners to seriously question the value of continuing the relationship or to agree to consult a helping professional. Though some people feel it is best to "let sleeping dogs lie," the airing of underlying dissatisfactions can be healthful for a relationship when it is done skillfully. Couples who reach an impasse can follow several courses of action that may be helpful.

LOOKING AT THE SITUATION FROM THE OTHER PERSON'S PERSPECTIVE
Some of the conflict may be resolved by (honestly!) saying something like, "I still disagree with you, but I can understand why you take your position." In this way, you recognize your partner's goodwill and, perhaps, lessen tensions.

SEEKING VALIDATING INFORMATION   On the other hand, if you do not follow your partner's logic, you can say something like, "Please believe me: I'm trying very hard to look at this from your point of view, but I can't follow your reasoning. Would you try to help me understand your point of view?"

TAKING A BREAK   Sometimes when we reach a stalemate, it helps to allow the problem to "incubate." If you and your partner allow each other's viewpoints to jell for a while, perhaps a resolution will dawn on one of you later on. If you wish, schedule a follow-up discussion so that the issue won't be swept under the rug.

TOLERATING DIFFERENTNESS   Although we tend to form relationships with people who share similar attitudes, there is never a perfect overlap. A partner who pretends to be your clone will most likely become a bore. Assuming that your relationship is generally rewarding and pleasurable, you may find it possible to tolerate certain differences between yourself and your partner. Respecting other people in part means allowing them to be who they are. When we have a solid sense of who we are as individuals and what we stand for, we are more apt to be able to tolerate differentness in our partners.

Relationships come to an end when the partners cannot resolve their differences. Yes, relationships sometimes do end when couples cannot resolve their differences. It is possible for relationships to continue and improve even when we reach impasses, however. We need to be able to tolerate differentness in other people if relationships are to improve. •

AGREEING TO DISAGREE When all else fails, we can agree to disagree on various issues. You can remain a solid, respected individual, and your partner can remain a worthwhile, effective person even if the two of you disagree from time to time. You can handle an impasse by focusing on the things that you and your partner have in common. Presumably there will be a number of them—some of them with little feet.

SUMMING UP

STAGES IN ROMANTIC RELATIONSHIPS

Levinger proposes an ABCDE model of romantic relationships, which refers to five stages: attraction, building, continuation, deterioration, and ending.
Attraction The major promoter of attraction is propinquity.
Building Similarity in the level of physical attractiveness, similarity in attitudes, and liking motivate us to build relationships.
Continuation Factors such as variety, caring, positive evaluations, perceived fairness in the relationship, lack of jealousy, and mutual feelings of satisfaction encourage us to continue relationships.
Jealousy Sexual jealousy is aroused when we suspect that an intimate relationship is threatened by a rival, or a partner shows interest in another. Jealousy produces feelings of mistrust
Deterioration Factors that foster deterioration include failure to invest time and energy in the relationship, deciding to put an end to it, or simply permitting deteriora-

tion to proceed unchecked. Relationships tend to end when the partners find little satisfaction in the affiliation, alternative partners are available, couples are not committed to preserving them and they expect them to falter.
Ending Relationships tend to end when the partners find little satisfaction in the affiliation, alternative partners are available, couples are not committed to preserving them, and they expect them to falter.

LONELINESS

Loneliness is a state of painful isolation, of feeling cut off from others.
Causes of Loneliness The causes of loneliness include lack of social skills, lack of interest in other people, lack of empathy, fear of rejection, lack of self-disclosure, cynicism about human nature, demanding too much too soon, general pessimism, and an external locus of control.

Coping with Loneliness People are helped to overcome loneliness by challenging self-defeating attitudes and social-skills training.

INTIMACY

Intimacy involves feelings of emotional closeness with another person and the desire to share each other's inmost thoughts and feelings.
Knowing and Liking Yourself An initial step toward intimacy with others is getting to know and like yourself so that you can identify your inmost feelings and develop the security to share them.
Trusting and Caring Intimate relationships require trust, caring, and tenderness.

Being Honest Honesty is a core feature of intimacy. However, not all of a person's past experiences must be revealed for a couple to have an intimate relationship.
Making a Commitment Truly intimate relationships are marked

by commitment or resolve to maintain the relationship through thick and thin.

Maintaining Individuality When the *I* Becomes *We* In healthy unions, a strong sense of togetherness does not eradicate individuality.

Communicating Communication is a two-way street. It embraces sending and receiving messages. We often express feelings through nonverbal channels such as tone of voice, gestures, body posture, and facial expressions.

COMMUNICATION SKILLS

Common Difficulties in Sexual Communication Couples may find it difficult to talk about sex because of the lack of an agreeable, common language. Many couples also harbor irrational beliefs about relationships and sex, such as the notion that their partners should know what they want, without their having to ask.

Getting Started Ways of getting started communicating include talking about talking, requesting permission to raise an issue, and granting their partner permission to say things that might be upsetting.

Listening to the Other Side Skilled listening involves such elements as active listening, paraphrasing, the use of reinforcement, and valuing your partner even when the two of you disagree.

Learning About Your Partner's Needs You can learn about partner's needs by asking questions, using self-disclosure, and asking your partner to level with you about an irksome issue.

Providing Information You can provide information by "accentuating the positive" and using verbal and nonverbal cues.

Making Requests In making requests, it is helpful to take responsibility for what happens to you, to be specific, to be assertive, and to use "*I talk.*"

Delivering Criticism In delivering criticism, it is helpful to evaluate your motives, pick a good time and place, be specific, express displeasure in terms of your own feelings, keep complaints to the present, and express criticism constructively and positively.

Receiving Criticism To receive criticism effectively, it is helpful to clarify your goals, ask clarifying questions, acknowledge the criticism, reject inappropriate criticisms, and negotiate differences.

When Communication Is Not Enough: Handling Impasses Partners can help manage impasses by trying to see things from the partner's perspective, seeking validating information, taking a break, tolerating differentness, and, when necessary, agreeing to disagree.

_____ Married people rarely if ever masturbate.

_____ Women who masturbate during adolescence are less likely to find gratification in marital coitus than women who do not.

_____ Women are more likely to reach orgasm through sexual intercourse than masturbation.

_____ Most women masturbate by inserting a finger or other object into the vagina.

_____ Heterosexuals do not fantasize about homosexual activity.

_____ Statistically speaking, oral sex is the norm for today's young married couples.

_____ African Americans are more likely than white Americans to engage in oral sex.

_____ When lovers fantasize about other people, the relationship is in trouble.

C H A P T E R   9

Sexual Techniques and Behavior Patterns

This is the chapter that describes sexual techniques and offers statistical breakdowns of "who does what with whom." There is great variety in human sexual expression. Some of us practice few, if any, of the techniques we describe in this chapter. Some of us practice most or all of them, at least some of the time. Many of us practice some of them some of the time. Our knowledge of the prevalences of these techniques comes from sex surveys that began with Kinsey and have continued with the work of Hunt, Wyatt, Janus and Janus, and others. Because surveys are plagued by problems such as nonrepresentative sampling, refusals to participate, and misrepresentations by respondents, we are somewhat restricted in our ability to generalize their results. We should thus think of surveys as providing our best "guestimates" of the prevalences of sexual behaviors.[1] They do not provide precise figures.

CNN Sex Survey Update

The readers of this textbook may be as varied in their sexual values, preferences, and attitudes as is society in general. Some of the techniques we describe may thus strike some readers as indecent. Our intention is to provide information about the diversity of sexual expression. We are not looking for common ground as to what sexual practices are acceptable. Nor is it our purpose to pass moral judgments or to invite readers to expand their sexual repertoires. Rather, we seek to inform readers about the range and diversity of sexual expression that exists in our society and elsewhere.

The human body is sensitive to many forms of sexual stimulation. Yet we reiterate the theme that biology is not destiny: A biological capacity does not impose a behavioral requirement. Cultural expectations, personal values, and individual learnings—not only the biological capacities of our sexual organs—determine our sexual behavior.

We begin by reviewing the techniques that people practice by themselves to derive sexual pleasure—masturbation and sexual fantasy. We then consider techniques that involve a sexual interaction with a partner.

SOLITARY SEXUAL BEHAVIOR

Various forms of sexual expression do not require a partner or are not generally practiced in the presence of a partner. Masturbation is one of the principal forms of one-person sexual expression. Whereas masturbation involves direct stimulation of the genitals, other forms of individual sexual experience, such as sexual fantasy, may or may not be accompanied by genital stimulation.

MASTURBATION

Learning Objective 1:
Summarize historical and religious views on masturbation.

> In solitude he pollutes himself, and with his own hand blights all his prospects for both this world and the next. Even after being solemnly warned, he will often continue this worse than beastly practice, deliberately forfeiting his right to health and happiness for a moment's mad sensuality.
>
> (J. H. Kellogg, M.D., *Plain Facts for Old and Young,* 1882.)

Masturbation
Sexual self-stimulation.

The word *masturbation* derives from the Latin *masturbari*, from the roots for "hand" and "to defile," which provide clues to historical cultural attitudes toward the practice. **Masturbation** may be practiced by means of manual stimulation of the genitals, perhaps

[1]A full discussion of the limitations of surveys is found in Chapter 2.

Dildo
A penis-shaped object.

Coitus interruptus
The practice of withdrawing the penis prior to ejaculation during sexual intercourse.

Activity: *Thinking About The Logic of Cultural Taboos Against Masturbation* This writing activity in the IM encourages students to examine the assumptions underlying masturbation taboos.

with the aid of artificial stimulation, such as an electric vibrator, or through the use of an object, such as a pillow or a **dildo,** that provides direct tactile stimulation of the genitals. Even before we conceive of sexual experiences with others, we learn in early childhood that touching our genitals produces feelings of pleasure.

Within the Judeo-Christian tradition, masturbation—"onanism"—has been strongly condemned as sinful. Early Judeo-Christian attitudes toward masturbation reflected the censure that was applied toward nonprocreative sexual acts. In the Judeo-Christian tradition, masturbation has been referred to as "Onanism," a name that is derived from the biblical story of Onan. According to the book of Genesis (38:9–11), Onan was the second-born son of Judah, whose oldest son, Er, had died without leaving an heir. Biblical law required that if a man died without leaving a male heir, his brother must take the widow as a wife (a union called a Levirate marriage) and rear their firstborn son as his brother's heir. Judah thus directed Onan to "Go in unto thy brother's wife, and perform the duty of a husband's brother unto her, and raise up seed to thy brother." But Onan "spilled [his seed] upon the ground" during sexual relations with his deceased brother's wife, and was struck down by God for his deed.

While "onanism" has come to be associated with Judeo-Christian condemnation of masturbation, Onan's act was one of **coitus interruptus,** not masturbation. Both acts, however, involve nonprocreative sex—spilling the seed. Moreover, Onan's punishment seems to have more to do with his failure to fulfill his levirate obligations than for spilling his seed (Bullough, 1976). Whatever its biblical origins, masturbation is clearly prohibited under the Jewish code of laws. Historians suspect that Jews and Christians in ancient times condemned sexual practices that do not lead to pregnancy because of the need that existed for an increase in their numbers. The need for progeny is also linked to the view that coitus in marriage is the only morally acceptable avenue of sexual expression.

The history of cultural attitudes toward masturbation in Western society has been, until very recently, one of almost continual condemnation of the practice on moral and religious grounds—even on medical grounds.

HISTORICAL MEDICAL VIEWS OF MASTURBATION Until recent years masturbation was thought to be physically and mentally harmful, as well as degrading. Various maladies have been erroneously linked to masturbation at one time or another, including epilepsy, heart attacks, insanity, cancer, sterility, and genital warts.

Concerned about the damage that they believed masturbation would cause to mind and body, many nineteenth-century physicians advised parents to take measures to prevent their children from masturbating. Various contraptions were introduced to keep children from touching themselves. Some of these devices were truly barbarous, as you can see in Figure 9.1.

Leading clergy and medical authorities of the nineteenth century were persuaded that certain foods had a stimulating effect on the sex organs. So one form of advice to

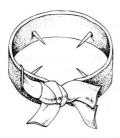

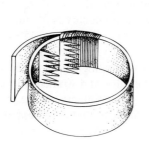

FIGURE 9.1 **Devices Designed to Curb Masturbation.** Because of widespread beliefs that masturbation was harmful, various contraptions were introduced in the nineteenth century to prevent the practice in children. Some of the devices were barbarous.

Notes: The dietary recommendations made by Graham and Kellogg sound like the health-food advice given today (eliminating coffee, tea, and chocolate, and eating more whole-grain products). Interestingly, physical fitness (which is related to age, diet, exercise, and heredity) is correlated with higher, not lower, levels of sexual activity.

Impotence
Recurrent difficulty in achieving or sustaining an erection sufficient to successfully engage in sexual intercourse. (The term has been replaced by the terms *male erectile disorder* or *erectile dysfunction,* as discussed in Chapter 15.)

Activity: Thinking About Sex and Athletic Performance This activity in the IM encourages students to think critically about the myths regarding the effects of sexual activity on athletic performance.

Discussion Question: What myths were you told about masturbation? What views do various religious groups hold about masturbation? What effects do myths and religious beliefs have on behavior?

parents focused on modifying their children's diets to eliminate foods that were believed to excite the sexual organs, notably coffee, tea, and chocolate, and to substitute "unstimulating" foods in their place, most notably grain products. In the 1830s the Reverend Sylvester Graham developed a cracker, since called the graham cracker, for the purpose of helping people keep their sexual impulses in check.

Yet another household name belongs to a man who made his mark by introducing a bland diet that was also intended to help people, especially youngsters, control their sexual impulses. In the nineteenth-century United States, medical advice was largely disseminated to the general public through pamphlets and guides written by leading medical authorities. One of the more influential writers was the superintendent of the Battle Creek Sanatorium in Michigan, Dr. J. H. Kellogg (1852–1943), better known to you as the father of the modern breakfast cereal. Kellogg, a follower of Graham, was especially concerned with the "dangers" of masturbation. Kellogg, like Graham, believed that sexual desires could be controlled by following a diet of simple foods, especially grain products, including the corn flakes he developed that have since borne his name. (We wonder how Kellogg would react today to the energizing, sugar-coated cereals that now bear his name.)

Graham and Kellogg were not alone. Several nineteenth-century scholars of sexuality joined the crusade against the perils of masturbation. Richard von Krafft-Ebing (in *Psychopathia Sexualis,* 1886) and Havelock Ellis (in *Studies in the Psychology of Sex,* 1900) condemned masturbation as psychologically dangerous. Krafft-Ebing linked masturbation to homosexuality. Masturbation, or so it was mistakenly believed, arrested the development of normal erotic instincts and led to heterosexual **impotence,** thus encouraging homosexuality.

Despite this history, scientific research has not found any empirical evidence that masturbation is physically or psychologically harmful. Masturbation does not cause insanity, grow hair on the hands, or cause warts or any of the other psychological and physical ills once attributed to the practice. Masturbation is physically harmless, save for the relatively few cases of injuries to the genitals that have occurred through excessively rough stimulation. Nor is it psychologically harmful, although it may be a sign of a psychological problem in the relatively few cases in which a person uses masturbation as an exclusive sexual outlet when other opportunities for sexual relationships are available. Moreover, people who consider masturbation wrong, harmful, or sinful may experience anxiety or guilt if they masturbate or feel the urge to masturbate. These negative emotions are linked to their attitudes toward masturbation, not to masturbation per se.

Despite the widespread condemnation of masturbation in our society, various surveys indicate that most people have masturbated at some point in their lives. The incidence of masturbation is generally greater among men than women, but there are undoubtedly many women who masturbate frequently and many men who rarely if ever do so. Almost all of the adult men and about two thirds of the adult women in Kinsey's samples (Kinsey et al., 1948, 1953) and the *Playboy* sample in the early 1970s (Hunt, 1974) reported that they had masturbated.

More recent surveys show that the percentage of women who report masturbating has risen to about 70 percent or higher, depending on the particular study (Reinisch, 1990). In a recent study of students in an urban university, the percentage who reported they had masturbated was 85 percent for women and 95 percent for men (Person et al., 1989). Seventy-one percent of the women and 83 percent of the men reported masturbating during the previous three-month period. Yet not all researchers find that the gender gap has narrowed to such an extent. A recent survey of students in a New England college found nearly twice as many men (81%) as women (45%) reporting some experience with masturbation (Leitenberg et al., 1993). About three in four men, as compared to only one in three women, reported masturbating during the previous year. Men who masturbated did so three times more often than did women who masturbated. It seems that despite the sexual revolution and the greater attention focused on female sexual pleasure in recent years, women may be less likely to find masturbation as pleasurable or acceptable as do men (Leitenberg et al., 1993). Women may still be subject to traditional socialization pressures that teach that sexual activity for pleasure's sake is more of a taboo for women than for men.

The results from this college sample concerning differences in masturbation frequency between men and women are mirrored in the Januses' nationwide sample (Janus & Janus, 1993). The Januses found that one in four men, as compared to only one in ten women, reported masturbating at least several times weekly. We need to caution, however, that the results of surveys based on limited samples of college students or other nonrepresentative samples, like the Janus and Janus sample, may not generalize more broadly. Moreover, we should also recognize that people may be less inclined to report a behavior like masturbation that still—despite the sexual revolution—has something of a taint associated with it.

Though masturbation tends to decline with age for both men and women, there may be an increase following a marital separation, divorce, or the death of a spouse (Hegeler & Mortensen, 1977). Still, continued masturbation was reported by nearly half (46%) of a sample of 800 adults 60 years of age or older (Starr & Weiner, 1981). This is a high level of acceptance of masturbation as a sexual outlet among people who were reared during a time when masturbation was generally viewed as harmful (Kammeyer et al., 1990).

Median
A type of average: The number exactly in the middle of a series, beneath which 50 percent of the cases fall.

Despite the common assumption that only adults who lack a coital partner continue to masturbate, evidence shows that masturbation is also prevalent among married people. Even in Kinsey's time, nearly 40 percent of married men and 30 percent of married women in their late twenties and early thirties reported masturbating. In more recent surveys, the majority of young married people report masturbating from time to time. Hunt (1974), for instance, found that, in the *Playboy* sample, 72 percent of husbands in their twenties and thirties masturbated, at a **median** rate of twice monthly. And 68 percent of wives of the same age masturbated, at a median rate of nearly 10 times a year. Sixty-eight percent of the nearly 100,000 married women surveyed by *Redbook* magazine reported masturbating (Tavris & Sadd, 1977). The Janus and Janus survey in the late 1980s and early 1990s found that 44 percent of the married men and 16 percent of the married women reported masturbating at least once a week. Only one in five married men and one in four married women reported never masturbating.

Married people rarely if ever masturbate. Today it seems that the majority of married people masturbate at least occasionally. •

Contemporary scholars see masturbation as harmless. They have even found therapeutic benefits for masturbation. Masturbation has emerged as a widely practiced form of treatment for women who have difficulty reaching orgasm (Kay, 1992) (see Chapter 15).

Although misinformation about masturbation persists, only 14 to 15 percent of the *Playboy* samples of 18- to 24-year-olds said that masturbation was wrong (Hunt, 1974). However, among respondents 55 years of age or older, nearly one in three said that masturbation was wrong. Many young people today view masturbation as a means of exploring their own bodies to learn what arouses them (Levy et al., 1987). Self-knowledge obtained through masturbation can be shared with a partner to enhance the sexual relationship. Orgasmic ability among women may also reflect underlying attitudes toward masturbation and willingness to learn about one's own orgasmic potential through self-stimulation.

The link between attitudes toward masturbation and orgasmic potential receives some support from a recent study of women that showed more negative attitudes toward masturbation among a group of women (21 to 40 years of age) who had never achieved orgasm in their lives than among a comparison group of orgasmic women (Kelly et al., 1990). Earlier, Kinsey and his colleagues reported links between prior masturbation and sexual satisfaction in marriage. Women who had masturbated during adolescence were more likely to find gratification in marital coitus than women who did not (Kinsey et al.,

1953). This evidence does not lead us to suggest that adolescents should masturbate as a way of guaranteeing adult sexual fulfillment. It may simply be that people who masturbate early are generally more open to exploring their sexuality and learning about the types of stimulation that arouse them. These attitudes may carry over into marriage, increasing the likelihood that women would seek the stimulation in coitus they need to achieve sexual gratification. On the other hand, it is also possible that adolescent masturbation sets the stage for marital sexual satisfaction by yielding information about the types of stimulation that are needed to bring about sexual gratification.

TRUTH OR FICTION?
REVISITED

Women who masturbate during adolescence are less likely to find gratification in marital coitus than women who do not. *Actually, women who masturbate during adolescence are more likely to find gratification in marital coitus than women who do not.* •

Other surveyists find that women achieve orgasm more reliably through masturbation than through coitus. Based on a sample of 3,000 women, Hite (1977) reported that 92 percent could reliably achieve orgasm through masturbation, as compared to only 30 percent who regularly did so through coitus. Hite's surveys are limited by biases such as very small return rates, so her percentages may not accurately reflect the general female population. Still, her findings are consistent with others' who suggest that masturbation may be a more reliable means of achieving orgasm than coitus (for example, Masters & Johnson, 1966), at least for women who accept masturbation as a sexual outlet.

TRUTH OR FICTION?
REVISITED

Women are more likely to reach orgasm through sexual intercourse than masturbation. *Women are actually more likely to reach orgasm through masturbation than through coitus.* •

REASONS FOR MASTURBATION People masturbate for many reasons. Some masturbate for pleasure or release of sexual tension. Others find that orgasms induced by masturbation can help relieve menstrual cramping, provide temporary relief from anxiety, or help induce sleep. Some masturbate as a sexual outlet when they are without a partner. Some people masturbate to learn about their sexual responsiveness. People today, concerned about the threat of AIDS, may use masturbation as a sexual outlet when they are without a regular partner, rather than engage in the riskier practice of seeking a casual sexual contact.

In our efforts to correct misinformation about masturbation, we do not wish to leave the impression that there is anything wrong with people who prefer *not* to masturbate. Nor do we wish to imply that everyone should masturbate. Although we may all have the capacity to experience pleasure from self-stimulation, let us again caution against transforming a biological capacity into a behavioral requirement.

TECHNIQUES OF MALE MASTURBATION

> Sex is like bridge—if you don't have a good partner, you'd better have a good hand.
>
> (Contemporary bathroom graffiti)

Although specific masturbation techniques vary widely among individuals, most men report that they masturbate by manual manipulation of the penis (Figure 9.2). Typically they take only one or two minutes to reach orgasm (Hite, 1981; Kinsey et al., 1948). Men tend to grip the penile shaft with one hand, jerking it up and down in a milking motion. Some men move the whole hand up and down the penis, while others use just two fingers, generally the thumb and index finger. Men usually shift from a gentler rubbing action during the flaccid or semi-erect state of arousal to a more vigorous milking motion once full erection takes place. Men are also likely to stroke the glans and frenulum lightly at the outset, but their grip tightens and their motions speed up as orgasm nears. At

FIGURE 9.2 **Male Masturbation.** Masturbation techniques vary widely, but most men report that they masturbate by manual manipulation of the penis. They tend to grip the penile shaft with one hand and jerk it up and down in a milking motion.

orgasm, the penile shaft may be gripped tightly, but the glans has become sensitive and contact with it is usually avoided. (Likewise, women usually avoid stimulating the clitoris directly during orgasm because of increased sensitivity.)

Some men use soapsuds (which may become irritating) as a lubricant for masturbation during baths or showers. Other lubricants, such as petroleum jelly or K-Y jelly, may also be used to reduce friction and to simulate the moist conditions of coitus.

A relatively few men prefer to masturbate by rubbing their penis and testicles against clothing or bedding (Kinsey et al., 1948). A few (perhaps a very few) men rub their genitals against inflatable dolls sold in sex shops. These dolls may come with artificial mouths or vaginas which can be filled with warm water to mimic the sensations of coitus. Artificial vaginas are also sold separately.

Men seeking novel stimulation may experiment by strapping vibrators to the backs of their hands. Electrical vibrators are not used very often by men, however, perhaps because they do not simulate the type of up-and-down motions of the penis that men favor. Most men rely heavily on fantasy or erotic photos or videos, but do not use sex-shop devices.

TECHNIQUES OF FEMALE MASTURBATION Techniques of female masturbation also vary widely, so much so that Masters and Johnson (1966) report never observing two women masturbating in precisely the same way. Even when the general technique was similar, women varied in the tempo and style of their self-caresses. But some general trends have been noted. Most women masturbate by massaging the mons, labia minora, and clitoral region with circular or back-and-forth motions (Hite, 1976; Kinsey et al., 1953). They may also straddle the clitoris with their fingers, stroking the shaft rather than the glans (see Figure 9.3, page 258). The glans may be lightly touched early during arousal, but because of its exquisite sensitivity, it is rarely stroked for any length of time during masturbation. Women typically achieve clitoral stimulation by rubbing or stroking the clitoral shaft or pulling or tugging on the vaginal lips. Some women also massage other sensitive areas, such as their breasts or nipples, with the free hand. Women, like men, rely heavily on fantasy during masturbation.

In contrast to the male myth (Kinsey and his colleagues [1953] describe it as a "male conceit") that women usually masturbate by simulating penile thrusting through the insertion of fingers or phallic objects into their vaginas, relatively few women actually do (Hite, 1976; Kinsey et al., 1953). Hite reported that only 1.5 percent of her respondents exclusively relied on vaginal insertion as a means of masturbation. Kinsey and his colleagues found that only one in five women had sometimes used vaginal insertions of objects during masturbation. Some women first experimented with the technique of vaginal insertions but then gave it up as they became more familiar with their sexual anatomy and capabilities. Others practiced the technique because their male partners found it sex-

FIGURE 9.3 **Female Masturbation.** Techniques of female masturbation vary so widely that Masters and Johnson reported never observing two women masturbating in precisely the same way. Most women masturbate by massaging the mons, labia minora, and clitoral region, however, either with circular or back-and-forth motions.

ually stimulating to watch them engage in this type of activity. Still, some women reported experiencing erotic pleasures from deep vaginal penetration.

TRUTH OR *FICTION?*
R E V I S I T E D

Most women masturbate by inserting a finger or other object into the vagina. Most women do not *masturbate by inserting a finger or other object into the vagina. Rather, they rely on clitoral stimulation.* •

Even when women do use insertion, they usually precede or combine it with clitoral stimulation. Sex shops sell dildos, which women can use to rub their vulvas or to insert vaginally. Penis-shaped vibrators may also be used in a similar fashion. Many women masturbate during baths, or spray their genitals with water-massage shower heads.

Hand-held electrical vibrators (see Figure 9.4) provide a constant massaging action against the genitals that can be erotically stimulating. Some women find this type of stimulation too intense, however, and favor the use of electrical vibrators that strap to the

CNN Moscow Sex Shop

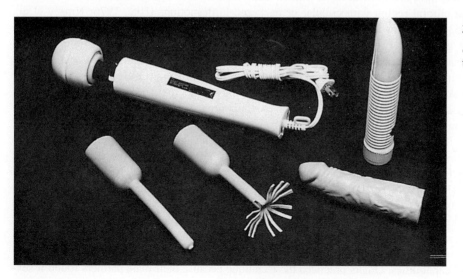

FIGURE 9.4 **Electrical Vibrators.** These are but a few of the many different types of electrical vibrators that are presently available.

back of the hand and cause the fingers to vibrate during manual stimulation of the genitals. This type of vibration may numb the hand that is attached to the vibrator, however. Women who use vibrators often experiment with different models to determine which offer the shape and intensity of vibration that suits their preferences.

SEXUAL FANTASY

Learning Objective 3: Describe the common sexual fantasies of males and females and the role fantasy plays in arousal and masturbation.

We classify sexual fantasies as sexual experiences that can occur without a partner, but many people also engage in fantasy during lovemaking. Some couples find it sexually arousing to share their fantasies with each other, or even to enact their fantasies with each partner playing a designated role. Strictly speaking, however, a fantasy is a private mental experience involving thoughts or images that are sexually arousing to the individual. Sexual fantasies may be experienced without accompanying sexual behavior, as in erotic dreams or daydreams. Sexual fantasies can also be incorporated in masturbation or sex with another person to heighten sexual response. Masturbators often require some cognitive form of stimulation, such as fantasy or reading or viewing erotica, to increase their arousal to the point of orgasm.

How common are sexual fantasies? Despite a popular belief that only people with deficient sex lives engage in sexual fantasies, evidence shows that the vast majority of men and women engage in sexual fantasies from time to time, especially during masturbation (Reinisch, 1990). One study of 212 married female college students found that 88 percent of them reported erotic fantasies. Most of them fantasized both during masturbation and coitus (Davidson & Hoffman, 1986). Another study showed that sexual daydreaming or fantasy in women was associated with greater sexual drive and activity and with a more positive sexual attitude (Purifoy et al., 1992)—hardly a pattern we would expect in people whose sex lives were deficient.

Sexual fantasies may be reasonably realistic, such as imagining sexual activity with an attractive classmate, or involve flights of fancy, such as making love to a movie star. The most common fantasy theme reported among a sample of 136 Canadian college women was intercourse with one's boyfriend or future husband (Pelletier & Herold, 1988).

Notes: In summarizing the results of a study of sexual behavior and attitudes among conservative Christians, V.E. Gil noted, "Respondents reported normative types and frequencies of fantasies. They experienced substantial to high levels of guilt about fantasizing" (p. 629). And "41 percent felt they were not in the best of God's grace after they experienced a fantasy" (p.635). (Gil, V.E. 1990. Sexual fantasy experiences and guilt among conservative Christians: An exploratory study. *Journal of Sex Research, 27*, 629-638.)

MASTURBATION FANTASIES In her book *My Secret Garden,* Nancy Friday (1973) compiled an anthology of erotic fantasies that women reported having during masturbation, daydreaming, and coitus. Here are some examples:

> Sometimes during sex, or just during the day, I think of what it would be like to trade husbands, that is, for me and my husband to have sex with a couple with whom we are good friends . . . me with the guy and my husband with the other wife (p. 47).

> I save my fantasizing for when I'm alone. I wait till evening, take a couple of drinks, and curl up in bed with a sexy book. Then when the drinks take hold I can imagine my hands are those of my lover.

> Other fantasies are just daydreams, which I have constantly. My favorite daydream is of me cooking or washing dishes, my lover comes in, puts his arms around me, and as we kiss and press against one another and our passion builds, I just reach behind me and turn off the stove, the dishes are forgotten, everything left wonderfully unfinished in this very interrupted state, as we go off to the bedroom to make love (p. 68).

Hunt (1974) reported that four out of five men and women in the *Playboy* sample who indicated that they masturbate report at least occasional fantasies when they do so. Let us note some gender similarities. The most common masturbation fantasy reported by both genders was "having intercourse with a loved one." But note some interesting differences: fantasizing making love to a stranger, making love to more than one person at a time, and forcing someone to engage in sexual activity were more commonly reported by men. Women, more often than men, reported fantasies of being forced to engage in sexual activity and engaging in sexual acts that they would never do in reality, presumably because they are forbidden. A more recent study of sexual fantasies reported in a college

Notes: "In brief, male sexual fantasies tend to be more ubiquitous, frequent, visual, specifically sexual, promiscuous, and active. Female sexual fantasies tend to be more contextual, emotive, intimate, and passive" (p. 529). (Ellis, B.J., and D. Symons. 1990. Sex differences in sexual fantasy: An evolutionary psychological approach. *Journal of Sex Research, 27*, 527–555.)

sample showed similar findings: Men more often reported sexual fantasy themes involving sex with other partners and forcing women into sexual activity (Person et al., 1989) (see Table 9.1).

Fantasy themes apparently parallel traditional gender stereotypes. Men are more likely to assume aggressive, dominant roles. Women are more apt to enact passive, submissive roles. Women may be more inclined to fantasize about forbidden acts because of the tighter controls that are generally placed on female sexuality in our culture. So perhaps cultural conditioning plays a role in determining fantasy themes.

These gender differences in fantasy themes may uncover deeper currents, however. From a sociobiological viewpoint, traits such as sexual aggressiveness and a predisposition toward impersonal sex may have yielded reproductive advantages to ancestral men. These traits may have rendered them more successful in mating with a larger number of women and fathering more children than their peers. Thus, whatever genes might have given rise to these behavior patterns would more likely have been transmitted down through the generations, perhaps even to the present time. The emergence of these themes in fantasy would thus be one more example of the expression of a natural gender difference.

Sociobiologists might conjecture that women are relatively more likely to fantasize about the images of familiar lovers because female reproductive success in ancestral times was more likely to depend on a close, protective relationship with a stable partner. Women can bear and rear only a relatively few offspring, so they would have had (and might still have) a relatively greater genetic investment in each reproductive opportunity.

Whether or not the wellsprings of sexual fantasy themes lie in our genetic heritages, we should not confuse sexual fantasies with overt behavior. Fantasies are private cognitive experiences that occur within a person's imagination. Most people do not intend to act out their fantasies. They simply use them as a means of inducing or enhancing sexual pleasure (Reinisch, 1990). As one woman noted,

> My fantasies are so personal, and the pleasure I get from them derives so much, I think, from the fact that they are private and locked away in my imagination, that I wouldn't dream of trying to make them come true . . . But act my fantasies out? Make them come true? No,

Sexual Fantasy. Sexual fantasies can be a powerful source of sexual stimulation.

absolutely not. My real life's not what they're about; I don't want those things to really happen to me, I simply want to imagine what it would be like. So that's where they'll stay.

(Friday, 1973, p. 288)

What Friday says here of women's fantasies also applies to men:

For many women, fantasy is a way of exploring, safely, all the ideas and actions which might frighten them in reality. In fantasy they can expand their reality, play out certain sexual variables and images in much the same way that children enter into fantasy as a form of play, of trying out desires, releasing energies for which they have no outlet in reality. Thinking about it, even getting excited over the image doesn't mean you want it as your reality . . . or else we all, night dreamers that we are, would be suppressed robbers, bisexuals, murderers, or even inanimate objects (p. 41).

Fantasizing about forcing someone into sexual activity, or about being victimized, does not mean that one wants these events to occur (Bond & Mosher, 1986; Reinisch, 1990). Women who imagine themselves being sexually coerced remain in control of their fantasies; real assault victims are not. Nor is it unusual for heterosexuals to have episodic homosexual fantasies, or for homosexuals to have occasional heterosexual fantasies, without any interest in carrying out these activities in reality.

Heterosexuals do not fantasize about homosexual activity. Heterosexuals may in fact fantasize about homosexual activity. Fantasies and behavior do not necessarily overlap. •

Why do people fantasize when they masturbate? Masturbation fantasies may serve several functions. For one, they may increase or facilitate sexual arousal. Sex therapists have encouraged their clients to practice sexual fantasies as a way of enhancing sexual arousal (e.g., Heiman & LoPiccolo, 1987). Sexual fantasies are highly arousing, in part because fantasizers can command the imagined sexual encounter. Fantasizers may imagine that people who will not give them the time of day find them irresistible and are willing to fulfill all of their sexual desires. Or fantasizers may picture improbable or impossible arousing situations, such as sexual activity on a commercial airliner or while skydiving. Some masturbation fantasies may be arousing because they permit us to deviate from traditional gender roles. Women might fantasize about taking an aggressive role or forcing someone into sexual activity. Men, by contrast, may imagine being overtaken by a horde of sexually aggressive women. Other fantasies involve sexual transgressions or "forbidden" behaviors, such as exposing oneself, doing a striptease before strangers, engaging in sexual activity with strangers, or sadomasochistic (S&M) sex.

Masturbation fantasies can also allow people to rehearse sexual encounters. We may envision the unfolding of an intended sexual encounter, from greeting a date at the door, through dinner and a movie, and finally to the bedroom. We can mentally rehearse what we would say and do as a way of preparing for the date. Finally, masturbation fantasies may fill in the missing love object when we are alone or our partners are away.

SEX WITH OTHERS

Many forms of sexual expression can only be experienced with a partner. In this section, we focus on various forms of heterosexual interactions between partners. In the next chapter, we discuss sexual interactions between gay male and lesbian partners.

Partners' feelings for one another, and the quality of their relationships, may be stronger determinants of their sexual arousal and response than the techniques that they employ. Partners are most likely to experience mutually enjoyable sexual interactions when they are sensitive to each other's sexual needs and incorporate techniques with which they are both comfortable. As with other aspects of sharing relationships, communication is the most important "sexual" technique.

FOREPLAY

Foreplay
Physical interactions that are sexually stimulating and set the stage for intercourse.

Learning Objective 4: Describe common foreplay techniques, such as kissing and breast and genital stimulation.

Teaching Tip: (Conduct the following only if your institution's ethics rules permit. Obviously, student participation must be voluntary.) Distribute index cards to all students. Ask them to write only "Male" or "Female" on their cards but to give no other identifying information. Then ask them to comment on foreplay preferences: time spent, behaviors, etc. Collect the cards and read them aloud to the class. Ask students to identify similarities and differences between males and females.

Various forms of noncoital sex, such as cuddling, kissing, petting, and oral-genital contact, can be used during **foreplay.** The pattern and duration of foreplay varies widely within and across cultures. Broude and Greene (1976) found that prolonged foreplay was the norm in about half of the societies in their cross-cultural sample. Foreplay was minimal in one in ten societies and virtually absent in about one third of them.

Within the United States, there is a gender difference in the amount of foreplay desired. A survey of college students revealed that women wanted longer periods of foreplay (and "afterplay") than men did (Denny et al., 1984). Since women usually require a longer period of stimulation during sex with a partner to reach orgasm, increasing the duration of foreplay may increase female coital responsiveness.

Foreplay is not limited to the human species. Virtually all species of mammals, from horses and sheep to dogs and chimpanzees, engage in various forms of foreplay. Depending on the particular species, mating pairs may rub, playfully nip, lick, or nuzzle each other's genitals for minutes or hours preceding coitus (Geer et al., 1984).

Kissing, genital touching, and oral-genital contact may also be experienced as ends in themselves, not merely as preludes to coitus. Yet some people object to petting for petting's sake, equating it with masturbation as a form of sexual activity without a "product." Many people behave as though all sexual contact must lead to coitus, perhaps because of the importance that our culture places on it (Levy et al., 1987). Because of this linkage, signals between partners may be misinterpreted. For example, when one partner approaches the other for some cuddling and light petting, the other may assume that these are overtures to coitus and feel rejected if the encounter does not culminate in coitus. Miscommunication can be avoided if partners convey their sexual intent in a way that is limit-setting but not rejecting (e.g., "I'd really like it if we just snuggled and cuddled for a while").

KISSING

Kissing is practiced almost universally in our culture, but it occurs less often among the world's cultures than manual or oral stimulation of the genitals (Frayser, 1985). Kissing is unknown in some cultures, such as among the Thonga of Africa and the Siriono of Bolivia. Variations in styles of "kissing" also exist across cultures (Ford & Beach, 1951). Instead of kissing, the Balinese of the South Pacific bring their faces close enough to each other to smell each other's perfume and feel the warmth of each other's skin. This practice has been wrongly dubbed "rubbing noses" by Europeans. Among some preliterate societies, kissing consists of sucking the partner's lips and tongue and allowing saliva to pass from one mouth to the other.

Couples may kiss for its own enjoyment or as a prelude to intercourse, in which case it is a part of foreplay. In *simple kissing,* the partners keep their mouths closed. Simple kissing may develop into caresses of the lips with the tongue, or into nibbling of the lower lip. In what Kinsey called *deep kissing,* which is also called French or soul kissing, the partners part their lips and insert their tongues into each other's mouths. Some prefer the lips parted slightly. Others open their mouths widely.

Kissing may also be an affectionate gesture without erotic significance, as in kissing someone good night. Some people are accustomed to kissing relatives and close friends affectionately on the lips. Others limit kissing relatives to the cheek. Sustained kissing on the lips and deep kissing are almost always erotic gestures.

Kissing is not limited to the partner's mouth. Kinsey found that more than nine husbands in ten kissed their wives' breasts. Women usually prefer several minutes of body contact and gentle caresses before desiring to have their partner kiss their breasts, or suck or lick their nipples. Women also usually do not prefer a hard sucking action unless they are highly aroused. Many women are reluctant to tell their partners that sucking hurts, because they do not want to interfere with their partner's pleasure (Masters & Johnson, 1970, 1979).

Other parts of the body are also often kissed, including the hands and feet, the neck and earlobes, the insides of the thighs, and the genitals themselves.

Kissing. Kissing is practiced almost universally in our culture, but is unknown in some other cultures. Kissing may be used as a form of foreplay preceding coitus or as an expression of affection and caring.

TOUCHING

Touching or caressing erogenous zones with the hands or other parts of the body can be highly arousing. Even simple hand-holding can be sexually stimulating for couples who are sexually attracted to one another. The hands are very rich in nerve endings.

Touching is a common form of foreplay. Both men and women generally prefer manual or oral stimulation of the genitals as a prelude to intercourse. Women generally prefer that direct caressing of the genitals be focused around the clitoris but not directly on the extremely sensitive clitoral glans. Men sometimes assume (often mistakenly) that their partners want them to insert their finger or fingers into the vagina as a form of foreplay. But not all women enjoy this form of stimulation. Some women go along with it because it's what their partners want (Knox, 1988) or because they think it's what their partners want. Ironically, men may do it because they assume that their partners want it. When in doubt, it would not hurt to *ask*. If you are not sure what to say, you can always blame us: "Listen, I read this thing in my human sexuality text, and I was wondering . . ."

Masters and Johnson (1979) noted gender differences with respect to preferences in foreplay. Men typically prefer direct stroking of their genitals by their partner early in lovemaking. Women, however, tend to prefer that their partners caress their genitals after a period of general body contact that includes holding, hugging, and nongenital massage. This is not a hard and fast (or slow) rule, but it concurs with other observations that men tend to be more genitally oriented than women. Women are more likely to view sex within a broader framework of affection and love.

TECHNIQUES OF MANUAL STIMULATION OF THE GENITALS   Here again, variability in technique is the rule, so partners need to communicate their preferences. The man's partner may use two hands to stimulate his genitals. One may be used to fondle the scrotum, by gently squeezing the skin between the fingers (taking care not to apply pressure to the testes themselves). The other hand may circle the coronal ridge and engage in gentle stroking of the penis, followed by more vigorous up and down movements as the man becomes more aroused.

The penis may also be gently rolled back and forth between the palms as if one were making a ball of clay into a sausage—increasing pressure as arousal progresses. Note that men who are highly aroused or who have just had an orgasm may find direct stimulation of the penile glans uncomfortable.

The woman may prefer that her partner approach genital stimulation gradually, following stimulation of other body parts. Genital stimulation may begin with light, stroking motions of the inner thighs and move on to the vaginal lips (labia) and the clitoral area. Women may enjoy pressure against the mons pubis from the heel of the hand, or tactile stimulation of the labia, which are sensitive to stroking motions. Clitoral stimulation can focus on the clitoral shaft or the region surrounding the shaft, rather than the clitoris itself, because of the extreme sensitivity of the clitoral glans to touch.

Moreover, the clitoris should not be stroked if it is dry, lest it become irritated. Since it produces no lubrication of its own, a finger may enter the outer portion of the vagina to apply some vaginal lubrication to the clitoral region.

Some, but not all, women enjoy having a finger inserted into the vagina, which can stroke the vaginal walls or simulate thrusting of the penis. Vaginal insertion is usually not preferred, if at all, until the woman has become highly aroused. Many women desire that their partners discontinue stroking motions while they are experiencing orgasm, but others wish stimulation to continue. The communication techniques described in Chapter 8 may help partners convey their preferences about genital stimulation. Men and women may physically guide their partners' hands or otherwise express their preferences as to the types of strokes they find most pleasurable.

If a finger is to be inserted into the vagina, it should be clean, and the fingernails should be well trimmed. Inserting fingers into the vagina that have been in the anus is dangerous, as they may transfer microbes from the woman's digestive tract, where they do no harm, to the woman's reproductive tract, where they can cause serious infections.

BREAST STIMULATION

Men are more likely to stimulate women's breasts than to have their own breasts fondled, even though the breasts (and especially the nipples) are erotically sensitive in both genders. Most, but not all, women enjoy breast stimulation. Masters and Johnson (1966) report that some women are capable of achieving orgasm from breast stimulation alone.

The hands and the mouth can be used to stimulate the breasts and the nipples. Since the desired type and intensity of breast stimulation varies from person to person, partners need to communicate their preferences.

The size of the breasts bears no relationship to the capacity for pleasure from stimulation. Some men whose partners are small-breasted, however, may not be inclined to engage in breast stimulation. They may assume (wrongly) that smaller-breasted women are less sensitive to this form of stimulation or that breast stimulation might make their partners uncomfortable by drawing attention to the size of their breasts.

Masters and Johnson (1979) find that gay men frequently stroke their partners' nipples before stimulating the penis itself. Although some heterosexual men enjoy having their breasts and nipples stimulated by their partners, many if not most do not, perhaps in part because they are unaware that their breasts are erotically sensitive. Cultural conditioning may also play a major part in men's reluctance to having their breasts stimulated: Men may feel uncomfortable receiving a form of stimulation that they have learned to associate with the stereotypical feminine sexual role.

ORAL-GENITAL STIMULATION

Fellatio
Oral stimulation of the male genitals.

Cunnilingus
Oral stimulation of the female genitals.

Learning Objective 5:
Describe fellatio and cunnilingus techniques and state how widely they are practiced among specific populations.

Oral stimulation of the male genitals is called **fellatio.** Fellatio is referred to by such slang terms as "blow job," "sucking," "sucking off," or "giving head." Oral stimulation of the female genitals is called **cunnilingus,** which is referred to by such slang expressions as "eating" (a woman) or "going down" on her.

The popularity of oral-genital stimulation has increased dramatically since Kinsey's day, especially among young married couples. Kinsey and his colleagues (1948, 1953) found that at least 60 percent of married, *college-educated* couples had experienced oral-genital contact. Such experiences were reported by only about 20 percent of couples who only had a high school education and 10 percent who only had a grade-school education. Oral sex has become increasingly acceptable to Americans across the educational spectrum. The *Playboy* survey in the early 1970s found that more than 90 percent of the married couples under 25 years of age—*across all educational levels*—reported they had engaged in oral-genital sex (Hunt, 1974). A more recent survey of married couples revealed similar findings: 90 percent of couples had engaged in fellatio, and 93 percent, in cunnilingus (Blumstein & Schwartz, 1983).

Statistically speaking, oral sex is the norm for today's young married couples. Oral-genital sex certainly has become the statistical norm for young married couples. According to recent surveys, more than 90 percent of them engage in this form of sexual expression. •

The Janus and Janus (1993) report on sexuality in contemporary U.S. society showed widespread acceptance of oral sex. Nearly 90 percent of the men and women in the Janus and Janus sample endorsed the belief that oral sex is either "very normal" or "all right." By contrast, only 29 percent of the men and 2 percent of the women polled viewed anal sex as either "very normal" or "all right."

Although there are dramatic changes in the incidence of oral-genital sexual activity from Kinsey's day to our own, there apparently are also persistent racial differences in the United States. Changes in the prevalence of oral sex among women are quite dramatic if we compare Kinsey's data with the results of Wyatt's sample of women in Los Angeles County (Wyatt, 1988a, 1988b). Among young white women (ages 18 to 36) in Kinsey's sample, 48 percent reported engaging in fellatio, as compared to 93 percent in Wyatt's sample. A similar increase was noted in the percentages of white women whose partners had engaged in cunnilingus—51 percent in Kinsey's sample, as compared to 87 percent in Wyatt's. Among African-American women, the percentage of women whose partners had engaged in cunnilingus rose from 18 percent in Kinsey's survey to 70 percent in Wyatt's. The percentages who reported they had engaged in fellatio increased from 15 percent in Kinsey's survey to 65 percent in Wyatt's. But Wyatt's sample was limited to women in Los Angeles and thus was not as geographically diverse as Kinsey's sample.

A recent national survey of more than 3,000 sexually active men between the ages of 20 and 39, conducted by the Battelle Human Affairs Research Center in Seattle, provides further evidence that oral sex has become the norm. Seventy-five percent of the men reported performing oral sex, whereas 79 percent reported receiving oral sex (Billy et al., 1993). Mirroring the racial differences observed by Wyatt between African-American and white women, African-American men in the Battelle survey were much less likely than their white counterparts to have performed or received oral sex (see Table 9.1). Moreover, whereas white men were about as likely to have performed oral sex as to have received oral sex, African-American men were much more likely to have had oral sex performed on them by their partners than the reverse.

In a 1980s survey of a college student sample, 81 percent of white females reported they had engaged in fellatio as compared to 47 percent of African-American females (Belcastro, 1985). Seventy-two percent of white males had performed cunnilingus, compared to 50 percent of African-American males. All in all, the available evidence indicates that although the prevalence of oral-genital sex since Kinsey's time has increased for both African-American and white Americans, African Americans remain relatively less likely than white Americans to engage in oral sexual activity.

TABLE 9.1 Reported experience with oral sex: Battelle survey of sexually active men ages 20 to 39

	African Americans (% reporting)	Whites (% reporting)	Overall (% reporting)
Performing oral sex	43	79	75
Receiving oral sex	62	81	79

Source: Adapted from Billy et al. (1993). Reprinted with permission.

African Americans are more likely than white Americans to engage in oral sex. False. A review of the available survey evidence from Kinsey's time to our own shows that white Americans are more likely than African Americans to engage in oral-genital sexual activity. •

As with touching, oral-genital stimulation can be used as a prelude to intercourse or as a sexual end in itself. If orgasm is reached through oral-genital stimulation, a woman may be concerned about tasting or swallowing a man's ejaculate. There is a lack of scientific evidence that swallowing semen is harmful to one's health, unless the man is infected with a sexually transmitted disease in which semen can act as a conduit of infections (Perry et al., 1989; Reinisch, 1990; Spitzer & Weiner, 1989). Note that oral-genital contact with the genitals of an infected partner, even without contact with semen, may transmit certain harmful organisms. Couples are thus advised to practice "safer sex" techniques (see Chapters 16 and 17) unless they know that they and their partners are free of sexually transmitted diseases (Reinisch, 1990).

Some women prefer not to taste or swallow semen because they find it to be "dirty," sinful, or repulsive. Others are put off by the taste or texture. Semen has a salty taste and a texture similar to the white of an egg. If couples are to engage in unprotected oral sex, open discussion of feelings can enhance pleasure and diminish anxiety. For example, the man can be encouraged to warn his partner or remove his penis from her mouth when he is nearing ejaculation.

Let us also dispel a couple of myths about swallowing semen. For one, it is impossible to become pregnant in this way. For another, semen is not fattening. Reinisch (1990) notes that the average amount of semen expelled in the ejaculate contains only about five calories.

TECHNIQUES OF FELLATIO   Although the word *fellatio* is derived from a Latin root meaning "to suck," a sucking action is generally not highly arousing. The up-and-down movements of the penis in the partner's mouth, or the licking of the penis, are generally the most stimulating. Gentle licking of the scrotum may also be highly arousing.

The mouth is stimulating to the penis because it contains warm, moist mucous membranes, as does the vagina. Muscles of the mouth and jaw can create varied pressure and movements. Erection may be stimulated by gently pulling the penis with the mouth (being careful never to touch the penis with the teeth) and simultaneously providing manual stimulation, as described earlier.

Higher levels of sexual arousal or orgasm can be promoted by moving the penis in and out of the mouth, simulating the motion of the penis in the vagina during intercourse. The speed of the motions can be varied, and manual stimulation near the base of the penis (firmly encircling the lower portion of the penis or providing pressure behind the scrotum) can also be stimulating.

Some people may gag during fellatio, a reflex that is triggered by pressure of the penis against the back of the tongue or against the throat. Gagging may be avoided if the man's partner grasps the shaft of the penis with one hand and controls the depth of penetration. Gagging is less likely to occur if the partner performing fellatio is on the top, rather than below, or if there is verbal communication about how deep the man may comfortably penetrate. Gagging may also be overcome by allowing gradually deeper penetrations of the penis over successive occasions while keeping the throat muscles relaxed.

TECHNIQUES OF CUNNILINGUS   Women can be highly aroused by their partner's tongue because it is soft, warm, and well-lubricated. In contrast to a finger, the tongue can almost never be used too harshly. A woman may thus be more receptive to direct clitoral contact by a tongue. Cunnilingus provides such intense stimulation that many women find it to be the best means for achieving orgasm. Some women cannot reach orgasm in any other way (Hite, 1976).

In performing cunnilingus, the partner may begin by kissing and licking the woman's abdomen and inner thighs, gradually nearing the vulva. Gentle tugging at or sucking of the labia minora can be stimulating, but the partner should take care not to bite. Many women

Notes: Remind students who engage in oral sex to practice safer sex by using condoms during fellatio (some stores carry flavored condoms) and dental dams (square pieces of latex rubber used by dentists during oral surgery) during cunnilingus.

enjoy licking of the clitoral region, and others desire sucking of the clitoris itself. The tongue may also be inserted into the vagina where it may imitate the thrusts of intercourse.

"69" The term *sixty-nine,* or *soixante-neuf* in French (pronounced swah-sahnt nuff), describes simultaneous oral-genital stimulation (see Figure 9.5). The numerals *6* and *9* are used because they resemble two partners who are upside down and facing one another.

The "69" position has the psychologically positive feature of allowing couples to experience simultaneous stimulation, but it can be an awkward position if two people are not similar in size. Some couples avoid 69 because it deprives each partner of the opportunity to focus fully on receiving or providing sexual pleasure. A person may find it distracting when receiving stimulation to have to focus on providing effective stimulation to someone else.

The 69 technique may be practiced side by side or with one partner on top of the other. But here again there are no strict rules, and couples often alternate positions.

ABSTAINING FROM ORAL SEX Despite the popularity of oral sex among couples today, those who desire to abstain from it should not consider themselves abnormal.

People offer various reasons for abstaining from oral sex. Although natural body odors may be arousing to some people, others are disturbed by the genital odors to which they are exposed. Some people object on grounds of cleanliness. They view the genitals as "dirty" because of their proximity to the urinary and anal openings. Concerns about offensive odors or cleanliness may be relieved by thoroughly washing the genitals beforehand.

Although some of the objections expressed by people who are reluctant to engage in oral sex may be overcome, others are more deeply rooted, such as beliefs that oral-genital contact is offensive or repulsive. Shyness and embarrassment may also deter interest in oral sex. A recent survey of college students found that shyness and embarrassment were the two most frequent reasons given for not engaging in oral sex (Gagnon & Simon, 1987). In one respect, oral sex is one of the most intimate types of lovemaking. After all, it provides a direct view of parts of the body we have been reared to keep private (Levy et al., 1987).

People may also object to oral sex because it is condemned by Judeo-Christian moral codes. In the Judeo-Christian tradition, any sexual contact that does not lead to procreation has been considered sinful. Couples may also be deterred from oral sex because it is illegal in many states, even for married couples. Some people object to oral sex on grounds that it is unnatural, even though many other species practice some form of oral-genital contact (Ford & Beach, 1951).

FIGURE 9.5 **Simultaneous Oral-Genital Contact.** The "69" position allows partners to share simultaneous oral-genital stimulation.

SEXUAL INTERCOURSE: POSITIONS AND TECHNIQUES

Learning Objective 6: List the four basic intercourse positions and the advantages and disadvantages of each.

Sexual intercourse, or *coitus* (from the Latin *coire*, meaning "to go together"), is sexual activity in which the penis is inserted into the vagina. Intercourse may take place in many different positions. Each position, however, must allow the genitals to be aligned so that the penis is contained by the vagina. In addition to varying positions, couples also vary the depth and rate of thrusting (in-and-out motions) and sources of additional sexual stimulation.

Though the number of possible coital positions is virtually endless, we will focus on four of the most commonly used positions: the male-superior (man-on-top) position, the female-superior (woman-on-top) position, the lateral-entry (side-entry) position, and the rear-entry position. Although not properly fitting the definition of sexual intercourse, we shall discuss anal intercourse as well, a sexual technique used by both heterosexual and gay male couples.

Missionary position
The coital position in which the man is on top. Also termed the *male-superior position.*

THE MALE-SUPERIOR (MAN-ON-TOP) POSITION The male-superior position ("superiority" is used purely in relation to body position, but has sometimes been taken as a symbol of male domination) has also been called the **missionary position.** In this position the partners face one another. The man lies above the woman, perhaps supporting himself on his hands and knees rather than applying his full weight against his partner (Figure 9.6). Still, movement is easier for the man than for the woman, which suggests that he is responsible for directing their activity.

Many students of human sexuality suggest that it is preferable for the woman to guide the penis into the vagina, rather than having the man do so. The idea is that the woman can feel the location of the vaginal opening and determine the proper angle of entry. To accomplish this, the woman must feel comfortable "taking charge" of the couple's lovemaking. With the breaking down of the traditional stereotype of the female as

FIGURE 9.6 **The Male-Superior Coital Position.** In this position the couple face one another. The man lies above the woman, perhaps supporting himself on his hands and knees rather than allowing his full weight to press against his partner. The position is also referred to as the *missionary position.*

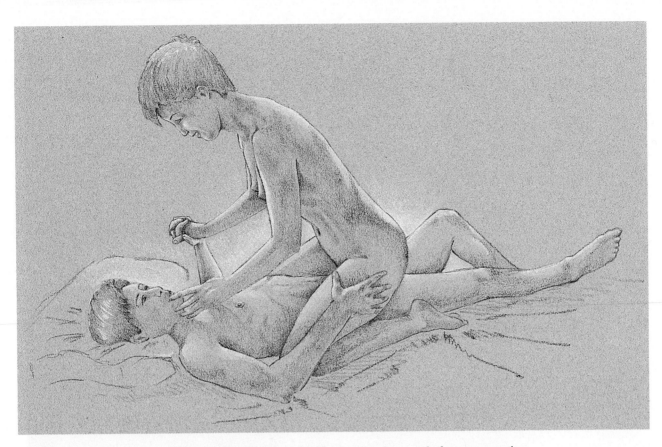

FIGURE 9.7 **The Female-Superior Coital Position.** In this position the couple face one another with the woman on top. The woman straddles the male from above, controlling the angle of penile entry and the depth of thrusting. The female-superior position puts the woman psychologically and physically in charge. The woman can assure that she receives adequate clitoral stimulation from the penis or the hand. The position also tends to be less stimulating for the male and may thus help him to control ejaculation.

Notes: In her 1990 book, *The Kinsey Institute New Report on Sex: What You Must Know to Be Sexually Literate,* Reinisch explores the origin of the term "missionary position." Among many similar stories is one about Pacific islanders who dubbed the man-on-top position the "missionary" position after witnessing this "unusual" practice among Western missionaries. According to Reinisch, this position is used most frequently among people in the United States, Japan, and some traditional groups in South America (p. 123).

passive, women are feeling more comfortable taking this role. On the other hand, if the couple prefers that the man guide his penis into his partner's vagina, the slight loss of efficiency need not trouble them, as long as he moves prudently to avoid hurting his partner.

The male-superior position has the advantage of permitting the couple to face one another so that kissing is easier. The woman may run her hands along her partner's body, stroking his buttocks and perhaps cupping a hand beneath his scrotum to increase stimulation as he reaches orgasm.

But the male-superior position makes it difficult for the man to caress his partner while simultaneously supporting himself with his hands. So the position may not be favored by women who enjoy having their partners provide manual clitoral stimulation during coitus. This position can be highly stimulating to the man, which can make it difficult for him to delay ejaculation. The position also limits the opportunity for the woman to control the angle, rate, and depth of penetration. It may thus be more difficult for her to attain the type of stimulation she may need to achieve orgasm, especially if she favors combining penile thrusting with manual clitoral stimulation. Finally, this position is not advisable during the late stages of pregnancy. At that time the woman's distended abdomen would force the man to arch severely above her, lest he place undue pressure against the woman's abdomen.

THE FEMALE-SUPERIOR (WOMAN-ON-TOP) POSITION   In the female-superior position the couple face one another with the woman on top. The woman straddles the male from above, controlling the angle of penile entry and the depth of thrusting (Figure 9.7). Some women maintain a sitting position; others lie on top of their partners. Many women vary their position.

FIGURE 9.8 **The Lateral-Entry Coital Position.** In this position the man and woman lie side by side, facing one another. The position allows each partner relatively free movement and easy access to the other. Because both partners rest easily on the bedding, it is an excellent position for prolonged coitus or for coitus when couples are fatigued.

Discussion Question: How can you communicate your position and stimulation preferences to a partner? Be specific. When, where, and what would you say or do?

In the female-superior position the woman is psychologically, and to some degree physically, in charge. She can move as rapidly or as slowly as she wishes with little effort, adjusting her body so as to vary the angle and depth of penetration. She can reach behind her to stroke her partner's scrotum, or lean down to kiss him.

As in the male-superior position, kissing is relatively easy. This position has additional advantages. The man may readily reach the woman's buttocks or clitoris in order to provide manual stimulation. Assuming that the woman is shorter than he is, it is rather easy for him to stimulate her breasts orally (a pillow tucked behind his head may help). The woman can, in effect, guarantee that she receives adequate clitoral stimulation, either by the penis or manually by his hand or her own. This position thus facilitates orgasm in the woman. As it tends to be less stimulating for the male, it may help him to control ejaculation. For these reasons this position is commonly used by couples who are learning to overcome sexual difficulties.

THE LATERAL-ENTRY (SIDE-ENTRY) POSITION In the lateral-entry position, the man and woman lie side by side, facing one another (Figure 9.8). This position has the advantages of allowing each partner relatively free movement and easy access to the other. The man and woman may kiss freely, and they can stroke one another's bodies with a free arm. The position is not physically taxing, because both partners are resting easily on the bedding. Thus it is an excellent position for prolonged coitus, or for coitus when couples are somewhat fatigued.

Let us note some disadvantages to this position. First, inserting the penis into the vagina while lying side by side may be awkward. Many couples thus begin coitus in another position and then change into the lateral-entry position—often because they wish to prolong coitus. Second, one or both partners may have an arm lying beneath the other that will "fall asleep" or become numb because of the constricted blood supply. Third, women may not receive adequate clitoral stimulation from the penis in this position. Of course, such stimulation may be provided manually (by hand) or by switching to another position after a while. Fourth, it may be difficult to achieve deeper penetration of the penis. The lateral position is useful during pregnancy (at least until the final stages, when the distension of the woman's abdomen may make lateral entry difficult).

THE REAR-ENTRY POSITION   In the rear-entry position, the man faces the woman's rear. In one variation (Figure 9.9), the woman supports herself on her hands and knees while the man supports himself on his knees, entering her from behind. In another, the couple lie alongside one another and the woman lifts one leg, draping it backward over her partner's thigh. The latter position is particularly useful during the later stages of pregnancy.

The rear-entry position may be highly stimulating for both partners. Men may enjoy viewing and pressing their abdomens against their partner's buttocks. The man can reach around or underneath to provide additional clitoral or breast stimulation, and the woman may reach behind (if she is on her hands and knees) to stroke or grasp her partner's testicles.

Potential disadvantages to this position include the following: First, this position is the mating position used by most other mammals, which is why it is sometimes referred to as *doggy style*. Some couples may feel uncomfortable about using the position because of its association with animal mating patterns. The position is also impersonal in the sense that the partners do not face one another, which may create a sense of emotional distance. Since the man is at the woman's back, the couple may feel that he is very much in charge—he can see her, but she cannot readily see him. Physically, the penis does not provide adequate stimulation to the clitoris. The penis also tends to pop out of

FIGURE 9.9 The Rear-Entry Coital Position. In this position the man faces the woman's rear. The rear-entry position is highly erotic for men who enjoy viewing and pressing their abdomens against their partner's buttocks. Some couples feel uncomfortable about using the position because of its association with animal mating patterns, however. The position is also impersonal in that the partners do not face one another, and the couple may dislike the feeling that the man is in charge because he can see his partner but she cannot readily see him.

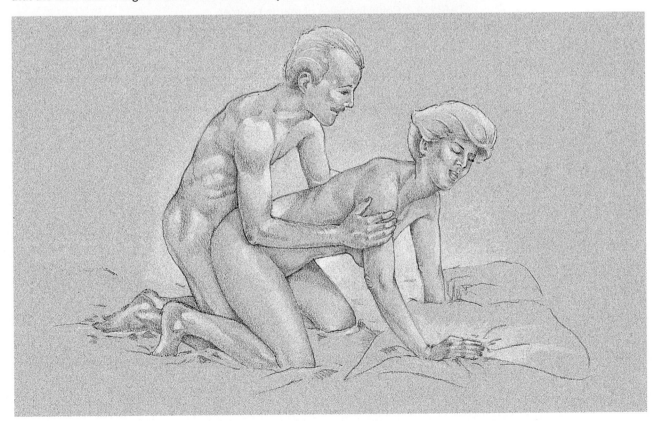

the vagina from time to time. Finally, air tends to enter the vagina during rear-entry coitus. When it is expelled, it can sound as though the woman has passed air through the anus—a possibly embarrassing though harmless occurrence.

Learning Objective 8: Describe the incidence and frequency of fantasy during coitus and the effects of fantasy on relationships.

USE OF FANTASY DURING COITUS   As with masturbation, mental excursions into fantasy during coitus may be used to enhance sexual arousal and response (Davidson & Hoffman, 1986). In a sense, coital fantasies allow couples to inject sexual variety and even offbeat sexual escapades into their sexual activity without being unfaithful. Fantasies were historically viewed as evil. People believed that fantasies, like dreams, were placed in the mind by agents of the devil. Despite this tradition, researchers find that most married people have engaged in coital fantasies (Crepault et al, 1977; Davidson & Hoffman, 1986; Hariton & Singer, 1974). In one study, 71 percent of the men and 72 percent of the women reported engaging in coital fantasies to enhance their sexual arousal (Zimmer et al., 1983). A more recent survey of a sample of 178 students, faculty, and staff members at a college in Vermont found that 84 percent reported fantasizing at least occasionally during intercourse (Cado & Leitenberg, 1990). Nor does there appear to be any connection between sexual dissatisfaction with one's relationship and the use of coital fantasies (Davidson & Hoffman, 1986). Thus coital fantasies are not a form of compensation for an unrewarding sexual relationship.

Lest you think that coital fantasies arise only out of sexual monotony in marriage, many if not most unmarried people also fantasize during sexual relations. In one study of sexually experienced, single undergraduates, Sue (1979) found that virtually the same percentages of men (58.6%) and women (59.4%) reported "sometimes" or "almost always" fantasizing during coitus.

Coital fantasies, like masturbation fantasies, run a gamut of themes. They include making love to another partner, group sex, orgies, images of past lovers or special erotic experiences, making love in fantastic and wonderful places, among others.

Table 9.2 shows the coital fantasies reported to E. Barbara Hariton (Hariton, 1973; Hariton & Singer, 1974) by a sample of married women from an affluent New York City

---

TABLE 9.2 Coital fantasies of married women

Fantasy	Percentage of Women Reporting Fantasy
Thoughts of an imaginary romantic lover enter my mind.	56
I relive a previous sexual experience.	52
I enjoy pretending that I am doing something forbidden.	50
I imagine that I am being overpowered or forced to surrender.	49
I am in a different place, like a car, motel, beach, woods, etc.	47
I imagine myself delighting many men.	43
I pretend that I struggle and resist before being aroused to surrender.	40
I imagine that I am observing myself or others having sex.	38
I pretend that I am another irresistibly sexy female.	38
I daydream that I am being made love to by more than one man at a time.	36
My thoughts center about feelings of weakness or helplessness.	33
I see myself as a striptease dancer, harem girl, or other performer.	28
I pretend that I am a whore or a prostitute.	25
I imagine that I am being forced to expose my body to a seducer.	19
My thoughts center around urination or defecation.	2

Source: Hariton, E.B., & Singer, J.L. (1974) Women's fantasies during sexual intercourse: Normative and theoretical implications. *Journal of Consulting and Clinical Psychology, 42,* 313–322. Copyright 1974 by the American Psychological Association. Reprinted by permission.

Are African Americans Sexually Permissive? Cultural Mythology Versus Some Facts

African Americans in our culture have long been stereotyped as more sexually permissive than whites (Wyatt, 1989). The perpetuation of this stereotype is based more on cultural biases than on scientific evidence. Evidence from Kinsey's time through the 1980s has shown that African-American teenagers begin intercourse at earlier ages, on the average, than white teenagers (Wyatt, 1989). Such research has largely failed to account for socioeconomic (social class) differences between the groups, however.

Researchers have begun to critically examine existing stereotypes of African-American sexuality. The 1988 National Survey of Family Growth, which surveyed nearly 8,500 American women ages 15 to 44, found that white women were more likely to have had 10 or more sexual partners than either African-American or Hispanic women (Lewin, 1992b). In another research effort, Philip Belcastro (1985) administered an anonymous sex survey to a racially mixed sample of more than 1,000 never-married, undergraduate students at a Midwestern university. Belcastro found that the similarities in the sexual behaviors of African-American and white students outweighed the differences. African-American and white students did not differ with respect to incidence of premarital coitus, coitus with a stranger, abortion, coital frequency, number of coital partners, use of condoms or diaphragms, and number of pregnancies (see Table 9.3). Some differences did emerge, however. African-

American males had their first coital experiences at an earlier age than white males, and had younger first partners. White females had relatively more coital partners with whom they had long-term (six months or longer) relationships. White males reported more masturbatory experience than African-American males. White females were more likely than African-American females to perform fellatio, masturbate their partner, and use birth-control pills and coitus interruptus. Belcastro's survey did not control for socioeconomic differences between the African-American and white samples, however. In addition, college students—African-American and white—are likely to be more affluent and better educated than their counterparts in the general population.

In another research effort, Gail Wyatt (1989) used Kinsey-style interviews to examine vari-

TABLE 9.3 Sexual behaviors of African-American and white college students

Behavior	Males (Means)		Females (Means)	
	African Americans	Whites	African Americans	Whites
Your age at first intercourse (years)	13.6	16.3*	16.2	16.8
Age of your first (heterosexual) coital partner	14.8	16.9*	18.6	19.2
Your age when you first masturbated (years)	13.3	13.1	12.6	14.3
Number of times you masturbate per month	4.7	6.5	2.2	3.4
Number of times a month you have intercourse	7.5	8.9	8.5	9.7
Number of heterosexual coital partners you have dated for 6 months or longer	2.9	2.2	1.5	2.0*
Number of partners you have cohabited with	2.4	1.9	2.0	1.2
Number of times you or your partner have become pregnant	1.5	1.0	1.2	1.1
Number of different coital partners in your lifetime	7.4	7.6	4.8	6.6

Source: Adapted from Belcastro, 1985, p. 65.
*Denotes statistically significant results comparing African Americans and Whites within gender.

continued

continued

ous aspects of sexual behavior among 126 African-American and 122 white American women, ages 18 to 36, from Los Angeles County. Wyatt's study is noteworthy for balancing white and African-American samples with respect to sociodemographic factors such as income level, education, and marital status. Wyatt reported no significant differences in age of first intercourse between the African-American and white women in her sample. The average age at first intercourse was 16.6 years for the total sample—16.5 years for African-American women and 16.7 years for white women, respectively—a nonsignificant difference. (These data are also remarkably similar to those obtained by Belcastro—see Table 9.3.) Factors that predicted age of first intercourse were similar across groups. For both groups, perceptions that one's parents were more influential than one's friends during adolescence and the eventual attainment of higher educational levels was associated with a delay in the age of first intercourse.

All in all, results of the Belcastro and Wyatt surveys fail to support the stereotype of African-American sexual permissiveness. The similarities between the races overshadowed

their differences. We should caution, however, that neither sample was a national probability sample. The results may thus not generalize to African Americans or white Americans in general.

Determining whether or not a group is sexually permissive depends on the criteria that one uses to define permissiveness. If age of coital initiation were the criterion of permissiveness, African-American males would be considered more permissive than white males, according to Belcastro's findings. If masturbating, performing fellatio, or masturbating one's partner were the criteria of permissiveness, white males and females would be deemed more permissive than their African-American counterparts.

Although more interracial research would be of interest, an even richer understanding of sexual behavior patterns might be gained by examining variability within racial groups according to such factors as socioeconomic status and family background.

Stereotypes of African-American Sexuality: A Commentary by Beverly Greene[1]

"Stereotypes and myths surrounding the sexuality of African Americans continue to abound even in the scholarly community.

The failure of empirical studies to support these stereotypes and the continuing preoccupation with them raises many important questions. We might ask why such beliefs are maintained with such tenacity when no evidence has ever really supported them. Some of the answers to these questions may be found in an understanding of the origins of such beliefs and the purpose served by them.

"Sexuality and race constitute two issues which elicit intense feelings in most people in our culture and both are explained in the context of cultural mythology rather than fact. Psychological science has unfortunately contributed to such stigmatization rather than mitigating it. The psychological literature is riddled with its share of scientific racism, designed to bear out popular belief and practice rather than conduct open and objective inquiry. This brings us back to the question of the origins of such thinking.

"Many of the racial stereotypes about African Americans, including myths about sexual prowess and appetite have their origins in the historical sexual objectification of African-American men and women by the dominant culture during the slave trade. During this period

---

suburb. The women included PTA members and regular churchgoers. Yet 65 percent—a strong majority—used coital fantasies. The use of fantasies was not a sign of marital difficulty. In fact, women who fantasized reported *better* sexual relations with their partners than did those who did not. The content of these fantasies suggests that they serve to introduce novelty or variety into their sexual relationships.

RELATIONSHIP ISSUES AND COITAL FANTASIES Studies of coital fantasies by Hariton and Singer (1974) and Sue (1979), among others, find that sexual fantasies during intercourse are common among couples with close relationships and are a means of facilitating sexual arousal. By facilitating sexual arousal, coital fantasies may help strengthen the intimate bond between the partners. Evidence does not show coital fantasies to be a sign of a troubled relationship.

African Americans were commodities, purchased and sold for a dollar amount much as any other property. Their price was usually determined by their ability to function as free labor and to produce offspring who would become free labor. The greater the capacity of the slave to reproduce, no matter with whom, the greater the price he or she would bring on the auction block. Forced to breed like animals at the behest of slave masters or be killed; regarded as animals like the plantation livestock; deprived of the option of legal marriages, as slaves could not make legal contracts; forced and frequent sexual relationships became a part of the norm, a part of the job about which there was no choice. African-American slaves in these situations were not only vulnerable to the sexual urges of their masters, they were blamed for them as well!

"The existence of such practices in the midst of a free and democratic society, founded on Christian ideals required some explanation. It became acceptable to view African Americans as innately inferior to whites, applying this argument to their capacity for sexual restraint as well. Thus, forced sexual promiscuity was viewed as an expression of this innate inferiority which circularly reinforced arguments in favor of continuing such practices.

"Once the realistic basis for such behavior was obscured and rationalized, it became harder to separate fact from myth. An additional purpose was served by this argument as well. Making African Americans the repository of sexual propensities found in all human beings across racial lines but deemed negative by dominant cultural norms, increased the perceived difference and distance between African and white Americans. This reinforced the acceptance of practices which would otherwise be unacceptable. Popular media depictions of African Americans continue to reinforce old myths, the most popular of which is that of sexual permissiveness, making it even more difficult to disentangle myth from fact. What is often most destructive is the tendency for some African Americans to believe that such myths about themselves are true, and to attempt to either act against them or to live up to them.

Beverly Greene

"It is hoped that new critical explanations of old data, and progressive studies will create a more accurate data base and lead to the evolution of a more factual understanding of this aspect of human behavior for African Americans."

Learning Objective 7: Compare the myths and facts about African-American sexual behavior.

[1]Beverly Green, Ph.D., is a clinical psychologist and Associate Professor of Psychology at St. John's University, Jamaica, New York. A Fellow of the American Psychological Association, she is co-editor of *Women of Color: Integrating Ethnic and Gender Identities in Treatment,* and *Psychological Perspectives on Lesbian and Gay Issues,* a publication of Division 44 of the American Psychological Association.

TRUTH OR *FICTION?*

R E V I S I T E D

When lovers fantasize about other people, the relationship is in trouble.
Evidence fails to show that coital fantasies are a sign of a troubled relationship. •

Partners are often reluctant to share their coital fantasies, or even to admit to them. This is especially true when the fantasy is about someone other than the partner. The fantasizer might fear being accused of harboring extramarital desires. Or the fantasizer might fear that the partner will interpret fantasies as a sign of rejection: "What's the matter, don't I turn you on anymore?" The advisability of self-disclosure is best weighed against one's partner's potential reactions to coital fantasies.

Learning Objective 9: Discuss who engages in anal intercourse and the necessary precautions to take.

ANAL INTERCOURSE   Anal intercourse can be practiced by heterosexual couples as well as gay male couples. It involves insertion of the penis into the rectum. The rectum is richly endowed with nerve endings and is thus highly sensitive to sexual stimulation. Anal intercourse is also referred to as "Greek culture," or lovemaking in the "Greek style" because of bisexuality among males in ancient Greece. It is also the major act that comes under the legal definition of sodomy. Both women and men may reach orgasm through receiving the penis in the rectum and thrusting.

In anal intercourse, the penetrating male situates himself behind his partner, though he may also lie above his partner in a face-to-face position. The receiving partner may supplement anal stimulation with manual stimulation of the clitoral region or penis to reach orgasm.

Women often report wanting their partner's fingers in the anus at the height of passion or at the moment of orgasm. A finger in the rectum at time of orgasm can heighten sexual sensation because the anal sphincters contract during orgasm. Although some men also want a finger in the anus, many resist because they associate anal penetration with the female role or with male homosexuality. The desire to be entered by one's partner is not an exclusively homosexual or heterosexual wish, however. Homosexuality refers to the eroticization of members of one's own gender, not the desire to penetrate or be penetrated.

Many couples are repulsed by the idea of anal intercourse. They view it as unnatural, immoral, or risky. Yet others find anal sex to be an enjoyable sexual variation, though perhaps not a regular feature of their sexual diet. The 1970s *Playboy* survey found that almost one quarter of the respondents below the age of 35 had engaged in anal sex during the preceding year, as compared with one in seven 35- to 44-year-olds and a scattering of respondents age 45 and above (Hunt, 1974). More recent data suggests that anal sex has become more prevalent among heterosexual couples since Kinsey's time. Only 15 percent of the white women ages 18 to 36 in the Kinsey sample reported engaging in anal sex, as compared to 53 percent in Wyatt's (1988a) Los Angeles sample. The percentages of African-American women in this age range who reportedly engaged in anal sex—9 percent in Kinsey's sample versus 21 percent in Wyatt's—has also shown a substantial increase. Other data from the 1980s showed that 25 percent of U.S. women reported engaging in anal intercourse occasionally, with 10 percent doing so regularly (Bolling & Voeller, 1987).

The Battelle national study of sexually active men in the 20 to 39 age group found somewhat lower percentages reporting experience with anal sex than those reported in samples based on women respondents. Only one in five men in the Battelle sample reported having engaged in anal intercourse (Billy et al., 1993). Anal intercourse was more commonly reported among better educated men. It is possible that anal sex may have declined in recent years because of heightened concerns about the spread of the AIDS virus through anal intercourse—see below. It is also possible that men are less likely than women to report heterosexual experiences with anal intercourse because of associations between anal sex and gay male sexual activity.

Couples who attempt anal intercourse should recognize that the rectum does not produce lubrication to facilitate entry of the penis. An artificial lubricant such as K-Y jelly should be used to ease entry. The receiving partner is likely to experience contraction of the anal musculature, or even pain, during the first attempt at anal penetration. Slow penetration allows the recipient to relax the anal sphincters gradually. Slow, gentle thrusting will help avoid tearing sensitive rectal tissue. Men and women can both receive a penis in the anus; it is a question of relaxation and lubrication. Anxiety will make anal intercourse more difficult because the anal sphincters, like other muscles in the body, tend to contract when people feel anxious.

Anilingus
Oral stimulation of the anus.

Many couples kiss or lick the anus in their foreplay. This practice is called **anilingus.** Oral-anal sex carries a serious health risk, however, because microorganisms causing intestinal diseases and various sexually transmitted diseases can be spread through oral-anal contact.

Many couples today hesitate to engage in anal intercourse because of the fear of AIDS and other sexually transmitted diseases (STDs). The AIDS virus and other microorganisms causing STDs such as gonorrhea, syphilis, and hepatitis can be spread by anal intercourse, because small tears in the rectal tissues may allow the microbes to enter the recipient's blood system. It is also true that women incur a greater risk of contracting the *human immunodeficiency virus,* or HIV, the virus that causes AIDS, from anal intercourse than from vaginal intercourse—just as receptive anal intercourse in gay men carries a high risk of infection (Voeller, 1991). However, monogamous partners who are both infection-free are at no risk of contracting HIV or other STD-causing organisms through anal or vaginal intercourse, or any other sexual act. HIV and other STD-causing organisms can only be transmitted by people who are infected with these organisms. But (and it's a big but!) people who are uncertain whether their partners are infected would be prudent to avoid anal intercourse, or at least to use a latex condom and a spermicide that is known to kill the AIDS virus. Further guidelines for reducing the risk of STDs, including AIDS, are provided in Chapters 16 and 17.

In this chapter, we observed many of the variations that exist in human sexual expression. No other species shows a similar range and diversity of sexual behaviors. People show diversity not only in sexual behavior, but also in sexual orientation—which is the focus of the following chapter.

SUMMING UP

SOLITARY SEXUAL BEHAVIOR

Masturbation Masturbation may be practiced by means of manual stimulation of the genitals, perhaps with the aid of an electric vibrator or an object that provides tactile stimulation. Within the Judeo-Christian tradition, masturbation has been condemned as sinful. Until recent years, masturbation was thought to be physically and mentally harmful, yet contemporary scholars see masturbation as harmless. Surveys indicate that most people have masturbated at some point in their lives.

Sexual Fantasy Sexual fantasies are often incorporated with masturbation or with sex with another person to heighten sexual response. Sexual fantasies range from the realistic to flights of fancy. Many people fantasize about sexual activities in which they would not actually engage.

SEX WITH OTHERS

Foreplay The pattern and duration of foreplay varies widely within and across cultures. Women usually desire longer periods of foreplay than men do.

Kissing Couples kiss for its own enjoyment or as a prelude to intercourse.

Touching Touching or caressing erogenous zones with the hands or other parts of the body can be highly arousing. Men typically prefer direct stroking of their genitals by their partner early in lovemaking. Women, however, tend to prefer that their partners caress their genitals after a period of general body contact.

Breast Stimulation Most, but not all, women enjoy breast stimulation. The hands and the mouth can be used to stimulate the breasts. The size of the breasts bears no relationship to the capacity to derive pleasure from stimulation.

Oral-Genital Stimulation The popularity of oral-genital stimulation has increased dramatically since Kinsey's day, but survey researchers find persistent differences in frequency of these activities between African and white Americans.

Sexual Intercourse: Positions and Techniques Couples today use a greater variety of coital positions than in Kinsey's time. Four of the most commonly used coital positions are the male-superior position, the female-superior position, the lateral-entry position, and the rear-entry position.

_____ Gay males and lesbians would prefer to be members of the opposite gender.

_____ Most gay males are "swishy," and most lesbians are "butch."

_____ Gay males and lesbians suffer from hormonal imbalances.

_____ Gay males unconsciously fear women's genitals because they associate them with castration.

_____ The American Psychiatric Association considers homosexuality a mental disorder.

_____ Many gay couples have lifestyles similar to those of married heterosexual couples and are as well adjusted.

C H A P T E R   *10*

Sexual Orientation

John, a nurse, was awarded custody of his 7-year-old son, Jacob, after a divorce. John's companion, Don, often picks Jacob up after school. "Who is that?" a teacher unfamiliar with the situation asked Jacob one day.

"That's my father's husband," Jacob replied matter-of-factly.

Alyson Publications, a Boston publisher, added two titles to its 1991 children's list: *Heather Has Two Mommies* and *Daddy's Roommate.*

Learning Objective 1:
Define sexual orientation and distinguish between sexual orientation, sexual identity, and sexual behavior.

As suggested by these slices of contemporary life reported by Gross (1991), it is becoming more common for children to be reared openly by gay male or lesbian couples. In most states, homosexuality is no longer grounds for parents to lose custody of their children. States have become more accepting of this living arrangement because of a lack of evidence that children reared by gay male and lesbian parents are less well adjusted than other children. Evidence does not support the fear that children raised by gay male or lesbian parents will be emotionally damaged or socially stigmatized (Baggett, 1992; Goleman, 1992b). Although they may face some teasing or ridicule, especially during adolescence, studies show that they do not suffer any psychological damage from being raised by gay parents (Goleman, 1992b). Nor, as leading sexologist John Money notes, does being raised by a homosexual parent cause children to become homosexual themselves or to develop gender-identity confusion (cited in Goleman, 1992b, p. C14).

In this chapter we discuss **sexual orientation,** the direction of one's romantic interests and erotic attractions—toward members of the same gender, the opposite gender, or both. We discuss how Kinsey and other researchers have conceptualized and categorized sexual orientations. We review theory and research concerning the origins of sexual orientation, with emphasis on homosexuality. We will see that gay males and lesbians, like their heterosexual counterparts, struggle to incorporate their sexuality within their personal identity, to find lovers, and to establish lifestyles that are emotionally and sexually rewarding. Unlike their heterosexual counterparts, however, gay males and lesbians in our culture must come to terms with their sexuality against a backdrop of societal intolerance. Let us begin by discussing the concept of sexual orientation—what it is and what it is not.

Sexual orientation
The directionality of one's sexual interests—toward members of the same gender, the opposite gender, or both genders.

Heterosexual orientation
Erotic attraction to, and preference for, developing romantic relationships with members of the opposite gender.

Homosexual orientation
Erotic attraction to, and preference for, developing romantic relationships with members of one's own gender. (From the Greek *homos,* meaning "same," not the Latin *homo,* which means "man.")

Gay males
Male homosexuals.

Lesbians
Female homosexuals. (After Lesbos, the Greek island on which, legend has it, female homosexuality was idealized.)

Bisexuality
Erotic attraction to, and interest in, developing romantic relationships with members of either gender.

SEXUAL ORIENTATION

Sexual orientation refers to one's erotic attraction toward, and interests in developing loving relationships with, members of one's own or the opposite gender. A **heterosexual orientation** refers to an erotic attraction to, and preference for developing romantic relationships with, members of the opposite gender. A **homosexual orientation** refers to an erotic attraction to, and preference for developing romantic relationships with, members of one's own gender. The term *homosexuality* denotes sexual interest in members of one's own gender and applies to both men and women. Homosexual men are often referred to as **gay males.** Homosexual women are generally called **lesbians** or *gay women.* Gay males and lesbians are also often referred to collectively as "gays" or "gay people." The term **bisexuality** is used to refer to an orientation in which one is sexually attracted to both males and females.

It is a common misconception that gay males and lesbians would prefer to be members of the opposite gender since they are attracted to members of their own gender (Renzetti & Curran, 1989). Like heterosexuals, however, gays have a gender identity that is consistent with their anatomic gender. Unlike transsexuals, gay males and lesbians do not see themselves as being trapped in the body of the opposite gender.

Gay males and lesbians would prefer to be members of the opposite gender. Actually, gay males and lesbians do not desire to change their gender. Their gender identity is consistent with their anatomic gender. •

Heterosexuals tend to focus almost exclusively on sexual aspects of homosexual relationships. But gay male and lesbian relationships, like heterosexual relationships, involve much more than sexual relations. Gay males and lesbians, like heterosexuals, spend only a small proportion of their time in sexual activity. More basic to a gay male or lesbian sexual orientation is the formation of romantic attachments with members of one's own gender that, like heterosexual relationships, provide a framework for love and sharing of life experiences (Peplau & Cochran, 1990). Although sex and love are common features of gay male, lesbian, and heterosexual relationships, neither is a *necessary* prerequisite for a relationship. Sexual orientations are not defined by sexual activity per se, but rather by the direction of one's romantic interests and erotic attractions.

Many gay men and lesbians protest the use of the term *homosexual,* because they feel that it draws too much attention to sexual behavior and because the term has carried a social stigma for many centuries. Many would prefer terms such as *gay male* or *lesbian sexual orientation,* or a term such as *homophile,* if a term must be used to set them apart. The Greek root *philia* suggests love and friendship rather than sexual behavior. Thus, a homophile is a person who develops romantic love and emotional commitment to members of the same gender. Sexual activity is secondary.

CLASSIFICATION OF SEXUAL ORIENTATION

Determining a person's sexual orientation would seem at first glance to be a clear-cut task. Some people are exclusively homosexual in terms of their self-identity and sexual behavior, whereas others are strictly heterosexual. Many people have varying degrees of homosexual and heterosexual feelings and experiences, however. Where might we draw the lines between homosexuality and heterosexuality? Or between these sexual orientations and bisexuality?

First, we should distinguish between homosexual *behavior* and homosexual *orientation* or *identity.* It is possible, indeed not unusual, for heterosexuals to have had some same-gender sexual experiences. A recent survey of more than 7,000 male readers of *Playboy* magazine showed that among those reporting sexual experiences with both men and women in adulthood, more than 2 out of 3 perceived themselves to be heterosexual rather than bisexual (Lever et al., 1992). For many of these men, sexual experiences with other men were limited to a brief period of their lives and did not alter their sexual orientations. Lacking heterosexual outlets, prison inmates may engage in homosexual activities while maintaining their heterosexual identity. They would prefer heterosexual relationships if these were available and are likely to return to a heterosexual lifestyle upon release from prison. Physical affection also helps some prisoners, male and female, cope with loneliness and isolation. Males who engage in homosexual prostitution may separate their sexual orientation from their "trade." Many fantasize about a female when permitting a client to fellate them. The behavior is homosexual. But the person's orientation may be heterosexual.

A Slice of Contemporary Life. Some gay couples consider themselves to be married, although their unions may not legally be recognized as marriages.

Notes: According to the *Oxford English Dictionary, Second Edition* (1989) the terms *homosexual* and *homosexuality* first appeared in print in 1892 in Krafft-Ebing's *Psychopathia Sexualis.*

Heteroerotic
Of an erotic nature and involving members of the opposite gender.

Homoerotic
Of an erotic nature and involving members of one's own gender.

Gay males and lesbians, too, may engage in heterosexual activity while maintaining a gay sexual orientation. Some gay males and lesbians even marry members of the opposite gender but continue to harbor unfulfilled desires for members of their own gender. Others may be bisexual, but have not acted upon their attraction to members of their own gender.

Consider too that one's sexual orientation may or may not become expressed in sexual behavior. Many people come to perceive themselves as gay or heterosexual long before they ever engage in sex with members of their own gender. Some people, whether gay or heterosexual, adopt a celibate lifestyle for religious or ascetic reasons and abstain from sexual relationships. Some remain celibate not by choice but by lack of available sexual opportunities.

People's erotic interests and fantasies may also shift over time. Gay males and lesbians may experience sporadic **heteroerotic** interests, whereas heterosexuals may occasionally have **homoerotic** interests. Many heterosexuals report sporadic or even frequent homoerotic fantasies, and many gay males and lesbians have heterosexual fantasies (Gordon & Snyder, 1989; Masters & Johnson, 1979). About 50 percent of one sample of lesbians reported that they are sometimes attracted to men (Bell & Weinberg, 1978).

Homosexuality and heterosexuality may thus not be mutually exclusive categories. People may have varying degrees of homosexual and heterosexual feelings and experiences. Kinsey and his colleagues recognized that the boundaries between homosexuality and heterosexuality are sometimes blurry. They thus proposed a continuum of sexual orientation rather than two opposite poles.

THE KINSEY CONTINUUM Before Kinsey, scientists generally viewed homosexuality and heterosexuality as separate categories. People were viewed as either homosexual or heterosexual in their psychological makeup and erotic interests. Kinsey and his colleagues (1948, 1953) found evidence of degrees of homosexuality and heterosexuality among U.S. inhabitants, however, with bisexuality representing a midpoint between the two. As Kinsey and his colleagues noted,

> The world is not to be divided into sheep and goats. . . . Only the human mind invents categories and tries to force facts into separated pigeonholes. The living world is a continuum in each and every one of its aspects (1948, p. 639).

Kinsey and his colleagues (1948, 1953) conceived a seven-point heterosexual-homosexual continuum (see Figure 10.1). People are located on the continuum according to their homosexual behavior and the magnitude of their attraction to members of their own gender. People in category 0 are considered exclusively heterosexual. People in category 6 are considered exclusively homosexual.

What percentage of the population, then, is homosexual? The percentages depend on the criteria one uses. Kinsey and his colleagues reported that about 4 percent of men and 1 to 3 percent of women in their samples were categorized as exclusively homosexual (6 on their scale). A larger percentage of people were considered predominantly homosexual (scale points 4 or 5) or predominantly heterosexual (1 or 2 on their scale). Some were classified as equally homosexual and heterosexual in orientation and could be labeled bisexual (scale point 3). The largest percentage of people were classified as exclusively heterosexual (scale point 0). Table 10.1 indicates the percentage of people who were classified according to the seven categories in Figure 10.1. Percentages varied according to marital status, age, level of education, and other factors. This particular table is based on people ages 20 to 35.

Married people were more likely than single people to be classified as exclusively heterosexual. During Kinsey's day, single young people had fewer heterosexual outlets, which may have encouraged them to seek homosexual outlets. Homosexual interests may have influenced some to delay marriage, however. Men, overall, were more likely than women to report homosexual experiences.

Between the poles of the continuum lie people with various degrees of homosexual interests and experience. Thirty-seven percent of men and 13 percent of the women told interviewers they had reached orgasm through homosexual activity at some time after

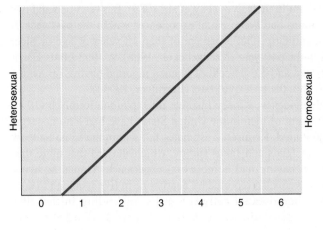

FIGURE 10.1 **The Kinsey Continuum.** Kinsey and his colleagues conceived a 7-point heterosexual-homosexual continuum that classifies people according to their homosexual behavior and the magnitude of their attraction to members of their own gender. People in category 0, who accounted for most of Kinsey's subjects, were considered exclusively heterosexual. People in category 6 were considered exclusively homosexual.

puberty. Fifty percent of men who remained single until age 35 reported they had reached orgasm through homosexual activity.

Many people in Kinsey's day were startled by these figures, since they meant that homosexual behavior, especially among males, was much more widespread than was generally believed. But Kinsey's figures for male homosexual activity may have been exaggerated. For instance, his finding that 37 percent of males had reached orgasm through homosexual activity was based on a sample that included a high proportion of former prisoners. Findings may also have been distorted by the researchers' efforts to recruit known gays into their samples. Once these sources of possible bias are corrected, the incidence of homosexual activity among males drops from 37 to about 25 percent. (Even this percentage is much higher than people suspected at the time.) Because Kinsey's sample was not drawn at random, however, we cannot say whether it represented the general population at the time.

A 1970 nationwide survey conducted by the Kinsey Institute obtained results (published in 1989) that were strikingly similar to Kinsey's early (adjusted) estimates: At least 20 percent of the randomly selected adult men in the United States had a homosexual

TABLE 10.1 Percentages of respondents ages 20 to 35 at each level of the Kinsey Heterosexual-Homosexual Continuum

Rating Category	Females (Percent)	Males (Percent)
0: Entirely heterosexual experience		
Single	61–72	53–78
Married	89–90	90–92
Previously married	75–80	
1-6: At least some homosexual experience	11–20	18–42
2-6: More than incidental homosexual experience	6–14	13–38
3-6: Homosexual as much or more than heterosexual	4–11	9–32
4-6: Mostly homosexual	3–8	7–26
5-6: Almost exclusively homosexual	2–6	5–22
6: Exclusively homosexual	1–3	3–16

Source: Based on data from Kinsey, A. C., et al. (1953). *Sexual behavior in the human female.* Philadelphia: W. B. Saunders, p. 488. Reprinted by permission of the Kinsey Institute for Research in Sex, Gender, and Reproduction, Inc.

experience to orgasm at some point in their lives (Fay et al., 1989). Between one and two percent of men in the United States had homosexual experiences within the past year. A 1988 national survey showed, similarly, that 3 percent of men 18 years of age or older had homosexual contacts within the past year (Michael et al., 1988). A 1993 Louis Harris poll found that 4.4 percent of men and 3.6 percent of women reported having sex with a member of their own gender within the past five years (Barringer, 1993d).

In examining the available evidence, Kinsey Institute director June Reinisch (1990) estimated that more than 25 percent of men in the United States have had a homosexual experience in their teens or adulthood. Reinisch's estimates fall within the same ballpark range as the results of the recent Janus and Janus survey, which showed that more than one in five men (22%) reported having had homosexual experiences (Janus & Janus, 1993). Homosexual experiences were also reported by nearly one in five women (17%).

Statistics concerning *past* homosexual activity can be misleading in that they may be limited to a single episode or to a brief period of adolescent experimentation. In half of the men who reported homosexual activity in Kinsey's sample, the experiences were limited to the ages between 12 and 14. In another third, they occurred by age 18 but never again in adulthood (Karlen, 1971). A generation later, the *Playboy* survey (Hunt, 1974) found that homosexual activity for most people was limited to adolescent experimentation. Moreover, 45 percent of males and 58 percent of females with homosexual experiences had limited them to one year of their lives. More than half had discontinued homosexual activity by age 16.

Kinsey's research also showed that sexual behavior patterns could shift during a person's lifetime, sometimes dramatically so (Sanders et al., 1990). Homosexual experiences or feelings, especially in adolescence, are common and do not mean that one will become exclusively homosexual in adulthood (Bullough, 1990).

What did Kinsey find with respect to more enduring patterns of homosexual activity? Estimates based on an analysis of Kinsey's data (Gebhard, 1977) suggest that 13 percent of the men and 7 percent of the women, or 10 percent for both genders combined, were either predominantly or exclusively homosexual in their interests and behavior for at least three years between the ages of 16 and 55.

Lately there has been considerable controversy concerning the percentages of people believed to be gay. Some researchers find much lower percentages of homosexual activity than Kinsey did. Considering data drawn from studies conducted in the United States, Asia, and Pacific island countries, Milton Diamond (1993) estimates that only about 5 percent of men and 2 to 3 percent of women across different cultures have at least once engaged in same-sex sexual activity since adolescence. Diamond notes that no cross-cultural studies show rates of homosexuality reaching the oft-cited figure of 10 percent of predominant or exclusive homosexuality attributed to Kinsey's work. Diamond also finds bisexual activities to be even less common than predominantly homosexual activity.

Lending support to Diamond's estimates are several recent, large-scale national surveys conducted in the United States, France, and Britain. In the United States, the Battelle survey of more than 3,000 sexually active men ages 20 to 39 found that only 2 percent of the men reported a sexual experience with another man during the previous ten years and only 1 percent reported being exclusively homosexual during this period (Billy et al., 1993). In Britain, researchers found that only 3.6 percent of the adult men surveyed reported ever having a male sexual partner (Johnson et al., 1992). In a French national survey, the figure was 4.1 percent (Spira et al., 1992).

Many factors can affect survey results, including the ways in which the questions are phrased, the social desirability of the professed behavior, the gender of the interviewer, and the manner in which the survey was conducted, such as by means of personal interviews, phone calls, or written surveys (Barringer, 1993a). For example, the Battelle study employed only female interviewers, and questions were asked in face-to-face interviews. It is possible that people are less willing to report behavior society deems socially undesirable in a face-to-face interview, even under anonymous conditions (Adler, 1993; Barringer, 1993a).

For all we know, sex surveys only reveal the percentages of people willing to admit to certain behaviors or sexual orientations, not the actual percentages that exist in the population. One of the major problems in counting the numbers of gay Americans is that "we can't count people who simply don't want to be counted" (Cronin, 1993). All things considered, the 1-percent figure of exclusive homosexuality reported in the Battelle study may only indicate the percentage of men who are willing to admit to being gay. It may not include men who hesitate to proclaim their sexual orientation because of the social stigma attached to homosexuality in our society (Isay, 1993; Cronin, 1993). Also excluded would be those gay men who have repressed or denied their sexuality because they have internalized social biases or psychological conflicts, or both (Isay, 1993). It would not be surprising if substantial numbers of gay men and lesbians simply cover up their orientation when asked by survey researchers or refuse to participate in such surveys (Cronin, 1993).

What, then, are we to make of the prevalence of predominant or exclusive homosexuality in our society? Although we lack a consensus of opinion among those in the scientific community (Cronin, 1993), it is reasonable to assume that the percentages of gay males and lesbians in the population fall somewhere between the 1-percent figure cited in the Battelle study and the 10-percent figure drawn from Kinsey's work. Whatever the actual figure may be, homosexual experiences and exclusive homosexuality are more common among men than women, perhaps by about a two-to-one margin (Diamond, 1993; Ellis et al., 1987; Hunt, 1974). The reasons for gender differences in homosexuality remain unclear.

All told, it doesn't appear that the prevalence in our society of homosexual experiences or of exclusive homosexuality has changed very much since Kinsey's day, despite the sexual revolution of the 1960s and 1970s (Gordon & Snyder, 1989). Today, however, gay males and lesbians are more visible, more accepting of themselves, and more willing to talk openly about their sexual orientation (Gordon & Snyder, 1989).

All in all, Kinsey's research impressed upon society the view that gays were more numerous than was commonly believed and that many heterosexual people had homosexual experiences or interests at one time or another. By underscoring the widespread occurrence of homosexual activity in our society, Kinsey may have contributed to the development of the gay rights movement (Bullough, 1984).

Learning Objective 2:
Compare and contrast the Kinsey continuum and Storm's two-dimensional model of sexual orientation.

CHALLENGES TO THE KINSEY CONTINUUM   Although the Kinsey continuum has been widely adopted by sex researchers, it is not universally accepted (Gonsiorek, 1982). Kinsey's view that exclusive heterosexuality and homosexuality lie at opposite poles of one continuum implies that the more heterosexual people are, the less homosexual they are, and vice versa (Sanders et al., 1990). This is akin to the traditional view of masculinity and femininity as representing opposite poles of the same continuum, such that the more masculine one is, the less feminine, and vice versa. We may also regard masculinity and femininity as independent personality dimensions, however (see Chapter 6). Some people may thus possess *both* masculine and feminine traits (that is, they may be psychologically androgynous). Similarly, heterosexuality and homosexuality may be separate dimensions rather than polar opposites.

Psychologist Michael Storms (1978, 1980), for one, has argued in favor of a model that treats homosexuality and heterosexuality as independent dimensions, so that one can be high or low on both dimensions at the same time. Storms (1980) suggests that there are separate dimensions of responsiveness to heterosexual ("heteroeroticism") and homosexual ("homoeroticism") stimulation, as shown in Figure 10.2. According to this model, bisexuals are high in both dimensions, whereas people who are low in both are essentially asexual. According to Kinsey, bisexuals would be *less* responsive to cross-gender stimulation than heterosexuals, but *more* responsive to same-gender stimulation. According to the two-dimensional model, however, bisexuals may be as responsive to cross-gender stimulation as heterosexuals, and as responsive to same-gender stimulation as gays.

To test this formulation, Storms (1980) investigated the erotic fantasies of heterosexuals, homosexuals, and bisexuals. Kinsey himself had argued that the content of erotic fantasies was an excellent gauge of sexual orientation. Kinsey might have predicted that bisexuals would have *fewer* heteroerotic fantasies than heterosexuals, and *more* homoerotic fantasies than heterosexuals. But Storms predicted that "bisexuals will report as *much* heteroerotic fantasy as heterosexuals and as much homoerotic fantasy as homosexuals" (p. 786).

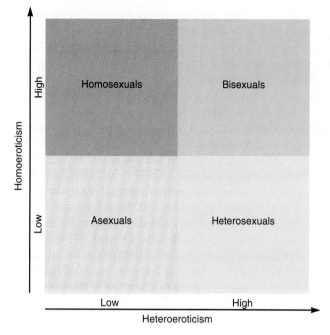

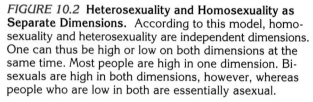

FIGURE 10.2 **Heterosexuality and Homosexuality as Separate Dimensions.** According to this model, homosexuality and heterosexuality are independent dimensions. One can thus be high or low on both dimensions at the same time. Most people are high in one dimension. Bisexuals are high in both dimensions, however, whereas people who are low in both are essentially asexual.

Storms found that heterosexual students reported significantly more fantasies about the opposite gender, and homosexual students reported more frequent homoerotic fantasies. Bisexuals, as predicted, reported a high level of both kinds of fantasies. Storms also found that gay students are more likely to have heteroerotic fantasies than heterosexuals are to have homoerotic fantasies. Given the stigma attached to homosexuality, it may be that heterosexuals are less likely to admit to homoerotic fantasies (even to themselves). It may also be that gays are influenced by the media and the culture at large, which, of course, consistently portray socially desirable heterosexual interactions.

Whatever the reasons, Storms did find that many bisexuals show a high level of sexual interest, as measured by erotic fantasies, in both men and women. Thus, it may be that heterosexual interest and homosexual interest are independent dimensions rather than opposite poles of one continuum. Yet most sex researchers continue to use the Kinsey scale for classifying sexual orientation, or some modification of it, rather than the Storms model (Sanders et al., 1990).

What can we conclude about the classification of sexual orientation? First, sexual orientation is probably too complex to reduce to a simple dichotomy between homosexuality and heterosexuality. As Kinsey and his colleagues noted, there is apparently a range of sexual experiences, feelings, and attractions between exclusive heterosexuality and exclusive homosexuality. Second, people's orientations and their behavior may differ. The two do not always go hand in hand. People who perceive themselves as heterosexual sometimes engage in homosexual activity, and vice versa. Finally, erotic desires and behaviors may change as people develop. The traditional view that people's sexual orientation is fixed at an early age is thus subject to question (Sanders et al., 1990). Our models of sexual orientation need to be flexible enough to accommodate these changes.

HOMOSEXUALITY AND BISEXUALITY

Learning Objective 3:
Define the terms *bisexual* and *ambisexual.*

Bisexuals respond sexually to both males and females. Bisexuals may have somewhat stronger attraction to one gender than the other, yet remain bisexual (Gordon & Snyder, 1989). Kinsey and his colleagues considered people rated as 3s to be bisexual (see Figure 10.1). Among 20- to 35-year-olds in Kinsey's samples, 9 to 32 percent of the men and 4 to 11 percent of the women were rated as 3s. But Kinsey based his findings on reports of bisexual behavior and erotic attraction to both genders, not on subjects' self-identities. Many millions of people have had both homosexual and heterosexual experiences, but we do not know how many of them would label themselves as bisexual (Zinik, 1985).

Bisexuals are sometimes said to "swing both ways," or to be "AC/DC" (as in "alternating current" and "direct current"). Some gays (and some heterosexuals) believe that claims to bisexuality are a "cop-out" that people use to deny being gay. Perhaps they fear leaving their spouses or "coming out" (declaring their homosexuality publicly). Others view bisexuality as a form of homosexual experimentation by people who are predominantly heterosexual. But many avowed bisexuals disagree and believe that they are capable of maintaining erotic interests in, and romantic relationships with, both genders. Bisexuality has not been as widely researched as homosexuality, but it may be that bisexuality is an authentic sexual orientation and not simply a "cover" for homosexuality (Gordon & Snyder, 1989).

Some bisexuals maintain erotic attraction to members of both genders and develop lifestyles that permit them to satisfy their dual inclinations. Others, however, feel pressured by heterosexuals and gays to commit themselves one way or another and find it difficult to bridge both worlds (Paul, 1984). And of course there are some gays who mask their orientation by adopting a bisexual lifestyle, such as getting married while maintaining clandestine homosexual liaisons.

Ambisexuals
People who have no preference for one gender over the other and who accept sex partners of either gender when the opportunity arises.

AMBISEXUALS In their study of homosexuality, Masters and Johnson (1979) found a subgroup of bisexuals they labeled **ambisexuals.** Ambisexuals differ from most bisexuals in that they have no current or past preferences for men or women. Given the opportunity, they fall into shallow, temporary sexual relationships with partners of either gender. They fail to develop intimate or enduring relationships. Of 12 ambisexuals studied by Masters and Johnson, only one woman had married. The marriage was described as something she agreed to for her husband's sake. She maintained an open lesbian relationship during its brief duration.

PERSPECTIVES ON HOMOSEXUALITY

CNN Gay Asylum

Homosexuality has existed throughout recorded history (Bullough, 1976), but attitudes toward homosexuality have varied widely across cultures and times. Homosexuality has been tolerated in some societies, openly encouraged in others, but condemned in most (Bullough, 1990). In this section we review historical and other perspectives on homosexuality. Through these perspectives we examine societal responses to homosexuality, evidence of homosexuality in cross-cultural and cross-species research, and the origins of sexual orientation in general and homosexuality in particular.

HISTORICAL PERSPECTIVES

Learning Objective 4:
Examine historical and cross-cultural homosexual practices and views of homosexuality.

In Western culture, few sexual practices have met with such widespread censure as homosexuality. Throughout much of Western history, homosexuality has been deemed sinful and criminal—an outrage against God and man (Bell & Weinberg, 1978). Within the Judeo-Christian tradition, homosexuality was regarded as a sin so vile that no one dared speak its name. Our legal system, grounded in this religious tradition, maintains criminal penalties for sexual practices commonly associated with homosexual sex, such as oral and anal sex.

Jews and Christians have traditionally referred to homosexuality as the Sin of Sodom. Hence the origin of the term *sodomy,* which generally alludes to anal intercourse (and sometimes to oral-genital contact). According to the book of Genesis, the city of Sodom was destroyed by the hand of God. Yet it is unclear what particular behavior incurred God's wrath. Pope Gregory III was not ambiguous, however, in his eighth-century account of the city's obliteration as a punishment for homosexuality.

Cross-Cultural Perspectives on Homosexual Behavior

Homosexual behavior is practiced in many preliterate societies. In their review of the literature on 76 preliterate societies, Ford and Beach (1951) found that in 49 societies (64%), male homosexual interactions were viewed as normal and deemed socially acceptable for some members of the group. The other 27 societies (36%) had sanctions, often severe, against homosexuality. Nevertheless, homosexuality persisted in these societies. In a more recent cross-cultural analysis, Broude and Greene (1976) found that homosexuality was present but uncommon in 41 percent of a sample of 70 of the world's non-European societies. It was rare or absent in 59 percent of these societies. Broude and Greene also found evidence of societal disapproval and punishment of homosexuality in 41 percent of a sample of 42 societies for which information was available.

Homosexual behavior among adult males appears to be more common in societies that highly value female virginity before marriage and separate young men and women (Davenport, 1976). Such factors may increase juvenile homosexual experimentation that may persist into adulthood. In the most common form of homosexuality among preliterate societies, men dress like women, perform women's tasks, and assume the receptive (female) sexual role in sexual behavior with other men (Ford & Beach, 1951).

Some societies permit or even require some forms of homosexual activity. In some societies, homosexual activities are acceptable between older and younger males or between adolescents, but not between adult men. The Siwans of North Africa expected all juvenile males to engage in homosexual

relations with older men ('Abd Allah, 1917). Fathers arranged for unmarried sons to be given to older men. Almost all men were reported to have had such homosexual relationships as boys. Later, between the ages of 16 and 20, they all married women.

Homosexual activities are sometimes limited to rites that mark the young male's initiation into manhood. In some preliterate societies, semen is believed to boost strength and virility. Older males thus transmit semen to younger males through oral or anal homosexual activities. Young Kukukuku males in New Guinea, for example, form homosexual liaisons to swallow each other's semen (Money & Ehrhardt, 1972).

Among the Sambian people of New Guinea, a tribe of warlike headhunters, 9- to 12-year-old males leave their parents' households and live in a "clubhouse" with other prepubertal and ado-

---

The book of Leviticus in the Old Testament was also clear in its condemnation of homosexuality and of the severe penalties that can be expected from its practice:

> If a man lies with a man as with a woman, both of them have committed an abomination; they shall be put to death, their blood is upon them.
> (Leviticus 20:13)

Homosexuality was not the only sexual act considered sinful by the early Christians (Bancroft, 1974). Any nonprocreative sexual act was considered sinful, even when practiced in marriage. With the fall of the Roman Empire, the influence of Christianity spread across western Europe. Christian beliefs were eventually encoded into secular law. By the late Middle Ages, most civil statutes throughout western Europe contained penalties for nonprocreative sexual acts involving the discharge of semen, including oral or anal sex, masturbation, homosexual acts, and bestiality (Boswell, 1990). Homosexual practices continue to be condemned today by Roman Catholic and Greek Orthodox churches, by most Protestant and Jewish denominations, and by Islam.

The Catholic church draws a distinction between a homosexual orientation and homosexual behavior, however. The behavior is considered sinful, not the orientation.

lescent males. There they undergo homosexual rites of passage. They drink "men's milk" (semen) by performing fellatio on older males to acquire the fierce manhood of the headhunter (Herdt, 1981; Money, 1990; Stoller & Herdt, 1985). The initiate is enjoined to ingest as much semen as he can, "as if it were breast milk or food" (Herdt, 1981, p. 235). Ingestion of semen is believed to give rise to puberty. Following puberty, adolescents are fellated by younger males (Baldwin & Baldwin, 1989). By the age of 19, however, young men are expected to take brides and enter exclusively heterosexual relationships.

These practices of Sambian culture might seem to suggest that the sexual orientations of males are fluid and shapable. The practices refer to *behavior,* however, and not *orientation.* "Homosexuality" among Sambians takes place within a cultural context that bears little resemblance to consensual homosexuality in Western society. The prepubertal Sambian male does not seek homosexual liaisons of his own accord; he is removed from his parental home, by force if necessary, and thrust into homosexual encounters by older males (Baldwin & Baldwin, 1989).

Little is known about lesbianism in non-Western cultures. Evidence of lesbianism was found by Ford and Beach in only 17 of the 76 societies they studied. Perhaps it was more difficult to acquire data about female sexuality. Perhaps female sexual behavior in general, not just homosexual activity, was more likely to be repressed. Of course, it is also possible that women are less likely than men to develop homosexual interests or lifestyles. Whatever the reasons for it, this cross-cultural evidence is consistent with data from our own culture (Hunt, 1974; Kinsey et al., 1948, 1953) that homosexual activity and interests are less common among females.

Why are some societies more tolerant of homosexual behavior than others? One reason may lie in societal perceptions of the need to either curb or increase the population. A lack of tolerance for homosexuality is often found in cultures that perceive a need to expand their populations (Ember & Ember, 1990). Condemnation of homosexuality among the early Jews and Christians, for example, may have issued from the need of these ancient cultures to increase their numbers. Societies that encounter population pressures because of periodic famines tend to be more tolerant of homosexuality (Ember & Ember, 1990).

Sin is a temporary state from which a sinner, including a homosexual sinner, can be freed by behavioral change, contrition, and repentance (Boswell, 1990).

CROSS-SPECIES PERSPECTIVES

Learning Objective 5: Summarize the information on same-gender sexual behavior in other species.

Many of us have observed pets and other animals engaging in behaviors that resemble homosexual contacts among humans, such as attempting to mount others of their own gender. We should be careful, though, about drawing comparisons between the behavior of humans and lower animals. Superficially similar behaviors may not have the same function in other species.

A male baboon may present his rear and allow himself to be mounted by another male. This behavior may resemble anal intercourse among gay men. Is the behavior sexually motivated, however? Mounting behavior among male baboons may represent a type of dominance ritual in which lower-ranking males adopt a submissive (feminine) posture to ward off attack from more dominant males (Nadler, 1990). (Some homosexual acts among humans may also involve themes of dominance, such as in the case of a dominant male prisoner forcing a less dominant one to submit to anal intercourse.) In other cases male baboons may be seeking favors or protection from the more dominant males (Nadler, 1990; Zuckerman, 1981). Among juvenile animals, homosexual behaviors may also represent a type of play. Females may also attempt to mount other females, but here too, the motivations may not be the same as those of humans.

More direct comparisons of homosexual acts by humans and other animals require clearer evidence of *sexual* motivation in homosexual activity in other animal species. Here the evidence is more variable both within and across species. Sexual motivations do appear to play a role in some, but not all, male-male and female-female interactions, for example, in fellatio and anal intercourse to ejaculation among juvenile male orangutans and in thrusting by one adult female gorilla against another (Harcourt et al., 1981). Chevalier-Skolnikoff (1976) observed encounters between male rhesus monkeys that appeared to be sexually motivated. The monkeys engaged in manual manipulation of the genitals, oral-genital stimulation, and rear mounting with occasional penetration. Most of the homosexual pairings were between adult and younger males. There even appeared to be close affectional ties between the partners. The intensity of the relationships declined as the young male approached sexual maturity, however. Researchers have failed to find evidence among nonhuman primates, however, of the type of prolonged, exclusive homosexuality found among humans that occurs even when heterosexual opportunities are available (Beach, 1976).

ATTITUDES TOWARD HOMOSEXUALITY IN CONTEMPORARY SOCIETY

Learning Objective 6: Discuss contemporary attitudes toward homosexuality, including the topics of homophobia, gay bashing, gay activism, and stereo-typing.

Toni, a 20-year-old lesbian college student, was incredulous that her parents believed she had *chosen* her sexual orientation. They saw her lesbianism as linked to the general rebelliousness that had been stirred by attending a school known for its "radical" image. Toni was infuriated that they believed that she would "get over" lesbianism once she decided to accept adult responsibilities.

(The Authors' Files)

Most people in our society view homosexuality—and homosexuals—negatively. Sixty-seven percent of respondents to one poll conducted during the 1960s expressed the belief that homosexuality was obscene and vulgar (Weinberg & Williams, 1974). Fewer than 20 percent believed that laws against homosexuality (technically, laws against sodomy) should be lifted. Studies during the 1970s showed that the majority of people in the United States viewed homosexuals as "sick" (Steffensmeier & Steffensmeier, 1974), "sinful" (Pattison, 1974), and "dangerous" (Morin & Garfinkle, 1978). A 1987 U.S. survey found that 75 percent of respondents felt that sexual relations between members of the same gender are "always wrong"—a statistic that is virtually the same as the 74 percent of respondents in a 1973 survey (Davis & Smith, 1987) who believed the same thing. Still, some changes may be in the offing. A smaller percentage (40%) of the 1987 respondents, as compared to 51 percent in the 1973 survey, would bar gays from teaching in a college or university. More recently, a 1992 national Gallup poll found that the great majority (78%) of Americans favor equal employment opportunities for homosexuals ("Job rights for homosexuals backed in poll," 1992). Two out of three Americans favor health insurance and inheritance rights for gay spouses. Yet fewer than one in three favored legally sanctioned gay marriages and about a third supported the right of gay couples to adopt children. And Americans were about equally split on the issues of whether gays should be permitted to teach in elementary schools or become members of the clergy.

Many of those who would bar gays from teaching and other activities rely on popular myths to support their cause, such as the myth that, given the chance, gays will seduce and recruit children into a homosexual lifestyle (Gordon & Snyder, 1989). Such beliefs have been used to bar homosexual couples from becoming adoptive or foster parents and to deny them custody or visitation rights to their own children following divorce (Renzetti & Curran, 1989). Some people who would bar gays from interactions with children fear that the children would be molested. Arguments based on this fear are as

Sexual Contact or Play? Is same-gender contact between primates, like the orangutans shown here, motivated by sexual drives or by other motives such as dominance or play? We should be careful about drawing comparisons between humans and other animals based on their observed behavior only.

logical as proposing that heterosexual men should be barred from such roles because some heterosexual men are child molesters or rapists. More than 90 percent of cases of child molestation involve heterosexual male assailants (Gelles & Cornell, 1985; Gordon & Snyder, 1989). Nor has it been shown that children reared or taught by gay men or lesbians are more likely to become gay themselves. One study found that 36 of 37 children who were reared by lesbian or transsexual couples developed a heterosexual orientation (Green, 1978). Nor has it been shown that children reared by gay parents are more likely to encounter gender-identity conflicts (Dullea, 1988). Finally, there is no evidence that gay teachers lure children into homosexuality (McCary & McCary, 1982).

Homophobia

A cluster of negative attitudes and feelings toward homosexuals and homosexuality, including intolerance, hatred, and fear. (From Greek roots meaning "fear" [of members of the] "same" [gender]).

Gay bashing

Violence against homosexuals.

HOMOPHOBIA **Homophobia** takes many forms, including use of derogatory names (such as *queer, faggot,* and *dyke*); telling disparaging "queer jokes"; barring gays from housing, employment, or social opportunities; taunting (verbal abuse); and **gay bashing.** Homophobic tendencies of one form or another seem commonplace in our society and may even be the norm among U.S. heterosexuals.

Homophobia derives from root words meaning "fear of homosexuals." Some people believe that intense negative feelings toward gays stem from, and serve to mask, deep-seated fears of homosexual feelings within oneself. While homophobia is more common among heterosexuals, gay people themselves can be homophobic. This form of homophobia, called *internalized homophobia,* stems from the internalization of the negative societal attitudes toward gays (Gonsiorek, 1988).

Although some psychologists link homophobia to fears of homosexuality within the self, homophobic attitudes may also be embedded within a cluster of stereotypical gender-role attitudes toward family life, including beliefs in male dominance and the belief that it is natural and appropriate for women to sacrifice for their husbands and children (Krulewitz & Nash, 1980; Marsiglio, 1993; Morin & Garfinkle, 1978). People who have a strong stake in maintaining stereotypical gender roles may feel more readily threatened by homosexuality, since gays appear to confuse or reverse these roles (MacDonald et al., 1972; MacDonald & Games, 1974).

Negative attitudes toward gays remain pervasive in our society. A 1988 national survey of young men ages 15 to 19 showed that nine of ten felt that sex between men was "disgusting" and three of five could not even see themselves being friends with a gay person (Marsiglio, 1993). Homophobic attitudes were more common among those who

Gay Bashing

"Mr. and Mr. Right." Gay activists seek legislation that would make it easier for gay couples to obtain health benefits spousal insurance, and other benefits accorded to married heterosexual couples.

identified with a traditional male gender role and those who held a fundamentalist religious orientation. Similarly, researchers find that college students who hold a conservative political orientation tend to be more accepting of negative attitudes toward homosexuality than are liberal students (Lottes & Kuriloff, 1992). Another university sample found male students to be more homophobic in their attitudes than women (Kunkel & Temple, 1992).

Generally speaking, heterosexual men are relatively less tolerant of gays than are heterosexual women (Herek, 1988; Kite, 1984; Seltzer, 1992), perhaps because they are more sensitive to the threat of discovering homosexual impulses within themselves. Consistent with this view, heterosexual males tend to hold more negative attitudes toward gay men than toward lesbians (Kite, 1992). In a study conducted by your first author (Nevid, 1983), college men and women were shown either explicit homosexual films (either gay male or lesbian) or heterosexual films. Their emotional responses and their attitudes toward gays were measured. The homosexual films elicited more negative emotional states—more anger, anxiety, and depression—in both genders than did the heterosexual films. However, negative *attitudes* toward gays were exacerbated by exposure to the films only in men and only in those men who viewed films of gay males. It appears that men are more sensitive to cues of homosexual threat and more likely to react to displays of sexual interactions between members of their own gender with both negative feelings and a hardening of their attitudes toward gays.

GAY BASHING AND THE AIDS EPIDEMIC   Although strides toward social acceptance of gays have been made since Kinsey's day, the advent of AIDS has added fuel to the fire of hatred and prejudice. When AIDS first appeared, it primarily struck the gay male community. Some people in the larger society believed that the epidemic was a plague sent by God to punish gays for sinful behavior. Gordon and Snyder (1989) point out that it is as logical to think that God sent Legionnaire's disease to punish Legionnaires.

According to Renzetti and Curran (1989), the AIDS epidemic served as a pretext that some people used to attack gay males, whom they blamed for spreading the disease. With the epidemic, there has been a concomitant dramatic rise in the incidence of *gay bashing*—acts of violence against gay men (Greer, 1986). Although better reporting may have accounted for some of the rise, violent incidents (against gay men *and* gay women) rose by an average of 42 percent in 1990 over the previous year in Boston, Chicago, Los Angeles, Minneapolis/St. Paul, New York, and San Francisco (Brozan, 1991). Anti-gay incidents in these cities included harassment, physical assault, robbery, arson, extortion, vandalism, bomb threats, and homicide.

Gay bashing also occurs on college campuses. A large percentage (77%) of 121 lesbian and gay male undergraduate students in one survey at Pennsylvania State University reported they had been verbally insulted, and nearly one in four (22%) reported that they had been chased by others (D'Augelli, 1992a). Six reported being physically assaulted. Most of the victimizers were fellow students, and few incidents of victimization were reported to the authorities. Students, too, tend to hold gay men more responsible for behaviors that put themselves at risk of contracting AIDS. A recent study found that students assigned a greater amount of blame to a hypothetical person who had contracted AIDS when the person was identified as a gay male than when the person was identified as a heterosexual male (Anderson, 1992).

Ironically, the percentage of gay men who account for new cases of AIDS has been steadily declining (see Chapter 17). By contrast, the percentages of persons who contract AIDS by sharing contaminated hypodermic syringes while injecting drugs, and by heterosexual intercourse, have been on the upswing. With the exception of infected babies who are born to mothers with the disease, and the isolated cases of transmission via transfusions with contaminated blood, it is *one's behavior, not the group to which one belongs, that places one at risk for AIDS.*

HOMOSEXUALITY AND THE LAW   During the past generation, gay men and lesbians have organized effective political groups to fight discrimination and to overturn the sodomy laws that have traditionally targeted them. Despite their success, sodomy laws are still on the books in 24 states and the District of Columbia (Press et al., 1986). Sodomy laws prohibit "unnatural" sexual acts, even between consenting adults. Although homosexuality itself is not illegal, certain sexual acts which many gays (and heterosexuals) practice, such as anal intercourse and oral-genital contact, fall under the legal definition of sodomy in many states. Sodomy laws also typically prohibit sexual contacts with animals. Although sodomy laws are usually intended to apply equally to all adults, married or unmarried, heterosexual or homosexual, the vast majority of prosecutions have been directed against gays. A 1986 Supreme Court decision in the case of *Hardwick v. Bowers* let stand a sodomy law in Georgia that makes it a crime punishable by a maximum term of 20 years for consenting adults to engage in either oral-genital or anal-genital sexual contact. The decision was a blow to gay rights organizations, which had looked to the Supreme Court to overturn sodomy laws nationwide. Instead, the court held that states retain the right to enact sodomy laws and impose criminal penalties.

Many other countries, including Mexico, Holland, Italy, Spain, England, France, and the Scandinavian countries have decriminalized homosexual acts (Carrera, 1981). In Canada, a consensual sexual act is prosecutable under sodomy laws only if one of the participants is under 21 years of age or the act is performed in public.

GAY ACTIVISM Nowhere in the United States have gays been more politically effective than in San Francisco. They are well represented on the city police force and in other public agencies. The national incidence of homosexuality has probably not increased since Kinsey's day, but the coming out of many gays, and their flocking to more tolerant urban centers, has rendered them formidable political forces in these locales.

The Mattachine Society, named after medieval gay court jesters, was the first powerful gay rights organization. At first, membership was kept secret to protect members' social standing in the community. Today, however, members' names are published and many heterosexual supporters are listed in their ranks. Founded in Los Angeles in 1950, the Mattachine Society now has chapters in most metropolitan areas. The society publishes the *Mattachine Newsletter* and *Homosexual Citizen.* Another newsletter, the *Advocate,* has become the nation's best-known gay newsletter.

The largest lesbian organization is the Daughters of Bilitis, named after the Greek courtesan who was loved by the lesbian poet Sappho. Founded in 1956, the group provides a forum for sharing social experiences and pursuing equal rights. The organization's newsletter is the *Ladder.*

Gay Rights. Gay men and lesbians have been joined by many heterosexuals in demonstrations demanding equal access of gays to housing, jobs, and other opportunities and, as shown here, protesting violence against gays.

Notes: Raids of gay bars and police harassment of gays were common in the 1960s. On Friday June 27, 1969, when the police came to raid the Stonewall Inn, a gay bar in Greenwich Village, patrons refused to go quietly and rioting followed. Within weeks, the Gay Liberation Front formed in New York City.

Notes: As of September 1993, discrimination based on sexual orientation was banned under national law in four countries: New Zealand, France, Denmark, and the Netherlands. (Taking the Lead. 1993, *Ms. 4* (3), 16.)

Butch
A lesbian who assumes a traditional masculine gender role.

The AIDS epidemic has had a profound effect on the political agenda of gay rights organizations. These organizations have mounted a vigorous effort to combat the AIDS epidemic on several fronts:

1. To lobby for increased funding for AIDS research and treatment.
2. To educate the gay and wider communities of the dangers associated with high-risk sexual behavior.
3. To encourage gay men and others to adopt safer sex practices, including the use of latex condoms (see Chapter 17).
4. To protect the civil rights of people with AIDS and carriers of the virus that causes AIDS (the *human immunodeficiency virus [HIV]*) with respect to employment, housing, medical and dental treatment, and medical insurance.
5. To provide counseling and support services for people with AIDS and those infected with HIV.

Although some gay rights organizations work within the mainstream political process, others, such as the militant *Act-Up* organization, have taken a more strident and confrontational stance to secure more funding for AIDS research and treatment.

Outing, gays unmasking the identities of other gays without their consent, has been adopted by some militant groups who believe that to effectively combat discrimination it is necessary to force people "out of the closet." Many gays have responded vehemently to this practice, calling it a "gay witch hunt."

CULTURAL STEREOTYPES   Are gay men *swishy* and gay women **butch**? Most people in the United States assume that a person's sexual orientation is inextricably entwined with his or her gender role (Storms, 1980). People thus expect gays to show evidence of role reversals. They expect a gay man to have feminine traits and a lesbian to be masculine.

This presumed link between gender role and sexual orientation, along with media portrayals of gays, has led to the stereotypes of the swishy, effeminate gay male and the butch lesbian. Many people think of gay males as swinging their hips, carrying wrists limply, offering weak handshakes, articulating words crisply (women enunciate words somewhat more clearly than men do), being overly emotional and dramatic, and wearing garish clothing—presumably to attract other gays. Lesbians, by contrast, are thought to be direct and curt in gesture and speech, to crop their hair, to wear drab, tailored clothing, and not to use makeup or shave their underarms or legs.

But research has shown that as few as 15 percent of the gay population fit these stereotypes (Kinsey et al., 1948; Pomeroy, 1966). In fact, a survey of college athletes on five university campuses found that a rather high percentage had engaged in homosexual fellatio (36%) or anal intercourse (18%) (Garner & Smith, 1977). About 8 percent were exclusively homosexual. Gay men are found among professional athletes, including football, baseball, and basketball players, even though fear of ostracism may deter them from "coming out."

TRUTH OR FICTION?

R E V I S I T E D

Most gay males are "swishy," and most lesbians are "butch." *Not so. Most gay males are not "swishy," nor are most lesbians "butch." Only a minority of gays fit these stereotypes.* •

Queens
Gay men who play exaggerated effeminate roles.

Drag queens
Queens who parade around in women's clothing.

Gay men who play exaggerated effeminate roles are called **queens** in the gay community. Some, called **drag queens,** parade around in women's dresses. Many gay men and lesbians frown on queens and drag queens, believing that they help perpetuate stereotypes and arouse hostility in heterosexuals.

A common belief among heterosexuals is that one partner in a gay relationship typically assumes the "masculine" role in the relationship, and the other, the "feminine" role. Although it is true that some gay relationships are structured at least in part along traditional gender roles, many are characterized by a sharing of roles, as noted by researchers Letitia Anne Peplau and Susan Cochran (1990):

A WORLD OF DIVERSITY

Homosexual Behavior and Machismo

Why do some gay males prefer the inserter role during anal intercourse, and others the insertee role? Carrier (1980) suggests that preferences for the inserter or receptive role in male homosexual relations may reflect gender-role expectations of the larger society. For example, Mexican mestizo[1] culture places a strong value on the hypermasculine ideal of manliness commonly known as *machismo*. Men are expected to be dominant and independent and women, submissive and dependent. Boys are expected to grow up to be as manly as possible; any sign of femininity is discouraged. Because of the strict gender-role divisions in mestizo culture, gay males may encounter cultural pressures to adhere more strictly to either the inserter (masculine) or insertee (feminine) role. In the United States and Canada, where gender roles are more flexible, gay males frequently shift roles.

Carrier also reports that societies with more strictly defined gender roles tend to attach a greater stigma to men who assume the passive or receptive sexual role in anal sexual activity. In some societies, such as Brazil, men who have sexual relations with other men are not considered gay if they perform the dominant role in the sex act (Brooke, 1993).

[1]Mestizos are Mexicans of mixed Indian and Spanish ancestry. Mestizos are the largest population group of Mexicans and represent the dominant culture in the country (Carrier, 1980).

Teaching Tip: Instead of lecturing about the myths and stereotypes associated with gay men and lesbians, have students volunteer things they've heard people say (you can identify them easily; they are child molesters; they have AIDS; they all try to "recruit" or proposition straight people; they don't have children; within a couple one plays the male role and one plays the female role; etc.) Write each of these on the chalkboard and discuss the facts about each one.

Femme
A lesbian who assumes a traditional feminine gender role.

In general, research suggests that most lesbians and gay men today actively reject traditional husband-wife or masculine-feminine roles as a model for enduring relationships. Most lesbians and gay men are in "dual-worker" relationships, so that neither partner is the exclusive "breadwinner" and each partner has some measure of economic independence. Further, examinations of the division of household tasks, sexual behavior, and decision making in homosexual couples find that clear-cut and consistent husband-wife roles are uncommon. In many relationships, there is some specialization of activities, with one partner doing more of some jobs and less of others. But it is rare for one partner to perform most of the "feminine" activities and the other to perform most of the "masculine" tasks. That is, a partner who usually does the cooking does not necessarily also perform other feminine tasks such as shopping or cleaning. Specialization seems to be based on more individualistic factors, such as skills or interests (p. 344).

STEREOTYPES AND SEXUAL BEHAVIOR   Among heterosexuals, sexual aggressiveness is linked to the masculine gender role, and sexual passivity to the feminine. Some heterosexuals assume (often erroneously) that in gay male and lesbian relationships, one partner consistently assumes the masculine role in sexual relations, and the other, the feminine.

Many gay couples vary the active and passive roles, however (Masters & Johnson, 1979). Among gay male couples, for example, roles in anal intercourse (*inserter* versus *insertee*) and in fellatio are often reversed. Contrary to popular assumptions, sexual behavior between lesbians seldom reflects distinct butch-**femme** gender roles. In one study of lesbians, 91 percent reported orally stimulating their partner's genitals, and 96 percent reported receiving oral-genital stimulation (Saghir & Robins, 1973). Typically, partners alternate roles or simultaneously perform and receive oral stimulation. Many gays claim that the labels of *masculine* and *feminine* only represent the straight community's efforts to pigeonhole them in terms straights can understand.

BIOLOGICAL PERSPECTIVES

Is sexual orientation an *inborn* trait that is transmitted genetically, like eye color or height? Does it reflect hormonal influences? Biological perspectives focus on the role of genetics and hormonal influences in shaping one's sexual orientation.

GENETICS AND SEXUAL ORIENTATION   Considerable evidence exists that homosexuality runs in families (Pillard, 1990; Pillard & Weinrich, 1986). In one study, for example, 22 percent of the brothers of a sample of 51 predominantly homosexual men were either bisexual or homosexual themselves. This is nearly four times the proportion expected in the general population (Pillard & Weinrich, 1986). Although such evidence is consistent with a genetic explanation, families also share a common environment.

Twin studies also shed light on the possible role of heredity. **Monozygotic** (MZ), or identical, twins develop from a single fertilized ovum and share 100 percent of their heredity. **Dizygotic** (DZ), or fraternal, twins develop from two fertilized ova and, like other brothers and sisters, share only 50 percent of their heredity. Thus if homosexuality is transmitted genetically, it should be found about twice as often among identical twins of gays as among fraternal twins. Since MZ and DZ twins who are reared together share similar environmental influences, differences in the degree of **concordance** for a given trait between the types of twin pairs are further indicative of genetic origins.

Several studies have identified gay men who had either identical (MZ) or fraternal (DZ) twin brothers in order to examine the prevalences of homosexuality in their twin brothers. In an early study, Kallmann (1952) found 100 percent concordance for homosexuality among the identical twin brothers of gay men, as compared to 12 percent concordance for fraternal twin pairs in which one of the brothers was identified as gay. This seemed strong evidence indeed of genetic factors in homosexuality. Later studies have found much lower concordance rates among MZ twins (Bailey & Pillard, 1991; Eckert et al., 1986; McConaghy & Blaszczynski, 1980). These studies found many instances of MZ twins in which one identical twin member was gay and the other in the pair was not. Still, MZ twins do appear to have a higher concordance rate for homosexuality than DZ twins. Bailey and Pillard (1991) reported a 52 percent concordance rate for homosexuality among MZ twin pairs versus 22 percent among DZ twin pairs in their sample. In another recent study, researchers reported a concordance rate for homosexuality of 66 percent in MZ twins, as compared to 30 percent among DZ twins, lending even further support to the role of heredity in sexual orientation (Whitam et al., 1993). Bear in mind, however,

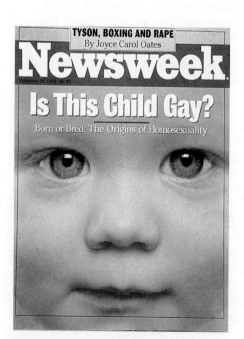

TYSON, BOXING AND RAPE
By Joyce Carol Oates

Newsweek

Is This Child Gay?
Born or Bred: The Origins of Homosexuality

Is This Child Gay? Is sexual orientation innate or learned?

that MZ twins are more likely to be dressed alike and treated alike than DZ twins, so their greater concordance for homosexuality may at least in part reflect environmental factors. The greater concordance between MZ twins may only signify that MZ twins are likely to react more similarly than DZ twins to the same *environmental* influences (Bancroft, 1990).

The prominent sexologist John Money (1987b) argues that genetic factors appear to play a role in the development of, but do not directly govern, one's sexual orientation. Psychosocial influences also play an important role. Most researchers believe that sexual orientation is affected by a complex interplay of biological and psychosocial influences.

In 1993, researchers at the National Cancer Institute (NCI) found evidence linking a region on the X sex chromosome to a homosexual orientation in men (Angier, 1993a; Begley, 1993; Hamer et al., 1993). The researchers found that gay males in a sample of 114 gay men were more likely to have gay male relatives on their mothers' side of the family than would be expected based on the prevalence of a gay male sexual orientation in the general population. Yet they did not have a greater than expected number of gay male relatives on their paternal side of the family. This pattern of inheritance is consistent with genetic traits, like hemophilia, that are linked to the X sex chromosome, which men receive from their mothers.

The researchers then went on to examine the X sex chromosome in 40 pairs of gay male, nontwin brothers. In 33 of the pairs, the brothers had identical DNA markers on the end tip of the X chromosome (Angier, 1993a; Begley, 1993). For brothers overall in the general population, about half would be expected to have inherited this identical chromosomal structure. It is suspected, therefore, that this chromosomal region may hold a gene that predisposes men to a gay male sexual orientation. This snippet contains hundreds of genes, any of which may be involved in genetic transmission of sexual orientation.

The researchers cautioned that they hadn't found a particular gene linked to sexual orientation, just a general location of where the gene may be found (Angier, 1993a). Nor do scientists know how such a gene, or combination of genes, might account for sexual orientation. Perhaps a particular gene or genes govern the development of proteins that sculpt parts of the brain in ways that favor the development of a gay male sexual orientation (Begley, 1993). Yet the researchers warned against overinterpreting their findings (Angier, 1993a). For one thing, whatever role such a gene or genes might play, they would not fully explain homosexuality in men. For one thing, a number of the gay brothers, 7 of the 40 pairs, did not have the chromosomal marker in common. Moreover, what the researchers did not do, and what remains to be done, is to see if the heterosexual brothers of gay men also share the same DNA sequence on their X sex chromosomes (Hubbard, 1993); if they did, then the DNA sequence could not be considered a genetic marker for homosexuality. At present, we can say that the NCI evidence further strengthens the case that some form of inheritance is involved in the development of homosexuality in males. Similar research on lesbians is under way.

Many gay males hailed the NCI findings as further evidence that their sexual orientation is biologically determined, not a personal choice that could be turned on or off like a light switch. Evidence of genetic determinants of sexual orientation undercuts the arguments of those opposed to gay rights who claim that homosexuality is a form of voluntary behavior that should be subjected to regulation (Henry, 1993).

Evidence of genetic determinants might also help ease concerns of heterosexual parents that exposure to gay teachers might lead impressionable youngsters to become gay themselves and may also alleviate misplaced guilt by parents who discover that their offspring are gay (Henry, 1993). On the other hand, evidence of a "gay gene" might lead people to view homosexuality as a biological defect or an aberration. Finding a "gay gene" would also raise ethical concerns (Begley, 1993; Burr, 1993). For example, if a test for detecting the gene were available, would prospective parents be inclined to abort fetuses that carried it? As one geneticist put it, "This [evidence of genetic factors in homosexuality] is a two-edged sword. It can be used to benefit gays by allowing them to make the case that the trait for which they're being discriminated against is no worse than skin color. On the other hand, it could get interpreted to mean that different is pathological" (Henry, 1993, p. 39). Whatever the contributions of our genetic inheritance to our sexual identity, geneticists recognize that sexual attraction and desire are complex and varied phenomena whose origins may never be fully understood and that are not simply programmed by one's genes (Henry, 1993; Hubbard, 1993).

HORMONAL INFLUENCES AND SEXUAL ORIENTATION   Since sex hormones strongly influence the mating behavior of other species (Crew & Moore, 1986), researchers have looked into possible hormonal factors in determining sexual orientation in humans.

Activating effects
Those effects of sex hormones that influence the level of the sex drive but not sexual orientation.

Testosterone is essential to male sexual differentiation (see Chapter 6). Thus, the levels of testosterone and its by-products in the blood and urine have been suspected as a possible influence of sexual orientation, at least in males. Research has failed to connect sexual orientation in either gender with differences in the levels of either male or female sex hormones in adulthood (Feder, 1984; Meyer-Bahlburg, 1979). Nor has the sexual orientation of gay males been altered by increasing their testosterone levels (Gartrell, 1982). In adulthood, testosterone appears to have **activating effects.** That is, it affects the intensity of sexual desire, but not the preference for partners of the same or opposite gender (Whalen et al., 1990).

What of the possible *prenatal* effects of sex hormones? Experiments have been performed in which pregnant rats were given antiandrogen drugs that block the effects of testosterone. When the drugs were given during critical periods when the fetuses' brains were becoming sexually differentiated, male offspring were likely to show feminine mating patterns as adults (Ellis & Ames, 1987). The adult males became receptive to mounting attempts by other males and failed to mount females (Ward, 1972).

Do prenatal sex hormones play a similar role in determining sexual orientation in humans? The answer is unclear. There is a lack of direct evidence of a relationship between hormonal imbalances during prenatal development and sexual orientation. We do know that the genitals of homosexual men were not feminized during prenatal development (Whalen et al., 1990). It remains possible, however—though speculative—that imbalances in prenatal sex hormones may cause brain tissue to be sexually differentiated in one direction even though the genitals are differentiated in the other. Scientists speculate that a similar mechanism may explain transsexualism (e.g., Money, 1987b).

Discussion Question: If researchers find solid evidence for biological "causes" of homosexuality, how do you think this will affect people's attitudes toward gay men and lesbians?

Recent evidence supports the view that there are structural differences between the brains of heterosexual and homosexual men. In 1991, Simon LeVay, a neurobiologist at the Salk Institute in La Jolla, California, carried out autopsies on the brains of 35 AIDS victims—19 homosexual men and 16 (presumably) heterosexual men. He found that a segment of the hypothalamus—specifically, a cell group called the third interstitial nucleus of the anterior hypothalamus—in the brains of the gay men was less than half the size of the same segment in the heterosexuals. The same brain segment was larger in the brain tissues of heterosexual men than in brain tissues obtained from a comparison group of six presumably heterosexual women. No significant differences in size were found between the brain tissues of the homosexual men and the women, however.

Since his subjects had suffered from AIDS, critics of LeVay's research suggest that the structural differences in the hypothalamus might have been due to the effects of AIDS and were unrelated to the men's sexual orientation. This does not appear to be the case, however, because the size difference was found only in the brains of the homosexual men and not in the brains of heterosexual men who had suffered from AIDS. LeVay's findings are intriguing, but they are preliminary. We do not know, for example, whether the structural differences found by LeVay are innate. Nor should LeVay's findings be taken to mean that biology is destiny. As Richard Nakamura, a government scientist with the National Institute of Mental Health, commented, "This [LeVay's findings] shouldn't be taken to mean that you're automatically homosexual if you have a structure of one size versus a structure of another size" (Angier, 1991).

The belief that homosexuality is innate or inborn has many adherents in the scientific and general communities. Support for the possible influences of prenatal hormonal factors in "sculpting" the brain in a masculine or feminine direction is based largely on animal studies, however. Direct evidence with people is lacking. We must also be careful in generalizing results from other species to our own.

Although there is no direct evidence that homosexuality is caused by prenatal hormonal factors, we can cite some indirect evidence. For example, excessive prenatal androgens masculinize the genitals of women with androgenital syndrome (see Chapter 6). Researchers have followed a group of women born with this syndrome. Their genitals were surgically corrected after birth and they were reared as females. By puberty, some of them showed homosexual interests (Bancroft, 1990; Ehrhardt et al., 1985). But also recall the cases of the two pseudohermaphrodites with androgenital syndrome who were studied by Money and Ehrhardt (1972). Although these children, whom we referred to as Abby and James in Chapter 6, were born with ambiguous genitals, their gender identities and sexual orientations were apparently determined by the gender in which they were reared, not by prenatal hormones.

Even if the link between prenatal hormones and sexual orientation is upheld in future research, John Money (1987) argues that such prenatal influences would not automatically produce a specific, predictable adult sexual orientation—because people are not robots. Early learning experiences also affect one's sexual orientation.

Learning Objective 8: Summarize the psychoanalytic and learning theories of the reasons for homosexuality and examine the link between early gender nonconformity and later homosexuality.

Polymorphously perverse
In psychoanalytic theory, being receptive to all forms of sexual stimulation.

Displacement
In psychoanalytic theory, a defense mechanism that allows one to transfer unacceptable wishes or desires onto more appropriate or less threatening objects.

Castration anxiety
In psychoanalytic theory, a man's fear that his genitals will be removed. Castration anxiety is an element of the Oedipus complex and is implicated in the directionality of erotic interests.

Penis envy
In psychoanalytic theory, the girl's wish to have a penis.

PSYCHOLOGICAL PERSPECTIVES

Do family relationships play a role in the origins of one's sexual orientation? What of one's childhood sexual experiences? Psychoanalytic theory and learning theory provide two of the major psychological approaches to understanding the origins of sexual orientation.

PSYCHOANALYTIC VIEWS   Sigmund Freud, the originator of psychoanalytic theory, believed that children enter the world **polymorphously perverse.** That is, prior to internalizing social inhibitions, children are open to all forms of sexual stimulation. However, through proper resolution of the Oedipus complex, a boy will forsake his incestuous desires for his mother and come to identify with his father. As a result, his erotic attraction to his mother will eventually be transferred, or **displaced,** onto more appropriate *female* partners, who perhaps resemble the "girl that married dear old dad." A girl, through proper resolution of her Electra complex, will identify with her mother and also seek heteroerotic stimulation when she becomes sexually mature.

In Freud's view, homosexuality results from failure to resolve the Oedipus complex by successfully identifying with the parent of the same gender. In men, faulty resolution of the Oedipus complex is most likely to result from a "classic pattern" in which there is an emotionally "close-binding" mother and a "detached-hostile" father. A boy reared in such a family may come to identify with his mother sexually and even to "transform himself into her" (Freud, 1922/1959, p. 40), becoming effeminate and eventually developing sexual interests in other men.

Freud believed that unresolved **castration anxiety** also plays a role in male homosexuality. In the Oedipus complex, the boy unconsciously comes to fear that his father, out of rivalry for the mother, will retaliate by removing the organ that the boy has come to associate with sexual pleasure through experiences with masturbation. If the Oedipus complex is not successfully resolved, castration anxiety may continue to persist in later life. When sexually mature, the man will not be able to tolerate sex with women, whose lack of a penis arouses castration anxiety within himself.

The Electra complex in little girls follows a somewhat different course. Freud believed that little girls become envious of boys' penises, since they lack their own. This concept of **penis envy** was one of Freud's most controversial beliefs. In Freud's view, jealousy leads little girls to resent their mothers, whom they blame for their anatomic "deficiency," and to turn from their mothers to their fathers as sexual objects. They now desire to possess the father, because the father's penis provides what they lack. But incestuous desires bring the girl into competition with her mother. Motivated by fear that her mother will withdraw her love if the desires persist, the girl normally forsakes them and identifies with her mother. She then develops traditional feminine interests and eventually seeks heteroerotic stimulation. She supplants her childhood desire for a penis with a desire to marry a man and bear children. The baby, emitted from between her legs, is the ultimate penis substitute.

A girl who does not resolve her penis envy in childhood may "manifest homosexuality, . . . exhibit markedly masculine traits in the conduct of her later life, choose a masculine vocation, and so on" (Freud, 1922/1959, p. 50). The residue of this unresolved complex is continued penis envy, the striving to become a man by acting like a man and seeking sexual satisfaction with women: lesbianism.

In Freud's view, a homosexual orientation is one result of assuming the gender role normally taken up by the opposite gender. The gay male is expected to be effeminate, and the lesbian, masculine. But, as noted in research into gender-typed behavior and homosexuality, this stereotypical view of gays is far from universal. Nor do the cross-gender behaviors found in some adult gay men or women necessarily derive from Oedipal problems. Biological and other psychosocial factors may be implicated.

A nagging problem of Freudian theory is that many of its concepts, such as castration anxiety and penis envy, are believed to operate at an unconscious level. As such, they lie beyond the scope of scientific observation and measurement. We cannot learn whether boys experience castration anxiety by asking them, since the theory claims that **repression** will keep such anxieties out of awareness. Nor can we directly learn about penis envy by interviewing girls.

Repression
In psychoanalytic theory, the most basic defense mechanism through which threatening ideas and impulses are ejected from conscious awareness.

TRUTH O R *FICTION?*

R E V I S I T E D

Gay males unconsciously fear women's genitals because they associate them with castration. The belief that "castration anxiety" in gay males is aroused by heterosexual intercourse has not been scientifically demonstrated and remains speculative. •

RESEARCH ON PSYCHOANALYTIC THEORIES OF HOMOSEXUAL DEVELOPMENT

Psychoanalysts—psychotherapists trained in the Freudian tradition—have researched homosexuality largely through case studies. These studies have been carried out almost exclusively with gay males who were in therapy at the time. In 1962, psychoanalyst Irving Bieber reported the results of questionnaires filled out by 77 psychiatrists on 106 homosexual clients. In 1976, he reported the results of similar surveys of homosexual clients.

Bieber claimed to find the "classic pattern" among gay males of a dominant, "smothering" mother and a passive, detached father. As the clients described them, the mothers were overprotective, seductive, and jealous of their sons. The fathers were aloof, unaffectionate, and hostile toward them. The father, being detached, may have failed to buffer the close mother-son relationship. The parents were typically unhappy, and the mother may have substituted a "close-binding" relationship with her son for the failed marital relationship. This classic pattern was believed to result in the boy's developing a fear of heterosexual contacts. A female partner would unconsciously represent his mother. Desire for her would stir unconscious fears of retaliation by the father—that is, castration anxiety.

Bieber's findings may be criticized on several grounds. First, the subjects were all in analysis, and many wanted to become heterosexual. Thus we may not be able to generalize the results to well-adjusted gay men. Second, the analysts may have chosen cases that confirmed their theoretical perspectives. Third, no clear evidence exists that gay males either fear or are repulsed by female genitalia. To the contrary, many gay males have successfully, and often repeatedly, engaged in heterosexual coitus. They may simply not be sexually attracted to women or may find gay male relationships more satisfying. Fourth, many *hetero*sexual men have family backgrounds that fit the classic pattern, and the families of many gay men do *not* fit the pattern. Researchers from the Kinsey Institute found that heterosexual males identified with their mothers as often as gay males did. A seductive mother-son relationship had little if any bearing on sexual orien-

Father-Son Relationship. Does the quality of the father-son relationship play a role, as some theorists suspect, in the development of homosexuality in men? According to a recent study, gay men perceived themselves as having been more distant from their father during childhood than did heterosexual men. The question is, why.

tation (Bell et al., 1981). Parent-child relations were only weakly linked to lesbianism as well. Finally, retrospective accounts of childhood relationships with parents are subject to gaps in memory and distortions.

More recent evidence has brought the issue of familial closeness between gay men and their parents into closer perspective. Richard Pillard and his colleagues (Pillard et al., 1982; Pillard & Weinrich, 1986; Pillard, 1990) found that gay males described themselves as more distant from their fathers during childhood than did either heterosexual controls or the gay men's own heterosexual brothers. The gay men in their sample also reported greater closeness to their mothers. Still, the father's psychological distance from the son may have reflected the *son's* alienation from him, not the reverse. That is, the son may have been so attached to his mother, or so disinterested in traditional masculine activities, that he rebuffed paternal attempts to engage him in conventional father-son activities.

To sum up, family characteristics may play a role in some cases of homosexual development, but there is great variation among the families of gay males and lesbians, and no one pattern applies in all cases (Isay, 1990). Family dynamics may be one of many contributing factors shaping sexual orientation.

Intrapsychic conflict
In psychoanalytic theory, conflict among the psychic (mental) structures of the id, ego, and superego.

LEARNING THEORIES   Learning theorists agree with Freud that early experiences play an important role in the development of sexual orientation. They focus on the role of reinforcement of early patterns of sexual behavior, however, rather than on the resolution of **intrapsychic conflicts.** People generally repeat pleasurable activities and discontinue painful ones. Thus, people may learn to engage in homosexual activity if childhood homosexual experimentation is connected with sexual pleasure. If sexual motivation is high, as it tends to be during adolescence, and the only outlets are with others of one's own gender, adolescents may experiment with same-gender sexual activity. If these encounters are pleasurable, and heterosexual experiences are unpleasant, a firmer gay male or lesbian sexual orientation may develop (Gagnon & Simon, 1973). Conversely, if pain, anxiety, or social disapproval are connected with early same-gender contacts, the child may learn to inhibit homosexual feelings and develop a firmer heterosexual orientation.

Although learning may play a role in the development of a gay male or lesbian sexual orientation, learning theorists have thus far failed to identify specific learning experiences that would lead to these orientations. Most adolescent same-gender encounters, even if pleasurable, do not lead to an adult gay male or lesbian sexual orientation. Many heterosexuals have had adolescent encounters with members of their own gender without swaying their adult orientations. This is true even of people whose early heterosexual interactions were fumbling and frustrating. Moreover, the overwhelming majority of gay males and lesbians had a developing homosexual identity *before* they had same-gender sexual encounters, pleasurable or otherwise (Bell et al., 1981).

GENDER NONCONFORMITY

Discussion Question:
Examine the idea that one of the biggest insults to boys is to be called a "sissy" and to men is to be called "feminine." Calling a girl a "tomboy" or a woman "masculine" does not carry the same sting. Are males who "act like" females seen as less valuable? In what way does this reflect the sexism in our culture?

 Gay Census

Although the stereotypes of the effeminate gay male and the masculine lesbian are exaggerated, research finds that gay males and lesbians report a greater incidence of cross-gender behavior as children than do heterosexual reference groups. Many gay males and lesbians have childhood recollections of acting and feeling "different" from their peers from a young age—some gay males can recall feeling different as early as the age of 3 or 4 (Isay, 1990). Feelings of differentness were often related to cross-gender behaviors. Saghir and Robins (1973) reported that two thirds (67%) of the gay males they studied, as compared to only 3 percent of the heterosexual male reference group, perceived themselves to have been effeminate during childhood. Gay males from various groups, such as prisoners, psychiatric patients, and members of gay rights organizations more often reported that they avoided participating in competitive sports as children, were more fearful of physical injury, and were more likely to avoid getting into fights, than did heterosexual males (McConaghy, 1987). Gay males are also more likely to recall feeling more sensitive than their peers during childhood, crying more easily, having their feelings more readily hurt, having more artistic interests, and having fewer male buddies but more female playmates (Isay, 1990). Gay males were also more likely than their heterosexual counterparts to have preferred "girls' toys" and playing with girls to playing with trucks or guns, or engaging in rough-and-tumble play—preferences that led to their being called "sissies" (Adams & Chiodo, 1983; Bell et al., 1981; Green, 1987). Gay men also recall more cross-dressing during childhood, preferring the company of older women to older men, and engaging in childhood sex play with other boys rather than with girls (Whitam, 1977).

Saghir and Robins also found evidence of masculine-typed behavior among lesbians as children, although the differences between the lesbian and heterosexual samples were not as great as those between the male gay and heterosexual samples. Lesbians were more likely than heterosexual women to perceive themselves as having been "tomboys" as children, to have preferred rough-and-tumble games to playing with dolls, and to have preferred wearing boys' clothing to "cutesy" dresses. Seventy percent of the lesbians sampled, as compared to only 16 percent of the female heterosexual reference group, considered themselves tomboys in childhood.

The above studies relied on retrospective reports of adults about their childhoods, and memories may be distorted or incomplete. Other investigators have followed boys who were identified as effeminate in childhood to see if they later developed a gay male sexual orientation. A series of these longitudinal studies reveals that the majority of very effeminate or "sissy" boys become gay or bisexual in adulthood (Brody, 1986; Green, 1979, 1985; Zuger, 1984). Richard Green (1985) tracked the development of 44 highly effeminate boys for 15 years. Thirty-three (75%) of them turned out to be gay or bisexual. As boys, they differed from their peers. Although many boys occasionally dress up in their mothers' clothes or play with dolls, these "sissy boys" assumed traditional feminine interests exclusively. They played for hours at a time with Barbie dolls and frequently dressed in girls' clothes. They showed no interest in rough-and-tumble games or competitive sports. Researchers believe that cross-gender interest patterns lead sissy boys to become alienated and isolated from male peers, and often, from their fathers as well (Brody, 1986).

How might extreme childhood effeminacy lead to a gay male sexual orientation? Green speculates that the social detachment of these boys from male peers and role models (especially fathers) creates strong, unfulfilled cravings for male affection, which lead them to seek males as partners in sex and love relationships in adolescence and adulthood. Alan Bell of the Kinsey Institute offers a different explanation. He believes that self-perceptions of differentness and social distance from other males during childhood lead these boys to develop erotic attractions that are also different from the other boys, namely erotic attractions toward members of their own gender (Brody, 1986).

Bear in mind that not all of these highly effeminate boys turned out to be gay. Note, too, that not all gay males show cross-gender behavior as children (Carrier, 1986). Although some gay men report engaging in few if any gender-conforming behaviors in childhood, others report as many typically masculine behaviors and as few feminine behaviors in childhood as heterosexual men (Phillips & Over, 1992). Moreover, perhaps

5 percent of heterosexual males cross-dressed as children (Carrier, 1986; Harry, 1983). Still, the finding that some heterosexual males showed cross-gender behavior as children, or that some gay men showed masculine behaviors in childhood, does not invalidate the general connection between excessive cross-gender behavior and the development of a gay male sexual orientation in some cases, any more than the incidence of tallness in women invalidates the link between gender and height (McConaghy, 1987). It remains unclear whether early effeminacy reflects genetic factors, prenatal influences (such as hormonal imbalances), early experiences, or some combination of these factors.

All in all, the origins of sexual orientation remain mysterious and complex, just as mysterious as the causes of heterosexuality. In reviewing theories and research, we are left with the impression that there may be no single cause of sexual orientation. Sexual orientation may represent a complex set of erotic attractions and behaviors that springs from multiple origins, involving psychosocial and biological factors. Genetic and biochemical factors (such as hormone levels) may affect the prenatal organization of the brain. These factors, in combination with early socialization experiences, may give rise to a gay male or lesbian, heterosexual, or bisexual sexual orientation. The precise influences and interactions of these factors have so far eluded researchers.

ADJUSTMENT OF GAY MALES AND LESBIANS

Despite the widespread belief that there is something wrong with gay men and lesbians, evidence has failed to show that these groups are more emotionally unstable or more subject to psychiatric disorders (like anxiety and depression) than their heterosexual counterparts (Reiss, 1980). Nor have researchers been able to distinguish between gays and heterosexuals on the basis of psychological tests (Reiss, 1980). Homosexuality itself is no longer considered a form of mental illness. In 1973 the American Psychiatric Association voted to drop homosexuality per se from its listing of mental disorders although the listing still includes a diagnostic category that applies to people who suffer persistent and marked distress or confusion about their sexual orientations (American Psychiatric Association, 1993).

TRUTH OR *FICTION?*

R E V I S I T E D

The American Psychiatric Association considers homosexuality a mental disorder. *The American Psychiatric Association has not considered homosexuality to be a mental disorder since 1973.* •

Gay men, lesbians, and bisexuals occupy all socioeconomic and vocational levels and follow a variety of lifestyles. Researchers find gay men and lesbians overall to be

Homosexuals and Adjustment. Researchers find that in general gay men and lesbians are as well adjusted as heterosexuals. Gay couples who are closely committed to one another are also as well adjusted as committed heterosexual couples.

more highly educated that most Americans (Cronin, 1993). Bell and Weinberg (1978) found variations in adjustment in the gay community that seem to mirror the variations in the heterosexual community. Gay people who lived with partners in stable, intimate relationships—so-called close couples—were about as well adjusted as married heterosexuals. Older gays who lived alone and had few sexual contacts were more poorly adjusted. So, too, are many heterosexuals who have similar lifestyles. All in all, differences in adjustment seem more likely to reflect the lifestyle than sexual orientation.

Most gay males and lesbians who share close relationships with their partners are satisfied with the quality of their relationships. Researchers find that heterosexual and gay couples report similar levels of satisfaction with their relationships (Kurdek & Schmitt, 1986a; Peplau & Cochran, 1990). In one study, for example, heterosexual, gay male, and lesbian couples all scored in the "well-adjusted" range and could not be distinguished on an inventory measuring marital satisfaction (Ramsay et al., 1978). In another study, gay males and lesbians in enduring relationships generally reported high levels of love, attachment, closeness, caring, and intimacy (Peplau & Cochran, 1980). Yet not all gay relationships, as not all heterosexual relationships, are satisfying. Among both groups, satisfaction is higher when both partners feel that the benefits they receive from the relationship outweigh the costs (Duffy & Rusbult, 1985/1986). Like heterosexuals, gay men and lesbians are happier in relationships where they share power and make joint decisions (Kurdek & Schmitt, 1986b).

In sum, researchers have not found that gay men and lesbians suffer from more psychological distress than heterosexuals. Researchers also find bisexuals to be about as well adjusted as heterosexuals and gay men and women (Coleman, 1987).

Much of the research on gay lifestyles has focused on the younger gay male and lesbian population. Although we know less about the aging process in gays, research indicates that aging gay men and lesbians (50 to 73 years of age) who are active in the gay community generally report high levels of life satisfaction and acceptance of aging (Quam & Whitford, 1992). Developing and maintaining a sense of belonging or group identification among gay people may be helpful in navigating life's passages, as it is in the general population.

TREATMENT OF HOMOSEXUALITY   People who view homosexuality as an illness see it as something to be "cured," perhaps by medical or psychological means. However, the great majority of gay men and lesbians do not seek professional assistance to change their sexual orientations. Most see their sexual orientations as integral parts of their personal identities. Bell and Weinberg (1978) found only a few gays who were interested in changing their sexual orientation—even if a "magic pill" were available to bring about the change (see Table 10.2). Only a minority of Bell and Weinberg's sample had *ever* considered discontinuing homosexual activity.

TABLE 10.2 Percentage of gays who wish they had received a "magic heterosexuality pill" at birth or could receive one today

	White Males	African-American Males	White Females	African-American Females
Desire magic pill at birth?	28	23	16	11
Desire magic pill today?	14	13	5	6

Source: Bell, A. P., & Weinberg, M. S. *Homosexualities: A study of diversity among men and women.* Copyright © 1978 by Simon & Schuster, p. 339. Reprinted by permission.

A few gay men and lesbians do express an interest in changing their orientations, however. Helping professionals have tried to assist them in a variety of ways. At one time, when it was commonly believed that hormonal imbalances influenced one's sexual orientation, hormone treatments were in vogue. There is no evidence that they were effective—fortunately they also seem to have been harmless (Meyer-Bahlburg, 1979).

A few psychotherapists have reported some success. For example, Bieber (1976) claimed that about one in four clients changed his or her sexual orientation through psychoanalytic psychotherapy. But critics charge that these clients were highly motivated to change, and that some of them began therapy as bisexuals. Their change in lifestyle may be attributable to their initial motivation to change, and not to the therapy itself.

Masters and Johnson (1979) employed methods used to treat sexual dysfunctions (see in Chapter 15) to "reverse" patients' gay male or lesbian sexual orientations. For example, they involved gay males in pleasurable activities with women, such as massage and genital stimulation, at a relaxed pace. Masters and Johnson reported a failure rate of 20 percent for the gay men and 23 percent for the lesbians they treated in their therapy program. At a 5-year follow-up, more than 70 percent of the clients continued to engage in heterosexual activity (Schwartz & Masters, 1984). These patients do not seem representative of the general homosexual population, however. Most of the patients were bisexuals. More than half were married to members of the opposite gender. Only about one in five was exclusively homosexual. All, moreover, were presumably motivated to switch their sexual orientations. In any event, changes in sexual behavior per se do not denote changes in basic sexual orientation.

Isay (1990), a psychoanalyst, argues that gay men and women often enter therapy because of conflicts that arise from social pressure and prejudice, and from related problems in accepting their homosexual identities. The role of the therapist, he argues, should be to help unburden the client of conflict and promote a more gratifying life as a gay person.

GAY IDENTITY: COMING TO TERMS WITH BEING GAY

Learning Objective 10: Explain the "coming out" process.

Gay males and lesbians in our culture struggle to come to terms with their sexual orientations against a backdrop of social condemnation and antagonism. The process of establishing a gay male or lesbian identity may thus be a long and painful struggle.

COMING OUT

Gay men and lesbians often speak of the process of accepting their sexual orientations as "coming out," or as "coming out of the closet." Coming out is a two-pronged process: coming out to oneself (recognizing one's gay male or lesbian sexual orientation) and coming out to others (declaring oneself to the world). Coming out can create a sense of pride in one's sexual orientation and foster the ability to form emotionally and sexually satisfying relationships with gay male or lesbian partners.

COMING OUT TO ONESELF   Many gay people have a difficult time coming to recognize, let alone to accept, their sexual orientation. Some have even considered or attempted suicide because of problems in self-acceptance:

> It [suicidal thinking] was because of my homosexuality. I was completely depressed that my homosexuality was leading me nowhere. My life seemed to be going around in a circle. I was still fighting against recognition of my homosexuality. I knew what I was but I didn't want to be.

> [I had] the feeling that homosexuality was a hopeless existence. I felt there was no future in it, that I was doomed to be alone. And from my Catholic background, I felt that homosexuality was very evil.

> (Bell & Weinberg, 1978, p. 202)

Notes: "The suicide attempt rate among gay teenage boys is estimated to be from 30 to 40 percent, and that for teenage lesbians 20 percent, both far above the 10 percent rate for teenagers overall. It has been estimated that as many as 30 percent of the teenagers who commit suicide are gay" (p. 364). (Evall, J. 1991. Sexual orientation and adoptive matching. *Family Law Quarterly, 25.*)

Some gay people have great difficulty coming to terms with their sexuality; others, almost none. Coming to recognize and accept their sexuality may involve the gradual stripping away of barriers of denial. Or it may be a sudden awakening, in which long-standing homoerotic interests focus on a particular person of the same gender, as with a graduate student named David:

> In college [David's] closest friend was gay. Although this friend had wanted to have sex with David and the attraction was mutual, David still could not associate this attraction with a sexuality that was not acceptable to him. In his first year of graduate school, when he was about 23, he fell in love and then suddenly and with a great sense of relief recognized and acknowledged to himself that he was homosexual. He then had sex for the first time and has subsequently been . . . open about his sexuality.
>
> (Isay, 1990, p. 295)

Recognition of one's gay sexual orientation may be only the first step in a lifelong process of sexual identity formation: the acceptance of being gay as part of one's self-definition (Isay, 1990). The term *gay* or *homosexual identity* refers to the subjective or psychological sense of being gay.

Some gay men and lesbians who have not yet come to recognize or accept their gay sexual orientation enter heterosexual marriages. For some, marriage is a means of testing heterosexual feelings. For others, it may represent an attempt to conceal or overcome their sexual orientation (Bell & Weinberg, 1978). Perhaps 20 percent of gay males and a higher percentage of lesbians get married at least once (Bell & Weinberg, 1978). But such marriages tend to be unhappy and short-lived. They may be strained by one partner's concealing her or his gay sexual orientation, or they may buckle from the open acknowledgment of being gay. Virtually all such marriages in Bell and Weinberg's study eventually ended in separation or divorce.

COMING OUT TO OTHERS　There are different patterns of "coming out" to others. Coming out occasionally involves an open declaration to the world. More often a person may decide to inform only one or perhaps a few select people. The person might tell close friends but not family members. In a society that holds negative attitudes toward gay people, many gay men and lesbians are reluctant to declare their sexual orientation, even to friends and family (Wells & Kline, 1987). Disclosure is fraught with the risk of loss of jobs, friendships, and social standing (Padesky, 1988). A social worker who counsels lesbians described some fears of coming out to others expressed by her clients:

> Will I lose my job, will I lose my house, will I lose my children, will I be attacked? I've seen people lose a job. Even if you don't lose it, you become marginal, excluded either actively or through uncomfortable vibes.
>
> (Cited in Barrett, 1990, p. 470)

Gay men and lesbians can anticipate a range of reactions from family members, often negative ones, including denial, anger, and rejection. Family members and loved ones may refuse to hear or be unwilling to accept reality, as Martha Barron Barrett notes in her book *Invisible Lives,* which chronicles the lives of a sample of lesbians in the contemporary United States:

> Parents, children, neighbors, and friends of lesbians deny, or compartmentalize, or struggle with their knowledge in the same way the women themselves do. "My parents know I've lived with my partner for six years. She goes home with me. We sleep in the same bed there. The word *lesbian* has never been mentioned." "I told my mother and she said, 'Well, now that's over with. We don't need to mention it again.' She never has, and that was ten years ago. I don't know if she ever told my father." A husband may dismiss it as "just a phase," a boyfriend may interpret it as a sexual tease, a straight woman may believe "she's just saying that because she couldn't get a man."
>
> The strong message is, "Keep it quiet." Many lesbians do that by becoming invisible. . . . They leave their lesbian persona at home when they go to work on Monday morning. On Friday they don it again. That weekend at home, the flip side of the double life, is what most of heterosexual society never sees.
>
> (Barrett, 1990, p. 52)

Some families are more accepting. They may have had prior suspicions and prepared themselves for the news that their family member is gay. Though families may be initially rejecting, they often eventually come to at least a grudging acceptance that their child is gay.

PATTERNS OF GAY MALE AND LESBIAN SEXUAL ACTIVITY

Learning Objective 11: Compare the sexual techniques of gay male, lesbian, and heterosexual partners.

Heterosexuals are often confused about the sexual practices of gay couples. They may wonder, "Just what do they do?" Generally speaking, gay couples express themselves sexually through as wide a range of activities as heterosexual couples, with the exception of vaginal intercourse. But there are shades of difference between gay and heterosexual couples in sexual techniques.

SEXUAL TECHNIQUES

Gay male couples tend to engage in such sexual activities as kissing, hugging, petting, mutual masturbation, fellatio, and anal intercourse. Laboratory observations of sexual relations between gay males by Masters and Johnson (1979) showed that gay males spent a good deal of time caressing their partners' bodies before approaching the genitals. After hugging and kissing, 31 of 42 gay male couples observed by Masters and Johnson used oral or manual nipple stimulation.

Not all gay males enjoy or practice anal intercourse, but most who do alternate between being the inserter and the insertee. The frequency of anal intercourse among gay males is apparently declining in the face of the AIDS epidemic (Catania et al., 1991; Centers for Disease Control, 1990a).

Risks of infection and of injury to the rectum or anus are associated with another sexual practice called "fisting." Although fisting is not unique to gay males, it is apparently most common among them (Lowry & Williams, 1983). This practice involves the insertion of the fist or hand into the rectum, usually after the bowels have been evacuated with an enema.

Activity: *Thinking About Whether or Not Gay Men and Lesbians Make Better Lovers* This IM activity encourages students to think critically about the characteristics of a good lover and to examine the similarities and differences in heterosexual and homosexual lovemaking techniques.

Sexual techniques practiced by lesbians vary. The great majority of lesbian couples report kissing, manual and oral breast stimulation, and manual and oral stimulation of the genitals (Kinsey et al., 1953). Manual genital stimulation is the most common and most frequent sexual activity among lesbian couples (Bell & Weinberg, 1978). Most lesbian couples also engage in genital apposition. That is, they position themselves so as to rub their genitals together rhythmically (Kinsey et al., 1953). Like gay males, lesbians spend a good deal of time holding, kissing, and caressing each other's bodies before they approach the breasts and genitals. By contrast, heterosexual males tend to move quickly to stimulate their partners' breasts or start directly with genital stimulation (Masters & Johnson, 1979).

Like heterosexual women, lesbians are less genitally oriented and less fixated on orgasm than men. Lesbians generally begin stimulating their partners with more general genital stimulation rather than direct clitoral stimulation, whereas heterosexual males often begin by stimulating the clitoris (Masters & Johnson, 1979). Nor do lesbian couples generally engage in deep penetration of the vagina with fingers. Rather, they may use more shallow vaginal penetration, focusing stimulation on the vaginal lips and entrance. Images of lesbians strapping on dildos for vaginal penetration exist more in the imagination of uninformed heterosexuals than in the sexual repertoire of lesbian couples (Masters & Johnson, 1979). The emotional components of lovemaking—gentle touching, cuddling, and hugging—are important elements of sexual sharing in lesbian relationships.

GAY LIFESTYLES

Learning Objective 12: Examine the variations in the lifestyles of gay men and lesbians.

One of the mistakes that lay people (and some researchers) make is to treat gay people as if they were all the same. According to Bell and Weinberg (1978), gays do not adopt a single, stereotypical lifestyle. That is why the authors termed their report *Homosexualities: A Study of Diversity Among Men and Women*. Variations in sexual expression exist within and across sexual orientations. Statements about homosexuality or heterosexuality must take into account individual differences in lifestyles.

Gay men and lesbians in larger U.S. urban centers can usually look to gay communal structures to provide services and support. These include gay rights organizations, gay-oriented newspapers, magazines, and bookstores, housing cooperatives, medical services, and other support services (Gagnon, 1990). The gay community provides a sense of acceptance and belonging that gays do not typically find in society at large. Gays still encounter discrimination in the workplace, in housing, and in the military. Restrictions on gay males participating in the armed services has been a continuing controversy. In 1993, President Bill Clinton encountered stiff opposition when he sought to follow through on his campaign pledge to permit openly gay men and women to serve in the military. As a compromise measure, he proposed a "don't ask, don't tell" policy which would permit gay males and lesbians to serve so long as they do not publicly express or reveal their sexual orientation. Moreover, military officials would be prohibited from inquiring about the sexual orientation of recruits or initiating investigations in the absence of a public display or disclosure of a homosexual orientation ("Defense dept. suspends its policy on homosexuals," 1993). The constitutionality of this policy remained unclear as of this writing ("High court lets Pentagon put gay policy into effect," 1993).

 Lesbian Parents

Gay rights organizations fight for rights for gays to participate fully in society—to teach in public schools, to adopt children, to live together in sanctioned relationships, and to serve openly and proudly in the military. Cafés and social clubs provide places where gay men and lesbians can socialize and be open about their sexual orientations. Many such establishments also serve as meeting places for casual sexual "pickups," although the advent of AIDS has greatly curtailed such activity. Organizations like New York's Gay Men's Health Crisis (GMHC) provide medical, social, and psychological assistance to gay males who have been afflicted by AIDS.

Not all gays feel that they are a part of the "gay community" or participate in gay rights organizations, however. For many, their sexual orientation is a part of their identity, but not a dominant theme that governs their social and political activities.

LIFESTYLE DIFFERENCES BETWEEN GAY MALES AND LESBIANS

Much of our knowledge of lifestyle patterns among gay males and lesbians comes from research that predates the AIDS epidemic. Researchers in the 1970s found that gay males were more likely than lesbians to engage in casual sex with many partners; lesbians more often confined their sexual activity to a committed, affectionate relationship (Bell & Weinberg, 1978). Bell and Weinberg reported that 84 percent of gay males, as compared to about 7 percent of lesbian women, reported having more than 50 partners in their lifetimes. Seventy-nine percent of gay males in their study, as compared to only 6 percent of lesbians, reported that more than half of their partners had been strangers.

Even in this age of AIDS, a recent survey found that only about half of gay men (between 40% and 60%), but about three in four lesbians, are currently involved in a steady relationship (Peplau & Cochran, 1990). Even within committed relationships, gay males tend to have more permissive attitudes toward extracurricular sexual activity and more frequent sexual contacts outside their primary relationships (Peplau & Cochran, 1990).

Cruising
The name homosexuals give to searching for a sex partner.

Traditionally, the gay bar was an arena for making sexual contacts (Bell & Weinberg, 1978). **Cruising** is the name gays give to searching for a sex partner, principally for casual sex. One "cruises" and one can "be cruised." Gay males were more likely than lesbians to cruise in public places, like gay bars. Lesbians were more likely to find partners among friends, at work, and at informal social gatherings.

Today, with the threat of AIDS hanging over every casual sexual encounter, cruising has lost popularity. Most gay baths, long a setting for casual sexual contacts, have closed down because of AIDS—either because public health officials were concerned that they encouraged high-risk sexual practices or because patrons stopped frequenting them.

The closing of many gay bath houses is but one sign of changes in gay communities that have occurred since the advent of AIDS. Many gay males have changed their behavior to prevent contracting or spreading AIDS. Evidence shows that as a group, gay males

Facing the Crisis. The gay male community has responded to the AIDS crisis through the development of telephone hot-lines, support services, and safer sex programs.

have become more likely to limit or avoid anal and oral sex, especially with new partners, to use latex condoms when they do practice these techniques, to limit their sexual contacts to partners they know well, and to rely more on masturbation as a sexual outlet (Centers for Disease Control, 1990a, 1990c; Lourea et al., 1986; Schechter et al., 1984; Siegel et al., 1988). Despite the advent of AIDS, some gay men, like some heterosexuals, continue to practice high-risk sexual behaviors, such as unprotected anal intercourse and sex with multiple partners.

Research also shows that "extracurricular" sexual activity continues to be commonplace among gay male couples. In one recent survey of 943 gay males and 1,510 married heterosexual males who had been living with a partner for 2 to 10 years, 79 percent of the gay males reported sex with another partner during the preceding year, as compared to only 11 percent of the heterosexual males (Blumstein & Schwartz, 1990). Among couples who had been together for longer than 10 years, 94 percent of gay men reported extracurricular activity at some time during their primary relationships.

VARIATIONS IN GAY LIFESTYLES

Close couples
Bell and Weinberg's term for gay couples whose relationships resemble marriage in their depth of commitment and exclusiveness.

Bell and Weinberg (1978) found that about three out of four gay couples they studied could be classified according to one of five lifestyles: *close couples, open couples, functionals, dysfunctionals,* and *asexuals.* **Close couples** strongly resembled marriages. They involved deep emotional commitment and few outside sexual relationships. Almost three times as many lesbians (28%) as gay males (10%) lived in such committed, intimate relationships. Gays living in close relationships showed fewer social and psychological problems than those in any other lifestyle.

TRUTH OR *FICTION?*

R E V I S I T E D

Many gay couples have lifestyles similar to those of married heterosexual couples and are as well adjusted. Many gay couples have lifestyles that are similar to those of married heterosexual couples, and they are, in fact, as well adjusted. They are called "close couples" by Bell and Weinberg. •

Open couples
Bell and Weinberg's term for gay couples who live together but engage in secret affairs.

Functionals
Bell and Weinberg's term for gays who live alone, have adapted well to a swinging lifestyle, and are sociable and well adjusted.

Partners in **open couples** lived together but engaged in clandestine affairs. Gays in open couples were not as well adjusted as those in close couples, but their overall adjustment compared to that of heterosexuals. Still other gays lived alone and had sexual contacts with numerous partners—a kind of "swinging singles" gay lifestyle. Some of those who lived alone, **functionals,** appeared to have adapted well to their swinging lifestyle and were sociable and well adjusted. Others, called **dysfunctionals,** had sexual, social, or psychological problems. Dysfunctionals were often anxious, unhappy, and found it difficult to form intimate relationships. **Asexuals** also lived alone but were distinguished by having few sexual contacts. They tended to be older than gays in the other groups.

Dysfunctionals
Bell and Weinberg's term for gays who live alone and have sexual, social, or psychological problems.

Asexuals
Bell and Weinberg's term for gays who live alone and have few sexual contacts.

Although they did not have the adjustment problems of dysfunctionals, they too did not form intimate relationships. Despite being largely asexual in terms of their behavior, their sexual orientation was clearly gay.

The Bell and Weinberg study described diversity of lifestyles in the gay community in the 1970s, before the AIDS epidemic struck. Although such lifestyles continue today to a certain extent, the AIDS epidemic has curtailed, though not eliminated, promiscuous sexual contacts within the gay community. The specter of AIDS has had a more profound effect on the lifestyles and sexual practices of gay males than any other group in society.

SUMMING UP

SEXUAL ORIENTATION

Sexual orientation describes the directionality of one's sexual and romantic interests—toward members of the same gender, the opposite gender, or both. The term *homosexuality* denotes sexual and romantic interest in members of one's own gender and applies to both men and women.

Classification of Sexual Orientation Kinsey and his colleagues found evidence of degrees of homosexuality and heterosexuality, with bisexuality representing a midpoint between the two. Heterosexuality and homosexuality may be separate dimensions rather than polar opposites, however.

Homosexuality appears to be about twice as common among men as women.
Homosexuality and Bisexuality Bisexuals respond sexually to both males and females.

PERSPECTIVES ON HOMOSEXUALITY

Historical Perspectives
Throughout much of Western history, homosexuality has been deemed sinful and criminal.
Cross-Cultural Perspectives
Homosexual *behavior* is practiced by at least some members of many preliterate societies.
Cross-Species Perspectives
Many animals engage in behaviors that resemble homosexual contacts among humans, but we must be cautious in ascribing motives to animals.
Attitudes Toward Homosexuality in Contemporary Society The majority of people in our society view homosexuality and homosexuals negatively. Views of homosexuality had become more tolerant until recent

years, when the advent of AIDS stoked the embers of antihomosexual attitudes. Some researchers suggest that homophobia stems from, and serves to mask, deepseated fears of homosexual feelings within oneself. During the past generation, gay males and lesbians have organized effective political groups to fight discrimination and overturn antisodomy laws that have traditionally targeted homosexuals.
Biological Perspectives
Evidence of a genetic contribution to homosexuality is accumulating. Research has failed to connect sexual orientation with reliable differences in current (adult) levels of sex hormones. Prenatal sex hormones may play a role in deter-

mining sexual orientation in humans, however. There may also be (hormonally induced) structural differences between the brains of heterosexual and gay men.
Psychological Perspectives
Psychoanalytic theory connects homosexuality with unconscious castration anxiety and improper resolution of the Oedipus complex. Learning theorists focus on the role of reinforcement of early patterns of sexual behavior.
Gender Nonconformity
Although only a few gays fit the stereotypes of swishy men and butch women, research finds that homosexuals report a greater incidence of cross-gender behavior as children than do heterosexual reference group.

ADJUSTMENT OF GAY MALES AND LESBIANS

Evidence has failed to show that gay males, lesbians, and bisexuals are more emotionally unstable or more subject to psychiatric disorders than heterosexuals are. Gays occupy all socioeconomic and vocational levels and follow a variety of lifestyles. Most gay males and lesbians are satisfied with their sexual orientations, but some seek to become heterosexual.

GAY IDENTITY: COMING TO TERMS WITH BEING GAY

Gay people in our culture struggle to come to terms with their sexual orientation against a backdrop of social condemnation and antagonism.

Coming Out Coming out is a two-pronged process: coming out to oneself and coming out to others. Coming to recognize and accept one's gay sexual orientation may occur as a gradual process or a sudden awakening. The term *gay* or *homosexual identity* refers to the subjective or psychological sense of being gay.

PATTERNS OF GAY MALE AND LESBIAN SEXUAL ACTIVITY

Gay people generally express themselves sexually through as wide a range of activities as heterosexuals, with the exception of vaginal intercourse.
Sexual Techniques Gay males spend a good deal of time caressing their partners' bodies before approaching the genitals. Gay males who practice anal intercourse usually alternate between being the inserter and insertee. Manual genital stimulation is the most common and most frequent sexual activity among lesbians. Lesbians spend much time holding, kissing, and caressing their partners' bodies before approaching the breasts and genitals.

GAY LIFESTYLES

Gays do not adopt a single, stereotypical lifestyle.
Lifestyle Differences Between Gay Males and Lesbians Gay males are more likely than lesbians to engage in casual sex with many partners. Lesbians more often confine sexual activity to a committed, affectionate relationship. Many gay males have changed their sexual behavior to prevent contracting or spreading AIDS.
Variations in Gay Lifestyles The majority of gays studied by Bell and Weinberg could be classified according to one of five lifestyles: close couples, open couples, functionals, dysfunctionals, and asexuals.

CHAPTER OUTLINE

_____ Prolonged athletic activity may decrease fertility in the male.

_____ A "test-tube baby" is grown in a large laboratory dish throughout the nine-month gestation period.

_____ For the first week following conception, a fertilized egg cell is not attached to its mother's body.

_____ Pregnant women can have one or two alcoholic beverages a day without harming their babies.

_____ A baby signals its mother when it is ready to be born.

_____ One U.S. birth in four is by Caesarean section.

_____ Couples should abstain from sexual activity for at least six weeks following childbirth.

C H A P T E R *11*

Conception, Pregnancy, and Childbirth

On an unusually balmy day in late October, Elaine and her husband Dennis rush to catch the train to their jobs in the city. Elaine's work day is outwardly much the same as any other. Within her body, however, a drama is unfolding. Yesterday, hormones had caused a follicle in her ovary to rupture, releasing its egg cell, or ovum. Like all women, Elaine possessed at birth all the ova she would ever have, each encased in a sac or follicle. How this particular follicle was selected to mature this month and release its ovum remains a mystery. For the next day or so, however, Elaine will be capable of conceiving.

When Elaine used her ovulation-timing kit the previous morning, it showed that she was about to ovulate. So later that night, Elaine and Dennis had made love, hoping that Elaine would conceive. When Dennis ejaculated, hundreds of millions of sperm were deposited within Elaine's vagina. Only a few thousand survived the journey through the cervix and uterus to the Fallopian tube that contained the ovum, released just hours earlier. Of these, a few hundred remained to bombard the ovum. Only one succeeded in penetrating the ovum's covering, resulting in conception. From a single cell formed by the union of sperm and ovum, a new life begins to form. The **zygote** is but $1/175$ of an inch across—a tiny beginning. But Elaine must wait a few weeks before a pregnancy test reveals that she is pregnant.

Four months into her pregnancy, Elaine decides to undergo an **amniocentesis** in order to check for the presence of chromosomal abnormalities, such as **Down syndrome.** Elaine is 37, and she is aware that Down syndrome occurs more frequently among children born to women in their late thirties and forties. Amniocentesis also indicates the gender of the fetus. Although many parents prefer to know the gender of their baby before it is born, Elaine and Dennis ask their doctor not to inform them. "Why ruin the surprise?" Dennis explains to his friends. So the baby's gender is recorded in the obstetrician's records, and Elaine and Dennis are left to debate boys' names and girls' names for the next few months.

Zygote
A fertilized ovum.

Amniocentesis
A procedure for drawing off and examining fetal cells in the amniotic fluid to determine the presence of various disorders in the fetus.

Down syndrome
A chromosomal abnormality that leads to mental retardation, caused by an extra chromosome on the twenty-first pair.

CONCEPTION: AGAINST ALL ODDS

Learning Objective 1:
Describe the process of conception.

Conception is the union of a sperm cell and an ovum. On one hand, conception is the beginning of a new human life. Conception is also the end of a fantastic voyage, however, in which a viable ovum, one of only several hundred that will mature and ripen during a woman's lifetime, unites with one of several hundred *million* sperm produced by the man in the average ejaculate.

Spontaneous abortion
The sudden, involuntary expulsion of the embryo or fetus from the uterus before it is capable of independent life.

Ova carry X sex chromosomes. Sperm carry either X or Y sex chromosomes. Girls are conceived from the union of an ovum and an X-bearing sperm, boys from the union of an ovum and a Y-bearing sperm. Sperm that bear Y sex chromosomes appear to be faster swimmers than those bearing X sex chromosomes. This is one of the reasons that between 120 and 150 boys are conceived for every 100 girls. What seem to be natural balancing factors favor the survival of female fetuses, however. Male fetuses are more likely to be lost in a **spontaneous abortion,** which often occurs during the first month of pregnancy. In many cases of early spontaneous abortion, the woman never realizes that she had been pregnant. Despite spontaneous abortions, boys still outnumber girls at birth by a ratio of 106 to 100 (Purtillo & Sullivan, 1979). Boys also suffer from a higher incidence of infant mortality, however, which further equalizes the numbers of boys and girls in the population by the time they mature to the point of pairing off.

The 200 to 400 million sperm in an average ejaculate may seem a wasteful investment, since only one can fertilize an egg. Only one in 1,000 will ever arrive in the vicinity

FIGURE 11.1 **Human Sperm Swarming Around an Ovum in a Fallopian Tube.** Fertilization normally occurs in a Fallopian tube, not in the uterus.

Zona pellucida
A gelatinous layer that surrounds an ovum. (From roots meaning "zone that light can shine through.")

Hyaluronidase
An enzyme that briefly thins the zona pellucida, enabling one sperm to penetrate. (From roots meaning "substance that breaks down a glasslike fluid.")

Learning Objective 2:
Identify the various methods of increasing the chances of conception and their success rates.

of an ovum, however. Millions deposited in the vagina simply flow out of the woman's body because of gravity, unless she remains prone for quite some time. Normal vaginal acidity kills many more. Many surviving sperm swim against the current of fluid coming from the cervix, through the os and into the uterus. Surviving sperm may reach the Fallopian tubes 60 to 90 minutes after ejaculation. About half the sperm end up in the wrong tube—that is, the one not containing the egg. Perhaps some 2,000 sperm find their way into the right tube. Fewer still manage to swim the final 2 inches against the currents generated by the cilia that line the tube.

Recent research suggests that the journey of sperm is not random or blind. In 1991, David Garber of the University of Texas Southwestern Medical Center and his colleagues discovered that fertile ova secrete a compound that appears to attract sperm cells. In 1992, Belgian researcher Marc Parmentier and his colleagues reported that sperm cells contain odor receptors that had earlier been found only in the nasal cavity. It is thus conceivable (pardon the pun) that sperm cells are attracted to ova through a variation of the sense of smell. At this point, however, Parmentier considers such conclusions to be "very, very speculative" (Angier, 1992b, p. A19).

Scientists in 1993 announced that they had identified a gene in sea urchins that makes a protein that enables a sperm cell to recognize an egg cell and unite with it during fertilization ("Newly found protein is sperm's key to egg," 1993). The protein lies on the surface of the egg and serves as a kind of guidance system that directs the sperm to the egg. The protein acts to keep away sperm from other species, so that only sperm from the animal's own species can bind to the egg. Although sea urchins are not human beings, scientists hope that a similar protein may be found on the surface of the human egg cell. Such knowledge could lead to the development of new contraceptive drugs that might work at the molecular level by blocking the action of this protein. This knowledge may also lead to improved techniques for treating problems of infertility.

Fertilization normally occurs in a Fallopian tube. (Figure 11.1 shows sperm swarming around an egg in a Fallopian tube.) Ova contain chromosomes, proteins, fats, and nutritious fluid and are surrounded by a gelatinous layer called the **zona pellucida.** This layer must be penetrated if fertilization is to occur. Sperm that have completed their journey secrete the enzyme **hyaluronidase,** which briefly thins the zona pellucida, enabling one sperm to penetrate. Once a sperm has entered, the zona pellucida thickens, locking other sperm out. The corresponding chromosomes in the sperm and ovum line up opposite each other. Conception occurs as the chromosomes from the sperm and ovum combine to form 23 new pairs, which carry a unique set of genetic instructions.

OPTIMIZING THE CHANCES OF CONCEPTION

Some couples may wish to optimize their chances of conceiving during a particular month so that birth occurs at a desired time. Others may have difficulty conceiving and wish to maximize their chances for a few months before consulting a fertility specialist. Some fairly simple procedures can dramatically increase the chances of conceiving for couples without serious fertility problems.

The ovum can be fertilized for about 4 to 20 hours after ovulation. Sperm are most active within 48 hours after ejaculation. So one way of optimizing the chances of conception is to engage in coitus within a few hours of ovulation. There are a number of ways to predict ovulation.

USING THE BASAL BODY TEMPERATURE CHART   Few women have perfectly regular cycles, so they can only guess when they are ovulating. A basal body temperature (BBT) chart (see Figure 11.2, page 308) may help provide a more reliable estimate.

As shown in the figure, body temperature is fairly even before ovulation, and early morning body temperature is generally below 98.6 degrees Fahrenheit. But just prior to ovulation, basal temperature dips slightly. Then, on the day following ovulation, temperature tends to rise by about 0.4 to 0.8 degree above the level before ovulation and to remain higher until menstruation. In using the BBT method, a women attempts to detect these temperature changes by tracking her temperature just after awakening each morning but before rising from bed. Thermometers that provide finely graded readings, such as electronic digital thermometers, are best suited for determining these minor changes. The couple record the woman's temperature and the day of the cycle (as well as the day of the month) and indicate whether they have engaged in coitus. With regular charting for six months, the woman may learn to predict the day of ovulation more accurately—assuming that her cycles are fairly regular.

Opinion is divided as to whether it is better for couples to have coitus every 24 hours or every 36 to 48 hours for the several-day period during which ovulation is expected. More frequent coitus around the time of ovulation may increase the chances of conception. Relatively less frequent (that is, every 36 to 48 hours) coitus leads to a higher sperm count during each ejaculation. Most fertility specialists recommend that couples seeking to conceive a baby have intercourse once every day or two during the week in which the woman expects to ovulate. Men with lower than normal sperm counts may be advised to wait 48 hours between ejaculations, however (Speroff et al., 1985).

ANALYZING URINE FOR LUTEINIZING HORMONE Over-the-counter kits are more accurate than the BBT method and predict ovulation by analyzing the woman's urine for the surge in luteinizing hormone (LH) that precedes ovulation by about 12 to 24 hours. The kits are expensive, however, and careful testing of the woman's urine each morning is required.

TRACKING THE VAGINAL MUCUS Women can track the thickness of their vaginal mucus during the phases of the menstrual cycle by rolling it between their fingers and noting changes in texture. The mucus is thick, white, and cloudy during most phases of the cycle, but becomes thin, slippery, and clear for a few days preceding ovulation. A day or so after ovulation the mucus again thickens and becomes opaque.

ADDITIONAL CONSIDERATIONS Coitus in the male-superior position allows sperm to be deposited deeper in the vagina and minimizes leakage of sperm out of the vagina due to gravity. Women may improve their chances of conceiving by lying on their backs and drawing their knees close to their breasts following ejaculation. This position, perhaps aided by the use of a pillow beneath the buttocks, may prevent sperm from dripping out quickly and elevates the pool of semen in relation to the cervix, causing gravity to work for rather than against conception. Women may also avoid standing, and lie as still

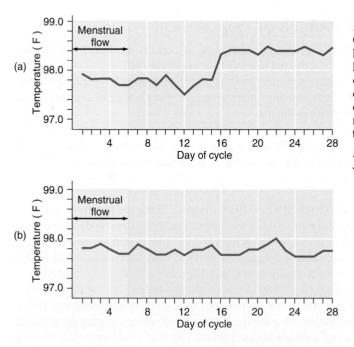

FIGURE 11.2 A Basal Body Temperature (BBT) Chart. Body temperature dips slightly just prior to ovulation, rises about 0.4 to 0.8 of a degree following ovulation, and remains elevated through the course of the cycle. Part (a) represents a cycle in which a sustained elevation in temperature occurred following ovulation on day 15. Part (b) shows no sustained temperature rise, which is indicative of an absence of ovulation in this cycle.

Source: Adapted from Kolodny, R. C., Masters, W.H., and Johnson, V.E. (1979). *Textbook of sexual medicine.*

as possible, for about 30 to 60 minutes following ejaculation to help sperm move toward the cervical opening.

Women with severely retroverted or "tipped" uteruses may profit from supporting themselves on their elbows and knees and having their partners enter them from behind. Again, this position helps prevent semen from dripping out of the vagina.

The man should penetrate the woman as deeply as possible just prior to ejaculation, hold still during ejaculation, then withdraw slowly in a straight line to avoid dispersing the pool of semen.

SELECTING THE GENDER OF YOUR CHILD

Folklore is filled with peculiar beliefs about methods of preselecting the gender of one's children. Some cultures have advised coitus under the full moon to conceive boys. The Greek philosopher Aristotle suggested that making love during a north wind would beget sons, but a south wind would produce daughters. Eating sour foods was once suggested to parents seeking to have boys. Those seeking girls were advised to consume sweets. Husbands who yearned to have boys were sometimes advised to wear their boots to bed. The thesis that the right testicle was responsible for seeding boys was popular at one time. Eighteenth-century French noblemen were advised to have their left testicles removed if they wanted to sire sons. It should go without saying that none of these methods worked. More recent methods sound more reasonable, if less colorful. Not all scholars concur that they are much more reliable, however.

SHETTLES'S APPROACH   Landrum Shettles (1982) notes that sperm bearing the Y sex chromosome are smaller than those bearing the X sex chromosome and are faster swimmers. But sperm with the X sex chromosome are more durable. From these assumptions, Shettles and other researchers derive a number of strategies for choosing the gender of one's children.

In order to increase the chances of having a boy, (1) the man should not ejaculate for several days preceding his partner's expected time of ovulation; (2) the couple should engage in coitus on the day of ovulation; (3) the man should be penetrating deeply at the moment of ejaculation; and (4) the woman can lower the acidity of the vagina and make it more hospitable to sperm bearing Y sex chromosomes by douching with 2 tablespoons of baking soda to a quart of warm water before coitus.

In order to increase the chances of having a girl, (1) the couple should engage in coitus two days (or slightly more) before ovulation; (2) the woman should raise the acidity of the vagina by douching with 2 tablespoons of vinegar per quart of warm water before coitus; (3) the woman should avoid orgasm following her partner's ejaculation on the (debatable) assumption that orgasm facilitates the journey of sperm; and (4) the man should ejaculate at a shallow depth of penetration.

A combination of these methods has been asserted to result in the conception of a child of the desired sex in about 80 percent of cases (Kogan, 1973), but many observers regard these figures as exaggerated (Carson, 1988).

SPERM-SEPARATION PROCEDURES   Several sperm-separation procedures are now in use (Jancin, 1988). One is based on the relative swimming rates of Y- and X-bearing sperm. In this method, which is intended to increase the chances of conceiving a boy, semen is placed at the top of a test tube containing albumin. Albumin, a thick liquid protein that is similar to egg white, slows the progress of X-bearing sperm to a greater degree than it does the faster-swimming Y-bearing sperm. The Y-bearing sperm move to the bottom more quickly than the X-bearing sperm. The sperm at the bottom of the tube are then collected and used in artificial insemination. This method reportedly has led to conception of boys 75 percent of the time, as compared to the usual 53 percent (Glass & Ericsson, 1982).

Other sperm-separation methods rely on the differences in electrical charges of the two types of sperm to separate them. Sperm-separation approaches in general reportedly have success rates of about 80 percent (Carson, 1988).

Where Are the Millions of Missing Women?

Cultural preferences for boys might cause the proportion of male births to mushroom in many cultures if gender pre-selection were more available. Because of gender preferences, gender-preselection technology has been criticized as "stupen-dously sexist" (Powledge, 1981).

Consider the potential effects of gender preselection in China, a culture that has imposed a one-child-per-family limit in order to reduce its population, now estimated to be 1.17 billion people (Kristof, 1993). Shulan Jiao and his colleagues at the Chinese Academy of Sciences note that the preference of Chinese families for boys is already jeopardizing China's family-planning goal of one child per family. The preference stems from the belief that men are nat-urally superior to women. Thus, it is considered a "misfortune" for a family to be without a male child (Jiao et al., 1986, p. 357). Given this traditional prejudice against girls, what might happen if Chinese couples could select the gender of their children but continued to be pressured to have just one child? Might China's population problems

be eliminated in a generation? What of successive generations? Would sufficient numbers of girls be born to stabilize the pop-ulation?

Some form of "family plan-ning" after birth may already be taking place in China and other nations (Kristof, 1991a, 1993). A review of 1989 birth records in China shows that female births are about 8 percent lower than would be normally expected, which translates into some 900,000 "missing" infant girls annually (Kristof, 1993). Are these infant girls, as some sus-pect, killed at birth by midwives on the orders of parents who are intent on having sons? Or are they reared secretly by parents who seek to evade the one-child-per-family rule? As ultrasound equipment in Chinese hospitals has become more widely avail-able, perhaps parents are mak-ing use of such techniques to learn whether the fetus is male, and if not, electing to abort the pregnancy and try again (Kristof, 1993). Most Chinese deny that female infanticide is a common practice, but Kristof (1991a) reports that some newborn girls are drowned by midwives who

keep a bucket by the mother's side for this purpose. The births may be reported as stillbirths.

Many cultures other than China have traditionally placed greater value on the births of sons than daughters, in part because sons are typically raised to fulfill breadwinner roles that provide parents with economic security in their old age. Based on the usual male-to-female birth ratio, Kristof (1991a) estimated that nearly 23 million women are "missing" in India, 3 million in Pakistan, 1.6 million in Bangladesh, 600,000 in Egypt, and 200,000 in Nepal. The prevalence of infanticide is unknown, but in many cases the baby girls apparently die early from various kinds of neglect. For example, family members may view an infant daughter with diarrhea as a nuisance, even though they view the same prob-lem in a boy as a medical crisis that requires the intervention of a doctor. When there is a contest for scarce food in an impover-ished household, boys may be given preference.

All in all, the world is a more dangerous place for infant girls.

INFERTILITY AND ALTERNATIVE WAYS OF BECOMING PARENTS

Infertility
Inability to conceive a child.

For couples who want children, there are perhaps few problems more frustrating than the inability to conceive. Physicians often recommend that couples try to conceive on their own for six months before seeking medical assistance. The term **infertility** is usually not applied until the failure to conceive has persisted for more than a year.

Infertility represents a pressing health concern for millions of Americans. This is partially the result of a steep rise in couples who postpone childbearing until their thirties and even forties. Infertility occurs in about one couple in 20 in which the woman is in

Discussion Question: The *definition* of infertility has been changing. Infertility used to be defined as the failure of a couple to conceive on their own for five years. This length of time was first lowered to two years and later lowered to one year. What forces may have played a role in these changes? What effects might the changes in definition have had?

Motility
Self-propulsion. A measure of the viability of sperm cells.

Autoimmune response
The production of antibodies that attack naturally occurring substances that are (incorrectly) recognized as being foreign or harmful.

Learning Objective 4: Describe the causes of infertility in males and females.

her twenties (Menken et al., 1986). The proportion of infertile couples rises to one in four among couples in their thirties (Silber, 1991). Overall, about one in twelve U.S. couples in which the wife is under the age of 45 is infertile (Leary, 1990). Another 10 percent have fewer children than they want (Gordon & Snyder, 1989). Moreover, many women, about one in four, experience at least one period of infertility during their reproductive years (Jones & Toner, 1993). About half of couples with infertility eventually succeed in conceiving a child (Jones & Toner, 1993). As we see, there are many different treatment options available, ranging from drugs to stimulate ovulation to the use of newer reproductive technologies, such as in vitro fertilization.

MALE FERTILITY PROBLEMS

Although most concerns about fertility have traditionally centered on the woman, fertility specialists believe that the source of infertility among couples is now roughly about equal between males and females—40 percent of the time problems are primarily traced to females and 40 percent to males, and in 20 percent of cases the cause is unknown or attributed to problems shared by both partners (Hatcher et al., 1990).

About one young man in 20 in the United States is believed to be infertile. Fertility problems in the male reflect abnormalities such as (1) low sperm count; (2) large numbers of irregularly shaped sperm, such as sperm with malformed heads or tails; (3) low sperm **motility** (sluggish movement); (4) chronic diseases like diabetes, as well as infectious diseases like sexually transmitted diseases; (5) injury to the testes; (6) an **autoimmune response** in which antibodies produced by the man deactivate his own sperm; and (7) a pituitary imbalance and/or thyroid disease. Problems in producing normal, abundant sperm may be caused by genetic factors, advanced age, hormonal problems, diabetes, injuries to the testes, varicose veins in the scrotum, drugs (alcohol, narcotics, marijuana, tobacco), exposure to environmental toxins or excess heat, and emotional stress.

Sperm production gradually declines with age, but normal aging does not produce infertility. Men in late adulthood have fathered children, even though conception may require more attempts.

Low sperm count (or the absence of sperm) is the most common problem. Sperm counts of 40 million to 150 million sperm per milliliter of semen are considered normal, and a count of fewer than 20 million is generally regarded as low. Sperm production may be low among men with undescended testes that were not surgically corrected prior to puberty. Frequent ejaculation can reduce sperm counts. Sperm production may also be impaired in men whose testicles are consistently 1 or 2 degrees above the typical scrotal temperature of 94 to 95 degrees Fahrenheit (Leary, 1990). Frequent hot baths and tight-fitting underwear can also reduce sperm production, at least temporarily. In an early study, Robinson and Rock (1967) constructed an athletic supporter that raised scrotal temperature by about 1.7 degrees Fahrenheit. Wearing the device for seven weeks lowered sperm counts by about 25 percent. Some men may encounter fertility problems from prolonged athletic activity, use of electric blankets, or even long, hot baths. In such cases the problem can be readily corrected. Male runners with fertility problems are often counseled to take some weeks off to increase their sperm counts.

Sometimes the sperm count is adequate, but prostate, hormonal, or other factors deprive sperm of motility or cause them to be deformed. Motility can also be hampered by scar tissue from infections, which may prevent sperm from passing through parts of the male reproductive system, such as the vas deferens. To be considered normal, sperm must be able to swim for at least two hours following coitus and most (60% or more) must be normal in shape (Glass, 1986).

TRUTH OR *FICTION?*

R E V I S I T E D

Prolonged athletic activity may decrease fertility in the male. True. Prolonged athletic activity can raise the temperature of the scrotum, providing a less-than-optimal environment for sperm. •

Discussion Question:
Should insurance plans pay for fertility treatments? If your answer is yes, should insurance plans limit the choices of infertility treatments based on factors such as cost per attempt, success rates, or age of prospective mother?

Artificial insemination
The introduction of sperm in the reproductive tract through means other than sexual intercourse.

Notes: In 1989 in Tennessee, a divorcing couple battled over their seven frozen embryos. The judge ruled that "life begins at conception" and awarded custody of the "children, existing in vitro" to the wife. The Tennessee Court of Appeals ordered joint custody, stating that "even after viability, human embryos are not given legal status equivalent to that of a person already born." The question is whether these embryos are "lives" or property to be divided. (*New England Journal of Medicine,* October 25, 1990, 1200–1202; *Ms.,* May/June 1991.)

Endometriosis
An abnormal condition in which endometrial tissue is sloughed off into the abdominal cavity rather than out of the body during menstruation. The condition is characterized by abdominal pain and may cause infertility.

Treatment of male infertility has not progressed as rapidly as treatment of female infertility, but some progress has been made. Sperm counts have been increased by surgical repair of the varicose veins in the scrotum, and microsurgery can be helpful in opening blocked passageways that prevent the outflow of sperm (Silber, 1991). Experimenters are now investigating the effects on sperm production of special cooling undergarments. One device, described as a kind of athletic supporter that is kept slightly damp with distilled water, has been approved by the Federal Drug Administration. Seventy percent of the men whose infertility is due to higher-than-normal scrotal temperatures show increased sperm count and quality with the wearing of cooling undergarments (Leary, 1990; Silber, 1991).

ARTIFICIAL INSEMINATION The sperm of men with low sperm counts can be collected and quick-frozen. The sperm from multiple ejaculations can then be injected into a woman's uterus at the time of ovulation. This is one **artificial insemination** procedure. The sperm of men with low sperm motility can also be injected into their partners' uteruses, so that the sperm begin their journey closer to the Fallopian tubes. Sperm from a donor can be used to artificially inseminate a woman whose partner is completely infertile or has an extremely low sperm count. The child then bears the genes of one of the parents, the mother. A donor can be chosen who resembles the man in physical traits and ethnic background.

FEMALE FERTILITY PROBLEMS

The major causes of infertility in women include (1) ovulation irregularity or failure to ovulate; (2) obstructions or malfunctions of the reproductive tract, which are often caused by infections or diseases involving the woman's reproductive tract; and (3) endometriosis. Additionally, declining hormone levels of estrogen and progesterone that occur with aging may prevent the ovum from becoming fertilized or remaining implanted in the uterus.

About 10 to 15 percent of female infertility problems stem from ovulation failure (Frisch, 1988). Many factors can play a role in failure to ovulate, including hormonal irregularities, malnutrition, genetic factors, stress, and chronic disease. Failure to ovulate may occur in response to extreme dieting, as in the case of the eating disorder *anorexia nervosa.* But even women who are only 10 to 15 percent below their normal body weights may fail to ovulate (Frisch, 1988).

Ovulation may often be induced by the use of fertility drugs such as *clomiphene* (Clomid), which stimulates the pituitary gland to secrete FSH and LH, which in turn stimulates maturation of ova. Clomiphene leads to conception in 80 to 90 percent of cases of infertility that are due *solely* to irregular or absent ovulation (Reinisch, 1990). But since infertility can have multiple causes, only about 50 percent of women who use clomiphene become pregnant. Another infertility drug, Pergonal, contains a high concentration of FSH, which directly stimulates maturation of ovarian follicles. Like clomiphene, Pergonal is associated with high rates of success in. women with infertility due to the failure to ovulate. Clomiphene and Pergonal have been linked to multiple births, including quadruplets and even quintuplets. Only a relatively small percentage (less than 10%) of such pregnancies result in multiple births, however.

Other causes of female infertility include cervical mucus that impedes the passage of sperm, antibodies produced by the woman that destroy sperm, and local infections that scar the Fallopian tubes and other organs, impeding the passage of sperm or ova. Such infections include pelvic inflammatory disease (PID)—an inflammation of the woman's internal reproductive tract that can be caused by various infectious agents, such as the bacteria responsible for gonorrhea and chlamydia (see Chapter 16). Women who have a history of one or more episodes of PID stand about a 20 percent chance of becoming sterile (Menken et al., 1986).

In **endometriosis**, cells break away from the uterine lining (the endometrium) and become implanted and grow elsewhere. When they develop on the surface of the ovaries or Fallopian tubes, they may block the passage of ova or impair conception for reasons

Laparoscopy

A medical procedure in which a long, narrow tube (laparoscope) is inserted through an incision in the navel, permitting the visual inspection of organs in the pelvic cavity. (From the Greek *lapara,* meaning "flank.")

Rubin test

A test in which carbon dioxide gas is blown through the cervix and its progress through the reproductive tract is tracked to determine whether or not the Fallopian tubes are blocked.

Learning Objective 5: List and describe alternate ways of becoming parents.

that are not well understood. About 15 percent of cases of female sterility are believed to be due to endometriosis (Halme, 1985). Hormone treatments and microsurgery are sometimes successful in reducing the blockage to the point that women can conceive. A physician may suspect endometriosis during a pelvic exam, but it is diagnosed with certainty by **laparoscopy.** A long, narrow tube is inserted through an incision in the navel, permitting the physician to inspect the organs in the pelvic cavity visually. The incision is practically undetectable.

Suspected blockage of the Fallopian tubes may also be checked by a **Rubin test** or a **hysterosalpingogram.** In a Rubin test, carbon dioxide gas is blown through the cervix. Its pressure is then monitored to determine whether it flows freely through the Fallopian tubes into the abdomen or is trapped in the uterus. In the more common hysterosalpingogram, the movement of an injected dye is monitored by X-rays. This procedure may be uncomfortable.

Several new methods have been recently introduced to help couples, with problems such as blocked Fallopian tubes, bear children.

IN VITRO FERTILIZATION   When Louise Brown was born in England in 1978 after being conceived by the method of **in vitro fertilization** (IVF), the event made headlines around the world. Louise was dubbed the world's first test-tube baby, although conception took place in a laboratory dish (not a test tube) and the fetus developed normally within the mother's uterus after implantation. With in vitro fertilization, the woman is first given fertility drugs to stimulate ovum production. Mature ova are then surgically removed from an ovary and placed in a laboratory dish along with the father's sperm. Fertilized ova are then injected into the mother's uterus to become implanted in the uterine wall.

TRUTH OR FICTION?

REVISITED

A "test-tube baby" is grown in a large laboratory dish throughout the nine-month gestation period. A "test-tube baby" is actually conceived in a laboratory dish (which is similar to a test tube, perhaps), but the fertilized egg is then placed in the mother's uterus where it must become implanted if it is to develop to term. •

Hysterosalpingogram

A test in which a dye is injected into the reproductive tract and its progress is tracked by X-rays to determine whether or not the Fallopian tubes are blocked. (From roots meaning "record of," "uterus," and "Fallopian tubes.")

In vitro fertilization

A method of conception in which mature ova are surgically removed from an ovary and placed in a laboratory dish along with sperm.

Gamete intrafallopian transfer (GIFT)

A method of conception in which sperm and ova are inserted into a Fallopian tube to encourage conception.

GIFT   In a more recently developed procedure, **gamete intrafallopian transfer,** or GIFT, sperm and ova are inserted together into a Fallopian tube where it is hoped fertilization will occur. Unlike in vitro fertilization, conception occurs in a Fallopian tube rather than in a laboratory dish.

ZIFT   ZIFT (**zygote intrafallopian transfer**) involves a combination of IVF and GIFT. Sperm and ova are combined in a laboratory dish. Following fertilization, the zygote is placed in the mother's Fallopian tube to begin its journey to the uterus for implantation. ZIFT has an advantage over GIFT in that the fertility specialists can ascertain that fertilization has occurred before insertion is performed.

DONOR IVF   **Donor IVF** is a variation of the IVF procedure in which the ovum is taken from another woman, fertilized, and then injected into the uterus or Fallopian tube of the intended mother. The procedure is used in cases in which the intended mother does not produce ova.

EMBRYONIC TRANSFER   A similar method for women who do not produce ova of their own is **embryonic transfer.** In this method a woman volunteer is artificially inseminated by the male partner of the infertile woman. Five days later the embryo is removed from the volunteer and inserted within the uterus of the mother-to-be, where it is hoped that it will implant in the uterine wall and be carried to term.

In vitro and transfer methods are costly, and they succeed in only a minority of cases. IVF or GIFT procedures typically cost about $5,000 per attempt. Still, measurable progress is being made in these methods. In the mid-1980s the top IVF clinics reported

Zygote intrafallopian transfer (ZIFT)
A method of conception in which an ovum is fertilized in a laboratory dish and then placed in a Fallopian tube.

Donor IVF
A variation of in vitro fertilization in which the ovum is taken from one woman, fertilized, and then injected into the uterus or Fallopian tube of another woman.

Embryonic transfer
A method of conception in which a woman volunteer is artificially inseminated by the male partner of the intended mother, after which the embryo is removed from the volunteer and inserted within the uterus of the intended mother.

Surrogate mother
A woman who is impregnated through artificial insemination, with the sperm of a prospective father, carries the embryo and fetus to term, and then gives the child to the prospective parents.

Learning Objective 6:
Examine the biological and psychological effects of pregnancy.

Teaching Tip: Instead of lecturing about the alternative methods of becoming a parent, have students suggest and describe them. Then discuss how many "parents" each resulting infant would have. Discuss the moral and legal issues surrounding each method.

success rates not much higher than 15 or 20 percent, even with multiple attempts. Advances in techniques have recently increased success rates at the better clinics to 40 percent or higher (Elmer-Dewitt, 1991). Success with in vitro fertilization drops off sharply with increasing age in women, declining from nearly 30 percent in women in their mid-twenties to 10 to 15 percent in women in their late thirties (Toner et al., 1991). As success remains elusive in many cases, frustration and lack of hope often lead couples to consider dropping out of infertility treatment programs (Blenner, 1992). Moreover, the stress of coping with infertility often takes a toll on marital adjustment (Ulbrich et al., 1990).

SURROGATE MOTHERS The use of **surrogate mothers** has become more commonplace in recent years among couples in which the woman is infertile. Still, the occurrence of surrogacy is relatively rare, with only some 2,000 births by surrogacy reported during the 1980s ("Women under assault," 1990). For a fee in the range of $10,000 to $20,000 plus medical expenses, the surrogate mother is artificially inseminated by the husband of the infertile woman and carries the baby to term. The surrogate signs a contract to turn the baby over to the infertile couple. Such contracts have been invalidated in some states, however, so that surrogate mothers in these states cannot be compelled to hand over the babies.

Adoption represents yet another way to resolve infertility. Despite the occasional conflicts in which adoptive parents are pitted against biological parents who have changed their minds about giving their children up for adoption, most adoptions result in the formation of loving new families. Because fewer single mothers are relinquishing healthy newborns for adoption, this form of adoption is harder to come by than it was in the past. Yet it is still very much an option. Additionally, many couples seek to adopt infants from other countries or infants with special needs and older children who desperately need loving families.

PREGNANCY

Women and men react to the news of a pregnancy in different ways. For those who are psychologically and economically prepared, the pregnancy may be greeted with joyous celebration. Some women feel that pregnancy helps fulfill their sense of womanhood:

> Being pregnant meant I was a woman. I was enthralled with my belly growing. I went out right away and got maternity clothes.

> It gave me a sense that I was actually a woman. I had never felt sexy before . . . I felt very voluptuous.

> (*Our Bodies, Ourselves,* 1979, pp. 259–260)

On the other hand, an unwanted pregnancy may evoke fear. Even couples who desire pregnancy may have mixed feelings upon learning the news.

In this section we examine biological and psychological aspects of pregnancy, including early signs of pregnancy, prenatal development, possible biological complications, effects of drugs and sex on pregnancy, and the psychological experiences of pregnant women and fathers. First, however, we invite you to consider the question, "Should you have a child?"

EARLY SIGNS OF PREGNANCY

For many women the first sign of pregnancy is missing a period. This signal may be greeted with joy or despair, depending on whether they want the pregnancy and are prepared for it. But some women have irregular menstrual cycles or may miss a period because of stress. So missing a period is not a fully reliable indicator. Some women also experience cyclic bleeding or spotting during pregnancy, although the blood flow is usually lighter than normal. If a woman's basal body temperature remains high for about three weeks after ovulation, there is reason to suspect pregnancy even if she spots two weeks after ovulation.

PREGNANCY TESTS

You may have heard your parents say that they learned your mother was pregnant by means of the "rabbit test," in which a sample of the woman's urine was injected into a laboratory animal. This procedure, which was once commonly used to confirm pregnancy, relied on the fact that women produce **human chorionic gonadotropin** (HCG) shortly after conception. HCG causes rabbits, mice, or rats to ovulate.

Today, pregnancy may be confirmed in minutes by means of tests that directly detect HCG. Tests can detect HCG in the urine as early as the third week of pregnancy. A blood test—the *beta subunit HCG radioimmunoassay* (RIA)—can accurately detect HCG in the woman's blood as early as the eighth day of pregnancy, or about five days preceding her expected period.

Over-the-counter home pregnancy tests are also available. They too test the woman's urine for HCG and are intended to be used as early as one day after a missed period. Laboratory-based tests are considered 98 or 99 percent accurate, but home-based tests performed by laypersons are nearly 10 percent less accurate (Hicks & Iosefsohn, 1989). A woman should see a physician if she suspects that she is pregnant or to confirm a home pregnancy test result.

About a month after a woman misses her period, a health professional may be able to confirm pregnancy by pelvic examination. Women who are pregnant usually show **Hegar's sign.** Hegar's sign is softness of a section of the uterus between the uterine body and the cervix, which may be palpated (felt) by the woman's physician by placing a hand on the abdomen and two fingers in the vagina.

EARLY EFFECTS OF PREGNANCY

Just a few days after conception, a woman may note tenderness of the breasts. Hormonal stimulation of the mammary glands may make the breasts more sensitive and cause sensations of tingling and fullness.

Morning sickness, which may actually occur throughout the day, refers to the nausea, food aversions, and vomiting experienced during pregnancy. About half of all pregnant women experience morning sickness during the first few months of pregnancy (Thompson, 1993). In some cases, morning sickness is so severe that the woman cannot eat regularly and must be hospitalized to ensure that she and the fetus receive adequate nutrition. Morning sickness usually subsides by about the twelfth week of pregnancy. Pregnant women may also experience greater-than-normal fatigue during the early weeks, so that they sleep longer and fall asleep more readily than usual. Frequent urination, which may also be experienced, is caused by pressure from the swelling uterus on the bladder.

MISCARRIAGE (SPONTANEOUS ABORTION)

Miscarriages have many causes, including chromosomal defects in the fetus and abnormalities of the placenta and uterus. About three in four miscarriages occur in the first 16 weeks of pregnancy, and the great majority of these occur in the first seven weeks (Samuels & Samuels, 1986). Some miscarriages occur so early that the woman is not aware that she was pregnant.

Following a miscarriage, a couple may feel a deep sense of loss, especially when the miscarriage occurs later in pregnancy. The couple who suffer a miscarriage may undergo a period of mourning (Blakeslee, 1988; Cole, 1987). Emotional support from friends and family often help the couple cope with the loss. In most cases women who miscarry can carry subsequent pregnancies to term.

SEX DURING PREGNANCY

Most health professionals concur that coitus is safe throughout the course of pregnancy until the start of labor, provided that the pregnancy is developing normally and the woman has no

Whose Baby Is It?

On March 27, 1986, a baby was born to Mary Beth Whitehead, a married mother of two children. The father was not Mary Beth's husband, but another man, William Stern, who with his wife Elizabeth had hired Mary Beth as a surrogate mother. The Sterns had been unable to conceive a child on their own because of Elizabeth's infertility. For a fee of $10,000, Mary Beth agreed to be inseminated with William's sperm, carry the resulting pregnancy to term, and deliver the baby to the Sterns upon birth, surrendering her parental rights. Mary Beth did give the baby, named Sara by Mary Beth, and Melissa by the Sterns, to the Sterns three days after its birth. She then changed her mind and demanded custody, setting in motion a court battle for "Baby M" that eventually led to a ruling by the New Jersey Supreme Court that invalidated the surrogacy contract and voided Mrs. Stern's adoption of the baby. The court held that a contract that requires a natural mother to surrender her baby at birth is invalid. Moreover, it held that the payment of money to a surrogate for surrendering parental rights may have represented a criminal act of "baby selling." Whereas Mary Beth was affirmed as the child's legal mother, the court held that the best interests of the child would be served by awarding custody to the baby's natural father, William Stern. Mrs. Whitehead, as both the legal and natural mother, was awarded visitation rights.

Other surrogacy cases are still before the courts, so the legality of surrogacy remains unsettled. Some states, following suit from the "Baby M" ruling, have invalidated surrogacy contracts, so surrogate mothers cannot be compelled to hand over the babies. Rights to custody, however, generally are determined based on what is "best" for the child (Cahill, 1988).

Superficially, surrogate motherhood might seem the mirror image of the technique in which a fertile woman is artificially inseminated with the sperm of a donor. But many important psychological and social issues are raised by the practice. For one thing, sperm donors usually do not know the identity of the women who have received their sperm. Nor do they observe their children developing within the mothers-to-be. However, surrogate mothers are involved through the entire process of prenatal development. Some surrogates, like Mrs. Whitehead, have a genetic link to the babies they conceive, having been artificially inseminated by the husbands of infertile women. Others, however, carry to term a fetus conceived in a laboratory dish from the sperm and ovum of the infertile couple and then implanted in their uterus. In the second case both members of the infertile couple contribute their genes to the resulting child while the surrogate serves merely a gestational role and has no genetic connection to the baby. Who, then, is the baby's "natural" mother?

Ethical and legal dilemmas revolve around the facts that most surrogate mothers contribute an ovum to the child and that, even when the child is conceived in a laboratory dish, surrogate mothers nevertheless sense the babies developing within them and can grow attached to them. Opponents of surrogacy argue that it represents a form of "baby selling" or exchange of parenting rights for money. Defenders, however, point out that surrogate mothers are paid for the services they provide, such as being artificially inseminated and carrying the pregnancy to term, not for turning over their parenting rights (Gostin, 1988; Steinbock, 1988). To some social critics, surrogate motherhood is one more instance of exploitation of the poor by the rich. That is, surrogacy exploits poor and undereducated women who are forced by economic necessity to sell their intimate services to more affluent but infertile couples (Gostin, 1988; Radin, 1987). From this perspective, the surrogate mother allows her body to be used (as a prostitute might allow her body to be used), and ultimately she must surrender the child that she might wish to retain. However, some surrogates are primarily motivated by the feelings of self-worth that derive from performing an altruistic act for others by providing them with a child they could not otherwise have (Steinbock, 1988). In such cases it is far from clear that the surrogate is being exploited (Steinbock, 1988). On the other hand, opponents argue that surrogacy is degrading to pregnant women, as it treats them simply as vessels (Annas, 1988). Civil libertarians have argued that people in our society hold rights to privacy that permit them to exercise choice in reproductive matters, including a right to bear children for infertile couples, so long as their actions cause no actual harm to others, especially the resulting child (Robertson, 1988). Note, however, that there are very few answers about the long-term effects of surrogacy and other alternative ways of becoming parents on the children involved (Elias & Annas, 1986).

Ethical and legal concerns about surrogacy also call into question some of the new reproductive technologies, such as donor IVF and embryonic transfer. It is now possible for women to have babies after menopause (by receiving donor eggs) or to become grandmothers to their own children (by using eggs donated by their daughters) (Kolata, 1994). It may even become possible in the near future for a woman to receive a transplanted ovary from an aborted fetus and later give birth to a child whose biological mother was the aborted fetus (Kolata, 1994). These reproductive technologies have leapfrogged ahead of society's efforts to grapple with their ethical, moral, and legal implications. What if a woman volunteer who undergoes donor IVF or embryonic transfer later changes her mind and demands parental rights, arguing that she has a genetic link to the resulting child even though she didn't carry it to term? The legal basis of such claims has not yet

been tested in the courts. Should women who donate their eggs to infertile couples be paid? Might such donation exploit poor women who may become egg donors because of economic pressures? Most women receiving donor IVF typically obtain eggs from unpaid volunteers (typically friends or relatives), but several medical centers have compiled lists of paid egg donors, typically college women who are generally attracted by the money (about $2,000 for each egg-removal procedure; Kolata, 1991f). Why shouldn't

egg donors be paid, advocates argue, since men who donate sperm are typically paid for their services? (Admittedly men are paid much less, about $40 each time. But egg donation is a riskier, more intrusive, and time-consuming process than sperm donation.) In your opinion, where should the line be drawn in determining how far medical science should be permitted to go in providing reproductive alternatives to infertile couples?

Gestational Carrier. Advances in reproductive technology now make it possible for women to have babies after menopause (by receiving donor eggs) or to become grandmothers to their own children (by using eggs donated by their daughters). This woman, age 45, is a gestational carrier for her daughter; an egg from her daughter was fertilized by sperm from her daughter's husband and then implanted in her uterus. The woman's daughter could not have children of her own because she was born without a uterus.

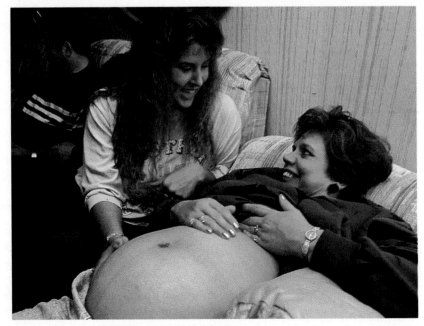

QUESTIONNAIRE

Should You Have a Child?

Deciding whether or not to have children is among the most significant life decisions you're likely to face. Children have a way of needing a generation (or a lifetime) of love and support. We have no simplistic answers to this question, no standardized questionnaire that yields a score for a "Go."

Instead, we offer the following questionnaire to help you consider some of the reasons to have or not to have children. This listing of reasons may offer you some insight into your own motives. You can check the blank spaces of the pros and cons to see how many pros you come up with and how many cons. But we don't pretend that each item in the list is equal in weight, or that your total score should govern your decision. You be the judge. It's your life (and, perhaps, your children's lives) and your choice.

Reasons to Have Children

Researchers have compiled the following reasons for having children (Berelson, 1979; Campbell et al., 1982; Daniels & Weingarten, 1982; Hoffman & Manis, 1978). Check those that seem to apply to you:

_____ 1. *Personal experience.* Having children is a unique experience. To many people, no other experience compares with having the opportunity to love them, experience their love, help shape their lives, and watch them develop.

_____ 2. *Personal pleasure.* There is fun and pleasure in playing with children, taking them to the zoo and the circus, and viewing the world through their fresh, innocent eyes.

_____ 3. *Personal extension.* Children carry on our family heritage, and some of our own wishes and dreams, beyond the confines of our own mortality. We name them after ourselves or others in our families, and see them as extensions of ourselves. We identify with their successes.

_____ 4. *Loving relationship.* Parents have the opportunity to establish extremely close and cherished bonds with other human beings.

_____ 5. *Personal status.* Within our culture, parents are afforded respect just because they are parents. Consider the commandment: "Honor thy father and thy mother."

_____ 6. *Personal competence.* Parenthood is a challenge. Competence in the social roles of mother or father is a potential source of gratification to many people.

_____ 7. *Personal responsibility.* Parents have the opportunity to be responsible for the welfare and education of their children.

_____ 8. *Companionship for the later years.* Many people expect their children will provide them with comfort, companionship, and perhaps crucial aid, in their later years.

_____ 9. *Moral worth.* Some people feel that having children provides the opportunity for a moral, selfless act in which they place the needs of others—their children—ahead of their own.

_____ 10. *Religious beliefs.* The biblical injunction to bear fruit and multiply" is followed by many people across a range of religious affiliations.

---

history of miscarriages. But women who experience bleeding or cramps during pregnancy may be advised by their obstetricians not to engage in coitus (Samuels & Samuels, 1986).

Masters and Johnson (1966) reported an initial decline in sexual interest among pregnant women during the first trimester, followed by increased interest during the second trimester and then another decline during the third. They also noted that many women decrease their sexual activity and have less interest during the first trimester because of fatigue, nausea, or misguided concerns that coitus will harm the embryo or fetus. Also during the first trimester, vasocongestion may cause tenderness of the breasts, discouraging fondling or sucking. But by and large, coital rates remain high through the first two trimesters and then fall sharply in the eighth and ninth months (Mills, 1981; Solberg et al., 1974). Researchers in Israel reported a gradual decline in sexual drive and

Reasons Not to Have Children

Researchers have also compiled reasons cited by many couples for deciding not to have children (Benedek & Vaughn, 1982; Bernard, 1975; Campbell et al., 1982; McFalls, 1983; Sunday & Lewin, 1985). Check those that you endorse:

_____ 1. *Strain on earth's resources.* Because the world is overpopulated, it is wrong to place additional strain on limited resources. More children will only geometrically increase the problem of overpopulation.

_____ 2. *Time together.* Child-free couples may be able to spend more time together as a couple and develop a more intimate relationship.

_____ 3. *Freedom.* Children have a way of erasing leisure time. They may also make it more difficult to pursue educational and vocational advancement. Child-free couples may be more able to live spontaneously, to go where they please and do as they please.

_____ 4. *Dual careers.* Child-free couples may both pursue meaningful careers without distraction.

_____ 5. *Financial drain.* Children are a financial burden, especially considering the costs of child care and education.

_____ 6. *Difficulty.* Parenthood is demanding. It requires sacrifice of time, money, and energy, and not everyone makes a good parent.

_____ 7. *Irrevocable decision.* Once you have children, the decision cannot be changed.

_____ 8. *Failure.* Some people fear that they will not be good parents. People with poor relationships with their own parents may fear that they will repeat the same mistakes their parents made with them.

_____ 9. *Other children.* People can enjoy children other than their own, such as nieces and nephews, or become "big brothers" or "big sisters," without assuming the full brunt of parental responsibility.

_____ 10. *Sense of danger.* The world is perceived to be a dangerous place, with the threats, for example, of crime, environmental destruction, and nuclear war. It is better not to bring children into such a world.

As we noted, there is no one "score" that will determine whether or not you should have a child. Nor will you necessarily feel the same way about having a child at the age of 20 as you may at 30 or 40. Just as selecting an appropriate career may take several years, evaluating your motivations about parenthood may also take time and considerable self-examination before you reach a decision that is right for you.

Source: Adapted from Rathus & Nevid, 1992, p. 558. Reprinted with permission.

---

frequency of intercourse and orgasm during pregnancy among a sample of 219 women, with the greatest decline occurring during the third trimester (Hart et al., 1991). Pain during intercourse is also commonly reported, especially in the third trimester (Ulbrich et al., 1990).

Postpartum
Following birth.

A survey by Solberg and his colleagues (Solberg et al., 1974), which was based upon interviews with 260 **postpartum** women, revealed that the male-superior coital position was reported to be the most popular before pregnancy, and also through the first two trimesters of pregnancy. As the woman's abdominal region swelled, however, the male-superior position became unwieldy. The female-superior, lateral-entry, and rear-entry positions were popular alternatives. In the final month, the lateral-entry position was used more frequently than the male-superior position. Note that manual and oral sex can continue as usual. Although oral sex is generally considered safe during pregnancy, blowing air into the pregnant woman's vagina is to be avoided, since it can introduce life-threatening air bubbles into the mother's bloodstream (Samuels & Samuels, 1986).

Some women are concerned that the uterine contractions of orgasm may dislodge a recently implanted embryo. Such concerns are unfounded, unless the woman has a history of miscarriage or is presently at risk of miscarriage. Women may also be concerned that orgasmic contractions during the final month may induce labor. Evidence on the issue is mixed, however. Yet it may be prudent for women with a history of miscarriage or who show evidence of early cervical ripening to abstain from intercourse during the third trimester (Herbst, 1979). Again, women and their partners are advised to consult their obstetricians. (Few obstetricians in the 1990s will make parents feel guilty that they retain their interest in sex during pregnancy.)

PSYCHOLOGICAL CHANGES DURING PREGNANCY

A woman's psychological response to pregnancy reflects her desire to be pregnant, her physical changes, and her attitudes toward these changes. Women with the financial, social, and psychological resources to meet the needs of pregnancy and child rearing may welcome pregnancy. Some describe it as the most wondrous experience of their lives. Other women may question their ability to handle their pregnancies and childbirth. Or they may fear that pregnancy will interfere with their careers or their mates' feelings about them. In general, women who want to have a baby and choose to become pregnant are better adjusted through their pregnancies.

The first trimester may be difficult for women who are ambivalent about pregnancy. At that stage symptoms like morning sickness are most pronounced, and women must come to terms with being pregnant. The second trimester is generally less tempestuous. Morning sickness and other symptoms have largely vanished. It is not yet difficult to move about, and the woman need not yet face the delivery. Women first note fetal movement during the second trimester, and for many the experience is stirring:

> I was lying on my stomach and felt—something, like someone lightly touching my deep insides. Then I just sat very still and . . . felt the hugeness of having something living growing in me. Then I said, No, it's not possible, it's too early yet, and then I started to cry. . . . That one moment was my first body awareness of another living thing inside me.
>
> (*Our Bodies, Ourselves,* 1979, p. 262.)

Looking Forward to Parenthood. A couple's reactions to pregnancy reflect the degree to which they want and are prepared for the child.

During the third trimester it is normal, especially for first-time mothers, to worry about the mechanics of delivery and whether the child will be normal. The woman becomes increasingly heavy and literally "bent out of shape." It may become difficult to get up from a chair or out of bed. She must sit farther from the steering wheel when driving. Muscle tension from supporting the extra weight in her abdomen may cause backaches. She may feel impatient in the days and weeks just prior to delivery.

Men, like women, respond to pregnancy according to the degree to which they want the child. Many men are proud and look forward to the child with great anticipation. In such cases, pregnancy may bring parents closer together. But fathers who are financially or emotionally unprepared may consider the pregnancy a "trap."

Now and then an expectant father experiences some signs of pregnancy, including morning sickness and vomiting. This reaction is termed a **sympathetic pregnancy.**

Sympathetic pregnancy
The experiencing of a number of signs of pregnancy by the father.

PRENATAL DEVELOPMENT

Learning Objective 7:
Trace prenatal development through the germinal, embryonic, and fetal stages.

Suppose you and a friend, who is Chinese, were born at the same time. Your friend may consider herself to be nine months older than you, even though you both have the same birthdate. Why? According to the Chinese, a person's age is calculated from the time of conception, rather than birth. This Chinese tradition appears to acknowledge the fact that the nine months of pregnancy are indeed eventful.

We can date pregnancy from the onset of the last menstrual cycle before conception, which makes the normal gestation period equal to 280 days. We can also date pregnancy from the date at which fertilization was assumed to have taken place, which normally corresponds to a day two weeks after the beginning of the woman's last menstrual cycle. In this case, the normal gestation period is 266 days.

Once pregnancy has been confirmed, the delivery date may be calculated by *Nagele's rule.* Jot down the date of the first day of the last menstrual period. Add seven days. Subtract three months. Then add one year. For example, if the last period began on November 12, 1995, adding seven days yields November 19, 1995. Then subtracting three months yields August 19, 1995. Adding one year gives a "due date" of August 19, 1996. Few babies are born exactly when they are due,[1] but the great majority are delivered during a ten-day period that spans the date.

Shortly following conception, the single cell that results from the union of sperm and egg begins to multiply—becoming two cells, then four, then eight, and so on. During the weeks and months that follow, tissues, structures, and organs begin to form, and the fetus gradually takes on the unmistakable shape of a human being. By the time the fetus is delivered at birth, it consists of hundreds of billions of cells, more cells than there are stars in the Milky Way galaxy. Prenatal development can be divided into three periods: the *germinal stage,* which corresponds to about the first two weeks; the *embryonic stage,* which coincides with the first two months; and the *fetal stage.* We also commonly speak of prenatal development in terms of three trimesters of three months each.

THE GERMINAL STAGE

Germinal stage
The period of prenatal development prior to implantation in the uterus.

Period of the ovum
Germinal stage.

Within 36 hours after conception, the zygote divides into two cells. It then divides repeatedly, becoming 32 cells within another 36 hours as it continues its journey to the uterus. It takes the zygote perhaps three or four days to reach the uterus. This mass of dividing cells then wanders about the uterus for perhaps another three or four days before it begins to become implanted in the uterine wall. The process of implantation takes about another week. This period from conception to implantation is termed the **germinal stage,** or the **period of the ovum** (see Figure 11.3, see page 322).

[1]The second and third authors wish to boast, however, that their daughters Allyn and Jordan were born precisely on their due dates. At least one of them has been just as compulsive ever since. The first author adds that he and his wife Judy had their son Michael within one day of the due date. (Close but no cigar, notes the third author.)

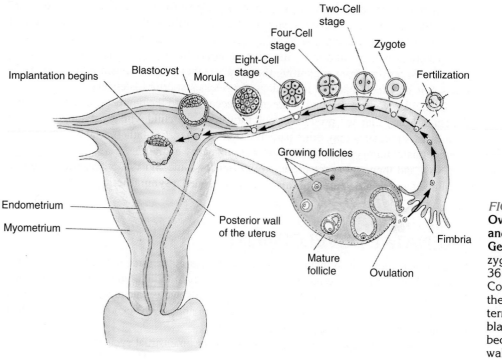

Two-Cell stage

Four-Cell stage

Zygote

Eight-Cell stage

Fertilization

Blastocyst

Morula

Implantation begins

Growing follicles

Endometrium

Myometrium

Posterior wall of the uterus

Mature follicle

Ovulation

Fimbria

FIGURE 11.3 **The Ovarian Cycle, Conception, and the Early Days of the Germinal Stage.** The zygote first divides about 36 hours after conception. Continuing division creates the hollow sphere of cells termed the blastocyst. The blastocyst normally becomes implanted in the wall of the uterus.

For the first week following conception, a fertilized egg cell is not attached to its mother's body. True. During the germinal period, a fertilized egg cell is in fact not attached to its mother's body. Later it becomes implanted in the uterine wall. •

Blastocyst

A stage within the germinal stage of prenatal development, when the embryo is a sphere of cells surrounding a cavity of fluid.

Embryonic disk

The platelike inner part of the blastocyst which differentiates into the ectoderm, mesoderm, and endoderm of the embryo.

Trophoblast

The outer part of the blastocyst, from which the amniotic sac, placenta, and umbilical cord develop.

Embryonic stage

The stage of prenatal development that lasts from implantation through the eighth week, and which is characterized by the differentiation of the major organ systems.

Several days into the germinal stage, the cell mass takes the form of a fluid filled ball of cells, which is called a **blastocyst.** Already some cell differentiation has begun. Cells begin to separate into groups that will eventually become different structures. Within a thickened mass of cells that is called the **embryonic disk,** two distinct inner layers of cells are beginning to form. These cells will become the embryo and eventually the fetus. The outer part of the blastocyst, called the **trophoblast,** consists of several membranes from which the amniotic sac, placenta, and umbilical cord eventually develop.

Implantation may be accompanied by some bleeding, which results from the usual rupturing of some small blood vessels that line the uterus. Bleeding can also be a sign of a miscarriage—though most women who experience implantation bleeding do not miscarry but go on to have normal pregnancies and deliver healthy babies.

THE EMBRYONIC STAGE

The period from implantation to about the eighth week of development is called the **embryonic stage.** The major organ systems of the body begin to differentiate during this stage.

Development of the embryo may be described as following two general trends—**cephalocaudal** and **proximodistal.** The apparently oversized heads depicted in Figure 11.4 represent embryos and fetuses at various stages of prenatal development. You can see that the growth of the head (the cephalic region) takes precedence over the growth of the lower parts of the body. You can also think of the body as containing a central axis that coincides with the spinal cord. The growth of the organ systems that lie close to this axis (that is, *proximal* to the axis) takes precedence over those that lie further away toward the extremities (that is, *distal* to the axis). Relatively early maturation of the brain and organ systems that lie near the central axis allows these organs to play important roles in the further development of the embryo and fetus.

Cephalocaudal

From the head downward. (From Latin roots meaning "head" and "tail.")

Proximodistal

From the central axis of the body outward. (From Latin roots meaning "near" and "far.")

Ectoderm

The outermost cell layer of the newly formed embryo, from which the skin and nervous system develop.

Neural tube

A hollow area in the blastocyst from which the nervous system will develop.

As the embryonic stage unfolds, the nervous system, sensory organs, hair, nails, teeth, and the outer layer of skin begin to develop from the outer layer of cells, or **ectoderm,** of the embryonic disk. By about three weeks after conception, two ridges appear in the embryo; the ridges fold together to form the **neural tube,** which then develops into the nervous system. From the inner layer of the embryonic disk, or **endoderm,** will come the respiratory and digestive systems, and such organs as the liver and the pancreas. A short time later in the embryonic stage, the middle layer of cells, or **mesoderm,** will differentiate and begin to develop into the reproductive, excretory, and circulatory systems, as well as the skeleton, muscles, and the inner layer of the skin.

During the third week of development, the head and blood vessels begin to form. By the fourth week, a primitive heart begins beating and pumping blood in a fetus that measures but a fifth of an inch in length. The heart will continue to beat without rest for every minute of every day for perhaps the better part of a century. By the end of the first month of development we can see the beginnings of the arms and legs, in the form of "arm buds" and "leg buds." The mouth, eyes, ears, and nose begin to take shape at this time. The brain and other parts of the nervous system also begin to develop.

The arms and legs develop in accordance with the proximodistal principle. First the upper arms and legs develop, then the forearms and lower legs. Then the hands and feet

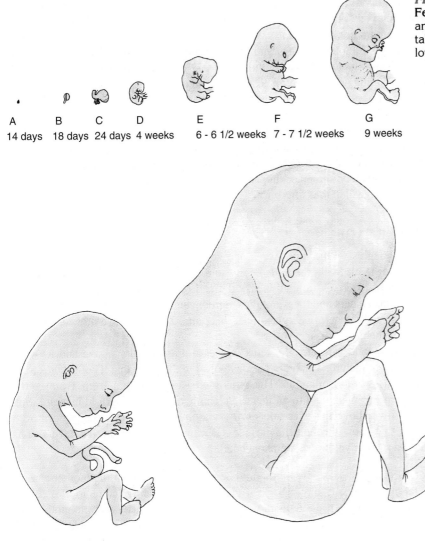

FIGURE 11.4 Human Embryos and Fetuses. Development is cephalocaudal and proximodistal. Growth of the head takes precedence over the growth of the lower parts of the body.

A — 14 days B — 18 days C — 24 days D — 4 weeks E — 6 - 6 1/2 weeks F — 7 - 7 1/2 weeks G — 9 weeks

H, 11 weeks

I, 15 weeks

Endoderm

The inner layer of the newly formed embryo, from which the lungs and digestive system develop.

Mesoderm

The central layer of the embryo, from which the bones and muscles develop.

Amniotic sac

The sac containing the fetus.

Amniotic fluid

Fluid within the amniotic sac that suspends and protects the fetus.

Placenta

An organ connected to the fetus by the umbilical cord. The placenta serves as a relay station between mother and fetus, allowing the exchange of nutrients and wastes.

Umbilical cord

A tube that connects the fetus to the placenta.

form, followed by webbed fingers and toes by about six to eight weeks into development. The webbing is gone by the end of the second month. By this time the head has become rounded and the limbs have elongated and separated. Facial features are visible. All this is happening in an embryo that is about 1 inch long and weighs $1/30$ of an ounce. It is during the second month that nervous impulses begin to travel through the developing nervous system.

THE AMNIOTIC SAC   The embryo—and later on, the fetus—develop within a protective environment in the mother's uterus called the **amniotic sac**, which is surrounded by a clear membrane. The embryo and fetus are suspended within the amniotic sac in a medium of **amniotic fluid.** The amniotic fluid acts like a shock absorber. It cushions the embryo from damage that might result from the mother's movements. The fluid also helps maintain a steady temperature within the amniotic sac.

THE PLACENTA   Nutrients and waste products are exchanged between mother and embryo (or fetus) through a mass of tissue called the **placenta.** The placenta is unique in origin. It develops from material supplied by both mother and embryo. Toward the end of the first trimester, it becomes a flattish, round organ about 7 inches in diameter and 1 inch thick—larger than the fetus itself. The fetus is connected to the placenta by the **umbilical cord.** The mother is connected to the placenta by the system of blood vessels in the uterine wall. The umbilical cord develops about five weeks after conception and reaches 20 inches in length. It contains two arteries through which maternal nutrients reach the embryo. A vein transports waste products back to the mother.

The circulatory systems of mother and embryo do not mix. A membrane in the placenta permits only certain substances to pass through, such as oxygen (from the mother to the fetus); carbon dioxide and other wastes (from the embryo or fetus to the mother, to be eliminated by the mother's lungs and kidneys); nutrients; some microscopic disease-causing organisms—including, sadly, those that cause German measles and AIDS; and some drugs, including aspirin, narcotics, alcohol, and tranquilizers.

The placenta is also an endocrine gland that secretes hormones that preserve the pregnancy, stimulate the uterine contractions that induce childbirth, and help prepare the breasts for breast-feeding. Some of these hormones may also cause the signs of pregnancy. HCG (human chorionic gonadotropin) stimulates the corpus luteum to continue to produce progesterone. The placenta itself secretes increasing amounts of estrogen and progesterone. Ultimately, the placenta passes from the woman's body after delivery. For this reason it is also called the "afterbirth."

THE FETAL STAGE

The fetal stage begins by the ninth week and continues until the birth of the baby. By about the ninth or tenth week, the fetus begins to respond to the outside world by turning in the direction of external stimulation. By the end of the first trimester, all the major organ systems, the fingers and toes, and the external genitals have been formed. The gender of the fetus can be determined visually at this point. The eyes have now also become clearly distinguishable.

During the second trimester the fetus increases dramatically in size and its organ systems continue to mature. The brain has developed to the point that it contributes to the regulation of basic body functions. The fetus increases its weight from 1 *ounce* to 2 *pounds* and grows from about 4 to 14 inches in length, a three- to fourfold increase. Soft, downy hair grows above the eyes and on the scalp. The skin turns ruddy because of blood vessels that show through the surface. (During the third trimester, layers of fat beneath the skin will give the red a pinkish hue.)

FETAL MOVEMENTS   Usually by the middle of the fourth month the mother can feel the first fetal movements. It may seem as if the fetus has suddenly "come to life." By the end of the second trimester, the fetus moves its limbs so vigorously that the mother may complain of being kicked—often at 4 A.M. It opens and shuts its eyes, sucks its thumb, alternates between periods of wakefulness and sleep, and perceives lights and sounds. The fetus also does somersaults, which the mother will definitely feel. Fortunately, the

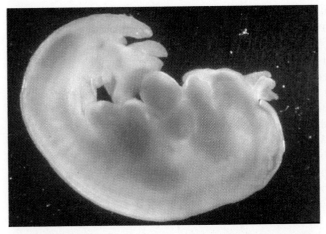

(a) 4–5 weeks

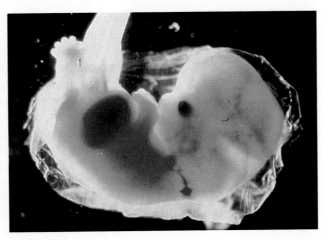

(b) 7th week

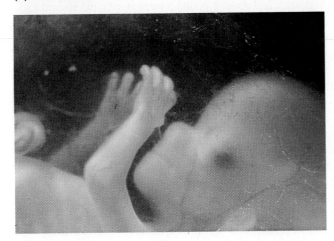

(c) 4½ months

Prenatal Development. Human growth and development are most dramatic prior to the birth. Within a few months, a human fetus advances from weighing a fraction of an ounce to several pounds, and from one cell to an organism composed of trillions of cells.

Age of viability
The age at which a fetus can sustain independent life.

Cephalic presentation
Emergence of the baby headfirst from the womb.

Breech presentation
Emergence of the baby feet-first from the womb.

Learning Objective 8:
Describe the effects on the fetus of maternal diet, maternal diseases and disorders, maternal and paternal use of drugs, and other environmental influences.

umbilical cord will not break or become wrapped around the fetus in a dangerous way, no matter how acrobatic the fetus becomes in its turns and somersaults.

Near the end of the second trimester the fetus approaches the **age of viability.** Still, only about one baby in ten born at the end of the second trimester who weighs under 2 pounds will survive, even with intense medical efforts.

During the third trimester the organ systems of the fetus continue to mature and become larger. The heart and lungs become increasingly capable of maintaining independent life. Typically during the seventh month the fetus turns upside down in the uterus so that it will be headfirst, or in a **cephalic presentation,** for delivery. But some fetuses do not turn during this month; if such a fetus is born prematurely it can have either a **breech presentation** (bottom first) or a shoulder-first presentation, which could complicate the problems of prematurity. The closer to term (the full nine months) the baby is born, the more likely it is that the presentation will be cephalic. If birth occurs at the end of the eighth month, the odds are overwhelmingly in favor of survival.

During the final months of pregnancy, the mother may become concerned that the fetus seems to be less active than it was previously. But most of the time this change in activity is perfectly normal. The fetus has grown so large that it is cramped in the uterus and its movements are constricted.

ENVIRONMENTAL INFLUENCES ON PRENATAL DEVELOPMENT

Advances in scientific knowledge have not only made us more aware of the changes that take place during prenatal development. They have also heightened our awareness of the problems that can occur and what might be done to prevent them. We focus in this next section on the environmental factors that affect prenatal development. These include the mother's diet, maternal diseases and disorders, and the mother's use of drugs.

THE MOTHER'S DIET It is a common misconception that the fetus will take only what it needs from its mother. If this were true, mothers would not need to be very concerned about their diets. But malnutrition in the mother can adversely affect fetal development. During the final trimester, for instance, the fetus gains weight rapidly. Maternal malnutrition during this stage has been linked to low birth weight and increased mortality during the first year of life (Wardlaw & Insel, 1990). Pregnant women who are well nourished are more likely to deliver babies of average or above average size. Their children are also less likely to develop colds and more serious respiratory disorders as infants.

A woman can expect to gain at least 20 pounds during pregnancy because of the growth of the placenta, amniotic fluid, and the fetus itself. Most women will gain about 25 pounds or so (Thompson, 1993). Overweight women may gain less, and slender women may gain as much as 30 pounds. Regular weight gains are most desirable, about $1/2$ pound a week during the first half of pregnancy and about 1 pound a week during the second half.

Teratogens
Environmental influences or agents that can damage an embryo or fetus. (From the Greek *teras*, meaning "monster.")

MATERNAL DISEASES AND DISORDERS Environmental influences or agents that can harm the embryo or fetus are called **teratogens.** These include drugs taken by the mother, such as alcohol and even aspirin, as well as substances produced by the mother's body, such as Rh-positive antibodies. Other teratogens include the metals lead and mercury, radiation, and disease-causing organisms such as viruses and bacteria. Although many disease-causing organisms cannot pass through the placenta to infect the embryo or fetus, some extremely small organisms, such as those causing syphilis, measles, mumps, and chicken pox, can. Some disorders such as toxemia are not transmitted to the embryo or fetus but can adversely affect the environment in which it develops.

Critical period of vulnerability
A period of time during which an embryo or fetus is vulnerable to the effects of a teratogen.

CRITICAL PERIODS OF VULNERABILITY Exposure to particular teratogens causes the greatest harm during certain **critical periods of vulnerability.** Critical periods correspond to the times at which the structures that are most affected by the particular teratgens are developing. The heart, for example, develops rapidly from the third to the fifth week following conception. As Figure 11.5 shows, the heart may be most vulnerable to certain teratogens at this time. The arms and legs, which develop later, are considered most vulnerable from the fourth through the eighth week of development. Since it is during the embryonic stage that the major organ systems differentiate, the embryo is generally most vulnerable to the effects of teratogens during this stage.

Let us now consider some of the most damaging effects of specific maternal diseases and disorders.

Rubella
A viral infection that can cause mental retardation and heart disease in an embryo. Also called *German measles.*

RUBELLA (GERMAN MEASLES) **Rubella** is a viral infection. Women who contract rubella during the first month or two of pregnancy, when rapid differentiation of major organ systems is taking place, may bear children who are deaf or who develop mental retardation, heart disease, or cataracts. Risk of these defects declines as pregnancy progresses.

Nearly 85 percent of women in the U.S. had rubella as children and so acquired immunity. Women who do not know whether they have had rubella may be tested; if they are not immune they can be vaccinated *prior to pregnancy.* Inoculation during pregnancy is considered risky because the vaccine causes a mild case of the disease in the mother, which can affect the embryo or fetus. Increased awareness of the dangers of rubella during pregnancy, and of the preventative effects of inoculation, has led to a dramatic decline in the number of children born in the United States with defects caused by rubella, from about 20,000 cases in 1964–1965 to fewer than 100 in 1983 (Franklin, 1984).

Syphilis
A sexually transmitted disease caused by a bacterial infection.

SYPHILIS Maternal **syphilis** may cause miscarriage or **stillbirth,** or be passed along to the child in the form of congenital syphilis. Congenital syphilis can impair the vision and hearing, damage the liver, or deform the bones and teeth.

Routine blood tests early in pregnancy can diagnose syphilis and other problems. Because the bacteria that cause syphilis do not readily cross the placental membrane during

Stillbirth
The birth of a dead fetus.

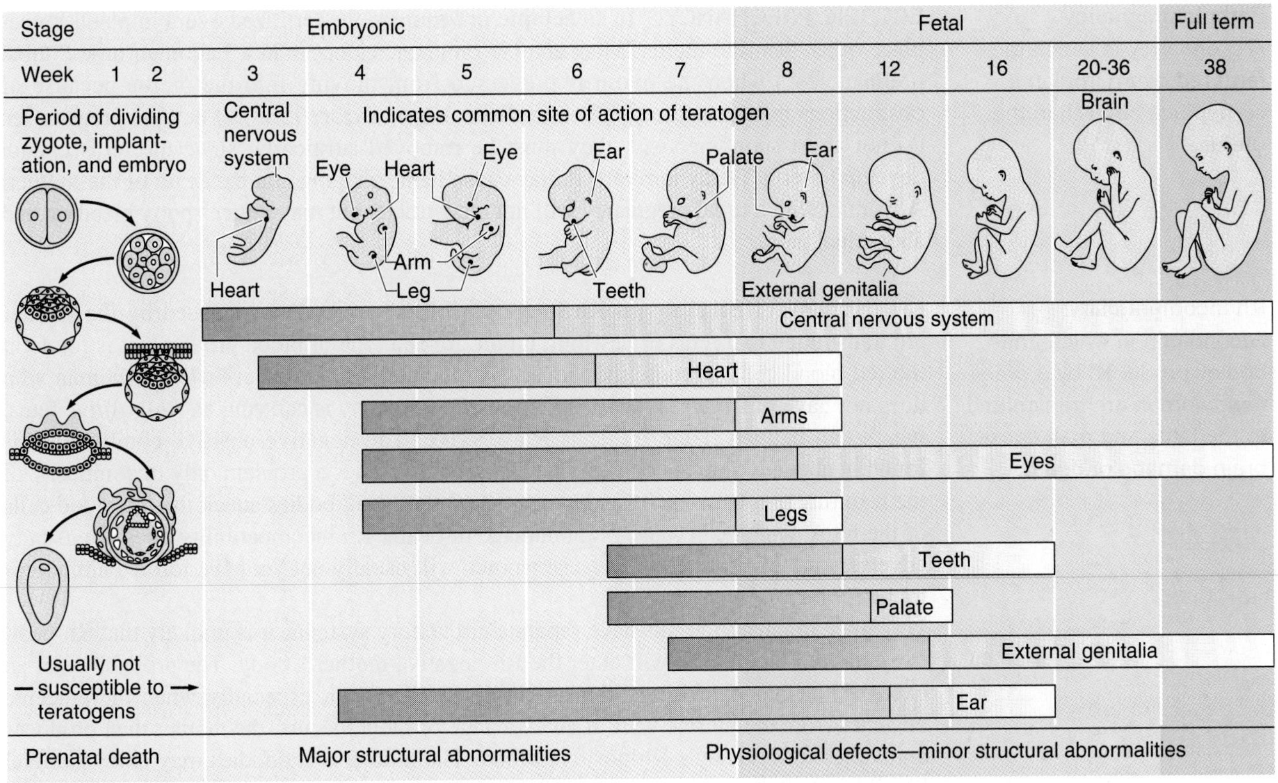

Stage		Embryonic						Fetal				Full term
Week	1 2	3	4	5	6	7	8	12	16	20-36	38

FIGURE 11.5 **Critical Periods in Prenatal Development.** The developing embryo is most vulnerable to teratogens when the organ systems are taking shape. The periods of greatest vulnerability of organ systems are shown in gray. Periods of lesser vulnerability are shown in yellow.

Source: Rathus, S.A. (1988). *Understanding Child Development.* Copyright © 1988 by Holt, Rinehart, & Winston, Inc. Reprinted with permission.

the first months of pregnancy, the fetus will probably not contract syphilis if an infected mother is treated successfully with antibiotics before the fourth month of pregnancy.

Acquired immunodeficiency syndrome (AIDS)
A sexually transmitted disease that destroys white blood cells in the immune system, leaving the body vulnerable to various "opportunistic" diseases.

ACQUIRED IMMUNODEFICIENCY SYNDROME (AIDS) **Acquired immunodeficiency syndrome** disables the body's immune system, leaving victims vulnerable to fatal illnesses (such as respiratory diseases and some types of cancer) that a healthy immune system would normally keep in check. The *human immunodeficiency virus* (HIV), which causes AIDS, can be transmitted through the placenta and infect the fetus in utero (Koop, 1987). The virus is also known to be transmitted to children by breast-feeding (Rogers, 1985). Children of infected mothers have also contracted the virus during childbirth. The usual rupturing of blood vessels in both the mother and baby during childbirth provides an opportunity for the virus to be transmitted through the blood.

Toxemia
A life-threatening condition that is characterized by high blood pressure.

TOXEMIA **Toxemia** is a life-threatening condition characterized by high blood pressure, that may afflict women late in the second or early in the third trimester of pregnancy. Its first stage, *preeclampsia,* is diagnosed by protein in the urine, swelling from fluid retention, and high blood pressure, and may be relatively mild. As preeclampsia worsens, the mother may have headaches and visual problems from the raised blood pressure, along with abdominal pain. If left untreated, the disease may progress to the final stage, *eclampsia,* which can lead to maternal or fetal death. Babies born to women with toxemia are often undersized or premature.

Toxemia appears to be linked to malnutrition, although the causes are unclear. Ironically, undernourished women may gain weight rapidly through fluid retention, but their swollen appearance may discourage them from eating. Pregnant women who gain weight rapidly but have not increased their food intake should consult their obstetricians.

Ectopic pregnancy
A pregnancy in which the fertilized ovum implants someplace other than the uterus.

ECTOPIC PREGNANCY   In an **ectopic pregnancy,** the fertilized ovum implants someplace other than the uterus. Most ectopic pregnancies occur in a Fallopian tube ("tubal pregnancies") when the ovum is prevented from moving into the uterus because of obstructions that result from infection (Schenker & Evron, 1983). If ectopic pregnancies do not abort spontaneously, they must be removed surgically, since the fetus cannot develop to term. Delay in removal may cause hemorrhaging and the death of the mother. A woman with a tubal pregnancy will not menstruate, but may notice spotty bleeding and abdominal pain.

Rh incompatibility
A condition in which antibodies produced by a pregnant woman are transmitted to the fetus and may cause brain damage or death.

RH INCOMPATIBILITY   In **Rh incompatibility,** antibodies produced by the mother are transmitted to a fetus or newborn infant. *Rh* is a type of blood protein that is found in the red blood cells of some individuals. Rh incompatibility occurs when a woman who does not have this blood factor, and is thus *Rh negative,* is carrying an *Rh-positive* fetus, which can happen if the father is Rh-positive. The negative-positive combination is found in about 10 percent of U.S. marriages but becomes a problem only in a minority of the resulting pregnancies. In such cases the mother's antibodies attack the red blood cells of the fetus, which can cause brain damage or death. Rh incompatibility does not usually adversely affect a first child because women will usually not yet have formed antibodies to the *Rh* factor.

Since mother and fetus have separate circulatory systems, it is unlikely that Rh-positive fetal red blood cells will enter the Rh-negative mother's body. The probability of an exchange of blood increases during childbirth, however, especially when the placenta detaches from the uterine wall. If an exchange of blood occurs, the mother then produces antibodies to the baby's Rh-positive blood. The mother's antibodies may enter the fetal bloodstream and cause a condition called *fetal erythroblastosis,* which can result in anemia, mental deficiency, or even the death of the fetus or newborn infant.

Fortunately, blood-typing of pregnant women significantly decreases the threat of uncontrolled erythroblastosis. If an Rh-negative mother is injected with the vaccine Rhogan within 72 hours after delivery of an Rh-positive baby, she will not develop the dangerous antibodies, and thus will not pass them on to the fetus in a subsequent pregnancy. A fetus or newborn child at risk for erythroblastosis may also receive a preventive blood transfusion, in order to remove the mother's Rh-positive antibodies from its blood.

DRUGS TAKEN BY THE MOTHER (AND FATHER)   Many couples are not aware that some widely used drugs, including such nonprescription drugs as aspirin, have been associated with birth abnormalities. In the 1960s the drug thalidomide was marketed to pregnant women as a presumably safe treatment for nausea and insomnia. Tragically, the drug caused birth deformities, including stunted or missing limbs, in nearly 8,000 babies born to mothers who used the drug before it was taken off the market. Maternal use of certain illegal drugs such as cocaine and marijuana may also place the fetus at risk (Chasnoff et al., 1985; Fried et al., 1984).

Paternal use of certain drugs also may expose the fetus to possible dangers. One question that remains unanswered is whether drugs might alter the genetic material in the father's sperm. It does appear that the use of certain substances by those who come into contact with a pregnant woman can be harmful to the developing fetus. For example, the mother's exposure to cigarette smoke in the environment can hurt the fetus. Exposure to marijuana smoke may also harm the fetus.

Some widely used over-the-counter drugs, such as aspirin, can have dangerous effects on a fetus. If you are pregnant, or suspect that you are, it is advisable to consult your obstetrician before taking any and all drugs, not just prescription drugs. Your obstetrician can usually direct you to a safe and effective substitute for a drug that could prove harmful to a developing fetus.

ANTIBIOTICS   Several antibiotics may be harmful to a fetus, especially if taken during certain periods of fetal development. Tetracycline may yellow the teeth and deform the bones. Other antibiotics have been implicated in deafness and jaundice.

Notes: Doctors have known for at least 250 years about the negative effects on the fetus of heavy alcohol use by a woman during pregnancy. Despite this, fetal alcohol syndrome (FAS) is currently the leading cause of mental retardation worldwide, with an incidence rate of 1.9 cases per 1000 live births. Children diagnosed with FAS have an average IQ of 68–70. (Wilton, J. M. 1991. Compelled hospitalization and treatment during pregnancy: Mental health status as models for legislation to protect children from prenatal drug and alcohol exposure. *Family Law Quarterly,* 25.)

DES

Diethylstilbestrol: an estrogen that was once given to women at risk for miscarriage to help maintain pregnancy.

HORMONES The hormones progestin and DES have sometimes been used to help women at risk of miscarriage maintain their pregnancies. When taken at about the time that sex organs differentiate, progestin—which is similar in composition to male sex hormones, can masculinize the external sex organs of embryos with female (XX) sex chromosomal structures. Progestin taken during the first trimester has also been linked to increased levels of aggressive behavior during childhood.

DES (short for *diethylstilbestrol*), a powerful estrogen, was given to many women at risk for miscarriage between the 1940s and 1960s to help maintain their pregnancies. DES is suspected of causing cervical and testicular cancer in some of the children whose mothers used it when pregnant. Other problems have been reported as well. Daughters whose mothers used DES during their pregnancies have been found to have a higher than expected rate of miscarriages and premature deliveries (Barnes et al., 1980). Sons whose mothers were DES users during their pregnancies have higher than expected rates of infertility (Stenchever et al., 1981). The DES users themselves appear to be at high risk of some serious medical problems, such as breast cancer (Greenberg et al., 1984).

VITAMINS Many pregnant women are prescribed daily doses of multivitamins to maintain their own health and to promote the development of a healthy pregnancy. "Too much of a good thing" may be hazardous, however. High doses of vitamins such as A, B_6, D, and K have been linked to birth defects. Vitamin A excesses have been linked with cleft palate and eye damage, whereas excesses of vitamin D are linked to mental retardation.

NARCOTICS Narcotics such as heroin and methadone can readily pass from mother to fetus through the placental membrane. Narcotics are highly addictive and it appears that fetuses of mothers who use them regularly during their pregnancies can become addicted to them in utero (Oro & Dixon, 1987). At birth, such babies may undergo withdrawal and show muscle tension and agitation. Women who use narcotics are advised to notify their obstetricians so that measures can be taken to aid the infants prior to and following delivery.

TRANQUILIZERS AND SEDATIVES The tranquilizers Librium and Valium can readily cross the placental membrane and are suspected of causing birth defects such as harelip. Sedatives, such as the barbiturate *phenobarbital,* are suspected of decreasing testosterone production and causing reproductive problems in boys of mothers who take them during pregnancy.

HALLUCINOGENICS Use of hallucinogenic drugs such as marijuana and LSD during pregnancy is linked to chromosomal damage in fetuses (National Academy of Sciences, 1982). The active ingredient in marijuana, THC, readily crosses the placenta, as does LSD. Use of marijuana can lead to decreased androgen production in male fetuses, which can interfere with the process of sexual differentiation. Research provides evidence that preschoolers whose mothers used marijuana during their pregnancies suffered more neurological and visual problems than did children of nonusers (Fried, 1986).

ALCOHOL Mothers who drink heavily during pregnancy expose the fetus to greater risk of birth defects, infant mortality, and growth deficiencies in later development (Streissguth et al., 1980). Maternal drinking during the fifth month of pregnancy has been associated with dysfunctions of the central nervous system (Streissguth et al., 1983). Children whose mothers drank during pregnancy frequently perform poorly in school, even when they possess average intelligence (Shaywitz et al., 1980).

Nearly 40 percent of children whose mothers drank heavily during pregnancy develop **fetal alcohol syndrome** (FAS). FAS is a cluster of symptoms typified by developmental lags and characteristic facial features, such as an underdeveloped upper jaw, flattened nose, and widely spaced eyes. Infants with FAS are often smaller than average and have smaller than average brains. They may be mentally retarded, lack coordination, and have deformed limbs and heart problems. They tend to be poorer at sucking than normal babies and tend not to catch up to the normal babies in size (Hollestedt et al., 1983).

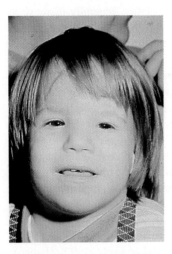

Fetal Alcohol Syndrome. The children of many mothers who drank alcohol during pregnancy show FAS—a syndrome that is characterized by developmental lags and such facial features as an underdeveloped upper jaw, flattened nose, and widely spaced eyes.

Fetal alcohol syndrome

A cluster of symptoms caused by maternal drinking in which the child shows developmental lags and characteristic facial features, such as an underdeveloped upper jaw, flattened nose, and widely spaced eyes.

FAS has even been found among the children of mothers who drank only two ounces of alcohol a day during the first trimester (Astley et al., 1992). The critical period for the development of the facial features associated with FAS seems to be the third and fourth weeks of prenatal development, when the head is starting to take shape (Streissguth et al., 1984).

TRUTH OR *FICTION?*

R E V I S I T E D

Pregnant women can have one or two alcoholic beverages a day without harming their babies. *Actually, there is no safe minimal amount of drinking for pregnant women. Pregnant women are advised to abstain from alcohol, period.* •

CIGARETTE SMOKING At least one in four pregnant women in 1990 smoked (U.S. Department of Health and Human Services [USDHHS], 1991; Floyd et al., 1993). Cigarette smoke contains several constituents, including carbon monoxide gas and the stimulant nicotine, that are transmitted from the mother's bloodstream to the fetus. Maternal smoking increases the risk of spontaneous abortion, complications during pregnancy such as premature rupturing of the amniotic sac, stillbirth, premature birth, low birth weight, and early infant mortality (English & Eskenazi, 1992; Floyd et al., 1993; USDHHS, 1992). These health risks, including low birth weights, generally increase in relation to the amount smoked, but even women smoking fewer than one pack a day stand a higher risk of pregnancy and birth complications than do nonsmokers (Floyd et al., 1993; Mayer et al., 1990).

Low birth weight is the most common risk factor for early infant death and disease (USDHHS, 1992). Maternal smoking during pregnancy more than doubles the risk of low birth weight (Mayer et al., 1990). As many as one in four cases of low birth weight could be prevented if mothers-to-be quit smoking during pregnancy (USDHHS, 1990). The earlier the pregnant smoker quits, the less the risk of delivering a low-birth-weight baby (Windsor & Orleans, 1986). Early cessation during pregnancy may lower the risk to a level similar to that of nonsmokers (Windsor & Orleans, 1986). Simply cutting down on smoking during pregnancy does not appear to offer much protection in preventing low birth weight, however (USDHHS, 1990).

Maternal smoking also has important acute effects on fetal heart rate (Graca et al., 1991) and increases the risk of sudden infant death syndrome (SIDS) (Feng, 1993; Haglund & Cnattingius, 1990; Malloy et al., 1992; Schoendorf & Kiely, 1992; Zhang & Fried, 1992). Maternal smoking has also been linked to reduced lung function in newborns (Hanrahan et al., 1992) and asthma in childhood (Martinez et al., 1992). Evidence also points to reduced attention spans, hyperactivity, and lower IQs and achievement test scores in children exposed to maternal smoking during and following pregnancy (Streissguth et al., 1984).

Smoking by the father (or other household members) may be dangerous to a fetus because secondary smoke (smoke exhaled by the smoker or emitted from the tip of a lit cigarette) may be absorbed by the mother and passed along to the fetus. Evidence shows that the children of fathers who smoke bear a greater risk of birth defects and infant mortality (Evans, 1981). Passive exposure to secondhand smoke during infancy is also linked to increased risk of SIDS (Schoendorf & Kiely, 1992).

Researchers estimate that among the 56 million women in the United States of reproductive age at greatest risk of becoming pregnant, 34 million drink, 18 million smoke cigarettes, and 6 million use marijuana (Adams et al., 1989). Researchers also report that many women do not change their drug use habits until after learning they are pregnant, which may occur weeks into a pregnancy at a time when the damage to the fetus has already occurred. Health experts advise women who may become pregnant, whether intentionally or not, to cease drug and alcohol use, including cigarette smoking, prior to any possibility of conception. Unfortunately, many women are unwilling or unable to change their drug use habits even after learning they are pregnant. Among women who smoke, only one in five quit smoking when they become pregnant (Floyd et al.,

1993). Moreover, many of those who do quit relapse later in pregnancy or following delivery (Windsor & Orleans, 1986).

OTHER AGENTS   X-rays increase the risk of malformed organs in the fetus, especially within the first month and a half following conception. Antihistamines, used commonly for allergies, may also deform the fetus. Use of the acne medication Accutane has been linked to birth defects and stillbirths.

In short, women are advised to consult their obstetricians before using any substance during pregnancy. Drugs that help women may harm their fetuses. Fortunately, less harmful substitutes are often available.

CHROMOSOMAL AND GENETIC ABNORMALITIES

Learning Objective 9: Discuss possible chromosomal and genetic abnormalities in the fetus and the tests used to detect them.

Not all of us are fortunate enough to have the normal complement of chromosomes, and some of us have genes that threaten our health or even our existence. Sometimes the genetic codes that contribute to our uniqueness also create problems. In this section we consider a number of the disorders shown in Table 11.1 and discuss ways of detecting them prior to birth.

DOWN SYNDROME   The risk of a child having Down syndrome increases with the mother's age, as shown in Table 11.2 (see page 332). Down syndrome is caused by an extra chromosome on the twenty-first pair. In about 95 percent of cases, Down syndrome is transmitted by the mother (Antonarakas et al., 1991). The inner corners of the

---

TABLE 11.1 Some chromosomal and genetic abnormalities

Cystic fibrosis	A genetic disease in which the pancreas and lungs become clogged with mucus, which impairs the processes of respiration and digestion.
Down syndrome	A condition characterized by a third chromosome on the twenty-first pair. The child with Down syndrome has a characteristic fold of skin over the eye and mental retardation. The risk of a child's exhibiting the syndrome increases as parents increase in age.
Hemophilia	A sex-linked disorder in which the blood fails to clot properly.
Huntington's chorea	A fatal neurological disorder whose onset occurs in middle adulthood.
Neural tube defects	Disorders of the brain or spine, such as *anencephaly,* in which part of the brain is missing, and *spina bifida,* in which part of the spine is exposed or missing. Anencephaly is fatal shortly after birth, but some spina bifida victims survive for a number of years, albeit with severe handicaps.
Phenylketonuria	A disorder in which children cannot metabolize phenylalanine, which builds up in the form of phenylpyruvic acid and causes mental retardation. The disorder can be diagnosed at birth and controlled by diet.
Retina blastoma	A form of blindness caused by a dominant gene.
Sickle cell anemia	A blood disorder that mostly afflicts African Americans, in which deformed blood cells obstruct small blood vessels, decreasing their capacity to carry oxygen, and heightening the risk of occasionally fatal infections.
Tay-Sachs disease	A fatal neurological disorder that primarily afflicts Jews of European origin.

Source: Rathus, S.A. (1988). *Understanding Child Development.* Copyright © 1988 by Holt, Rinehart, & Winston, Inc. Reprinted with permission.

TABLE 11.2 Risk of giving birth to a Down-syndrome infant in relation to the mother's age

Maternal age	Frequency of down syndrome infants among births	Maternal age	Frequency of down syndrome infants among births
30	1/885	40	1/109
31	1/826	41	1/85
32	1/725	42	1/67
33	1/592	43	1/53
34	1/465	44	1/41
35	1/365	45	1/32
36	1/287	46	1/25
37	1/225	47	1/20
38	1/176	48	1/16
39	1/139	49	1/11

Source: Samuels, M. & Samuels, N. (1986). *The well pregnancy book.* Copyright © 1986 by Mike Samuels, M.D. and Nancy Samuels. Reprinted by permission of Simon & Schuster.

eyes of people with the syndrome have a downward-sloping crease of skin that gives them a superficial likeness to Asians. This is why the syndrome was once dubbed *mongolism,* a moniker that has since been rejected because of racist overtones.

Children with Down syndrome have characteristic round faces; wide, flat noses; and protruding tongues. They often suffer from respiratory problems and heart malformations, problems that tend to claim their lives by middle age—the "prime of life" when most of us are reaching our vocational heights. People with Down syndrome are also moderately mentally retarded, but they usually can learn to read and write. With a little help from family and social agencies, they may hold jobs and lead largely independent lives. Despite their intellectual limitations, they are as capable of feeling as the rest of us, and they usually have warm, loving relationships with their families.

SICKLE CELL ANEMIA AND TAY-SACHS DISEASE Sickle cell anemia and Tay-Sachs disease are genetic disorders that are most likely to afflict certain racial and ethnic groups. Sickle cell anemia is most prevalent in the United States among African Americans. One of every 375 African Americans is affected by the disease, and 8 percent are carriers of the sickle cell trait (Leary, 1993b). In sickle cell anemia, the red blood cells assume a sickle shape—hence the name—and they form clumps that obstruct narrow blood vessels and diminish the supply of oxygen. As a result, victims can suffer problems ranging from swollen, painful joints to potentially lethal problems like pneumonia, and heart and kidney failure. Infections are a leading cause of death among those with the disease (Leary, 1993b).

Tay-Sachs disease is a fatal neurological disease of young children. Only one in 100,000 people in the United States is affected, but among Jews of Eastern European background the figure rises steeply to one in 3,600 (Hubbard & Wald, 1993). The disease is characterized by degeneration of the central nervous system and gives rise to retardation, loss of muscle control and paralysis, blindness, and deafness. Victims seldom live beyond the age of 5.

SEX-LINKED GENETIC ABNORMALITIES Some genetic defects, such as hemophilia, are sex linked, in that they are carried only on the X sex chromosome. They are transmit-

Recessive trait
A trait that is not expressed when the gene or genes involved have been paired with dominant genes. Recessive traits are transmitted to future generations, however, and are expressed if they are paired with other recessive genes.

Chorion
The membrane that envelopes the amniotic sac and fetus.

ted from generation to generation as **recessive traits.** Females, each of whom has two X sex chromosomes, are less likely than males to be afflicted by sex-linked disorders, because the genes that carry the disorder would have to be present on both of their sex chromosomes for the disorder to be expressed. Sex-linked disorders are more likely to afflict sons of female carriers because they only have one X sex chromosome, which they inherit from their mothers. England's Queen Victoria was a hemophilia carrier and transmitted the condition to many of her children, who in turn carried it into several ruling houses of Europe. For this reason hemophilia has been dubbed the "royal disease."

METHODS OF AVERTING CHROMOSOMAL AND GENETIC ABNORMALITIES

Based upon information about a couple's medical background and family history of genetic defects, genetic counselors help couples appraise the risks of passing along genetic defects to their children. Some couples facing a high risk of passing along genetic defects to their children decide to adopt. Other couples decide to have abortions if the fetus is determined to have certain abnormalities. Various medical procedures such as the following are used to detect the presence of these disorders in the fetus.

Amniocentesis is performed about 15 to 17 weeks into pregnancy. Fluid is drawn from the amniotic sac (or "bag of waters") with a syringe. Fetal cells in the fluid are grown in a culture and examined under a microscope for the presence of biochemical and chromosomal abnormalities. *Chorionic villus sampling (CVS)* is performed about 10 to 11 weeks into pregnancy. A narrow tube is used to snip off material from the **chorion,** which is a membrane that contains the amniotic sac and fetus. The material is then analyzed. CVS is somewhat riskier than amniocentesis, so most obstetricians prefer to use the latter. The tests detect Down syndrome, sickle cell anemia, Tay-Sachs disease, spina bifida, muscular dystrophy, Rh incompatibility, and up to about 60 other hereditary conditions. The tests also allow parents to find out whether they will have a girl or a boy.

In an ultrasound procedure, high-pitched sound waves are bounced off the fetus, like radar, revealing a picture of the fetus on a TV monitor and allowing the obstetrician to detect certain abnormalities. Obstetricians also use ultrasound to locate the fetus during amniocentesis, in order to lower the probability of injuring it with the syringe.

Parental blood tests can suggest the presence of problems such as sickle cell anemia, Tay-Sachs disease, and neural tube defects (Hobbins, 1991). Still other tests examine fetal DNA, and can indicate the presence of Huntington's chorea, cystic fibrosis, and other disorders.

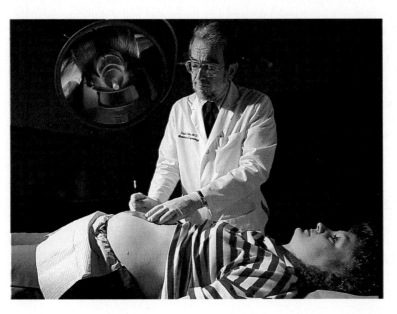

Amniocentesis. In this type of prenatal testing, cells sloughed off by the fetus into amniotic fluid are withdrawn by a syringe and examined for genetic and chromosomal abnormalities.

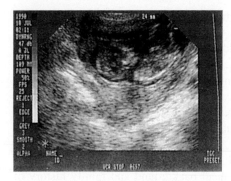

Ultrasound Image. An ultrasound image of the first author's son, Michael Nevid, at approximately 12 weeks following conception. The head and upper torso (facing upwards) can be seen in the upper middle section of the picture. He was handsome even then, his father points out.

CHILDBIRTH

Early in the ninth month of pregnancy, the fetus's head settles in the pelvis. This is called "dropping" or "lightening," and the woman may actually feel lighter, since this change decreases pressure on the diaphragm. About a day or so before the beginning of labor, the woman may notice blood in her vaginal secretions. This represents the rupturing of superficial blood vessels in the birth canal, caused by pressure on the pelvis by the fetus. At this time tissue that had plugged the cervix, possibly preventing entry of infectious agents from the vagina, becomes dislodged. There is a resultant discharge of bloody mucus, unfortunately called the "bloody show." Also about this time one woman in ten has a rush of warm "water" from the vagina. The "water" is actually amniotic fluid, and it means that the amniotic sac has burst. Labor usually begins within a day after the rupture of the amniotic sac. For most women the amniotic sac does not burst until the end of the first stage of childbirth, as described below. Some other common signs of impending labor include indigestion, diarrhea, abdominal cramps, and an ache in the small of the back. Labor begins with the onset of regular uterine contractions.

The first uterine contractions the woman encounters are called **Braxton-Hicks contractions** or so-called false labor contractions. They are relatively painless and tend to increase in frequency. They are false in that they do not widen the cervix or advance the baby through the birth canal. They are also less regular and painful than labor contractions and may serve to warm up the muscles that will be used in delivery. "Real" contractions, in contrast to the Braxton-Hicks contractions, become more intense when the woman moves around or walks.

The initiation of labor may involve the secretion of hormones by the fetal adrenal and pituitary glands that stimulate the placenta and mother's uterus to secrete **prostaglandins.** Prostaglandins cause labor contractions by exciting the uterine musculature. It would make sense for the fetus to have a mechanism for signaling the mother that it is mature enough to sustain independent life. The mechanisms that initiate and maintain labor are not fully understood, however. Later in labor the pituitary gland releases **oxytocin,** a hormone that stimulates contractions strong enough to expel the baby.

Braxton-Hicks contractions
So-called false labor contractions that are relatively painless.

Prostaglandins
Uterine hormones that stimulate uterine contractions.

Oxytocin
A pituitary hormone that stimulates uterine contractions.

TRUTH OR *FICTION?*
REVISITED

A baby signals its mother when it is ready to be born. *Babies probably do (chemically) signal their mothers when they are ready to sustain independent life.* •

THE STAGES OF CHILDBIRTH

Childbirth begins with the onset of labor and progresses through three stages.

THE FIRST STAGE   In the first stage uterine contractions **efface** and **dilate** the cervix to about 4 inches (10 cm) in diameter, so that the baby may pass through it. It is the stretching of the cervix that causes most of the pain of childbirth. A woman may experi-

Efface
To become thin.

Dilate
To open or widen.

Transition
The process during which the cervix becomes nearly fully dilated and the head of the fetus begins to move into the birth canal.

Episiotomy
A surgical incision in the perineum that widens the birth canal, preventing random tearing during childbirth.

Perineum
The area between the vulva and the anus.

Notes: Until the development of forceps in the seventeenth century, men were not involved in the childbirth process. In the United States, childbirth continued to be the province of midwives until the late 1800s and early 1900s, during which time medicine gained almost complete control of childbirth. "Midwifery almost ceased to exist in the United States, and for the first time in history, an entire society of women were attended in childbirth by men" (p. 57). (Rothman, Barbara Katz. 1982. *In Labor: Women and Power in the Birthplace.*)

ence little or no pain if her cervix dilates easily and quickly. The first stage may last from a couple of hours to more than a day. Twelve to 24 hours of labor is considered about average for a first pregnancy. In later pregnancies labor takes about half this time.

The initial contractions are usually mild and spaced widely apart, at intervals of 10 to 20 minutes. They may last 20 to 40 seconds. As time passes, contractions become more frequent and long, strong, and regular.

Transition is the process that occurs when the cervix becomes nearly fully dilated and the baby's head begins to move into the vagina, or birth canal. Contractions usually come quickly during transition. Transition usually lasts about 30 minutes or less and is often accompanied by feelings of nausea, chills, and intense pain.

THE SECOND STAGE   The second stage of childbirth follows transition and begins when the cervix has become fully dilated and the baby begins to move into the vagina and first appears at the opening of the birth canal (Figure 11.6). The woman may be taken to a delivery room for the second stage of childbirth. The second stage is shorter than the first stage, lasting from a few minutes to perhaps a few hours, and ending with the birth of the baby.

Each contraction of the second stage propels the baby farther along the birth canal (vagina). When the baby's head becomes visible at the vaginal opening, it is said to have *crowned*. Typically the baby emerges fully a few minutes after crowning.

An **episiotomy** may be performed on the mother when the baby's head has crowned. Episiotomies are controversial, however. The incision can be painful in itself and cause discomfort and itching as it heals. In some cases the discomfort interferes with coitus for months. Many obstetricians today no longer perform episiotomies routinely, but most health professionals concur that an episiotomy is preferable to the random tearing that can occur if the tissues of the **perineum** become extremely effaced.

With or without an episiotomy, the baby's passageway to the external world is a tight fit at best. As a result, the baby's facial features and the shape of its head may be temporarily distended. The baby may look as if it has been through a prizefight. Its head may be elongated, its nose flattened, and its ears bent. Although parents may be concerned whether the baby's features will assume a more typical shape, they almost always do.

THE THIRD STAGE   During the third, or placental, stage of childbirth, which may last from a few minutes to an hour or more, the placenta is expelled. Detachment of the placenta from the uterine wall may cause some bleeding. The uterus begins the process of contracting to a smaller size. The attending physician sews up the episiotomy or any tears in the perineum.

IN THE NEW WORLD   As the baby's head emerges, mucus is cleared from its mouth by means of suction aspiration to prevent the breathing passageway from being obstructed. Aspiration is often repeated once the baby is fully delivered. Now that suction aspiration is used, newly delivered babies are no longer routinely held upside down to help expel mucus. Nor is the baby slapped on the buttocks to stimulate breathing, as in so many old films.

Once the baby is breathing adequately, the umbilical cord is clamped and severed about 3 inches from the baby's body. (After the birth of your second and third authors' third child, your third author was invited by the obstetrician to cut the umbilical cord—but it was difficult for him to hear what the obstetrician said from his hiding place. The third author seized the scissors and cut the umbilical cord herself, squirting blood all over the glasses of the obstetrician. "Who gave the obstetrician the right to determine who would cut the umbilical cord!" your second author wanted to know.) The stump of the umbilical cord will dry and fall off in its own time, usually in seven to ten days.

While the mother is in the third stage of labor, the nurse may take the baby away and perform certain procedures, such as administering drops of silver nitrate or an antibiotic ointment (erythromycin) into the baby's eyes, a procedure that is required by most states to prevent bacterial infections in the newborn's eyes. Typically the baby would now also be footprinted and (if the birth has taken place in a hospital) given a plastic identification bracelet. Since neonates do not manufacture vitamin K on their own, the baby may also

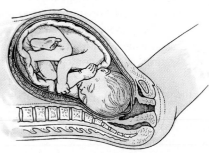

1. The second stage of labor begins

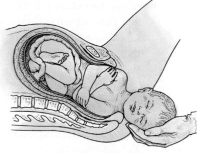

2. Further descent and rotation

3. The crowning of the head

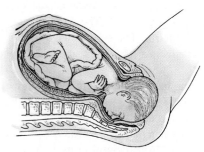

4. Anterior shoulder delivered

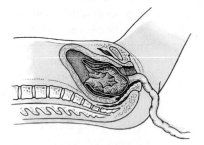

5. Posterior shoulder delivered

6. The third stage of labor begins with separation of the placenta from the uterine wall

FIGURE 11.6 **The Stages of Childbirth.** In the first stage, uterine contractions efface and dilate the cervix to about 4 inches so that the baby may pass. The second stage begins with movement of the baby into the birth canal and ends with birth of the baby. During the third stage the placenta separates from the uterine wall and is expelled through the birth canal.

receive an injection of the vitamin to ensure that her or his blood will clot normally in case of bleeding.

METHODS OF CHILDBIRTH

Learning Objective 11: Discuss historical and current methods of childbirth, including the use of anesthesia, preparation for childbirth, and the need for and frequency of Caesarean sections.

Until this century childbirth was usually an event that happened at home and involved the mother, a midwife, family, and friends. These days women in the United States and Canada typically give birth in hospitals attended by obstetricians who use surgical instruments and anesthetics to protect mothers and children from infection, complications, and pain. Medical procedures have saved many lives but have also made childbearing more impersonal. Social critics argue that it has taken control over their own bodies away from women and, through the use of drugs, denied many women the experience of giving birth.

MEDICATED CHILDBIRTH

In sorrow thou shalt bring forth children.

(Genesis 3:16)

The Bible suggests that the ancients saw suffering as a woman's lot. But during the past two centuries, science and medicine have led to the expectation that women should experience minimal discomfort during childbirth. Today some anesthesia is used to minimize or eliminate pain in most U.S. deliveries.

General anesthesia
The use of drugs to put people to sleep and eliminate pain, as during childbirth.

General anesthesia first became popular when Queen Victoria of England delivered her eighth child under chloroform anesthesia in 1853. General anesthesia, like the chloroform of old, induces unconsciousness. The drug sodium pentothal, a barbiturate, induces general anesthesia when it is injected directly into a vein in the arm. Barbiturates may also be taken orally to reduce anxiety while the woman remains awake. Women may also receive tranquilizers like Valium or narcotics like Demerol that help them relax and blunt pain without inducing sleep.

Anesthetic drugs, as well as tranquilizers and narcotics, decrease the strength of uterine contractions during delivery and may thus delay the process of cervical dilation and therefore prolong labor. They also weaken the woman's ability to push the baby through the birth canal. Because they cross the placental membrane, they also lower the newborn's overall responsiveness.

Local anesthesia
Anesthesia that eliminates pain in a specific area of the body, as during childbirth.

Regional or **local anesthetics** block pain in certain areas of the body without generally depressing the mother's alertness or putting her to sleep. In a *pudendal block,* the external genitals are numbed by local injection. In an *epidural block* and a *spinal block,* an anesthetic is injected into the spinal canal, which temporarily numbs the mother's body below the waist. The needles used for these injections do not come into contact with the spinal cord itself, which prevents the possibility of paralysis. Local anesthesia apparently decreases the responsiveness of the baby at birth (Murray et al., 1981). There is little convincing evidence that medicated childbirth leads to serious, long-term consequences for children, however (Ganitsch, 1992).

Natural childbirth
A method of childbirth in which women use no anesthesia but are given other strategies for coping with discomfort and are educated about childbirth.

NATURAL CHILDBIRTH   Partly as a reaction against the use of anesthetics, English obstetrician Grantly Dick-Read endorsed **natural childbirth** in his 1932 book *Childbirth Without Fear.* Dick-Read argued that women's labor pains were heightened by their fear of the unknown and resultant muscle tensions. Many of Dick-Read's contributions came to be regarded as accepted practice in modern childbirth procedures, such as the emphasis on informing women about the biological aspects of reproduction and childbirth, the encouragement of physical fitness, and the teaching of relaxation and breathing exercises.

(a)   **(b)**   **(c)**

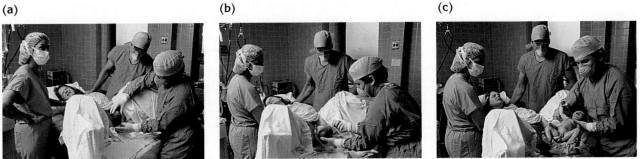

Coming into the World. These photos show a baby's birth from the appearance of the head in the vaginal opening (a) to the emergence of the baby from the mother's vagina (c). Note how the obstetrician uses suction aspiration to remove mucus from the baby's mouth (b).

Lamaze method

A childbirth method in which women learn about childbirth, learn to relax and to breathe in patterns that conserve energy and lessen pain, and have a coach (usually the father) present at childbirth. Also termed *prepared childbirth*.

PREPARED CHILDBIRTH: THE LAMAZE METHOD The French obstetrician Fernand Lamaze visited the former Soviet Union, in 1951, and found that many Russian women bore babies without anesthetics and without reporting a great deal of pain. Lamaze returned to Western Europe with some of the techniques the women used, and they are now usually termed the **Lamaze method,** or *prepared childbirth*. Lamaze (1981) argued that women can learn to conserve energy during childbirth and reduce the pain of uterine contractions by associating the contractions with other responses, such as thinking of pleasant mental images, such as beach scenes, or engaging in breathing and relaxation exercises.

A pregnant woman typically learns the Lamaze method by attending classes accompanied by a "coach"—usually the father—who will aid her in the delivery room by timing contractions, offering emotional support, and coaching her in the breathing and relaxation exercises. The woman and her partner also receive more general information about childbirth. The father is integrated into the process, and many couples report that their marriages are strengthened as a result. Both parents take pride in "their" accomplishment of bringing the child into the world (Bing, 1983). The Lamaze method takes a flexible attitude toward the use of anesthetics. The woman is usually encouraged to "take charge" and request anesthetics if she wants them.

Women using the Lamaze method report generally positive feelings about childbirth and their babies (Leifer, 1980). Many women report some pain during delivery and choose to use anesthetics, but the Lamaze method appears to enhance women's self-esteem by helping them gain a greater sense of control over the delivery process.

Notes: In a recent study, women having their first babies were each accompanied by a woman who had had a baby herself and who offered continuous emotional support during hospital labor and delivery. Compared to a control group, these women had fewer Caesarean sections, less use of anesthesia, shorter labors, and fewer forceps deliveries. (Kennell, Klaus, McGrath, Robertson, & Hinkley. 1991. Continuous emotional support during labor in a U.S. hospital: A randomized controlled trial. *Journal of the American Medical Association, 265* (17), 2197–2201.)

Caesarean section

A method of childbirth in which the fetus is delivered through a surgical incision in the abdomen.

Transverse position

A crosswise birth position.

CAESAREAN SECTION In a **Caesarean section,** the baby is delivered through surgery rather than naturally through the vagina. The term is derived from the Latin for "to cut." Julius Caesar is said to have been delivered in this way, but health professionals believe this unlikely (Brody, 1989b). In a Caesarean section (C-section for short) the woman is anesthetized and incisions are made in the abdomen and uterus so that the surgeon can remove the baby. The incisions are then sewn up and the mother can begin walking, often on the same day, although generally with some discomfort for a while.

C-sections are most likely to be advised when normal delivery is difficult or threatening to the health of the mother or child. Vaginal deliveries can become difficult if the baby is large or the mother's pelvis is small or misshapen, or if the mother is overly tired or in a weakened state. Herpes infections in the birth canal can also be bypassed by C-section (Ganitsch, 1992). C-sections are also likely to be performed if the baby presents for delivery in the breech position (feet downward) or the **transverse position** (lying crosswise), or if the baby is in distress.

Use of the C-section has mushroomed. Nearly one million births in 1991 were by Caesarean section, which works out to nearly one of every four births, as compared to about one in ten births in 1975 (Morbidity and Mortality Weekly Report, 1993; Samuels & Samuels, 1986). The rate remained virtually unchanged from 1989 to 1991. Some health professionals claim that the increased rate of C-sections reflects improvements in medical technology, such as the advent of fetal monitors that allow doctors to detect fetal distress. But critics claim that many C-sections are unnecessary and reflect overly aggressive medical practices. Even the federal government's Centers for Disease Control and Prevention (CDC) believes that many of the Caesarean deliveries in 1991, about one in three, were unnecessary ("U.S. Says 349,000 Caesareans in 1991 were not necessary," 1993). The CDC hopes to lower the rate of Caesareans in the United States to 15 per 100 births by the year 2000, a level the agency considers to be medically appropriate. Yet even health officials at the agency believe that this goal may be unrealistic.

TRUTH OR FICTION?

R E V I S I T E D

One U.S. birth in four is by Caesarean section. *The use of Caesarean section has mushroomed to nearly 25 percent of deliveries in the early 1990s, and critics of this trend have raised concerns as to how many of them are medically necessary.* •

Until recently, medical opinion held that once a woman had a C-section, subsequent deliveries also had to be performed by C-section to prevent the uterine scar from rupturing during labor. Evidence has shown that uterine rupturing is actually rare, however (Samuels & Samuels, 1986). Today, many obstetricians encourage women with prior C-sections who fall into certain low-risk groups to attempt subsequent vaginal deliveries. The number of women who are delivering vaginally after having had an earlier Caesarean section has been on the increase in recent years, from 13 percent in 1988 to 20 percent in 1990 and to 24 percent in 1991 (Morbidity and Mortality Weekly Report, 1993).

ALTERNATIVES TO THE HOSPITAL: WHERE SHOULD A CHILD BE BORN?

Learning Objective 12:
Compare hospitals and alternative locations for giving birth.

In the United States most births occur in hospitals. The major advantage of giving birth in a hospital is that medical equipment and personnel are available to handle complications that may arise. But hospital deliveries have their disadvantages. Hospitals are often impersonal and very expensive, although the costs to the parents may be offset by medical insurance. Giving birth in a hospital tends to instill the perception that pregnancy is an illness, rather than a healthy, natural process. In addition, the social environment of the hospital tends to encourage patients to assume a passive role and surrender responsibility for their care to the doctor. For various reasons, then, many pregnant women and their partners have sought alternative places to deliver their children.

Discussion Question:
Think about the ways we talk about the birth process. If, as we often say, doctors "deliver" babies, then what does the mother do? If pregnancy and birth are not disease states, why do we speak of pregnant women as "patients"? And why do many articles in women's or parenting magazines refer to "medical management" of childbirth, instead of providing information to assist women during pregnancy, labor, and birth? What purposes do various language choices serve?

BIRTH CENTERS   Birth centers seek to provide the atmosphere associated with home delivery. Birth centers typically have some medical equipment available and are frequently located within or adjacent to medical centers to permit immediate access to medical facilities (for example, if an emergency C-section is needed). Such centers are intended only for women who are deemed to be at low risk for birth complications (Toussie-Weingarten & Jacobwitz, 1987).

The birthing room itself is typically decorated and furnished cheerfully, like a bedroom. Family members, friends, and siblings of the baby may be present to share the experience. Women in labor can move about the room freely and eat, drink, rest, or chat with friends and family as they wish. Following the birth the family generally remains together in the room, sharing what for most is a loving and joyous experience. These days even maternity wards in U.S. hospitals seem to be assuming much of the comforting ambience of birthing centers (Ganitsch, 1992).

HOME BIRTHS   Home birth provides familiar surroundings and the psychological sense that the woman and her family are more fully in control. Some advocates of home childbirth argue that it is safe enough for women who have been medically screened for potential complications and who have a history of normal births. Critics charge that it is not possible to screen women for every possible complication, however, and that home delivery exposes the mother and child to unnecessary risks, especially if unexpected complications occur. Many physicians refuse to deliver babies in the mother's home (Toussie-Weingarten & Jacobwitz, 1987).

 Midwives

BIRTH PROBLEMS

Learning Objective 13:
Explain the causes, the effects at birth, and the effects later in a child's life of anoxia, preterm delivery, and low birth weight.

Most deliveries are uncomplicated, or "unremarkable" in the medical sense—although using that word to describe what for many parents is the most remarkable experience of their lives is an irony. Problems can and do occur, however. Some of the most common birth problems are anoxia and the birth of preterm and low-birth-weight babies.

ANOXIA

Anoxia
Oxygen deprivation.

Prenatal **anoxia** can cause various problems in the neonate and can affect later development, leading to such complications as brain damage and mental retardation. A prolonged cutoff of oxygen to the brain during delivery can also result in cerebral palsy and possibly death.

The baby is supplied with oxygen through the umbilical cord. The tight passage through the birth canal squeezes the umbilical cord. Temporary squeezing, like holding one's breath for a moment, is unlikely to cause problems. (In fact, slight oxygen deprivation at birth is not unusual because the transition from receiving oxygen through the umbilical cord to breathing on its own may not happen immediately after the baby emerges.) Anoxia can result if constriction of the cord is prolonged, however. Prolonged constriction is more likely to occur with a breech presentation, because the baby's head presses the umbilical cord against the birth canal during delivery. Fetal monitoring can help detect anoxia early, however, before damage occurs. An immediate C-section can be performed if the fetus appears to be in distress.

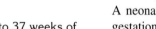
Black Health Care

PRETERM AND LOW-BIRTH-WEIGHT CHILDREN

Preterm
Born prior to 37 weeks of gestation.

A neonate is considered to be premature, or **preterm,** if it is born before 37 weeks of gestation. The normal period of gestation is 40 weeks. Prematurity is generally linked with low birth weight, since the fetus normally makes dramatic gains in weight during the last weeks of pregnancy. Regardless of the length of its gestation period, a newborn baby is considered to have a low birth weight if it weighs less than 5 pounds (about 2,500 grams).

Preterm or low-birth-weight babies face a heightened risk of infant mortality. A birth weight of $3\frac{1}{4}$ pounds (1,500 grams) is considered to be the cutoff point with respect to the likelihood of mortality. In a study in New York City, about 60 percent of newborns who were below this cutoff weight died during their first year, compared with only 5.5 percent of babies who weighed 1,500 to 2,500 grams (about 3 to 5 pounds) at birth (Kessner, 1973).

Surfactants
Substances that prevent the walls of the airways from sticking together.

Respiratory distress syndrome
A cluster of breathing problems, including weak and irregular breathing, to which preterm babies are especially prone.

Preterm babies are relatively thin because they have not yet formed the layer of fat that accounts for the round, robust appearance of most full-term children. Their muscles are immature, which weakens their sucking and breathing reflexes. Also, in the last weeks of pregnancy fetuses secrete **surfactants** that prevent the walls of their airways from sticking together (Avery & Merritt, 1991). Muscle weakness and incomplete lining of the airways with surfactants can cause a cluster of problems known as **respiratory distress syndrome,** which is responsible for many neonatal deaths. Preterm babies may also suffer from underdeveloped immune systems, which leave them more vulnerable to infections.

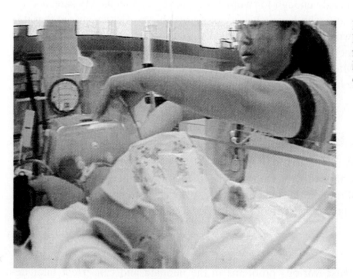

Neonatal Intensive Care. Preterm and low-birth-weight babies often need intensive medical care immediately following birth. Many preterm and low-birth-weight babies are born to mothers who receive inadequate or no prenatal care.

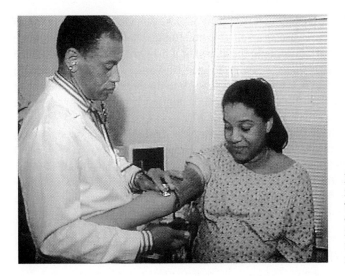

Prenatal Care. The incidence of low-birth-weight babies is clearly connected to the quality of prenatal care. In this clinic, a woman is having her blood pressure checked as part of a prenatal examination. Many women in the United States—especially poor women—do not receive adequate prenatal care, however, and some receive no care at all.

Preterm infants usually remain in the hospital for a time, where they can be monitored and placed in incubators that provide a temperature-controlled environment and confer some protection from disease. If necessary, they may also receive oxygen.

THE POSTPARTUM PERIOD

The weeks following delivery are called the postpartum period. The first few days postpartum are frequently happy ones. The long wait is over, as are the discomforts of childbirth. A sizable number of women experience feelings of depression, however, in the days and sometimes weeks and months following childbirth.

MATERNAL DEPRESSION

Mood changes following childbirth are experienced by many new mothers. During the days or weeks following the delivery of their babies, anywhere from 50 to 80 percent of new mothers (Harding, 1989) experience periods of sadness, tearfulness, and irritability that are commonly called the "postpartum blues," the "maternity blues," or the "baby blues." This downswing in mood typically occurs around the third day after delivery (Samuels & Samuels, 1986). The baby blues usually last about 48 hours and are generally believed to be a normal response to hormonal and psychological changes that attend childbirth (Harding, 1989; Samuels & Samuels, 1986).

Some mothers experience more persistent and severe mood changes, called **postpartum depression** (PPD) (Whiffen, 1992). PPD may last a year or even longer. PPD can involve extreme sadness or despair, apathy, changes in appetite and sleep patterns, low self-esteem, and difficulty concentrating. A recent study found that 9.3 percent of those in a sample of 1,033 married, middle-class, first-time mothers from the Pittsburgh area who had full-term, healthy infants had experienced PPD (Campbell & Cohn, 1991). Some researchers (e.g., Gitlin & Pasnau, 1989) estimate that PPD affects up to 15 percent of new mothers.

Like the "maternity blues," PPD may reflect a combination of physiological and psychological factors. Hormonal changes may play a role in PPD, but women with PPD are more likely than those with the maternity blues to have been susceptible to depression before and during their pregnancies (O'Hara et al., 1984). Psychosocial factors such as stress, a troubled marriage, or the need to adjust to an unwanted or sick baby may all increase a woman's susceptibility to PPD (Gitlin & Pasnau, 1989; Mansnerus, 1988;

Postpartum depression
Persistent and severe mood changes during the postpartum period, involving feelings of despair and apathy and characterized by changes in appetite and sleep, low self-esteem, and difficulty concentrating.

CNN Unequal Treatment

O'Hara et al., 1984, 1991). Adjusting to a new baby imposes inevitable changes on parents, and change is usually stressful in itself (Nevid, Rathus & Greene, 1994). Some women encounter depression in adjusting to the arrival of a baby that had not been wanted or planned. Depression is also likely to be prolonged in women who feel helpless in meeting the demands they face (Cutrona, 1983). First-time mothers, single mothers, and mothers who lack social support from their partners or family members face the greatest risk of PPD (Gitlin & Pasnau, 1989; Mansnerus, 1988).

New fathers may also have bouts of depression. New mothers are not the only ones who must adjust to the responsibilities of parenthood. Fathers too may feel overwhelmed or unable to cope. Perhaps more fathers might experience the "paternity blues" but for the fact that mothers generally shoulder the lion's share of child-rearing chores. New fathers who suffer from depressed moods tend to interact less with their babies and are less accepting of their parenting role (Zaslow et al., 1985).

BREAST-FEEDING VERSUS BOTTLE-FEEDING

For various reasons only a minority of U.S. women breast-feed their children. One reason is that many women return to the workforce shortly following childbirth and are unavailable for regular feedings. Some choose to share feeding chores with the father, who is equally equipped to prepare and hold a bottle, but not to breast-feed. Other women find breast-feeding inconvenient or unpleasant. Long-term comparisons of breast-fed and bottle-fed children show few, if any, significant differences (Wardlaw & Insel, 1990). Breast-feeding does reduce the general risk of infections to the baby, however, by transmitting the mother's antibodies to the baby (Wardlaw & Insel, 1990). Breast-feeding also reduces the incidence of allergies in babies, particularly in allergy-prone infants (Wardlaw & Insel, 1990).

The hormones prolactin and oxytocin are involved in breast-feeding. **Prolactin** stimulates production of milk, or **lactation,** two to three days after delivery. Oxytocin causes the breasts to eject milk and is secreted in response to suckling. When an infant is weaned, secretion of prolactin and oxytocin is discontinued, and lactation comes to an end.

Uterine contractions that occur during breast-feeding help return the uterus to its typical size. Breast-feeding also delays resumption of normal menstrual cycles. Breast-feeding is not a perfectly reliable birth-control method, however. (But nursing women are advised not to use birth-control pills, since the hormone content of the pills is passed to the infant through the milk.)

Should a woman breast-feed her baby? Although breast-feeding has some benefits for both mother and infant, each woman must weigh these benefits against the difficulties breast-feeding may pose for her. These include assuming the sole responsibility for nighttime feedings, the physical demands of producing and expelling milk, and tendencies for soreness in the breasts, as well as the inconvenience of being continually available to meet the infant's feeding needs. Women should breast-feed because they want to, not because they feel they must.

RESUMPTION OF OVULATION AND MENSTRUATION

For close to a month after delivery, women experience a reddish vaginal discharge called **lochia.** A nonnursing mother does not resume actual menstrual periods until 2 to 3 months postpartum. The first few cycles are likely to be irregular. Many women incorrectly assume that they will resume menstruating following childbirth by first having a menstrual period and then ovulating two weeks later. In most cases the opposite is true. Ovulation precedes the first menstrual period after childbirth. Thus, a woman may become pregnant before the menstrual phase of her first postpartum cycle. Some women, but not all, who suffered premenstrual syndrome before their pregnancies are often delighted to find that their periods give them less discomfort after the birth of their children.

Learning Objective 15:
Discuss the advantages and disadvantages of breast-feeding and bottle-feeding.

Notes: In the United States, the popularity of breast-feeding began to decline in the 1930s. By 1946, the proportion of women breast-feeding was 65 percent; in 1956, it was 37 percent; in 1966, it was 27 percent, and by 1971, 14 percent. The incidence of breast-feeding has increased from its low point in the early 1970s, particularly among middle-class, educated mothers (p. 307). (Corea, Gena. 1985. *The Mother Machine: Reproductive Technologies From Artificial Insemination to Artificial Wombs.*)

Prolactin
A pituitary hormone that stimulates production of milk. (From roots meaning "for milk")

Lactation
Production of milk by the mammary glands.

Lochia
A reddish vaginal discharge that may persist for a month after delivery. (From the Greek *lochios,* meaning "of childbirth.")

RESUMPTION OF SEXUAL ACTIVITY

The resumption of sexual activity depends on a couple's level of sexual interest, the healing of episiotomies or other injuries, fatigue, the recommendations of obstetricians, and, of course, tradition. Obstetricians usually advise a 6-week waiting period for safety and comfort.

Couples should abstain from sexual activity for at least six weeks following childbirth. *Couples should probably abstain from* coitus *for about six weeks postpartum, but many other kinds of sexual activities are safe and do not cause discomfort. (Check with your obstetrician.)* •

Postpartum prohibitions against sex are virtually universal. They are found in 94 percent of the world's societies (Frayser, 1985). The prohibitions usually do not last longer than six months, although among some peoples they may apply for two years or more.

Women will typically prefer to delay coitus until it becomes physically comfortable, generally when the episiotomy or other lacerations have healed and the lochia has ended. This may take several weeks. Women who breast-feed may also find they have less vaginal lubrication, which can cause some discomfort during coitus. K-Y jelly or other lubricants may help in such cases.

The return of sexual interest and resumption of sexual activity may take longer for some couples than for others. Sexual interest depends more on psychological than on physical factors. Many couples encounter declining sexual interest and activity in the first year following childbirth, generally because child care can sap energy and limit free time. One of the big challenges that new parents face is learning to incorporate lovemaking within their busy schedules. Generally speaking, couples whose sexual relationships were satisfying before the baby arrived tend to show greater sexual interest and to resume sexual activity earlier than those who had less satisfying relationships beforehand. (No surprise.)

Notes: In May 1994, New York State amended its civil right laws to enable a nursing mother who has been harassed in a public place to file a civil suit. Florida passed a similar law in 1993. (Basu Rekha. 1994. Restoring right to feed baby. *Des Mones Register, 1T,* May 30.)

SUMMING UP

CONCEPTION: AGAINST ALL ODDS

Conception is the union of a sperm cell and an ovum. Ova carry X sex chromosomes. Sperm carry either X or Y sex chromosomes. Girls are conceived from the union of an ovum and an X-bearing sperm, boys from the union of an ovum and a Y-bearing sperm. Fertilization normally occurs in a Fallopian tube. **Optimizing the Chances of Conception** Optimizing the

chances of conception is engaging in coitus at the time of ovulation. Ovulation can be predicted by calculating the woman's basal body temperature, analyzing the woman's urine for luteinizing hormone, or tracking the thickness of vaginal mucus. **Selecting the Gender of Your Child** Strategies for gender preselection have been derived

from the fact that sperm bearing the Y sex chromosome are faster swimmers but less durable than those bearing the X sex chromosome. Several sperm-separation procedures are used to ensure that a couple conceives a child of a particular gender. None of these methods is perfectly reliable, however.

INFERTILITY AND ALTERNATIVE WAYS OF BECOMING PARENTS

Male Fertility Problems

Fertility problems in the male include low sperm count, irregularly shaped sperm, low sperm motility, certain chronic or infectious diseases, trauma to the testes, an autoimmune response to sperm, and pituitary imbalances and/or thyroid disease.

Female Fertility Problems

The major causes of infertility in women include irregular or absent ovulation, obstructions or malfunctions of the reproductive tract, and endometriosis. Failure to ovulate may often be overcome by fertility drugs. Methods for overcoming other female fertility problems include in vitro fertilization, GIFT, ZIFT, donor IVF, embryonic transfer, and surrogate motherhood.

PREGNANCY

Early Signs of Pregnancy

Early signs include a missed period, presence of HCG in the blood or urine, and Hegar's sign.

Pregnancy Tests Pregnancy tests detect the presence of HCG—human chorionic gonadotropin—in the woman's urine or blood.

Early Effects of Pregnancy

Early effects include tenderness in the breasts and morning sickness.

Miscarriage (Spontaneous Abortion) Miscarriages have many causes, including chromosomal defects in the fetus and abnormalities of the placenta and uterus.

Sex During Pregnancy Most health professionals concur that in most cases coitus is safe until the start of labor.

Psychological Changes During Pregnancy A woman's psychological response to pregnancy reflects her desire to be pregnant, her physical changes, and her attitudes toward these changes. Men, like women, respond to pregnancy according to the degree to which they want the child.

PRENATAL DEVELOPMENT

The Germinal Stage The germinal stage is the period from conception to implantation.

The Embryonic Stage The embryonic stage begins with implantation and extends to about the eighth week of development and is characterized by differentiation of the major organ systems. The embryo develops within the amniotic sac. Nutrients and waste products are exchanged between mother and embryo through the placenta.

The Fetal Stage The fetal stage begins by the ninth week and continues until the birth of the baby. The fetal stage is characterized by continued maturation of the fetus's organ systems and dramatic increases in size.

Environmental Influences on Prenatal Development Environmental factors that affect prenatal development include the mother's diet, maternal diseases and disorders, and drugs. Maternal malnutrition has been linked to low birth weight and infant mortality. Exposure to particular teratogens causes the greatest harm during critical periods of vulnerability.

Chromosomal and Genetic Abnormalities Chromosomal and genetic abnormalities can lead to cystic fibrosis, Down syndrome, hemophilia, Huntington's chorea, neural-tube defects, phenylketonuria, retina blastoma, sickle cell anemia, and Tay-Sachs disease. Parental blood tests, amniocentesis, and ultrasound allow parents to learn whether their children have or are at risk for many such disorders.

CHILDBIRTH

The Stages of Childbirth In the first stage uterine contractions efface and dilate the cervix so that the baby may pass. The first stage may last from a couple of hours to more than a day. The second stage lasts from a few minutes to a few hours and ends with the birth of the baby. During the third stage the placenta is expelled.

Methods of Childbirth Contemporary methods for facilitating childbirth include medicated childbirth, natural childbirth, the Lamaze method, and Caesarean section.

Alternatives to the Hospital: Where Should a Child Be Born? In the United States most births occur in hospitals. Some parents seeking more intimate arrangements, however, opt for a birth center or home delivery.

BIRTH PROBLEMS

Anoxia Prenatal anoxia can cause brain damage and mental retardation in the child.

Preterm and Low-Birth-Weight Children Preterm and low-birth-weight babies have a heightened risk of infant mortality. A baby born before 37 weeks of gestation is considered preterm.

THE POSTPARTUM PERIOD

Maternal Depression Transient mood changes following childbirth are experienced by many new mothers. Women with postpartum depression experience lingering depression following childbirth.
Breast-Feeding Versus Bottle-Feeding Breast-feeding is connected with fewer infections and allergic reactions in the baby than bottle-feeding. Long-term studies show few differences between children whose parents used one of the other feeding method, however.
Resumption of Ovulation and Menstruation The first few menstrual cycles following childbirth are likely to be irregular.
Resumption of Sexual Activity Obstetricians usually advise a 6-week waiting period following childbirth before resuming coitus, but couples need not wait this long to enjoy other forms of sexual activity.

C H A P T E R 12

Contraception and Abortion

It was a stifling day in July 1912. Margaret Sanger (1883–1966), a nurse practitioner, was summoned to the house of a woman near death from a botched self-induced abortion. Her husband had called a doctor, and the doctor sent for Sanger. Together, doctor and nurse worked feverishly through the days and nights that followed to stem an infection that had taken hold in the woman. Sanger later commented,

> never had I worked so fast, never so concentratedly. The sultry days and nights were melted into a torpid inferno. It did not seem possible there could be such heat, and every bit of food, ice, and drugs had to be carried up three flights of stairs. . . .

Discussion Question: Try to imagine what life would be like if both contraception and abortion were illegal. Would you break the law and try to obtain condoms or a diaphragm? How would you feel about a person's being charged with the crime of possessing a condom or diaphragm? Would you break the law and help teach women how to prevent pregnancy?

After two interminable weeks, the woman began to recover. Her neighbors, who had feared the worst, came to express their joy. But the woman, who smiled wanly at those who came to see her, appeared more depressed and anxious than would be expected of someone who was recovering from a grave illness. By the end of the third week, when Sanger prepared to leave her patient, the woman, Mrs. Sachs, voiced the fear that was haunting her. Her face registered deep despair as she explained to Sanger that she dreaded becoming pregnant again and facing a choice between attempting another abortion, which she feared might kill her, and bearing a baby whose care it was beyond her means to support. She pleaded for information about contraception but Sanger could offer none. In 1912 it was a crime even for health professionals like Margaret Sanger to dispense information about contraceptives. Abortions, too, were illegal. Sanger tried to comfort her and promised to return to talk again.

Three months later she received another urgent call. It was Mr. Sachs. His wife was sick again—from the same cause. As Sanger recalled,

> for a wild moment I thought of sending someone else, but actually, of course, I hurried into my uniform, caught up my bag, and started out. All the way I longed for a subway wreck, an explosion, anything to keep me from having to enter that home again. But nothing happened, even to delay me. I turned into the dingy doorway and climbed the familiar stairs once more. The children were there, young little things.
>
> Mrs. Sachs was in a coma and died within ten minutes. I folded her still hands across her breast, remembering how they had pleaded with me, begging so humbly for the knowledge which was her right. I drew a sheet over her pallid face. Jake was sobbing, running his hands through his hair and pulling it out like an insane person. Over and over again he wailed, "My God! My God! My God!"
>
> (Sanger, 1938)

Today, partly because of the work of Margaret Sanger, who went on to become a key advocate for birth control, information about contraceptives may be disseminated freely throughout the United States.

Birth control includes both contraception—techniques to prevent conception from occurring—and induced abortion, which refers to the purposeful termination of a pregnancy before the embryo or fetus is capable of surviving outside the womb. This chapter first discusses the history of contraception. Then we examine methods of contraception and abortion.

CONTRACEPTION

Learning Objective 1: Define contraception and trace the history of methods of contraception.

People have been devising means of contraception since they became aware of the relationship between coitus and conception. Ironically, the safest and most effective method of contraception is also the least popular: abstention. The Bible contains many references

Coitus interruptus
A method of contraception in which the penis is withdrawn from the vagina prior to ejaculation. Also referred to as the *withdrawal method*.

TRUTH OR FICTION?
———————————
R E V I S I T E D

Condom
A sheath made of animal membrane or latex that covers the penis during coitus and serves as a barrier to sperm following ejaculation.

Learning Objective 2:
Discuss the history of contraception law in the United States.

Notes: In a 1989 book entitled *Pregnancy, Contraception, and Family Planning Services in Industrialized Countries* (by Jones, Forrest, Henshaw, Silverman, and Torres), the authors point out that the total abortion rate and pregnancy rate is higher in the United States than in most of the 20 industrialized countries they studied. This can be attributed at least partially to the lack of readily available information about contraceptives, especially in the mass media, and to the fact that family planning services are provided by obstetricians and gynecologists rather than by general practitioners and family planning clinics.

to contraceptive techniques, including vaginal sponges and contraceptive concoctions, as well as **coitus interruptus,** or withdrawal. The story of Onan, for example, implies knowledge of the withdrawal method.

Ancient Egyptian methods of birth control included douching after coitus with wine and garlic, and soaking crocodile dung in sour milk and stuffing the mixture deep within the vagina.

Ancient Egyptians used crocodile dung as a contraceptive substance. The ancient Egyptians did use crocodile dung as a contraceptive substance. •

The dung mixture apparently blocked the passage of sperm through the cervix and also soaked up sperm (Tannahill, 1980). The dung may also have done its job through a social mechanism—it may have discouraged all but the most ardent suitors.

Greek and Roman women placed absorbent materials within the vagina to absorb semen. The use of sheaths or coverings for the penis has a long history (Hatcher et al., 1994; Reinisch, 1990). Sheaths worn over the penis as decorative covers can be traced back to ancient Egypt (1350 B.C.). Penile sheaths made of linen were first described in European writings in 1564 by the Italian anatomist Fallopius (from whom the name of the Fallopian tube is derived). Such penile sheaths were used, without success, as a barrier against syphilis. The term **condom** was not used to describe penile sheaths until the eighteenth century, when sheaths made of animal intestines became popular as a means of preventing sexually transmitted diseases and unwanted pregnancies. Among the early advocates of condoms as a method of contraception was the Italian adventurer and writer Giovanni Casanova (1725–1798), whose name we now associate with men who are known for their amorous adventures. James Boswell (1740–1795), the biographer of Samuel Johnson, described his use of "armor," or condoms, in his graphic *London Journal.* On one occasion, however, he was so enamored with a street prostitute that he neglected to use his armor and contracted gonorrhea. Condoms made of rubber (hence the slang "rubbers") were introduced shortly after Charles Goodyear's invention of the process of vulcanization of rubber in 1843. Many other forms of contraception were also used widely in the nineteenth century, including withdrawal, vaginal sponges, and douching.

CONTRACEPTION IN THE UNITED STATES: THE LEGAL BATTLE

As methods of contraception grew more popular in the nineteenth century, opponents waged a battle to make contraception illegal. One powerful opponent of contraception was Anthony Comstock, who served for a time as the secretary of the New York Society for the Suppression of Vice. Comstock lobbied successfully for passage of a federal law in 1873—the Comstock law—that prohibited the dissemination of birth-control information through the mail on the grounds that it was "obscene and indecent." Many states passed even more restrictive laws, outlawing passage of information from one person to another, even from physician to patient.

Consider the resistance that Margaret Sanger met when she challenged the laws restricting disclosure of information about contraception. In 1914 she established the National Birth Control League, which published the magazine *The Woman Rebel. Rebel* did not publish birth-control information but challenged the view that it was obscene. Nevertheless, charges were brought against Sanger, and she fled to Europe before her trial. During her self-imposed exile, she visited birth-control clinics in the Netherlands. When the charges against her in the United States were dropped in 1916, Sanger returned and established a birth-control clinic in Brooklyn, New York. The clinic was closed by the police and Sanger was arrested. Released on bail, she reopened the clinic and was thereupon sentenced to 30 days in jail. She successfully appealed the sentence. In 1918 the courts ruled that physicians must be allowed to disseminate information that might aid in the cure and prevention of disease. Dismantling of the Comstock law had begun. With the financial support of a wealthy friend, Katherine Dexter McCormack, Sanger spurred research into the use of hormones as one approach to contraception. In 1960, only six years before Sanger's death, oral contraception—"the pill"—was finally marketed in the United States. In 1965 the Supreme Court struck down the last impediment to free use of contraception: a law preventing the sale of contraceptives in Connecticut (*Griswold v. Connecticut,* 1965). In 1973 abortion was in effect legalized by the Supreme Court in the case of *Roe v. Wade,* permitting women to terminate unwanted pregnancies.

Today, contraceptives are advertised in popular magazines and sold through vending machines in college dormitories. U.S. history is not a one-way road to unrestricted use of birth control, however. Recent Supreme Court decisions have set aside bits and pieces of *Roe v. Wade,* giving the states more discretion over the regulation of abortion and restricting access to abortions for minors. Public programs that provide high-school students with condoms to reduce the risks of teenage pregnancy and transmission of the AIDS virus—especially programs that do not require parental consent—have created a storm of controversy. Use of **artificial contraception** continues to be opposed by many groups, including the Catholic church. Yet many individual Catholics, including many priests, hold liberal attitudes toward contraception.

SELECTING A METHOD OF CONTRACEPTION

If you believe that you and your partner should use a method of contraception, how will you determine which one is right for you? There is no simple answer. What is right for your friends may be wrong for you. You and your partner will make your own selections, but there are some issues you may want to consider:

1. *Convenience.* Is the method convenient? The convenience of a method depends on a number of factors: Does it require a device that must be purchased in advance? If so, can it be purchased over the counter as needed, or are a consultation with a doctor and a prescription required? Can the method be used effectively at a moment's notice, or, like the birth-control pill, does it require weeks or months to reach maximum effectiveness?

   Some couples feel that few things dampen ardor and spontaneity more quickly than the need to pay attention to a contraceptive device in the heat of passion. Use of contraceptives like the condom and the diaphragm need not interrupt sexual activity, however. Both partners can share in putting the contraceptive device in or on. Some couples find that this becomes an erotic aspect of their lovemaking.

2. *Moral acceptability.* A method that is morally acceptable to one person may be objectionable to another. For example, some oral contraceptives prevent fertilization; others allow fertilization to occur but then prevent implantation of the fertilized ovum in the uterus. In the second case, the method of contraception may be considered to produce a form of early abortion, which is likely to concern people who object to abortion no matter how soon after conception it occurs. Yet the same people may have no moral objection to preventing fertilization.

3. *Cost.* Methods vary in cost. Some more costly methods involve devices (such as the diaphragm, the cervical cap, and the IUD) or pills (oral contraceptives) that require initial and follow-up medical visits in addition to the cost of the devices themselves. Other methods, such as rhythm methods, are essentially free.

4. *Sharing of responsibility.* Most forms of birth control place the burden of responsibility largely, if not entirely, on the woman. The woman must consult with her doctor to obtain birth-control pills or other prescription devices, such as diaphragms, cervical caps, Norplant, and IUDs. The woman must take birth-control pills reliably or check to see that her IUD remains in place.

   Some couples prefer methods that allow for greater sharing of responsibility, such as alternating use of the condom and diaphragm. A man can also share the responsibility for the birth-control pill by accompanying his partner on her medical visits, sharing the expense, and helping her remember to take her pill.

5. *Safety.* How safe is the method? What are the side effects? What health risks are associated with its use? Can your partner's health or comfort be affected by its use?

Artificial contraception
A method of contraception that applies a human-made device.

Learning Objective 3: List eight issues to consider when choosing a contraceptive.

Notes: Worldwide, over 100 million acts of sexual intercourse take place each day. These acts result in 910,000 conceptions and 356,000 sexually-transmitted bacterial and viral infections. About 50 percent of the conceptions are unplanned and about 25 percent are unwanted. Over 300 million couples worldwide do not have access to family planning services. (World Health Organization, 1992.)

Notes: The lifetime risk of dying from pregnancy-related causes is 1 in 21 in Africa, 1 in 54 in Asia, 1 in 73 in South America, 1 in 6,366 in North America, and 1 in 9,850 in Northern Europe. (Starrs, Ann. Preventing the tragedy of maternal deaths: A report on the International Safe Motherhood Conference held in Nairobi, Kenya, 1987.)

---

6. *Reversibility.* Reversibility refers to the effects of a birth-control technique or device. In most cases the effects of birth-control methods can be fully reversed by discontinuing their use. In other cases reversibility may not occur immediately, as with oral contraceptives. One form of contraception, surgical sterilization, should be considered irreversible, although some surgical attempts at reversal have been successful.

7. *Protection against STDs.* Birth-control methods vary in the degree of protection they afford against STDs like gonorrhea, chlamydia, and AIDS. This is especially important to people who are sexually active with one or more partners who are *not known to be free of infectious diseases.*

Contraceptives not only prevent conception, they also prevent sexually transmitted diseases (STDs). *Some contraceptives do help prevent STDs as well as conception. Most methods, however, offer no protection against STDs.* •

8. *Effectiveness.* Techniques and devices vary widely in their effectiveness in actual use. Despite the widespread availability of contraceptives, about two of three pregnancies in the United States are unplanned, and of these, about half result from contraceptive failures (Angier, 1993a). Researchers find that women using poor methods of contraception often overestimate the effectiveness of the contraception they use (Whitley & Hern, 1991). The failure rate for a particular method refers to the percentage of women who become pregnant when using the method for a given period of time, such as during the first year of use. Most contraceptive methods are not used correctly all or even much of the time. Thus it is instructive to compare the failure rate among people who use a particular method or device *perfectly* (consistently and correctly) with the failure rate among *typical* users. Failure rates among typical users are often considerably higher because of incorrect, unreliable, or inconsistent use. Table 12.1 shows the failure rates, continuation rates, reversibility, and degree of protection against STDs associated with various contraceptive methods.

METHODS OF CONTRACEPTION

Let us now consider various methods of contraception, including oral contraceptives (the pill), intrauterine devices (IUDs), diaphragms, cervical caps, spermicides, condoms, douching, withdrawal (coitus interruptus), timing of ovulation (rhythm), and some new developments in contraception, such as Norplant.

ORAL CONTRACEPTIVES (THE PILL)

An **oral contraceptive** is commonly referred to as a birth-control pill, or simply "the pill." Thirty-two types of birth-control pills are marketed in the United States today (Mishell, 1989). They vary in the type and dosages of hormones they contain. Birth-control pills fall into two major categories: combination pills and minipills.

Combination pills (such as Ortho-Novum, Ovcon, and Loestrin) contain a combination of synthetic forms of the hormones estrogen and progesterone (progestin). Most combination pills provide a steady dose of synthetic estrogen and progesterone. Other combination pills, called *multiphasic* pills, vary the dosage of these hormones across the menstrual cycle to reduce the overall dosages to which the woman is exposed and possible side effects. The **minipill** contains synthetic progesterone (progestin) only.

Available only by prescription, oral contraceptives are used by 28 percent of women in the United States who use reversible (nonsterilization) forms of contraception, or some 19 million women (Angier, 1993a). Use of the pill has been on the increase in recent years, especially among married women (Forrest & Fordyce, 1993). Birth-control pills are the most popular forms of contraception among single women of reproductive age.

TABLE 12.1 Approximate failure rates of various methods of birth control (in percentages of women using the method who become pregnant within the first year of use)

Method	% of Women Experiencing an Accidental Pregnancy within the First Year of Use		% of Women Continuing Use at One Year[3]	Reversibility	Protection Against Sexually Transmitted Diseases (STDs)
	Typical Use[1]	Perfect Use[2]			
Chance[4]	85	85		Yes (unless fertility has been impaired by exposure to STDs	no
Spermicides[5]	21	6	43	yes	some
Periodic Abstinence	20		67	yes	no
Calendar		9			
Ovulation Method		3			
Sympto-Thermal[6]		2			
Post-Ovulation		1			
Withdrawal	19	4		yes	no
Cervical Cap[7]					
Parous Women*	36	26	45	yes	some[8]
Nulliparous Women**	18	9	58	yes	some[8]

[1]Among typical couples who initiate use of a method (not necessarily for the first time), the percentage who experience an accidental pregnancy during the first year if they do not stop use for any other reason.

[2]Among couples who initiate use of a method (not necessarily for the first time) and who use it perfectly (both consistently and correctly), the percentage who experience an accidental pregnancy during the first year if they do not stop use for any other reason.

[3]Among couples attempting to avoid pregnancy, the percentage who continue to use a method for one year.

[4]The percentages failing in columns (2) and (3) are based on data from populations where contraception is not used and from women who cease using contraception in order to become pregnant. Among such populations, about 89% become pregnant within one year. This estimate was lowered slightly (to 85%) to represent the percentage who would become pregnant within one year among women now relying on reversible methods of contraception if they abandoned contraception altogether.

[5]Foams, creams, gels, vaginal suppositories, and vaginal film.

[6]Cervical mucus (ovulation) method supplemented by calendar in the pre-ovulatory and basal body temperature in the post-ovulatory.

*A woman who has borne children

**A woman who has not borne children

Birth Control Pills. Oral contraceptives come in various types and dispensers, several of which are shown here.

HOW THEY WORK Women cannot conceive when they are already pregnant because their bodies suppress maturation of egg follicles and ovulation. The combination pill "fools" the brain into acting as though the woman is already pregnant, so that no additional ova mature or are released. If ovulation does not take place, a woman cannot become pregnant.

In a normal menstrual cycle, low levels of estrogen during and just after the menstrual phase stimulate the pituitary gland to secrete FSH, which in turn stimulates the maturation of ovarian follicles. The estrogen in the combination pill inhibits FSH production, so follicles do not mature. The progesterone (progestin) inhibits the pituitary's secretion of LH, which would otherwise lead to ovulation. The woman continues to have menstrual periods, but there is no unfertilized ovum to be sloughed off in the menstrual flow.

The combination pill is taken for 21 days of the typical 28-day cycle. Then, for seven days, the woman either takes no pill at all or an inert placebo pill to maintain the habit of taking a pill a day. The sudden drop in hormone levels causes the endometrium to disintegrate and menstruation to follow three or four days after the last pill has been taken. Then the cycle is repeated.

The progestin in the combination pill also increases the thickness and acidity of the cervical mucus. The mucus thus becomes a more resistant barrier to sperm and inhibits development of the endometrium. Therefore, even if an egg were somehow to mature and become fertilized in a Fallopian tube, sperm would not be likely to survive the pas-

TABLE 12.1 (continued)

Method	% of Women Experiencing an Accidental Pregnancy within the First Year of Use		% of Women Continuing Use at One Year[3]	Reversibility	Protection Against Sexually Transmitted Diseases (STDs)
	Typical Use[1]	Perfect Use[2]			
Sponge					
Parous Women	36	20	45	yes	some[8]
Nulliparous Women	18	9	58	yes	some[8]
Diaphragm[7]	18	6	58	yes	some[8]
Condom Alone					
Female	21	5	56	yes	yes[8]
Male	12	3	63	yes	yes[8]
Pill	3		72	yes	no, but may reduce the risk of PID[9]
Progestin Only		0.5			
Combined		0.1			
IUD					
Progesterone T	2.0	1.5	81	yes, except if fertility is impaired by infection	no, and may increase the risk of PID[9]
Copper T 380A	0.8	0.6	78		
Depo-Provera	0.3	0.3	70	yes	no
Norplant (6 capsules)	0.09	0.09	85	yes	no
Female Sterilization	0.4	0.4	100	not usually	no
Male Sterilization	0.15	0.10	100	not usually	no

[7]With spermicidal cream or jelly.

[8]These methods provide better protection against STDs if a spermicide such as nonoxynom 9 is used simultaneously.

[9]Pelvic inflammatory disease.

Sources: For failure rates and percentages of women discontinuing use, adapted from Hatcher, R.A., Trussell, J., Stewart, F., Stewart, G.K., Kowal, D., Guest, F., Cates, W., Jr., & Policar, M.S. (1994). *Contraceptive technology,* 16th revised edition. New York: Irvington Publishers Inc.

For reversibility and protection against sexually transmitted diseases, adapted from Reinisch (1990). © (1990) by the Kinsey Institute for Sex, Gender, and Reproduction. From the book THE KINSEY INSTITUTE NEW REPORT ON SEX. Reprinted by permission of St. Martin's Press, New York, NY.

sage through the cervix. Even if sperm were somehow to succeed in fertilizing an egg, the failure of the endometrium to develop would mean that the fertilized ovum could not become implanted in the uterus. Progestin may also impede the progress of ova through the Fallopian tubes and make it more difficult for sperm to penetrate ova.

The minipill contains progestin but no estrogen. Minipills are taken daily through the menstrual cycle, even during menstruation. They act in two ways. They thicken the cervical mucus to impede the passage of sperm through the cervix, and they render the inner lining of the uterus less receptive to a fertilized egg. Thus, even if the woman does conceive, the fertilized egg will pass from the body rather than becoming implanted in the uterine wall. Since it contains no estrogen, the minipill does not usually prevent ovulation (Hatcher et al., 1988). The combination pill, by contrast, works directly to prevent ovulation. Since ovulation and fertilization may occur in women who use the minipill, some people see use of the minipill as an early abortion method. Others, however, reserve the term "abortion" for methods of terminating pregnancy following successful implantation.

EFFECTIVENESS OF BIRTH-CONTROL PILLS   The failure rate of the birth-control pill associated with perfect use is very low—a half of one percent or less depending on the type of pill (see Table 12.1). The failure rate increases to 3 percent in typical use. Failures can occur when women forget to take the pill for two days or more, when they

"Do I look like a mother to you?"

[fine print text]

Planned Parenthood Poster.
She does, if you look at the statistics. One million teenage girls in the U.S. become pregnant each year and the pregnancy rate has been going up (see Chapter 13).

do not use backup methods when they first go on the pill, and when they switch from one brand to another. But forgetting to take the pill even for one day may alter the woman's hormonal balance, allowing ovulation—and fertilization—to occur.

REVERSIBILITY   Use of oral contraceptives may temporarily reduce fertility after they are discontinued, but is not associated with permanent infertility (Mishell, 1989). Nine of ten women begin ovulating regularly within three months of suspending use (Reinisch, 1990). Users of the pill who frequently start and stop usage may later incur fertility problems, however (Reinisch, 1990). When a woman appears not to be ovulating after going off the pill, a drug like clomiphene is often used to induce ovulation.

ADVANTAGES AND DISADVANTAGES   The great advantage of oral contraception is that when used properly it is nearly 100 percent effective. Unlike many other forms of contraception, such as the condom or diaphragm, its use does not interfere with sexual spontaneity or diminish sexual sensations. The sex act need not be interrupted, as it would be by use of a condom.

Birth-control pills may also have some *healthful* side effects. They appear to reduce the risk of rheumatoid arthritis, ovarian cysts, pelvic inflammatory disease (PID), and fibrocystic (benign) breast growths. The use of the pill regularizes menstrual cycles and reduces menstrual cramping and premenstrual discomfort. The pill may also be helpful in the treatment of iron-deficiency anemia and facial acne. Considerable scientific evidence shows that the use of the combination pill reduces the risks of ovarian and endometrial cancer, even for a number of years after the woman has stopped taking the pill (Hatcher et al., 1994; Mishell, 1989). Moreover, the pill's protective effects against invasive ovarian cancer increases steadily with the length of use (Whittemore et al., 1992).

The pill does have some disadvantages. It confers no protection against STDs. Moreover, it may reduce the effectiveness of antibiotics used to treat STDs. Going on the pill requires medical consultation, so a woman must plan to begin using the pill at least several weeks before becoming sexually active or before discontinuing the use of other contraceptives and must incur the expense of medical visits.

The main drawbacks of birth-control pills are potential side effects and possible health risks. The estrogen in combination pills may produce such side effects as nausea and vomiting, fluid retention (feeling "bloated"), weight gain, increased vaginal discharge, headaches, tenderness in the breasts, and dizziness (Shapiro, 1988). Many of these side effects are temporary, but when they persist, women may be switched from one pill to another, perhaps to one with lower doses of hormones. Pregnant women produce high estrogen levels in the corpus luteum and placenta. The combination pill artificially raises levels of estrogen, so it is not surprising that women who use it may have side effects that mimic the early signs of pregnancy, such as weight gain or nausea ("morning sickness"). Weight gain can result from estrogen (through fluid retention) or progestin (through increased appetite and development of muscle). Oral contraceptives may also increase blood pressure in some women, but clinically significant elevations are rare in women using the low-dose pills that are available today (Hatcher et al., 1994). Still, it is wise for women who use the pill to have their blood pressure checked regularly (Mishell, 1989). Women who encounter problems with high blood pressure from taking the pill are usually switched to another form of contraception.

Many women have avoided using the pill because of the risk of blood clots. The lower dosages of estrogen found in most types of birth-control pills today are associated with much lower risk of blood clots than was the case in the 1960s and 1970s when higher dosages were typically used (Wharton & Blackburn, 1988). Still, women who are at increased risk for blood clotting problems, such as those with a history of circulatory problems or stroke are typically advised against using the pill.

Women who are considering using the pill need to weigh the benefits and risks in terms of their own health profile in consultation with their gynecologists or health care providers. For the great majority of young, healthy women in their twenties and early thirties, there is very little chance of developing blood clots or other cardiovascular problems from using the pill (Hatcher et al., 1994; Layde et al., 1982; Mant et al., 1987; Porter et al., 1982, 1985). Moreover, women who use the pill are no more likely than nonusers to develop cardiovascular problems later in life—even women who had used the pill for more than 10 years (Stampfer et al., 1988).

Some women, however, should simply not be on the pill (Calderone & Johnson, 1989; Hatcher et al., 1994; Mishell, 1989; Reinisch, 1990). These include women with a history of circulatory problems or blood clots, and those who have suffered a heart attack or stroke or have a history of coronary disease, breast or uterine cancer, undiagnosed genital bleeding, liver tumors, or sickle cell anemia (because of associated blood-clotting problems). Because of their increased risk of cardiovascular problems, caution should be exercised when using the combination pill with women over 35 years of age who are heavy smokers (15 or more cigarettes daily) (Hatcher et al., 1994). Nursing mothers should also avoid using the pill, as the hormones may be passed to the baby in the mother's milk.

Since the risks of cardiovascular complications generally increase with age, many women over the age of 35 have been encouraged by their gynecologists to use other forms of birth control. As a result, the pill is used by only one woman in 50 between the ages of 35 and 44, as compared to one woman in six in the 25 to 34 age category and one woman in four in the 15 to 24 age group (Statistical Abstract of the United States, 1990). Recent studies, however, show no increased risk of serious cardiovascular disease among healthy, nonsmoking women up to the age of 45 who use oral contraceptives containing lower dosages of estrogen (Mishell, 1989). Many health professionals today, including the American College of Obstetricians and Gynecologists, believe that healthy nonsmokers ages 35 to 44 can continue to use oral contraceptives safely (Mishell, 1989; Upton, 1987).

The pill may also have psychological effects. Some users report depression or irritability. Switching brands or altering doses may help. Evidence remains lacking concerning the effects of today's lower-estrogen pills on sexual desire.

Progestin fosters male secondary sex characteristics, so women who take the minipill may develop acne, facial hair, thinning of scalp hair, reduction in breast size, vaginal dryness, and missed or shorter periods. Irregular or so-called breakthrough bleeding between menstrual periods is a common side effect of the minipill (Reinisch, 1990). Irregular bleeding should be brought to the attention of a health professional. Because they can produce vaginal dryness, minipills can hinder vaginal lubrication during intercourse, decreasing sexual sensations and rendering sex painful.

Researchers have also examined suspected links between the use of the pill and certain forms of cancer, especially breast cancer, since breast cancer is sensitive to hormonal changes. Results from several large-scale studies show no overall increase in the rates of breast cancer among pill users, but it remains possible that some subgroups of women who use the pill may be at increased risk (Hatcher et al., 1994). The evidence linking use of the pill with increased risk of cervical cancer is mixed, with some studies showing such a link and others showing none (Hatcher et al., 1994).

Women considering the pill are advised to have a thorough medical evaluation to rule out contraindications (reasons for *not* using the pill). The evaluation should include a detailed medical and family history, and a physical exam including a Pap smear, assessment of blood pressure, screening for sexually transmitted diseases (STDs), urinalysis, breast and pelvic exam, and possibly an EKG (electrocardiogram). Women who begin to use the pill, regardless of their age or risk status, should pay attention to changes in their physical condition, have regular checkups, and promptly report any physical complaints or unusual symptoms to their physicians (Reinisch, 1990).

"MORNING-AFTER" PILLS   The so-called morning-after pill, or postcoital contraceptive, actually refers to several types of pills that have high doses of estrogen and progestin. Since they are not taken regularly, they do not prevent ovulation from occurring. Instead, they stop fertilization from taking place or prevent the fertilized egg from implanting in the uterus (Hoffman, 1993). In that respect, then, some people consider them an early abortion technique. Morning-after pills are most effective when taken within 72 hours after ovulation (Shapiro, 1988). Women who wait to see whether they have missed a period are no longer candidates for the morning-after pill. Depending on the brand, either four, six, or eight pills are prescribed.

TRUTH O R *FICTION?*

R E V I S I T E D

There is an effective oral contraceptive that can be taken the morning after unprotected intercourse. *Yes, there are oral contraceptives that can be taken the morning after unprotected intercourse. They are termed "morning-after" pills.* •

Morning-after pills have a higher hormone content than most birth-control pills. For this reason, nausea is a common side effect, occurring in perhaps 70 percent of users. Nausea is usually mild and passes within a day or two after treatment, but it can be treated with anti-nausea medication (Hatcher et al., 1994). Vomiting should be brought to the attention of a physician, since the woman may need to take additional pills to make up for ones possibly lost in vomiting (Hatcher et al., 1994).

Because of the strength of the dosage, the morning-after pill is not recommended as a regular form of birth control. We also know little about possible long-term health complications. Morning-after pills are *one-time* forms of "emergency" protection (Hatcher et al., 1994), which may be most appropriate to use following rape or when regular contraceptive devices fail (for example, if a condom breaks or a diaphragm becomes dislodged). The morning-after pill is generally effective in preventing implantation of a fertilized ovum, but health professionals caution that when it fails, the fetus may be damaged by exposure to the hormones it contains.

INTRAUTERINE DEVICES

Intrauterine device
A small object that is inserted into the uterus and left in place to prevent conception. Abbreviated *IUD*.

Learning Objective 5:
Describe how IUDs work and discuss their effectiveness, reversibility, advantages, and disadvantages.

Camel drivers setting out on long desert journeys placed round stones in the uteruses of female camels to prevent them from becoming pregnant and lost to service. The stones may have acted as primitive **intrauterine devices** (IUDs). IUDs are small objects of various shapes that are inserted into the uterus. IUDs have been used by humans since Greek times. Today, they are inserted by a physician or nurse practitioner into the uterus and usually left in place for a year or more. Fine plastic threads or strings hang down from the IUD into the vagina, so that the woman can check to see that it remains in place.

IUDs are used by about 1.5 million women in the United States and more than 80 million women around the world (Altman, 1991a). Nearly 60 million IUD users are in China, where nearly one in three married women uses an IUD during her childbearing years. By contrast, IUDs are used by only about 3 percent of married women of childbearing age in the United States (Shapiro, 1988). Married women in the United States are more than twice as likely as single women to use an IUD (Statistical Abstract of the United States, 1990).

IUDs achieved their greatest popularity in the United States in the 1960s and 1970s. Then there was a sharp dropoff in their use during the 1980s, largely because of negative publicity about a popular model, the Dalkon Shield, whose use was linked to a high incidence of pelvic infections (Cole, 1989) and tubal infertility (Darling et al., 1992).

Figure 12.1 shows some of the shapes (from loops and spirals to Ts and 7s) and materials (from silver to gold and from copper to plastic) that have been used with IUDs. Only two remain on the market in the United States, however: the Progestasert T, which releases small quantities of progesterone (progestin) daily, and the Copper T 380A (ParaGard), a T-shaped, copper-based device (Cole, 1989). Because the Progestasert T must be replaced annually, and any insertion carries some risk of infection, health authorities recommend the use of the ParaGard device, which can be used for upwards of 8 years, unless the woman is allergic to copper (Hatcher et al., 1994).

HOW THEY WORK We do not know exactly how IUDs work. A foreign body, such as the IUD, apparently irritates the uterine lining. This irritation gives rise to mild inflammation and the production of antibodies which may be toxic to sperm or to fertilized ova and/or may prevent fertilized eggs from becoming implanted. Inflammation may also impair prolif-

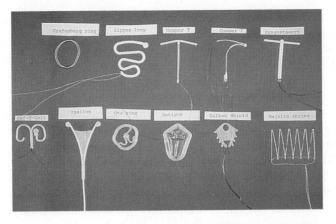

FIGURE 12.1 **Some of the Shapes and Materials That Have Been Used in Intrauterine Devices.** Only two IUDs remain on the market in the United States: the Progestasert T, which releases small quantities of progestin (upper far right), and the Copper T 380A (ParaGard), a T-shaped, copper-based device (upper middle).

eration of the endometrium—another impediment to implantation. Progestin released by the Progestasert T also has effects like the progestin-only minipill; that is, it lessens the likelihood of fertilization and implantation. Action on fertilized ova may be considered to constitute an early abortion. Since IUDs may not prevent fertilization, people who oppose abortion, regardless of how soon it occurs after conception, also oppose the IUD.

EFFECTIVENESS The failure rate associated with the typical use of Progestasert T is about 2 percent see Table 12.1). Most failures occur within three months of insertion, often because the device shifts position or is expelled. ParaGard is the most effective IUD, with a first-year failure rate in typical use of 0.8 percent.

The IUD may irritate the muscular layer of the uterine wall, causing contractions that expel it through the vagina. The device is most likely to be expelled during menstruation, so users are advised to check their sanitary napkins or tampons before discarding them. Women who use IUDs are advised to check the string several times a month to ensure that the IUD is in place. Spontaneous expulsions occur in 2 to 10 percent of users within the first year of use (Hatcher et al., 1994). Women who have not borne children have a higher expulsion rate (about 7%) than women who have (3%) (Reinisch, 1990). Some family-planning clinics advise women to supplement their use of IUDs with other devices for the first three months, when the risks of a shift in position or expulsion are greatest.

Aspirin and antibiotics may also decrease IUD effectiveness. Women using IUDs may substitute a non-aspirin pain reliever, like acetaminophen (e.g., Tylenol, Datril), and use supplemental devices when they are taking antibiotics.

REVERSIBILITY IUDs may be removed readily by professionals. Nine out of ten former IUD users, who wish to do so, become pregnant within a year (Reinisch, 1990).

ADVANTAGES AND DISADVANTAGES The IUD has three major advantages: (1) it is highly effective; (2) it does not diminish sexual spontaneity or sexual sensations; and (3) once in place, the woman need not "do anything" more to prevent pregnancy (other than check to see that it remains in place). The small risk of failure is reduced in effect to zero if the couple also use an additional form of birth control, such as the diaphragm or condom.

The IUD also does not interfere with the woman's normal hormonal production. Users continue to produce pituitary hormones that stimulate ovarian follicles to mature and rupture, thereby releasing mature ova and producing female sex hormones.

If IUDs are so effective and relatively "maintenance free," why are they not more popular? One reason is that insertion is sometimes painful. Another reason is possible troublesome side effects and potential for even more serious health complications. The most common side effects are excessive menstrual cramping, irregular bleeding (spotting) between periods, and heavier than usual menstrual bleeding (Cole, 1989; Reinisch, 1990). These usually occur shortly following insertion and are among the primary reasons women ask to have the device removed. A more serious concern is the possible risk of pelvic inflammatory disease (PID), a serious disease that can become life-threatening if left untreated (Hatcher et al., 1994). A recent review of the scientific evidence suggests that women who use the IUD may have a small increased risk of PID (Cates & Stone, 1992b). It appears that the risk of infection is associated more with the insertion of the device (bacteria may enter the woman's reproductive tract during insertion) than with use of the device itself (Cates & Stone, 1992b).

One of the principal dangers of PID is that it can produce scar tissue that blocks the Fallopian tubes, causing infertility. Women with active, recent, or recurrent pelvic infections should not use an IUD (Hatcher et al., 1994). Caution should be exercised if an IUD is used in women who have known risk factors for PID, such as a recent episode of gonorrhea or chlamydia, or recurrent episodes of these STDs, or sexual contact with multiple partners or with a partner who has multiple sexual partners. All in all, the IUD may be best suited to women who have completed their families and who are advised not to use oral contraceptives (Mishell, 1989).

Another risk in using an IUD is that the device may perforate (tear) the uterine or cervical walls, which can cause bleeding, pain, and adhesions and become life-threatening. Perforations are usually caused by improper insertion and occur in perhaps one case in 1,000 (Reinisch, 1990). IUD users are also at greater risk for ectopic pregnancies, both during and after usage, and for miscarriage. Ectopic pregnancies occur in about 5 percent of women who become pregnant while using an IUD (Cole, 1989). IUD use is not recommended for women with a history of ectopic pregnancy (Cole, 1989). Women who become pregnant while using the IUD stand about a 50–50 chance of miscarriage (Hatcher et al., 1994).

Despite the fact that the IUD irritates uterine tissues, there is no evidence that IUD users run a greater risk of cancer. Long-term data on the health effects of IUD use is limited, however.

Another drawback to the IUD is its cost. The typical cost of an IUD insertion in a family planning clinic ranges between $200 and $300 (Hatcher et al., 1994). The potential expulsion of the device presents yet another disadvantage. Moreover, the IUD, like the pill, offers no protection against STDs. Finally, like the pill, IUDs place the burden of contraception entirely on the woman.

THE DIAPHRAGM

Diaphragm
A shallow rubber cup or dome, fitted to the contour of a woman's vagina, that is coated with a spermicide and inserted prior to coitus to prevent conception.

Diaphragms were once used by about one third of U.S. couples who practiced birth control. When invented in 1882, they were a breakthrough. Their popularity declined only in the 1960s with the advent of the pill and the IUD. Today, only one married white woman in 20, and one married African-American woman in 50, ages 15 to 44, regularly use the diaphragm (Statistical Abstract of the United States, 1990). Overall, 3 percent of U.S. women using reversible forms of contraception use the diaphragm (Angier, 1993a).

The diaphragm is a shallow cup or dome made of thin latex rubber (Figure 12.2). The rim is a flexible metal ring covered with rubber. Diaphragms range from 2 to 4 inches in diameter to allow a precise fit.

Diaphragms are available by prescription and must be fitted to the contour of the vagina by a health professional. Several sizes and types of diaphragms may be tried during a fitting. Women practice insertion in a health professional's office so they can be guided as needed.

Learning Objective 6:
Describe the diaphragm, the contraceptive sponge, and the cervical cap, and discuss how they are used, how they work, their effectiveness, their reversibility, and their advantages and disadvantages.

HOW IT WORKS   The diaphragm is inserted and removed by the woman, much like a tampon. It is akin to a condom in that it forms a barrier against sperm when placed snugly over the cervical opening. Yet it is unreliable as a barrier alone. Thus, the diaphragm should be used in conjunction with a spermicidal cream or jelly. The diaphragm's main function is to keep the spermicide in place.

HOW IT IS USED   The diaphragm should be inserted no more than two hours before coitus, since the spermicides that are used may begin to lose effectiveness beyond this time.

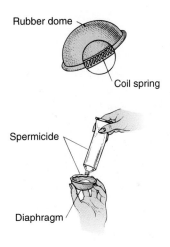

FIGURE 12.2 **A Diaphragm.** The diaphragm is a shallow cup or dome made of latex. Diaphragms must be fitted to the contour of the vagina by a health professional. The diaphragm forms a barrier to sperm but should be used in conjunction with a spermicidal cream or jelly.

Rubber dome

Coil spring

Spermicide

Diaphragm

Some health professionals, however, suggest that the diaphragm may be inserted up to six hours preceding intercourse. (It seems reasonable to err on the side of caution and assume that there is a two-hour time limit.) The woman or her partner places a tablespoonful of spermicidal cream or jelly on the inside of the cup and spreads it inside the rim. (Cream spread outside the rim might cause the diaphragm to slip.) The woman opens the inner lips of the vagina with one hand and folds the diaphragm with the other by squeezing the ring. She inserts the diaphragm against the cervix, with the inner side facing upward (see Figure 12.3, page 360). Her partner can help insert the diaphragm, but the woman is advised to check its placement. Some women prefer a plastic insertion device, but most find it easier to insert the diaphragm without it. The diaphragm should be left in place *at least six hours* to allow the spermicide to kill any remaining sperm in the vagina (Hatcher et al, 1994). It should not be left in place for longer than 24 hours to guard against toxic shock syndrome (TSS).

After use, the diaphragm should be washed with mild soap and warm water and stored in a dry, cool place. When cared for properly, a diaphragm can last about two years. Women may need to be refitted after pregnancy or a change in weight of about ten pounds or more.

EFFECTIVENESS If used consistently and correctly, the failure rate of the diaphragm is estimated to be 6 percent during the first year of use (see Table 12.1). In typical use, however, the failure rate is believed to be three times as high—18 percent. Some women become pregnant because they do not use the diaphragm during every coital experience. Others may insert it too early or not leave it in long enough. The diaphragm may not fit well, or it may slip—especially if the couple is acrobatic. A diaphragm may develop tiny holes or cracks. Women are advised to inspect the diaphragm for signs of wear and consult their health professionals when in doubt. Effectiveness also is seriously compromised when the diaphragm is not used along with a spermicide that is applied correctly (Trussell et al., 1993).

REVERSIBILITY The effects of the diaphragm are fully reversible. In order to become pregnant, the woman simply stops using it. The diaphragm has not been shown to influence subsequent fertility.

ADVANTAGES AND DISADVANTAGES The major advantage of the diaphragm is that when used correctly it is a safe and relatively effective means of birth control and does not alter the woman's hormone production or reproductive cycle. The diaphragm can be used as needed, whereas the pill must be used daily and the IUD remains in place whether or not the woman engages in coitus. Another advantage is the virtual absence of side effects. The few women who are allergic to the rubber in the diaphragm can switch to a plastic model. Another advantage is that spermicides that contain nonoxynol-9 may provide some, but not total, protection against sexually transmitted diseases (STDs), including AIDS, genital herpes, trichomonas ("trich"), syphilis, and perhaps chlamydia (Reinisch, 1990).

The major disadvantage is the high pregnancy rate associated with typical use. Nearly one in five typical users (18%) of the diaphragm combined with spermicidal cream or jelly become pregnant during the first year of use (Hatcher et al., 1994). Another disadvantage is the need to insert the diaphragm prior to intercourse, which the couple may find disruptive. Another disadvantage is that the woman's partner may find the taste of the spermicides used in conjunction with the diaphragm to be unpleasant during oral sex. The pressure exerted by the diaphragm against the vaginal and cervical walls may also irritate the urinary tract and cause urinary or even vaginal infections. Switching to a different size diaphragm or one with a different type of rim may help alleviate this problem. About one woman or man in 20 may develop allergies to the particular spermicide that is used, which can lead to irritation of the genitals. This problem may also be alleviated by switching to another brand.

SPERMICIDES

Spermicides are chemical agents that kill sperm. They come in different forms, including jellies and creams, suppositories, aerosol foam, and a contraceptive film. Contraceptive (vaginal) sponges also contain spermicides. Spermicides should be left in place in the vagina (no douching) for *at least six to eight hours* after coitus (Hatcher et al., 1994).

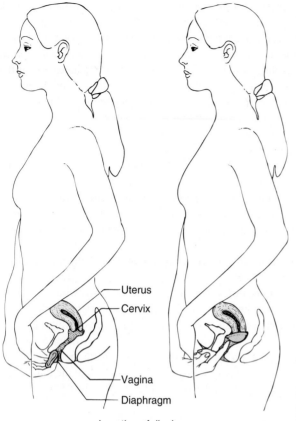

Uterus

Cervix

Vagina

Diaphragm

Insertion of diaphragm

FIGURE 12.3 **Insertion and Checking of the Diaphragm.** Women are instructed in insertion of the diaphragm by a health professional. In practice, a woman and her partner may find joint insertion an erotic experience.

HOW THEY ARE USED   Spermicidal jellies, creams, foam, and suppositories should be used no more than 60 minutes preceding coitus to provide for maximum effectiveness (Hatcher et al., 1994) . Spermicidal jellies and creams come in tubes with plastic applicators that introduce the spermicide into the vagina (see Figure 12.4). Spermicidal foam is a fluffy white cream with the consistency of shaving cream. It is contained in a pressurized can and is introduced with a plastic applicator in much the same way as spermicidal jellies and creams.

Vaginal suppositories are inserted into the upper vagina, near the cervix, where they release spermicide as they dissolve. Unlike spermicidal jellies, creams, and foam, which become effectively immediately when applied, suppositories must be inserted no less than 10 to 15 minutes before coitus so that they have sufficient time to dissolve (Hatcher et al., 1994).

Spermicidal film consists of thin, 2-inch-square sheets that are saturated with spermicide. When placed in the vagina, they dissolve into a gel and release the spermicide. The spermicidal film should be inserted at least five minutes before intercourse to allow it time to melt and for the spermicide to be dispersed (Hatcher et al., 1994). It remains effective for upwards of one hour (Hatcher et al., 1994). One disadvantage of the film that some users have noted is a tendency for it to adhere to the fingertips which makes it difficult to insert correctly.

HOW THEY WORK   Spermicides coat the cervical opening, blocking the passage of sperm and killing sperm by chemical action.

EFFECTIVENESS   Typically,the first-year failure rate of spermicides used alone is high, about 18 to 21 pregnancies per year per 100 users (Hatcher et al., 1994; Reinisch,

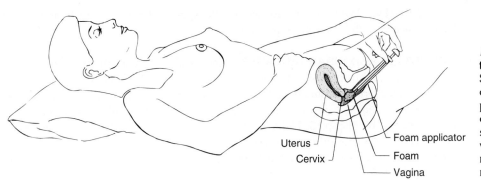

FIGURE 12.4 **The Application of Spermicidal Foam.** Spermicidal jellies and creams come in tubes with plastic applicators. Spermicidal foam comes in a pressurized can and is applied with a plastic applicator in much the same way as spermicidal jellies and creams.

Uterus
Cervix
Foam applicator
Foam
Vagina

1990). When used correctly and consistently, the failure rate is estimated to drop to about 6 pregnancies per 100 users in the first year. All forms of spermicide are more effective when they are combined with other forms of contraception, such as the condom.

REVERSIBILITY   Spermicides have not been linked with any changes in reproductive potential. So couples who wish to become pregnant simply stop using them.

Notes: For those who have sex infrequently or those who wish to carry a contraceptive with them, spermicidal foam comes in small prefilled single-use applicators with a carrying case. The Today sponge and condoms are also small and easy to carry.

ADVANTAGES AND DISADVANTAGES   The major advantages of spermicides are that they do not alter the woman's natural biological processes and are applied only as needed. Unlike a diaphragm, they do not require a doctor's prescription or a fitting. They can be bought in virtually any drugstore, and the average cost per use of the foam variety is modest—about 50 cents. Spermicides that contain nonoxynol-9 may also provide some protection against organisms that give rise to STDs.

The major disadvantage is the high failure rate among typical users. Foam often fails when the can is not shaken enough, when too little is used, when it is not applied deeply enough within the vagina near the cervix, or when it is used after coitus had begun.

Spermicides are generally free of side effects, but can cause vaginal or penile irritation in some people. This problem can sometimes be alleviated by changing brands. Some partners find the taste of spermicides unpleasant. (Couples can engage in oral sex before applying spermicides.) Spermicides may pose a danger to an embryo, so women who suspect they are pregnant are advised to suspend usage until they find out for certain.

THE CONTRACEPTIVE SPONGE

The Today Sponge. The contraceptive sponge contains a spermicide that is activated when the sponge is immersed in water prior to being inserted in the vagina. Placed high in the vagina against the cervix, the sponge absorbs sperm and the spermicide it contains kills them by chemical action.

Introduced in the 1980s, the contraceptive sponge, also called the vaginal sponge, is one of the newer forms of contraception. It is a soft, round ball of polyurethane, about 2 inches in diameter, that contains the potent spermicide nonoxynol-9 and is marketed under the brand name Today. The sponge is discarded after use. Available without a prescription, they cost about $1.25 to $1.50 each.

HOW IT WORKS   The spermicide in the sponge is activated when the sponge is immersed in water. The woman then inserts the sponge high in the vagina against the cervix. As a barrier, the sponge blocks and literally soaks up the ejaculate. The spermicide kills nearby sperm. The sponge must be left in place for six hours after coitus.

EFFECTIVENESS   The effectiveness of the sponge in typical use is low, with first-year pregnancy rates ranging between 18 percent among nulliparous women (women who have not borne children) to 36 percent among parous women (women who have borne children) (Hatcher et al., 1994).

METHODS OF CONTRACEPTION

REVERSIBILITY We have no evidence that the sponge affects fertility. Couples who wish to conceive a child simply stop using it.

ADVANTAGES AND DISADVANTAGES One prime advantage of the sponge is that a woman can begin using it on the very day that it is needed. Unlike the diaphragm, it does not require prior consultation, fitting, or prescription. Also unlike the diaphragm and other spermicides, it may be inserted up to 24 hours before coitus, so sexual spontaneity need not be disrupted. Unlike spermicides and foams, the sponge provides 24 hours of continuous protection and need not be reinserted before each subsequent act of intercourse within the 24-hour period. The sponge is also tasteless and odorless. Since the spermicide is long-lasting, users are also not likely to get involved in clock-watching.

Now, the disadvantages. Perhaps one in 20 men and women experiences mild irritation from the spermicide. Some women report that the sponge is uncomfortable, and some report difficulty removing it. About 6 percent of women in one study discontinued using the sponge because they found it difficult to remove (Edelman et al., 1984). There is a very, very slight chance—about one case in every two million uses (Faich et al., 1986)—of developing toxic shock syndrome (TSS). The chances of developing TSS can be decreased further by not wearing the sponge for longer than a 24–30 hour period (Hatcher et al., 1994). Finally, despite its convenience, the sponge does not offer the level of protection against unwanted pregnancies in regular use that is afforded by other contraceptive methods.

THE CERVICAL CAP

The cervical cap, like the diaphragm, is a dome-shaped latex cup. It comes in different sizes and must be fitted by a health professional. It is smaller than the diaphragm, about the size of a thimble, and is meant to fit snugly over the cervical opening.

The Cervical Cap. In the shape of a thimble, the cervical cap fits snugly over the cervical opening and should be used with a spermicide, filling about a third of it.

HOW IT IS USED Like the diaphragm, the cap is intended to be used with a spermicide applied inside it (Hatcher et al., 1994).When inserting it, the woman (or her partner) fills the cap about a third full of spermicide. Then, squeezing the edges together, the woman inserts the cap high in the vagina, so that it presses firmly against the cervix. The woman can test the fit by running a finger around the cap to ensure that the cervical opening is covered. It should be left in place for at least six hours after intercourse (Hatcher et al., 1994). The cap provides continuous protection for upwards of 48 hours without the need for additional spermicide, no matter how many times intercourse occurs (Hatcher et al., 1994). To reduce the risk of toxic shock syndrome, the cap should not be left in place longer than 48 hours. Like the diaphragm, it should be cleaned after every use and checked regularly for wear and tear. The cap typically costs about $22, not including the cost for the medical visit which is necessary to fit the device. When cared for properly, the cap should last for upwards of three years.

HOW IT WORKS Like the diaphragm, the cervical cap forms a barrier and also holds spermicide in place against the cervix, preventing sperm from passing into the uterus and Fallopian tubes, and killing sperm by chemical action.

EFFECTIVENESS The failure rate in typical use is estimated to be high and equal to that of the contraceptive sponge, ranging from 18 percent in nulliparous women to 36 percent in parous women (Hatcher et al., 1994). Failures may be attributed, at least in part, to the cap's becoming dislodged and to changes in the cervix during the menstrual cycle, which can cause the cap to fit less snugly over the cervix.

REVERSIBILITY There is no evidence that the cervical cap affects fertility.

ADVANTAGES AND DISADVANTAGES Like the diaphragm, the cap is a mechanical device that does not affect the woman's hormonal production or reproductive cycle. The cap may be especially suited to women who cannot support a diaphragm because of lack of vaginal muscle tone. Because of concern that the cap may irritate cervical tissue, however, Mishell (1989) recommends that it should only be used by women with a normal Pap smear and that a repeat Pap smear be performed three months following initial use.

Some women find the cap uncomfortable. The cap can also become dislodged during sex or lose its fit as the cervix changes over the menstrual cycle. Reported side effects include the possibility of recurrent urinary tract infections and allergic reactions or sensitivities to the rubber or spermicide. Other potential disadvantages include the expense and inconvenience of being fitted by a health professional. Moreover, some women are shaped so that the cap does not remain in place.

The effectiveness of the cervical cap, and of the contraceptive sponge, is considerably greater among women who have not previously given birth than those who have (Trussell et al., 1993). The reasons for such differences remain unknown. Women who have previously given birth may wish to consult their gynecologists concerning the suitability of these devices for them.

CONDOMS

Prophylactic
An agent that protects against disease.

Learning Objective 8: Describe how condoms are used, and discuss their effectiveness, reversibility, advantages, and disadvantages.

Condoms are also called "rubbers," "safes," **prophylactics** (because latex condoms protect against STDs), and "skins" (referring to those that are made from animal viscera). Condoms lost popularity with the advent of the pill and the IUD. They are less effective than the pill or IUD, may disrupt sexual spontaneity, and can decrease coital sensations because they prevent the penis from actually touching the vaginal wall.

Condoms have been making a comeback, however, because those made of latex rubber can help prevent the spread of the AIDS virus, the *human immunodeficiency virus* (HIV), and other STDs, and to a lesser extent, because of concerns about side effects of the pill and the IUD. Largely because of concerns about AIDS and other STDs, use of condoms among unmarried women jumped from 18 percent in 1987 to 33 percent in 1992 (Forrest & Fordyce, 1993). Unmarried women are more likely to report using condoms than are married women. Overall, 17 percent of U.S. women who use reversible forms of contraception use condoms (Angier, 1993). Condoms vary in price but average about 50 cents each (Hatcher et al., 1994).

Condom advertisements have appeared in mainstream media, including such magazines as *People, GQ, Cosmopolitan,* and *Playboy* (Hochman, 1992) and on major television networks. In a 1994 television commercial, a man and a woman are shown hurriedly undressing. The man tells the woman that he forgot to bring a condom with him, whereupon she tells him that he best forget it (making love, that is). Whether the media campaign will lead to increased usage in the general population remains to be seen.

The renewed popularity of condoms has also been spurred by the increased assertiveness of contemporary women, who have made the point (which should be obvious, but all too often is not) that contraception is as much the man's responsibility as the woman's. Condoms alter the psychology of sexual relations. By using a condom the man assumes much of the responsibility for contraception. Condoms are the only contraceptive device worn by men, and the only readily reversible method of contraception that is available to men (Gordon & Snyder, 1989). Condoms can be easily obtained without a prescription from pharmacies, family-planning clinics, and even from vending machines that are found in some college dormitories.

Some condoms are made of latex rubber. Thinner, more expensive condoms ("skins") are made from the intestinal membranes of animals. The latter allow greater sexual sensation, but do not protect as well against STDs. Only latex condoms are effective against the tiny AIDS virus. Condoms made of animal intestines have pores large enough to permit the AIDS virus and other viruses, such as the one that causes hepatitis B, to slip through (Goldsmith, 1987; Lytle et al., 1990). Some condoms are plain on the ends, whereas others have nipples or reservoirs (see Figure 12.5, page 364) that catch semen and may help prevent the condom from bursting during ejaculation.

HOW IT WORKS   A condom is a cylindrical sheath that serves as a barrier, preventing the passage of sperm and disease-carrying microorganisms from the man to his partner.

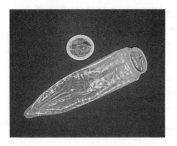

FIGURE 12.5 **Condoms.** Some condoms are plain-tipped, whereas others have nipples or reservoirs that catch semen and may help prevent the condom from bursting during ejaculation. Only latex condoms form effective barriers to the tiny AIDS virus.

It also helps prevent infected vaginal fluids (and microorganisms) from entering the man's urethral opening or from penetrating through small cracks in the skin of the penis.

HOW IT IS USED The condom is rolled onto the penis by the man or his partner once erection is achieved and before contact between the penis and the vagina (see Figure 12.6). If the condom is *not* used until moments before the point of ejaculation, sperm-carrying fluid from the Cowper's glands or from preorgasmic spasms may already have passed into the vagina. Nor does the condom afford protection against STDs if it is fitted after penetration.

Condoms can—but rarely do—fall off or break. Researchers report that between 1 and 2 percent of condoms break or fall off during vaginal or anal intercourse or when withdrawing the penis following intercourse (Cates & Stone, 1992a; Trussell et al., 1992). However, condoms do sometimes slip down the shaft of the penis without falling off. Trussell and colleagues report a 9.5 percent occurrence of some slippage during intercourse and 17 percent during withdrawal. Yet complete slippage occurred in fewer than 1 percent of occasions of intercourse. To use a condom most effectively and to help prevent it from either breaking or falling off, a couple should observe the following guidelines[1]:

- Use a condom each and every time you have intercourse. Inexperienced users should also practice putting a condom on before they have the occasion to use one with a partner.
- Handle the condom carefully, making sure not to damage it with your fingernail, teeth, or other sharp objects.
- Place the condom on the erect penis before it touches the vulva.
- For uncircumcised men, pull back the foreskin before putting on the condom.
- If you use a spermicide, place some inside the tip of the condom before placing the condom on the penis. You may also wish to use additional spermicide applied by an applicator inside the vagina to provide extra protection, especially in the event of breakage of the condom.
- Do not pull the condom tightly against the tip of the penis.
- For a condom without a reservoir tip, leave a small empty space—about a half inch—at the end of the condom to hold semen, yet do not allow any air to be trapped at the tip. Some condoms come equipped with a reservoir (nipple) tip that will hold semen.
- Unroll the condom all the way to the bottom of the penis.
- Ensure that adequate vaginal lubrication during intercourse is present, possibly using lubricants if necessary. But use only water-based lubricants such as contraceptive jelly or K-Y jelly. Never use an oil-based lubricant that can weaken the latex material, such as petroleum jelly (Vaseline), cold cream, baby oil or lotion, mineral oil, massage oil, vegetable oil, Crisco, hand or body lotions, and most skin creams. Do not use saliva as a lubricant because it may contain infectious organisms, such as viruses.
- If the condom breaks during intercourse, withdraw the penis immediately and put on a new condom and use more spermicide.
- After ejaculation, carefully withdraw the penis while it is still erect.
- Hold the rim of the condom firmly against the base of the penis as the penis is withdrawn to prevent the condom from slipping off.
- Remove the condom carefully from the penis, making sure that semen doesn't leak out.
- Check the removed condom for evidence of any tears or cracks. If any are found, immediately apply a spermicide containing nonoxynol-9 directly to the penis and within the woman's vagina. Wrap the used condom in a tissue and discard it in the garbage. Do not flush it down the toilet, as condoms may cause problems in the sewers. Wash your hands thoroughly with soap and water.

Since condoms can be eroded by exposure to body heat or other sources of heat, they should not be kept for any length of time in a pocket or the glove compartment of a

[1]Adapted from Centers for Disease Control pamphlet, *Condoms and Sexually Transmitted Diseases . . . Especially AIDS* (HHS Publication FDA 90–4329), and other sources.

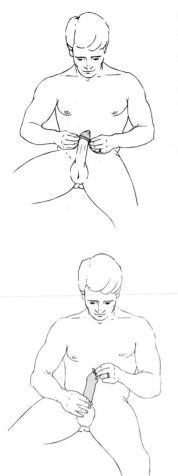

FIGURE 12.6 **Fitting a Condom on the Penis**
First the rolled-up condom is placed on the head of the penis, and then it is rolled down the shaft of the penis. If a condom without a reservoir tip is used, a one-half-inch space should be left at the tip for the ejaculate to accumulate.

car. Nor should a condom ever be used more than once. Here are some other things you should *never* do with a condom:

- Never use teeth, scissors, or sharp fingernails to open a package of condoms. Open the condom package carefully to avoid tearing or puncturing the condom.
- Never test a condom by inflating it or stretching it.
- Never use a condom after its expiration date. Check the package for the expiration date (if any) before using a condom. The expiration date is not the manufacturing (mfg) date.
- Never use damaged condoms. Condoms that are sticky, discolored, brittle, or appear otherwise damaged, or that show signs of deterioration, should never be used, regardless of their expiration date. A condom that sticks to itself or feels gummy is damaged and should not be used.
- Never use a condom if the sealed packet containing the condom is damaged, or cracked or brittle, as the condom itself may be damaged or defective.
- Do not open the sealed packet until you are ready to use the condom. A condom contained in a packet that has been opened can become dry and brittle within a few hours, causing it to tear more easily. The box that contains the condom packets, however, may be opened at any time.
- Never use the same condom twice. Use a new condom each time you have intercourse. Also, use a new condom if you switch the site of intercourse, such as from the vagina to the anus, or from the anus to the mouth, during a single sexual act.
- If you want to carry a condom with you, place it in a loose jacket pocket, or purse, not in your pant's pocket, or in a wallet held in your pant's pocket, where it might be exposed to body heat.
- Never buy condoms from vending machines that are exposed to extreme heat or placed in direct sunlight.

EFFECTIVENESS   In typical use, the failure rate of the male condom is estimated at 12 percent (see Table 12.1). That is, 12 women whose male partners rely on condoms alone for contraception can expect to become pregnant during the first year of use. This rate can be reduced to perhaps 2 or 3 percent if the condom is used consistently and correctly and combined with the use of a spermicide (Hatcher et al., 1994; Reinisch, 1990). The effectiveness of a condom and spermicide combined rivals that of the birth-control pill, when used correctly and consistently.

REVERSIBILITY   The condom is simply a mechanical barrier to sperm and does not compromise fertility. Therefore, a couple who wish to conceive a child simply discontinue its use.

ADVANTAGES AND DISADVANTAGES   Condoms have the advantage of being readily available for use as needed. They can be purchased without prescription. They require no fitting and can remain in sealed packages until needed. They are readily discarded after use. The combination of condoms and spermicides containing the ingredient nonoxynol-9 has the additional advantage of increased contraceptive effectiveness and protection against various STD-causing organisms, including the virus that causes AIDS. Some condoms contain this spermicidal agent as a lubricant. When in doubt, ask the pharmacist.

Condoms do not affect production of hormones, ova, or sperm. Women whose partners use condoms ovulate normally. Men who use them produce sperm and ejaculate normally. With all these advantages, why are condoms not more popular?

One disadvantage of the condom is that it may render sex less spontaneous. This concern was reported by nearly 70 percent of the respondents to a *Consumer Reports* (1989) survey. The couple must interrupt lovemaking to apply the condom. Condoms may also lessen sexual sensations somewhat, especially for the man—latex condoms more so than animal membrane sheaths. The dulling of sexual sensations is a reason men often give for refusing to use them. Another disadvantage is that condoms sometimes slip off or tear, allowing sperm to leak through.

Teaching Tip: The failure rate of condoms used with a spermicide is almost as low as that of oral contraceptives. Condoms and spermicides are both available over-the-counter and relatively inexpensive. And, condoms offer "unparalleled protection" from STDs, especially if combined with a spermicide containing Nonoxynol-9. Ask students: Why don't more people choose condoms and spermicides? Should the information about the advantages be more widely available? To whom? Via what media? If their answer is no, have them state why not. If their answer is yes, have them suggest a program to make this possible.

Douche
To rinse or wash the vaginal canal by inserting a liquid and allowing it to drain out.

Learning Objective 9: Describe withdrawal and discuss its effectiveness, reversibility, advantages, and disadvantages.

On the other hand, condoms are almost entirely free of side effects (an advantage reported by 70 percent of female respondents to the same *Consumer Reports* survey). They offer protection against STDs that is unparalleled among contraceptive devices. They can also be used without prior medical consultation. Both partners can share putting on the condom, which makes it into an erotic part of their lovemaking, not an intrusion. The use of textured or ultra-thin condoms may increase sensitivity, especially for the male. Thus many couples find that advantages outweigh disadvantages. Sex in the age of AIDS has given condoms a new respectability, even a certain trendiness. Notice, for example, the new "designer colors" and styles on display at your local pharmacy. Advertisers now also target women in their ads, suggesting that women, like men, can come prepared with condoms.

It is tempting to claim that the condom has a perfect safety record and no side effects. Let us settle for "close to perfect." Some people may have allergic reactions to the spermicides with which some lubricated condoms are coated, or which the woman may apply herself. In such cases the couple may need to use a condom without a spermicidal lubricant or stop using supplemental spermicides. Some men and women are allergic to the latex material in condoms.

Women have an absolute right to insist that their male sex partners wear latex condoms, assuming that their partners are not latex-sensitive. STDs such as gonorrhea and chlamydia (see Chapter 16) do far more damage to a woman's reproductive tract than to a man's. Condoms can help protect women from vaginitis, pelvic inflammatory disease (PID), infections that can harm a fetus or cause infertility, and most importantly, AIDS.

DOUCHING

Many couples believe that if a woman **douches** shortly after coitus, she will not become pregnant. Women who douche for contraceptive purposes often use syringes to flush the vagina with water or a spermicidal agent. The water is intended to wash sperm out; the spermicides, to kill them. Shapiro (1988) considers douching totally ineffective, however, because large numbers of sperm may be beyond the range of the douche within seconds after ejaculation. In addition, squirting a liquid into the vagina may even propel sperm *toward* the uterus. Douching, at best, has a failure rate among typical users of 40 percent (Reinisch, 1990)—much too high to be considered reliable.

Regular douching may also alter the natural chemistry of the vagina, increasing the risk of vaginal infection. In short, douching is a "non-method" of contraception.

WITHDRAWAL (COITUS INTERRUPTUS)

Withdrawal means that the man removes his penis from the vagina before ejaculating. The Canadian folksinger Gordon Lightfoot recalls some advice his grandfather gave him. The grandfather, who had sired a large family, told young Gordon that unless he wanted to do the same, he had best take a lesson from the Canadian Pacific Railroad and learn to pull out on time. But despite the grandfather's colorful comparisons, withdrawal is not a very effective method of birth control.

EFFECTIVENESS Withdrawal has a first-year failure rate among typical users ranging from 19 to 23 percent (Hatcher et al., 1994; Reinisch, 1990). There are several reasons for these failures. The man may not withdraw in time. Even if the penis is withdrawn just before ejaculation, some ejaculate may still fall on the vaginal lips and sperm may find their way to the Fallopian tubes. Active sperm may also be present in the *pre*-ejaculatory secretions of fluid from the Cowper's glands, a discharge of which the man is usually unaware and cannot control. These sperm are capable of fertilizing an ovum even if the man withdraws before orgasm. Because of its unreliability and high failure rate, we consider withdrawal, like douching, to be a non-method of contraception. Yet despite its unreliability, 6 percent of unmarried women rely on withdrawal as a means of birth control (Shapiro, 1988).

FERTILITY AWARENESS METHODS (RHYTHM METHODS)

Learning Objective 10:
Name and explain the four
fertility awareness tech-
niques and discuss their
effectiveness, advantages,
and disadvantages.

Fertility awareness, or *rhythm,* methods rely on awareness of the fertile segments of the woman's menstrual cycle. Terms such as *natural birth control* or *natural family planning* are also used to refer to these methods. The essence of such methods is that coitus is avoided on days when conception is most likely. Fertility awareness methods are used by about 3 percent of married women ages 15 to 44, but by less than 1 percent of single women (Statistical Abstract of the United States, 1990). Women ages 25 to 44 are more than twice as likely as 15- to 24-year-olds to use rhythm methods. Since the rhythm method does not employ artificial devices, it is acceptable to the Roman Catholic church.

HOW THEY WORK   A number of rhythm methods are used to predict the likelihood of conception. They are the mirror images of the methods that couples use to increase their chances of conceiving (see Chapter 11). Methods for enhancing the chances of conception seek to predict ovulation so the couple can arrange to have sperm present in the woman's reproductive tract about that time. As methods of *birth control,* rhythm methods seek to predict ovulation so that the couple can *abstain* from coitus when the woman is fertile.

Calendar method
A fertility awareness (rhythm) method of contraception that relies on prediction of ovulation by tracking menstrual cycles, typically for a 10- to 12-month period, and assuming that ovulation occurs 14 days prior to menstruation.

THE CALENDAR METHOD   The **calendar method** assumes that ovulation occurs 14 days prior to menstruation. The couple abstains from intercourse during the period that begins 3 days prior to day 13 (because sperm are unlikely to survive for more than 72 hours in the female reproductive tract) and ends two days after day 15 (because an unfertilized ovum is unlikely to remain receptive to fertilization for longer than 48 hours). The period of abstention thus covers days 10 to 17 of the woman's cycle.

When a woman has regular 28-day cycles, predicting the period of abstention is relatively straightforward. Women with irregular cycles are generally advised to chart their cycles for 10 months to a year to determine their shortest and longest cycles. The first day of menstruation counts as day 1 of the cycle. The last day of the cycle is the day preceding the onset of menstruation.

Consider a woman whose cycles vary from 23 to 33 days. In theory she will ovulate 14 days before menstruation begins. (To be safe she should assume that ovulation will take place anywhere from 13 to 15 days before her period.) Applying the rule of "three days before" and "two days after," she should avoid coitus from day 5 of her cycle, which corresponds to three days before her earliest expected ovulation (computed by subtracting 15 days from the 23 days of her shortest cycle and then subtracting 3 days), through day 22, which corresponds to 2 days after her latest expected ovulation (computed by subtracting 13 days from the 33 days of her longest cycle and then adding 2 days). Another way of determining this period of abstention would be to subtract 18 days from the woman's shortest cycle to determine the start of the "unsafe" period and 11 days from her longest cycle to determine the last "unsafe" day. The woman in the example has irregular cycles. She thus faces an 18-day abstention period each month—quite a burden for a sexually active couple.

Most women who follow the calendar method need to abstain from coitus for at least 10 days during the middle of each cycle (Reinisch, 1990). Moreover, the calendar method cannot ensure that the woman's longest or shortest menstrual cycles will occur during the 10- to 12-month period of baseline tracking. Some women, too, have such irregular cycles that the range of "unsafe" days cannot be predicted reliably even if baseline tracking is extended.

Basal body temperature (BBT) method
A fertility awareness method of contraception that relies on prediction of ovulation by tracking the woman's temperature during the course of the menstrual cycle.

THE BASAL BODY TEMPERATURE (BBT) METHOD   In the **basal body temperature (BBT) method,** the woman tracks her body temperature on awakening each morning to detect the small changes that occur directly before and after ovulation. A woman's basal body temperature sometimes dips slightly just before ovulation and then tends to rise between 0.4 and 0.8 degree Fahrenheit just before, during, and after ovulation. It remains elevated until the onset of menstruation. (The rise in temperature is caused by the increased production of progesterone by the corpus luteum during the luteal phase of the cycle.) Thermometers that provide finely graded readings, such as electronic thermometers, are best suited for determining minor changes. A major problem with the BBT method is that it does not indicate the several *unsafe* preovulatory days during which sperm deposited in the vagina may remain viable. Rather, the BBT method indicates when a woman *has* ovulated. Thus, many women use the calendar method to predict the number of "safe" days prior to ovulation and the BBT method to determine the number of "unsafe" days after. A woman would avoid coitus during the "unsafe" preovulatory period (as determined by the calendar method) and then for three days when her temperature rises and remains elevated. A drawback of the BBT method is that changes in body temperature may also result from factors unrelated to ovulation, such as infections, sleeplessness, or stress. So some women triple check themselves by also tracking their cervical mucus.

THE CERVICAL MUCUS (OVULATION) METHOD   Evelyn and John Billings (1974) were among the first to describe the **ovulation method,** which relies upon tracking changes in the **viscosity** of the cervical mucus. Following menstruation, the vagina feels rather dry. There is also little or no discharge from the cervix. These dry days are relatively safe. Then a mucous discharge appears in the vagina that is first thick and sticky, and white or cloudy in color. Coitus (or unprotected coitus) should be avoided at the first sign of any mucus. As the cycle progresses, the mucous discharge thins and clears, becoming slippery or stringy, like raw egg white. These are the **peak days.** This mucous discharge, called the *ovulatory mucus,* may be accompanied by a feeling of vaginal lubrication or wetness. Ovulation takes place about a day after the last peak day (about four days after this ovulatory mucus first appears). Then the mucus becomes cloudy and tacky once more. Intercourse may resume four days following the last peak day.

One problem with this method is that some women have difficulty detecting changes in the mucous discharge. Such changes may also result from infections, certain medications, or contraceptive creams, jellies, or foam. Sexual arousal may also induce changes in viscosity.

OVULATION-PREDICTION KITS   Predicting ovulation is somewhat more accurate with an ovulation-prediction kit. The kits allow women to test their urine daily for the presence of luteinizing hormone (LH). LH levels surge upward about 12 to 24 hours prior to ovulation. Ovulation-prediction kits are more accurate than the basal body temperature method. Some couples use the kits to enhance their chances of conceiving a child by engaging in coitus when ovulation appears imminent. Others use them as a means of birth control to find out when to avoid coitus. When used correctly, ovulation-predicting kits are between 95 to 100 percent accurate (Reinisch, 1990).

Ovulation kits are expensive and require that the woman's urine be carefully tested each morning. Nor do they reveal the full range of the unsafe *pre*ovulatory period during which sperm may remain viable in the vagina. A couple might thus choose to use the kits to determine the unsafe period following ovulation, and the calendar method to determine the unsafe period preceding ovulation.

EFFECTIVENESS   The estimated first-year failure rate in typical use is 20 percent, which is high but no higher than the use of contraceptive devices such as the cervical cap, contraceptive sponge, or the female condom (see Table 12.1). Still, perhaps one in five typical users will become pregnant during the first year of use. (You may have heard the joke, "What do you call people who use the rhythm method? Parents!") Fewer failures occur when these methods are applied conscientiously, when a combination of rhythm methods is used, and when the woman's cycles are quite regular. Restricting coitus to the post-ovulatory period can reduce the pregnancy rate to 1 percent (Hatcher et al., 1994). The trick is to be able to reliably determine when ovulation occurs. The pregnancy rate can be reduced to practically zero if rhythm methods are used with other forms of birth control, such as the condom or diaphragm.

ADVANTAGES AND DISADVANTAGES   Because they are a natural form of birth control, rhythm methods appeal to many people who, for religious or other reasons, pre-

Ovulation method
A fertility awareness method of contraception that relies on prediction of ovulation by tracking the viscosity of the cervical mucus.

Viscosity
Stickiness, consistency.

Peak days
The days during the menstrual cycle during which a woman is most likely to be fertile.

Discussion Question:
Describe the personal characteristics and the type of relationship that would make a couple good candidates for using fertility awareness methods of contraception.

fer not to use artificial means. Since no devices or chemicals are used, there are no side effects or health complications. Nor do they cause any loss of sensation, as condoms do. Nor is there disruption of lovemaking, as with condoms, diaphragms, or foam, although lovemaking could be said to be quite "disrupted" during the period of abstention. Rhythm methods are inexpensive, except for ovulation-prediction kits. Both partners may share the responsibility for rhythm methods. The man, for example, can take his partner's temperature or assist with the charting. All rhythm methods are fully reversible. To conceive, the couple may simply discontinue timing ovulation, or they may decide to engage in coitus at about the time of ovulation.

A disadvantage is the fact that the reliability of rhythm methods is low. Rhythm methods may be unsuitable for women with irregular cycles. Women with irregular cycles who ovulate as early as a week after their menstrual flows can become pregnant even if they only engage in unprotected intercourse when they are menstruating, since some sperm remaining in a woman's reproductive tract may survive for up to eight days and fertilize an ovum that is released at that time (Reinisch, 1990). Moreover, the rhythm method requires abstaining from coitus for several days, or perhaps weeks, each month. Rhythm methods also require that records of the menstrual cycle be kept for many months prior to implementation. Unlike diaphragms, condoms, or spermicides, rhythm methods cannot be used at a moment's notice. Finally, rhythm methods do not offer any protection against STDs.

STERILIZATION

Sterilization
Surgical procedures that render people incapable of reproduction without affecting sexual activity.

Learning Objective 11: Explain the procedures used in male and female sterilization and discuss the effectiveness, advantages, and disadvantages of the procedures.

Today many people decide to be sterilized when they plan to have no children or no more children. With the exception of abstinence, sterilization is the most effective form of contraception. Yet the prospect of **sterilization** arouses strong feelings because a person is transformed all at once, and presumably permanently, from someone who might be capable of bearing children to someone who cannot. This transformation often involves a profound change in self-concept. These feelings are especially strong in men and women who link fertility to their sense of masculinity or femininity.

Still, more than a million sterilizations are performed in the United States each year. It is the most widely used form of birth control among married couples ages 30 and above (Reinisch, 1990). Nineteen percent of the respondents in a 1992 national sample of nearly 7,000 women ages 15 to 50 reported being sterilized, whereas 12 percent reported having partners who had undergone a vasectomy. Married women were far more likely to rely on a permanent method of contraception (tubal sterilization or vasectomy) than were single women (48% versus 11%).

Vasectomy
The surgical method of male sterilization in which sperm are prevented from reaching the urethra by cutting each vas deferens and tying it back or cauterizing it.

MALE STERILIZATION   The male sterilization procedure used today is the **vasectomy.** Current estimates indicate that about 500,000 vasectomies are performed each year in the United States (Altman, 1993j). In all, more than 15 percent of men in the United States have had vasectomies.

A vasectomy is usually carried out in a doctor's office, using local anesthesia, in 15 to 20 minutes. Small incisions are made in the scrotum. Each vas is cut, a small segment is removed, and the ends are tied off or cauterized (to prevent them from growing back together) (Figure 12.7). Now sperm can no longer reach the urethra. Instead, they are harmlessly reabsorbed by the body.

The man can usually resume sexual relations within a few days. Since some sperm may be present in his reproductive tract for a few weeks, however, he is best advised to use an additional contraceptive method until his ejaculate shows a zero sperm count. Some health professionals recommend that the man have a follow-up sperm count a year after his vasectomy, to ensure that the cut ends of the vas deferens have not grown together—a complication that occurs in about 1 percent of cases (Reinisch, 1990).

Vasectomy does not diminish sex drive or result in any change in sexual arousal, erectile or ejaculatory ability, or sensations of ejaculation. Male sex hormones and sperm are still produced by the testes. Without a passageway to the urethra, however, sperm are

Notes: During the period from 1905 to 1972, over 70,000 Americans were involuntarily sterilized. The floodgates of involuntary sterilization opened in 1927, when a Supreme Court decision legitimized sterilization of socially inadequate persons. Those targeted for sterilization were the severely disabled, the epileptic, inmates of prisons and mental institutions, drunkards, and the "feeble-minded." The term *feeble-minded* was broadly applied and often included the poor, uneducated, homeless, and orphans. (Discovery Journal: The Lynchburg Story. 1994. *Discovery Channel,* July 2, 9–10pm.)

no longer expelled with the ejaculate. Since sperm account for only about 1 percent of the ejaculate, the volume of the ejaculate is not noticeably different.

Though there are no confirmed long-term health risks of vasectomy (Reinisch, 1990), two recent studies of more than 73,000 men who had undergone vasectomies raise concerns that the procedure may not be as risk-free as people generally believe. The studies showed that men who had had vasectomies more than 20 years earlier faced a slightly increased risk of prostate cancer (Altman, 1993j; Giovannucci et al., 1993a; Giovannucci et al., 1993b). The studies found a link, a statistical association or correlation, between vasectomies and the risk of prostate cancer, but did not establish a causal connection. It is possible that other factors may explain the greater risk faced by vasectomized men than the vasectomy itself. The results also conflict with earlier studies showing either no link between vasectomies and the risk of prostate cancer or even a *lower* risk among vasectomized men. Medical experts caution against overreacting to the newer findings and urge that more research is needed to clarify the relationship between vasectomy and prostate cancer (Altman, 1993g; Perlman et al., 1993). In the meantime, medical experts recommend that men who have had vasectomies make sure to get annual checkups for signs of prostate cancer (Altman, 1993g).

The vasectomy is nearly 100 percent effective. Fewer than two pregnancies occur during the first year among 1,000 couples in which the man has undergone a vasectomy (see Table 12.1). The few failures stem from sperm remaining in the male's genital tract shortly after the operation, or the growing together of the segments of a vas deferens.

Reversibility is simple in concept but not in practice. Thus, vasectomies should be considered permanent. In an operation to reverse a vasectomy, called a **vasovasotomy,**

FIGURE 12.7 **Vasectomy.** The male sterilization procedure is usually carried out in a doctor's office, using local anesthesia. Small incisions are made in the scrotum. Each vas deferens is cut and the ends are tied off or cauterized to prevent sperm from reaching the urethra. Sperm are harmlessly reabsorbed by the body after the operation.

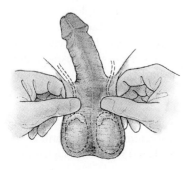

1. Location of vas deferens
2. Injection of local anesthetic
3. Incision over vas deferens

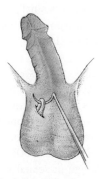
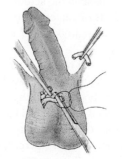
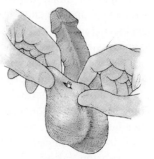

4. Isolation of vas from surrounding tissue

5. Removal of segment of vas; tying of ends

6. Return of vas to position; incision is closed and process is repeated on the other side

the ends of the vas deferens are sewn together, and in a few days they grow together. Estimates of success at reversal, as measured by subsequent pregnancies, depend on several factors and range from 16 to 79 percent (Hatcher et al., 1994). Some vasectomized men develop antibodies that attack their own sperm. The production of antibodies does not appear to endanger the man's health (Hatcher et al., 1994), but it may contribute to infertility following reconnection (Reinisch, 1990).

Major studies conducted over a 15-year period revealed no deaths due to vasectomy in the United States (Reinisch, 1990). Few documented complications of vasectomies have been reported in the medical literature. Minor complications are reported in 4 or 5 percent of cases, however. They typically involve temporary local inflammation or swelling after the operation. Ice packs and anti-inflammatory drugs, such as aspirin, may help reduce swelling and discomfort. More serious but rarer medical complications include infection of the epididymis (Reinisch, 1990).

FEMALE STERILIZATION   Nearly 4 in 10 (39%) married women in the United States, under the age of 45 have been surgically sterilized (Statistical Abstract of the United States, 1990). **Tubal sterilization,** also called *tubal ligation,* is the most common method of female sterilization. Tubal sterilization prevents ova and sperm from passing through the Fallopian tubes. It is estimated that 650,000 tubal sterilizations are performed each year in the United States (Altman, 1993h).

The two principal surgical procedures for tubal sterilization are *minilaparotomy* and *laparoscopy.* In a **minilaparotomy,** a small incision is made in the abdomen, just above the pubic hairline, to provide access to the Fallopian tubes. Each tube is gently brought out through the incision and cut and either tied back or clamped with a clip. The surgeon then allows the tubes to slip back into place. In a **laparoscopy** (Figure 12.8) (sometimes called "belly button surgery"), the Fallopian tubes are approached through a small incision in the abdomen just below the navel. The surgeon then inserts a narrow, lighted viewing instrument called a *laparoscope* through the incision to locate the tubes. A small section of each of the tubes is cauterized, cut, or clamped. The woman usually returns to her daily routine in a few days and can resume coitus when it becomes comfortable. In an alternative sterilization procedure, a **culpotomy,** the Fallopian tubes are approached through an incision in the back wall of the vagina.

None of these methods disrupts sex drive or sexual response. Surgical sterilization does not induce premature menopause or alter the woman's production of sex hormones. The menstrual cycle is undisturbed. The unfertilized egg is simply reabsorbed by the body, rather than being sloughed off in the menstrual flow.

A **hysterectomy** also results in sterilization. A hysterectomy is a major operation that is commonly performed because of cancer or other diseases of the reproductive tract; however, it is inappropriate as a method of sterilization. Hysterectomy carries the risks of major surgery and, when the ovaries are removed along with the uterus, it induces a "surgical menopause" because the woman no longer produces female sex hormones. In 1978 the Department of Health, Education and Welfare forbade funding of hysterectomies intended as sterilization procedures.

Female sterilization is highly effective in preventing pregnancy, although slightly less effective than male sterilization. Overall, about one woman in two hundred (0.4%) is likely to become pregnant in the first year following a tubal sterilization (Hatcher et al., 1994), most likely the result of a failed surgical procedure or an undetected pregnancy at the time of the procedure. Like vasectomy, tubal ligation should be considered irreversible. Reversals are successful, as measured by subsequent pregnancies, in 43 to 88 percent of cases, depending on the particular procedure (Hatcher et al., 1994). Reversal is difficult and costly, however.

Fewer than one sterilization operation in 100 can be surgically reversed. *Actually, many sterilization operations can be reversed surgically. Since reversal is not guaranteed, however, people contemplating sterilization are wise to look upon it as permanent.* •

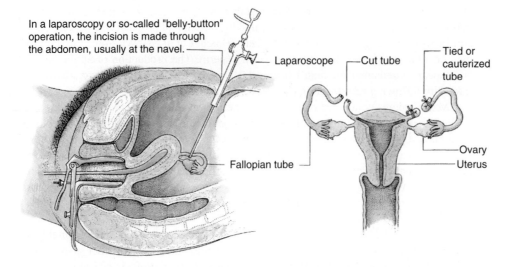

In a laparoscopy or so-called "belly-button" operation, the incision is made through the abdomen, usually at the navel.

Laparoscope

Cut tube

Tied or cauterized tube

Fallopian tube

Ovary

Uterus

FIGURE 12.8 **Laparoscopy.** In this method of female sterilization, the surgeon approaches the Fallopian tubes through a small incision in the abdomen just below the navel. A narrow instrument called a *laparoscope* is inserted through the incision, and a small section of each Fallopian tube is cauterized, cut, or clamped to prevent ova from joining with sperm.

Discussion Question:
Female sterilization, as compared to male sterilization, is costlier, sometimes requires the use of a general anesthetic, and more often results in medical complications. Why, then, are many more women than men sterilized each year in the United States?

Sterilized women are no more likely than nonsterilized women to experience psychological problems (Hatcher et al., 1994). About 2 to 11 percent of women incur medical complications, however, depending on the types of surgery and anesthesia (Reinisch, 1990). The most common complications are abdominal infections, excessive bleeding, inadvertent punctures of nearby organs, and scarring. The use of general anesthesia (typical in laparoscopies and in some minilaparotomies) poses additional risks, as in any major operation. In fact, most of the deaths that are attributed to tubal sterilization actually result from the anesthesia (Reinisch, 1990). The overall death rate is quite small, however: two to five deaths per 100,000 operations.

ADVANTAGES AND DISADVANTAGES OF STERILIZATION The major advantages of sterilization are effectiveness and permanence. Sterilization is nearly 100 percent effective. Following surgery the couple need not do anything more to prevent conception. The permanence is also its major drawback, however. People sometimes change their minds about wanting to have children.

Sterilization procedures create varying risks of complications following surgery, with women generally incurring greater risks than men. Another disadvantage of sterilization is that it affords no protection against STDs (Cates & Stone, 1992b). People who are sterilized may still wish to use condoms and spermicides for protection against STDs.

NEW DEVELOPMENTS IN CONTRACEPTION

Learning Objective 12:
Describe the advantages and disadvantages of the new contraceptives Norplant, Depo-Provera, and the female condom, and discuss possible future developments in contraception.

 Norplant

Sherryl Connelly noted that "History will be made when some resourceful scientist perfects a method of contraception that is absolutely sure, guaranteed safe and convenient, too" (1981, p. 62). That day is far off—but let us consider some methods that have recently been introduced or are under development.

NORPLANT One new technique that is receiving a great deal of attention is a contraceptive implant, known commercially as *Norplant,* consisting of six matchstick-sized silicone tubes containing progestin that are surgically embedded under the skin of a woman's upper arm. The tubes can be implanted in about 10 minutes under local anesthesia (Lewin, 1991a). They release a small, steady dose of progestin into the woman's blood-

Norplant. Norplant consists of matchstick-like rods that are implanted under the skin of the woman's upper arm. The rods release a steady dose of progestin, the same hormone contained in the so-called minipill. While the progestin doesn't usually prevent ovulation, it renders a contraceptive effect by thickening the cervical mucus to impede the passage of sperm and by making the uterine lining less receptive to implantation of a fertilized ovum.

stream, providing continuous contraceptive protection for as long as five years after implantation (Hatcher et al., 1994; Lewin, 1991a). About 100,000 U.S. women received Norplant implants in just the first year following its approval in 1990 as a contraceptive device (Lewin, 1991a). The progestin in the Norplant system suppresses ovulation and thickens the cervical mucus so that sperm cannot pass. The contraceptive effect occurs within 24 hours of insertion. After five years the spent tubes are replaced. An alternative contraceptive implant, Norplant-2, consists of two hormone-releasing tubes that provide at least three years of protection (Liskin & Blackburn, 1987; Sivin, 1988).

A major advantage of Norplant is the convenience of having a supply of contraception that is automatically dispensed and literally less than an arm's length away at all times. The woman need not remember to take a pill a day, insert a contraceptive device before coitus, or check to see that an IUD is in place. Moreover, Norplant is reported to have an extremely low failure rate of less than 1 percent per year across five years (Sivin, 1988). The failure rate approximates that of surgical sterilization. Unlike sterilization, however, Norplant is fully reversible. Removal of the implants restores a normal likelihood of pregnancy. The most commonly reported side effect is a pattern of abnormal menstrual bleeding (Hatcher et al., 1994; Mishell, 1989). Many health professionals concerned about finding ways to reduce teenage pregnancy rates have greeted the introduction of Norplant with enthusiasm. School-based programs have been initiated to make Norplant available to young women, which has fueled the debate concerning whether schools should be involved in distributing contraceptives to minors (see Chapter 13).

THE FEMALE CONDOM   Another innovation is the female condom. The device consists of a polyurethane (plastic) sheath, $6^{1}/_{2}$ inches in length and $1^{1}/_{2}$ to 2 inches in diameter, that is used to line the vagina during intercourse. It is held in place at each end by a flexible plastic ring. The female condom provides a secure but flexible shield that barricades against sperm but allows the penis to move freely within the vagina during coitus. It can be inserted as long as eight hours preceding intercourse, but should be removed (carefully following instructions) immediately after intercourse (Hatcher et al., 1994). A new one must be used for each repeated act of intercourse.

Like the male condom, the female condom may offer some protection against STDs. Dr. Mary E. Guinan (1992) of the Centers for Disease Control notes that a "hidden epidemic" of HIV infection in women is emerging, and points out that women can use the female condom if their partners refuse to wear a male condom. Cynthia Pearson (1992) of the National Women's Health Network notes that the female condom "for the first time [gives] women control over exposure to sexually transmitted disease, including AIDS."

The female condom (brand name *Reality*) was approved for marketing in the United States in 1993 (Leary, 1993b). It was approved with the provision that it carry a warning on its label that it appears to be less effective than the male latex condom in preventing pregnancies and transmission of sexually transmitted diseases. During test trials, the pregnancy rate was estimated to range between 21 and 26 percent, but is estimated to be as low as 5 percent among perfect users (Hatcher et al., 1994; Leary, 1993b). The pregnancy rate in actual use remains to be determined. We also lack evidence concerning the effectiveness of the female condom in providing protection against HIV and other STDs (Centers for Disease control, 1993b).

Many women also complain that the female condom is bulky and difficult to insert (Stewart, 1992). Still, it is the first barrier method of contraception that women control themselves. The naming of the device *Reality* suggests that it may be used most widely by women faced with the reality of male partners who refuse to use condoms themselves or who fail to use them consistently or properly. Each female condom costs about $2.50, or about five times the costs of the male condom.

Female Condom. The female condom is a polyurethane sheath that covers the vaginal entrance, preventing the passage of sperm from the penis to the vagina. The female condom may also offer some protection against sexually transmitted diseases (STDs).

OTHER METHODS   Another recently developed contraceptive device for women is the *vaginal ring*. It can be worn in the vagina for three months before replacement (Monier & Laird, 1989). Shaped like a diaphragm, the ring contains either a combination of estrogen and progestin or progestin only. The hormones are slowly released and pass

A WORLD OF DIVERSITY

Birth-Rate News—A Contraception Revolution Has Swept the Third World

A contraceptive revolution—a remarkable success story—has gone largely unnoticed in the West. It is as impressive as the green revolution in agriculture, and perhaps equally important in averting widespread famine in many developing countries. Birth rates have been falling in many poor, developing countries in the third world—the result of an aggressive campaign to promote the use of modern contraceptive methods.

Women in the third world are averaging 3.9 children, and more than 50 percent of the women use some form of contraception, according to UN estimates. This is a stunning change from the 8 percent who used contraception in 1965 when they were averaging more than six children. Some of the most notable successes

have occurred in Thailand, Indonesia, Mexico, Colombia, Brazil, and Bangladesh. In Bangladesh, for example, fertility rates dropped by 21 percent between 1970 and 1991, from 7 children per woman to 5.5. The use of contraceptives among married women of reproductive age rose during this period from 3 percent to 40 percent. In Thailand, the average number of children per woman was cut in half, from 4.6 in 1975 to 2.3 in 1987 (Stevens, 1994).

All this portends further significant declines in family size if sufficient investment in family planning is made in the 1990s. This investment will determine whether the world's population grows from 5.4 billion today to a stabilized 10 billion to 12 billion as early as the year 2045 or 15

billion to 20 billion by 2100, according to UN projections.

The global population's growth rate has declined faster than many experts thought possible in the late 1960s. This decline has come mainly as a result of the voluntary use of public and private family-planning services, not through coercive measures. There are still third world states, primarily in sub-Saharan Africa and the Islamic world, where the use of birth control remains low and fertility remains high. But even in several of these—Kenya, Egypt, Zimbabwe—the acceptance of contraceptives seems to be growing.

A remarkable feature of this revolution is the near-universality in the third world in adopting family-planning policies and the absence of political risk in doing

Notes: According to a February 1992 report by the Population Crisis Committee, the five worst family-planning records for 1991 belong to Haiti, Malawi, the Philippines, Saudi Arabia, and the United States. Family size in the United States has increased yearly since 1988. The report attributes the increase to shrinking funds for family planning services and the erosion of abortion rights.

into the bloodstream through the mucosal lining of the vagina. The vaginal ring is a convenient means of receiving a continuous dose of hormones without having to remember to take a pill. It is expected to be available in the United States by the mid-1990s. Research on the effectiveness of the vaginal ring is under way.

Depo-Provera (medroxyprogesterone acetate) is a long-acting, synthetic form of progesterone that works as a contraceptive by inhibiting ovulation. The progesterone signals the pituitary gland in the brain to stop producing hormones that would lead to the release of mature ova by the ovaries (Leary, 1992c). Administered by injection once every three months, Depo-Provera is an effective form of contraception, with reported failure rates of less than one pregnancy per 100 women during the first year of use (Hatcher et al., 1994). Depo-Provera has been used by more than 30 million women in more than 90 countries worldwide since it was first marketed in 1969, yet its approval in the United States was delayed for years, largely because of concerns over possible risks of breast cancer and potential side effects (Leary, 1992c). A review by the Food and Drug Administration (FDA) found the overall cancer risk, including the risk of breast cancer, to be minimal, and the drug finally achieved FDA approval as a contraceptive in 1992 (Barringer, 1992a). A World Health Organization study of 12,000 women also

so. Nearly all developing countries provide contraceptive services. Family-planning programs are credited with having reduced the world population by more than 400 million from what it otherwise would be (Stevens, 1994). Another surprising feature has been the low investment needed to reduce birth rates.

The World Bank estimates that developing countries spend a total of $3 billion yearly on family planning. If the UN projection of a world population of 6 billion by 1999 is not to be exceeded, the people in developing countries will require 44 billion condoms, 9 billion cycles of oral contraceptives, 150 million sterilization operations, and 310 million intrauterine devices or Norplant insertions. This means the annual cost of family-planning programs in the third world will triple, to about $9 billion. Global assistance will have to increase.

Failure to give adequate support to family-planning programs for the rest of the 1990s would be measured in billions of people added before the world's population is stabilized.

Source: Adapted from Sinding & Segal (1991, December 19). Birth-rate news. *The New York Times,* p. A31.

Women in China Are Educated About the Use of Contraceptive Devices.
A contraceptive revolution is taking place among many developing nations. The United Nations estimates that more than 50 percent of the women in developing nations now use some form of contraception.

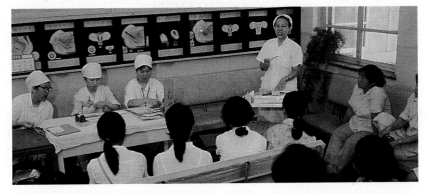

CNN Male Pill

Notes: According to a Knight-Ridder News Service article (*Des Moines Register,* January 14, 1992), Ortho Pharmaceutical Corporation is the only U.S. company researching male contraceptives. Dr. Spyros Pavloy, director of male contraceptive research at Vanderbilt University Medical Center said, "If we had all the money we need, we could have a male contraceptive in the next five or six years."

found no linkage between the drug and the risk of ovarian or cervical cancer (Walt, 1993). Yet the drug may produce various side effects, such as weight gain, menstrual irregularity or suspension of menstruation, and spotting between periods (Hatcher et al., 1994). Studies have also linked the use of the drug to *osteoporosis,* a disease involving bone loss that can lead bones to become brittle and easily fractured (Leary, 1992c). Despite such concerns, the FDA approved the use of Depo-Provera as a contraceptive, believing that its benefits outweighed its risks (Walt, 1993). Depo-Provera may be especially appealing to women seeking long-term contraception who cannot afford the $500 to $800 cost of the time-released contraceptive implant Norplant (Leary, 1992c). Depo-Provera is expected to be priced at a level comparable to that of birth-control pills used for an equivalent period of time, about $200 annually.

Still other methods of contraception are in experimental stages, including sterilization techniques that promise greater reversibility. Also in the experimental stage is a so-called male pill, an oral contraceptive for men. The male sex hormone testosterone has shown some promise in reducing sperm production. The pituitary gland normally stimulates the testes to produce sperm. Testosterone suppresses the pituitary, in turn suppressing sperm production. Men who have received testosterone injections have shown

A Male Contraceptive.
Researchers are exploring the role of testosterone injections as a form of contraception. Here, a technician examines a sample of a man's sperm displayed on a television monitor.

declines in sperm production. Potential complications include an increased risk of prostate cancer. Testosterone also appears to increase cholesterol levels in the bloodstream, which may heighten the risk of cardiovascular disease.

Another approach was suggested when investigators in China found extremely low birth rates in communities in which cottonseed oil was used in cooking. They extracted a drug from the cotton plant, *gossypol,* which shows promise as a male contraceptive. Chinese studies reveal the drug to be nearly 100 percent effective in preventing pregnancies. The drug appears to nullify sperm production without affecting hormone levels or the sex drive. However, toxic effects of gossypol have limited its acceptability as a male contraceptive (Mishell, 1989; Xu et al., 1988).

Some men are infertile because they produce antibodies that destroy their own sperm. It is also speculated that vasectomy causes some men's bodies to react to their own sperm as foreign substances and produce antibodies. This is an immunological response to sperm. Some researchers have suggested that it may be possible to develop ways to induce the body to produce such antibodies. Ideally this procedure would be reversible.

Applying ultrasound waves to the testes has been shown to produce reversible sterility in laboratory rats, dogs, and monkeys. As with the IUD, no one is quite certain how ultrasound works in inducing temporary sterilization. Moreover, its safety with men has not been demonstrated.

ABORTION

Induced abortion
The purposeful termination of a pregnancy before the embryo or fetus is capable of sustaining independent life. (From the Latin *abortio,* meaning "that which is miscarried.")

 Russian Abortion

Notes In a national survey of 281 clinics released November 4, 1993 by the Fund for the Feminist Majority, staff at 21 percent of the clinics said they had received death threats, 18 percent had received bomb threats, 16 percent had faced blockades by anti-choice protesters, and 10 percent had been targets of chemical attacks.

An **induced abortion** (in contrast to a spontaneous abortion, or miscarriage) is the purposeful termination of a pregnancy before the embryo or fetus is capable of sustaining independent life. Perhaps more than any other contemporary social issue, induced abortion (hereafter referred to simply as abortion) has divided neighbors and family members into opposing camps.

Thirty-seven million abortions worldwide, including more than 1.5 million in the United States, are performed each year (Smolowe, 1993; Statistical Abstract of the United States, 1990). The great majority of abortions in the United States—about 90 percent—occur during the first trimester, a time when they are safest to the woman and least costly to perform (Centers for Disease Control, 1992b). Women who have abortions are more likely to be unmarried than married by a ratio of approximately four to one (Henshaw & Silverman, 1988).

Women of color in the United States have proportionally more abortions than white women (Centers for Disease Control, 1992b). There are about 55 abortions per 1,000 women of color reported each year, as compared to 23 for white women. Although the proportion of women having abortions is greater among women of color than white women, most abortions are performed on white women (Centers for Disease Control, 1992b). We should also note that these statistics probably underestimate the actual rates of abortion, especially for higher income women who have greater access to private health care providers, as many abortions performed in private settings are reported under some other medical classification than abortion.

Abortion is practiced widely in Canada, Japan, Russia, and many European nations. It is less common in underdeveloped nations, largely because of sparse medical facilities. Abortion is rarely used as a primary means of birth control. It usually comes into play when other methods have failed.

More than half (54.6%) of the women having abortions are in their twenties. Women ages 15 to 19 account for about one in four (25.2%) abortions. The remainder of women having abortions are either under the age of 15 (1.0%), between 30 and 39 years of age (17.8%), or are 40 or older (1.4%) (Henshaw & Silverman, 1988). Nearly half of the women seeking abortions are mothers who bear substantial family responsibilities (Russo et al., 1992). There are many reasons why women have abortions, including psychological factors as well as external circumstances. Obtaining an abortion is often

QUESTIONNAIRE

Pro-Choice or Pro-Life? Where Do You Stand?

What does it mean to be "pro-life" on the abortion issue? What does it mean to be "pro-choice"? Which position is closer to your own views about abortion? How strongly do you identify with your espoused position?

The *Reasoning About Abortion Questionnaire (RAQ)* (Parsons et al., 1990) assesses agreement with pro-life or pro-choice lines of reasoning about abortion. To find out which position is closer to your own, indicate your level of agreement or disagreement with each of the following items by circling the number that most closely represents your feelings. Then refer to the key in the appendix to interpret your score.

1 = **Strongly Agree**

2 = **Agree**

3 = **Mixed Feelings**

4 = **Disagree**

5 = **Strongly Disagree**

1. Abortion is a matter of personal choice.
   1 2 3 4 5

2. Abortion is a threat to our society. 1 2 3 4 5

3. A woman should have control over what is happening to her own body by having the option to choose abortion.   1 2 3 4 5

4. Only God, not people, can decide if a fetus should live.   1 2 3 4 5

5. Even if one believes that there may be some exceptions, abortion is still basically wrong.   1 2 3 4 5

6. Abortion violates an unborn person's fundamental right to life.   1 2 3 4 5

7. A woman should be able to exercise her rights to self-determination by choosing to have an abortion.   1 2 3 4 5

8. Outlawing abortion could take away a woman's sense of self and personal autonomy.
   1 2 3 4 5

9. Outlawing abortion violates a woman's civil rights.   1 2 3 4 5

10. Abortion is morally unacceptable and unjustified.   1 2 3 4 5

11. In my reasoning, the notion that an unborn fetus may be a human life is not a deciding issue in considering abortion.   1 2 3 4 5

12. Abortion can be described as taking a life unjustly.   1 2 3 4 5

13. A woman should have the right to decide to have an abortion based on her own life circumstances.   1 2 3 4 5

14. If a woman feels that having a child might ruin her life, she should consider an abortion.
   1 2 3 4 5

15. Abortion could destroy the sanctity of motherhood.   1 2 3 4 5

16. An unborn fetus is a viable human being with rights.   1 2 3 4 5

17. If a woman feels she can't care for a baby, she should be able to have an abortion.
   1 2 3 4 5

18. Abortion is the destruction of one life for the convenience of another.   1 2 3 4 5

19. Abortion is the same as murder.   1 2 3 4 5

20. Even if one believes that there are times when abortion is immoral, it is still basically the woman's own choice.   1 2 3 4 5

Source: Parsons, N.K., Richards, H.C., & Kantor, G.D.P. (1990). Validation of a scale to measure reasoning about abortion. *Journal of Counseling Psychology, 37,* 107–112. Copyright © 1990 by the American Psychological Association. Reprinted by permission.

motivated by a desire to reduce the risk of physical, economic, psychological, and social disadvantages that the woman perceives for herself and her present and future children should she take the pregnancy to term (Russo et al., 1992).

The national debate over abortion has been played out in recent years against a backdrop of demonstrations, marches, and occasional acts of violence, such as fire-bombings of abortion clinics. The right-to-life (pro-life) movement asserts that human life begins at conception and thus views abortion as the murder of an unborn child (Sagan & Druyan, 1990). Many in the pro-life movement brook no exception to their opposition to abortion. Some would permit abortion to save the mother's life, however, or when a pregnancy results from rape or incest.

The pro-choice movement contends that abortion is a matter of personal choice and that the government has no right to interfere with a woman's right to terminate a pregnancy. Pro-choice advocates argue that women should be free to control what happens within their bodies, and should have the right to terminate a pregnancy.

Viable
Capable of sustaining independent life outside the womb.

Moral concerns about abortion often turn on the question of when human life begins. Does it begin at conception? When the embryo becomes implanted in the uterus? When the fetus begins to assume a human shape or develops human facial features? When the fetus becomes **viable?** At birth?

In his thesis on *ensoulment,* the thirteenth-century Christian theologian Saint Thomas Aquinas wrote that a male fetus does not acquire a human soul until 40 days after conception; a female fetus does not acquire a soul until after 80 days. Scientists, too, have attempted to define when human life can be said to begin. Astronomer Carl Sagan (Sagan, 1977; Sagan & Druyan, 1990), for example, writes that fetal brain activity can be considered a secular or scientific marker of human life. Brain activity is needed for thought, the quality that is considered most "human" by many. Brain wave patterns typical of children do not begin until about the thirtieth week of pregnancy. Before then, the human fetus lacks the brain architecture to begin thinking (Sagan & Druyan, 1990). Of course, this line of thinking raises the question of whether fetal brain wave activity can be equated with thought. (What would a fetus "think" about?) Moreover, some argue that a newly fertilized ovum carries the *potential* for human thought in the same way that the embryonic or fetal brain does. It could even be argued that sperm cells and ova are living things in that they carry out the biological processes characteristic of cellular life. All in all, the question of when *human* life begins is a matter of definition that is apparently unanswerable by science.

HISTORICAL AND LEGAL PERSPECTIVES ON ABORTION

Learning Objective 13: Summarize the history of abortion, the changing abortion laws in the United States, and attitudes toward abortion.

Societal attitudes toward abortion have varied across cultures and times in history. Abortion was permitted in ancient Greece and Rome, but women in ancient Assyria were impaled on stakes for attempting abortion. Neither the Old Testament nor the New Testament specifically prohibits abortion (Sagan & Druyan, 1990). For much of its history, the Roman Catholic church held to Saint Thomas Aquinas's belief that ensoulment of the fetus did not occur for at least 40 days after conception. In 1869, Pope Pius IX declared that human life begins at conception. Thus an abortion at any stage of pregnancy became murder in the eyes of the Church and grounds for excommunication (Luker, 1984). The Roman Catholic church has since opposed abortion during any stage of pregnancy.

In colonial times and through the mid-nineteenth century, women in the United States were permitted to terminate a pregnancy until such time as the "quickening" (the point at which the woman was first able to feel the fetus stirring within her) (Sagan & Druyan, 1990). Few women were prosecuted for abortion, because quickening was determined by the woman's self-report (Sagan & Druyan, 1990). More restrictive abortion laws emerged after the Civil War, spurred by the need to increase the population and by concerns voiced by physicians about protecting women from botched abortions at the hands of "surgical butchers" (Lader, 1970). By 1900 virtually all states in the union had enacted legislation banning abortion *at any point* during pregnancy, except when necessary to save the woman's life (Faux, 1989).

Abortions were legal in the United States prior to the Civil War. *Yes, prior to the Civil War, abortions were legal until the point in the pregnancy when the woman sensed fetal movements.* •

Notes: One extreme example of anti-abortion violence was the March 10, 1993 murder of Dr. David Gunn, a Florida ob/gyn who performed abortions. Gunn was shot by Michael Griffin outside the Pensacola Women's Medical Services Clinic. Griffin was convicted of first degree murder and sentenced to life in prison with no chance of parole for 24 years. ("Clinton letter condemns anti-abortion violence," *Des Moines Register*, 3A, March 14, 1994.)

Notes: According to a 1994 publication by the Alan Guttmacher Institute, entitled *Family Planning Perspectives*, 1,529,000 abortions were performed in the United States in 1992. For the period of 1988–1992, the rate of abortions per 1000 women of child-bearing age dropped by 5 percent. During the same period, the number of abortion providers per 100,000 child-bearing-age women dropped by 202 percent.

Abortion laws remained essentially the same until the late '60s when some states liberalized their abortion laws under rising public pressure. Then, in 1973, the U.S. Supreme Court in effect legalized abortion nationwide in the landmark *Roe v. Wade* decision.

Roe v. Wade held that a woman's right to an abortion was protected under the right to privacy guaranteed by the Constitution. The decision legalized abortions for any reason during the first trimester, leaving the decision to have an abortion entirely in the hands of the woman. In its ruling the Court also noted that a fetus is not considered a person and is thus not entitled to constitutional protection. The Court ruled that states may regulate a woman's right to have an abortion during the second trimester to protect her health, such as by requiring her to obtain an abortion in a hospital rather than a doctor's office. The Court also held that when a fetus becomes viable, its rights override the mother's right to privacy. Because the fetus may become viable early in the third trimester, states may prohibit third-trimester abortions, except in cases in which an abortion is necessary to protect a woman's health or life. Although legislative actions and later court decisions have somewhat narrowed abortion rights, *Roe v. Wade* has withstood repeated challenges.

In 1977, Congress enacted the Hyde amendment, which denies Medicaid funding for abortions except in cases in which the woman's life is endangered. In *Harris v. McRae* (1980), the U.S. Supreme Court essentially upheld the Hyde amendment (and similar state legislation) by ruling that federal and state governments are not required to pay for abortions for poor women who are receiving public assistance.

Since *Roe v. Wade*, 33 states have also enacted laws requiring parental consent or notification before a minor may have an abortion (Carlson, 1990). Sixty-nine percent of adults in the United States believe that parental permission should be required before teenage girls can have abortions (Carlson, 1990). Many pregnant teenage girls, however, especially those living in families with alcoholic or abusive parents, fear telling their parents that they are pregnant. In 1990 rulings involving state laws in Ohio and Minnesota, the U.S. Supreme Court upheld the rights of states to require that a minor seeking an abortion notify at least one parent and wait 48 hours before an abortion can be performed. The Court provided an "escape clause," however: The minor girl may go before a judge instead. Carlson (1990) notes that many pregnant teenagers who are reluctant to reveal pregnancies to their parents may also hesitate to reveal them to authority figures such as judges. A 1993 U.S. Supreme Court ruling let stand a Mississippi law requiring minors to obtain approval either from both parents or from a judge.

Parental consent laws have widespread popular support; three of four adults support such provisions, including many abortion rights supporters (Lewin, 1992b). Yet, with or without the rules, the majority of girls seeking abortions do consult with their parents before going through with their plans. One of the arguments favoring parental approval is the belief that parents know what is best for their children. However, opponents say that parental consent laws only serve to delay girls from getting safer early abortions, forcing them to postpone getting abortions until the second trimester when the risks are greater. Even in states that allow minors seeking abortions to obtain consent from a third party, most usually a judge, the delays involved can heighten the risks the girl faces (Pliner & Yates, 1992).

In 1989 a decision by the U.S. Supreme Court in a Missouri case, *Webster v. Reproductive Health Services,* considerably narrowed abortion rights granted previously under *Roe v. Wade*. By a five-to-four split decision, the Supreme Court upheld Missouri state laws (1) restricting public employees from performing or assisting in abortions, except in cases in which an abortion was needed to save a woman's life; (2) prohibiting the use of public facilities for performing abortions; and (3) requiring doctors to perform medical tests to determine the viability of a fetus before granting a woman's request for an abortion if she is believed to be at least 20 weeks pregnant. Although the

Notes: A publication entitled *National Survey of State Laws* contains detailed charts of state laws governing abortion, the definition of legal abortion, consent and/or notice requirements, penalties for violating the laws, residency requirements, waiting periods, and licensing requirements for abortionists. (Leiter, Richard A. (Ed.). 1993. *National Survey of State Laws.* Detroit, MI: Gale Research.)

Discussion Question: Recently a news commentator, in describing the polls regarding abortion attitudes said the problem is that many people in the United States are both pro-life and pro-choice. Analyze this idea. Do any of you consider yourself to be both pro-life and pro-choice?

Webster decision did not ban abortions, it made it more difficult (and expensive) for women to obtain late second-trimester abortions by allowing states to require medical testing for viability at 20 weeks. The 20-week stipulation is unlikely to have a major impact, however, because 91 percent of abortions occur within the first 12 weeks of pregnancy (McKinney, 1989). States would also be permitted to ban abortions performed in public facilities or by public employees, which would make it more difficult for poor women to obtain abortions.

ATTITUDES TOWARD LEGALIZED ABORTION National public opinion polls taken since *Roe v. Wade* have consistently shown that a majority of people in the United States support the decision legalizing abortion (Gordon & Snyder, 1989). There is little difference in support for abortion between Catholics, Jews, and Protestants (Gordon & Snyder, 1989). Public support for abortion increased during the 1960s and 1970s but decreased slightly between 1980 and 1985 (Gillespie et al., 1988).

Most people in the United States favor legalized abortion but not under all circumstances (Scott & Schuman, 1980). A 1993 ABC News/*Washington Post* poll found that a woman's right to have an abortion was approved by a margin of 2 to 1, 65 percent versus 33 percent. Yet, according to a 1989 Gallup poll, only 27 percent of Americans believe that a woman should have a right to an abortion for any reason (Gallup, 1989). A large majority believe that women should be permitted to have an abortion if the pregnancy results from rape or incest, if the woman's life or health is threatened, or if the child is likely to be born seriously deformed. A majority feel that abortion should be illegal, however, for a woman who does not want or cannot afford a child. Even a great majority of American Catholics and Protestants endorse abortion under certain conditions, such as when the woman's health is endangered, when there is a chance of birth defects, or when a woman becomes pregnant as the result of rape ("A sparser flock with changing views," 1993). Support for abortion under other conditions is lower, however, with fewer than half endorsing abortions in the case of a single woman who doesn't want to marry (38% of Catholics and 44% of Protestants approving) or of a married woman who doesn't want more children (37% of Catholics and 43% of Protestants approving).

Although some consider abortion a "women's issue," men are as likely if not more likely to be pro-choice (Scott & Schuman, 1980). Among people who support abortion rights, however, women as a group feel more strongly about the issue than men do, are more likely to consider a congressional candidate's stance on abortion to be a litmus test for support, and are more likely to take social action.

Abortion Rights. Pro-choice or pro-life? More than twenty years after the landmark *Roe v. Wade* decision, the issue of legalized abortion continues to polarize our society.

Notes: A publication entitled *National Survey of State Laws* contains detailed charts of state laws governing abortion. The information for each state includes the definition of illegal abortion, the definition of legal abortion, consent and/or notice requirements, penalties for violating the laws, residency requirements, waiting periods, and licensing requirements for abortionists. (Leiter, Richard A. (Ed.). 1993. *National Survey of State Laws*. Detroit, MI: Gale Research.)

 Abortion Doctor

Learning Objective 14: Describe six methods of abortion, including RU-486, the possible complications associated with each, and the time period during pregnancy in which each can be performed.

Vacuum aspiration Removal of the uterine contents by suction. An abortion method used early in pregnancy. (From the Latin *aspirare,* meaning "to breathe upon.")

The controversy over abortion has led to an overall decline in the number of abortion providers (Boodman, 1993; Lacayo, 1993; National Abortion Rights Action League Fact Sheet, 1993). Nationwide, 83 percent of counties have no abortion provider. Two states, North Dakota and South Dakota, have just one abortion provider each, so women seeking abortions must often travel to other states. Many women who seek abortions at abortion clinics must navigate through a daunting maze of pro-life picketers to gain entrance through clinic doors.

THE RISKS OF ABORTION AROUND THE WORLD—FOR RICHER OR POORER

An abortion performed by a physician during the first trimester is safer than continuing a pregnancy to term (Gordon & Snyder, 1989). Abortions in the second trimester create varying degrees of risk, depending on the procedure. The overall mortality rate associated with legal abortions in the United States has remained extremely low, with fewer than one death reported per 100,000 procedures performed (Centers for Disease Control, 1992; Koonin, 1992). In Mexico, where abortion is illegal, more than 100,000 women die annually from illicit, unsanitary abortions (Bonavoglia, 1991). Those who die are primarily poor women who have no recourse to sanitary abortions elsewhere. Rich women in countries that prohibit abortions typically have little or no difficulty obtaining safe abortions (Gordon & Snyder, 1989). Of course, all this discussion of risk refers to risk to the *mother.* Abortion kills the embryo or fetus, which is the root of the controversy.

Many people in the U.S. pro-choice movement argue that if abortions were to be made illegal again, thousands of women, especially poor women, would die or suffer serious physical consequences from botched, nonsterile abortions. People in the pro-life movement counter that alternatives to abortion such as adoption are available to pregnant women and that no one is forced to have an abortion. Pro-choice advocates argue that the debate about abortion should be framed not only by notions of the mother's right to privacy but also by the issue of the quality of life of an unwanted child. They argue that minority and physically or mentally disabled children are often hard to place for adoption. These children often spend their childhoods being shuffled from one foster home to another. Pro-life advocates counter that killing a fetus eliminates any potential that it might have, despite hardships, of living a fruitful and meaningful life. The debate about abortion continues with no consensus in the offing.

METHODS OF ABORTION

Regardless of the moral, legal, and political issues that surround abortion, there are a number of abortion methods in use today.

VACUUM ASPIRATION, or suction curettage, is the safest and most common method of abortion (Calderone & Johnson, 1989). It accounts for more than 90 percent of abortions in the United States (National Center for Health Statistics, 1986). It is relatively painless and inexpensive. It can be done with little or no anesthesia in a medical office or clinic but can be performed only during the first trimester (Calderone & Johnson, 1989). Later, thinning of the uterine walls increases the risks of perforation and bleeding. In the procedure the cervix is usually dilated first by insertion of progressively larger curved metal rods, or "dilators," or by insertion, hours earlier, of a stick of seaweed called *Laminaria digitata. Laminaria* expands as it absorbs cervical moisture, providing a gentler means of opening the os. Then an angled tube connected to an aspirator (suction machine) is inserted through the cervix into the uterus. The uterine contents are then evacuated (emptied) by suction (Figure 12.9). Possible complications of the procedure include perforation of the uterus, infection, cervical lacerations, and hemorrhaging, but these are rare.

TRUTH OR *FICTION?*
R E V I S I T E D

The D & C is the most widely used type of abortion method in the United States today. *Vacuum aspiration, and not the D & C, is the most widely used abortion method in the United States today.* •

A CLOSER LOOK

RU-486

An abortion pill that causes a chemically induced abortion has recently been introduced by a French manufacturer. Called RU-486, the pill contains mifepristone, a chemical that induces early abortion by blocking the effects of progesterone, the hormone that stimulates proliferation of the endometrium, that allows implantation of the fertilized ovum, and that is required for the placenta to develop. The chemical in RU-486 greatly diminishes the chances that a fertilized ovum will be implanted or that a placenta will develop to sustain its growth. The drug should not be used after the forty-seventh day following the last menstrual period (Riding, 1990). By the early 1990s, more than 150,000 women in Europe had used the drug ("Easier way found for abortion pill," 1993).

The effectiveness of RU-486 is enhanced when a woman takes hormones called prostaglandins, generally by injection, 48 hours after taking the drug (Riding, 1990; Swahn et al., 1985). Prostaglandins also help reduce the risk of hemorrhaging (Riding, 1990). Clinical trials based on more than 2,000 women in France have established that RU-486 is as effective as vacuum aspiration when it is used along with prostaglandins up to three weeks beyond the date of the missed period (Silvestre et al., 1990). In European studies involving more than 60,000 women, RU-486 was effective in inducing abortions in 96 percent of cases (Leary, 1993a).

A new method involving the oral administration of prostaglandin (Cyotec) following the use of RU-486 was recently

introduced (Smolowe, 1993). The use of this technique does not require the woman to go to a clinic for a follow-up injection of the hormone. French researchers report that RU-486 works just as well when combined with an oral dose of prostaglandin as when the hormone is taken by injection ("Easier way found for abortion pill," 1993). Making an abortion as seemingly simple as swallowing a combination of pills has intensified the debate over the use of RU-486. Pro-life groups consider abortion murder, whether induced by surgery or a pill, and they urge that mothers give up unwanted children for adoption rather than terminate their pregnancies.

RU-486 and other similar drugs (called antiprogestins) may have much broader uses than inducing abortion (Leary, 1993a). RU-486 shows promise as an alternative to the morning-after pill, since it produces less nausea and vomiting than the drugs now used as morning-after pills (Smolowe, 1993). There may also be some medical uses for RU-486 in combating endometriosis, fibroid tumors, benign brain tumors, and even breast cancer (Leary, 1993a).

Supporters of RU-486 argue that it offers a safe, noninvasive substitute for more costly and unpleasant abortion procedures (Segal, 1990). They also assert that RU-486 may reduce the numbers of women who die each year from complications from self-induced abortions. Such women are usually too poor to avail themselves of legally sanctioned abortion facilities, or they live in third world countries that lack adequate medical services

(Riding, 1990). Yet even the developer of the RU-486, Dr. Etienne-Emile Baulieu, recognizes that taking RU-486 does not eliminate the anguish over having an abortion. "It's insulting to women to say that abortion now will be as easy as taking aspirins. . . . It is always difficult, psychologically and physically, sometimes tragic" (Smolowe, 1993, p. 51). Moreover, questions remain about the safety of the procedure (Carper, 1993). Commonly reported side effects include heavy menstrual bleeding, lasting about 10 days on the average, and menstrual cramping.

RU-486 has not yet been introduced in the United States, largely because of opposition by pro-life groups (Riding, 1990; Segal, 1990). In 1993, President Bill Clinton expressed support for making the drug available to women in the United States, which would reverse the former administration's policy of barring the drug from the country (Hilts, 1993; Leary, 1993c; Smolowe, 1993). Because of the time needed to arrange for a U.S. manufacturer for the drug and obtain the necessary approval from the FDA, experts believe that the drug will not be widely available in the United States until the mid-1990s at the earliest (Leary, 1993c). Still, if RU-486 does arrive in the U.S. (and it may well have arrived by the time you read these pages), it is expected to further ignite the already heated abortion debate because it will make abortions more accessible and difficult to regulate (Smolowe, 1993).

 RU-486

Notes: In May 1994, the French manufacturer of RU-486, Roussel Uclaf, gave all patent rights for the pill to a nonprofit research group, the Population Council. The research group will begin clinical trials in the fall of 1994. (Coming to America: RU-486. 1994. *Time,* May 30, 21.)

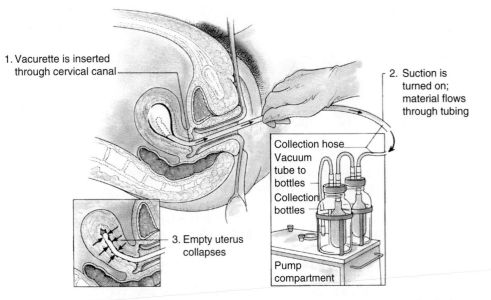

1. Vacurette is inserted through cervical canal

2. Suction is turned on; material flows through tubing

Collection hose
Vacuum tube to bottles
Collection bottles

3. Empty uterus collapses

Pump compartment

Figure 12.9 Vacuum Aspiration. This is the safest and most common method of abortion, but it can only be performed during the first trimester. An angled tube is inserted through the cervix in the uterus, and the uterine contents are then evacuated (emptied) by suction.

D & C

Abbreviation for *dilation and curettage,* an operation in which the cervix is dilated and uterine contents are then gently scraped away.

DILATION AND CURETTAGE (D & C) The **D & C** was once the customary method of performing abortions. It now accounts for only 1 percent of U.S. abortions (National Center for Health Statistics, 1986). It is usually performed 8 to 20 weeks following the last menstrual period (LMP). Once the cervix has been dilated, the uterine contents are scraped from the uterine lining with a blunt scraping tool.

D & Cs are carried out in a hospital, usually under general anesthesia. The scraping increases the chances of hemorrhaging, infection, and perforation. Because of these risks, D & Cs have largely been replaced by the vacuum aspiration method (Calderone & Johnson, 1989). D & Cs are still used to treat various gynecological problems, however, such as abnormally heavy menstrual bleeding.

D & E

Abbreviation for *dilation and evacuation,* an abortion method in which the cervix is dilated prior to vacuum aspiration.

DILATION AND EVACUATION (D & E) The **D & E** is used most commonly during the second trimester, when vacuum aspiration alone would be too risky. The D & E combines suction and the D & C. First the cervix is dilated. The cervix must also be dilated more fully than with vacuum aspiration to allow for passage of the larger fetus. Then a suction tube is inserted to remove some of the contents of the uterus. But suction alone cannot safely remove all uterine contents. So the remaining contents are removed with forceps. A blunt scraper may also be used to scrape the uterine wall to make sure that the lining has been removed fully. Like the D & C, the D & E is usually performed in the hospital under general anesthesia. Most women recover quickly and relatively painlessly. In rare instances, however, complications can arise. These include excessive bleeding, infection, and perforation of the uterine lining (Thompson, 1993).

Intra-amniotic infusion

An abortion method in which a substance is injected into the amniotic sac to induce premature labor. Also called *instillation.*

INDUCING LABOR BY INTRA-AMNIOTIC INFUSION Second trimester abortions are sometimes performed by chemically inducing premature labor and delivery. The procedure, which must be performed in a hospital, is called instillation, or **intra-amniotic infusion.** It is usually performed when fetal development has progressed beyond the point at which other methods are deemed safe. A saline (salt) solution or a solution of prostaglandins (hormones that stimulate uterine contractions during labor) is injected into the amniotic sac. Prostaglandins may also be administered by vaginal suppository. Uterine contractions (labor) begin within a few hours after infusion. The fetus and placenta are expelled from the uterus within the next 24 or 48 hours.

Japan's Abortion Agony: In a Country That Prohibits the Pill, Reality Collides with Religion

Japan may be the richest, most technologically advanced nation in the world, but it depends on an antiquated system of birth control that forces women to rely heavily on abortion in a society that at the same time disapproves of it.

Japan's abortion rate is one of the highest among the world's industrialized nations. One reason for this is the lack of birth-control alternatives. The government bans the use of the birth-control pill as a contraceptive, and doctors do not encourage sterilization, IUDs, or diaphragms. Nearly 75 percent of Japanese continue to use condoms and rhythm methods despite their high failure rate.

Over the years Japanese officials defended the ban against the pill by arguing that

oral contraceptives are unsafe and would promote promiscuity ("Still no pill for Japan," 1992). In 1992, a review by the Health and Welfare Ministry found birth-control pills to be safe, but decided to uphold the ban because of concerns about AIDS. Though Japan has had relatively few AIDS cases by international standards (fewer than 500 by mid-1991), the health ministry feared that lifting the ban on the pill might discourage condom use and lead to an epidemic of AIDS. Some women in Japan are able to skirt the ban by consulting sympathetic physicians who are willing to prescribe them presumably to treat gynecological complaints.

In part because of limited contraceptive options, the Japanese use condoms more

than any other people in the world. They are widely available in drugstores, supermarkets, and vending machines; embarrassed housewives can buy them from door-to-door saleswomen. Abortion is the widely used backup for failed contraception. And yet, though abortions have now been legal and easily accessible in Japan for over 40 years, women who have them feel stigmatized because abortion is regarded by many Japanese, even those who accept it, as "killing a baby."

The majority of Japanese draw little distinction between a fetus and an infant. According to Samuel Coleman, the author of *Family Planning in Japanese Society,* the reasons lie at least partially in Shinto and Buddhism, Japan's two major religions.

Intra-amniotic infusion accounts for only about 3 percent of all abortions (National Center for Health Statistics, 1986). Medical complications, risks, and costs are greater with this procedure than with other methods of abortion. Overly rapid labor can tear the cervix, but previous dilation of the cervix with *Laminaria* lessens the risk. Perforation, infection, and hemorrhaging are rare if prostaglandins are used, but about half the recipients experience nausea and vomiting, diarrhea, or headaches. Saline infusion can cause shock and even death if the solution is carelessly introduced into the bloodstream.

Hysterotomy
An abortion method in which the fetus is removed by Caesarean section.

HYSTEROTOMY   The **hysterotomy** is, in effect, a Caesarean section. Incisions are made in the abdomen and uterus, and the fetus and uterine contents are removed. Hysterotomy may be performed during the late second trimester, between the sixteenth and twenty-fourth weeks LMP. It is performed very rarely, usually only when intra-amniotic infusion is not advised. A hysterotomy is major surgery that must be carried out under general anesthesia in a hospital. Like any major surgery, hysterotomy involves a risk of surgical complications accompanying the use of general anesthesia and a potential for postoperative infection.

Although neither religion promotes active opposition to abortion, Buddhism is based on the ideal of overcoming one's sense of ego. In this context, a woman who aborts wrongly puts her ego before her fetus. Shinto, an ancient religion based on ancestor and nature worship, holds that an aborted fetus can place a curse on the woman who aborts.

Offerings at the Temple

Hiroshi Hihara is a gynecologist in Tokyo. He makes his living on infertility work and abortions, many of them for married women whose method of contraception has failed. Although Hihara is a member of a Buddhist temple, he does not consider himself religious. But he says he is not comfortable with abortion. "Abortion is legal and approved of by the government, and if a patient wants it, I can't turn her down," he says. "She's entitled to it. But I am not happy to do it." And yet he performs some 200 abortions a year, and quietly admits, when asked, that his fees from abortion represent "a large portion of my income."

Caught in this moral and economic trap, he resolves his feelings in a uniquely Japanese way. First, he tells each abortion patient to make an offering after the operation at any of the Buddhist temples selling miniature stone statues, or *mizuko-juko*, which women can buy in memory of an aborted fetus. Thousands of such statues stand on display at temples these days, and although some are for miscarriages and stillborn children, the vast majority are for abortions. Many of the statues are decorated with crocheted hats, plastic bibs, and little pinwheels, all put there by women to keep the soul of the aborted fetus warm and amused.

Abortion First, Contraception Second

Debate is going on over whether to legalize the pill and promote other forms of birth control such as the diaphragm. Whether Japanese women will use the pill if legalized is an open question. In a June 1990 survey released by one of Japan's largest newspapers, results showed that fewer than 10 percent of Japanese women would use it even if it were available.

Adapted from Bumiller, 1990.

PSYCHOLOGICAL CONSEQUENCES OF ABORTION

Learning Objective 15: Describe the findings from the research on the psychological consequences of abortion in the United States and Japan.

The woman who faces an unwanted pregnancy may experience a range of negative emotions, including

> . . . fear ("What will I do now?"), self-anger ("How could I let this happen?"), guilt ("What would my parents think if they knew I was pregnant?"), ambivalence ("Will I be sorry if I have an abortion? Will I be sorry if I don't?"), and sometimes desperation ("Is suicide a way out?").

(Knox, 1988, p. 455)

Choosing to have an abortion is typically a painful decision—perhaps the most difficult decision a woman will ever make. Even women who make a decision to have an abortion without hesitation may have feelings of guilt, remorse, anger, and sadness. Although the woman's partner is often overlooked in the research on abortion, he too may encounter such feelings (Shostak et al., 1984).

Women's reactions depend on various factors, including the support they receive from others (or the lack thereof) and the strength of their relationships with their partners. Women with greater support from their male partners or parents tend to show a

Notes: In one study of 1004 married women who came to an abortion clinic in St. Louis, MO, researchers found that fewer than 1 in 20 women failed to notify their husbands voluntarily. Of those who told their husbands, 99.5 percent reported that their husbands agreed with their decisions to choose an abortion. This high rate of communication and agreement is surprising when you consider that 28.7 percent of these women reported that they had been raped, battered, or both within their marriages. (Smith, H. W., and Kronauge, C. 1990. The politics of abortion: Husband notification legislation, self-disclosure, and marital bargaining. *Sociological Quarterly, 31(4)*, 585–598.)

more positive emotional reaction following an abortion (Armsworth, 1991). Generally speaking, the sooner the abortion occurs, the less stressful it is. Women who have a difficult time reaching an abortion decision, who blame the pregnancy on their character, who have lower expectations before the abortion concerning their ability to cope afterwards, and who perceive less social support from important others in their lives, tend to experience more emotional distress shortly following the abortion than do others (Major & Cozzarelli, 1992). However, there is little evidence that abortions result in diagnosable psychological disorders (Armsworth, 1991). Still, women may profit from talking with confidants or helping professionals before the abortion and afterwards.

Many men are very concerned and supportive of their partners; others seek to detach themselves from the situation. They may consider the pregnancy the woman's responsibility: "She's the one who let herself get pregnant." Some men reproach the woman for failing to take precautions. No wonder feminists insist that men share full responsibility for pregnancies.

Women's negative feelings tend to be more severe before the abortion than afterwards. Shortly afterward the woman is likely to feel a sense of relief (David, 1978; Gordon & Snyder, 1989). Feelings of sadness or regret, however, may occur later on, although they tend not to be severe or prolonged (Wassenberg & Nass, 1977). Women interviewed about a year after an abortion generally show good psychological adjustment (Burnell & Norfleet, 1987). Recollection of the abortion may evoke passing feelings of sadness for years afterward, however (Gordon & Snyder, 1989). Some who have abortions in their teens or early twenties may have profound regret if they have difficulty becoming pregnant when they want to do so later on. They may think that they destroyed their one chance for motherhood (Gordon & Snyder, 1989).

All in all, few women who have abortions regret their decisions. Only 8 percent of the women in one national survey who had had an abortion felt that they had made the wrong choice (Nass et al., 1984).

The World of Diversity feature (see pages 384–385) provides some perspective on the ways in which some citizens of the wealthiest nation on the Pacific rim cope with their feelings about abortion.

SUMMING UP

Birth control includes both contraception and induced abortion.

CONTRACEPTION

Contraception in the United States: The Legal Battle

In the United States, Anthony Comstock lobbied successfully for passage of a federal law in 1873 that prohibited the dissemination of birth-control information through the mail on the grounds that it was obscene and indecent. In 1918 the courts ruled that physicians must be allowed to disseminate information that might aid in the cure and prevention of disease, and dismantling of the Comstock law had begun.

Selecting a Method of Contraception Issues surrounding the choice of a method of contraception involve their convenience, moral acceptability, cost, sharing of responsibility between the partners, safety, reversibility, the protection they afford from sexually transmitted diseases (STDs), and effectiveness.

METHODS OF CONTRACEPTION

Oral Contraceptives (The Pill) Birth-control pills include combination pills and minipills. Combination pills contain estrogen and progestin and fool the brain into acting as though the woman is already pregnant, so that no additional ova mature or are released. Minipills contain progestin, thicken the cervical mucus to impede the passage of sperm through the cervix, and render the inner lining of the uterus less receptive to a fertilized egg. Oral contraception is nearly 100 percent effective. The main drawbacks are side effects and potential health risks.

"Morning-after" pills prevent implantation of a fertilized ovum in the uterus.

Intrauterine Devices (IUDs) The IUD apparently irritates the uterine lining, causing inflammation and the production of antibodies that may be toxic to sperm or fertilized ova and/or may prevent fertilized eggs from becoming implanted. The IUD is highly effective, but there are possible troublesome side effects and the potential for serious health complications.

The Diaphragm The diaphragm should be used with a spermicidal cream or jelly. The diaphragm must be fitted by a health professional.

Spermicides Spermicides block the passage of sperm and kill sperm. Their failure rate is high, but spermicides that contain nonoxynol-9 may also provide some protection against organisms that give rise to STDs.

The Contraceptive Sponge The sponge blocks and soaks up the ejaculate, while the spermicide it contains kills sperm.

The Cervical Cap Like the diaphragm, the cap is most effective when used with a spermicide.

Condoms Latex condoms afford protection against STDs. Condoms are the only contraceptive device worn by men, and the only readily reversible method of contraception that is available to men.

Douching Douching is ineffective for contraception, because large numbers of sperm may be found beyond the range of the douche within seconds after ejaculation.

Withdrawal (Coitus Interruptus) Withdrawal requires no special equipment but has a high failure rate.

Fertility Awareness Methods (Rhythm Methods) Rhythm methods rely on awareness of the fertile segments of the woman's menstrual cycle. Rhythm methods include the calendar method, the basal body temperature method, and the cervical mucus method. Their failure rate is high in typical use.

Sterilization Sterilization methods should be considered permanent, although they may be reversed in many cases. The vasectomy is usually carried out under local anesthesia in 15 to 20 minutes. Female sterilization methods prevent ova and sperm from passing through the Fallopian tubes.

New Developments in Contraception The contraceptive implant, Norplant, consists of tubes containing progestin that are surgically embedded under the skin of the woman's upper arm. Norplant provides continuous contraceptive protection for as long as five years.

The female condom is fitted over the vaginal opening and provides a shield that blocks sperm but allows the penis to move freely.

The vaginal ring can be worn in the vagina for three months and delivers a continuous dose of hormones that relieves a woman of having to remember to take a pill.

Depo-Provera is injected and supplies a continuous dosage of long-acting progesterone, which acts to inhibit ovulation.

ABORTION

Historical and Legal Perspectives on Abortion In colonial times and through the mid-nineteenth century, women in the United States were permitted to terminate a pregnancy until "quickening" occurred. More restrictive abortion laws came into being after the Civil War.

In 1973, the U.S. Supreme Court in effect legalized abortion nationwide in the landmark *Roe v. Wade* decision.

Methods of Abortion Abortion methods in use today include vacuum aspiration, D & C, D & E, induction of labor by intra-amniotic infusion, and hysterotomy.

Psychological Consequences of Abortion Although choosing to have an abortion is typically a painful decision, women interviewed about a year after an abortion generally show good psychological adjustment.

_____ Many boys are born with erections.

_____ Infants often engage in pelvic thrusting at 8 to 10 months of age.

_____ Most children learn the facts of life from parents or from school sex education programs.

_____ Sex education encourages sexual activity among children and adolescents.

_____ Nocturnal emissions in boys accompany erotic dreams.

_____ Petting is practically universal among adolescents in the United States.

_____ More than one million adolescent girls in the United States become pregnant each year.

_____ In some school districts, condoms are distributed to adolescents without parental consent.

C H A P T E R *13*

Sexuality in Childhood and Adolescence

> My heart leaps up when I behold
> A rainbow in the sky:
> So was it when my life began,
> So is it now I am a man,
> So be it when I shall grow old
> Or let me die!
> The Child is father of the Man:
> And I could wish my days to be
> Bound each to each by natural piety.
>
> (William Wordsworth, "My Heart Leaps Up")

What a life it would be, indeed, were our hearts to swell with the wonders of the world throughout our lives. In this chapter we begin our chronicle of sexual behavior across the life span, and we see the ways in which the child is father of the man. Within children's personal and social experiences lie the seeds of later sexual competence and self-esteem; or the seeds of incompetence, guilt, and shame. Through the next chapter we shall see that our sexuality remains an integral part of our lives throughout our lives—one that has the potential to help our hearts leap up for all our days.

INFANCY (0 TO 2 YEARS): A SEARCH FOR THE ORIGINS OF HUMAN SEXUALITY

Learning Objective 1: Summarize the information on infants' capacity for sexual response, including the information on masturbation and genital play.

Babies develop their sucking reflex as fetuses. The sucking reflex allows babies to gain nourishment, which is necessary for survival. But as Sigmund Freud hypothesized, infants also seem to reap sensual pleasure from sucking fingers, pacifiers, nipples, or whatever else fits into the mouth. This is not surprising, given the sensitivity of the mouth's mucosal lining.

Stimulation of the genitals in infancy may also produce sensations of pleasure. Parents who touch their infants' genitals while changing or washing them may discover the infants smiling or becoming excited. Infants discover the pleasure of self-stimulation (masturbation) for themselves when they gain the capacity to manipulate their genitals with their hands.

THE INFANT'S CAPACITY FOR SEXUAL RESPONSE

It is not uncommon for boys to be born with erections, and most have erections during the first few weeks. In an early study, Halverson (1940) followed nine boys between the ages of 3 and 20 weeks and found that seven attained erections at least daily. Incidence of erection varied from none to 40 a day. Erections were often accompanied by fretful crying, stretching, and stiff flexing of the limbs.

TRUTH OR *FICTION?*
R E V I S I T E D

Many boys are born with erections. *Many boys are indeed born with erections. Ultrasound has revealed erections even in fetuses.* •

Signs of sexual arousal in infant girls, such as vaginal lubrication, are less readily detected. Yet evidence of lubrication and genital swelling has been reported (Martinson, 1976).

Do not interpret children's responses according to adult concepts of sexuality, however. Lubrication and erection are reflexes, not necessarily signals of "interest" in sex.

Infants have the biological capacity for these reflexes, but we cannot say what, if anything, the reflexes "mean" to them.

PELVIC THRUSTING   Pelvic thrusting is observed in infant monkeys, apes, and humans. These observations led ethologist John Bowlby (1969) to suggest that infantile sexual behavior may be the rule in mammals, not the exception. Thrusting has been observed in humans at 8 to 10 months of age (Lewis & Kagan, 1965) and seems to be an expression of affection. Typically, the infant clings to the parent, nuzzles, and thrusts and rotates the pelvis for several seconds.

TRUTH OR *FICTION?*

R E V I S I T E D

Infants often engage in pelvic thrusting at 8 to 10 months of age. *True, but there is no reason to believe that thrusting means the same thing to infants that it does to adults.* •

ORGASM   At least some infants seem capable of sexual responses that closely resemble orgasm. Kinsey and his colleagues (1953) noted that baby boys show behaviors that resemble adult orgasm by as early as 5 months; baby girls, as early as 4 months. Orgasmic responses in boys are similar to those in men—but without ejaculation. Ejaculation only occurs after puberty.

MASTURBATION

Masturbation is typical for infants and young children and tends to start between 6 and 12 months, although usually somewhat earlier among boys than girls (Bieber, 1975). At early ages children usually masturbate by rubbing the genitals against a soft object, such as a towel, bedding, or a doll. As the child matures and becomes capable of more coordinated hand movements, direct manual stimulation of the genitals often becomes preferred.

Bakwin (1973) observed infant girls apparently masturbating to orgasm. A 5-month-old would press her legs together, then lift them and bear down till her face reddened. A 7-month-old threw her rag doll on the floor and pressed her body against it rhythmically. A 14-month-old girl would press her legs together and "get red in the face" (p. 53). After apparently reaching an orgasmlike state, she would relax, perspiring, and look exhausted.

Masturbation to orgasm is rare until the second year, however (Reinisch, 1990). Some children begin masturbating to orgasm later. Some never do. All in all, however,

Parent-Child Bonding. Parents who form warm and affectionate relationships with their children may help them develop the ability to form loving attachments later in life.

Cross-Cultural Perspectives on Childhood Sexuality

Though we are born with the capacity for sexual response, our expression of sexuality largely reflects the culture in which we are reared. Every culture pressures its people to discriminate between socially acceptable and unacceptable behavior. We may not fully conform to the teachings of our -culture, but most of us within a given culture develop similar behavior patterns and attitudes.

Cultures vary in their attitudes and practices concerning human sexuality, and in particular, childhood and adolescent sexuality. Some may be characterized as sexually permissive, others as sexually restrictive or semirestrictive. Broude and Greene (1976) analyzed attitudes toward, and frequency of, premarital sex among 114 of the world's societies. Most societies (55%) either disapproved of or

disallowed premarital sex among females. About one in four societies (24%) permitted girls to engage in premarital sex; another 21 percent tolerated female premarital sex if it was discreet. Despite societal prohibitions, premarital sex among females was common in 17 percent of the societies sampled and was universal or nearly so in 49 percent of societies. Female premarital sex was uncommon but occurred occasionally in 14 percent of societies and was rare or absent in only 20 percent of societies. Premarital sex among males occurred even more frequently. Among 107 societies in their cross-cultural sample, male premarital sex was universal or nearly so in 60 percent, "typical" in 18 percent, atypical but occurring occasionally in 10 percent, and rare or absent in only 12 percent.

Sexually Permissive Societies
Based on their review of ethnographic studies, Ford and Beach (1951) noted that when masturbation was permitted in a society, children progressed from occasional genital touching to more purposeful masturbation by about 6 to 8 years of age.

Sexually permissive cultures also tend to permit sexual expression among peers. Among the Seniang people of Oceania, boys and girls publicly simulate coitus without fear of reproach by adults (Ford & Beach, 1951). The Lesu of Oceania believe that it is normal for children to imitate coital positions. The Chewu people of Africa believed that childhood sexual experimentation is necessary for adult fertility. Children were expected to erect small huts outside the village, where they played husband and wife.

---

an orgasmic response from masturbation is common among children, as it is among adults (Reinisch, 1990).

GENITAL PLAY

Discussion Question:
Some day-care centers have one bathroom with several toilets, which are used by boys and girls. How do you think day-care workers should handle this situation? At nap time in a day-care center, a worker may find that a child masturbates himself or herself to sleep. How might a daycare worker approach this situation?

Children in the United States typically do not engage in genital play with others until about the age of 2. Then, as an expression of their curiosity about their environment and other people, they may investigate other children's genitals, or hug, cuddle, kiss, or climb on top of them. None of this need cause concern. Spiro (1965) describes 2-year-olds at play in an Israeli kibbutz:

> Ofer [a boy] and Pnina [a girl] sit side by side on chamber pots. . . . Ofer puts his foot on Pnina's foot, she then does the same—this happens several times. . . . Finally, Pnina shifts her pot away, then moves back, then away . . . they laugh . . . . Pnina stands up, lies on the table on her stomach, . . . Ofer pats her buttocks. . . . Ofer kicks Pnina gently, and they laugh. . . Pnina touches and caresses Ofer's leg with her foot . . . says "more more". . . Ofer stands, then Pnina stands, both bounce up and down . . . both children are excited, bounce, laugh together . . . Pnina grabs Ofer's penis, and he pushes her away . . . she repeats, he pushes her away, and turns around . . . Pnina touches his buttocks (p. 225).

The Lecha people of the Himalayas believed that girls do not attain physical maturity unless they engage in early sexual intercourse. During early childhood, Lecha children engaged in mutual masturbation and attempted copulation. Girls began to engage in regular sexual intercourse by age 11 or 12. Among the Trobrianders of the South Pacific, girls were usually initiated into sexual intercourse by 6 or 8 years of age, boys by age 10 or 12. Among the Muria Gond of India, boys and girls as young as age 10 lived together in dormitories and spent their evenings dancing, singing, and pairing off for sex (Elwin, 1968).

Societies that permit sex play among children also tend to encourage open discussion of sex and to allow children to observe sexual behavior among adults. Among the Trukese of the South Pacific, children learned about sex by observing and asking adults. Lesu children, too, would observe adults, but there was at least one taboo: They were not to watch their own mothers.

Sexually Restrictive Societies
Ford and Beach (1951) found that only a minority of preliterate societies were sexually restrictive. Some, like the Apinaye people of South America, responded to children's sexual experimentation with threats and punishments. The Apinaye warned their children not to masturbate and thrashed them if they were suspected of doing so. Among the Kwoma of New Guinea, boys were warned never to touch their genitals, even when urinating. They risked having their penises beaten with a stick if they touched them.

Sexually restrictive societies discourage masturbation and sex play among children. Children who disobey are punished. Such societies also tend to be close-mouthed about sex. Parents try to keep their children ignorant about reproduction. Premarital sex and watching adults engage in sex are also restricted.

Societies that prohibit adolescent girls from engaging in sexual activity generally impose the same restrictions on boys (Barry & Schlegel, 1984). Still, though restrictions may be placed on boys, many societies hold to a sexual double standard by which boys are allowed greater sexual freedom than girls.

There is no reason to infer that Ofer and Pnina were seeking sexual gratification. Rough-and-tumble play, including touching the genitals, is common among children.

EARLY CHILDHOOD (3 TO 8 YEARS)

SUSAN: Once my younger sister and I were over at a girl friend's house playing in her bedroom. For some reason she pulled her pants down and exposed her rear to us. We were amazed to see she had an extra opening down there we didn't know about. My sister reciprocated by pulling her pants down so we could see if she had the same extra opening. We were amazed at our discovery, our mothers not having mentioned to us that we had a vagina!

CHRISTOPHER: Nancy was a willing playmate, and we spent many hours together examining each other's bodies as doctor and nurse. We even once figured out a pact that we would continue these examinations and watch each other develop. That was before we had started school.

(Morrison et al., 1980, p. 19)

Childhood Sexuality? Children have a natural inquisitiveness about sexual anatomy.

These recollections of early childhood show children's curiosity about sexual anatomy. Children often reciprocate exhibition of their bodies. The unwritten rule seems to be, "I'll show you mine if you'll show me yours."

MASTURBATION

Learning Objective 2:
Discuss masturbation in early childhood suggest how parents might react if they discover their children masturbating.

KIM: I began to masturbate when I was 3 years old. My parents. . . tried long and hard to discourage me. They told me it wasn't nice for a young lady to have her hand between her legs.

When I was five I remember my mother discovering that I masturbated with a rag doll I slept with. She was upset, but she didn't make a big deal about it. She just told me in a matter-of-fact way, "Do you know that what you're doing is called masturbating?" That didn't make much sense to me, except I got the impression she didn't want me to do it.

(Morrison et al., 1980, pp. 4, 5)

Because of the difficulties in conducting such research, statistics concerning the incidence of masturbation in children is largely speculative. Parents may not wish to respond to questions concerning the sexual conduct of their children. Or if they do, they may have a tendency to present their children as little "gentlemen" and "ladies" and perhaps underreport their sexual activity. Their biases may also lead them not to perceive their children's genital touching as masturbation. Many parents will not even permit their adolescent children to be interviewed about their sexual behavior (Fisher & Hall, 1988), let alone their younger children. When we are asked to look back as adults, our memories may be less than accurate.

We can only conclude that some children masturbate whereas others do not. Prevalences are highly speculative. But it does appear that children masturbate more frequently by the age of 4 or 5 (Reinisch, 1990).

HETEROSEXUAL BEHAVIOR

Learning Objective 3:
Describe typical heterosexual and same-gender sexual play among children ages three to eight.

ALICIA: On my birthday when I was in the second grade, I remember a classmate, Tim, walked home with a friend and me. He kept chasing me to give me kisses all over my face, and I acted like I didn't want him to do it, yet I knew I liked it a lot; when he would stop, I thought he didn't like me anymore.

(Morrison et al., 1980, pp. 21, 29)

Three- and 4-year-olds commonly express affection through kissing. Curiosity about the genitals may also occur by this stage. Sex games like "show" and "playing doctor" may begin earlier but become common between the ages of 6 and 10 (Reinisch, 1990). Much of this sexual activity takes place in same-gender groups, although mixed-gender sex games are not uncommon. Children may exhibit their genitals to each other, touch each other's genitals, or even masturbate together.

SAME-GENDER SEXUAL BEHAVIOR

> ARNOLD: When I was about 5, my cousin and I . . . went into the basement and dropped our pants. We touched each other's penises, and that was it. I guess I didn't realize the total significance of the secrecy in which we carried out this act. For later. . . my parents questioned me . . . and I told them exactly what we had done. They were horrified and told me that that was definitely forbidden.
>
> (Morrison et al., 1980, p. 24)

Despite Arnold's parents' "horror," same-gender sexual play in childhood does not presage adult sexual orientation (Reinisch, 1990). It may, in fact, be more common than heterosexual play. It typically involves handling the other child's genitals, although it may include oral or anal contact. It may also include an outdoor variation of the game of "show" in which boys urinate together and see who can reach farthest or attain the highest trajectory.

PREADOLESCENCE (9 TO 13 YEARS)

Learning Objective 4: Discuss the incidence of masturbation and of heterosexual and same-gender sexual behaviors among preadolescents.

During preadolescence children typically form relationships with a close "best friend" that enable them to share secrets and confidences. The friends are usually peers of the same gender. Preadolescents also tend to socialize with larger networks of friends in gender-segregated groups. At this stage boys are likely to think that girls are "dorks." To girls at this stage, "dork" is too good a word to apply to most boys.

Preadolescents grow increasingly preoccupied with and self-conscious about their bodies. Their peers pressure preadolescents to conform to dress codes, standards of "correct" slang, and to group standards concerning sex and drugs. Peer disapproval can be an intense punishment.

Sexual urges are experienced by many preadolescents, but they may not emerge until adolescence. Sigmund Freud had theorized that sexual impulses are hidden, or latent, during preadolescence, but many preadolescents are quite active sexually during the so-called latency period.

MASTURBATION

> PAUL: When I was about 10, stories about masturbation got me worried. A friend and I went to a friend's older brother whom we respected and asked, "Is it really bad?" His reply stuck in my mind for years. "Well, it's like a bottle of olives—every time you take one out, there is one less in there." We were very worried because we thought we'd run out before we got to girls.
>
> (Morrison et al., 1980, pp. 6–8)

Kinsey and his colleagues (1948, 1953) reported that masturbation is the primary means of achieving orgasm during preadolescence for both genders. They found that 45 percent of males and 15 percent of females masturbated by age 13. Based on the *Playboy* survey of sexual behavior in the 1970s, Hunt (1974) reported that about two thirds (63%) of the males sampled, and one third (33%) of the females, reported masturbating by age 13. The frequencies of masturbation in childhood have apparently increased since Kinsey's time, with the increases proportionally greater among girls.

HETEROSEXUAL BEHAVIOR

Preadolescent sex play often involves mutual display of the genitals, with or without touching. Such sexual experiences are quite common and do not appear to impair future sexual adjustment (Leitenberg et al., 1989).

Talking to Your Children About Sex

"Daddy, where do babies come from?"

"What are you asking me for? Go ask your mother."

Most children do not find it easy to talk to their parents about sex (Coles & Stokes, 1985). The parents may not find it any easier. Nearly half (47%) of the teens polled in a national survey said they would ask their friends, siblings, or sex partners if they desired information about sex. Only about a third (36%) would turn to their parents (Coles & Stokes, 1985). Three out of four say that it is hard to talk about sex with their fathers. More than half (57%) find it difficult to approach their mothers. Regrettably, information received from peers is likely to be strewn with inaccuracies. Misinformed teenagers run a higher risk of unwanted pregnancies and STDs.

Yet most young children are curious about where babies come from, about what makes little girls different from little boys, and so on. Parents who avoid answering such questions convey their own uneasiness about sex and may teach children that sex is something to be ashamed of, not something they should discuss openly.

Some parents resist talking about sex with their children because they are insecure in their own knowledge. Reinisch (1990) argues that parents need not be sex experts to talk to their children about sex, however. Parents can turn to books in the local bookstore to fill in gaps in knowledge, or to books that are intended for parents to read to their children. They can also admit that they do not know the answer to a particular question. Reinisch suggests that children will respect parents who display such honesty.

In answering children's questions, parents need to be sensitive to what their children can understand. The 4-year-old who wants to know where babies come from is probably not interested in detailed biological information. It may be sufficient to say, from "Mommy's uterus" and then point to mother's abdominal region. Why say "tummy"? "Tummy" is wrong and confusing.

In their *Family Book About Sexuality,* Calderone and Johnson (1989) offer parents some pointers:

1. *Be willing to answer your child's questions about sex.*

Parents who respond to their children's questions about sex by saying, "Why do you want to know that?" squelch further questioning. The child is likely to interpret the parent's response as meaning, "You shouldn't be interested in that."

2. *Use appropriate language.* As children develop awareness of their sexuality, they need to learn the names of their sex organs. They also need to learn that the "dirty words" that others use to refer to the sexual parts of the body are not acceptable in most situations, since they carry emotional connotations that can arouse negative feelings.

Nor should parents use "silly words" to describe sexual organs. As June Reinisch (1990) notes,

Another way parents send out negative messages about sexuality is by using silly words (or no words at all) to describe sexual anatomy. Whether they call genitals "pee-pee" or "privates" or nothing at all, parents are telling children that these body parts are significantly different, embarrassing, mysterious, or taboo compared to such other body parts as the eyes, nose,

---

Although preadolescents tend to socialize in same-gender groups, interest in the opposite gender among heterosexuals tends to gradually increase as they approach puberty. One survey of 946 10- to 17-year-olds in a middle- and upper-middle-class Pennsylvania suburb found increasing interest in romantic involvement with the opposite gender from the age of 10 to the age of 13 (Broderick, 1966).

Group dating and mixed-gender parties often provide preadolescents with their first exposure to heterosexual activities. Couples may not begin to pair off until early or mid-adolescence.

SAME-GENDER SEXUAL BEHAVIOR

Much preadolescent sexual behavior among members of the same gender is simply exploration. Some incidents reflect lack of availability of partners of the opposite gender.

and knees, which have names openly used in conversation (p. 248).

3. *Give advice in the form of information that the child can use to make sound decisions, not as an imperial edict.* State your own convictions, but label your beliefs as your own, rather than as something you are trying to impose on your child. Parents are not as likely to be effective by "laying down the law" as by relating convictions in firm but loving ways— by providing information and encouraging discussion. Reinisch (1990) suggests combining information about sex with expressions of the parent's values and beliefs.

Parents of teenage children often react to sexual experimentation with threats or punishments, which may cause adolescents to rebel or tune them out. Or the adolescent may learn to associate sex with fear and anger, which may persist even in adult relationships. Parents may find it more constructive to convey concern about the consequences of children's actions in a loving and nonthreatening way that invites an open

response. Say, for example, "I'm worried about the way you are experimenting, and I'd like to give you some information that you may not have. Can we talk about it?" (Calderone & Johnson, 1989, p. 141).

4. *Share information in small doses.* Pick a time and place that feels natural for such discussions, such as when the child is preparing for bed or when you are riding in the car.

5. *Encourage the child to talk about sex.* Children may feel embarrassed about talking about sex, especially with family members. Make the child aware that you are always available to answer questions. Be "askable." But let the child postpone talking about a sensitive topic until the two of you are alone or the child feels comfortable. Books about sexuality may help a child open up. They can be left lying around or given to the child with a suggestion such as, "This is a good book about sex, or at least I thought so. If you read it, then, maybe we can talk about it" (Calderone & Johnson, 1989, p. 136).

6. *Respect privacy rights.* Most of us, parents and children alike, value our privacy at certain times. A parent who feels uncomfortable sharing a bathroom with a child can simply tell the child that Daddy (or Mommy) likes to be alone when using the bathroom. Or the parent might explain, "I like my privacy, so please knock and I'll tell you if it's okay to come in. I'll do the same for you" (Calderone & Johnson, 1989, p. 137). This can be said without a scolding or harsh tone. Privacy rights in the bedroom can be established by saying in a clear and unthreatening way, "Please knock when the door's closed and wait to be invited in" (Calderone & Johnson, 1989, p. 138). But it is just as important for the parent to respect the same rights to privacy that the parent expects from the child. The child is likely to feel grateful for the respect and to show respect in return.

As with younger children, same-gender experiences during preadolescence may be more common than heterosexual experiences (Leitenberg et al., 1989). These activities are usually limited to touching of each other's genitals or mutual masturbation. Since preadolescents generally socialize within their genders, it is not surprising that their sexual explorations may also be within their genders. Most same-gender sexual experiences involve single episodes or short-lived relationships and are not signs of a budding gay orientation (Hunt, 1974).

SOURCES OF SEXUAL INFORMATION

Learning Objective 5: List the sources of sexual information most often used by preadolescents.

How do preadolescents learn about sex? Early studies repeatedly showed that peers were the primary source of sexual knowledge. A 1915 survey of 948 college men revealed that 85 percent had learned the "facts of life" from peers (cited in Gagnon, 1965, p. 223). The

Chastity Class

Discussion Question:
School sex-education programs rarely begin before fifth or sixth grade. Then, usually what is taught is body parts and their functions. What topics would you include in a sex-education curriculum for sixth graders (children about age 11)?

Playboy survey in the 1970s (Hunt, 1974) showed that peers remained the main source of sexual information for both genders. The next most often cited source was "reading," but the reading was mostly unguided and the information gained was unreliable.

School-based sex education programs were relatively rare as late as the early 1970s, despite the fact that an overwhelming majority of parents supported sex education in the schools (Norman & Harris, 1981). Sex education programs became more common in the 1970s and 1980s. By the late 1980s, about six in ten teenagers received some form of sex education in the schools (Kenney et al., 1989).

Today, 47 states mandate or recommend teaching sex education (Haffner, 1993). But the content and length of sex education programs vary widely. Most programs continue to emphasize the biological aspects of puberty and reproduction (Haffner, 1993). Few focus on joint sexual activity, abortion, masturbation, sexual orientation, and other aspects of human sexual experience. Sexual pleasure is hardly ever mentioned. According to Deborah Haffner, Executive Director of SEICUS (Sex Education and Information Council of the U.S.), what is missing in sex education today is any discussion of sex. Fewer than 10 percent of young people receive comprehensive sex education, according to SEICUS.

Despite the increased number of sex education programs, peers apparently remain the major source of information (Papini et al., 1988; Thornburg & Aras, 1986). Sex education, however, does appear to be having an impact. A national survey of teenagers in the 1980s found that schools had become the primary source of information about reproduction (for one teen in two) and about birth control (for 37% of teens) (Coles & Stokes, 1985); see Table 13.1. Yet "friends" and "books/media" remained the primary source of information about topics like masturbation and sexual techniques. Few teens relied on their parents. All too often, parents and the schools relegate responsibility for the more value-laden subjects (such as birth control, homosexuality, and sexual techniques) to the street corner (Coles & Stokes, 1985).

TRUTH OR *FICTION?*
————————————
R E V I S I T E D

Most children learn the facts of life from parents or from school sex education programs. *Actually, most children learn many of the facts of life from peers or unguided reading. Is the lamp on the street corner the key guiding light for U.S. youth?* •

Sex education in the schools, especially about value-laden topics, remains a source of controversy. Some people argue that sex education ought to be left to parents and religious authorities. But the data suggest that the real alternatives to the schools are peers and the corner newsstand, which sells more copies of "adult" magazines than of textbooks. Many parents are also concerned that teaching such subjects as sexual techniques and contraception encourages sexual experimentation. Yet research has failed to demonstrate that exposure to sex education increases early sexual experimentation (Eisen & Zellman, 1987; Hayes, 1987).

TRUTH OR *FICTION?*
————————————
R E V I S I T E D

Sex education encourages sexual activity among children and adolescents. *Actually, researchers have not been able to find any evidence that sex education increases sexual activity among children and adolescents.* •

Many school programs that offer information about contraception and other sensitive topics are limited to high school juniors and seniors. Sexual experimentation often begins earlier, however. Most sexually active teens in Coles and Stokes's (1985) sample began engaging in intercourse by age 15. Fifty percent of the sexually active teenage boys, and 18 percent of the sexually active teenage girls, began by 13.

Accurate information in preadolescence might prevent various sexual mishaps (Coles & Stokes, 1985). Many teens, for example, erroneously believe that a female cannot get pregnant while standing up or from her first coital experience. Others believe that douching protects them from sexually transmitted diseases (STDs) or unwanted pregnancies.

398
CHAPTER 13   SEXUALITY IN CHILDHOOD AND ADOLESCENCE

TABLE 13.1 Primary source of information by topic (in percentages of respondents)

	School	Parents	Sex Partner	Friends	Books/ Media	Clinic/ Doctor	Sibling
Reproduction	50	23		15	9		2
Birth Control	37	17	1	17	20	4	4
Masturbation	21	12	1	32	30	1	3
Homosexuality	22	14	1	26	35		2
Sexual Techniques	14	9	17	26	32		2

Because of rounding, percentages may not total 100.
Source: From *Sex and the American Teenager* by R. Coles and G. Stokes. Copyright © 1985 by Rolling Stone Press. Reprinted by permission of HarperCollins Publishers.

ADOLESCENCE

Adolescence is bounded by the advent of puberty at the lower end and the capacity to take on adult responsibilities at the upper end. In our society adolescents are "neither fish nor fowl," as the saying goes—neither children nor adults. Adolescents may be able to reproduce and be taller than their parents, but they may not be allowed to get driver's licenses or attend R-rated films. They are prevented from working long hours and must usually stay in school until age 16. They cannot marry until they reach the age of "consent." The message is clear: Adults see adolescents as impulsive, and they must be restricted for "their own good." Given these restrictions, a sex drive heightened by surges of sex hormones, and media inundation with sexual themes, it is not surprising that many adolescents are in conflict with their families about "going around" with certain friends, sex, and using the family car.

PUBERTY

Puberty begins with the appearance of **secondary sex characteristics** and ends when the long bones make no further gains in length (see Table 13.2, pages 402–403). The appearance of strands of pubic hair are often the first visible signs of puberty. Pubic hair tends to be light colored, sparse, and straight at first. Then it spreads and grows darker, thicker, and coarser. Puberty also involves changes in **primary sex characteristics.** Once puberty begins, most major changes occur within three years in girls and within four years in boys (Rutter, 1980).

Toward the end of puberty, reproduction becomes possible. The two principal markers of reproductive potential are **menarche** in the girl and the first ejaculation in the boy. But these events do not generally herald immediate fertility.

Girls typically experience menarche between the ages of 10 and 18. In the mid-1800s, European girls typically achieved menarche by about age 17 (see Figure 13.1, page 400). The age of menarche has declined sharply since then among girls in Western nations, most likely because of improved nutrition and health care. In the United States, the average age of menarche by the 1960s and 1970s had dropped to between $12\frac{1}{2}$ and 13 (Chumlea, 1982). Why?

Puberty
The stage of development during which reproduction first becomes possible. Puberty begins with the appearance of *secondary sex characteristics* and ends when the long bones make no further gains in length. (From the Latin *puber,* meaning "of ripe age.")

Secondary sex characteristics
Physical characteristics that differentiate males and females and that usually appear at puberty but are not directly involved in reproduction, such as the bodily distribution of hair and fat, development of the muscle mass, or deepening of the voice.

Primary sex characteristics
Physical characteristics that differentiate males and females and are directly involved in reproduction, such as the sex organs.

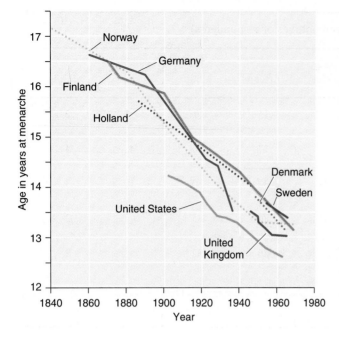

FIGURE 13.1 **The Decline in Age at Menarche.** The age at menarche has been declining since the mid-1800s among girls in Western nations, apparently because of improved nutrition and health care. Menarche may be triggered by the accumulation of a critical percentage of body fat.

Source: J. M. Tanner (1973). *Growth in Adolescence.* 2nd edition. Oxford: Blackwell Scientific Publications.

Menarche

The onset of menstruation; first menstruation. (From Greek roots meaning "month" [*men*] and "beginning" [*arche*].)

Anovulatory

Without ovulation.

One view is that a critical body weight (perhaps 103 to 109 pounds) triggers pubertal changes such as menarche, and children today do tend to achieve larger body sizes sooner (Frisch, 1974). Menarche may also be triggered by the accumulation of a certain percentage of body fat. This theory is supported by the finding that menarche comes later to girls who have a lower percentage of body fat, such as athletes (Frisch, 1983). Whatever the exact triggering mechanism, the average age at which girls experience menarche has leveled off in recent years.

PUBERTAL CHANGES IN THE FEMALE   First menstruation, or menarche, is the most obvious sign of puberty in girls. Yet other, less obvious changes have already taken place that have set the stage for menstruation. Sometime between 8 and 14 years of age, release of FSH by the pituitary gland causes the ovaries to begin to secrete estrogen. Estrogen has several major effects on pubertal development. For one, it stimulates the growth of breast tissue ("breast buds"), perhaps as early as age 8 or 9. The breasts usually begin to enlarge during the tenth year.

Estrogen also promotes the growth of the uterus and the thickening of the vaginal lining. It also stimulates growth of fatty and supporting tissue in the hips and buttocks. This tissue and the widening of the pelvis cause the hips to become rounded and permit childbearing. But growth of fatty deposits and connective tissue varies considerably. Some women may have pronounced breasts; others may have relatively large hips.

Small amounts of androgens produced by the female's adrenal glands, along with estrogen, stimulate development of pubic and underarm hair, beginning at about age 11. Excessive androgen production can darken or thicken facial hair.

Estrogen causes the labia to grow during puberty, but androgens cause the clitoris to develop. Estrogen stimulates growth of the vagina and uterus.

Estrogen typically brakes the female growth spurt some years before that of the male. Girls deficient in estrogen during their late teens may grow quite tall, but most tall girls reach their heights because of normal genetically determined variations, not estrogen deficiency.

Estrogen production becomes cyclical in puberty and regulates the menstrual cycle. Following menarche, a girl's early menstrual cycles are typically **anovulatory.** Girls cannot become pregnant until ovulation occurs, which may lag behind menarche by as much as two years. At first ovulation may not be reliable, so a girl may be relatively infertile. Some teenagers are highly fertile soon after menarche, however (Reinisch, 1990).

CHANGES IN THE MALE   At puberty the hypothalamus signals the pituitary to increase production of FSH and LH. These releasing hormones stimulate the testes to increase their output of testosterone. Testosterone prompts growth of the male genitals: the testes, scrotum, and penis. It fosters differentiation of male secondary sex characteristics: the growth of facial, body, and pubic hair, and the deepening of the voice. Testicle growth, in turn, accelerates testosterone production and pubertal changes. The testes continue to grow and the scrotal sac becomes larger and hangs loosely from the body. The penis widens and lengthens, and pubic hair appears.

By age 13 or 14, erections become frequent. Indeed, many junior high school boys dread that they may be caught between classes with erections, or asked to stand before the class. Under the influence of testosterone, the prostate and seminal vesicles—the organs that produce semen—increase in size and semen production begins. Boys typically experience their first ejaculation by age 13 or 14 (Thornburg & Aras, 1986), most often through masturbation (Kinsey et al., 1948). There is much variation, however. First ejaculations may occur as early as age 8 or not until the early twenties (Reinisch, 1990). Mature sperm are not usually found in the ejaculate until about a year after the first ejaculation, at age 14 on the average (Kulin et al., 1989). But sperm may be present in the first ejaculate (Reinisch, 1990), so pubertal boys should not assume that they have an infertile "grace period" following first ejaculation. About a year after first ejaculation, boys may also begin **nocturnal emissions,** which are also called "wet dreams" because of the belief that nocturnal emissions accompany erotic dreams—which need not be so.

Nocturnal emission
Involuntary ejaculation of seminal fluid while asleep. Also referred to as a "wet dream," although the individual need not be dreaming about sex, or dreaming at all.

Nocturnal emissions in boys accompany erotic dreams. *Despite the alias "wet dreams," nocturnal emissions in boys need not accompany erotic dreams.* •

Larynx
A structure of muscle and cartilage at the upper end of the trachea that contains the vocal cords; the voice box.

Underarm hair appears at about age 15. Facial hair is at first a fuzz on the upper lip. A beard does not appear for another two or three years. Only half of U.S. boys shave (of necessity) by age 17. The beard and chest hair continue to develop past the age of 20. At 14 or 15 the voice deepens because of the growth of the **larynx** and the lengthening of the vocal cords. Development is gradual, and the voices of adolescent boys sometimes crack embarrassingly.

Boys and girls undergo general growth spurts during puberty. Girls usually shoot up before boys. Individuals differ, however, and some boys spurt sooner than some girls.

Increases in muscle mass produce increases in weight. The shoulders and the circumference of the chest widen. At age 20 or 21, men stop growing taller because testosterone prevents the long bones from making further gains in length.

Puberty. Puberty marks the passage from childhood to young adulthood. Toward the end of puberty, reproduction becomes possible. Reproductive maturity, however, does not necessarily go hand-in-hand with responsible sexual decision-making.

Teaching Tip: Instead of lecturing about the physical and psychological changes associated with puberty, have students suggest what they would tell fifth or sixth graders. Encourage students to consider including information on specific body changes, average age of these changes, feelings, the wide range of "normal" development, and the problems experienced by early and late maturing boys and girls. Have students discuss what information they would *not* teach fifth and sixth graders.

TABLE 13.2 Stages of pubertal development

In Females	
Beginning sometime between ages 8 and 11	Pituitary hormones stimulate ovaries to increase production of estrogen. Internal reproductive organs begin to grow.
Beginning sometime between ages 9 and 15	First the areola (the darker area around the nipple) and then the breasts increase in size and become more rounded. Pubic hair becomes darker and coarser. Growth in height continues. Body fat continues to round body contours. A normal vaginal discharge becomes noticeable. Sweat and oil glands increase in activity, and acne may appear. Internal and external reproductive organs and genitals grow, which makes the vagina longer and the labia more pronounced.
Beginning sometime between ages 10 and 16	Areola and nipples grow, often forming a second mound sticking out from the rounded breast mound. Pubic hair begins to grow in a triangular shape and to cover the center of the mons. Underarm hair appears. Menarche occurs. Internal reproductive organs continue to develop. Ovaries may begin to release mature eggs capable of being fertilized. Growth in height slows.
Beginning sometime between ages 12 and 19	Breasts near adult size and shape. Pubic hair fully covers the mons and spreads to the top of the thighs. The voice may deepen slightly (but not as much as in males). Menstrual cycles gradually become more regular. Some further changes in body shape may occur into the young woman's early twenties.

Note: This table is a general guideline. Changes may normally appear sooner or later than shown, and not always in the indicated sequence.

Source: Copyright © 1990 by the Kinsey Institute for Research in Sex, Gender, and Reproduction. From *The Kinsey Institute New Report on Sex.* Reprinted with permission from St. Martin's Press, New York, NY.

Gynecomastia
Overdevelopment of a male's breasts. (From Greek roots meaning "woman" [*gyneco-*] and "breast" [*mastos*].)

Nearly one in two boys experiences temporary enlargement of the breasts, or **gynecomastia.** Gynecomastia probably stems from the small amount of female sex hormones secreted by the testes.

MASTURBATION

Learning Objective 7: Discuss the ages at which males and females typically begin masturbating to orgasm and the incidence of masturbation among teenagers.

Masturbation is a major sexual outlet during adolescence. Nearly all males and about two thirds of the females in the *Playboy* survey reported that they had masturbated to orgasm by the end of adolescence (Hunt, 1974). About half of the adolescent boys (46%) in Coles and Stokes's (1985) national survey of 1,067 teenagers, but only about a quarter of the girls (24%), reported masturbating. The average age at which teenagers in the Coles and Stokes survey reported they started to masturbate was 11 years 8 months.

A Southern California survey of 641 teenagers showed that boys who masturbate do so two to three times a week, on the average, as compared to about once a month for girls (Hass, 1979). Researchers find no links between adolescent masturbation and early sexual activity (for example, frequency of intercourse, number of different partners, age upon first intercourse) and sexual adjustment during young adulthood (Leitenberg et al., 1993).

Many teens still think of masturbation as shameful (Coles & Stokes, 1985). Only about one in three (31%) of the teens surveyed by Coles and Stokes reported feeling

Beginning sometime between ages 9 and 15	Testicles begin to grow. Skin of the scrotum becomes redder and coarser. A few straight pubic hairs appear at the base of the penis. Muscle mass develops and boy begins to grow taller. The areola grows larger and darker.
Beginning sometime between ages 11 and 16	The penis begins to grow longer. The testicles and scrotum continue to grow. Pubic hair becomes coarser, more curled, and spreads to cover the area between the legs. The body gains in height. The shoulders broaden. The hips narrow. The larynx enlarges, resulting in a deepening of the voice. Sparse facial and underarm hair appears.
Beginning sometime between ages 11 and 17	The penis begins to increase in circumference as well as in length (though more slowly). The testicles continue to increase in size. The texture of the pubic hair is more like an adult's. Growth of facial and underarm hair increases. Shaving may begin. First ejaculation occurs. In nearly half of all boys, gynecomastia (breast enlargement) occurs, which then decreases in a year or two. Increased skin oils may produce acne.
Beginning sometime between ages 14 and 18	The body nears final adult height and the genitals achieve adult shape and size, with pubic hair spreading to the thighs and slightly upward toward the belly. Chest hair appears. Facial hair reaches full growth. Shaving becomes more frequent. For some young men, further increases in height, body hair, and muscle growth and strength continue into their early twenties.

Teaching Tip: Acquire at least five or six books about the physical changes associated with puberty that have a reading level appropriate for children ages eight to twelve. Pass these around the class. Ask students if they knew what to expect at puberty. Ask those who didn't if they wish they had known.

completely free of guilt over masturbation. One in five felt a "large amount" or "a great deal" of guilt. The others felt a "small" or "medium" amount of guilt.

HETEROSEXUAL BEHAVIOR

Young people today start dating and "going steady" earlier than in past generations. These changes have implications for teenage pregnancy. Teens who date earlier (by age 14) are more likely to engage in premarital sex before the end of high school (Miller et al., 1986). Teens who initiate sexual intercourse earlier are also less likely to use contraception and more likely to incur an unwanted pregnancy. If the young woman decides to keep her baby, she is also more likely to have to leave school and scuttle educational and vocational plans (Furstenberg, 1976). Early dating does not always lead to early coitus, however. Nor does early coitus always lead to unwanted pregnancies (Berger, 1988). Still, some young women find their options in adulthood restricted by a chain of events that began in early adolescence (Berger, 1988).

PETTING   Many adolescents use petting to express affection, satisfy their curiosities, heighten their sexual arousal, and reach orgasm while avoiding pregnancy and maintaining virginity.

Menarche in Cross-Cultural Perspective

I'll never forget seventh grade when it seemed all my friends were menstruating but me. At first I was thinking of coming to school one day and telling them I had gotten my first period but I was afraid that they'd know I was lying so I didn't. Pretty soon no one talked about it much so by the time I did get my first period no one really cared—except my mother who told me I was now a woman.

I began menstruating when I was twelve. I remember feeling great ambivalence about it. I was a little frightened by the blood, and resented having to wear a "diaper." I was sure everyone would be able to tell I had a belt and pad on! On the other hand, I was excited to know that I could become pregnant—that I had become a woman.

My mother showed me how to roll up and wrap a used sanitary napkin in Kleenex. I really did it perfectly my first try and went out to show my mother, who had company in the living room. They giggled; though I got no negative messages about it, I felt embarrassed.

(Morrison et al., 1980, pp. 70–73)

These recollections of college women reflect common attitudes toward menstruation. Some pubescent girls see it as a sign of "becoming a woman." They anxiously await menarche. They compete with friends to see who will be first to arrive on the doorstep of adulthood. The second quote shows that many people mistakenly believe that menstruation signals reproductive capacity. Yet such capacity may lag behind menarche by more than a year.

Girls tend to be more likely to share news of first menstruation with friends than boys are to tell other boys of their first ejaculation (Brooks-Gunn et al., 1986; Gaddis & Brooks-Gunn, 1985). Menstruation is perceived as a biological event that signals a passage to womanhood. Ejaculation is perceived as a sexual event, however. Boys may also feel embarrassed to disclose the experience to friends because it typically occurs during masturbation.

In different times, in different places, menarche has had different meanings. The Thais view menarche as transforming a girl into a complete woman (Gardiner & Gardiner, 1991). The Kurtatchi, who live on an island off the green coast of New Guinea, greet menarche with an elaborate ceremony (Matlin, 1987). The girl's mother announces the event to friends and relatives, who go into seclusion with the girl. They paint their bodies in preparation for public ceremonies. The girl and her entourage emerge from seclusion, perform a dance, and blow on a conch shell. The girl parades among the rejoicing villagers. Then there is a feast.

Among Hindu families in India, the onset of menstruation signifies the loss of the girl's purity (Kumar, 1991). During menstruation, she is expected to abstain from cooking food for the family or participating in religious ceremonies. A menstruating girl may be expected to cease daily activities and spend time alone in her room, a practice of isolation that may continue even into her marriage.

The *Playboy* survey found petting nearly universal among adolescents in the 1970s (Hunt, 1974). Nor has petting gone out of fashion among today's teens. An overwhelming majority (97%) of teenagers sampled in a 1980s survey had engaged in kissing (a form of light petting) by the age of 15 (Coles & Stokes, 1985). Girls tended to engage in kissing earlier than boys, perhaps because girls tend to mature faster. By age 13, 73 percent of the girls and 66 percent of the boys had engaged in kissing.

TRUTH OR FICTION?
REVISITED

Petting is practically universal among adolescents in the United States.
Petting does turn out to be practically universal among U.S. adolescents. •

ORAL SEX   The incidence of premarital oral sex has increased two- or threefold since Kinsey's time. In the 1980s, about four in ten (41%) of the 17- and 18-year-old girls in the Coles and Stokes (1985) survey reported that they had performed fellatio. About a third of the boys reported performing cunnilingus. Many girls reported they had engaged in fellatio more for their partners' pleasure than their own.

A 1982 survey of 16-year-old high school students revealed even higher rates of oral sex (Newcomer & Udry, 1985). Fifty-three percent of the 256 boys sampled and 42 percent of the 289 girls reported engaging in oral sex. More students had engaged in oral sex than in coitus. Some couples maintain a kind of *technical virginity* by substituting oral sex for intercourse (Gagnon & Simon, 1987). This seems to represent a reversal of the traditional *sexual script* in which couples would not begin engaging in oral sex, if at all, until some point after they had begun having intercourse.

Some adolescent couples engage in oral sex, but not coitus, as a mode of birth control. As one 17-year-old New York girl put it, "That's what we used to do before we could start having sex, because we didn't have protection and stuff" (Coles & Stokes, 1985, p. 60).

Learning Objective 8: Cite the average age of first intercourse, the incidence of premarital intercourse, and the motives and factors that influence when teens will engage in intercourse.

PREMARITAL INTERCOURSE   Today, more than half of our teenagers are having sex (Haffner, 1993). Many young people feel as if they are caught betwixt and between. On the one hand, adults tell them to wait until they're older, to "just say no." On the other hand, the movies and television programs they see, and the stories they hear from their peers, reinforce the belief that everybody's "doing it."

The incidence of premarital intercourse, especially for females, has increased dramatically since Kinsey's day. In Kinsey's time, the sexual double standard held firm. Women were expected to remain virgins until marriage, but society looked the other way for men. Not surprisingly, Kinsey and his colleagues found a much greater incidence of premarital coitus among men. By the age of 20, 77 percent of the single men but only 20 percent of the single women reported that they had engaged in premarital coitus. Of those still single by age 25, the figures rose to 83 percent for men but only 33 percent for women. The discrepancy between the genders is partly explained by the fact that men were often sexually initiated by prostitutes (Hunt, 1974). By the time of the *Playboy* survey in the early 1970s (Hunt, 1974), 95 percent of the men and 81 percent of the women in the 18- to 24-year-old category reported that they had engaged in premarital intercourse—a striking increase among young women since Kinsey's day. Increased rates of premarital coitus among young women should not be confused with sexual promiscuity, however. Kinsey found that 53 percent of the females who had engaged in premarital coitus had done so with one partner only (Kinsey et al., 1953). The 1970s *Playboy* survey, conducted during the heyday of the sexual revolution, found virtually the same percentage (54%) (Hunt, 1974).

Discussion Question: Do statistics about the age of first intercourse match your perceptions of your peers' behavior? At what age did your peers begin having intercourse? Do you believe your peers were usually truthful about their sexual experiences?

Sexual activity among adolescents in the United States has increased since the 1970s (Centers for Disease Control, 1991f). Surveys in the early 1970s found that about half (46 to 57% across studies) of the women sampled had engaged in premarital sex by the age of 19 (Kantner & Zelnik, 1972; Sorensen, 1973), compared to fewer than 20 percent in Kinsey's day. By 1979, 65 percent—nearly two out of three—young, never-married women 19 years of age who lived in metropolitan U.S. areas had engaged in sexual intercourse (Zeman, 1990) (see Table 13.3, page 406). By 1988, among 19-year-old, never-married adolescents living in metropolitan U.S. areas, 78 percent of the girls and 86 percent of boys had initiated sexual intercourse (Zeman, 1990).

Premarital sex has become the norm in our society. The Janus and Janus nationwide sample taken during the late 1980s and early 1990s found that even among adults today who identify themselves as very religious, seven in ten reported having had premarital sexual experiences (Janus & Janus, 1993). Young people today are also initiating sexual intercourse at younger ages. Kinsey found that 7 percent of white females had engaged in intercourse by the age of 16. By 1979, 22 percent of 15-year-old girls in U.S. metropolitan areas had engaged in coitus, with the figure rising to 27 percent by 1988 (Zeman, 1990). By 1988, about one in three 15-year-old boys also reported coital experiences (Zeman,

TABLE 13.3 Percentages of adolescent boys and girls in metropolitan U.S. areas who engaged in sexual intercourse, 1979 vs. 1988

	Boys		Girls	
Age	1979	1988	1979	1988
15	n/a	33	22	27
16	n/a	50	27	34
17	56	66	47	52
18	66	72	54	70
19	78	86	65	78

Source:Newsweek, 1990. Reprinted with permission. Source of data for girls: National Survey of Family Growth; for boys: Urban Institute.

1990). Today, the average age of first intercourse among girls in the United States is 16; for boys, 15.5 (U.S. Department of Health and Human Services, 1990c).

Although teenage sexual activity has increased nationwide, sexual activity appears to have declined in the 1980s among college women on some campuses, perhaps in response to mounting fears of AIDS and increased conservatism. For example, 37 percent of college women at one university who were surveyed during the early 1980s reported they were sexually active, as compared to about 50 percent of the women surveyed five years earlier (Gerrard, 1987).

In sum, the incidence of premarital sex has increased since Kinsey's day, dramatically so among females. Rates of premarital sex among young men have traditionally been higher, but the gender gap has narrowed considerably.

MOTIVES FOR INTERCOURSE   Premarital intercourse is motivated by a number of factors. Sex hormones, especially testosterone, activate sexual arousal. Thus the pubertal surge of hormones directly activates sexual arousal, at least among boys (Brooks-Gunn & Furstenberg, 1989). Hormonal changes may also have indirect effects on sexual experimentation (Brooks-Gunn & Furstenberg, 1989). Hormonal changes stoke the development of secondary sex characteristics. Adolescents whose secondary sex characteristics develop early may begin dating earlier, which may increase the likelihood of progressing toward sexual intercourse at an earlier age. Some early maturers may be pressured into dating or sex—psychologically ready or not.

For some adolescents, sexual intercourse is perceived as the natural outgrowth of love, or as expressed by Betsy, of the belief that one is in love:

> I was seventeen when I had my first sexual experience. I had been going out with my boyfriend for about five months, during which time he had been continually pressuring me to have sex. He made it seem as though I had to comply or he would end the relationship. Because I was deeply in love with him (or so I thought), I allowed it to happen.
>
> (Copyright © 1991 by McIntyre, Formichella, Osterhout, and Gresh by arrangement with AVON BOOKS, p. 64)

Adolescents may consider intercourse a sign of maturity, a way for girls to reward a boyfriend for remaining loyal, or a means of punishing parents. Some adolescents engage in coitus in response to peer pressure, especially from close friends. Adolescents whose friends have engaged in sexual intercourse are more likely to engage in intercourse themselves (Sack et al., 1984). Coles and Stokes (1985) found that for 78 percent of the virgins in their national sample, few if any of their friends had engaged in intercourse; this was true of only 28 percent of the nonvirgins.

Notes: For parents who hope their children's attitudes toward sex will be similar to their own, open communication about sex may increase the likelihood. In one study of twenty-two 12- to 14-year-olds and their parents, the correlation between the parents' and children's sexual attitudes was significantly higher in the families that communicated more openly about sex. [Fisher, T. 1986. Parent-child communication about sex and young adolescents' sexual knowledge and attitudes. *Adolescence, 21*(83).]

Sometimes the pressure comes from dating partners:

MEGAN (18, California): I have felt pressure before. My first boyfriend pressured me because he knew I loved him and that he could take advantage of my feelings. I was blinded by my feelings and I had sex with him. I hated it.

AMY (18, Washington, D.C.): I was sexually pressured by my second boyfriend. He didn't love me, but he did want to have sex. I helped him sneak into my room in the middle of the night. Just before we were about to have sex, I realized that it wasn't something I wanted to do. I wanted my first time to be with someone I loved and who loved me. I stopped him, although he tried everything to get me to say yes. The next day we broke up, and I couldn't have been happier.

MATT (18, New York): My girlfriend pressured me and I didn't handle it very well. I submitted so she wouldn't be mad or disappointed.

FACTORS IN PREMARITAL INTERCOURSE Researchers find that many young people who abstain from premarital coitus do so for religious or moral reasons (Coles & Stokes, 1985; Miller & Bingham, 1989). Family influences and religious values are important determinates of adolescent sexual experience (White & DeBlassie, 1992). Other reasons include fear of being caught, of pregnancy, or of disease.

A study of 142 low-income, African-American adolescent females (ages 13–18) at an inner-city health clinic in Dallas found that girls who were not sexually active, about one in three, tended to be younger and more career oriented, to have a father at home, to hold more conservative values about sexuality, and to be more influenced by family values, than were the sexually active girls (Keith et al., 1991).

Teens who have higher educational goals and do better in school are less likely to engage in coitus than less academically oriented teens (Brooks-Gunn & Furstenberg, 1989; Hofferth & Hayes, 1987). The causal connection between school performance and premarital sex is difficult to discern, because adolescents who do well in school are also more likely to come from better functioning families.

Not surprisingly, older teens are more likely than younger ones to engage in premarital intercourse (Miller & Bingham, 1989). The likelihood of premarital intercourse is also linked to early dating, especially early steady dating (Brooks-Gunn & Furstenberg, 1989; Miller et al., 1986). Adolescents who begin dating earlier may be more likely to progress through stages of petting to coitus.

Other researchers focus on relationships between family factors and premarital intercourse. Children whose parents are separated or divorced are more likely than those from intact homes to engage in premarital intercourse (Coles & Stokes, 1985). Perhaps parents who have "failed" in their marital relationships lack credibility in advising their adolescent children (Coles & Stokes, 1985). Perhaps divorced mothers communicate more permissive attitudes than married mothers (Thornton & Camburn, 1987). Single parents, because of time constraints, may also be less capable of supervising their children (Newcomer & Udry, 1987). So teenagers from single-parent homes may have greater opportunities for privacy, especially when the parent is employed outside the home (Coles & Stokes, 1985). Moreover, a teenager may interpret a single parent's becoming sexually active with dates as tacit approval of premarital sex.

The quality of the relationship between teens and their parents may also be important (Brooks-Gunn & Furstenberg, 1989). Teens who feel that they can talk to their parents are less likely to engage in coitus than those who describe communication with their parents as poor (Inazu & Fox, 1980; Jessor & Jessor, 1977).

Adolescents whose parents are very permissive and impose very few rules and restrictions are also more likely to engage in premarital intercourse (Hogan & Kitigawa, 1985; Miller et al., 1986). Parents who show an interest in their children's behavior and communicate their concerns and expectations with understanding and respect may best influence their children to show sexual restraint.

Notes: Although religious young women are more likely to postpone first intercourse, they are less likely to use a prescription method of contraception if they do have sex. (Studer, M., and Thornton, A. 1987. Adolescent religiosity and contraceptive usage. *Journal of Marriage and the Family, 49,* 117–128.)

Ethnic Differences in Premarital Intercourse, Adolescent Use of Contraception, and Resolution of Unwanted Pregnancies

Trends toward early intercourse are found among many ethnic groups in the United States. Wyatt's (1988a, 1988b) samples of white and African-American women in the Los Angeles area in the 1980s, for example, showed that first intercourse for both groups had occurred at an earlier age than was the case with Kinsey's samples. Virtually all (98%) of the women in Wyatt's samples (Wyatt, 1988a, 1988b, 1989), both African American and white, reported that they had engaged in premarital coitus by the age of 20. A 1988 national probability sample of 18- to 19-year old women in the United States also showed a relatively high percentage of women of both races (74% among whites, 78% among blacks) reporting having engaged in sexual intercourse (Forrest & Singh, 1990).

As compared to white teens, African-American teens tend to begin coitus about two years earlier, on the average, and are more likely in dating relationships to progress directly from light petting to intercourse (Brooks-Gunn & Furstenburg, 1989). Earlier initiation to coitus and more rapid progression from petting to intercourse may place African-American females at greater risk of unwanted pregnancies (Brooks-Gunn & Furstenberg, 1989; Smith & Udry, 1985).

A review of the available research on ethnicity and sexual behavior in college students shows Asian-American and Hispanic-American students to be somewhat more conservative sexually than their African-American or (non-Hispanic) White American counterparts

(Baldwin et al., 1992; Padilla & O'Grady, 1987). A recent survey of 114 Chinese-American students attending the University of California at Berkeley showed that more than 60 percent approved of premarital intercourse for couples who are in love or engaged to be married (Huang & Uba, 1992). Four in ten reported engaging in premarital intercourse themselves. By contrast, a much lower proportion (fewer than one in ten) of the respondents in a recent survey of Chinese students in Hong Kong reported having premarital intercourse (Chan, 1990). The experience of living in a sexually permissive culture like the United States seems to have had a somewhat liberalizing influence on the sexual behavior and attitudes of young Chinese Americans. Lending support to this interpretation is the finding from the Berkeley survey that level of acculturation to U.S. society was associated with both greater sexual experience and more permissive attitudes. Still, the prevalence of premarital sex among Asian-American students, including the Chinese-American students in the Berkeley sample, is low by comparison with the general U.S. college population.

There are also informative ethnic group differences in the use of contraception. Hispanic-American adolescents, for example, are less likely than non-Hispanics to use contraception (Darabi et al., 1986). Horowitz (1983) attributes the low rate of use of contraceptives by Hispanic-American teens not to lack of knowledge about birth control, but to conflict between

sexual activity and the conservative sexual values with which they are reared. The use of contraception may be a nagging reminder that one's sexual behavior is inconsistent with one's sexual values. A survey of Mexican-American and Anglo undergraduates at a southern California state university with a large Mexican-American enrollment found that Mexican-American students were more conservative and traditional in their sexual attitudes and reported less sexual experience than their Anglo counterparts (Padilla & O'Grady, 1987). Another researcher reports that Mexican-American women tend to delay first intercourse in comparison to non-Hispanic White women (Slonim-Nevo, 1992).Yet other research shows that the more often Hispanic-American adolescent females engage in intercourse, the more likely they are to use effective contraception (Durant et al., 1990). Perhaps it becomes more difficult to maintain a veneer of denial of sexual activity as the young woman becomes more sexually active.

The survey by Padilla and O'Grady (1987) also revealed that Mexican-American students held more conservative attitudes than Anglo students concerning masturbation, abortion, and premarital and extramarital relationships. Mexican-American students less frequently engaged in sexual intercourse, had fewer coital partners, and reported masturbating less often than their Anglo counterparts. They also identified more strongly than Anglo students with a traditional Judeo-Christian value system. The Padilla and O'Grady survey

Learning Objective 9: Discuss
ethnic and cross-cultural differences in premarital intercourse,
use of contraception, teenage
pregnancy, and resolution
of unwanted pregnancies.

CNN Israel, Pizza, and Sex

was based on one college sample of 165 Mexican-American students (86 male, 79 female) and 99 Anglo students (47 male, 52 female). They may not represent the Mexican-American community at large.

A longitudinal study in Houston, Texas, sheds light on some ethnic differences in the resolution of teenage pregnancies (Buchanan & Robbins, 1990). The data shown in Table 13.4 are based on a sample of more than 2,000 males from the Houston school district who were first evaluated in seventh grade and then ten years later. By age 21, rates of adolescent pregnancies among the sexual partners of these young men were greater among African Americans (24%) than white (12%) or Hispanic Americans (16%).

Abortions were more often used as a means for resolving adolescent pregnancies among whites in this sample than among African Americans or Hispanic Americans. Among African Americans and Hispanic Americans, adolescent pregnancies were more often carried to term, with a greater percentage of adolescent fathers among the Hispanics either marrying or living with the mothers.

The problem of teen pregnancy cuts across all ethnic, religious and socioeconomic groupings and has become a major social problem in our society. Although most everyone agrees with the need to prevent teens from becoming pregnant, how to accomplish this goal has become the subject of a major national debate, as we will see later in the chapter.

Ethnic Differences in Use of Contraception. Researchers find ethnic differences in contraceptive use among sexually active adolescents. How might cultural factors explain variations in use of contraceptives?

TABLE 13.4 Consequences for males of adolescent pregnancy and its resolution, by racial/ethnic group (in percentages)

	Those whose partners experienced pregnancy by age 21	Those whose partners had abortions	Those whose partners had the child; couple did not marry or cohabit	Those whose partners had the child; couple married or cohabited
African American (N = 627)	24	16	56	28
White (N = 1666)	12	58	8.	34
Hispanic American (N = 240)	16	29	16	55
Total (N = 2533)	15	38	28	34

Source: Adapted from Buchanan & Robbins (1990). Early adult psychological consequences for males of adolescent pregnancy and its resolution. *Journal of Youth and Adolescence, 19,* 413–424. Reprinted with permission from Plenum Publishing.

The First Time

MARK: As we had no place to go, we went out into the woods with several blankets and made love. It was like something out of a Woody Allen movie. I couldn't get my pants off because I was shaking from nerves and from the cold. The nerves and cold made it all but impossible for me to get an erection and then after I had and we made love I couldn't find the car keys.

AMY: My first sexual experience occurred after the Junior Prom in high school in a car at the drive-in. We were both virgins, very uncertain, but very much in love. We had been going together since eighth grade. The experience was somewhat painful. I remember wondering if I would look different to my mother the next day. I guess I didn't because nothing was said.

(Morrison et al., 1980, p. 608)

There is always a first time. Given the inexperience and awkwardness of at least one member of the couple, and frequent feelings of guilt and fear, it is not surprising that most people, like Mark and Amy, don't get it quite right the first time. Adolescent boys and girls often report different concerns about first intercourse. The girl is more likely to be concerned about whether she is doing the right thing. The boy is more likely to be concerned about whether he is doing the

thing right (Children's Defense Fund, 1988). Women are more likely than men to be physically and psychologically disappointed with the experience and to feel guilty afterwards (Darling et al., 1992). One study of 300 sexually experienced college students found that only 28 percent of the women considered their first encounter physically or psychologically satisfying. Yet 81 percent of college men were physically satisfied, and 67 percent were psychologically satisfied (Darling & Davidson, 1986).

Negative attitudes among women toward their first coital experience may have cultural roots. A recent cross-cultural comparison between American and Swedish women showed that American women reported more negative emotional experiences to their first premarital coitus than did Swedish women (Schwartz, 1993). Sweden has more permissive sexual attitudes than the United States has.

Negative emotional consequences of first intercourse may more closely reflect cultural norms or standards than the act itself. Perhaps this explains why women raised in a more sexually restrictive culture, like the United States, were more likely to experience negative emotional reactions such as guilt, fear, and anxiety than their Swedish counter-

parts who were raised in a society that is more tolerant of sexual experimentation, especially for women. Then again, perhaps the young men of Sweden were more responsive to their partners' needs.

Coles and Stokes (1985) found that most adolescent boys (60%) reported feeling "glad" after their first intercourse (see Table 13.5). Most adolescent girls (61%) expressed ambivalence. One in ten girls (11%) reported feeling "sorry," as compared to only 1 percent of boys. Some females have guilt or remorse over losing their virginity. Others find first intercourse painful or uncomfortable, in part because of the tearing of the hymen, in part because penetration may have been rushed or forced. For one 15-year-old New York girl, the pain was more than she had anticipated:

[I] wasn't expecting it to hurt that much. It was like total pain. Even after the first minutes of pain, it's still like you're too sore to enjoy anything. I didn't expect that at all.

(Coles & Stokes, 1985, p. 74)

Yet for some, the quality of the relationship tempered pain:

We were both so excited. We hadn't been able to sleep the night before. I can't remember that much leading up to it, but we had sex a few times—I guess

TEENAGERS' VALUES AND THE SEXUAL DOUBLE STANDARD Do young people today subscribe to the traditional double standard that allows greater sexual freedom for men than for women? It may be premature to drive the nails into the coffin of the sexual double standard, but a common standard for judging acceptability of premarital sex may be emerging. A study of 666 undergraduate students in a Midwestern university showed no evidence of the double standard; students were not differently disposed toward the acceptability of premarital sex for one gender or the other (Sprecher, 1989b).

about three times—that night. He really enjoyed it; I found it emotionally nice, but painful. It was like a *good* hurt, but still it hurt; it was uncomfortable. But it was something we both felt really good about.

(Coles & Stokes, 1985, p. 74)

Young women are more likely to find their first coital experience satisfying when their partners are loving, gentle, and considerate (Weiss, 1983).

Women in Wyatt's (1988a, 1988b) sample began having intercourse at younger ages than those in Kinsey's. Living in more liberated times, those in Wyatt's sample were relatively less committed to their first partners, but still tended to have more positive reactions than Kinsey's sample. Fifty-nine percent of the white women in Wyatt's sample and 42 percent of the African-American women reaped at least some enjoyment from their first intercourse, as compared to 40 percent of the white and 14 percent of the African-American women in Kinsey's sample.

First intercourse is often awkward, even fumbling. The partners are still learning about their own sexual responses and how to please each other:

KAREN (23, New York): I had sexual intercourse for the first time at age 18. My boyfriend

and I had been going out for a year. For several months before we had intercourse we engaged in a lot of petting but not much genital contact. I was the more aggressive partner and I was the one who suggested we have intercourse. It was very awkward; the first time we tried, he couldn't get in.

(Copyright © 1991 by McIntyre, Formichella, Osterhout, and Gresh by arrangement with AVON BOOKS, pp. 50–51)

Let us note some gender differences in choice of first partners. For first-time intercourse, evidence from student surveys shows that females are more likely than males to have been involved in a committed relationship with their partners (Darling et al., 1992). In Zelnik and Shah's (1983) sample, about two of three of the women

reported that their first partner was someone they were "going steady with" or "engaged to." Only half as many men were going steady with or engaged to their first partner. Males were much more likely (43% versus 11% for women) to say that their first partner was "just a friend" or someone they had "just met." Coles and Stokes (1985) report that more teenage males (32%) than females (13%) described their first partners as "just friends." These gender differences may reflect the traditional double standard that accords greater sexual freedom to men. Men are expected to "sow their wild oats" with casual partners. Women are expected to save themselves for a man with whom they share strong emotional ties and an enduring relationship.

TABLE 13.5 Feelings about first intercourse (percentage)

	Sorry	Ambivalent	Glad	No Feelings
Males	1	34	60	5
Females	11	61	23	4

Source: From *Sex and the American Teenager* by R. Coles and G. Stokes. Copyright © 1985 by Rolling Stone Press. Reprinted by permission of HarperCollins Publishers.

According to the Coles and Stokes (1985) national survey, teenagers express only slightly more approval of casual sex for boys than for girls.

TEENAGE PREGNANCY   More than one million teenage girls in the United States become pregnant each year (Alan Guttmacher Institute, 1991). This amounts to one in every 10 girls between the ages of 15 and 19, and one in five sexually active girls. Nearly 40 percent of teenage pregnancies, or nearly 400,000 annually, end in abortion. Although

A WORLD OF DIVERSITY

Rates of Teenage Pregnancy at Home and Abroad

Although overall rates of teenage pregnancy have been increasing in the United States, there are interesting ethnic and social class differences. Rates of teenage pregnancy are more prevalent among women of color, women from lower socio-economic classes, and urbanites (Hechtman, 1989). Poverty is an especially strong predictor of teenage pregnancy (Jencks & Mayer, 1990). African-American and Hispanic-American teenagers, many of whom are poor, are twice as likely as whites to become pregnant (Alan Guttmacher Institute, 1991). African-American girls have the highest birth rate overall. Yet the Hispanic teenage pregnancy rate is growing faster than all other ethnic and racial groups, including African Americans (Shapiro,

1992). Non-Hispanic white teenage pregnancy rates have also risen in the past decade, but at a slower rate than either African-American or Hispanic teens.

The rate of teenage pregnancy in the United States is more than double the rates in Canada, France, Great Britain, and Sweden, and more than five times greater than the rates in the Netherlands (Jones, 1985). Adolescent females in the United States, however, are no more likely to engage in sexual intercourse than adolescents in these other countries. What, then, might account for the two- to fivefold greater number of teenage pregnancies in the United States?

Several factors appear to account for these international

differences (Jones, 1985; Wallace & Vienonen, 1989). First, fewer U.S. teenagers have access to family-planning services that provide contraceptives at low or no cost. Second, U.S. teenagers who use contraception are much less likely to use birth-control pills, one of the most effective forms of contraception. Third, the other countries, except for Canada, provide more extensive community- and school-based sex education programs. Other factors, too, may be involved. For example, young men in these other countries tend to accept somewhat more responsibility for birth control than do their American counterparts (Hess et al., 1993).

Discussion Question: Is there a double standard about premarital sex among your friends? Was there a double standard when you were in high school? What evidence can you cite for your answer? How have attitudes changed since you were sixteen?

some of the remainder of these pregnancies result in miscarriages, nearly 500,000 produce live births (Kantrowitz, 1990a). Rates of teenage pregnancy have been increasing and have reached a higher level than at any time since the early 1970s (National Research Council, 1993). The proportion of out-of-wedlock births among teenagers also shot up during the 1970s and 1980s. Among young women 15 to 17 years of age in the period 1985–1989, 81 percent of births occurred out of wedlock, as compared to 41 percent in 1965–1969 and 59 percent in 1975–1979 (Pear, 1991). Two of three teenage mothers today are unmarried, as compared to 15 percent in 1960. Among African-American teenage mothers, 92 percent are unmarried (National Research Council, 1993).

Some pregnant teenagers planned their pregnancies, but the great majority did not. Nine in ten pregnancies among unmarried teenagers were unplanned (Alan Guttmacher Institute, 1991).

TRUTH OR FICTION?

R E V I S I T E D

More than one million adolescent girls in the United States become pregnant each year. *It is true that there are more than one million adolescent pregnancies in the United States each year. Nearly 40 percent of them end in abortion.* •

The consequences of unplanned teenage pregnancies can be devastating to mothers, their children, and to society as a whole. Even young people themselves perceive teenage

TABLE 13.6 Type of birth control used by sexually active teenagers (percentages)

	Rhythm	Withdrawal	Condom	The Pill	Diaphragm	Foam	IUD
First Time	3	18	62	11	3	1	0
Most Recent Time	4	17	54	45	4	4	2

Source: From *Sex and the American Teenager* by R. Coles and G. Stokes. Copyright © 1985 by Rolling Stone Press. Reprinted by permission of HarperCollins Publishers.

Learning Objective 11: Discuss the issues surrounding teen pregnancy, including the impact on the teenage mother's life, the impact on the children of teenage mothers, and the role of teen fathers.

parenthood to be disastrous (Moore & Stief, 1992). Teenage mothers are more likely to live in poverty and to receive welfare than their peers (Grogger & Bronars, 1993). Half of teenage mothers quit school and go on public assistance (Kantrowitz, 1990a). Few receive consistent emotional or financial help from the fathers, who generally cannot support themselves, much less a family. Working teenage mothers earn just half as much as those who give birth in their twenties (National Research Council, 1993). Barely able to cope with one baby, many young mothers who give birth at age 15 or 16 have at least one more baby by the time they are 20. Among teenage girls who become pregnant, nearly one in five will become pregnant again within a year. More than 31 percent will have a repeat pregnancy within two years (Alan Guttmacher Institute, 1991). Undereducated, unskilled, and overburdened, these young mothers face a constant uphill struggle.

Medical complications associated with teenage childbearing are highest of any group of fertile women except for those in their late forties (Hess et al., 1993). In addition to high rates of miscarriage and stillbirths, children born to teenagers are at greater risk of prematurity, birth complications, and infant mortality (Honig, 1978; Mencken,

Teenage Pregnancy. More than 1 million teenage girls in the United States become pregnant each year. What are the costs of teenage pregnancy—to the girls themselves, to their children, and to society at large?

1972). These problems are largely the result of inadequate prenatal care, not the age of the mother. Children of pregnant teenagers who receive adequate prenatal care seem to be at no greater risk of these problems than those of older women (Martinson, 1985; Trussell, 1988).

Children of teenage mothers are at greater risk of physical, emotional, and intellectual problems in their preschool years, due to poor nutrition and health care, family instability, and inadequate parenting (Broman, 1981; Furstenberg et al., 1987, 1989; Hechtman, 1989; Trussell, 1988). They are more aggressive and impulsive as preschoolers than are children of older mothers (Furstenberg et al., 1989). They do more poorly in school. They are also more likely to suffer maternal abuse or neglect (Felsman et al., 1987; Kinard & Reinherz, 1987).

A number of factors have contributed to the increase in teenage pregnancy, including a loosening of traditional taboos on adolescent sexuality (Hechtman, 1989). Impaired family relationships, problems in school, emotional problems, misunderstandings about reproduction or contraception, and lack of contraception also play roles (Hechtman, 1989). Some adolescent girls believe that a baby will elicit a commitment from their partners, or fill an emotional void. Some become pregnant as a way of rebelling against parents. Some poor teenagers view early childbearing as the best of the severely limited options they perceive for their futures. But the largest number become pregnant because of misunderstandings about reproduction and contraception or miscalculations about the odds of conception. Even many who are relatively well informed about contraception fail to use it consistently (Hechtman, 1989).

More attention has been focused on teenage mothers, but young fathers bear an equal responsibility for teenage pregnancies. A survey based on a nationally representative sample of 1,880 young men ages 15 through 19 showed that socioeconomically disadvantaged young men in particular appeared to view paternity as a source of self-esteem and were consequently more likely than more affluent young men to say that fathering a child would make them feel like a real man and that they would be pleased, or at least not as upset, with an unplanned pregnancy (Marsiglio, 1993a). Consistent with these attitudes, young men living in poorer conditions were less likely to have used an effective contraceptive method during their last sexual experience.

Teenage fathers are more likely to have problems in school—both behavioral and academic—and to hold more pessimistic attitudes toward the future than their peers (Hanson et al., 1989). Steady dating also increased the risk of teenage fatherhood.

CONTRACEPTIVE USE AMONG SEXUALLY ACTIVE TEENS   Sexually active teenagers use contraception inconsistently, if at all (Bachrach, 1984; Furstenberg, 1984). Contraception is most likely to be used by teens in stable, monogamous relationships (Baker et al., 1988). Even teens in monogamous relationships tend to use ineffective methods of contraception or to use effective methods inconsistently, however (Polit-

Discussion Question:
During a recent television interview, Senator Daniel Patrick Moynihan (D-New York) said that never before in history has a society had as high a percentage of its babies born to and raised by single women. What impact do you think this will have on our society?

Learning Objective 12:
Discuss contraception use and the factors that determine contraception use among sexually active teens.

Contraception Clinic. A young woman receives counseling about the use of birth control pills. Should schools provide contraceptive services to sexually active students? Should parents have a say in whether their children receive such services?

O'Hara & Kahn, 1985). About one in five sexually active teens in the Coles and Stokes (1985) national sample relied on withdrawal or the rhythm method the first and last times they had intercourse (see Table 13.6).

Various factors determine use of contraceptives (Beck & Davies, 1987). Teenage girls who engage in more frequent intercourse are more likely to use contraception and to use more effective methods (DuRant & Sanders, 1989). Teens whose peers use contraceptives are more likely to use them themselves (Jorgensen et al., 1980). Older teenagers are more likely than younger ones to use contraception (Mosher & Bachrach, 1987). Younger teens who are sexually active may be less likely to use contraception because they lack information about contraception and because they do not always perceive the repercussions of their actions (Handler, 1990). Younger teens may also have less access to contraceptives.

Teenage boys are more likely than teenage girls to know how to obtain and use condoms correctly, according to the results of a California survey of more than 1,000 high school students (Leland & Barth, 1992). Boys are also more likely to have used birth control during their first or most recent sexual experience. It appears that girls are more uncomfortable than boys in obtaining or using contraception, especially condoms (Leland & Barth, 1992).

Poor family relationships and communication with parents are associated with inconsistent contraceptive use (Brooks-Gunn & Furstenberg, 1989). Poor performance in school and low educational ambitions predict irregular contraceptive use, as they also predict early sexual initiation.

When asked to explain why they don't use contraceptives, sexually active teens often cite such factors as sexual infrequency ("don't have intercourse often enough to use it") and disruption of sexual spontaneity ("interferes with sex") (Coles & Stokes, 1985). Some teenagers get "carried away" and do not wish to disrupt sex by applying birth-control devices. For others, coitus is an unplanned, "spur of the moment" experience (Zelnik & Shah, 1983).

Myths also decrease likelihood of using birth control (Allgeier, 1981; Kelley, 1981; Oskamp & Mindick, 1981). Some adolescents believe that they are too young to become pregnant. Others believe that pregnancy results only from repeated coitus, or will not occur if they are standing up. Still other adolescents simply do not admit to themselves that they are engaging in coitus. Concerns about side effects are also given as reasons for failure to use contraception (Washington et al., 1983).

Teenagers who focus on the long-term consequences of their actions are more likely to use contraceptives. The quality of the relationship is also a factor. Satisfaction with the relationship is associated with more frequent intercourse *and* more consistent use of contraception (Jorgensen et al., 1980). More consistent contraceptive use is found in relationships in which the young woman takes the initiative in making decisions and resolving conflicts.

Let us note that many adolescents today who use condoms do so more because of fear of AIDS than to protect themselves against unwanted pregnancies (Lewin, 1991b). A reduction in teenage pregnancies may be a side effect of this trend.

Learning Objective 13: List and evaluate the suggested strategies for combating teenage pregnancy.

COMBATING TEENAGE PREGNANCY: A ROLE FOR THE SCHOOLS?   Various means have been recommended to combat the problem of teenage pregnancy, including requiring universal sex education in schools, distribution of free contraceptive services to teens, greater openness between parents and children in talking about sex, and use of the media to disseminate information about responsible sex practices and contraception (Warren, 1992). Noting the effects of sex education in other industrialized countries, many helping professionals believe that the rate of teenage pregnancy in the United States, and the spread of AIDS and other sexually transmitted diseases, could be curtailed through extensive sex education, including comprehensive coverage of contraception, and through programs that provide teens with ready access to contraceptives.

Pregnancy prevention programs in the schools range from encouraging teens to delay early sex ("saying no to early sex") to providing information about contraception to distributing condoms directly to students or referring students to contraceptive clinics (Berger, 1991; Furstenberg et al., 1989; Hayes, 1987). The vast majority of sex educators,

A CLOSER LOOK

Should Public Schools Provide Students with Contraceptives?

Alarmed by the threat of AIDS and the epidemic of teenage pregnancy, some school districts now distribute contraceptives, such as condoms, to students (Lewin, 1991a). Most school districts require parental consent. Others, such as the huge New York City school system, do not (Berger, 1991). Clinics that protect the confidentiality of their teenage clients often make active attempts to involve the parents in some way, usually by providing opportunities for family counseling, parent advisory groups, and parent-child communication training (Beck & Davies, 1987).

TRUTH OR FICTION?

REVISITED

In some school districts, condoms are distributed to adolescents without parental consent. *Condoms are indeed distributed to adolescents in some school districts without parental consent—but not without controversy.* •

Today only a few contraceptive counseling programs specifi-

cally reach out to males. Those that do so are typically stymied by poor participation rates (e.g., Gordon & DeMarco, 1984). There is a discrepancy between the attitudes of teenage males and their behavior (Beck & Davies, 1987). Young men generally voice strong opinions that birth control is the responsibility of both partners, but few use family-planning services even when they are available.

Reducing the rate of teenage pregnancy may require a coordinated strategy of advocating sexual restraint on the one hand and providing contraceptive services and sexual counseling on the other. Few adults believe that teenage pregnancy is desirable. It is questionable, however, whether society can reach a consensus concerning the social and moral acceptability of programs that offer contraceptive services to teens, especially programs that do not require parental consent. Many parents oppose such programs because they fear that they compromise family cohesiveness and parental authority. Many parents believe that they, not the schools, should dispense information to their children about contraception and be the ones to decide whether their chil-

dren should be given contraceptives. Many oppose giving adolescents contraceptives on moral and religious grounds. Opponents also argue that more emphasis should be placed on encouraging abstinence than on distributing contraceptives. Some opponents believe that distributing contraceptives to teens encourages premarital sex.

Advocates of these programs argue that the requiring of parental consent would only discourage participation by large numbers of sexually active teens. They note that many teens become sexually active despite educators' encouragement to abstain. Given this reality, they argue, society has a responsibility to help protect sexually active teens from unwanted pregnancies and AIDS.

Handing out condoms is not likely to reduce teenage pregnancy or the spread of sexually transmitted diseases unless the "handouts" are accompanied by counseling that focuses on their proper use. Sexually active teenagers also need to learn how to communicate the need for contraception with their partners. More comprehensive reproductive health care clinics have been established in some schools,

Discussion Question: Recently several schools and churches have received a great deal of publicity for soliciting written pledges from young people that they will remain abstinent until marriage. Do you think these young people will keep their pledges?

86 percent, recommend abstinence to their students as the best way to prevent pregnancy and AIDS (Kantrowitz, 1990b). Fewer than half inform their students about how to obtain contraceptives. Although three out of four large school districts in the United States provide some instruction about the methods of contraception and the use of condoms to prevent the spread of AIDS and other sexually transmitted diseases, only about four in ten provide information about specific clinics or doctors whom students can contact to receive contraceptives (Kenney et al., 1989).

Evidence supports the effectiveness of programs that counsel abstinence, at least among younger teens. A school-based sex education program focused on the development of skills needed to resist social and peer pressure to initiate sexual activity encour-

which combine condom distribution with sexual counseling. But are they effective in lowering the rates of teenage pregnancy? Thus far, these programs have failed to produce a significant dent in schoolwide pregnancy rates (Kirby et al., 1992, 1993). Whatever the effects of these school-based programs in reducing teenage pregnancy rates, the important functions they serve in providing much needed primary health care to young people who may not have access to other health care providers should not be ignored (Kirby et al., 1993).

The introduction of the contraceptive device Norplant has added a new wrinkle to the debate over distributing contraceptives in the schools. The advantage of Norplant is that once implanted, it offers around-the-clock protection against unwanted pregnancies for several years without any additional effort required. Baltimore, which is beset with one of the highest teen pregnancy rates in the United States, has become the first city in the nation to offer Norplant to teenage girls in a school-based clinic in the attempt to combat teenage pregnancies (Kantrowitz, 1992;

Lewin, 1992a). In Baltimore, one in 10 girls ages 15 to 17 have babies ("For high school girls, Norplant debate hits home," 1993). Most live in poverty. Until the experimental program, Norplant was too expensive for most teens to afford, costing about $350 for the chemical and an additional $150 to $500 for the implantation. The Norplant program is located in a school in an impoverished inner-city, community, where the problem of teenage pregnancy is most acute. Here, a 16-year-old teenage mother in Baltimore expresses her hopes that Norplant will enable her to finish high school and pursue a college education without becoming pregnant again:

> I don't know what I would do if I had another baby. . . I share a crowded bedroom with two younger sisters, and it's so small and cluttered with bunk beds and cribs. I've tried to find a job, but there aren't any, and my stepfather is out of work. I want to go to art school, and I always dreamed of having fun on a college campus. . . . I wanted Norplant to help me finish school.

(New York Times, March 7, 1993, p. 28)

It is too early to tell whether the Baltimore Norplant program will prove successful. Yet it has already sparked considerable controversy. Though some proponents hail Norplant as a "silver bullet" against teen pregnancies, others believe that it will encourage teenage promiscuity. As one local clergyman put it, "Norplant sends a message that it is O.K. to have sex as long as you don't get pregnant" ("Plan for wider use of Norplant by girls dividing Baltimore," 1993). Opponents also point out that Norplant does not offer any protection against sexually transmitted diseases. Some opponents consider the use of Norplant in inner-city schools to be a racist tool. Some worry about potential side effects or medical risks, especially in a population of inner-city teens who may not see a physician regularly. Proponents argue that Norplant is needed because teens fail to use other forms of contraception consistently or at all, even if they are made available to them.

 Education and Morality

aged younger (junior high school) teens to postpone sexual involvement (Howard & McCabe, 1990). Program participants also had fewer pregnancies than students who did not participate in the program. However, programs that rely on the "just say no" model to encourage abstinence are less effective in persuading high school students to abstain from sexual activity (Wilson & Sanderson, 1988).

Because many teenagers are or will become sexually active, our society faces the question of whether the public schools should make contraceptive services or contraceptives themselves available to sexually active teens. This issue is the focus of heated debate among parents, educators, health officials, and other public officials in various communities in the United States and Canada. (See A Closer Look section.)

Learning Objective 14:
Describe the incidence of
same-gender sexual behav-
ior among teenagers and the
additional stresses experienced by gay and
lesbian teenagers.

Notes: In the March 1992
issue of the Marvel Comic
Alpha Flight, superhero
Northstar disclosed his
homosexuality. Would
teenage years be easier for
gay and lesbian teens if
they had openly gay role
models? Do comic book
superheroes count?

SAME-GENDER SEXUAL BEHAVIOR

About 5 percent of the adolescents in the Coles and Stokes (1985) national survey reported same-gender sexual experiences. An earlier survey found that more than nine out of ten reported same-gender experiences among adolescents were between peers (Sorensen, 1973). Seduction of adolescents by gay male and lesbian adults was relatively rare. Most adolescent same-gender sexual encounters are transitory (Chilman, 1979). They most often include mutual masturbation, fondling, and genital display.

Many gay males and lesbians of course develop a firm sense of being gay during adolescence. Coming to terms with adolescence is often a difficult struggle, but it is often more intense for gay people (Baker, 1990) (see Chapter 10). Adolescents can be particularly cruel in their stigmatization, referring to gay peers as "homos," "queers," "faggots," and so on. Many adolescent gays thus feel isolated and lonely and decide to cloak their sexual orientation. Many do not express their sexual orientation at all until after their high school years.

Adding to the strain of developing a gay identity in a largely hostile society is the threat of AIDS, which is all the more pressing a threat to young gay males because of the toll that AIDS has inflicted on the gay male community (Baker, 1990).

In this chapter we have chronicled sexuality in childhood and adolescence. In the next chapter we continue our journey through the life span.

SUMMING UP

INFANCY (0 TO 2 YEARS): A SEARCH FOR THE ORIGINS OF HUMAN SEXUALITY

The Infant's Capacity for Sexual Response It is known that fetuses suck their fingers in the womb, and that males have erections. Stimulation of the genitals in infancy may produce sensations of pleasure. Pelvic thrusting has been observed in humans as early as 8 months of age. Masturbation may begin as early as 6 to 12 months. Some infants seem capable of sexual responses that closely resemble orgasm.
Masturbation Self-stimulation for pleasure (masturbation) typically occurs among children as young as 6 to 12 months of age.
Genital Play Typically, children in the U.S. do not engage in genital play with others until about the age of 2.

EARLY CHILDHOOD (3 TO 8 YEARS)

Masturbation Statistics concerning the incidence of masturbation at ages 3 to 8 is speculative.
Heterosexual Behavior In early childhood, children show curiosity about the genitals and may play "doctor."
Same-Gender Sexual Behavior Same-gender sexual play may be more common than heterosexual play and does not presage adult sexual orientation.

PREADOLESCENCE (9 TO 13 YEARS)

Preadolescents tend to socialize with best friends and with large groups, and to become self-conscious about their bodies.

Masturbation Masturbation is apparently the primary means of achieving orgasm during preadolescence for both genders.

Heterosexual Behavior Preadolescent sex play often involves mutual display of the genitals, with or without touching. Group dating and mixed-gender parties often provide preadolescents with their first exposure to heterosexual activities.

Same-Gender Sexual Behavior Much preadolescent same-gender sexual behavior involves sexual exploration and is short-lived.

Sources of Sexual Information Despite the increased availability of sex-education programs, peers apparently remain the major source of sexual information.

ADOLESCENCE

Adolescence is bounded by the advent of puberty at the lower end and the capacity to take on adult responsibilities at the upper end. The conflicts and distress experienced by many adolescents apparently reflect the cultural expectations to which they are exposed.

Puberty Pubertal changes are ushered in by sex hormones. Puberty begins with the appearance of secondary sex characteristics and ends when the long bones make no further gains in length. Once puberty begins, most major changes in primary sex characteristics occur within three years in girls and within four years in boys.

Masturbation Masturbation is a major sexual outlet during adolescence.

Heterosexual Behavior Adolescents today date and "go steady" earlier than in past generations, a change that has apparently increased the incidence of teenage pregnancy. Many adolescents use petting as a way of achieving sexual gratification without becoming pregnant or losing one's virginity. The incidence of premarital intercourse, especially for females, has increased dramatically since Kinsey's day.

Sexually active teenagers use contraception inconsistently, if at all. Thus, more than one million teenage girls in the United States become pregnant each year.

Same-Gender Sexual Behavior Most adolescent same-gender sexual encounters are transitory. Coming to terms with adolescence is often more intense for gay males and lesbians, largely because homosexuality is stigmatized in our society.

_____ "Singlehood" (forgive the word) has become a more common U.S. lifestyle over the past few decades.

_____ Marriage is losing its popularity as a style of life.

_____ In the ancient Hebrew and Greek civilizations, wives were viewed as their husbands' property.

_____ Most of today's sophisticated young people see nothing wrong with an occasional extramarital fling.

_____ Few women can reach orgasm after the age of 70.

_____ People who are paralyzed due to spinal-cord injuries cannot become sexually aroused or engage in coitus.

C H A P T E R   *14*

Sexuality in Adulthood

People entering adulthood today face a wider range of sexual choices and lifestyles than those in earlier generations. The sexual revolution loosened traditional constraints on sexual choices, especially for women. Couples experiment with lifestyles that would have been unthinkable a generation or two earlier. The numbers of couples who cohabit, or "live together," skyrocketed in the 1970s and 1980s. A few couples have experimented with "open marriages" and "group marriages," which openly disavow the traditional marital covenant of sexual exclusiveness. Some married couples not only permit their spouses to take lovers, but also share their extramarital experiences through "swinging." An increasing number of young people choose to remain single as a way of life, not merely as a way station preceding the arrival of Mr. or Ms. Right.

In this chapter, we discuss diverse forms of adult sexuality in U.S. society today, including singlehood, marriage, and such alternate lifestyles as cohabitation, open marriage, and group marriage. (Although we focus on lifestyles among heterosexuals in this chapter, a diversity in lifestyles also exists among gays [see Chapter 10].) We also explore sexuality in late adulthood. Young people are often surprised to learn that most older people (probably including their own parents and grandparents) maintain active sex lives. We also see that most disabled people also have sexual feelings and lead active sex lives.

Let us begin as people begin—with singlehood.

SINGLEHOOD

Recent years have seen a sharp increase in the numbers of single young people in our society. "Singlehood" (forgive the term!), not marriage, is now the most common lifestyle among people in their early twenties. Though marriages may be made in heaven, a greater percentage of Americans are saying heaven can wait. By 1991, one in four people in the United States 18 years of age and older had never married, as compared to about one in six in 1970 and one in five in 1980 (Barringer, 1992b; Barringer, 1992c). The rate of marriages has also fallen off, with the proportion of people in the United States tying the knot in 1991 reaching a 25-year low (Barringer, 1992c). By 1988, nearly 80 percent of single men in the 20 to 24 age range were unmarried, up from 55 percent in 1970 (U.S. Bureau of the Census, 1990a). The percentage of single women in this age group nearly doubled, from 36 percent in 1970 to 61 percent in 1988. By the mid-1980s, about one in four U.S. households consisted of a single adult. This represented a threefold increase since 1960 (U.S. Bureau of the Census, 1985; "Living alone and loving it," 1987).

Although most people do get married by their late twenties, never-married singles still account for some 43 percent of the men and 30 percent of the women in the 25 to 29 age group (U.S. Bureau of the Census, 1990a). In fact, the proportion of people who remain single into their late twenties and early thirties more than doubled from 1970 to the mid-1980s (U.S. Bureau of the Census, 1990a).

"Singlehood" (forgive the word) has become a more common U.S. lifestyle over the past few decades. True, more people are remaining single into their twenties and thirties than was the case a generation or two ago. •

Several factors contribute to the increased proportion of singles. For one thing, more people now postpone marriage to pursue educational and career goals (Barringer, 1991). Many young people are deciding to "live together," at least for a while, rather than get married. Too, people are getting married at later ages (Kornblum, 1988). The increased prevalence of divorce in recent years also swells the ranks of single adults.

Singles' Scene. There is no one "singles' scene" today. Some singles meet in singles bars or health clubs, others in more casual settings such as the neighborhood laundromat while sorting laundry, while still others meet via computer networks or TV dating services.

Serial monogamy

A pattern of involvement in one exclusive relationship after another, as opposed to engaging in multiple sexual relationships at the same time.

Celibacy

Complete sexual abstinence. (Sometimes used to describe the state of being unmarried, especially in the case of people who take vows to remain single.)

Learning Objective 2:
Identify the people most likely to cohabit, the reasons they give for cohabiting, the styles of cohabitation, and the relationship between cohabitation and later marriage.

Another factor is that less social stigma is attached to remaining single today (Kammeyer et al., 1990). Though single people are less likely today to be perceived as socially inadequate or as failures, some singles still encounter traditional prejudices (Kammeyer et al., 1990). Men who have never married may be suspected of being gay. Single women may feel that men perceive them as "loose."

Single people do not necessarily choose to be single. Some remain single because they have not yet found Mr. or Ms. Right. A survey of nearly 500 single Canadians found that most had remained single because they had not yet found the right person or because their standards for a marital partner were high (Austrom & Hanel, 1985).

Many young people today see singlehood as an alternative, open-ended way of life, however, not just as a temporary stage that precedes marriage. As career options for women have expanded, they are not as financially dependent on men as were their mothers and grandmothers. A number of career women, like young career-oriented men, choose to remain single (at least for a time) to focus their energies on their careers (Current Population Reports, 1985).

Singlehood is not without its problems. The most frequent complaint among single people is loneliness (Janus & Janus, 1993; Kammeyer, 1990). Some 85 percent of singles surveyed in one study complained about loneliness (Simenauer & Carroll, 1982). Some singles express concerns about a lack of a steady, meaningful social relationship. Others, usually women, mention fears about their physical safety. Some people living alone may find it difficult to satisfy their needs for intimacy, companionship, sexual gratification, and emotional support. Despite these concerns, most singles are well-adjusted and content, not at all fitting the stereotypes of loneliness and depression (Rollins, 1986). Singles who have a greater number of friends and a supportive social network tend to be more satisfied with their lifestyles (Austrom & Hanel, 1985).

Where do singles meet? Singles' bars, popular meeting places for singles during the sexual revolution of the 1960s and 1970s, have lost much of their cachet in the face of the threat of AIDS and other sexually transmitted diseases (STDs). In certain respects, health clubs have become the singles' bars of the 1990s. Dating services, especially videodating services, have become popular, as have personal advertisements. Singles also meet under more mundane circumstances, such as when sorting their laundry in neighborhood laundromats that are frequented by young singles. Many still meet in more traditional ways, such as by introductions from friends or family or in social gatherings and parties. (Your second author notes that she is regularly approached by young men in gray flannel suits in the supermarket in the early evening. Your third author would like her to find another time to shop.)

There is no one "singles' scene" today. Single people differ in their sexual interests and lifestyles. Many achieve emotional and psychological security through a network of intimate relationships with friends. Most are sexually active. Many of those who are sexually active practice **serial monogamy.** Other singles have a primary sexual relationship with one steady partner but occasional brief relationships with others. Still others, even in this age of AIDS, pursue a series of casual sexual encounters, or "one-night stands."

Some singles remain celibate, either by choice or for lack of opportunity. People choose **celibacy** for a number of reasons. Nuns and priests choose celibacy for religious reasons. Others believe that celibacy allows them to focus more of their energies and attention on their work or to commit themselves to an important cause. They see celibacy as a temporary accommodation to other pursuits. Others remain celibate because they view sex outside of marriage as immoral or sinful. Still others remain celibate because they find the prospects of sexual activity aversive or unalluring, or because of fears of STDs.

COHABITATION: DARLING, WOULD YOU BE MY POSSLQ?

There is nothing I would not do
If you would be my POSSLQ

(Charles Osgood)

Cohabitation
Living together as though married but without legal sanction.

Notes: In reviewing data from the National Survey of Families and Households (NSFH), a survey of 13,017 people conducted in 1987–1988, researchers concluded that "three-quarters of the decline in the proportion of women married for the first time by age 25 was offset by increased cohabitation" (p. 926). They also found that 40 percent of cohabiting households include children. (Bumpers, L. L., Sweet, J. A., and Cherlin, A. 1991. The role of cohabitation in declining rates of marriage. *Journal of Marriage and the Family, 53,* 913–927.)

Notes: According to the 1991 book *The Spousal Equivalent Handbook: A Legal and Financial Guide to Living Together* by J. Duff and G. G. Truitt, nonmarital cohabitation is still forbidden by law in ten states: Arizona, Florida, Illinois, Michigan, Mississippi, New Mexico, North Carolina, North Dakota, Virginia, and West Virginia.

POSSLQ? This unromantic abbreviation was introduced by the U.S. Bureau of the Census to refer to **cohabitation.** It stands for People of Opposite Sex Sharing Living Quarters and applies to unmarried couples who live together.

Although cohabitation has not become fully accepted into the social mainstream, society has developed a more tolerant attitude toward cohabiting couples. We seldom hear people today refer to cohabitation as "living in sin" or "shacking up" as we once did. People today are more likely to refer to cohabitation with value-free expressions such as "living together." (Only government statisticians seem to use the acronym POSSLQ.)

Perhaps the current tolerance reflects societal adjustment to the explosive increase in the numbers of cohabiting couples. Or perhaps the numbers of cohabiting couples have increased as a consequence of increased social acceptability. (Also, as one parent of a woman in her twenties told one of the authors, "I'd rather have her living with [him] than running around singles' bars and getting AIDS.") By the mid-1980s, nearly one out of three single U.S. women between the ages of 20 and 29 had cohabited at one time or another (Tanfer, 1987).

The numbers of households consisting of unmarried adults of the opposite gender living together in the United States increased 80 percent during the 1980s, from 1.6 million couples in 1980 to 2.9 million couples in 1990 (United States Bureau of the Census, 1990a). By 1992, the number had increased to 3.3 million (Saluter, 1992). Not all of these households consist of romantically involved couples. The government keeps statistics only on unrelated people of the opposite gender living together, not on the numbers who share the same bed. Some people live with members of the opposite gender for economic reasons or because of circumstances, not because they are romantically involved. Yet it is reasonable to assume that a considerable majority of cohabitors are romantically involved couples.

Attitudes toward cohabitation reveal an age gradient. By the early 1980s, only 29 percent of young people ages 18 to 34 disapproved of cohabitation, as compared to 51 percent of people ages 35 to 49 and 71 percent of people age 50 and above (Merit, 1982). Forty-three percent of the men and 35 percent of the women in a sample of 500 college students reported that they could see themselves living together with a partner (Billingham & Sack, 1986). A national fertility survey of Canadian women also found less approving attitudes toward cohabitation among older women, as well as among those living in rural areas, those with less education, non-Catholics, and those who attend church more frequently. Regional differences also came into play, as women living in Quebec tended to be more approving than women in other provinces (Wu & Balakrishnan, 1992).

WHO ARE THE COHABITORS?

Much of the attention on cohabitation has been focused on college students living together, but cohabitation is more prevalent among the less well-educated and less affluent classes (Kammeyer et al., 1990). The cohabitation rate is about twice as high among African-American couples as white couples (U.S. Bureau of the Census, 1987). Fifty-five percent of male cohabitors, and 41 percent of female cohabitors, have never been married

(United States Bureau of the Census, 1990a). About one cohabiting couple in three have children living in their household (Saluter, 1992). About one cohabitor in three is divorced. Cohabitors are less likely than noncohabitors to belong to a church or to attend church services (Watson, 1983). Cohabitation is most common among young people. Six out of ten male cohabitors and nearly seven out of ten female cohabitors are under 35 years of age (United States Bureau of the Census, 1990a).

REASONS FOR COHABITATION

Notes: J. Duff and G. G. Truitt, authors of the 1991 book *The Spousal Equivalent Handbook: A Legal and Financial Guide to Living Together* recommend that *all* cohabitants (partners of the same sex, single partners without children, divorced partners with children, etc.) sign a written agreement addressing such issues as financial responsibility, property ownership, life insurance benefits, and durable and medical powers of attorney.

Why do people cohabit? One reason is that cohabitation may represent an alternative to the loneliness that can accompany living alone. Romantic partners may have deep feelings for one another but not be ready to get married. Some couples prefer cohabitation because it provides a consistent intimate relationship without the legal and economic entanglements of marriage (Renzetti & Curran, 1989).[1]

Economic factors come into play as well. Emotionally committed couples may decide to cohabit because of the economic advantages of sharing household expenses. Cohabiting individuals who receive public assistance (social security or welfare checks) may risk losing their support if they get married. Younger couples may cohabit secretly to maintain parental support that they might lose if they were to get married or to openly reveal their living arrangements.

STYLES OF COHABITATION

Like singlehood, styles of cohabitation vary. Most of them can be classified into one of three types (Kammeyer, 1990):

1. *Part-time/limited cohabitation.* Two people start dating each other. One person starts spending more time at the residence of the other. As the relationship deepens, staying over becomes more frequent. The visitor brings more and more clothes and belongings, so that the couple are practically living together. The couple may not reach a formal decision to live together. Rather, they may "drift" into cohabitation and only recognize the fact once they are essentially living together.
2. *Premarital cohabitation.* This is a style of cohabitation in which two people who expect to get married decide to first live together. Typically the couple shares a single residence, which they jointly maintain and manage. They also share an awareness and expectation that marriage is in the offing. They may have already made the decision to get married. In a variation called *trial marriage,* however, the couple seeks to test the relationship by cohabiting before making a commitment to marriage (Macklin, 1978).
3. *Substitute marriage.* In this type of cohabitation, a couple makes a long-term commitment to live together without entering into a legal marriage. A variety of motivations may be involved in establishing this commitment. For example, a divorced person may be reluctant to enter another marriage.

COHABITATION AND LATER MARRIAGE: A BENEFIT OR A RISK?

Cohabiting couples may believe that cohabitation will strengthen their eventual marriage by helping them to iron out the kinks in their relationship. Yet cohabitors who later marry may run a greater—not lesser—risk of divorce than noncohabitors. Statistics from a national survey of households reveal that the likelihood of divorce within ten years of marriage is nearly twice as great among married couples who cohabited before marriage (Riche, 1988). A Swedish study found that the likelihood of marital dissolution was 80 percent greater among women who had cohabited before a first marriage than among women who had not (Bennett et al., 1988).

[1]Some people, however, have brought "palimony" suits against former cohabiting partners. They have claimed that a contractual relationship existed between the parties concerning division of assets and responsibilities for financial support.

Researchers have found evidence of poorer communication (in the opinion of the wife) and lower marital satisfaction overall (for both partners) among couples who had cohabited before marriage (DeMaris & Leslie, 1984). A Canadian study found higher levels of marital satisfaction, especially among wives, in married couples who had not cohabited before marriage than in those who had (Watson, 1983). Others, too, have found somewhat lower levels of marital satisfaction among prior cohabitors (Booth & Johnson, 1988).

We must be cautious about drawing causal conclusions from correlational data, however. None of the couples in these studies were *randomly assigned* to cohabitation or noncohabitation. Therefore, *selection factors*—the factors that lead some couples to cohabit and others not to cohabit—may explain the results (Kammeyer, 1990). Cohabitors tend to be more committed to personal independence (Blumstein & Schwartz, 1983). They also tend to be less traditional and less religious than noncohabitors (Kammeyer, 1990). All in all, people who cohabit prior to marriage tend to be less committed to the values and interests traditionally associated with the institution of marriage (Bennett et al., 1988). The attitudes of cohabitors, and not cohabitation itself, may thus account for their higher rates of marital dissolution.

Then, too, some researchers have found no link between marital adjustment or satisfaction and prior cohabitation (e.g., Newcomb & Bentler, 1980; Watson & DeMeo, 1987). Still, it is clear that living together before marriage is no guarantee of a successful or happy marriage.

Finally, let us also note that only about a third of cohabiting couples eventually marry (Clayton & Voss, 1977). Most of the others break up within three years. Termination of the relationship, not marriage, is thus the most likely outcome of cohabitation (Yamaguchi & Kandel, 1985). Still, despite the eventual outcome, about four of five cohabiting couples report that they are satisfied with their relationships (Risman et al., 1981).

MARRIAGE

Learning Objective 3: Summarize the history of marriage and cite the percentage of people who marry.

The social institution of marriage is found in all human societies. Most people in every known society, sometimes nearly all, get married at least once (Ember & Ember, 1990; Kammeyer, 1990).

Marriage is our most common lifestyle. In some cultures, such as among the Hindu of India, marriage is virtually universal, with more than 99 percent of the females eventually marrying (Petersen, 1975). In the United States, most people (90% of the males and 93% of the females) marry at least once by the age of 40 (Kammeyer, 1990).

TRUTH OR FICTION?

R E V I S I T E D

Marriage is losing its popularity as a style of life. Not so. Marriage remains extremely popular. Even among people who adopt nontraditional lifestyles, most eventually enter into traditional marriages. •

In the United States, about 65 percent of the adult men and 60 percent of the adult women are currently married and living with their spouses (U.S. Bureau of the Census, 1990a). Some 5 million people get married each year (Statistical Abstract of the United States, 1987). With more people delaying marriage in favor of pursuing educational and career goals, the average (median) age of first marriage has been rising steadily over the past few decades, and is now 26.5 years for men and 24.4 years for women (Saluter, 1992). This represents an increase of three years for both men and women since 1975.

HISTORICAL PERSPECTIVES

Marriage in Western culture has a long and varied history. Among the ancient Hebrews, men dominated the important aspects of life. This system was known as **patriarchy.** The man of the house had the right to choose wives for his sons and could himself take concubines or additional wives. He alone could institute divorce—a practice still found among Orthodox Jews. Although he could dally, his wife had to be scrupulous in the

Patriarchy
A form of social organization in which the father or eldest male runs the group or family. Government, rule, or domination by men. (From the Greek *pater,* meaning "father," and *archein,* meaning "to rule")

Wedding Days. The social institution of marriage is found in all human societies. The particular type of marriage ceremony or ritual used to mark a couple's entry into marriage depends on the culture, as these photos illustrate.

Chattel
A movable piece of personal property, such as furniture or livestock. (From the Old French word meaning "cattle."

maintenance of her virtue. Failure to bear children was grounds for divorce. The wife was clearly considered to be part of the property of the man of the house: a **chattel.**

In classical Greece women were similarly viewed as the property of men. Their central purposes were to care for the household and to bear children. Rarely were they viewed as suitable companions for men. During the Golden Age of Greece men would turn to high-class prostitutes for sensual sex and sophisticated conversation—not to their wives. In the city-state of Sparta, marriage rites in ancient times were not very formal: the man simply dragged his "bride" to his house and locked her in.

TRUTH OR FICTION?
—————————
R E V I S I T E D

In the ancient Hebrew and Greek civilizations, wives were viewed as their husbands' property. Yes, wives were in fact viewed as their husbands' property—as chattels. The women's movement has fought to throw off the weight of millennia of oppressive practices! •

Discussion Question:
What expectations do you have about marriage? About a spouse's behavior? How important is it to discuss your expectations prior to marriage? (Topics to discuss prior to marriage can include religion; where you will spend holidays; how decisions about having children will be made; whether one spouse will stay home full time with young children; who will do which household tasks; how money decisions will be made; how often the couple will visit extended family members; etc.)

The Romans also had a powerful patriarchy. The oldest man directed family life and could, if he wished, sell his children into slavery and arrange their marriages and divorces. Marriages were typically arranged for financial or political gain. Women were in effect given by their fathers to their husbands.

The Christian tradition also has a strong patriarchal foundation. Male dominance was legitimized by Biblical scripture, as we can see in this passage from the New Testament: "Wives, submit to your own husbands, as unto the Lord. For the husband is the head of the wife, as Christ is the head of the church" (Ephesians 5:23–24).

Patriarchal traditions in Western culture gradually weakened with time, and women came to be viewed as loving companions rather than mere chattels. They were gradually given more household responsibilities and were recognized as being capable of profiting from education. The notion that a married woman might rightfully seek personal fulfillment through a career unrelated to her husband's needs is a relatively recent development, however. The perception that married women have a right to sexual fulfillment is also new. As late as the nineteenth century, sex in marriage was largely seen as a means of rearing children and satisfying the husband's sexual needs (Kammeyer, 1990). The husband determined when the couple would engage in intercourse and how it would be done. There were certainly some caring and sensitive husbands at the time, but a social historian characterized typical nineteenth-century sexual relations between husbands and wives as "brief and brutal," with "little evidence that women derived much pleasure from it" (Shorter, 1982, p. 9). Sex was viewed, even among educated classes, as a husband's right and a wife's duty (Kammeyer, 1990). Marriage manuals of the time held that a woman's role was to submit to her husband's advances in order to please him (Gordon, 1978). Women, it was believed, should be motivated sexually only by the desire for children.

TABLE 14.1 A comparison of traditional and modern marriages

Traditional Marriage	Modern Marriage
The emphasis is on ritual and traditional roles.	The emphasis is on companionship.
Couples do not live together before marriage.	Couples may live together before marriage.
The wife takes the husband's last name.	The wife may choose to keep her maiden name.
The husband is dominant; the wife is submissive.	Neither spouse is dominant or submissive.
The roles for the husband and the wife are specific and rigid.	Both spouses have flexible roles.
There is one income (the husband's).	There may be two incomes (the couple may share the breadwinning role).
The husband initiates sexual activity; the wife complies.	Either spouse may initiate (or refuse) sex.
The wife takes care of the children.	The parents share child-rearing chores.
Education is considered important for the husband, not for the wife.	Education is considered equally important for both spouses.
The husband's career decides the location of the family residence.	The career of either spouse may determine the location of the family residence.

Source: Adapted by permission from *Choices in Relationships* by D. Knox Copyright © 1988 by West Publishing Company. All rights reserved.

Marital roles in modern society have changed, and are changing still. Some couples still adhere to traditional gender roles that ascribe breadwinning responsibilities to the husband and child care and homemaking roles to the wife. U.S. couples today are more likely to share or even reverse marital roles, however. Table 14.1 lists some of the discriminating features of traditional and so-called modern marriages.

WHY DO PEOPLE MARRY?

Throughout Western history the institution of marriage has served to meet certain personal and cultural needs. Marriage legitimizes sexual relations and provides a legal sanction of deeply committed intimate relationships. It permits the maintenance of a home life and provides an institution in which children can be supported economically and socialized into adopting the norms of the family and the culture at large. Marriage has restricted sexual relations so that a man could be assured—or at least could assume—that his wife's children were his. Marriage also permitted the orderly transmission of wealth from one family to another and from one generation to another. Wealth could be transmitted from one family to the family of the bride or the groom, and from the father to his sons or his sons-in-law. As late as the seventeenth and eighteenth centuries, most European marriages were arranged by the parents of the bride and groom, generally on the basis of how the marriage would benefit the families (Kammeyer, 1990).

Notions like romantic love, equality, and the very radical concept that men as well as women would do well to aspire to the ideal of faithfulness are quite recent additions to the structure of marriage in Western society. Not until the nineteenth century did the notion of love as a basis for marriage become widespread in Western culture (Kammeyer, 1990). In some preliterate societies, the very idea of being in love is considered a laughable concept—hardly a basis for marriage.

Today, because more people believe that premarital sex is acceptable between two people who feel affectionate toward one another, the desire to engage in sexual inter-

Activity: *Thinking Critically About Whether People Are Naturally Monogamous.* This IM activity encourages students to think critically about how we define which behaviors are "natural" for humans.

Monogamy
Marriage to one person.

Polygamy
Simultaneous marriage to more than one person.

Polygyny
A form of marriage in which a man is married to more than one woman at the same time.

Polyandry
A form of marriage in which a woman is married to more than one man at the same time.

Learning Objective 5: Describe the influences of age, race, social class, and religion on mate selection in the United States.

Homogamy
The practice of marrying people who are similar in social background and standing. (From Greek roots meaning "same" [*homos*] and "marriage" [*gamos*].)

course is less likely to motivate marriage. Marriage provides a sense of emotional and psychological security, however, and opportunities to share feelings, experiences, and ideas with someone with whom one forms a special attachment. Desires for companionship and intimacy are thus central goals in contemporary marriages. Even in these more liberated times, young people (ages 17 to 23) today strongly endorse the traditional ideal that marriage is a lifetime commitment (Moore & Stief, 1992).

TYPES OF MARRIAGE

There are two major types of marriage: **monogamy** and **polygamy.** In monogamy, a husband and wife are wed only to each other. But let us not confuse monogamy, which is a form of matrimony, with sexual exclusivity. People who are monogamously wedded often do have extramarital affairs, as we shall see, but they are considered to be married to only one person at a time. In polygamy, a person has more than one spouse and is permitted sexual access to each of them.

    Polygyny is by far the most prevalent form of polygamy among the world's societies (Ford & Beach, 1951; Frayser, 1985). **Polyandry** is practiced only rarely (see Chapter 1). In polygynous societies, men are permitted to have multiple wives if they can support them; more rarely a man will have one wife and one or more concubines. The man's first wife typically has higher status than the others. Economic factors and the availability of prospective mates usually limit the opportunities for men to wed more than one woman at a time, however. In many cases, only wealthy men can afford to support multiple wives and the children of these unions. In addition, few if any societies have enough women to allow most men to have two or more wives (Ember & Ember, 1990). For these reasons, even in societies that prefer polygyny, fewer than half of the men at any given time actually have multiple mates (Ford & Beach, 1951).

WHOM DO WE MARRY: ARE MARRIAGES MADE IN HEAVEN OR IN THE NEIGHBORHOOD?

Most preliterate societies regulate the selection of spouses in some way (Ember & Ember, 1990). The incest taboo, universal across cultures, proscribes matings between immediate or close relatives. Societal rules and customs also determine which persons are desirable mates and which are not. Even in Western cultures where mate selection is presumably "free," factors such as race, social class, and religion often determine the categories of persons within which we may seek mates. Parents today seldom arrange marriages, although they may still encourage their child to date that wonderful son or daughter of the solid churchgoing couple who live down the street. People in our culture tend to marry others from the same geographical area and social class. Since neighborhoods are often made up of people from a similar social class, storybook marriages like Cinderella's are the exception to the rule (Ember & Ember, 1990).

    We tend to marry people who attract us: people similar to us in physical attractiveness, who share reasonably similar attitudes on important matters, and who seem likely to meet our material, sexual, and psychological needs. We often marry people who physically resemble us in various ways, such as in skin and eye color, as well as in such subtle characteristics as the width of the nose and the thickness of the lips—even the length of the earlobe and the distance between the eyes (Diamond, 1986). We are more often than not similar to our mates in such characteristics as height, personality traits, and intelligence (Buss, 1984; Lesnik-Oberstein & Cohen, 1984).

    The concept of "like marrying like" is termed **homogamy.** We usually marry people of the same race. Interracial marriages account for fewer than one in every two hundred marriages (U.S. Bureau of the Census, 1991c). Moreover, more than nine of ten marriages are between people of the same religion. Marriages between individuals who are alike may stand a better chance of survival, since the partners are more likely to share their values and attitudes (Berger, 1988). Dissimilar couples, however, can work to overcome the barriers that divide them by developing shared interests and mutual respect for their differences.

Babies and Marriage? Not Exactly Like the Horse and Carriage

Once upon a time, it is said, babies and marriage went together largely like the proverbial horse and carriage. Today, however, the connection is no longer so solid. The percentages of single-parent families has been heading upward, more than doubling from 12 percent to 26 percent between 1970 and 1990 (Barringer, 1992c). By the latter half of the 1980s, more than half of the children born to 18- and 19-year-olds in the United States were born out of wedlock (O'Connell, 1991). A 1993 U.S. Census Bureau report showed that nearly one in four (24%) never-married women today become mothers, up from 15 percent in 1982 (DeParle, 1993; "More single mothers," 1993). The sharpest increases were found among white women (more than doubling from 6.7 percent to 14.6 percent), among women who had graduated from college (also more than doubling from 3.0 percent to 6.4 percent), and among women in professional and managerial jobs (nearly tripling from 3.1 percent to 8.3 percent). The numbers of unmarried African-American and Hispanic-American women becoming mothers had also risen, but not as sharply as among white women (DeParle, 1993).

Demographers and sociologists suggest a number of reasons for the upturn in out-of-wedlock births. For one thing, there is less stigma attached to bearing children out of wedlock today (Bachu, 1991). Unmarried women who become pregnant today are thus less likely to seek the sanction of marriage. Another reason is that more people are postponing marriage to pursue educational or career goals, or because they haven't met someone that meets their marital expectations (Barringer, 1992c). The state of the economy may also play an important role. Troubled economic conditions may discourage people from making a commitment during times they don't feel economically secure (Barringer, 1992c). Whatever the reason, women who delay marriage spend a longer period of time as singles during which they can become accidentally pregnant (Bumpas, 1991). Day care has also become more available, making it easier for single women to rear children (Rindfuss, 1991).

Why the sharp increase in out-of-wedlock births among better educated, professionally employed women? It appears that the social acceptability of single parenthood within the middle class has risen while women's increased earning power provides them with the economic means to raise a child alone (Seligmann, 1993). Although women's earnings, on the average, still fall below those of men, the earning power of well-educated professional women has risen to the point that they are no longer economically dependent on men. DeParle (1993) observes that the "feminist revolution has left many women with a new sense of independence. Witnessing the high divorce rates around them, many women no longer trust the institution of marriage" (p. A1). Moreover, many single, well-educated women today who are facing the relentless ticking of their biological clocks with no prospective partner in the offing are opting for motherhood anyway (Lawson, 1993). As one 39-year-old single mother whose son is now nearly four years old commented,

> Ideally, [my son]. . . would have a father who adored me and adored him. . . but we don't have that . . . I always wanted to have a child, . . . I knew so many women who were waiting for that Alan Alda type to come along, and wanting a committed relationship. And they were waiting and waiting.

(Seligmann, 1993, p. 53)

A national organization, Single Mothers by Choice, which was formed to help single mothers cope with raising children alone, now has some 2,000 members in 20 chapters nationwide (Lawson, 1993).

Most single mothers, however, are neither well-educated

Mating gradient
The tendency for women to "marry up" (in social or economic status) and for men to "marry down."

We also tend to follow *age homogamy*. Age homogamy—the selection of a partner who falls in one's own age range—may reflect the tendency to marry early in adulthood. Persons who marry late or who remarry tend not to select partners so close in age. Bridegrooms tend to be two to five years older than their wives, on the average, in European, North American, and South American countries (Buss, 1988).

Some marriages also show a **mating gradient.** The stereotype has been that an economically established older man would take an attractive, younger woman as his wife. But

nor professionally employed. Most are women with little education who are either unemployed or underemployed. The challenges they face are not those of balancing the responsibilities of career and motherhood but of coping with the daily struggles of survival. The United States Census Bureau reports that nearly 50 percent of unwed mothers failed to finish high school and only 6 percent had bachelor's degrees (Lawson, 1993). A record number of unmarried mothers now depend on welfare payments to survive (DeParle, 1993). Children from single-parent households, overall, have more educational, financial, and emotional problems than those from dual-parent households.

Out-of-wedlock births have shot up since the 1960s, especially among African-Americans (Chideya, 1993). Two of three first births to African-American women under the age of 35 are now out of wedlock (Chideya, 1993). A majority of African-American children (58%) now live in single-parent households, as compared to 20 percent of white children (Barringer, 1992c). (About 25% of these new parents of children born out of wedlock are, however, living together, or cohabiting [Bumpas, 1991]. Children born within these relationships will thus be reared in

two-parent families.) An African-American child today has but a one-in-five chance of being raised by two parents (Chideya, 1993). The greater prevalence of out-of-wedlock births among African Americans is found at both the low and high end of the income spectrum. It's not the institution of marriage that has lost favor. A *Newsweek* poll of single African-American adults showed that 88 percent wanted to get married (Chideya, 1993). But the dream of marriage has been hammered in the last 25 years. The economic dislocation that began in the 1970s and 1980s, when the nation shifted from an industrial to a service base, was particularly devastating to African-American men, who

had migrated north in vast numbers to well-paying manufacturing jobs that to a large extent no longer exist (Chideya, 1993).

The connection between marriage and bearing children varies widely among industrialized nations. In Japan, for example, only 1 percent of children are born out of wedlock (O'Connell, 1991). In Sweden, however, cohabitation is so common that about 50 percent of children are born out of wedlock (O'Connell, 1991). With the exception of Japan, sharp increases in the numbers of unmarried mothers have occurred in recent years in other industrialized democracies, as they have in the United States (DeParle, 1993).

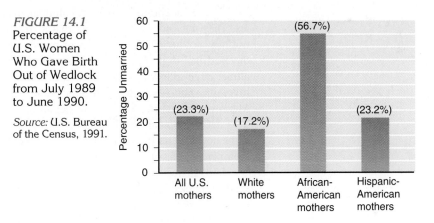

FIGURE 14.1
Percentage of U.S. Women Who Gave Birth Out of Wedlock from July 1989 to June 1990.

Source: U.S. Bureau of the Census, 1991.

by and large, with boring predictability, we are attracted to and marry the boy or girl (almost) next door. Most marriages seem to be made not in heaven, but in the neighborhood.

WHO HAS HIS HEAD IN THE CLOUDS? (HINT: THE QUESTION IS *NOT* PHRASED IN SEXIST LANGUAGE)   When it comes to picking a mate, men tend to be the romantics; women, the pragmatists (Berger, 1988). Men are more likely to believe that each person has one true love whom they are destined to find (Peplau & Gordon,

1985). Men are more likely to believe in love at first sight. Women, on the other hand, are more likely to value financial security as much as passion. Women are more likely to believe that they could form a loving relationship with many individuals. Women are also less likely to believe that love conquers all, especially economic problems.

MARITAL SEXUALITY

Learning Objective 6:
Describe the changes since the Kinsey studies in marital foreplay, the frequency, techniques, and duration of marital sex, and the satisfaction husbands and wives express about marital sex.

Patterns of marital sexuality vary across cultures, yet anthropologists have noted some common threads (Ember & Ember, 1990). Privacy for sexual relations is valued in almost all cultures. Most cultures also place restrictions on coitus during menstruation, during at least some stages of pregnancy, and for a time after childbirth.

Until the sexual revolution of the 1960s and 1970s, Western culture could be characterized as sexually restrictive, even in its attitudes toward marital sex. Hunt noted that "Western civilization has long had the rare distinction of contaminating and restricting the sexual pleasure of married couples more severely than almost any other" (1974, p. 175).

THE SEXUAL REVOLUTION HITS HOME

We usually think of the sexual revolution in terms of the changes in sexual behaviors and attitudes that occurred among young unmarried people. It also ushered in profound changes in marital sexuality, however. Compared to Kinsey's "pre-revolution" samples from the late 1930s and 1940s, married couples today engage in coitus more frequently and for longer durations of time. They report higher levels of sexual satisfaction and engage in a greater variety of sexual activities.

The sexual revolution also helped dislodge traditional male dominance in sexual behavior. In essence, male dominance is the view that sexual pleasure is meant for men but not women, and that it is the duty of women to satisfy their husbands' sexual needs and serve as essentially passive "receptacles." Assumptions of male dominance are found even in the writing of the (for his time) liberated Kinsey. Nowhere are they more evident than in his (and his colleagues') comment that men, who have the biological capacity to ejaculate a few moments after entry, need not feel bound to "wait" for women to reach orgasm (Kinsey et al., 1948, p. 580).

People caught up in social revolutions may not perceive themselves as revolutionaries. They may not even be aware that a "revolution" is taking place. The sexual revolution was not heralded by parades or massive demonstrations. There was no "storming of the Bastille" to proclaim sexual freedom. Organizations promoting "free love" did not attract large followings. Even the most famous slogan of the sexual revolution—"Make love, not war"—was more an indictment of the Vietnam War than a call for free love. Moreover, social movements are begun by a few but are spread by the perception that they define popular trends. Married people, as well as singles, thus made sexual decisions not only on the basis of their religious teachings and personal values, but also on their perceptions of the current norm.

Liberalizing trends were communicated through popular media. Hundreds if not thousands of books and magazines with sexual content crammed bookstore shelves and supermarket display cases. During Kinsey's day, books like Henry Miller's *Tropic of Cancer* and D. H. Lawrence's *Lady Chatterley's Lover* were censored in the United States. Now they are readily available but so tame when compared to the racy content of books and magazines today that they barely raise any eyebrows. Similarly, since the late 1960s pornographic films have been shown in adult theaters across the nation. In many places the audiences include middle-class couples and college students, not just "dirty old men." The VCR has brought sexually explicit films into middle-class suburban homes.

Scientific findings were also liberalizing influences. Kinsey's and Masters and Johnson's findings that normal women were capable not only of orgasm but also of multiple orgasms punctured long-standing beliefs that sexual gratification was the birthright of men alone. Masters and Johnson's 1966 book, *Human Sexual Response,* is one of the few technical books to ever become a national best-seller. Alex Comfort's 1972 book

The Joy of Sex, a profusely illustrated sex manual for couples, broke records by remaining on the *New York Times* best-seller list for more than a decade. TV shows, films, and radio talk shows began to portray women as sexual initiators who enjoy sex. All of these influences have encouraged U.S. women to forgo the traditional passive approach to sexuality.

The affluence of the post–World War II years also encouraged more young people to pursue a college education and live away from home. College liberates not only through exposure to great books and scientific knowledge, but also through challenging students' attitudes by bright, knowledgeable peers from different backgrounds. Prejudice and myth are often analyzed and discarded.

Americans have also become more mobile. Jobs carry young people thousands of miles from home. Their sexual attitudes are influenced by new acquaintances from many parts of the country and from people from other nations, not just by a few people from "the neighborhood."

The development of effective contraceptives also permitted sex to be separated from reproduction. Motives for sexual pleasure became more open. All these liberalizing forces have led to changes in the frequency of marital sex and in techniques of foreplay and coitus since Kinsey's day.

CHANGES IN DURATION AND TECHNIQUES OF FOREPLAY Married women in Kinsey's sample reported an average (median) length of foreplay of about 12 minutes. This figure rose to nearly 15 minutes among the wives in the *Playboy* survey (Hunt, 1974). Kinsey found that men at lower educational levels engaged in briefer periods of foreplay, generally lasting but a minute or two before penetration. The length of foreplay rose to 5 to 15 minutes among college-educated men. In a dramatic shift in sophistication since Kinsey's day, Hunt found that the typical duration of foreplay in the 1970s was 15 minutes for college-educated and noncollege males alike. Foreplay was relatively longer in duration among younger married couples than their elders, however.

Marital foreplay has also become more varied since Kinsey's day. Couples today use a wider variety of foreplay techniques, including oral stimulation of the breasts and oral-genital contact (Blumstein & Schwartz, 1983; Hunt, 1974).

CHANGES IN FREQUENCY OF MARITAL COITUS How frequently do married couples engage in coitus? A comparison of the reports from Kinsey's couples and the *Playboy* survey couples (Table 14.2) shows increases in coital frequency at every age level.

TABLE 14.2 Median weekly frequency of marital coitus, male and female estimates combined (Kinsey and *Playboy* surveys)

KINSEY (1948, 1953)		PLAYBOY (1974)	
Age	**Frequency**	**Age**	**Frequency**
16–25	2.45	18–24	3.25
26–35	1.95	25–34	2.55
36–45	1.40	35–44	2.00
46–55	.85	45–54	1.00
55–60	.50	55 & over	1.00

Source: Reproduced with permission from Playboy Enterprises, Inc. from *Sexual Behavior in the 1970s* by Morton Hunt. Copyright © 1974 by Morton Hunt.

Neither Kinsey nor Hunt found a link between coital frequency and educational or socioeconomic level. Both researchers found coitus to be most frequent among younger age groups, however. Coitus tends to decline with age, a finding reported by Kinsey, Hunt, and by other researchers (e.g., Ade-Ridder, 1985; Palmore, 1981). Regardless of a couple's age, sexual frequency also appears to decline with years of marriage (Blumstein & Schwartz, 1990).

CHANGES IN TECHNIQUES AND DURATION OF COITUS In coitus, as foreplay, the marital bed since Kinsey's day has become a stage on which the players act more varied roles. Today's couples use greater variety in coital positions.

Kinsey's subjects mainly limited coitus to the male-superior position. As many as 70 percent of Kinsey's males used the male-superior position exclusively (Kinsey et al., 1948). Perhaps three couples in ten used the female-superior position frequently. One in four or five used the lateral-entry position frequently; and about one in ten, the rear-entry position. Younger and more highly educated men showed greater variety, however. Hunt (1974), by comparison, found that three quarters of the married couples in the *Playboy* survey used the female-superior position at least occasionally. More than half had used the lateral-entry position, and about four in ten had used the rear-entry position.

An often overlooked but important difference between Kinsey's and Hunt's samples involved the length of intercourse. In Kinsey's time it was widely believed that the "virile" man ejaculated rapidly during intercourse. Kinsey estimated that most men reached orgasm within 2 minutes after penetration, many within 10 or 20 seconds. Kinsey recognized that women usually took longer to reach orgasm through coitus, and that some clinicians were already asserting that a man's ejaculation was "premature" unless he delayed it until "the female (was) ready to reach orgasm" (1948, p. 580). Yet Kinsey, trained as a biologist, observed that

> . . . in many species of mammals the male ejaculates almost instantly upon intromission, and that this is true of man's closest relatives among the primates. Students of sexual activity among chimpanzees, for instance, report that 10 to 20 seconds is all the time which is ordinarily needed to effect ejaculation in that species. Far from being abnormal, the human male who is quick in his sexual response is quite normal among the mammals, and usual in his own species . . . . It would be difficult to find another situation in which an individual who was quick and intense in his responses was labeled anything but superior, and that in most instances is exactly what the rapidly ejaculating male probably is, however inconvenient and unfortunate his qualities may be from the standpoint of the wife in the relationship.

(Kinsey et al., 1948, p. 580. Reprinted by permission of The Kinsey Institute for Research in Sex, Gender, and Reproduction, Inc.)

From an evolutionary standpoint, rapid ejaculation may have survival value. Copulating animals may be less aware of their surroundings, leaving themselves more vulnerable to predators in the bush. Males who ejaculated rapidly may have had reproductive advantages over those who delayed. Whatever the evolutionary roots that may once have favored rapid ejaculation, there is no apparent advantage for modern man. Instead, men who ejaculate rapidly may discourage their partners from participating in coitus, which might actually *reduce* their reproductive success.

Fortunately "from the standpoint of the wife in the relationship," even today's less educated couples appear to be more sophisticated than Kinsey's in their recognition of the need for sexual variety and their focus on providing and receiving sexual pleasure rather than simply rapidly reaching orgasm. In the *Playboy* survey, married men, including those without college educations, reported an average duration of intercourse of approximately 10 minutes (Hunt, 1974), about five times the duration estimated by Kinsey.

SEXUAL SATISFACTION

One index by which researchers measure sexual satisfaction, at least among women, is orgasmic consistency. Nearly all men reach orgasm consistently; not so women. After 15 years of marriage, 45 percent of the wives in Kinsey's study reported orgasm 90 to 100

Discussion Question:
Kinsey cites animal behavior to argue that quick ejaculation is "normal" or even "superior" male human behavior. For what other human sexual behaviors can animal behavior be used as a standard in arguing for "normalcy"? (Monogamous sexual relationships? Homosexual behavior? Sex play among the young of the species?)

Discussion Question:
What explanations would you suggest for why married women of all ages report somewhat less satisfaction than men with marital sex?

Sexual Satisfaction. Researchers find that marital closeness is linked to sexual satisfaction. Perhaps sexual pleasure contributes to marital closeness, or perhaps closeness helps couples achieve greater sexual satisfaction.

"A personal best for you, maybe."

Reproduced by special permission of Playboy magazine, © 1983.

percent of the time. This figure rose to 53 percent of the wives in the *Playboy* survey, who reported orgasm "all or almost all of the time" (Hunt, 1974, p. 212). The group of women surveyed in the 1970s in a large readership survey by *Redbook* magazine were younger and better educated than those in the Kinsey and *Playboy* surveys, and 63 percent of them reported reaching orgasm all or most of the time (Tavris & Sadd, 1977). After 15 years of marriage, 12 percent of the wives in Kinsey's study had not experienced orgasm. Seven percent of the *Playboy* survey's and 7 percent of the *Redbook Report's* wives reached orgasm "none" or "almost none" of the time.

Orgasm is not the only criterion for measuring pleasure or satisfaction in marital sex. The *Playboy* survey asked participants to rate their marital sexual relations during the past year from "very pleasurable" to "very nonpleasurable." The findings were rather positive: Two out of three married men rated marital coitus as "very pleasurable." Adding in those who rated coitus as "mostly pleasurable," the figures swell to 99 percent among 18- to 24-year-olds and drop only to 94 percent for those 45 and above (Hunt, 1974).

Six out of ten married women under 45 in the *Playboy* survey rated coitus "very pleasurable," although there was a marked dropoff among older women. Adding in those who considered coitus "mostly pleasurable," coitus earned an approval rating of 88 percent among 18- to 24-year-olds. It peaked at 93 percent for 35- to 44-year-olds, and declined to 83 percent among those over 55.

The perceived closeness of the marital relationship was also linked to the pleasure received from coitus. Marital coitus does not take place in an emotional vacuum. Generally speaking, the closer the relationship, the more enjoyable the sex. Sexual pleasure may contribute to marital closeness, just as closeness may render sex more enjoyable. The number of couples who have found that sex is *not* the answer to their problems indicates that sex is not enough to maintain a troubled relationship, however.

Other researchers have found that wives who talk openly to their husbands about their sexual feelings and needs report higher levels of sexual satisfaction (Banmen & Vogel, 1985; Tavris & Sadd, 1977). Women respondents to the *Redbook* survey who took an active role during sex were more satisfied with their sex lives than those who assumed the traditional passive female role (Tavris & Sadd, 1977).

EXTRAMARITAL SEX

It is as absurd to say that a man can't love one woman all the time as it is to say that a violinist needs several violins to play the same piece of music.

(Balzac)

Extramarital sex
Sexual relations between a married person and someone other than his or her spouse.

Conventional adultery
Extramarital sex that is kept clandestine (hidden) from one's spouse.

Extramarital sex (or "affairs") are usually conducted without the spouse's knowledge or approval. Such clandestine affairs are referred to as **conventional adultery** (Smith & Smith, 1974), infidelity, or simply "cheating." Some extramarital affairs are "one-night stands." Others persist for years.

Consensual adultery
Extramarital sex that is engaged in openly with the knowledge and consent of one's spouse.

Swinging
A form of consensual adultery in which both spouses share extramarital sexual experiences. Also referred to as *mate swapping*.

In **consensual adultery,** extramarital relationships are conducted openly with the knowledge and consent of the partner and sometimes even with the partner's participation, as in **swinging.**

Not all people subscribe to Balzac's view regarding marital fidelity. Some people engage in extramarital sex for variety. Some have affairs to break the routine of a confining marriage (Ellis, 1977). Others enter affairs for reasons similar to the nonsexual reasons adolescents often have for coitus: as a way of expressing hostility toward a spouse or of retaliating for injustice. Husbands and wives who engage in affairs often report that they are not satisfied with, or fulfilled by, their marital relationships.

Sometimes the sexual motive is less pressing than the desire for emotional closeness. In one study, some women who reported affairs said they had been seeking someone whom they could "talk" to or "communicate" with (Atwater, 1982). Curiosity and desire for personal growth were more prominent motives for extramarital affairs than marital dissatisfaction among Atwater's (1982) respondents. Middle-aged people may have affairs to boost their self-esteem or prove that they are still attractive.

Men (whether single, married, or cohabiting) are generally more approving of extramarital affairs than are women (Glass & Wright, 1992). For those who have engaged in extramarital intercourse, men are more likely to cite a need for sexual excitement as a justification for an extramarital affair than are women, 75 percent versus 55 percent (Glass & Wright, 1992). Women are more likely to cite "falling in love" as a justification for their affairs than do men, 77 percent versus 43 percent. These data support the widely held view that "men separate sex and love; women appear to believe that love and sex go together and that falling in love justifies sexual involvement" (Glass & Wright, p. 361).

PATTERNS OF EXTRAMARITAL SEX

Learning Objective 7: Discuss the patterns of extramarital sex, attitudes toward it, and its effects.

How many people "cheat" on their spouses? Though viewers of television talk shows may think that everyone is cheating on everyone, recent surveys paint a different picture. An ABC News/Washington Post telephone poll found that only 7 percent of the wives and 13 percent of the husbands admitted to having extramarital affairs (Painter, 1987). A study conducted between 1988 and 1992 by the respected National Opinion Research Center reported similar results, with 21 percent of the husbands and 12 percent of the wives acknowledging marital infidelity ("Cheating going out of style but sex is popular as ever," 1993). Yet some surveys show somewhat higher prevalences of extramarital affairs. More than one in three men and more than one in four women who participated in the Janus and Janus survey reported having extramarital affairs (Janus & Janus, 1993). Experience with extramarital affairs was even reported by nearly one in three (31%) of the survey respondents who identified themselves as "very religious."

Having presented the percentages of reported extramarital sex, let us note one compelling limitation to these data. These reports cannot be verified, since people may not reveal whether they have "cheated" on their spouses. The frequencies of extramarital sex are probably underreported to an undetermined extent, especially in cases where respondents are not ensured of anonymity.

Although researchers agree that accurate figures on extramarital sex are lacking (Gordon & Snyder, 1989), researchers at the Kinsey Institute took into account the findings of a number of surveys in estimating that, overall, 37 percent of husbands and 29 percent of wives have had extramarital affairs (Reinisch et al., 1988).[2]

Not surprisingly, spouses who report engaging in extramarital sex tend to be less committed to their marriages (Beach et al., 1985) and express less marital satisfaction (Thompson, 1983). People whose close friends have had affairs are more likely to have them themselves (Atwater, 1982).

Some extramarital affairs are limited to a single episode or brief encounter. Others endure for years. Extended affairs tend to become highly intimate and emotionally

---

[2]Estimates are based on populations of white, relatively well-educated, middle-class, primarily urban U.S. inhabitants between the ages of 20 and 45. Information about other population groups is too sparse to provide a basis for estimates.

involving, but are generally strained by the clandestine nature of the relationship and the limited time that the partners can spend together. But perhaps because the veil of secrecy creates a certain intrigue, passions may burn brightly for a time. Yet jealousies and demands for commitment often strain such relationships to the breaking point.

ATTITUDES TOWARD EXTRAMARITAL SEX

The sexual revolution does not seem to have liberated attitudes toward extramarital sex. Most married people disapprove of it. Eighty to 98 percent of the *Playboy* sample reported that they would object to their mates' engaging in affairs (Hunt, 1974). Moreover, only 20 percent of those in the sample who reported having had affairs said that their mates were aware of them. Most married couples espouse the value of monogamy as the cornerstone of their marital relationship (Blumstein & Schwartz, 1990).

TRUTH OR FICTION?
———————————
R E V I S I T E D

Most of today's sophisticated young people see nothing wrong with an occasional extramarital fling. *Most of today's sophisticated young people do, in fact, see something wrong with an occasional extramarital fling. The sexual revolution never extended itself to extramarital affairs—at least among the majority of married people.*

CROSS-CULTURAL PERSPECTIVES ON EXTRAMARITAL SEX Most societies prohibit extramarital relationships for one or both spouses (Frayser, 1985). In cultures in which extramarital sex is permitted, husbands are typically allowed greater sexual freedom than wives. Frayser could find no societies that allowed extramarital sex for wives but not husbands.

Despite cultural prohibitions, extramarital sex among wives occurred anywhere from occasionally to universally in about three of four (73%) societies in a cross-cultural sample of 56 of the world's societies. It was rare or absent in about 27 percent of them (Broude & Greene, 1976). Male extramarital sex occurred from occasionally to universally in 80 percent of a sample of 55 societies. It was rare or absent in 20 percent of them.

Even in societies that permit extramarital relationships, social customs or controls typically regulate them (Frayser, 1985). Among the Aleut people of Alaska's Aleutian Islands, for example, men may offer visitors the opportunity to sleep with their wives as a gesture of hospitality. Among the Chukchee of Siberia, who often travel long distances from their homes, a married man is allowed to engage in sexual activity with his host's wife. The understanding is that he would reciprocate when the host visited him (Ford & Beach, 1951).

Kinship ties often determine sexual access to extramarital partners (Frayser, 1985). Among the people of the Marshall Islands in the Pacific, a woman is allowed to have a sexual relationship with her sister's husband. Among the Native American Comanches, a man is permitted to have intercourse with his brother's wife, if his brother consents. Customs sometimes limit extramarital intercourse to ceremonial occasions. The Fijians of Oceania, for example, engage in extramarital relationships only following the return of their men from warfare. In Western society, Mardi Gras and some out-of-town conventions represent ceremonial occasions for extramarital liaisons that might not be tolerated otherwise.

EFFECTS OF EXTRAMARITAL SEX

Discussion Question: What reasons have you heard people give for engaging in extramarital sex? What effects did extramarital sex have on relationships you've observed?

The discovery of infidelity can evoke a range of emotional responses. The spouse may be filled with anger, jealousy, even shame. Feelings of inadequacy and doubts about one's attractiveness and desirability may surface. Infidelity may be seen by the betrayed spouse as a serious breach of trust and intimacy. Marriages that are not terminated in the wake of the disclosure may survive in a damaged condition.

Not all marriages are destroyed or damaged by infidelity, however. Such outcomes are not inevitable (Ellis, 1977; Myers & Leggitt, 1975). Extramarital affairs may also be a symptom of a failing marriage rather than a cause.

The harm an affair does to a marriage may reflect the meaning of the affair to the individual and his or her spouse. If a person has an affair because the marriage is deeply troubled, the affair may be one more factor that speeds its dissolution. The effects on the marriage may depend on the nature of the affair. It may be easier to understand that a spouse has fallen prey to an isolated, unplanned encounter than to accept an extended affair (Kammeyer, 1990). In some cases the discovery of infidelity stimulates the couple to work to improve their relationship. If the extramarital activity continues, however, it may undermine the couple's efforts to restore their relationship.

SWINGING

Comarital sex
Swinging; mate-swapping.

Swinging—also called "mate-swapping" or **comarital sex**—is a form of consensual adultery in which both partners openly share sexual experiences with other people. Some swingers argue that swinging can help improve a marriage by reducing sexual boredom and increasing togetherness. This view draws support from studies that show that swinging leads to increased rates of coitus *between* the spouses and is associated with higher levels of marital satisfaction (Gilmartin, 1975; Wheeler & Kilmann, 1983). But these studies were limited to swinging couples who had made an adjustment to swinging. We do not know about the much larger numbers of couples who dropped out from swinging. A more recent study of 56 swinging couples showed no consistent relationship between swinging and marital satisfaction. Swinging was as likely to disrupt a marital relationship as to improve it (Levitt, 1988).

Most swingers seek to avoid emotional entanglements with their swinging partners, but they may fail to separate their emotions from their sexual activity. Emotional intimacy between swinging partners can be even more threatening to the swingers' primary relationships than sexual intimacy. For various reasons, most swinging couples drop out after a short period of experimentation (Murstein et al. 1985).

Swingers tend to be white, fairly affluent, well-educated, and to have but nominal religious affiliations (Jenks, 1985). Solid statistics on the prevalence of swinging are lacking, however. Observers of sexual trends suggest that swinging, like other nontraditional forms of matrimony, seems to have largely vanished from the social scene in recent years (Havemann & Lehtinen, 1990). The rising concern about AIDS, coupled with the more conservative social climate of the 1980s and early 1990s appears to have restricted swinging largely to a relatively few devotees of swinging magazines, which feature solicitations from couples seeking partners for swinging relationships. Even during the heyday of the sexual revolution, only 2 percent of married males and fewer than 2 percent of married females in the *Playboy* survey had "swung," and many of these individuals had tried it just once (Hunt, 1974).

DIVORCE

Learning Objective 8: Cite the percentage of marriages that end in divorce and discuss the costs of divorce for children, women, and men.

About half of all marriages in the United States end in divorce (U.S. Bureau of the Census, 1987), and half of these end within the first seven years (Fisher, 1987). The divorce rate in the United States rose steadily through much of the twentieth century (see Figure 14.2,) before leveling off in the 1980s (Kemper, 1983; Norton & Moorman, 1987). About one quarter (25.9%) of children below the age of 18 live in single-parent households (Barringer, 1991). Divorced women outnumber divorced men, in part because men are more likely to remarry following divorce (Saluter, 1992).

The relaxation of legal restrictions on divorce, especially the introduction of the so-called no-fault divorce, has made divorces easier to obtain. Until the mid-1960s, adultery was the only legal grounds for divorce in New York State. Other states were equally strict. But by 1985, no-fault divorce laws had been enacted in every state except South Dakota, allowing the granting of a divorce without a finding of marital misconduct (Weitzman, 1985). The increased economic independence of women has also contributed to the rising divorce rate. More women today have the economic means of breaking away

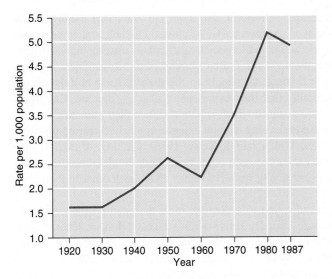

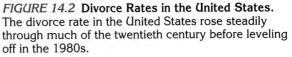

FIGURE 14.2 **Divorce Rates in the United States.**
The divorce rate in the United States rose steadily through much of the twentieth century before leveling off in the 1980s.

Notes: One working wife in four earns more than her husband. [*Bottom Line/ Personal* (1988, April 30). New York: Boardroom Reports, Inc.]

from a troubled marriage. Today, more people consider marriage an alterable condition than in prior generations. People today hold higher expectations of marriage than did their parents or grandparents. They expect marriage to be personally fulfilling as well as meet the traditional expectation of marriage as an institution for rearing children. Many demand the right to be happy in marriage. The most common reasons given for a divorce today are problems in communication and a lack of understanding (Kitson & Sussman, 1982). Years ago it was more likely to be lack of financial support (Kammeyer, 1990).

THE COST OF DIVORCE

Notes: The results of a 1980 nationwide telephone survey of 2033 married people indicate that both parental divorce and parental marital unhappiness (even though the marriage remains intact) are associated with more liberal attitudes toward divorce in adulthood. Experiencing divorce oneself is also associated with more liberal attitudes toward divorce. (Amato, P. R., and Booth, A. 1991. The consequences of divorce for attitudes toward divorce and gender roles. *Journal of Family Issues, 12(3)*, 306–322.)

Divorce is often associated with financial and emotional problems. When a household splits, the resources often cannot maintain the earlier standard of living for each partner. A woman who has not pursued a career may struggle to compete with younger, more experienced workers. Divorced mothers often face the combined stress of the sole responsibility for rearing their children (women receive custody in the majority of divorce cases) and the need to increase their incomes to make ends meet. Not surprisingly, single mothers (including divorced and never-married mothers) are more likely to report depression and less satisfaction with life than either single fathers or married parents (Burden, 1986). Divorced fathers may also find it difficult to pay alimony and child support while attempting to establish a new lifestyle.

Divorce may also prompt feelings of failure as a spouse and parent, loneliness and uncertainty about the future, and depression. Married people appear to be better able to cope with the stresses and strains of life, perhaps because they can rely on each other for emotional support (Pearlin & Johnson, 1977). Divorced and separated people have the highest rates of physical and mental illness in the population (Bloom et al., 1978; Nevid et al., 1994). Divorced people also have higher rates of suicide than married people (Trovato, 1986). On the other hand, divorce may be a time of personal growth and renewal. It can provide an opportunity for people to take stock of themselves and establish a new and hopefully more rewarding life for themselves.

Children also suffer in a divorce. Children's adjustment problems tend to increase in the first year following a divorce, but lessen somewhat by the end of the second year (Hetherington et al., 1982, 1983). Boys tend to show greater problems in adjustment, which often are manifested in conduct problems at school and increased anxiety and dependence. Girls, however, seem to fare better and often cannot be differentiated from girls from intact families on the basis of their adjustment.

Adjustment problems may endure. Wallerstein and Blakeslee (1989) reported that about four out of ten children in their case studies showed problems such as anxiety, academic underachievement, decreased self-worth, and anger ten years after the divorce. A "sleeper effect" was also described: Apparently well-adjusted children in divorced families developed problems in early adulthood, especially difficulties trusting that their partners in intimate relationships would make lasting commitments. Researchers attribute children's problems following divorce not simply to the divorce itself but also to the decline in the quality of parenting that they experience following divorce. Children's adjustment following divorce is enhanced when parents maintain their parenting responsibilities and set aside their differences long enough to agree upon child-rearing practices (Wallerstein & Blakeslee, 1989; Wallerstein & Kelly, 1980). Children of divorce also benefit when divorced parents encourage each other to continue to play important roles in their children's lives and avoid saying negative things about each other in their children's presence.

Despite the difficulties in adjusting to a divorce, most divorced people eventually bounce back. Most also become sexually active within a year (Hunt & Hunt, 1977). Nearly four out of five eventually remarry, on the average about three years following the divorce (Glick & Lin, 1986). Among older people, divorced men are more likely than divorced women to remarry (Richardson, 1985)—in part because men usually die earlier than women (and so fewer prospective husbands are available), in part because older men tend to remarry younger women. The proportion of divorced women who remarry appears to be declining (Norton & Moorman, 1987). Census data suggest that only about three of ten women over the age of 40 who got divorced in the 1980s will eventually remarry (Bumpas et al., 1988). (A similar situation exists among people who are widowed. Only about one in four widows, as compared to about one in two widowers, eventually remarry [Lown & Dolan, 1988].)

Remarriages are even more likely than first marriages to end in divorce (Lown & Dolan, 1988). After all, divorced people constitute a group who are relatively less inclined than the general population to persist in a troubled marriage (Spanier & Furstenberg, 1982). Many divorced people who remarry are also encumbered with alimony and child-support payments that strain their new marriages. Many bring children from their earlier marriages to their new ones.

By the beginning of the next century, the stepfamily is expected to be the most common family unit in the United States (CBS News, 1991). Six of ten stepfamilies eventually disband, often under the weight of the financial and emotional pressures of coping with the demands of a reconstituted family (CBS News, 1991). However, among remarriages that survive, the level of personal happiness in spouses is as high as among spouses in first marriages and much higher than the level among divorced people (Weingarten, 1985).

What of the long-term consequences of divorce? In one study, only one person in five reported that divorce had been a mistake five years after the fact (Wallerstein & Kelly, 1980). Most felt that the divorce had enhanced their lives. Most also reported that they had underestimated the emotional pain they would encounter, however. In another study, most divorced people reported that benefits of ending a bad relationship outweighed the emotional and financial costs (Albrecht et al., 1983).

ALTERNATIVE FORMS OF MARRIAGE

Marriages are generally based on the expectation of sexual exclusivity. Alternative or nontraditional marital styles, however, such as open marriages and group marriages, permit intimate relationships with people outside the marriage. Such alternative lifestyles attracted a flurry of attention during the heyday of the sexual revolution in the 1970s, but were even then more often talked about than practiced (Havemann & Lehtinen, 1990). Today, they find still fewer adherents.

OPEN MARRIAGE

Open marriage is based on the view that people's needs for intimacy are unlikely to be gratified through one relationship. Proponents argue that the core marriage can be

Elderly Divorce

Teaching Tip: Set up three columns on the chalkboard, one labeled "More people remaining single longer," one labeled "More cohabitation," and one labeled "More divorces." First have students discuss the possible causes of each trend. Second, discuss the societal impact of each trend. Third, if students view any of these trends negatively, have them suggest changes they think might halt or reverse the trends.

Learning Objective 9: Describe open marriage and group marriage and the effects of each on those involved.

Open marriage
A marriage that is characterized by the personal privacy of the spouses and the agreed-upon liberty of each spouse to form intimate relationships, which may include sexually intimate relationships, with people other than the spouse.

enhanced if the partners have the opportunity to develop emotionally intimate relationships with others (O'Neill & O'Neill, 1972).

The prevalence of open marriages, like that of swinging, remains unknown. Nor is there much data upon which to base conclusions about the success of open marriages. Rubin (1982) found no meaningful differences in marital adjustment between 130 couples with sexually open marriages and 130 couples who maintained sexual exclusivity. Still another study found no differences in the longevity of sexually open and sexually exclusive marriages over a five-year period (Rubin & Adams, 1986).

GROUP MARRIAGE

Group marriage also attracted some adherents during the sexual revolution of the 1960s and 1970s. In a group marriage, three or more people share an intimate relationship, although they are not legally married. Each member feels committed or married to at least two others. The major motive for group marriage is extension of intimacy beyond one spouse in order to increase personal fulfillment (Constantine & Constantine, 1973). Members of eight out of nine group marriages surveyed by the Constantines also admitted interest in a variety of sexual partners, however.

Group marriages differ from swinging in that participants share inmost thoughts and feelings and expect their bonds to be permanent. Group marriages, therefore, are not perceived merely as vehicles for legitimizing mate-swapping. Adherents expect children to profit by observing several adult role models and by escaping the "smothering" possessiveness of exclusive parent-child relationships.

Although they provide sexual variety, group marriages require adjustment to at least two other people—not just one. Moreover, legal and social problems can arise with respect to such issues as paternity and inheritance. Managing money may also be stressful, with arguments arising over joint accounts and who can spend how much for what. Sexual jealousies often arise as well. Given these problems, it is not surprising that group marriages are rare and have a high failure rate. Most dissolve within months or a few years (Macklin, 1980).

Group marriages are not unique to our culture. Although rare, other cultures have developed analogous marital customs (Werner & Cohen, 1990). Among the Chukchee people of Siberia, for example, group marriages sometimes involved as many as 10 couples. The men in such marriages, who considered themselves "companions-in-wives," had sexual rights to each wife.

All in all, the ideal of the traditional marriage remains strong in our culture. In a survey of 500 college students, only 13 percent of the males and a mere 3 percent of the females acknowledged willingness to participate in swinging (Billingham & Sack, 1986). Fewer still—5 percent of the males and 1 percent of the females—were willing to enter into group marriage. Men are somewhat more likely than women to participate or express an interest in lifestyles that permit greater sexual freedom and, perhaps, less personal responsibility (Knox, 1988). (The second author is not surprised.) But even most of those who have tried alternative lifestyles such as cohabitation, open marriage, or group marriage enter into traditional marriages at some time.

All in all, most adults in the United States feel about marriage the way Winston Churchill felt about democracy: It's flawed, laden with problems, and frustrating—but for most people, it's preferable to the alternatives.

SEX IN THE LATER YEARS

Which is the fastest growing segment of the U.S. population? People age 65 and above. More than 30 million U.S. inhabitants are age 65 and above, and their number is growing fast. This "graying" of the United States may have a profound effect on virtually every aspect of our lives, from the types of TV shows, movies, and consumer products that are produced to changes in the views we hold of older people, especially concerning their sexuality. Many people in our culture see sexual activity as appropriate only for the young (Reiss, 1988). This belief falls within a constellation of unfounded cultural myths about sexuality among older people, which includes the notions that older people are sexless, older people with sexual urges are abnormal, and older men with sexual interests are "dirty old men."

Researchers find that sexual daydreaming and sexual drive and activity tend to decline with age, whereas negative sexual attitudes tend to increase (Purifoy et al., 1992). However, research does not support the belief that people lose their sexuality as they age. Nearly all (95%) of the elderly people in one sample reported that they liked sex, and 75 percent reported that orgasm was essential to their sexual fulfillment (Starr & Weiner, 1982). People who are exposed to cultural views that sex among older people is deviant may renounce sex as they age, however. Those who remain sexually active may be bothered by guilt (Reiss, 1988).

Sexual activity among the elderly, as among other groups, is influenced not only by physical structures and changes, but by cultural expectations.

PHYSICAL CHANGES

Although many elderly people retain the capacity to respond sexually, physical changes do occur as the years pass (see Table 14.3). If we are aware of them, we will not view them as abnormal or find ourselves unprepared to cope with them. Many potential problems can be averted by changing our expectations or making some changes to accommodate the aging process.

CHANGES IN THE FEMALE   Many of the physical changes in women stem from decline in the production of estrogen around the time of menopause. The vaginal walls lose much of the elasticity and the thick, corrugated texture of the childbearing years. They grow paler and thinner.

As the vaginal walls thin and lose elasticity, coitus may become irritating. The thinning of the walls may also place greater pressure against the bladder and urethra during coitus, leading in some cases to symptoms of urinary urgency and burning urination. The condition, similar to honeymoon cystitis, may persist for days.

TABLE 14.3 Changes during sexual arousal often associated with aging

Changes in the Female	Changes in the Male
Reduced myotonia (muscle tension)	Longer time to erection and orgasm
Reduced vaginal lubrication	Need for more direct stimulation for erection and orgasm
Reduced elasticity of the vaginal walls	
Smaller increases in breast size during sexual arousal	Less semen emitted during ejaculation
	Erections may be less firm
Reduced intensity of muscle spasms at orgasm	Testicles may not elevate as high into scrotum
	Less intense orgasmic contractions
	Lessened feeling of a need to ejaculate during sex
	Longer refractory period

Source: Copyright © 1990 by The Kinsey Institute for Research in Sex, Gender, and Reproduction. From *The Kinsey Institute New Report on Sex.* Reprinted with permission from St. Martin's Press, New York, NY.

Sexuality and Aging. Despite stereotypes that stigmatize older people who are sexually active as somehow abnormal or deviant, it is perfectly normal for older people, even the advanced elderly, to have sexual urges and to maintain an active sexual life.

The vagina also shrinks in size. The labia majora lose much of their fatty deposits and become thin. The introitus becomes relatively constricted and penile entry may become somewhat difficult. This "problem" has a positive aspect: increased friction between the penis and vaginal walls may heighten sexual sensations. The body of the uterus decreases in size after menopause and no longer becomes so congested during sexual arousal. Following menopause, women also produce less vaginal lubrication and the lubrication that is produced may take minutes, not seconds, to appear. Lack of adequate lubrication is also a major reason for painful coitus.

Many of these changes may be slowed or reversed through estrogen-replacement therapy (see Chapter 3). Natural lubrication may also be increased through more elaborate foreplay. The need for more foreplay may encourage the man to become a more considerate lover. (He too will likely need more time to become aroused.) An artificial lubricant may also ease problems posed by difficult entry or painful thrusting.

Women's breasts show smaller increases in size with sexual arousal as they age, but the nipples still become erect. Because the muscle tone of the urethra and anal sphincters decreases, the spasms of orgasm become less powerful and fewer in number. Thus orgasms may feel less intense. The uterine contractions that occur during orgasm may become discouragingly painful for some postmenopausal women. Despite these changes, women can retain their ability to achieve orgasm well into their advanced years. Indeed, many women in their eighties have been found to experience orgasm as often as women in their early twenties (Kaplan & Sager, 1971). The subjective experience of orgasm also remains highly satisfying, despite the lessened intensity of muscular contractions (Katchadourian, 1987).

TRUTH OR *FICTION?*

REVISITED

Few women can reach orgasm after the age of 70. Actually, healthy women can retain the capacity for orgasm well into their advanced years. •

CHANGES IN THE MALE Age-related changes tend to occur more gradually in men than in women and are not clearly connected with any one biological event, as they are with menopause in the woman. Male adolescents may achieve erection in a matter of seconds through sexual fantasy alone. But after about age 50, men take progressively longer to achieve erection, and erections become less firm, perhaps because of lowered testosterone production. Older men may require minutes of direct stimulation of the penis to achieve an erection. Couples can adjust to these changes by extending the length and variety of foreplay.

Most men remain capable of erection throughout their lives. Erectile dysfunction is not inevitable with aging. Men generally require more time to reach orgasm as they age, however, which may also reflect lowered testosterone production. In the eyes of their sex partners, however, delayed ejaculation may make them better lovers.

The testes may decrease slightly in size and produce less testosterone with age. Testosterone production usually declines gradually from about age 40 to 60, and then begins to level off. However, the decline is not inevitable and may be related to the man's general health. Sperm production tends to decline as the seminiferous tubules degenerate, but viable sperm may be produced quite late in life. Men in their seventies, eighties, even nineties have fathered children.

Nocturnal erections tend to diminish in intensity, duration, and frequency as men age, but they do not normally disappear in healthy men (Reinisch, 1990; Schiavi et al., 1990). The refractory period tends to lengthen with age. An adolescent may require only a few minutes to regain erection and ejaculate again after a first orgasm, whereas a man in his thirties may require half an hour. Past age 50, the refractory period may increase to several hours.

As men age, the sensations of ejaculatory inevitability that occur during the emission stage of ejaculation may disappear. Older men produce less ejaculate, and it may seep rather than shoot out. Though the contractions of orgasm still begin at 0.8-second intervals, they become weaker and fewer. Still, the number and strength of spasms do not translate precisely into subjective pleasure. An elderly male may enjoy orgasm as thoroughly as he did at a younger age. Attitudes and expectations can be as important as the contractions themselves.

An 82-year-old man commented on his changing sexual abilities:

> I come maybe once in every three sexual encounters these days with my wife. My erection comes and goes, and it's not a big concern to us. I get as much pleasure from touching and thrusting as I do from an ejaculation. When I was younger it was inconceivable to me that I might enjoy sex without an orgasm, but I can see now that in those days I missed out on some pleasure by making orgasm such a focus.
>
> (Gordon & Snyder, 1989, p. 153)

Following orgasm, erection subsides more rapidly than in a younger man. A study of 65 healthy men ages 45 to 74 showed an age-related decline in sexual desire, arousal, and activity. Yet there were no differences between younger and older men in level of sexual satisfaction or enjoyment (Schiavi et al., 1990).

In sum, most physical changes do not bring a man or a woman's sexual life to a grinding halt. People's attitudes, sexual histories, and partners are usually more important factors in sexual behavior and enjoyment.

PATTERNS OF SEXUAL ACTIVITY

Despite the decline in certain physical functions, elderly people can continue to lead a vibrant and fulfilling sexual life. In fact, years of sexual experience may more than compensate for any diminution of physical responsiveness. In one survey of 800 U.S. inhabitants ages 60 through 91, nearly three out of four who had remained sexually active reported that lovemaking had become more rewarding over the years (Starr & Weiner, 1981). Unfortunately, people who overreact to expected changes in sexual response may conclude that their sexual lives are over and give up on sexual activity or even on expressing any physical affection (Reinisch, 1990).

Ninety-four percent of the men and 84 percent of the women in Kinsey's samples remained sexually active at the age of 60. Even the very elderly tend to maintain a sexual interest. Half of the 60- to 91-year-olds surveyed by Starr and Weiner (1981) reported sexual relations on a regular basis; and half of these, at least once a week. A more recent study of 200 healthy 80- to 102-year-olds reported that 30 percent of the women and 62 percent of the men still engaged in intercourse (Bretschneider & McCoy, 1988). Sex therapist Helen Singer Kaplan (1990) concludes:

Teaching Tip: Instead of lecturing about sexual behavior in later years, pose the following questions to students. Allow discussion to proceed on each until the major points have been discussed. 1) What myths do we believe about the sex lives of people over 50, 60, or 70 years of age? 2) What physiological changes occur in females? In males? 3) What effects do these changes have on sexual behavior? 4) Which sexual behaviors with what frequency are typical of older adults?

The loss of sexuality is not an inevitable aspect of aging. . . . The results of these studies are remarkable in their consensus: Without exception, each investigator found that, providing they are in good health, the great majority of people remain sexually functional and active on a regular basis until virtually the end of life. Or, to put it more succinctly, 70 percent of healthy 70-year-olds remain sexually active, and are having sex at least once a week, and typically more often than that . . . .

Although it is widely believed that sex no longer matters after middle age, the opposite is true, and sex often becomes *more* and not *less* important as a person grows older. Because sex is among the last pleasure-giving biological processes to deteriorate, it is potentially an enduring source of gratification at a time when these are becoming fewer and fewer, and a link to the joys of youth. These are important ingredients in the elderly person's emotional well-being (pp. 185, 204).

Coital frequency does tend to decline with age. One study of spouses married for more than 50 years showed that nearly half (47%) had discontinued intercourse, and 92 percent reported a decline over the years (Ade-Ridder, 1985). Several factors played a role in declining activity, including physical problems, boredom, and cultural attitudes toward sex among the aging. Despite general trends, sexuality among the elderly is variable (Knox, 1988). Many elderly people engage in intercourse, oral sex, and masturbation at least as often as when younger; some become disgusted by sex; others simply lose interest. A six-year longitudinal study of older married couples found that one in five actually increased their coital frequency over time (Palmore, 1981).

Coital frequency, however, is not synonymous with sexual satisfaction. In a Canadian study of 215 married people who were middle-aged and older (51 to 81 years of age), those age 65 or above showed lower coital frequency than younger respondents (Libman, 1989). No sizable differences emerged in the level of sexual satisfaction between older and younger groups, however.

Masturbation also generally declines with age for both men and women, although an increase may occur following a marital separation, divorce, or death of a spouse (Hegeler & Mortensen, 1977). Still, continued masturbation was reported by nearly half (46%) among a sample of people ages 60 to 91 (Starr & Weiner, 1981). This is a high level of acceptance among people who were reared during a time when masturbation was generally viewed as harmful (Kammeyer et al., 1990).

Couples may accommodate to the physical changes of aging by broadening their sexual repertoire to include more diverse forms of stimulation. Many respondents to a *Consumer Reports* survey reported using oral-genital stimulation, sexual fantasy, sexually explicit materials, anal stimulation, vibrators, and other sexual techniques to offset problems in achieving lubrication or erection (Brecher, 1984). Sexual satisfaction may be derived from manual or oral stimulation, cuddling, caressing, and tenderness, as well as from intercourse to orgasm (Kammeyer, 1990).

The availability of a sexually interested and supportive partner may be the most important determinant of continued sexual activity. In one survey, the most common reason women gave for discontinuing sexual activity was the death of their husbands (Pfeiffer et al., 1972). Lack of a partner is a special concern for women. Women's life expectancy exceeds men's by an average of seven years (71.3 years for men versus 78.3 years for women). This is one reason that one older woman in two lives without a spouse, as compared to one man in five (Gordon & Snyder, 1989). About 50 percent of all women over the age of 65 have been widowed, as compared to only 13 percent of men over age 65 (U.S. Bureau of the Census, 1987). Not surprisingly, loneliness was the problem most frequently reported (55%) among a sample of 36 widows (Haas-Hawkings et al., 1985).

Perhaps nowhere is sexuality among the elderly subject to greater distortions than in nursing homes and "old-age" homes (Gordon & Snyder, 1989; Pratt & Schmall, 1989). The staff of these facilities tend to treat the residents as sexless beings and may be stunned to discover them involved in sexual activity. In many cases sexual activities among residents are actively discouraged. Gordon and Snyder (1989) argue that no one—not staff members of the facilities, nor the person's own children—has a right to dictate to older persons about sex.

SEX AND DISABILITY

Sex and the Disabled.
Most people with disabilities have the same sexual needs, feelings, and desires as people without disabilities, and they are capable of expressing their sexuality in ways that can be pleasurable for themselves and their partners.

Learning Objective 11:
Discuss the myths about and the societal reactions to the sexuality of disabled people.

Like the elderly, people with disabilities, especially those whose physical disabilities render them dependent on others, are often seen as occupying a permanent and sexless childlike role (Asch & Rousso, 1985). Such views are based on misconceptions about the sexual functioning of people with disabilities. Some of these myths and stereotypes may be eroding, however, in part due to the success of the civil and social rights movements of the disabled in the 1970s and the attention focused on the sexuality of people with disabilities in such films as *Coming Home, Born on the Fourth of July,* and *My Left Foot* (Knight, 1989).

A person may have been born with or acquire a bodily impairment, or suffer a loss of function or a disfiguring change in appearance. Although the disability may require the person to make adjustments in order to perform sexually, most people with disabilities have the same sexual needs, feelings, and desires as people without disabilities. Their ability to express their sexual feelings and needs depends on the physical limitations imposed by their disabilities, their adjustment to their disabilities, and the availability of partners. The establishment of mature sexual relationships generally demands some distance from one's parents. Therefore, persons with disabilities who are physically dependent on their parents may find it especially difficult to develop sexual relationships (Knight, 1989). Parents who acknowledge their children's sexual development can be helpful by facilitating dating. Far too often, parents become overprotective:

> Adolescent disabled girls have the same ideas, hopes, and dreams about sexuality as able-bodied girls. They will have learned the gender role expectations set for them by the media and others and may experience difficulty if they lack more substantive educational information about sexuality and sex function. In addition their expectations may come in conflict with the family which may have consistently protected or overindulged the child and not permitted her to "grow up.". . . In many cases the families are intensely concerned about the sexual and emotional vulnerability of the daughter and hope that "nothing bad" will happen to her. They may, therefore, encourage her to wear youthful clothing and to stay a safe little girl. The families can mistakenly assume there may be no sexual life ahead of her and protect her from this perceived bitter reality with youthful clothing and little-girlish ways. The result can be, of course, that the young emerging woman may become societally handicapped in learning how to conduct herself as a sexual woman. She will be infantilized.

> (Cole, 1988, pp. 282–283)

In such families young people with disabilities get the message that sex is not for them (Stavros, 1991). As they mature they may need counseling to help them recognize the normalcy of their sexual feelings and to help them make responsible choices for exploring their sexuality.

CEREBRAL PALSY

Cerebral palsy
A muscular disorder that is caused by damage to the central nervous system (usually prior to or during birth) and characterized by spastic paralysis.

Discussion Question: How could we change societal myths about disabled peoples' sexuality? Be specific. What do we teach? To whom? When?

Cerebral palsy does not generally impair sexual interest, capacity for orgasm, or fertility (Reinisch, 1990). Depending on the nature and degree of muscle spasticity or lack of voluntary muscle control, however, afflicted people may be limited in their types of sexual activities and coital positions.

The importance of sex education for disabled people is highlighted by a case of a man with cerebral palsy:

> A 40-year-old man with moderate cerebral palsy came to see me for sexual counseling. When asked why he came for counseling, he said, "I think I'm old enough to learn about sex." He was college educated, fully employed, and had been living by himself, away from his parents, for three years. In questioning him further, I found that the extent of his sexual knowledge was he knew he had a penis but knew nothing about the human sexual response or about female anatomy. When I asked him if any "white, sticky stuff" ever came out of his penis, he replied, "Yes, and doesn't that have something to do with my cerebral palsy?"

> (Knight, 1989, p. 186)

People with disabilities such as cerebral palsy often suffer social rejection during adolescence and perceive themselves as unfit or unworthy of intimate sexual relationships, especially with people who are not disabled. They are often socialized into an asexual role. Sensitive counseling can help them understand and accept their sexuality, promote a more positive body image, and provide the social skills to establish intimate relationships (Edmonson, 1988; Rousso, 1982).

SPINAL-CORD INJURIES

Learning Objective 12: Describe the challenges associated with sexual relations between people with various disabilities and their partners.

Persons who suffer physical disabilities as the result of traumatic injuries or physical illness must not only learn to cope with their physical limitations but also adjust to a world designed for nondisabled people (Trieschmann, 1989). Spinal-cord injuries affect about 6,000 to 10,000 people annually in the United States (Seftel et al., 1991). The majority of persons who suffer disabling spinal-cord injuries are young, active males. Automobile or pedestrian accidents account for about half of these cases. Other common causes include stabbing or bullet wounds, sports injuries, and falls. Depending on the location of the injury to the spinal cord, a loss of voluntary control (paralysis) can occur in either the legs (*paraplegia*) or all four limbs (*quadriplegia*). A loss of sensation may also occur in parts of the body that lie beneath the site of injury. Most people who suffer such injuries have relatively normal life spans, but the quality of their lives is profoundly affected.

The effect of spinal-cord injuries on sexual response depends on the site and severity of the injury. As you may recall (see Chapter 4), men have two erection centers in the spinal cord, a higher one located in the lumbar region that controls psychogenic erections, and a lower one, the sacral erection center, that controls reflexive erections. When damage occurs at or above the level of the lumbar center, the man loses the capacity for psychogenic erections, the kinds of erections that occur in response to mental stimulation alone, such as when viewing erotic films or fantasizing. They may still be able to achieve reflexive erections from direct stimulation of the penis, as these erections are controlled by the sacral erection center located in a lower portion of the spinal cord. However, they cannot feel any genital sensations because the nerve connections to the brain are severed. Men with damage to the sacral erection center lose the capacity for reflexive erections but can still achieve psychogenic erections so long as their upper spinal cords remain intact (Spark, 1991). Overall, researchers find that about three of four men with spinal-cord injuries are able to achieve erections but only about one in ten continue to ejaculate naturally (Geiger, 1981; Spark, 1991). Others can be helped to ejaculate with the aid of a vibrator (Szasz & Carpenter, 1989). Their brains may help to fill in some of the missing sensations associated with coitus and even orgasm. When direct stimulation does not cause erection, the woman can stuff the limp penis into the vagina and gently thrust her hips, taking care not to dislodge the penis.

Although the frequency of sexual activity among spinal-cord-injured men tends to decline following the injury (Alexander et al., 1993), a study of almost 1,300 men with these injuries found that about one out of three (35%) continued to engage in sexual intercourse (Spark, 1991). Only about one in five of the men received any kind of sexual counseling to help them adjust sexually to their disability. The men typically reported increased interest in alternative sexual activities, especially those involving areas above the level of the spinal injury, such as those involving the mouth, lips, neck, and ears.

In women, as in men, retention of sexual response depends on the site and severity of the injury (Seftel et al., 1991). Women may lose the ability to experience genital sensations or to lubricate normally during sexual stimulation. However, breast sensations may remain intact, making this area even more erotogenic. Most women with spinal-cord injuries can engage in coitus, become impregnated, and deliver vaginally. A recent survey of 27 spinal-cord-injured women showed that about half were able to experience orgasm after their injuries (Kettl et al., 1991). Some also report "phantom orgasms" that provide intense psychological pleasure and that are accompanied by nongenital physical sensations that are similar to those experienced by nondisabled women (Perduta-

Fulginiti, 1992). Spinal-cord-injured women can heighten their sexual pleasure by learning to use fantasized orgasm, orgasmic imagery, and amplification of their physical sensations (Perduta-Fulginiti, 1992).

People who are paralyzed due to spinal-cord injuries cannot become sexually aroused or engage in coitus. *Actually, people who are paralyzed due to spinal-cord injuries usually* can *become sexually aroused and engage in coitus. Most spinal-cord-injured women can become impregnated and bear healthy children.* •

Couples facing the challenge of spinal-cord injury may expand their sexual repertoire to focus less on genital stimulation (except to attain the reflexes of erection and lubrication) and more on parts of the body that retain sensation. Stimulation of some areas of the body such as the ears, the neck, and the breasts (in both men and women) can yield pleasurable erotic sensations (Knight, 1989; Seftel et al., 1991).

SENSORY DISABILITIES

Sensory disabilities, such as blindness or deafness, do not directly affect genital responsiveness. Still, a person's sexuality may be affected in a number of ways. A person who has been blind since birth or early childhood may have difficulty understanding a partner's anatomy. Sex education curricula have been designed specifically to enable visually impaired people to learn about sexual anatomy via models. Anatomically correct dolls may be used to simulate positions of intercourse.

Deaf persons, too, often lack knowledge about sex. Their ability to comprehend the social cues involved in forming and maintaining intimate relationships may also be impaired. Sex education programs based on sign language are helping many hearing-impaired people become more socially perceptive as well as knowledgeable about the physical aspects of sex. Persons with visual and hearing impairments often lack self-esteem and self-confidence, which makes it difficult for them to establish intimate relationships. Sexual counseling may help them become more aware of their sexuality and develop social skills.

OTHER PHYSICAL DISABILITIES AND IMPAIRMENTS

Arthritis
A progressive disease that is characterized by inflammation or pain in the joints.

Specific disabilities pose particular challenges to, and limitations on, sexual functioning. **Arthritis** may make it difficult or painful for sufferers to bend their arms, knees, and hips during sexual activity (Ehrlich, 1988). Coital positions that minimize discomfort and the application of moist heat to the joints before sexual relations may be helpful.

A male amputee may find that he is better balanced in the lateral or female-superior position than in the male-superior position (Knight, 1989). A woman with limited hand function may find it difficult or impossible to insert a diaphragm and may need to request assistance from her partner or switch to another contraceptive (Cole, 1988). Sensitivity to each other's needs is as vital to disabled couples as to the nondisabled.

PSYCHOLOGICAL DISABILITIES

Persons with psychological disabilities, such as mental retardation, are often stereotyped as incapable of understanding their sexual impulses. The retarded are sometimes assumed to maintain childlike innocence through their lives, or to be devoid of sexuality. Some stereotype the retarded in the opposite direction: as having stronger-than-normal sex drives and being incapable of controlling them (Reinisch, 1990). Some mentally retarded people do act inappropriately—by masturbating publicly, for example. The stereotypes are exaggerated, however, and even many of those who act inappropriately can be trained to follow social rules (Reinisch, 1990).

Parents and caretakers often discourage the retarded from learning about their sexuality or teach them to deny or suppress their sexual feelings. Although the physical changes of puberty may be delayed in mentally retarded people, most develop normal sexual needs (Edmonson, 1988). Most are capable of learning about their sexuality and can be guided into rewarding and responsible intimate relationships.

One of the greatest impediments to sexual fulfillment among people with disabilities is finding a loving and supportive partner. Some people engage in sexual relations with people with disabilities out of sympathy. By and large, however, the partners are other people with disabilities or nondisabled people who have overcome stereotypes that portray disabled people as undesirable. Many partners have had some prior positive relationship with a person with a disability, usually during childhood (Knight, 1989). Experience facilitates acceptance of the idea that a disabled person can be desirable. Depending on the nature of the disability, the nondisabled partner may need to be open to assuming a more active sexual role to compensate for the limitations of the partner with the disability. Two partners with disabilities need to be sensitive to each other's needs and physical limitations. People with disabilities and their partners may also need to expand their sexual repertoires to incorporate ways of pleasuring each other that are not as fixated on genital stimulation.

The message is simple: Sexuality may enrich the lives of nearly all adults at virtually any age.

SUMMING UP

SINGLEHOOD

Recent years have seen a sharp increase in the numbers of single young people in our society.

Reasons include increased permissiveness toward premarital sex and, particularly for women, the

desire to become established in a career. No one lifestyle characterizes single people.

COHABITATION: DARLING, WOULD YOU BE MY POSSLQ?

Who Are the Cohabitors?
Cohabitation is more prevalent among the less well-educated and less affluent classes.
Reasons for Cohabitation
Some couples prefer cohabitation because it provides a consistent intimate relationship without the legal and economic entanglements

of marriage. Some emotionally committed couples cohabit because of the economic advantages of sharing household expenses.
Styles of Cohabitation
Sociologists have noted three styles of cohabitation: part-time/limited cohabitation, premarital cohabitation, and substitute marriage.

Cohabitation and Later Marriage: A Benefit or a Risk? Cohabitors who later marry may run a greater risk of divorce than noncohabitors, perhaps because cohabitors are a more liberal group.

MARRIAGE

Marriage is found in all human societies and is our most common lifestyle.
Historical Perspectives In historic patriarchies, the man of the house had the right to choose

wives for his sons and could himself take concubines or additional wives.
Why Do People Marry?
Throughout Western history, marriages have legitimized sexual

relations, sanctioned the permanence of a deeply committed intimate relationship, provided for the orderly transmission of wealth, and provided a setting for child rearing. In Western society today, romantic love is seen as an essential aspect of marriage.

Types of Marriage The major types of marriage are monogamy and polygamy. Polygamy includes polygyny and polyandry.

Whom Do We Marry: Are Marriages Made in Heaven or in the Neighborhood? People in the United States tend to marry within their geographical area and social class. They tend to marry people similar in physical attractiveness, who share similar attitudes, and who seem likely to meet their material, sexual, and psychological needs.

MARITAL SEXUALITY

Until the sexual revolution, Western culture could be characterized as sexually restrictive, even in its attitudes toward marital sex.

The Sexual Revolution Hits Home Married couples today engage in coitus more frequently and for longer durations of time than in Kinsey's day. They report higher levels of sexual satisfaction and engage in a greater variety of sexual activities.

Sexual Satisfaction U.S. women are more likely to reach orgasm through marital sex than in Kinsey's day. Wives take more active sexual roles than in Kinsey's day.

EXTRAMARITAL SEX

In most cases extramarital relationships are conducted without the spouse's knowledge or approval. People may have affairs for sexual variety, to punish their spouses, to achieve emotional closeness, or to prove that they are attractive.

Patterns of Extramarital Sex Precise figures on the prevalence of extramarital sex are lacking.

Effects of Extramarital Sex The discovery of infidelity can evoke anger, jealousy, even shame. Affairs often, but not always, damage marriages.

Attitudes Toward Extramarital Sex Extramarital sex continues to be viewed negatively by the majority of married people in our society.

Swinging Only a small minority of married couples engage in swinging.

DIVORCE

About half the marriages in the United States end in divorce. Reasons include relaxed restrictions on divorce, greater financial independence among women, and the idea that marriages should be happy.

The Cost of Divorce Divorce is often associated with financial and emotional problems, however. Divorce can give rise to feelings of failure and depression, and make it difficult to rear children.

ALTERNATIVE FORMS OF MARRIAGE

Alternative marital styles such as open marriages and group marriages permit intimate relationships with people outside the marriage.

Open Marriage Open marriages allow each partner open companionship and personal privacy, which may allow sexual intimacy with others.

Group Marriage In a group marriage, three or more people share an intimate relationship, although they are not legally married.

SEX IN THE LATER YEARS

There are a number of unfounded cultural myths about sexuality among older people, including the stereotypes that older people are sexless and that older people with sexual urges are abnormal.

Physical Changes Physical changes as the years pass can impair sexual activity. Many potential problems can be averted by changing our expectations and making changes to accommodate the aging process.

Patterns of Sexual Activity Sexual activity tends to decline with age, but continued sexual activity can boost self-esteem and be an important source of gratification.

SEX AND DISABILITY

People with disabilities may suffer from prejudice that depicts them as sexless or as lacking the means to express their sexual needs or feelings.

Cerebral Palsy Cerebral palsy does not usually impair sexual interest, capacity for orgasm, or fertility, but afflicted people may be limited in their types of sexual activities and coital positions.

Spinal-Cord Injuries People with spinal-cord injuries may be paralyzed and lose sensation below the waist. They often respond reflexively to direct genital stimulation, however, and are often fertile and can bear children.

Sensory Disabilities Sensory disabilities do not directly affect sexual response but may impair sexual knowledge and social skills.

Psychological Disabilities Most mentally retarded people can learn the basics of their own sexuality and develop responsible intimate relationships.

_____ Sexual dysfunctions are rather rare.

_____ The most common cause of painful intercourse in women is vaginal infection.

_____ Women on the island of Inis Beag off the Irish coast are biologically incapable of experiencing orgasm.

_____ In sex therapy, a man with erectile dysfunction is taught how to will an erection.

_____ Many sex therapists recommend masturbation as the treatment for women who have never been able to reach orgasm.

_____ A man can be prevented from ejaculating by squeezing his penis when he feels that he is about to do so.

C H A P T E R *15*

Sexual Dysfunctions and Sex Therapy

Until recently, Derek Jones, 39, and his wife Pam, 37, had not attempted coitus for five years. Their sexual relations had been limited to fondling and caressing each other and to occasional oral-genital contact. They had given up at coitus because of Derek's persistent difficulty in attaining and sustaining erections. But recently they had begun trying again. Some nights Derek would have an erection enabling him to penetrate, only to find that he ejaculated too rapidly. Many nights he was unable to perform at all. Each failure was yet another blow to Derek's self-esteem. Pam kept secret her belief that he could not perform because he was no longer sexually attracted to her.

Terry, 24, has decided she is built differently from friends and women she reads about. They all reach orgasm, it seems, at the drop of a hat. But she has never managed "one of those things." Her husband David, also 24, is considerate, but Terry knows that he, too, is frustrated and feels guilty with every ejaculation. Why should he enjoy sex if Terry cannot? Sex has become a chore rather than a source of pleasure, and David has been having some difficulty attaining erection. Terry wonders whether she should try to fake orgasm to hold on to him. But she is too embarrassed to ask a friend how to act.

(The Authors' Files)

Sexual dysfunction
Persistent or recurrent difficulties in becoming sexually aroused or reaching orgasm.

Discussion Question: What if early sex education emphasized how common it is to have sexual problems occasionally? What if sex education emphasized mutual pleasure instead of goal-oriented sex to orgasm? Might fewer people experience shame, guilt, and anxiety about sexual performance?

Derek and Terry have **sexual dysfunctions.** That is, they have difficulties in becoming sexually aroused or reaching orgasm. Many of us are troubled by sexual problems from time to time. Men occasionally have difficulty achieving an erection or ejaculate more rapidly than they would like. Most women occasionally have difficulty achieving orgasm or becoming sufficiently lubricated. People are not considered to have a sexual dysfunction unless the problem is persistent and causes distress, however.

Although there are different types of sexual dysfunctions, they share some common features (see Table 15.1). People with sexual dysfunctions may avoid sexual opportunities for fear of failure. They may anticipate that sex will result in frustration or physical pain rather than pleasure and gratification. Because of the emphasis placed upon sexual competence in our culture, people with sexual dysfunctions may feel inadequate or incompetent, feelings that diminish their self-esteem. They may experience a range of negative emotions, including guilt, shame, frustration, depression, and anxiety.

Many people with sexual dysfunctions find it difficult to talk about their problems with others, even their spouses or helping professionals. A woman who is unable to achieve orgasm with her husband may begin faking orgasms

---

TABLE 15.1 Common features of sexual dysfunctions

Fear of failure	Fears relating to failure to achieve or maintain erection or failure to reach orgasm.
Assumption of a spectator role rather than a performer role	Monitoring and evaluating your body's reactions during sex.
Diminished self-esteem	Thinking less of yourself for failure to meet your standard of normality.
Emotional effects	Guilt, shame, frustration, depression, anxiety.
Avoidance behavior	Avoiding sexual contacts for fear of failure to perform adequately; making excuses to your partner.

Source: Adapted from *DSM–III–R*, (1987). American Psychiatric Association. pp. 291–292.

TABLE 15.2 Estimated prevalence of various current sexual dysfunctions (percentage of respondents reporting any problem)

Premature ejaculation	36–38	–
Erectile dysfunction	4–9	–
Inhibited male orgasm	4–10	–
Inhibited female orgasm	5–10	–

Source: Adapted from Spector, I. M., & Carey, M. P. (1990). Incidence and prevalence of the sexual dysfunctions: A critical review of the empirical evidence. *Archives of Sexual Behavior, 19,* 389-408. Reprinted with permission of Plenum Publishing.

rather than "make a fuss." A man with erectile dysfunction may find it difficult to voice his concerns to his physician during his annual physical. Many physicians are also uncomfortable talking about sexual matters. They may never inquire about sexual problems.

Because so many people are reluctant to admit to sexual difficulties, we do not have precise figures on their frequencies. The best information we have is based on a recent review of community surveys conducted during the past 40 years (Spector & Carey, 1990; see Table 15.2). Overall, slightly more than one in three men in community surveys (36–38%) report problems of premature (too rapid) ejaculation. Lower percentages report currently having difficulty achieving or maintaining erections (erectile dysfunction) or reaching orgasm (inhibited orgasm). A large community survey in Massachusetts of 1,709 men ages 40 to 70 found a much higher percentage of lifetime occurrence of erectile dysfunction in this age group. Fifty-two percent of the men polled had experienced the problem to varying degrees (Altman, 1993i). Erectile problems increased steadily with age. The prevalence of complete erectile failure increased from 5 percent among the 40-year-old men to 15 percent among the 70-year-olds. We caution that the methodologies of these various surveys differed, and none can be considered truly representative of the U.S. population at large. As a result, the actual prevalences of these problems in the general population as a whole may, and most probably do, vary from the reported rates.

TRUTH OR FICTION?

R E V I S I T E D

Sexual dysfunctions are rather rare. To the contrary—they are quite common. •

TYPES OF SEXUAL DYSFUNCTIONS

The most widely used system of classification of sexual dysfunctions is based upon the American Psychiatric Association's *Diagnostic and Statistical Manual of Mental Disorders* (the DSM). The DSM, which is now in its fourth edition, the DSM-IV, groups most sexual dysfunctions within the following four categories:

Sexual desire disorders Sexual dysfunctions in which people have persistent or recurrent lack of sexual desire or aversion to sexual contact.

1. **Sexual desire disorders** involve dysfunctions in sexual desire, interest, or drive, in which the person experiences a lack of sexual desire or an aversion to genital sexual contact.

Learning Objective 1: Name and describe the two sexual desire disorders and discuss factors that may contribute to their development.

Discussion Question: Speculate on the cause(s) of the gender shift in cases of lack of desire between the 1970s and the 1980s. What societal changes might account for this change? How much do our busy lifestyles contribute to lack of sexual desire?

2. **Sexual arousal disorders.** Sexual arousal is principally characterized by erection in the male and vaginal lubrication and swelling of the external genitalia in the female. In men, sexual arousal disorders involve recurrent difficulty in achieving or sustaining erections sufficient to successfully engage in sexual intercourse. In women, they typically involve failure to become sufficiently lubricated.

3. **Orgasm disorders.** Men or women may encounter difficulties achieving orgasm or may reach orgasm more rapidly than they would like. Women are more likely to encounter difficulties reaching orgasm; men are more likely to experience overly rapid orgasm (premature ejaculation). But some men experience inhibited orgasm during coitus, and a few women complain of overly rapid orgasms.

4. **Sexual pain disorders.** Both men and women may suffer from **dyspareunia** (painful intercourse). Women may experience **vaginismus,** which prevents penetration by the penis or renders penetration painful.

Sexual dysfunctions may also be classified as either lifelong or acquired. *Lifelong* dysfunctions have existed throughout the person's lifetime. *Acquired* dysfunctions develop following a period of normal functioning. They also may be classified as generalized or situational. *Generalized* dysfunctions affect a person's general sexual functioning. *Situational* dysfunctions affect sexual functioning only in some sexual situations (such as during coitus but not during masturbation) or occur with some partners but not with others. Consider, for example, a man who has never been able to achieve or maintain an erection during sexual relations with a partner but can do so during masturbation. His dysfunction would be classified as lifelong and situational.

SEXUAL DESIRE DISORDERS

Disorders of sexual desire involve lack of sexual desire or interest and/or aversion to genital sexual activity. Although the prevalence of these disorders in the general population is not known, sex therapists report an increase in their frequency over the past generation. They are now the most common complaint of couples seeking sex therapy (Spector & Carey, 1990; Stuart et al., 1987).

LACK OF SEXUAL DESIRE   People with little or no sexual interest or desire are said to have *hypoactive sexual desire disorder* (formerly called *inhibited sexual desire*). They also often report an absence of sexual fantasies. Whereas women accounted for most cases of low sexual desire in the mid-1970s (LoPiccolo & Friedman, 1988), the number of cases among men appears to have increased in recent years (Letourneau & O'Donohue, 1993) and may actually have surpassed the numbers accounted for by women (Spector & Carey, 1990). Whatever the actual gender distribution, the belief that men are always eager and willing to engage in sexual activity is no more than a myth (Knox, 1988).

Lack of sexual desire does not imply that a person is unable to achieve erection, lubricate adequately, or reach orgasm (Goleman, 1988). Some people with low sexual desire have such problems, but many can become sexually aroused and reach orgasm when stimulated adequately. Many enjoy sex, even if they are unlikely to initiate or seek genital sexual activity. Many appreciate the affection and closeness of physical intimacy, but have no interest in genital stimulation.

Hypoactive sexual desire is one of the most commonly diagnosed sexual dysfunctions (Letourneau & O'Donohue, 1993). Yet there is no clear consensus among clinicians and researchers concerning the definition of low sexual desire. How much sexual interest or desire is "normal"? There is no standard level of sexual desire—no 98.6-degree reading on the "sexual thermometer." Lack of desire is usually considered a problem when couples recognize that their level of sexual interest has gotten so low that little remains. Sometimes the lack of desire is limited to one partner. When one member of a couple is more interested in sex than the other, sex therapists often try to help the couple fashion a compromise in their level of sexual activity rather than focus only on boosting the interest of the disinclined partner (Goleman, 1988). They also try to uncover and

Hypogonadism
An endocrine disorder that reduces the output of testosterone.

resolve any underlying relationship problems that may dampen the sexual ardor of one or both partners.

Various biological and psychosocial factors such as hormonal deficiencies, depression, and marital dissatisfaction are believed to contribute to lack of desire. Numerous medical conditions may diminish sexual desire, including testosterone deficiencies, thyroid overactivity or underactivity, and temporal lobe epilepsy (Kresin, 1993). Sexual desire is stoked by testosterone, which is produced by men in the testes and by both genders in the adrenal glands. Women may experience less sexual desire when their adrenal glands are surgically removed. Low sexual interest, along with erectile difficulties, are also common among men with **hypogonadism** (Carani et al., 1990). Women with inhibited sexual desire usually have normal levels of the hormones testosterone, estrogen, and progesterone, however (Schreiner-Engle et al., 1989; Stuart et al., 1987). The role of hormones in lack of desire among physically healthy men and women remains unclear.

Researchers find men with hypoactive sexual desire disorder to be older than women with the disorder (Segraves & Segraves, 1991a). A gradual decline in sexual desire, at least among men, may be explained in part by the reduction in testosterone levels that occurs in middle and later life. Abrupt changes in sexual desire, however, are more often explained by psychological and interpersonal factors such as depression, emotional stress, and problems in the relationship (Goleman, 1988; Leiblum & Rosen, 1988; Schreiner-Engle & Schiavi, 1986).

In one study, women with low sexual desire reported less satisfaction with their marital relationships than did other women (Stuart et al., 1987). Women with low sexual desire also reported lower levels of enjoyment and emotional satisfaction in their sexual relationships with their husbands. Although dissatisfaction with the sexual aspects of their marital relationships may have reduced their sexual interest, such evidence is correlational and does not pinpoint cause and effect. Marital or sexual dissatisfaction may dampen sexual appetite, but lack of sexual desire may also increase marital strains and dissatisfaction.

Various psychological problems can contribute to low sexual desire (Letourneau & O'Donohue, 1993). Anxiety is the most commonly reported factor. Various types of anxiety may be involved in dampening sexual desire, including performance anxiety (anxiety over being evaluated negatively), anxiety involving fears of pleasure or loss of control, and deeper sources of anxiety relating to fears of castration or injury. Depression is also a common cause of inhibited desire. A history of sexual assault has also been linked to low sexual desire.

Marital Conflict and Sexual Desire. Not only may marital conflicts dampen sexual interest, lack of sexual interest may increase marital strain and dissatisfaction.

Parents as Models. Parental examples are important modeling influences in shaping a child's development. Parents who are warm and affectionate toward each other model loving interactions which can help children develop a healthy attitude toward intimate relationships.

Lack of sexual desire may also have childhood roots. In the Stuart study (Stuart et al., 1987), women with lower sexual desire more often perceived their parents as having negative attitudes toward sex and as displaying little affection toward one another than did women with normal levels of desire. Parental attitudes and examples set by parents may dampen the development of sexual interest in some women. So, too, may cultural controls placed on women's sexuality (Richgels, 1992). Fears of sexual arousal may also play a role, at least among people who hold back from becoming sexually aroused or experiencing sexual pleasure. Such people may be unaware that they are inhibiting their sexual desires.

Certain medications, including those used to control anxiety or hypertension, may also reduce desire. Changing medications or dosage levels may return the person's previous level of desire.

SEXUAL AVERSION DISORDER   People with low sexual desire may have little or no interest in sex, but they are not repelled by genital contact. Some people, however, find sex disgusting or aversive and avoid genital contact.

Sexual aversions are less common than lack of desire and remain poorly understood (Spark, 1991). Some researchers consider sexual aversion to be a *sexual phobia* or *sexual panic state* with intense, irrational fears of sexual contact and a pressing desire to avoid sexual situations (Kaplan, 1987). Sexual aversion in men is often associated with a history of erectile failure (Spark, 1991). Such men may find sexual situations anxiety-evoking because of their association with failure and shame. Their partners may also develop an aversion to sexual contact because of this anxiety and because of their own frustration. A history of sexual trauma, such as rape or childhood sexual abuse or incest, often figures prominently in cases of sexual aversion, especially in women.

SEXUAL AROUSAL DISORDERS

When we are sexually stimulated, our bodies normally respond with **vasocongestion,** which produces erection in the male and vaginal lubrication in the female. People with disorders of sexual arousal, however, fail to achieve or sustain the lubrication or erection necessary to facilitate sexual activity. Or they lack the subjective feelings of sexual pleasure or excitement that normally accompany sexual arousal (American Psychiatric Association, 1987).

Problems of sexual arousal have sometimes been labeled *impotence* in the male and *frigidity* in the female. But these terms are pejorative, so many professionals prefer to use less threatening, more descriptive, labels.

Learning Objective 2: Name the sexual arousal disorders in males and females and discuss factors that may contribute to their development.

Vasocongestion
Engorgement of blood vessels with blood, which swells the genitals and breasts during sexual arousal.

A Case of Lifelong Erectile Dysfunction: "The Singer in the Band"

Cliff, 29, was a singer in a rock band, playing local clubs and private parties. His hair was styled in the contemporary fashion of a rock star, but very little else about him fit the stereotype. He didn't drink, smoke, take drugs, or party to all hours of the night. Perhaps most surprisingly, Cliff was still a virgin. He did not expose this "secret," as he put it, to anyone but his therapist. The members of the band had wondered about his sexual orientation, since Cliff would reject the advances of female admirers. He dated infrequently and hardly ever beyond a first date. His hesitation to engage in coitus did not reflect a personal commitment to celibacy, homosexual leanings, or lack of sexual interest. He was immobilized by an overwhelming fear of failure to perform sexually. Cliff reported that he always felt best when he was singing—like he was on top of the world. "It was funny," he would say, "people would think I had everything going for me." They would not know that Cliff felt inadequate and inferior to other men because he couldn't perform "like a man."

Cliff had first attempted intercourse at 17 with a girl from the neighborhood. She had aggressively pursued him, even giving him written sexual invitations. He described their first encounter as a disaster. He lost his erection at the point of penetration and tried desperately but unsuccessfully to penetrate with a flaccid penis. There were several other such frustrating experiences in the next few years, always with the same disappointing outcome. Eventually, he gave up trying, finding excuses with his dating partners for his fear of pursuing sexual activity, breaking off relationships that had become too intimate.

(The Authors' Files)

Male erectile disorder
Persistent difficulty achieving or maintaining an erection sufficient to allow the man to engage in or complete sexual intercourse. Also termed *erectile dysfunction.*

MALE ERECTILE DISORDER   Sexual arousal disorder in the male, called **male erectile disorder** or *erectile dysfunction,* is characterized by persistent difficulty achieving or maintaining an erection sufficient to allow the completion of sexual activity. In most cases the failure is limited to sexual activity with partners, or with some partners and not others, and can thus be classified as *situational.* In rare cases the dysfunction is found during any sexual activity, including masturbation, and is thus considered *generalized.* Some men with erectile dysfunction are unable to attain an erection with their partners. Others can achieve erection but not sustain it (or recover it) long enough for penetration and ejaculation.

Experts estimate that 10 to 15 million men in the United States suffer from erectile dysfunction (Leary, 1992b). Perhaps another 10 million suffer from partial dysfunction. The incidence of erectile disorder increases with age and is believed to affect approximately one in three men over the age of 60. Men with *lifelong* erectile dysfunction (formerly called *primary* erectile dysfunction) never had adequate erectile functioning. Erectile dysfunction far more commonly develops after a period of normal functioning and is classified as *acquired erectile dysfunction* (formerly called *secondary* erectile dysfunction). Many such men engaged in years of successful coitus prior to the problem.

Occasional problems in achieving or maintaining erection are quite common. Fatigue, alcohol, anxiety over impressing a new partner, and other factors may account for a transient episode. Even an isolated occurrence can lead to a persistent problem if the man fears recurrence, however. The more anxious and concerned the man becomes about his sexual ability, the more likely he is to suffer **performance anxiety** during his next sexual opportunity. Anxiety can contribute to repeated failure, and a vicious cycle of anxiety and failure may develop.

Performance anxiety
Anxiety concerning one's ability to perform behaviors, especially behaviors that may be evaluated by other people.

A man with erectile difficulties may try to "will" an erection, which can compound the problem. Each failure may further demoralize and defeat him. He may ruminate about his sexual inadequacy, setting the stage for yet more anxiety. His partner may try to comfort and support him by saying things like, "It can happen to anyone," "Don't

TYPES OF SEXUAL DYSFUNCTIONS   **459**

worry about it," or "It will get better in time." But attempts at reassurance may be to no avail. As one client put it,

> I always felt inferior, like I was on probation, having to prove myself. I felt like I was up against the wall. You can't imagine how embarrassing this [erectile failure] was. It's like you walk out in front of an audience that you think is a nudist convention and it turns out to be a tuxedo convention.
>
> (Rathus & Nevid, 1991, p. 403)

The vicious cycle of anxiety and erectile failure may be interrupted if the man recognizes that occasional problems are normal and does not overreact. The emphasis in our culture on men's sexual prowess may spur them to view occasional failures as catastrophes rather than transient disappointments, however. Viewing occasional problems as an inconvenience, rather than a tragedy, may help avert the development of persistent erectile difficulties.

Performance anxiety is a prominent cause of erectile dysfunction, but so too are other psychological factors, such as depression, lack of self-esteem, and relationship problems (Leary, 1992b). Physiological factors can also play a causative role, as we shall see.

FEMALE SEXUAL AROUSAL DISORDER Women may encounter persistent difficulties becoming sexually excited or sufficiently lubricated in response to sexual stimulation. In some cases these difficulties are lifelong. In others they develop after a period of normal functioning. In some cases difficulties are pervasive and occur during both masturbation and sex with a partner. More often they occur in certain situations, as with some partners and not with others, or during certain sexual activities, like coitus, but not during others, such as oral-genital sex or masturbation.

Data on the prevalence of female sexual arousal disorder remains lacking (Morokoff, 1993). We do know that sexual arousal disorder in females often occurs together with other sexual disorders such as hypoactive sexual desire disorder and orgasm disorders (Segraves & Segraves, 1991b). Despite problems in becoming sexually aroused, women with sexual arousal disorders are often capable of engaging in coitus. Vaginal dryness may produce discomfort, however.

Sexual arousal disorder in the female, like that in the male, may arise from various physical factors (Graber, 1993). A thorough evaluation by a medical specialist (a urologist in the case of a male or a gynecologist in the case of a female) is recommended to uncover physical problems that may be involved. Any neurological, vascular, or hormonal problem that interferes with the lubrication or swelling response of the vagina to sexual stimulation may be a causative factor in sexual arousal disorders in women. For example, diabetes mellitus may lead to diminished sexual excitement in women because of the degeneration of the nerves servicing the clitoris and the blood vessel (vascular) damage it causes. Reduced estrogen production can also result in vaginal dryness. But problems in sexual arousal are more commonly traced to psychological causes. In some cases, women who harbor deep-seated anger and resentment toward their partners may find it difficult to turn off these feelings and become sexually aroused when they go to bed. In other cases, sexual trauma is implicated. Survivors of sexual abuse often find it difficult to respond sexually with their intimate partners. Childhood sexual abuse is especially prevalent in cases of sexual arousal disorder in women (Morokoff, 1993). Feelings of helplessness, anger, or guilt, or even flashbacks of the abuse, may surface when the woman begins sexual activity, dampening her ability to become aroused. Other psychosocial causes include anxiety or guilt about sex and ineffective stimulation by the partner (Morokoff, 1993).

Learning Objective 3:
Describe the three disorders of the orgasm phase and discuss factors that may contribute to their development.

ORGASM DISORDERS

There are three diagnosable disorders relating to the orgasm phase of the sexual response cycle: (1) inhibited female orgasm; (2) inhibited male orgasm; and (3) premature ejaculation.

Inhibited orgasm

A sexual dysfunction characterized by persistent or recurrent delay in reaching orgasm, or failure to reach orgasm at all, despite attaining a level of sexual stimulation of sufficient intensity to normally culminate in orgasm.

In **inhibited orgasm,** the man or woman is persistently delayed in reaching orgasm or does not reach orgasm at all, despite achieving sexual stimulation of sufficient intensity to normally culminate in orgasm. Inhibited orgasm is more common among women than men. In some cases a person can reach orgasm without difficulty while engaging in sexual relations with one partner, but not with another.

INHIBITED MALE ORGASM   Men with inhibited orgasm are described as having *delayed* or *retarded* ejaculation or *ejaculatory incompetence.*[1] The problem may be either lifelong or acquired, generalized or situational. There are very few cases of men who have never ejaculated (Kaplan, 1974). In most cases the disorder is limited to coitus. The man may be capable of ejaculating during masturbation or oral sex, but find it difficult if not impossible, despite high levels of sexual excitement, to ejaculate during intercourse. There is a common myth that men with inhibited orgasm and their female partners enjoy his condition, because it enables him to "go on forever" (Dekker, 1993). Actually, the experience is frustrating for both partners.

Inhibited male orgasm is relatively infrequent in the general population and in clinical practice, where it is among the least frequently diagnosed disorders (Dekker, 1993). Research on the problem has been scarce (Dekker, 1993), and only a few individual or multiple case reports have appeared in the literature (e.g., Masters & Johnson, 1970; Rathus, 1978).

Inhibited orgasm in males may be caused by physical problems such as multiple sclerosis (Kedia, 1983) or neurological damage that interferes with neural control of ejaculation. It may also be a side effect of certain drugs (Ban & Freyhan, 1980). Various psychological factors may also play a role, including performance anxiety, sexual guilt, and hostility toward the partner. Helen Singer Kaplan (1974) suggests that some men with inhibited orgasm may be unconsciously "holding back" their ejaculate from their partners because of underlying hostility or resentment. Masters and Johnson (1970) found that men with this problem frequently have strict religious backgrounds that may leave a residue of unresolved guilt about sex that inhibits ejaculation. Emotional factors such as fears of pregnancy and anger toward one's partner can also play a role.

As with other sexual dysfunctions, men with inhibited orgasm, and their partners, may "try harder." But trying harder often compounds rather than alleviates sexual problems. Sexual relations become a job to get done, a chore rather than an opportunity for pleasure and gratification.

Anorgasmic

Never having reached orgasm. (Literally, "without orgasm.")

INHIBITED FEMALE ORGASM   Women with inhibited female orgasm (also called *female orgasmic dysfunction*) are unable to achieve orgasm or have difficulty reaching orgasm following what would usually be an adequate amount of sexual stimulation. A woman who masturbates to a high level of sexual excitement but is unable to climax may be considered "orgasmically impaired." Women who have never achieved orgasm through any means are sometimes labeled **anorgasmic** or *pre*orgasmic.

The prevalence of anorgasmia appears to have fallen off in recent years. Kinsey and his colleagues (1953) reported that as many as 10 percent of adult U.S. women (Kinsey et al., 1953) were anorgasmic. By the 1970s, surveys reported that only 5 to 7 percent of female respondents reached orgasm either none or almost none of the time (Fisher, 1973; Levine & Yost, 1976). But anorgasmia should not be equated with orgasmic dysfunction (Wakefield, 1988). Whereas many anorgasmic women have difficulty achieving orgasm despite receiving adequate stimulation, others may never have had the opportunity to receive sufficient stimulation to reach climax.

A woman who is able to achieve orgasm through masturbation or perhaps through oral sex or manual stimulation may not necessarily achieve orgasm dependably during coitus with her partner (Stock, 1993). Penile thrusting during coitus alone may not pro-

---

[1]Just as we find terms like *impotence* and *frigidity* unnecessarily pejorative, we prefer to use the more clinical-sounding but less offensive *inhibited male orgasm* or *delayed ejaculation* rather than "retarded" ejaculation or ejaculatory "incompetence."

Spectator role
A role, usually taken on because of performance anxiety, in which people observe rather than fully participate in their sexual encounters.

vide sufficient clitoral stimulation to trigger an orgasmic response (see Chapter 9). An orgasmic dysfunction may be diagnosed, however, if orgasm during coitus was impaired by such factors as sexual guilt or performance anxiety. Women who try to force an orgasm may also find themselves unable to do so. They may assume a **spectator role** and observe rather than fully participate in their sexual encounters. "Spectatoring" may further decrease the likelihood of orgasm.

PREMATURE EJACULATION A second type of male orgasmic disorder, premature ejaculation, appears to be the most common male sexual dysfunction (Derogatis, 1980). Slightly more than one man in three in community surveys admits to currently experiencing problems involving premature ejaculation (Spector & Carey, 1990).

Premature ejaculation
A sexual dysfunction in which ejaculation occurs with minimal sexual stimulation and before the the man desires it.

Men with **premature ejaculation** ejaculate too rapidly to permit their partners or themselves to fully enjoy sexual relations. The degree of prematurity varies. Some men ejaculate during foreplay, even at the sight of their partner disrobing. But most ejaculate either just prior to or immediately upon penetration, or following a few coital thrusts (Kaplan, 1974).

Just what constitutes *prematurity*? Some definitions focus on a particular time period during which a man should be able to control ejaculation. Is ejaculation within 30 seconds of intromission premature? Within one minute? Ten minutes? There is no clear cutoff. Contemporary scholars argue that the focus should be on whether the couple is satisfied with the duration of coitus rather than on some predetermined length of time (Derogatis, 1980; Sloan, 1979).

Helen Singer Kaplan (1974) suggested that the label "premature" should be applied to cases in which men persistently or recurrently lack voluntary control over their ejaculations. This may sound like a contradiction in terms since ejaculation is a reflex, and reflexes need not involve thought or conscious control. Kaplan means, however, that a man may control his ejaculation by learning to regulate the amount of sexual stimulation he experiences so that it remains below the threshold at which the ejaculation reflex is triggered.

RAPID FEMALE ORGASM: CAN WOMEN REACH ORGASM TOO QUICKLY? The female counterpart to premature ejaculation, *rapid orgasm,* is so rarely recognized as a problem that it is generally ignored by clinicians and is not classified as a sexual dysfunction in the DSM system. Still, in some couples the woman experiences orgasm more rapidly than her partner and shows little interest in continuing sexual activity to allow her partner to achieve gratification. Many women who reach orgasm rapidly are open to continued sexual stimulation and capable of experiencing successive orgasms, however.

SEXUAL PAIN DISORDERS

Learning Objective 4:
Describe the sexual pain disorders and discuss factors that may contribute to their development.

For most of us, coitus is a source of pleasure. For some of us, however, coitus gives rise to pain and discomfort.

DYSPAREUNIA Dyspareunia, or painful coitus, can afflict men or women. Dyspareunia is one of the most common sexual dysfunctions and is also a common complaint of women seeking gynecological services (Quevillon, 1993).

Pain is a sign that something is wrong—physically or psychologically. Dyspareunia may result from purely physical causes, from purely emotional factors, or from an interaction of the two (Reid & Lininger, 1993). The most common cause of coital pain in women is inadequate lubrication. In such a case, additional foreplay or artificial lubrication may help. Vaginal infections or sexually transmitted diseases (STDs) may also produce coital pain, however. Allergic reactions to spermicides, even the latex material in condoms, can give rise to coital pain or irritation. Pain during deep thrusting may be caused by endometriosis or pelvic inflammatory disease (PID), from other diseases or structural disorders of the reproductive organs (Reid & Lininger, 1993), or by penile contact against the cervix.

The most common cause of painful intercourse in women is vaginal infection.
Actually, lack of adequate lubrication is the most common cause of coital pain in women. •

Psychological factors such as unresolved guilt or anxiety about sex or the lingering effects of sexual trauma may also be involved. These factors may inhibit lubrication and cause involuntary contractions of the vaginal musculature, making penetration painful or uncomfortable.

Painful intercourse is less common in men and is generally associated with genital infections that cause burning or painful ejaculation. Smegma under the penile foreskin of uncircumcised men may irritate the penile glans during sexual contact.

VAGINISMUS   Vaginismus involves an involuntary contraction of the pelvic muscles that surround the outer third of the vaginal barrel. Vaginismus occurs reflexively during attempts at vaginal penetration, making entry by the penis painful or impossible. These reflexive contractions are accompanied by a deep-seated fear of penetration (Beck, 1993). Some women with vaginismus are unable to tolerate penetration by any object, including a finger, tampon, or a physician's speculum (Shortle & Jewelewicz, 1986). The prevalence of vaginismus is unknown (Nathan, 1986).

The woman with vaginismus usually is not aware that she is contracting her vaginal muscles. In some cases, husbands of women with vaginismus develop erectile dysfunction after repeated failures at penetration (Masters & Johnson, 1970). Such marriages can remain unconsummated for years.

Vaginismus is caused by a psychological fear of penetration, rather than by a physical injury or defect (LoPiccolo & Stock, 1986). Women with vaginismus often have histories of sexual trauma or rape or of botched abortions that resulted in vaginal injuries. Though they may desire sexual relations and be capable of becoming sexually aroused and achieving orgasm, their unresolved fear of penetration triggers an involuntary spasm of the vaginal musculature at the point of penile insertion. Vaginismus can also be a cause or an effect of dyspareunia. That is, women who have suffered painful intercourse may develop a fear of penetration that leads to the development of an involuntary vaginal contraction. Or women with vaginismus may experience pain during coital attempts if the couple tries to force penetration.

ORIGINS OF SEXUAL DYSFUNCTIONS

Since sexual dysfunctions involve the sex organs, it was once assumed that they stemmed largely from organic or physical causes. Today the pendulum has swung, and it is widely believed that many, if not most, cases reflect psychosocial factors such as sexual anxieties, lack of sexual knowledge, or marital dissatisfaction. Research suggests that it is simplistic to assume that causes are either psychosocial or organic, however. Many cases involve the interaction of organic and psychological factors (Meisler & Carey, 1990; Mohr & Beutler, 1990).

ORGANIC CAUSES

Learning Objective 5:
Discuss the possible organic causes of various sexual dysfunctions, including hormonal, vascular, neurological, and chemical causes.

Physical factors, such as fatigue and lowered testosterone levels, can dampen sexual desire and reduce responsiveness. Fatigue may lead to erectile dysfunction and inhibited orgasm in men, and to orgasmic dysfunction and dyspareunia (because of inadequate lubrication) in women. These will be isolated incidents unless the person attaches too much meaning to them and becomes concerned about future performances, however. Dyspareunia, however, often reflects organic factors such as underlying infections. Various medical conditions can affect orgasmic functioning in both men and women, including diabetes mellitus, multiple sclerosis, spinal-cord injuries, complications from surgical procedures (such as removal of the prostate in men), endocrinological problems,

Inis Beag and Mangaia—Worlds Apart[2]

Let us invite you on a journey to two islands that are a world apart—sexually as well as geographically. The sexual attitudes and practices within these societies will shed some light on the role of cultural values in determining what is sexually normal and what is sexually dysfunctional.

Our first stop is the island of Inis Beag, which lies off the misty coast of Ireland. From the air Inis Beag is a green jewel, fertile and inviting. At ground level things do not appear quite so warm, however.

The residents of this Irish folk community do not believe that it is normal for women to experience orgasm. Anthropologist John Messenger (1971), who visited Inis Beag in the 1950s and 1960s, reported that any woman who finds pleasure in sex—especially the intense waves of pleasure that can accompany orgasm—is viewed as deviant. *Should women on Inis Beag, then, be diagnosed as orgasmically impaired?*

TRUTH OR FICTION?

REVISITED

Women on the island of Inis Beag off the Irish coast are bio- **logically incapable of experiencing orgasm.** *Not true. But they are reared to believe that orgasm is a deviant sexual response for women.* •

Premarital sex is all but unknown on Inis Beag. Prior to marriage, men and women socialize apart. Marriage comes relatively late—usually in their middle thirties for men and their middle twenties for women. Mothers teach their daughters that they will have to submit to their husbands' animal cravings in order to obey God's injunction to "be fruitful and multiply." *After this indoctrination, women show little interest in sex. Should they be diagnosed as having hypoactive sexual desire disorder?*

The women of Inis Beag need not be overly concerned about frequent sexual intercourse, however, since the men of the island believe, erroneously, that sexual activity will drain their strength. Consequently, men avoid sex on the eve of sporting activity or strenuous work. Because of taboos against nudity, married couples engage in intercourse with their underclothes on. Intercourse takes place in the dark—literally as well as figuratively.

During intercourse the man takes the male-superior position. The male is always the initiator. Foreplay is brief, rarely involving manual stimulation of the breasts and never including oral stimulation of the genitals. *Should people who have difficulty becoming sexually aroused under these circumstances be diagnosed as having sexual arousal disorders?* The man ejaculates as rapidly as he can, in the belief that he is the only partner with sexual needs and to spare his wife as best he can. Then he turns over and rapidly falls asleep. Once more the couple have done their duty. *Since the man ejaculates rapidly, should he be diagnosed as having premature ejaculation?*

Our next stop is Mangaia. Mangaia is a Polynesian pearl of an island. It lifts languidly out of the blue waters of the Pacific. It lies on the other side of the world from Inis Beag—in more ways than one.

From an early age, Mangaian boys and girls are encouraged to get in touch with their own sexuality through sexual play and masturbation (Marshall, 1971). At about the age of 13, Mangaian boys are initiated into manhood by adults

2This feature is adapted from Rathus & Nevid, 1992, pp. 459–460.

and use of some pharmacological agents, such as certain drugs used to treat hypertension and psychiatric disorders (Segraves & Segraves, 1993).

It was once believed that 95 percent of cases of erectile dysfunction resulted from psychological causes (Masters & Johnson, 1970). Recent evidence suggests that organic factors are more widely involved than was previously thought, however (Rajfer et al., 1992) and may account for a majority of cases of erectile dysfunction (Reinisch, 1990).

who instruct them in sexual techniques. Mangaian males are taught the merit of bringing their female partners to multiple orgasms before ejaculating. *Are Mangaian males who ejaculate before their partners have multiple orgasms suffering from premature ejaculation?*

Boys practice their new techniques with girlfriends on secluded beaches or beneath the listing fronds of palms. They may visit girlfriends in the evening in the huts where they sleep with their families. Parents often listen for their daughters to laugh and gasp so that they will know that they have reached orgasm with a visiting young man, called a "sleepcrawler." Usually they pre-tend to be asleep so as not to interfere with courtship and impede their daughters' chances of finding a suitable mate. Daughters may receive a nightly succession of sleepcrawlers.

Girls, too, learn techniques of coitus from their elders. Typically they are initiated by an experienced male relative. Mangaians look on virginity with disdain, because virgins do not know how to provide sexual pleasure. Thus, the older relative makes his contribution to the family by initiating the girl.

Mangaians, by the way, expressed concern when they learned that many European and U.S. women do not regularly experience orgasm during coitus. Orgasm is apparently universal among Mangaian women. Therefore, Mangaians could only assume that Western women suffered from some abnormality of the sex organs. *Do they?*

All in all, the sharp contrasts between Inis Beag and Mangaia illustrate how concepts of normality are embedded within a cultural context. Behavior that is judged to be normal in one culture may be regarded as abnormal in another. How might our own cultural expectations influence our judgments about sexual dysfunction?

Polynesia. Cultural expectations influence our judgments about sexual dysfunction. Some native Polynesian cultures have a permissive attitude toward sexuality that encourages children to explore their sexuality at an early age. In adulthood, men may be expected to bring their partners to orgasm several times before ejaculating. Do men in such societies, who ejaculate before their partners have multiple orgasms, suffer from premature ejaculation?

Psychological factors such as anxiety or depression may serve to perpetuate or exacerbate the problem even in cases with underlying organic causes, however (Melman et al., 1988; Reinisch, 1990).

Organic causes of erectile disorder affect the flow of blood to and through the penis or damage to the nerves involved in the control of the erection reflex (Appell, 1986; Spark, 1991). Erectile problems can arise when clogged or narrow arteries leading to the penis deprive the penis of oxygen (Blakeslee, 1993). Erectile disorder occurs in as many as 35 percent of 20- to 60-year-old men with diabetes mellitus, a disease that can damage blood vessels and nerves involved in erection. Nerve damage resulting from prostate surgery may also impair erectile response. Erectile dysfunction may also result from multiple sclerosis (MS), a disease in which nerve cells lose the protective coatings that facilitate transmission of neural messages. If MS affects the spinal cord, erectile dysfunction may result. As many as 50 percent of adult men with MS may have erectile disorder. There is no cure for MS, but sexual functioning may return during periods of remission. MS has also been implicated in inhibited orgasm in men (Kedia, 1983).

Syphilis, a sexually transmitted disease, can result in erectile failure if the bacteria that cause the disease invade the spinal cord and destroy the cells that control the erection reflex (Spark, 1991). Chronic kidney disease can also impair erectile response.

Other physical causes of erectile dysfunction are hypertension and endocrine disorders that impair testosterone production. With debilitating diseases such as cancer, emphysema, and heart disease, a general decline in health can also take its toll on sexual response.

Rajfer and his colleagues (1992) believe that most cases of erectile dysfunction involve a failure of the body to produce sufficient quantities of the substance nitric oxide. When nitric oxide comes into contact with the muscles encircling blood vessels in the penis, the muscles relax, allowing vasocongestion to occur and causing the penis to swell. A lack of nitric oxide allows blood to leak out of the penis and be reabsorbed by the body, thereby preventing the degree of engorgement necessary for the attainment and maintenance of erection. One approach to overcome erectile dysfunction is to inject the penis with a chemical that raises nitric oxide levels and thus relaxes the penile muscles to permit blood to flow more freely. (Unfortunately, no pill with a similar effect is in the offing [Kessler, 1992].)

Women may also encounter vascular or nerve disorders that impair genital blood flow, reducing lubrication and sexual excitement, rendering intercourse painful, and reducing their ability to reach orgasm.

Tumescence
Swelling; erection. (From the Latin *tumere,* meaning "to swell." *Tumor* has the same root.)

People with sexual dysfunctions are generally advised to undergo a physical examination to determine whether their problems are biologically based. Men with erectile dysfunction may be evaluated in a sleep center to determine whether they attain erections while asleep. Healthy men usually have erections during rapid-eye-movement (REM) sleep, which occurs every 90 to 100 minutes. Men with organically based erectile dysfunctions often do not have nocturnal erections. However, this technique, called nocturnal penile **tumescence,** or NPT, may lead to misleading results in perhaps 20 percent of cases (Meisler & Carey, 1990). NPT may thus be helpful but not definitive in suggesting whether erectile dysfunction is organically based (Mohr & Beutler, 1990).

Prescription drugs and illicit drugs are believed to account for one in four cases of erectile dysfunction (Leary, 1992b). Antidepressant medication and antipsychotic drugs may impair erectile functioning and inhibit ejaculation in men and interfere with orgasm in women (Segraves, 1988; Spark, 1991). Tranquilizers like Valium and Xanax may delay or prevent orgasm in either gender (Segraves, 1988). Antihypertensive drugs can lead to erectile failure (Segraves, 1988). Switching to hypertensive drugs that do not impair sexual response or adjusting dosage levels may help (Spark, 1991).

Central nervous system depressants such as alcohol, heroin, and morphine can reduce the sexual appetite and impair sexual functioning (Segraves, 1988). Regular marijuana use has also been associated with reduced sexual drive and performance (Nelson, 1988; Spark, 1991). Heavy drinking can damage the nerves that control erection and ejaculation (Spark, 1991). Narcotics also depress testosterone production, which can further dampen the sexual appetite and lead to erectile failure (Spark, 1991). Low sexual desire and erectile dysfunctions are common among chronic alcoholics and drug users (Cocores & Gold, 1989; Schiavi, 1990).

Despite the common belief that cocaine is an aphrodisiac, regular use can cause sexual dysfunctions such as erectile disorder and inhibited orgasm in males and reduced sexual desire in both genders (Weiss & Mirin, 1987). Some people report increased sexual pleasure from the initial use of cocaine, but repeated use can lead to dependency on the drug for sexual arousal. Long-term use may compromise the ability to experience sexual pleasure (Weiss & Mirin, 1987).

Occasional use of alcohol and other drugs can also lead to sexual difficulties when people misattribute their sexually dampening effects to underlying causes within themselves. If you are unable to perform sexually when you have had a few drinks and do not recognize that alcohol can depress your performance, you may believe that something else is wrong with you. This belief can create anxiety at your next sexual opportunity, which can prevent normal functioning. A second failure may set off a vicious cycle in which self-doubts prompt more anxiety, and anxiety results in repeated failure and heightened anxiety.

PSYCHOSOCIAL CAUSES

Learning Objective 6: Discuss the numerous psychosocial contributors to sexual dysfunctions.

Psychosocial factors are connected with sexual dysfunctions. These include—but are not necessarily limited to—cultural influences, psychosexual trauma, a gay sexual orientation, marital dissatisfaction, psychological conflict, lack of sexual skills, irrational beliefs, and performance anxiety.

Activity: *The Sexual Anxiety Inventory* This 25-item inventory in the IM allows students to compare their levels of sexual anxiety with those of other students.

CULTURAL INFLUENCES   Children reared in sexually repressive cultural or home environments may learn to respond to sex with feelings of anxiety and shame, rather than sexual arousal and pleasure. People whose parents instilled in them a sense of guilt over touching their genitals may find it difficult to accept their sex organs as sources of pleasure.

In Western cultures, sexual pleasure has traditionally been a male preserve. Young women may be reared to believe that sex is a duty to be performed for their husbands, not a source of personal pleasure. Although the traditional double standard may have diminished in the United States, girls may still be exposed to relatively more repressive attitudes. Women are more likely than men in our culture to be taught to repress their sexual desires and even to fear their sexuality (Nichols, 1990a). Cultural values encourage many young women to regard their maturing sexual urges as dangerous until proven safe (Vance, 1984). Self-control and vigilance—not sexual awareness and acceptance—become identified as feminine virtues. Women reared with such attitudes may be less likely to learn about their sexual potentials or express their erotic preferences to their partners. Compared to women who readily reach orgasm, sexually active but anorgasmic women report more negative attitudes toward masturbation, greater sexual guilt, and greater discomfort talking with their partners about sexual activities that involve direct clitoral contact (cunnilingus and manual stimulation) (Kelly et al., 1990).

Many women who are exposed to sex-negative attitudes during childhood and adolescence find it difficult to suddenly view sex as a source of pleasure and satisfaction once they are married. The result of a lifetime of learning to turn themselves off sexually may lead to difficulties experiencing the full expression of sexual arousal and enjoyment when an acceptable opportunity arises (Morokoff, 1993).

Given the prevailing double standard in our culture, we should not be surprised that restrictive cultural learning has a disproportionate impact on women. Men, too, may be handicapped by cultural misinformation and sexual taboos, however, as noted in the nearby A World of Diversity feature on erectile dysfunction.

PSYCHOSEXUAL TRAUMA   Learning theorists focus on the role of conditioned anxiety in explaining sexual dysfunctions. Sexual stimuli come to elicit anxiety when they have been paired with physically or psychologically painful experiences, such as rape, incest, or sexual molestation. Strong, conditioned anxiety can stifle sexual arousal. Unresolved anger and misplaced guilt can also make it difficult for victims of rape and other sexual traumas to respond sexually, even years afterward. Persons who have been sexually victimized may harbor feelings of disgust and revulsion toward sex or deep-seated fears of sex that make it difficult for them to respond sexually, even with loving partners.

Cross-Cultural Studies of Erectile Dysfunction

Erectile dysfunction is not limited to Western cultures. Evidence of erectile dysfunction was found in 80 percent of a cross-cultural sample of 40 preindustrial and industrializing societies (Broude & Greene, 1976). In some of these societies, cures were sought through the wearing of charms and other forms of magic. Although evidence of erectile dysfunction was not found in 20 percent of the societies sampled, we cannot assume that erectile dysfunction did not exist in them. It could also mean that erectile difficulties were not discussed.

In another cross-cultural study, Welch and Kartub (1978) found that cultural factors, especially cultural restrictiveness toward sex, were related to the incidence of erectile dysfunction.

Cultures that held more restrictive attitudes toward premarital sex among females, toward sex in marriage, and toward extramarital sex, reported a higher prevalence of erectile difficulties among men. Perhaps men who are reared in more sexually restrictive cultures are more prone to develop sexual anxiety, guilt, or inhibitions that interfere with sexual functioning. In our own culture, too, men who are reared in families that condemn sexual activity may develop shame and guilt about their own sexual desires and have difficulty expressing themselves sexually, even in marriage.

Cultural beliefs may also play a role in the development of erectile dysfunction. In India it is a common folk belief that semi-nal fluid is formed from blood and is precious. Each ejaculation is held to involve the loss of a significant amount of life energy. A psychiatric syndrome known as the Dhat syndrome afflicts men who become extremely anxious about the loss of seminal fluid through nocturnal emissions (Akhtar, 1988; Chadda & Ahuja, 1990; Malhotra & Wig, 1975). Men with this syndrome often seek medical attention in the attempt to curtail their nocturnal emissions. Erectile dysfunction sometimes occurs in men with Dhat syndrome because their fears about wasting precious seminal fluid make it difficult for them to perform sexually (Singh, 1985).

SEXUAL ORIENTATION Some gay males and lesbians test their sexual orientation by developing heterosexual relationships, even marrying and rearing children with partners of the opposite sex. Others may wish to maintain the appearance of heterosexuality to avoid the social stigma that society attaches to homosexuality. In such cases problems in arousal or performance with heterosexual partners can be due to a lack of heteroerotic interests. A lack of heterosexual response is not a problem for people who are committed to a gay lifestyle (Masters & Johnson, 1970), however. Sexual dysfunctions may also occur in gay relationships, as they do in heterosexual relationships.

INEFFECTIVE SEXUAL TECHNIQUES In some marriages couples practice a narrow range of sexual techniques because they have fallen into a certain routine or because one partner controls the timing and sequence of sexual techniques. A woman who remains unknowledgeable about the erotic importance of her clitoris may be unlikely to seek direct clitoral stimulation. The man who responds to a temporary erectile failure by trying to force an erection may be unintentionally setting himself up for repeated failure. The couple who fail to communicate their sexual preferences or to experiment with altering their sexual techniques may find themselves losing interest. Brevity of foreplay and coitus may contribute to female orgasmic dysfunction.

EMOTIONAL FACTORS Orgasm involves a sudden loss of voluntary control. Fear of losing control or "letting go" may block sexual arousal. Other emotional factors, especially depression, are often implicated in sexual dysfunctions (Beck, 1988). Women with inhibited sexual desire are more likely to report a history of depressive episodes (Schreiner-Engle & Schiavi, 1986). People who are depressed frequently report lessened sexual interest and may find it difficult to respond sexually. People who are exposed to a high level of emotional stress may also experience an ebbing of sexual interest and response.

RELATIONSHIP PROBLEMS   Relationship problems are important and often pivotal factors in sexual dysfunctions (Catalan et al., 1990; Leiblum & Rosen, 1991; Rust et al., 1988). Problems in a relationship are not so easily left at the bedroom door. Couples usually find that their sexual relationships are no better than the other facets of their relationships (Perlman & Abramson, 1982). Couples who harbor resentments toward one another may use the sexual arena as a field of combat. They may fail to become aroused by their partners or "withhold" orgasm to make their partners feel guilty or inadequate.

Problems in communication may also play a role. Troubled relationships are usually characterized by poor communication. Partners who have difficulty communicating about other matters may be unlikely to communicate their sexual desires to each other.

The following case highlights how sexual dysfunctions can develop against the backdrop of a troubled relationship:

After living together for six months, Paul and Petula are contemplating marriage. But a problem has brought them to a sex therapy clinic. As Petula puts it, "For the last two months he hasn't been able to keep his erection after he enters me." Paul is 26, a lawyer; Petula, 24, is a buyer for a large department store. They both grew up in middle-class, suburban families, were introduced through mutual friends, and began having intercourse, without difficulty, a few months into their relationship. At Petula's urging, Paul moved into her apartment, although he wasn't sure he was ready for such a step. A week later he began to have difficulty maintaining his erection during intercourse, although he felt strong desires for his partner. When his erection waned, he would try again, but would lose his desire and be unable to achieve another erection. After a few times like this, Petula would become so angry that she began striking Paul in the chest and screaming at him. Paul, who at 200 pounds weighed more than twice as much as Petula, would just walk away, which angered Petula even more.

It became clear that sex was not the only trouble spot in their relationship. Petula complained that he preferred to be with his friends and go to baseball games than to spend time with her. When they were together at home, he would become absorbed in watching sports events on television, and showed no interest in activities she enjoyed—attending the theater, visiting museums, etc. Since there was no evidence that the sexual difficulty was due to either organic problems or depression, a diagnosis of male erectile disorder was given. Neither Paul or Petula were willing to discuss their nonsexual problems

A Failure to Communicate. Problems in communication can lead to or exacerbate sexual dysfunctions. Sexual problems can arise when partners fail to communicate their sexual needs and desires. Problems may persist when couples fail to communicate about their sexual difficulties or seek solutions.

with a therapist. While the sexual problem was treated successfully with a form of sex therapy modeled after techniques developed by Masters and Johnson [see discussion later in the chapter] and the couple later married, Paul's ambivalences continued well into their marriage, and there were future recurrences of sexual problems as well.

(Adapted from Spitzer et al., 1989, pp. 149–150; reprinted from Rathus & Nevid, 1991, pp. 402–403)

Though couples with strongly committed and supportive relationships can generally develop effective coping strategies for overcoming even the most severe sexual problems, couples in relationships with unresolved conflicts may derive little if any benefit from even the most advanced psychological, medical, or surgical treatments of sexual dysfunctions (Leiblum & Rosen, 1991).

PSYCHOLOGICAL CONFLICTS   Within Freud's psychoanalytic theory, sexual dysfunctions are rooted in the failure to successfully resolve the Oedipus or Electra complexes of early childhood. Sexual encounters in adulthood arouse unconscious anxieties and hostilities that are believed to reflect unresolved conflicts, resulting in inhibition of sexual response.

A modern psychoanalytic theorist, Helen Singer Kaplan (1974), believes that sexual dysfunctions represent an interaction of *immediate* causes (such as poor techniques, marital conflict, performance anxiety, and lack of effective communication) and deep-seated or *remote* causes (such as unresolved childhood conflicts that predispose people to encounter sexual anxiety and hostility in adulthood). Kaplan believes there is value in combining direct behavioral techniques, which deal with the immediate causes of sexual dysfunctions, with psychoanalytic (insight-oriented) techniques that deal with the remote causes.

LACK OF SEXUAL SKILLS   Sexual competency involves the acquisition of sexual knowledge and skills and is based largely on learning. We generally learn what makes us and others feel good through trial and error and by talking and reading about sex. Some people may not develop sexual competency because of a lack of opportunity to acquire knowledge and experience—even within marriage. People with sexual dysfunctions may have been reared in families in which discussions of sexuality were off limits and early sexual experimentation was harshly punished. Such early influences may have squelched the young person's sexual learning and experimentation or led her or him to associate anxiety or guilt with sex.

Helen Singer Kaplan (1974) notes that premature ejaculators may have failed to learn to recognize the level of sexual arousal that directly precedes their ejaculatory threshold—the level of stimulation that triggers the ejaculatory reflex. As a result they may be less able to employ self-control strategies to delay ejaculation such as temporarily halting genital stimulation when they approach their "point of no return." Men with limited sexual experience are particularly unlikely to recognize their ejaculatory threshold and to regulate sexual stimulation so that it remains below this triggering point. Some men may try to delay ejaculation by keeping their minds blank or diverting their attention from sex (as by thinking about a forthcoming calculus exam). In so doing, they ignore their own sexual stimulation and do not learn "when to say when."

Although some men with premature ejaculation may have difficulty gauging their level of sexual arousal, research fails to show that premature ejaculators in general are less accurate than other men in making such judgments (Kinder & Curtiss, 1988; Strassberg et al., 1987). It may be that premature ejaculators are more physiologically sensitive to sexual stimulation, not that they are less capable of assessing their sexual arousal (Strassberg et al., 1987; Strassberg et al., 1990). Perhaps premature ejaculators simply require less stimulation to achieve orgasm.

IRRATIONAL BELIEFS   Psychologist Albert Ellis (1962, 1977) points out that irrational beliefs and attitudes may contribute to sexual dysfunctions. Negative feelings like anxiety and fear, Ellis submits, do not stem directly from the events we experience, but rather from our interpretations of these events. If a person encounters a certain event, like an erectile or orgasmic dysfunction on a given day, and then *believes* that the event is awful or catastrophic, he or she will exaggerate feelings of disappointment and set the stage for future problems.

PERFORMANCE ANXIETY   Anxiety—especially performance anxiety—plays important roles in the development of sexual dysfunctions. Performance anxiety occurs when a person becomes overly concerned with how well he or she performs a certain act or task. Performance anxiety may place a dysfunctional individual in a spectator rather than a performer role. Rather than focusing on erotic sensations and allowing involuntary responses like erection, lubrication, and orgasm to occur naturally, he or she focuses on self-doubts and fears, and thinks, "Will I be able to do it this time? Will this be another failure?"

Performance anxiety can set the stage for a vicious cycle in which a sexual failure leads to increased anxiety, which in turn leads to repeated failure, and so on. Sex therapists emphasize the need to break this vicious cycle by removing the need to perform.

In men, performance anxiety can inhibit erection while also triggering a premature ejaculation. (Erection, mediated by the parasympathetic nervous system, can be blocked by activation of the sympathetic nervous system in the form of anxiety. Since ejaculation, like anxiety, is mediated by the sympathetic nervous system, arousal of this system in the form of anxiety can increase the level of stimulation and thereby heighten the potential for premature ejaculation.)

In women, performance anxiety can reduce vaginal lubrication and contribute to orgasmic dysfunction. Women with performance anxieties may try to force an orgasm to occur, only to find that the harder they try, the more difficult it becomes. Forty years ago the pressures women faced regarding sex were similar to those in the sexually repressive culture of Inis Beag. They centered on the issue of whether or not to engage in sexual intercourse. Today, the pressures on both genders are more similar to those in the sexually permissive culture of Mangaia, in which both genders are expected to achieve certain standards of sexual performance.

TREATMENT OF SEXUAL DYSFUNCTIONS

Sex therapy
A collective term for short-term behavioral models for treatment of sexual dysfunctions.

When Kinsey conducted his surveys in the 1930s and 1940s, there was no effective treatment for sexual dysfunctions. At the time the predominant model of therapy for sexual dysfunctions was long-term psychoanalysis. Psychoanalysts believed that the sexual problem would abate only if the presumed unconscious conflicts that lay at the root of the problem were resolved through long-term therapy. Evidence of the effectiveness of psychoanalysis in treating sexual dysfunctions is still lacking, however.

Since that time behavioral models of short-term treatment, collectively called **sex therapy,** have emerged. These models aim to modify the dysfunctional behavior directly. Although they may focus on the problem behavior directly, sex therapists also recognize the importance of the partners' relationship. Relationship problems are often connected with sexual dysfunctions. Even if the relationship is not part of the problem, working with the couple as a unit can be part of the solution.

Although the particular approach may vary, sex therapies share a focus on (1) modifying self-defeating beliefs and attitudes; (2) fostering sexual competencies (sexual skills and knowledge); (3) fostering improved sexual communication; and (4) using behavioral "homework" exercises to enhance coital and noncoital stimulation while reducing performance anxiety. When feasible, sex therapy involves both sex partners. Individual therapy may be preferred in some cases, as we shall see. Therapists also find that simply granting people permission to engage in behaviors that enhance their sexual satisfaction, or imparting information to help them think more positively about sexuality and correct mistaken beliefs (such as the belief that "normal" women do not desire clitoral stimulation), may be sufficient to overcome many sexual problems without the need for specific behavioral exercises or more intensive therapy (Annon, 1974).

Let us begin with the groundbreaking work of Masters and Johnson.

THE MASTERS-AND-JOHNSON APPROACH

Learning Objective 8:
Compare Masters and Johnson's approach to sex therapy to Helen Singer Kaplan's approach.

Sensate focus exercises
Exercises in which sex partners take turns giving and receiving pleasurable stimulation in nongenital areas of the body.

Masters and Johnson pioneered the use of direct behavioral approaches to treating sexual dysfunctions in heterosexual couples (Masters & Johnson, 1970).[3] A therapy team (one man and one woman) focuses on the couple as the unit of treatment during a two-week residential program. Masters and Johnson consider the couple, not the individual, dysfunctional. A couple may describe the husband's erectile dysfunction as the problem, but this problem is likely to have led to a dysfunctional interaction between the couple by the time they seek therapy. Similarly, a man whose wife has an orgasmic dysfunction is likely to be anxious about his ability to provide effective sexual stimulation.

The dual-therapist team permits each partner to discuss problems with a member of his or her own gender. It reduces the chance of therapist bias in favor of the male or female partner and allows each partner to hear concerns expressed by another member of the opposite gender. Anxieties and resentments are aired in daily therapy sessions, but the focus of treatment is behavioral change. Couples perform daily sexual homework assignments, such as **sensate focus exercises,** in the privacy of their hotel rooms.

Sensate focus sessions are carried out in the nude. Partners take turns giving and receiving stimulation in nongenital areas of the body. Without touching the breasts or genitals, the giver massages or fondles the receiving partner in order to provide pleasure under relaxing and nondemanding conditions. Since genital activity is restricted, there is no pressure to "perform." The giving partner is "freed" to engage in trial-and-error learning about the receiving partner's sensate preferences. The receiving partner is also "freed" to enjoy the experience without feeling rushed to reciprocate or obliged to perform by becoming sexually aroused. The receiving partner's only responsibility is to direct the giving partner as needed. In addition to these general sensate focus exercises, Masters and Johnson used specific assignments designed to help couples overcome particular sexual dysfunctions.

Masters and Johnson have had an extraordinary influence on the development of sex therapy. Since 1970, when the first results of their treatment program were presented in their book *Human Sexual Inadequacy,* further developments in sex therapy have focused largely on variations of their approach rather than on the introduction of new approaches (Barlow, 1986).

Yet many contemporary sex therapists have departed from the Masters-and-Johnson format. Many do not treat clients in an intensive residential program. Many question the necessity of male/female cotherapist teams. Researchers find that one therapist is about as effective as two, regardless of the therapist's gender (Libman et al., 1985). Nor does the therapeutic benefit seem to depend to any great extent on whether the sessions are conducted within a short period of time, as in the Masters-and-Johnson approach, or spaced over time (Libman et al., 1985). Some success has also been reported in minimal contact programs in which participants are given written instructions rather than live therapy sessions (e.g., Takefman & Brender, 1984), although the results tend to be more variable than in therapist-administered treatments (Mohr & Beutler, 1990). Therapists have also departed from the Masters-and-Johnson approach by working individually with preorgasmic women rather than focusing on the couple as the unit of treatment. Group treatment programs have also been used successfully in treating orgasmic dysfunction in women (e.g., Killmann et al., 1987).

THE HELEN SINGER KAPLAN APPROACH

Kaplan (1974) calls her approach *psychosexual therapy.* Psychosexual therapy combines behavioral and psychoanalytic methods. Kaplan, as noted, believes that sexual dysfunctions have both *immediate* causes and *remote* causes (underlying intrapsychic conflicts that date to childhood). Kaplan begins therapy with the behavioral approach. She focuses on improv-

---

[3]Masters and Johnson later applied their therapy techniques to treating sexually dysfunctional homosexual couples (see Masters & Johnson, 1979).

ing the couple's communication, eliminating performance anxiety, and fostering sexual skills and knowledge. She uses a brief form of insight-oriented therapy when it appears that remote causes impede response to the behavioral program. In so doing, she hopes to bring to awareness unconscious conflicts that are believed to have stifled the person's sexual desires or responsiveness. Although Kaplan reports a number of successful case studies, there are no controlled studies demonstrating that the combination of behavioral and insight-oriented, or psychoanalytic techniques, is more effective than the behavioral techniques alone.

Let us now consider some of the specific techniques that sex therapists have introduced in treating several of the major types of sexual dysfunction.

DISORDERS OF SEXUAL DESIRE

Some sex therapists help kindle the sexual appetites of people with inhibited sexual desire by prescribing self-stimulation exercises combined with erotic fantasies (LoPiccolo & Friedman, 1988). Sex therapists may also assist dysfunctional couples by prescribing sensate focus exercises, enhancing communication, and expanding the couple's repertoire of sexual skills. Sex therapists recognize that inhibited desire is often a complex problem that requires more intensive treatment than do problems of the arousal or orgasm phases (Leiblum & Rosen, 1988). Helen Singer Kaplan (1987) argues that insight-oriented approaches are especially helpful in the treatment of inhibited sexual desire and sexual aversion to uncover and resolve the deep-seated psychological conflicts that are believed to stifle natural sexual desires.

When lack of desire is connected with depression, sexual interests may rebound when the depression lifts. Treatment in such cases may involve psychotherapy or chemotherapy, not sex therapy per se. Some cases of inhibited desire involve hormonal deficiencies, especially deficiencies in testosterone. But testosterone replacement therapy is believed to be successful only in the relatively few cases of bona fide testosterone deficiencies (Spark, 1991).

When problems in the relationship are involved, marital or couples therapy may be indicated to improve the relationship. Once interpersonal problems are ironed out, sexual interest may return.

Treatment of sexual aversion disorder may involve a multifaceted approach, including biological treatments such as the use of medications to reduce anxiety, and psychological treatments designed to help the individual overcome the underlying sexual phobia. Couples therapy may be used in cases where sexual aversions arise from problems in relationships (Gold & Gold, 1993). Sensate focus exercises may be used to lessen generalized anxiety about sexual contact. But fears of specific aspects of the sexual act may need to be overcome through behavioral exercises in which the client learns to manage the stimuli that evoke fears of sexual contact:

Bridget, 26, and Bryan, 30, were married for four years but had never consummated their relationship because Bridget would panic whenever Bryan attempted coitus with her. While she enjoyed foreplay and was capable of achieving orgasm with clitoral stimulation, her fears of sexual contact were triggered by Bryan's attempts at vaginal penetration. The therapist employed a program of gradual exposure to the feared stimuli to allow Bridget the opportunity to overcome her fears in small, graduated steps. First she was instructed to view her genitals in a mirror when she was alone—this in order to violate her long-standing prohibition against looking at and enjoying her body. While this exercise initially made her feel anxious, with repeated exposure she became comfortable performing it and then progressed to touching her genitals directly. When she became comfortable with this step, and reported experiencing pleasurable erotic sensations, she was instructed to insert a finger into the vagina. She encountered intense anxiety at this step and required daily practice for two weeks before she could tolerate inserting her finger into her vagina without discomfort. Her husband was then brought into the treatment process. The couple was instructed to have Bridget insert her own finger in her vagina while Bryan watched. When she was comfortable with this exercise, she then guided his finger into her vagina. Later he placed one and then two fingers into her vagina, while she controlled the depth, speed, and duration of penetration. When she felt ready, they proceeded to attempt penile penetration in the female superior position, which allowed her to maintain control over penetration. Over time, Bridget became more comfortable with penetration to the point that the couple developed a normal sexual relationship.

(Adapted from Kaplan, 1987, pp. 102–103)

DISORDERS OF SEXUAL AROUSAL

Men with chronic erectile dysfunction may believe that they have "forgotten" how to have an erection. They may ask their therapists to "teach" them or "show them" how. Some of our clients have asked us to tell them what they should think or picture in their minds to achieve an erection, or how they should touch their partners or be touched. Erection is an involuntary reflex, however, not a learned skill. The man need not learn how to have an erection any more than he need learn how to breathe.

In sex therapy, women who have trouble becoming lubricated and men with erectile problems learn that they need not "do" anything to become sexually aroused. As long as their problems are psychologically and not organically based, they need only receive sexual stimulation under relaxed circumstances, so that anxiety does not inhibit their natural reflexes.

TRUTH OR *FICTION?*

R E V I S I T E D

In sex therapy, a man with erectile dysfunction is taught how to will an erection. Untrue. Men with erectile dysfunction are actually taught that it is not possible to will an erection. One can only set the stage for erection (or vaginal lubrication) to occur, and then allow it to happen reflexively. •

In order to reduce performance anxiety, the partners engage in nondemanding sexual contacts: contacts that do not demand lubrication or erection. They may start with nongenital sensate focus exercises in the style of Masters and Johnson. After a couple of sessions, sensate focus extends to the genitals. The position shown in Figure 15.1 allows the woman easy access to her husband's genitals. She repeatedly "teases" him to erection and allows the erection to subside. Thus she avoids creating performance anxiety that could lead to loss of erection. By repeatedly regaining his erection, the man loses the fear that loss of erection means it will not return. He learns also to focus on erotic sensations for their own sake. He experiences no demand to perform, as the couple is instructed to refrain from coitus.

When the dysfunctional partner can reliably achieve sexual excitement (denoted by erection in the male and lubrication in the female), the couple does not immediately attempt coitus, since this might rekindle performance anxiety. Rather, the couple engages in a series of nondemanding, pleasurable sexual activities, eventually culminating in coitus.

In Masters and Johnson's approach, the couple begin coitus after about 10 days of treatment. The woman teases the man to erection while she is sitting above him, straddling his thighs. When he is erect, *she* inserts the penis—to avoid fumbling attempts at entry—and moves slowly back and forth in a *nondemanding way*. Neither attempts to reach orgasm. If erection is lost, teasing and coitus are repeated. Once the couple become confident that erection can be retained—or reinstated if lost—they may increase coital thrusting gradually to reach orgasm.

ORGASM DISORDERS

Women who have never experienced orgasm often harbor negative sexual attitudes that cause anxiety and inhibit sexual response. Treatment in such cases may first address these attitudes.

Masters and Johnson use a couples-oriented approach in treating anorgasmic women. They begin with sensate focus exercises. Then, during genital massage and later during coitus, the woman guides her partner in the caresses and movements that she finds sexually exciting. Taking charge helps free the woman, psychologically speaking, from the traditional stereotype of the passive, subordinate female role.

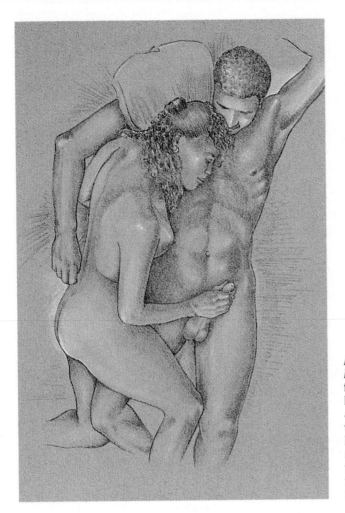

FIGURE 15.1 **The Training Position Recommended by Masters and Johnson for Treatment of Erectile Dysfunction and Premature Ejaculation.** By lying in front of her partner who has his legs spread, the woman has ready access to his genitals. In one part of a program designed to overcome erectile dysfunction, she repeatedly "teases" him to erection and allows the erection to subside. Thus she avoids creating performance anxiety that could lead to loss of erection. Through repeated regaining of erection, the man loses the fear that loss of erection means it will not return.

Masters and Johnson recommend a training position (see Figure 15.2, page 476) that gives the man access to his partner's breasts and genitals. She can guide his hands to show him the types of stimulation she enjoys. The genital play is *nondemanding.* The goals are to learn to provide and enjoy effective sexual stimulation, not to reach orgasm. The clitoris is not stimulated early, since doing so may produce a high level of stimulation before the woman is prepared.

After a number of occasions of genital play, the couple undertake coitus in the female-superior position (see Figure 15.3, page 477). This position allows the woman freedom of movement and control over her genital sensations. She is told to regard the penis as her "toy." The couple engages in several sessions of deliberately slow thrusting to sensitize the woman to sensations produced by the penis and break the common counterproductive pattern of desperate, rapid thrusting.

Orgasm cannot be willed or forced. When a woman receives effective stimulation, feels free to focus on erotic sensations, and feels that nothing is being demanded of her, she will generally reach orgasm. Once the woman is able to attain orgasm in the female-superior position, the couple may extend their sexual repertoire to other positions.

Masters and Johnson prefer working with the couple in cases of anorgasmia, but other sex therapists prefer to begin working with the woman individually through a program of directed masturbation (Barbach, 1975; Heiman & LoPiccolo, 1987). This approach assumes that the woman accepts masturbation as a therapy tool. Masturbation provides women with opportunities to learn about their own bodies at their own pace. It frees them of the need to rely on partners or to please partners. The sexual pleasure they experience

FIGURE 15.2 **The Training Position for Nondemanding Stimulation of the Female Genitals Recommended by Masters and Johnson and Helen Singer Kaplan.** This position gives the man access to his partner's breasts and genitals. She can guide his hands to show him the types of stimulation she enjoys.

helps counter lingering sexual anxieties. Although there is some variation among therapists, the following elements are commonly found in directed masturbation programs:

1. *Education.* The woman and her sex partner (if she has one) are educated about female sexuality.
2. *Self-exploration.* Self-exploration is encouraged as a way of increasing the woman's sense of body awareness. In the privacy of her home, she may hold a mirror between her legs to locate her sexual anatomical features. Kegel exercises may be prescribed to help tone and strengthen the pubococcygeous (PC) muscle that surrounds the vagina and increase her awareness of genital sensations and sense of control.
3. *Self-massage.* Once the woman feels comfortable about exploring her body, she creates a relaxing setting for self-massage. She chooses a time and place where she is free from external distractions. She begins to explore the sensitivity of her body to touch, discovering and then repeating the caresses that she finds pleasurable. At first self-massage is not concentrated on the genitals. It encompasses other sensitive parts of the body. She may incorporate stimulation of the nipples and breasts and then direct genital stimulation, focusing on the clitoral area and experimenting with hand movements. Nonalcohol-based oils and lotions may be used to enhance the sensuous quality of the massage and to provide lubrication for the external genitalia. Kegel exercises may also be performed during self-stimulation to increase awareness of vaginal sensations and increase muscle tension. Some women use their dominant hand to stimulate their breasts while the other hand massages the genitals. No two women approach masturbation in quite the same way. During the first few occasions

the woman does not attempt to reach orgasm, so as to prevent performance anxiety.

4. *Giving oneself permission.* The woman may be instructed to practice assertive thoughts to dispel lingering guilt and anxiety about masturbation. For example, she might repeat to herself, "This is my body. I have a right to learn about my body and receive pleasure from it."

5. *Use of fantasy.* Arousal is heightened through the use of sexual images, fantasies, and fantasy aids, such as erotic written or visual materials.

6. *Allowing, not forcing, orgasm.* It may take weeks of masturbation to reach orgasm, especially for women who have never achieved orgasm. By focusing on her erotic sensations and fantasies, but not demanding orgasm, the woman lowers performance anxiety and creates the stimulating conditions needed to reach orgasm.

7. *Use of a vibrator.* A vibrator may be recommended to provide more intense stimulation, especially for women who find that manual stimulation is insufficient.

8. *Involvement of the partner.* Once the woman is capable of regularly achieving orgasm through masturbation, the focus may shift to the woman's sexual relationship with her partner. Nondemanding sensate focus exercises may be followed by nondemanding coitus. The female-superior position is often used, as it increases the woman's ability to control the depth, angle, and rate of thrusting, which helps ensure that she receives the kinds of stimulation needed to reach orgasm.

TRUTH OR *FICTION?*

R E V I S I T E D

Many sex therapists recommend masturbation as the treatment for women who have never been able to reach orgasm. *Many sex therapists do in fact recommend masturbation as the treatment for women who have never been able to reach orgasm. Masturbation allows women (and men) to get in touch with their own sexual responses without relying on a partner.* •

FIGURE 15.3 **Coitus in the Female-Superior Position.** In treatment of female orgasmic dysfunction, the couple undertake coitus in the female-superior position after a number of occasions of genital play. This position allows the woman freedom of movement and control over her genital sensations. She is told to regard the penis as her "toy." The couple engages in several sessions of deliberately slow thrusting to sensitize the woman to sensations produced by the penis and break the common counterproductive pattern of desperate, rapid thrusting.

Kaplan (1974) suggests a bridge maneuver to assist couples who are interested in making the transition from a combination of manual and coital stimulation to coital stimulation alone as a means for reaching orgasm. Manual stimulation during coitus is used until the woman senses that she is about to reach orgasm. Manual stimulation is then stopped and the woman thrusts with her pelvis to provide the stimulation necessary to reach orgasm. Over time the manual clitoral stimulation is discontinued earlier and earlier. Although some couples may prefer this "hands-off" approach to inducing orgasm, Kaplan points out that there is nothing wrong with combining manual stimulation and penile thrusting. There is no evidence that reliance on clitoral stimulation means that women are sexually immature. As noted in Chapter 5, evidence has not borne out the theoretical psychoanalytic distinction between clitoral orgasms and vaginal orgasms.

Our focus has been on sexual techniques, but it is worth noting that a combination of approaches that focus on sexual techniques and underlying interpersonal problems may be more effective than focusing on sexual techniques alone, at least for couples whose relationships are troubled (Killmann et al., 1987; LoPiccolo & Stock, 1986).

INHIBITED MALE ORGASM Treatment of inhibited male orgasm generally focuses on increasing sexual stimulation and reducing performance anxiety (LoPiccolo & Stock, 1986). Masters and Johnson instruct the couple to practice nondemanding sensate focus

---

TABLE 15.3 Outcomes of sex therapy at the Masters & Johnson Institute (1959–1977)

Variables	N	Failures	Successes	Success Rate
Primary (Lifelong) Erectile Dysfunction	51	17	34	67%
Secondary (Acquired) Erectile Dysfunction	501	108	393	78%
Premature Ejaculation	432	17	415	96%
Inhibited Male Orgasm (Ejaculatory Incompetence)	75	18	57	76%
Male Totals	1,059	160	899	85%
Primary Orgasmic Dysfunction (Primary Anorgasmia)	399	84	315	79%
Secondary Orgasmic Dysfunction (Secondary Anorgasmia)	331	96	235	71%
Vaginismus	83	1	82	99%
Female Totals	813	181	632	78%
Combined Totals	1,872	341	1531	82%

Source: Adapted from Kolodny, R. C. (1981). Evaluating Sex Therapy: Process and Outcome at the Masters & Johnson Institute. *Journal of Sex Research, 17,* 301–318. Reprinted from *The Journal of Sex Research,* a publication of the Society for the Scientific Study of Sex; Mount Vernon, Iowa 42315 USA.

exercises for several days, during which the man makes no attempt to ejaculate. The couple is then instructed to bring the man to orgasm in any way they can, usually by the woman's stroking his penis. Once the man can ejaculate in the woman's presence, the woman brings him to the point at which he is about to ejaculate. Then, in the female-superior position, she inserts the penis and thrusts vigorously to bring him to orgasm. If he loses the feeling he is about to ejaculate, the process is repeated. Even if ejaculation occurs at the point of penetration, it often helps break the pattern of inability to ejaculate within the vagina.

Squeeze technique
A method for treating premature ejaculation whereby the tip of the penis is squeezed temporarily to prevent ejaculation.

PREMATURE EJACULATION In the Masters-and-Johnson approach, sensate focus exercises are followed by practice in the training position shown in Figure 15.1 to treat premature ejaculation. The woman teases her partner to erection and uses the **squeeze technique** when he indicates that he is about to ejaculate. She squeezes the tip of the penis, which temporarily prevents ejaculation from occurring. This process is repeated three or four times in a 15-to-20-minute session before the man purposely ejaculates.

In using the squeeze technique (which should only be used following personal instruction from a sex therapist), the woman holds the penis between the thumb and first two fingers of the same hand. The thumb presses against the frenulum. The fingers straddle the coronal ridge on the other side of the penis. Squeezing the thumb and forefingers together fairly hard for about 20 seconds (or until the man's urge to ejaculate passes) prevents ejaculation. The erect penis can withstand fairly strong pressure without discomfort, but erection may be partially lost.

TRUTH OR *FICTION?*

R E V I S I T E D

A man can be prevented from ejaculating by squeezing his penis when he feels that he is about to do so. A man can in fact be prevented from ejaculating by squeezing his penis when he feels that he is about to do so. The method should only be used following personal instruction from a sex therapist, however. •

After two or three days of these sessions, Masters and Johnson have the couple begin coitus in the female-superior position because it creates less pressure to ejaculate. The woman inserts the penis. At first she contains it without thrusting, allowing the man to get used to intravaginal sensations. If he signals that he is about to ejaculate, she lifts off and squeezes the penis. After some repetitions, she begins slowly to move backward and forward, lifting off and squeezing as needed. The man learns gradually to tolerate higher levels of sexual stimulation without ejaculating.

The alternate "stop-start" method for treating premature ejaculation was introduced by urologist James Semans (1956). The method can be applied to manual stimulation or coitus. For example, the woman can manually stimulate her partner until he is about to ejaculate. He then signals her to suspend sexual stimulation and allows his arousal to subside before stimulation is resumed. This process enables the man to recognize the cues that precede his point of ejaculatory inevitability or "point of no return" and to tolerate longer periods of sexual stimulation. When the "stop-start" technique is applied to coitus, the couple begin with simple vaginal containment with no pelvic thrusting, preferably in the female-superior position. The man withdraws if he feels he is about to ejaculate. As the man's sense of control increases, thrusting can begin along with variations in coital positions. The couple again stop when the man signals that he is approaching ejaculatory inevitability.

SEXUAL PAIN DISORDERS

Dyspareunia, or painful intercourse, generally calls for medical intervention to ascertain and treat any underlying physical problems, such as genital infections, that might give rise to painful sensations during intercourse. When dyspareunia is caused by vaginismus, successful treatment of vaginismus through a behavioral approach, described below, may eliminate pain.

VAGINISMUS Vaginismus is generally treated with behavioral exercises in which plastic vaginal dilators of increasing size are inserted to help relax the vaginal musculature. A gynecologist may first demonstrate insertion of the narrowest dilator; later, the woman herself practices insertion of wider dilators in the privacy of her home. The woman increases the size of the dilator only when she becomes capable of tolerating insertion and containment (for 10 or 15 minutes) of smaller ones without discomfort or pain. The woman herself—not her partner or therapist—controls the pace of treatment (LoPiccolo & Stock, 1986). The woman's or her partner's fingers (first the littlest finger, then two fingers and so on) may be used in place of the plastic dilators, with the woman controlling the speed and depth of penetration. When the woman is able to tolerate dilators (or fingers) equivalent in thickness to the penis, the couple may attempt coitus with the woman controlling the insertion of the penis under relaxed and nondemanding conditions. The idea is to avoid resensitizing her to fears of penetration. Since vaginismus often occurs among women with a history of sexual trauma, such as rape or incest, additional treatment for the psychological effects of these experiences may supplement the use of dilators (LoPiccolo & Stock, 1986).

EVALUATION OF SEX THERAPY

Learning Objective 10:
Evaluate various sex therapies in terms of their success rates in treating specific sexual dysfunctions

Masters and Johnson (1970) reported an overall success rate of about 80 percent in treating sexual dysfunctions in their two-week intensive program. Some dysfunctions proved more difficult to treat than others. An analysis of treatment results from 1950 to 1977 showed success rates ranging from 67 percent for primary erectile dsyfunction to 99 percent for vaginismus (Kolodny, 1981) (see Table 15.3, page 478). A follow-up of 226 initial successes after a 5-year period showed that 16 people, or 7 percent, experienced a "treatment reversal."

Masters and Johnson's critics note that they followed up on a disappointingly small percentage (29%) of their sample over a 5-year period. Thus, they may have seriously underestimated the actual number of treatment reversals (Adams, 1980; Zilbergeld & Evans, 1980). Zilbergeld and Evans (1980) also challenged their outcome measures. They argued that Masters and Johnson used a global measure of success or failure that was not tied to specific criteria.

Masters and Johnson's sample may also have been biased in at least two ways. It consisted only of people who were willing and could afford to spend two weeks at their institute for full-time therapy. These people were better educated and more affluent than the general population. Masters and Johnson also denied treatment to a number of people whom they considered not "really interested" in changing. Thus, their final sample may have been limited to people who were highly motivated. So some of the success of treatment may have been due to the clients' high level of motivation rather than to the treatment they received. Finally, the absence of a control group prevents us from knowing whether factors extraneous to the treatment itself may have been responsible for the apparent success.

Though other researchers have reported more modest levels of success in treating erectile disorder than those reported at the Masters and Johnson Institute (Barlow, 1986), long-term follow-up evaluations support the general effectiveness of sex therapy for erectile dysfunction (Everaerd, 1993). Yet problems do recur in some cases and are not always easily overcome (Everaerd, 1993). Some couples cope with recurring problems by using the techniques they learned during treatment, such as sensate focus exercises. The addition of biological treatments to the arsenal of treatments for erectile dysfunction has improved success rates to the point that virtually all erection problems can be successfully treated in one way or another (Reinisch, 1990).

We lack any controlled studies of treatments of inhibited male orgasm (Dekker, 1993). Other than the original Masters and Johnson studies, results have been generally disappointing, with most patients showing only modest if any improvement (Dekker, 1993). More research is needed to develop and demonstrate effective treatment approaches. Likewise, new techniques in treating low sexual desire are needed because presently available sex therapy techniques are often inadequate in treating the problem (Hawton, 1991).

Sex therapy approaches to treating vaginismus and premature ejaculation have produced more consistent levels of success (Beck, 1993; O'Donohue et al., 1993). Reported success in treating vaginismus has ranged as high as 80 percent (Hawton et al., 1990) to 100 percent in Masters and Johnson's original research (Masters & Johnson, 1970). Treatment of premature ejaculation has resulted in success rates exceeding 90 percent using the squeeze or stop-start techniques (Killmann & Auerbach, 1979). But there are few data on the long-term results of treatment for premature ejaculation (LoPiccolo & Stock, 1986). Nor do we know why these techniques are effective (Kinder & Curtiss, 1988). Because the squeeze technique carries with it some risk of discomfort, many therapists prefer using the stop-start method.

LoPiccolo and Stock (1986) found that 95 percent of a sample of 150 previously anorgasmic women were able to achieve orgasm through a directed masturbation program. About 85 percent of these women were able to reach orgasm through manual stimulation by their partners. Only about 40 percent were able to achieve orgasm during coitus, however. Generally speaking, couples-oriented treatment helps facilitate orgasm during coitus but is no guarantee that women will become orgasmic during coitus. Nevertheless, the goal of achieving orgasm through some form of genital stimulation with a cooperative partner, as through oral sex or by direct manual clitoral stimulation, is realistic for most women (LoPiccolo & Stock, 1986). Many couples who believe it is important for the woman to reach orgasm during coitus are able to accomplish this end by combining direct clitoral stimulation with coital stimulation (LoPiccolo & Stock, 1986).

Researchers have come to understand some of the factors that predict success in sex therapy. Couples are generally more likely to benefit from sex therapy if they have good relationships and are highly motivated (Hawton & Catalan, 1986; Killmann et al., 1987; McCabe & Delaney, 1992). It should come as little surprise that the success of treatment often depends on the quality of the relationship. Nor is it surprising that people are generally more successful when they are more motivated to take full advantage of the treatments they receive. It also appears that partners who acquire coping skills from therapy that they can use later, such as learning to respond to problems that arise by discussing them openly and by reinstating techniques learned in therapy, are generally better able to overcome recurrences of the problem (Hawton et al., 1986). Sex-therapy techniques may not be appropriate for people in whom profound personal problems or problems in the relationship underlie sexual dysfunctions (Pryde, 1989).

BIOLOGICAL TREATMENTS OF ERECTILE DYSFUNCTION

Biological or biomedical approaches may be helpful in treating erectile dysfunction, especially in cases in which organic factors are involved. Treatments include penile implants, hormone treatments, vascular surgery, and self-injections of drugs that induce erections.

IMPLANTS   A *penile implant* is a prosthetic device that is surgically implanted. About 20,000 men receive penile implants annually in the United States (Blakeslee, 1993). The costs for the surgery and the prosthesis are as high as $10,000 to $12,000. Most medical insurance plans cover only those cases in which organic causes of erectile dysfunctions are documented (Spark, 1991).

Two general types of implants are currently used: the semirigid and inflatable types (Diagnostic and Therapeutic Technology Assessment [DATTA], 1988). The semirigid implant is made of two rods of silicone rubber that remain in a *permanent* semirigid position. It is rigid enough for intercourse and also permits the penis to hang reasonably close to the body at other times. The inflatable type requires a more extensive surgical procedure. Cylinders are implanted in the penis. A fluid reservoir is placed near the bladder. A tiny pump is inserted in the scrotum. To attain erection, the man squeezes the pump several

Learning Objective 11: Describe the biomedical treatments available for erectile dysfunction, the success rates, and the satisfaction rates expressed by men who receive these treatments.

Discussion Question: How many of the men in the class would agree to each of the biomedical treatments for erectile dysfunction? Why or why not? How many of you would encourage a male partner to agree to one of these treatments? (Remember, partners of men with erectile dysfunction could receive sexual satisfaction through stimulation other than penile penetration.)

times, releasing fluid into the cylinders. When the erection is no longer needed, a release valve returns the fluid to the reservoir, deflating the penis (DATTA, 1988).

Inflatable implants tend to be preferred by men and their partners over the noninflatable, semirigid type (Beutler et al., 1986; DATTA, 1988), perhaps because the inflatable type can more closely duplicate the normal processes of tumescence and detumescence. Couples also find the inflatable type more aesthetically pleasing and sexually satisfying (DATTA, 1988). Some adverse side effects of penile implants have also been reported, including infection, pain, and erosion or perforation of the device (DATTA, 1988). The penile implant also damages the spongy tissues of the penis, impairing the man's ability to have normal erections. Penile implants do not in themselves affect sexual drive, sexual sensations, or ejaculation (DATTA, 1988).

Men who receive penile implants, and their partners, are generally pleased with them (Anderson & Wold, 1986; Beutler et al., 1984; Collins & Kinder, 1984). In one study of 35 implant recipients, only one said that he would not undergo the surgery again. The others expressed high levels of satisfaction and enhanced self-esteem (Coleman et al., 1985). Long-term follow-ups of sexual adjustment place the rate of satisfaction for men and their partners closer to 60 to 75 percent, however (LoPiccolo & Stock, 1986; Spark, 1991). Men with psychologically based erectile dysfunctions tend to show less long-term benefit than men with organically caused dysfunctions (Spark, 1991).

Given the irreversible nature of the surgery, it is especially important for men and their partners to receive counseling beforehand to correct unrealistic expectations (Shaw, 1989). An expert panel convened by the National Institutes of Health in 1992 called for men and their doctors to consider the alternative treatments that are available. The experts recommended that surgical solutions, such as the use of penile implants or vascular surgery, be employed only if less invasive techniques, such as sex therapy and the use of injections to stimulate erections, prove unsuccessful. Penile implants have been falling out of favor lately, for several reasons, including complications from surgery, mechanical malfunctions, and fears that the silicone material may prove harmful (Blakeslee, 1993).

VASCULAR SURGERY *Vascular surgery* may be helpful in the few cases of specific blockages in the blood vessels that supply the penis, or in which structural defects in the penis restrict blood flow (LoPiccolo & Stock, 1986). A type of arterial bypass operation may be used to reroute the blood vessels serving the penis around the area of blockage. Such operations have helped increase erections and restore sexual functioning in four out of five cases of men with vascular problems (Carmignani et al., 1987; Goldstein, 1987; Mohr & Beutler, 1990).

HORMONE TREATMENTS *Hormone (testosterone) treatments* may help restore sexual drive and erectile ability in men with abnormally low levels of testosterone (Carani et al., 1990; Spark, 1991). There is no evidence for its effectiveness in men with normal hormone levels (Segraves, 1988b). Testosterone has not been shown to help women who complain of lack of desire (Dow & Gallagher, 1989; Mathews et al., 1983) unless their problem follows a surgically induced menopause in which the testosterone-producing adrenal glands were removed along with the ovaries (Sherwin et al., 1985).

PENILE INJECTION The muscle relaxant *papaverine* typically produces an erection within 10 minutes after injection into the corpus cavernosum of the penis. The erection lasts as long as 1 to 4 hours (Althof et al., 1989; Mohr & Beutler, 1990). A physician teaches the man how to inject himself before coitus. By the end of 1989, more than 4,000 men in the United States, Europe, and Japan had participated in self-injection programs (Spark, 1991).

Papaverine induces erection by increasing nitric oxide levels in the penis, which in turn relaxes the muscles that surround the small blood vessels in the penis, causing them to dilate and allow blood to flow into the penis more freely. Papaverine may also be combined with the drug phentolamine, which overcomes nerve signals that would otherwise maintain the penis in a flaccid state (Spark, 1991). Perhaps 65 to 75 percent of men with erectile failure can achieve an erection through penile injections combining papaverine and phentolamine (Spark, 1991). The injections are most effective for men

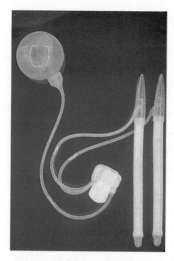

Penile Implants. The inflatable implant shown here consists of two cylinders which are placed in the penis. A fluid reservoir (top left) is placed near the bladder within the lower abdomen. A tiny pump (lower middle) is typically inserted in the scrotum. Squeezing the pump releases fluid into the cylinders, which inflates the penis. A release valve returns the fluid to the reservoir, deflating the penis.

whose erectile problems can be traced to neurological problems that impair the transmission of nerve signals that regulate erection (Spark, 1991; Szasz et al., 1987). Injections are less effective for men whose erectile disorders stem from vascular problems that restrict the flow of blood to the penis (Spark, 1991). Although the injections have also been used successfully with men whose erectile problems are psychologically based (Kiely et al., 1987), about one in three of these men fail to respond (Spark, 1991). A long-term study of self-injections with papaverine and phentolamine in 42 men showed significant improvements in sexual satisfaction, frequency of intercourse, and orgasm during coitus as judged by both the men and their partners (Althof et al., 1991).

Penile injections may cause some side effects, including bruises of the skin of the penis; prolonged, painful erections (*priapism*) that are not erotic or sexually satisfying and can last for 6 to 12 hours; fibrosis and nodules in the penis; some difficulties reaching orgasm or ejaculating; abnormal liver functioning; infections; dependency on the injections to induce erections; and diminished quality of erections over time (Althof et al., 1989; Mohr & Beutler, 1990; Renshaw, 1987; Spark, 1991; Turner et al., 1989). Nearly half the patients in one study declined or discontinued treatment because of such side effects (Althof et al., 1989). Many men find the idea of penile injections distasteful and reject the treatment out of hand or drop out after a short trial period (Gilbert & Gingell, 1991).[4] Still, some men do find the injections helpful, although the long-term effectiveness and risks of the treatment require further study. Researchers are investigating alternative treatments to injections. For example, drug companies are experimenting with creams that can promote erections when rubbed on the penis (Blakeslee, 1993).

VACUUM CONSTRICTION DEVICE   Sounding like something from the "what will they think of next" category, a recently introduced, noninvasive *vacuum constrictor device (VCD)* helps men achieve erections through vacuum pressure. The device (brand name: ErecAid), which costs about $400, consists of a cylinder that is connected to a hand-operated vacuum pump. The device creates a vacuum when it is placed over the limp penis and held against the body to create an airtight seal (Mohr & Beutler, 1990; Spark, 1991). The vacuum pressure forces an increased flow of blood into the penis, inducing an erection. Rubber bands placed around the base of the penis can maintain the erection for as long as 30 minutes. About 30,000 men were reported to be using the vacuum device by the early 1990s (Blakeslee, 1993).

Although the device has been used successfully by men with both organically and psychologically based erectile failure, side effects such as pain and discomfort and black-and-blue marks on the penis are common (Spark, 1991). Injuries to the penile tissues may also result from the rubber bands. The rubber bands also prevent normal ejaculation, so semen remains trapped in the urethra until the bands are released (Spark, 1991). The quality of the erections produced by the device is also considered inferior to spontaneous erections (Spark, 1991). Despite these drawbacks, men who use the device, and their partners, reportedly are generally satisfied with it (Cooper, 1987). The effectiveness of the device in routine use as well as its effects on the couple's sexual relations remain undetermined, however (Mohr & Beutler, 1990; Spark, 1991).

HOW DO YOU FIND A QUALIFIED SEX THERAPIST?

Learning Objective 12: Discuss the organizations people could contact and the questions they could ask to help them locate a qualified sex therapist.

How would you find a sex therapist if you had a sexual dysfunction? You might find advertisements for "sex therapists" in the yellow pages. But beware. Most states do not restrict usage of the term "sex therapist" to recognized professionals. In these states, anyone who wants to use the label may do so, including quacks and prostitutes.

Thus, it is essential to determine that a sex therapist is a member of a recognized profession (such as psychology, social work, medicine, or marriage and family counsel-

---

[4]Some women are also disconcerted by the procedure. But not all. One woman who approved the technique said, "When I'm in the mood I simply leave a syringe on the pillow and he gets the message." (Spark, 1991, p. 159).

ing) with training and supervision in sex therapy. Professionals are usually licensed or certified by their states. All states require licensing of psychologists and physicians, but some states do not license social workers or marriage counselors. If you have questions about the license laws in your state, contact your state's professional licensing board. The ethical standards of these professions prohibit practitioners from claiming expertise in sex therapy without suitable training.

If you are uncertain as to how to locate a qualified sex therapist in your area, you may obtain names of local practitioners from various sources, such as your university or college psychology department, health department, or counseling center; a local medical or psychological association; a family physician; or your instructor. You may also seek services from a sex-therapy clinic affiliated with a local medical center or medical school in your area, many of which provide services on a sliding scale depending on the patient's income level. You may also contact the American Association of Sex Educators, Counselors, and Therapists (AASECT), a professional organization that certifies sex therapists. They can provide you with the names of certified sex therapists in your area. They are located at 11 Dupont Circle, N.W., Suite 220, Washington, D.C. 20036. (Telephone number: 202-462-1171.)

Ethical professionals are not annoyed or embarrassed if you ask them (1) what their profession is, (2) where they earned their advanced degree, (3) whether they are licensed or certified by the state, (4) what fees they charge, (5) their plans for treatment, and (6) the nature of their training in human sexuality and sex therapy. If the therapist hems and haws, asks why you are asking such questions, or fails to provide a direct answer, beware.

Professionals are also restricted by the ethical principles of their professions from engaging in unethical practices, such as having sexual relations with their clients. The nature of therapy creates an unequal power relationship between the therapist and the client. The therapist is perceived as an expert whose suggestions are likely to carry great authority. Clients may thus be vulnerable to exploitation by therapists who misuse their therapeutic authority. Let's be absolutely clear here: There is no therapeutic justification for a therapist having sex with a client. Any therapist who makes a sexual overture toward a client, or tries to persuade a client to have sexual relations, is acting unethically.

SUMMING UP

Sexual dysfunctions are difficulties in becoming sexually aroused or reaching orgasm.

TYPES OF SEXUAL DYSFUNCTIONS

Sexual Desire Disorders
These disorders involve dysfunctions in sexual desire, interest, or drive, in which the person experiences a lack of sexual desire or an aversion to genital sexual contact.
Sexual Arousal Disorders
In men, sexual arousal disorders involve recurrent difficulty in achieving or sustaining erections sufficient to successfully engage in sexual intercourse. In women, they typically involve failure to become sufficiently lubricated.
Orgasm Disorders Women are more likely to encounter difficulties reaching orgasm, whereas men are more likely to have premature ejaculation.
Sexual Pain Disorders These disorders include dyspareunia and vaginismus.

ORIGINS OF SEXUAL DYSFUNCTIONS

Many sexual dysfunctions involve the interaction of organic and psychological factors.

Organic Causes Fatigue may lead to erectile dysfunction in men, and to orgasmic dysfunction and dyspareunia in women. Dyspareunia often reflects vaginal infections and STDs. Organic factors are believed to be involved in more than 50 percent of cases of erectile dysfunction. Medications and other drugs may also impair sexual functioning.

Psychosocial Causes Psychosocial factors that are connected with sexual dysfunctions include cultural influences, psychosexual trauma, homosexual inclinations, marital dissatisfaction, psychological conflict, lack of sexual skills, irrational beliefs, and performance anxiety. Children reared in sexually repressive cultural or home environments may learn to respond to sex with feelings of anxiety and shame, rather than sexual arousal and pleasure. Many people do not acquire sexual competencies because of a lack of opportunity to acquire knowledge and experience, even within marriage. Irrational beliefs and attitudes such as excessive needs for approval and perfectionism may also contribute to sexual problems. Performance anxiety may place a dysfunctional individual in a spectator rather than performer role.

TREATMENT OF SEXUAL DYSFUNCTIONS

Sex therapy aims to directly modify dysfunctional behavior by modifying self-defeating beliefs and attitudes, fostering sexual skills and knowledge, enhancing sexual communication, and behavioral exercises to enhance sexual stimulation while reducing performance anxiety.

The Masters-and-Johnson Approach Masters and Johnson pioneered the direct, behavioral approach to treating sexual dysfunctions. They employ a male and female therapy team during an in-residence, two-week program, which focuses on the couple as the unit of treatment. Sensate focus exercises are used to enable the partners to give each other pleasure in a nondemanding situation.

The Helen Singer Kaplan Approach Kaplan's *psychosexual therapy* combines behavioral and psychoanalytic methods.

Disorders of Sexual Desire Some sex therapists help kindle the sexual appetites of people with inhibited sexual desire through prescribing self-stimulation exercises combined with erotic fantasies.

Disorders of Sexual Arousal Men and women with impaired sexual arousal receive sexual stimulation from their partners under relaxed circumstances, so that anxiety does not inhibit their natural reflexes.

Orgasm Disorders Masters and Johnson use a couples-oriented approach in treating anorgasmic women. Other sex therapists prefer a program of directed masturbation to enable women to learn about their own bodies at their own pace and free them of the need to rely on partners or please partners. Premature ejaculation is usually treated with the squeeze technique or the stop-start method.

Sexual Pain Disorders Dyspareunia or painful intercourse is generally treated with medical intervention. Vaginismus is generally treated with plastic vaginal dilators of increasing size.

Evaluation of Sex Therapy The success of sex therapy has varied with the type of sexual dysfunction treated.

Biological Treatments of Erectile Dysfunction Biological approaches may be helpful in treating erectile dysfunction, especially when there is organic involvement. Treatments include penile implants, hormone treatments, vascular surgery, and self-injections of drugs that induce erections.

_____ About 80 percent of the women who contract gonorrhea never develop symptoms.

_____ Christopher Columbus brought more than beads, blankets, and tobacco back to Europe from the New World: he brought syphilis.

_____ Gonorrhea and syphilis may be contracted from toilet seats in public restrooms.

_____ If a syphilitic chancre (sore) goes away by itself, the infection does not require medical treatment.

_____ Men too can develop vaginal infections.

_____ Vaginitis is often caused by an overgrowth of infectious organisms that normally reside in the vagina.

_____ Many men whose partners have "trich" are also infected themselves, often unknowingly.

_____ Genital herpes can only be transmitted during flare-ups of the disease.

_____ Most people with genital warts have them on visible parts of the body.

_____ Pubic lice are of the same family of animals as crabs.

C H A P T E R *16*

Sexually Transmitted Diseases

Harold and Carin, both 20, have been dating for several months. They feel strong sexual attraction toward each other but have hesitated to become sexually intimate because of fears about AIDS. Harold believes that using condoms is no guarantee against infection and wants the two of them to be tested for HIV, the virus that causes AIDS. Carin has resisted undergoing an HIV test, partly because she feels insulted that Harold fears that she may be infected, and frankly, partly in fear of the test results. She has heard that symptoms may not develop for years after infection. She wonders whether she might have been infected by one of the men whom she had slept with in the past.

Stefanie has genital herpes. A 19-year-old pre-law student, she has had no recurrences since the initial outbreak two years earlier. But she knows that herpes is a lifelong infection and may recur periodically from time to time. She also knows that she may inadvertently pass the herpes virus along to her sexual partners, even to the man she eventually marries. She has begun thinking seriously about Steve, a man she has been dating for the past month. She would like to tell him that she has herpes before they become sexually intimate. Yet she fears that telling him might scare him away.

John, 21, a math and computer science major, is planning a career in computer operations, hoping one day to run the computer systems for a large corporation. He lives off campus with several of his buddies in a run-down house they've dubbed the "Nuclear Dumpsite." He has been dating Maria, a theater major, for several months. They have begun having sexual relations and have practiced "safer sex"—at least most of the time. During the past week he noticed a burning sensation while urinating. It seems to have passed now, so he figures that it was probably nothing to worry about. But he's not sure and wonders whether he should see a doctor.

(From *A Student's Guide to AIDS And Other Sexually Transmitted Diseases* by J. S. Nevid. Copyright © 1993 by Allyn & Bacon. Reprinted by permission.)

Sexually transmitted diseases
Diseases that are communicated through sexual contact. Abbreviated STDs.

Harold, Carin, Stefanie, and John express some of the fears and concerns of a generation of young people who are becoming sexually active at a time when the threat of AIDS and other STDs (**sexually transmitted diseases**) hangs over every sexual decision. Coming of age in this age of AIDS, young people today face the prospect of a lifetime of uncertainty and fear overshadowing their development of intimate relationships.

AIDS is indeed a scary thing, a very scary thing. But AIDS is only one of many STDs, although certainly the most deadly and frightening. It seems these days that every time you pick up a newspaper you read about AIDS. Every time you turn on the radio or a television set you hear about AIDS. We have been flooded with information about AIDS, yet other STDs pose much wider threats. In a study of more than 16,000 students on 19 U.S. college campuses, the virus that causes AIDS was found in 30 blood samples (Gayle et al., 1990), or about 0.2 percent of this population (one student in 500). *Chlamydia trachomatis* (the bacterium that causes chlamydia) and *human papilloma virus* (HPV) (the organism that causes genital warts) were each found in one sample in 10, or 10 percent of the college population! Chlamydia, virtually unheard of a generation ago, is now the most common bacterial STD in the United States, outpacing those old bacterial menaces gonorrhea and syphilis (U. S. Department of Health and Human Services [USDHHS], 1992).

The same college study found that although college students were reasonably well versed about AIDS, many are unaware that chlamydia can go undetected for years, and if left untreated can cause pelvic inflammation and scarring that can lead to infertility. Many, perhaps most, students were completely ignorant of HPV, a virus that causes genital warts and that is linked to cervical cancer. Yet the federal Centers for Disease Control and Prevention (CDC) estimates that as many as one million new cases of HPV infection occur annually in the United States—more than syphilis, genital herpes, and AIDS combined (Penn, 1993). Whereas about one million Americans are infected with HIV, more than one in five Americans, about 56 million, are infected with some other STD-causing virus, such as those causing genital warts, herpes, and hepatitis (Barringer, 1993e). *None of this is intended to downplay the threat of AIDS. AIDS is lethal, and one case is one case too many.*

There are also important links between HIV/AIDS and other STDs (USDHHS, 1992). For one thing, people appear to be at greater risk of becoming infected with HIV upon exposure to the virus if they already carry another STD. For another, the use of latex (rubber) condoms not only helps prevent the spread of HIV but also many other STD-causing organisms as well, such as those causing gonorrhea, chlamydia, and genital herpes (Cates & Stone, 1992a,b).

Sexually transmitted diseases (STDs) are diseases that are transmitted through sexual means, such as by vaginal or anal intercourse, or oral sex. They were formerly called *venereal diseases* (VD)—after Venus, the Roman goddess of love. Some STDs can be spread (and often are) through nonsexual contact as well as sexual contact. For example, AIDS and viral hepatitis may be spread by sharing contaminated needles. And yes, a few STDs (like "crabs") may be picked up from bedding or other objects, like moist towels, that harbor the infectious organisms that cause these STDs.

CNN Sex Disease

AN EPIDEMIC

STDs are epidemic in our society and around the world. More than 13 million people in the United States, including 2.5 million adolescents (about one in every six), contract an STD each year (American Social Health Association, 1989; Johnson, 1990). At least one

One in Ten. Researchers estimate that one college student in ten is afflicted with chlamydial infections and genital warts. Most students may be aware of the dangers of AIDS, but how many know about the risks posed by these more common STDs?

Talking to Your Partner About STDs

Many people find it difficult to discuss the issue of STDs with their partners. As one young woman explained:

> It's one thing to talk about "being responsible about STDs" and a much harder thing to do it at the very moment. It's just plain hard to say to someone I am feeling very erotic with, "Oh, yes, before we go any further, can we have a conversation about STDs?" It's hard to imagine murmuring into someone's ear at a time of passion, "Would you mind slipping on this condom or using this cream just in case one of us has an STD?" Yet it seems awkward to bring it up any sooner if it's not clear between us that we want to make love.

(*The New Our Bodies, Ourselves*, 1984, p. 267)

Because talking about STDs with sex partners can be difficult or awkward, many young people admit that they "wing it" (Wallis,

1987). They assume that their partners are free of STDs and hope for the best. Some people pretend that if you don't talk about AIDS and other STDs, they will simply go away. But the microbes causing AIDS, herpes, chlamydia, genital warts, and other STDs will not simply go away by not talking about them. Then there is the case of a young man from rural Illinois who reported that when he was 16, his mother ordered him to buy condoms. "Every weekend," he told an interviewer, "I had to show her that I had one with me or I would get grounded" (Johnson, 1990). The times, they are a-changing, in this age of AIDS.

But just how might you raise the subject of STDs? Timing is important. As the young woman quoted recognizes, it may be awkward to discuss STDs and the precautions you might take

at a point in your relationship when it is not yet clear that you and your partner will become sexually intimate. Though you need not "jump the gun," whatever time you do select, make sure that it occurs *before* any genital contact begins (by that we mean genital-genital, oral-genital, and anal-genital contact). Far too often, only *after* making love will one partner say something to the other, like this: "By the way, I hope that you're not infected with anything, are you?" Even more often, nothing at all is either said or done to prevent STDs. Let us suggest a few pointers that might make talking about STDs somewhat less awkward.[1]

You've gone out with Chris a few times and you're keenly attracted. Chris is attractive, bright, witty, shares some of your attitudes, and, all in all, is a powerful turn-on. Now the evening is

Teaching Tip: Have each student role-play telling a partner that he/she has an STD. Have the speaker tell the partner about the specific STD and explain that the partner needs to see a physician to be tested and treated.

in four Americans is likely to contract an STD at some point in their lives (Barringer, 1993e). Two of three cases affect people under the age of 25; one of four afflicts teenagers. Yet many young people remain largely uninformed about the dangers posed by the many different types of STDs.

Some readers have STDs today and do not even realize it. Ignorance is not bliss, however, because some STDs may not produce noticeable symptoms but still damage the internal reproductive system if left untreated. STDs can also be painful and, in the cases of AIDS and advanced syphilis, lethal. Women suffer disproportionately from the effects of STDs; they are more likely to develop infertility as the result of STDs spreading within the internal reproductive system (Barringer, 1993e; Rosenberg & Gollub, 1992). The best available estimates suggest that 100,000 to 150,000 women a year become infertile as a result of STDs (Barringer, 1993e). Overall, STDs are believed to account for between 15 and 30 percent of cases of infertility among women. In addition to their biological effects, STDs may exact an emotional toll on individuals and strain relationships to the breaking point. Nevertheless, many people find it difficult to discuss the issue with their partners, an issue we explore further in the accompanying feature, Talking to Your Partner About STDs.

There is a current surge in the incidence of many STDs, and it reflects several factors. One is the increased numbers of young people who engage in coitus, many of whom fail to use latex condoms (which can prevent the transmission of many STD-causing organisms) consistently, if at all. Another is the widespread use of the pill. Although birth-control pills are reliable methods of contraception, they do not prevent the spread of STDs, although some people may mistakenly believe that they do. Still another reason is that

winding down. You've been cuddling, and you think you know where things are heading.

Something clicks in your mind! You realize that as wonderful as Chris is, you don't know every place Chris has "been." As healthy as Chris looks and acts, you don't know what's swimming around in Chris's bloodstream. Chris may not know either. In a moment of pent-up desire, Chris may also (how should we put this delicately?)... lie about not being infected or about past sexual experiences.

What do you say now? How do you protect yourself without turning Chris off? Write some possible responses in the spaces provided, and then check below for some ideas.

1. _____

2. _____

3. _____

Ah, the clumsiness! If you ask about condoms or STDs, it is sort of making a verbal commitment to have sexual relations, and perhaps you're not exactly sure that's what your partner intends. And even if it's clear that's where you're heading, will you seem too straightforward? Will you kill the romance? The spontaneity of the moment? Sure you might—life has its risks. But which is riskier: an awkward moment or being infected with a fatal illness? Let's put it another way: Are you *really* willing to die for sex? Given that few verbal responses are perfect, here are some things you can try:

1. You might say something like this: "I've brought something and I'd like to use it. . . " (referring to a condom).

2. Or you can say, "I know this is a bit clumsy" (you are assertively expressing a feel

ing and asking permission to pursue a clumsy topic; Chris is likely to respond with "That's okay," or "Don't worry—what is it?")—"but the world isn't as safe as it used to be, and I think we should talk about what we're going to do."

The point to this is that your partner hasn't been living in a remote cave. Your partner is also aware of the dangers of STDs, especially of AIDS, and ought to be working with you to make things safe and unpressured. If your partner is pressing for unsafe sex and is inconsiderate of your feelings and concerns, you need to reassess whether you really want to be with this person. We think you can do better.

[1]Rathus & Nevid, 1992, p. 487. Reprinted with permission.

some infections, like chlamydia, often have no symptoms, so some infected individuals unwittingly pass them along to others (Goldsmith, 1989). Other identified risk factors include early sexual involvement and sex with multiple partners (Yarber and Parillo, 1992). Drug use is also associated with an increased risk of STDs, in part because people who abuse drugs are more likely than others to engage in unsafe sexual practices, and because certain forms of drug use, such as needle sharing, can directly transmit infectious organisms, like HIV.

Education is a critical component in curtailing the STD epidemic among young people (Yarber & Parillo, 1992). STD instruction is intended to promote responsible sexual decision making and to alter behaviors that put young people at risk of infection. However, education alone is not sufficient. Young people must be motivated to practice prevention and risk-reduction strategies if education is to have a meaningful effect on their behavior (Yarber & Parillo, 1992). Experts recognize that school-based STD education programs should not wait until the junior or senior year of high school to spread the message of STD prevention, since many adolescents are becoming sexually active at younger ages (see Chapter 13) (USDHHS, 1992).

In this chapter we discuss STDs that are caused by agents as diverse as bacteria, viruses, protozoa, and parasites. We discuss their incidence and transmission, symptoms, diagnosis, and treatment. We explore the sexual practices and behavior patterns that affect the risk of contracting STDs. In the next chapter we discuss HIV infection and AIDS, which to date, has eluded the efforts of researchers to develop a vaccine or cure. In the case of HIV/AIDS, education and prevention are the best weapons we have.

Learning Objective 2:
Discuss the incidence, transmission, symptoms, diagnosis, and treatment of gonorrhea.

BACTERIAL DISEASES

Bacteria
Plural of *bacterium,* a class of one-celled microorganisms that have no chlorophyll and can give rise to many illnesses. (From the Greek *baktron,* meaning "stick," referring to the fact that many bacteria are rod-shaped.)

Without the one-celled microorganisms we call **bacteria,** there would be no wine. Bacteria are essential to fermentation. They also play vital roles in our bodies' digestive systems. Unfortunately, bacteria also cause many diseases such as pneumonia, tuberculosis, and meningitis, along with the STDs gonorrhea, syphilis, and chlamydia.

GONORRHEA

Gonorrhea
A sexually transmitted disease (STD) caused by the *Neisseria gonorrhoeae* bacterium and characterized by

Gonorrhea—also known as "the clap" or "the drip"—was once the most widespread STD in the United States, but the rate of gonorrheal infection declined substantially during the 1980s (Centers for Disease Control [CDC], 1990d). The decline of the incidence of gonorrhea is one of the few (relative) success stories in the fight against STDs. Approximately three quarters of a million cases of gonorrhea occur annually (CDC, 1989a). Many cases of gonorrhea go unreported, however, so the actual incidence may be as high as 3 to 5 million cases per year. Most new cases of gonorrhea are contracted by young people between the ages of 20 and 24.

13. I dislike talking about STD with my peers.
    SA A U D SD

14. I would be uncertain about going to the doctor unless I was sure I really had an STD.
    SA A U D SD

15. I would feel that I should take my sex partner with me to a clinic if I thought I had an STD.
    SA A U D SD

16. It would be embarrassing to discuss STD with one's partner if one were sexually active.
    SA A U D SD

17. If I were to have sex, the chance of getting an STD makes me uneasy about having sex with more than one person.
    SA A U D SD

18. I like the idea of sexual abstinence (not having sex) as the best way of avoiding STD.
    SA A U D SD

19. If I had an STD, I would cooperate with public health persons to find the sources of STD.
    SA A U D SD

20. If I had an STD, I would avoid exposing others while I was being treated. SA A U D SD

21. I would have regular STD checkups if I were having sex with more than one partner.
    SA A U D SD

22. I intend to look for STD signs before deciding to have sex with anyone
    SA A U D SD

23. I will limit my sex activity to just one partner because of the chances I might get an STD.
    SA A U D SD

24. I will avoid sex contact any time I think there is even a slight chance of getting an STD.
    SA A U D SD

25. The chance of getting an STD would not stop me from having sex.   SA A U D SD

26. If I had a chance, I would support community efforts toward controlling STD.
    SA A U D SD

27. I would be willing to work with others to make people aware of STD problems in my town.   SA A U D SD

Source: Yarber, W. L., Torabi, M. R., & Veenker, C. H. (1989). Development of a three-component sexually transmitted diseases attitude scale. *Journal of Sex Education & Therapy, 15,* 36–49. Reprinted with permission.

a discharge and burning urination. Left untreated, gonorrhea can give rise to pelvic inflammatory disease (PID) and infertility. (From the Greek *gonos,* meaning "seed," and *rheein,* meaning "to flow," referring to the fact that in ancient times the penile discharge characteristic of the illness was erroneously interpreted as a loss of seminal fluid.)

Gonorrhea is caused by the *gonococcus* bacterium (see Table 16.1, page 494). A penile discharge that was probably gonorrhea is described in ancient Egyptian and Chinese writings and is mentioned in the Old Testament (Leviticus 15). Ancient Jews and Greeks assumed that the discharge was an involuntary loss of seminal fluid. In about 400 B.C. the Greek physician Hippocrates suggested that the loss stemmed from excessive sex or "worship" of Aphrodite (whom the Romans would later rename *Venus*). The term *gonorrhea* is credited to the Greek physician Galen, who lived in the second century A.D. Albert L. S. Neisser identified the gonococcus bacterium in 1879, and for this reason, the microorganism bears his name: *Neisseria gonorrhoeae.*

TRANSMISSION   Gonococcal bacteria require a warm, moist environment, like that found along the mucous membranes of the urinary tract in both men and women or the cervix in women. Outside the body, they die in about a minute. There is no evidence that gonorrhea can be picked up from public toilet seats or by touching dry objects (Calderone & Johnson, 1989; Reinisch, 1990). In rare cases, gonorrhea was contracted by contact with a moist and warm towel or sheet used immediately beforehand by an

TABLE 16.1 Causes, modes of transmission, symptoms, diagnosis, and treatment of major sexually transmitted diseases

STD and Pathogen	Modes of Transmission	Symptoms	Diagnosis	Treatment
Bacterial Diseases				
Gonorrhea ("clap," "drip"): Gonococcus bacterium (*Neisseria gonorrhoeae*).	Transmitted by vaginal, oral, or anal sexual activity, or from mother to newborn during delivery.	In men, yellowish, thick penile discharge, burning urination. In women, increased vaginal discharge, burning urination, irregular menstrual bleeding (most women show no early symptoms).	Clinical inspection, culture of sample discharge.	Antibiotics: ceftriaxone, spectinomycin, penicillin.
Syphilis: *Treponema pallidum.*	Transmitted by vaginal, oral, or anal sexual activity, or by touching an infectious chancre.	In primary stage, a hard, round painless chancre or sore appears at site of infection within 2 to 4 weeks. May progress through secondary, latent, and tertiary stages, if left untreated.	Primary-stage syphilis is diagnosed by clinical examination and by examination of fluid from a chancre in a dark-field test. Secondary-stage syphilis is diagnosed by blood test (the VDRL).	Penicillin, or doxycycline, tetracycline, or erythromycin for nonpregnant penicillin-allergic patients.
Chlamydia and **nongonococcal urethritis (NGU):** *Chlamydia trachomatis* bacterium; NGU in men may also be caused by *Ureaplasma urealycticum* bacterium and other pathogens.	Transmitted by vaginal, oral, or anal sexual activity; to the eye by touching one's eyes after touching the genitals of an infected partner; or to newborns passing through the birth canal of an infected mother.	In women, frequent and painful urination, lower abdominal pain and inflammation, and vaginal discharge (but most women are symptom-free). In men, symptoms are similar to but milder than those of gonorrhea—burning or painful urination, slight penile discharge (most men are also asymptomatic). Sore throat may indicate infection from oral-genital contact.	The Abbott Testpack analyzes a cervical smear in women; in men, an extract of fluid from the penis is analyzed.	Antibiotics: doxycycline, tetracycline, or erythromycin.
Vaginitis				
Bacterial vaginosis: *Gardnerella vaginalis* bacterium and others.	Can arise by overgrowth of organisms in vagina, allergic reactions, etc.; also transmitted by sexual contact.	In women, thin, foul-smelling vaginal discharge. Irritation of genitals and mild pain during urination. In men, inflammation of penile foreskin and glans, urethritis, and cystitis. May be asymptomatic in both genders.	Culture and examination of bacterium.	Oral treatment with metronidazole (brand name: Flagyl).
Candidiasis moniliasis (thrush, "yeast infection"): *Candida albicans*—a yeast-like fungus.	Can arise by overgrowth of fungus in vagina; may also be transmitted by sexual contact, or by sharing a washcloth with an infected person.	In women, vulval itching; white, cheesy, foul-smelling discharge; soreness or swelling of vaginal and vulval tissues. In men, itching and burning on urination, or a reddening of the penis.	Diagnosis usually made on basis of symptoms.	Vaginal suppositories, creams, or tablets containing miconazole, clotrimazole, or terconazole; modification of use of other medicines and chemical agents; keeping infected area dry.

(continued)

Adapted from Table 14.3 in Rathus, S.A. (1993). *Psychology,* 5th ed. Fort Worth: Harcourt Brace Jovanovich.

TABLE 16.1 (continued)

STD and Pathogen	Modes of Transmission	Symptoms	Diagnosis	Treatment
Vaginitis (continued)				
Trichomoniasis ("trich"): *Trichomonas vaginalis*— a protozoan (one-celled animal).	Almost always transmitted sexually.	In women, foamy, yellowish, odorous vaginal discharge; itching or burning sensation in vulva. Many women are asymptomatic. In men, usually asymptomatic, but mild urethritis is possible.	Microscopic examination of a smear of vaginal secretions, or of culture of the sample (latter method preferred).	Metronidazole (Flagyl).
Viral Diseases				
Oral herpes: *Herpes simplex virus-type 1 (HSV-1).*	Touching, kissing, sexual contact with sores or blisters; sharing cups, towels, toilet seats.	Cold sores or fever blisters on the lips, mouth, or throat; herpetic sores on the genitals.	Usually clinical inspection.	Over-the-counter lip balms, cold-sore medications; check with your physician, however.
Genital herpes: *Herpes simplex virus-type 2 (HSV-2).*	Almost always by means of vaginal, oral, or anal sexual activity; most contagious during active outbreaks of the disease.	Painful, reddish bumps around the genitals, thighs, or buttocks; in women, may also be in the vagina or on the cervix. Bumps become blisters or sores that fill with pus and break, shedding viral particles. Other possible symptoms: burning urination, fever, aches and pains, swollen glands; in women, vaginal discharge.	Clinical inspection of sores; culture and examination of fluid drawn from the base of a genital sore.	The antiviral drug acyclovir (brand name: Zovirax) may provide relief and prompt healing over, but is not a cure; herpes sufferers often profit from counseling and group support as well.
Hepatitis: hepatitis A, B, C, and D type viruses.	Sexual contact, especially involving the anus (especially hepatitis A); contact with infected fecal matter; transfusion of contaminated blood (especially hepatitis B and C).	Ranges from being asymptomatic to mild flu-like symptoms and more severe symptoms including fever, abdominal pain, vomiting, and "jaundiced" (yellowish) skin and eyes.	Examination of blood for hepatitis antibodies; liver biopsy.	Treatment usually involves bed rest, intake of fluids, and, sometimes, antibiotics to ward off bacterial infections that might take hold because of lowered resistance. Alpha interferon is sometimes used in treating hepatitis C.
Acquired immunodeficiency syndrome (AIDS): *Human immunodeficiency virus (HIV).*	HIV is transmitted by sexual contact; direct infusion of contaminated blood; from mother to fetus during pregnancy; or from mother to child through childbirth or breast-feeding.	Infected people may initially be asymptomatic or develop mild flulike symptoms, which may then disappear for many years prior to the development of "full-blown" AIDS. Full-blown AIDS is characterized by fever, weight loss, fatigue, diarrhea, and opportunistic infections such as rare forms of cancer (Kaposi's sarcoma) and pneumonia (PCP).	A blood test (ELISA) detects HIV antibodies in the bloodstream. The diagnosis of AIDS itself is made on the basis of CD4 cell counts and/or the appearance of indicator diseases in HIV-infected people.	There is no cure for AIDS. Drugs like AZT may provide a limited benefit for a limited period of time. Patients may profit from proper nutrition, exercise, counseling, and stress-management techniques.

(continued)

TABLE 16.1 *(continued)*

STD and Pathogen	Modes of Transmission	Symptoms	Diagnosis	Treatment
Viral Diseases				
Genital warts (venereal warts): *Human papilloma virus (HPV)*.	Transmission is by sexual and other forms of contact, such as with infected towels or clothing.	Appearance of painless warts, often resembling cauliflowers, on the penis, foreskin, scrotum, or internal urethra in men, and on the vulva, labia, wall of the vagina, or cervix in women. May occur around the anus and in the rectum of both genders.	Clinical inspection.	Methods include cryotherapy (freezing), podophyllin, burning, surgical removal.
Ectoparasitic Infestations				
Pediculosis ("crabs"): *Pthirus pubis* (pubic lice).	Transmission is by sexual contact, or by contact with an infested towel, sheet, or toilet seat.	Intense itching in pubic area and other hairy regions to which lice can attach.	Clinical examination.	Lindane (brand name: Kwell)—a prescription shampoo; nonprescription medications containing pyrethrins or piperonyl butoxide (brand names: RID, Triple X).
Scabies: *Sarcoptes scabiei.*	Transmission is by sexual contact, or by contact with infested clothing or bed linen, towels, and other fabrics.	Intense itching; reddish lines on skin where mites have burrowed in; welts and pus-filled blisters in affected areas.	Clinical inspection.	Lindane (Kwell).

infected person (Calderone & Johnson, 1989). Gonorrhea is almost always transmitted by unprotected vaginal, oral, or anal sexual activity, or from mother to newborn during delivery (Reinisch, 1990).

Pharyngeal gonorrhea
A gonorrheal infection of the pharynx (the cavity leading from the mouth and nasal passages to the larynx and esophagus) that is characterized by a sore throat.

Ophthalmia neonatorum
A gonorrheal infection of the eyes of newborn children who contract the disease by passing through an infected birth canal. (From the Greek *ophthalmos,* meaning "eye.")

A person who performs fellatio on an infected man may develop **pharyngeal gonorrhea**, which produces a throat infection. Mouth-to-mouth kissing and cunnilingus are less likely to spread gonorrhea. The eyes provide a good environment for the bacterium. Thus, a person whose hands come into contact with infected genitals and who inadvertently touches his or her eyes afterward may infect them. Infants have contracted gonorrhea of the eyes, **ophthalmia neonatorum,** when passing through the birth canals of infected mothers. This disorder may cause blindness but has become rare because the eyes of newborns are treated routinely with silver nitrate or penicillin ointment, which are toxic to gonococcal bacteria.

A gonorrheal infection may be spread from the penis to the partner's rectum during anal intercourse. A cervical gonorrheal infection can be spread to the rectum if an infected woman and her partner follow vaginal intercourse with anal intercourse. Gonorrhea is less likely to be spread by vaginal than penile discharges. Thus, lesbians are less likely than gay males to contract the disease.

Gonorrhea is highly contagious. Women may stand a slightly greater than 50 percent chance of contracting gonorrhea after just one exposure; men, a 20 to 25 percent risk of infection (Handsfield et al., 1984; Platt et al., 1983). The risks to women are believed to be greater because women retain infected semen in the vagina following intercourse (Reinisch, 1990). The risk of infection does increase with repeated exposure, for example, to 60 to 80 percent for men who have sex either four times with one infected woman or one time with each of four infected women (Reinisch, 1990).

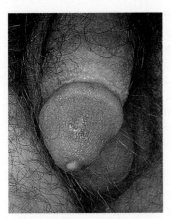

Gonorrheal Discharge.
Gonorrhea in the male often causes a thick, yellowish, pus-like discharge from the penis.

SYMPTOMS Most men experience symptoms within two to five days after infection. Symptoms include a penile discharge that is clear at first. Within a day it turns yellow to yellow-green, thickens, and becomes puslike. The urethra becomes inflamed, and urination is accompanied by a burning sensation. Thirty to 40 percent of males have swelling and tenderness in the lymph glands of the groin. Inflammation and other symptoms may become chronic if left untreated.

The initial symptoms of gonorrhea usually abate within a few weeks without treatment, leading victims to think of gonorrhea as being no worse than a bad cold. The truth of the matter is that even though the early symptoms fade, the gonococcus bacterium will usually continue to damage the body.

In women the primary site of the infection is the cervix, where it causes **cervicitis,** which may be accompanied by a yellowish to yellow-green puslike discharge that irritates the vulva. If the infection spreads to the urethra, women may also note burning urination. *About 80 percent of the women who contract gonorrhea are* **asymptomatic** *during the early stages of the disease, however.* Unfortunately, therefore, many infected women do not seek treatment until more serious symptoms develop. They may also innocently infect another sex partner.

About 80 percent of the women who contract gonorrhea never develop symptoms. *Though it is true that about 80 percent of the women who contract gonorrhea do not develop symptoms during the* early stages *of the disease, they may develop quite serious symptoms later on.* •

Cervicitis
Inflammation of the cervix.

Asymptomatic
Without symptoms.

Epididymitis
Inflammation of the epididymis.

Pelvic inflammatory disease
Inflammation of the pelvic region—possibly including the cervix, uterus, Fallopian tubes, abdominal cavity, and ovaries—that can be caused by organisms such as *Neisseria gonorrhoeae.* Its symptoms are abdominal pain, tenderness, nausea, fever, and irregular menstrual cycles. The condition may lead to infertility. Abbreviated *PID*.

When gonorrhea is not treated early, it may spread through the urogenital systems in both genders and strike the internal reproductive organs. In men, it can lead to **epididymitis,** which can cause fertility problems. Swelling and feelings of tenderness or pain in the scrotum are the principal symptoms of epididymitis. Fever may also be present. Occasionally the kidneys are affected. In women, the bacterium can spread through the cervix to the uterus, Fallopian tubes, ovaries, and other parts of the abdominal cavity, causing **pelvic inflammatory disease** (PID).

Symptoms of PID include cramps, other forms of abdominal pain and tenderness, cervical tenderness and discharge, irregular menstrual cycles, coital pain, fever, nausea, and vomiting. PID may also be asymptomatic. Whether or not women experience symptoms, PID can cause scarring that blocks the Fallopian tubes and impairs fertility. PID is a serious illness that requires aggressive treatment with antibiotics to fight the underlying infection (Reinisch, 1990). Surgery may also be needed to remove the infected tissue. Unfortunately, many women become aware of a gonococcal infection only when they experience the discomfort of PID.

These consequences are all the more unfortunate because gonorrhea, when diagnosed and treated early, clears up rapidly in over 90 percent of cases.

PID may also have nonsexual causes, such as the transfer to the genital tract of bacteria that normally exist in the rectum. This can occur if the woman wipes herself from the back to the front after a bowel movement. Infections transmitted during childbirth or through insertion of an IUD may also lead to PID.

DIAGNOSIS AND TREATMENT Diagnosis of gonorrhea involves clinical inspection of the genitals by a physician (e.g., a family practitioner, urologist, or gynecologist) and the culturing and examination of a sample of genital discharge (Ison, 1990; Judson, 1990). Antibiotics are the standard and almost always successful treatment for gonorrhea. Penicillin was once the favored antibiotic treatment, but the rise of penicillin-resistant strains of *Neisseria gonorrhoeae* has required that alternative antibiotics be used (Goldstein & Clark, 1990). A single injection of the antibiotic *ceftriaxone* is now recommended (CDC, 1989b). Ceftriaxone has an excellent effect against all strains of the gonococcus bacterium (Goldstein & Clark, 1990) and cures all forms of uncomplicated gonorrhea (Judson, 1990). An alternative antibiotic such as *spectinomycin* may be used

Learning Objective 3:
Discuss the history,
incidence, transmission,
symptoms, stages, and
treatment of syphilis.

Syphilis
An STD that is caused by
the *Treponema pallidum*
bacterium and that may
progress through several
stages of development—
often from a chancre to a
skin rash to damage to the
cardiovascular or central
nervous systems. (From the
Greek *siphlos*, meaning
"maimed" or "crippled.")

 Syphilis Surge

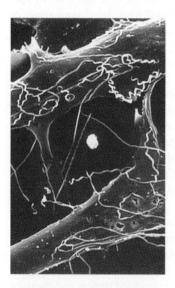

*FIGURE 16.1 Treponema
pallidum or Spirochete.*
Treponema pallidum is
the bacterium that causes
syphilis. Because of the spiral
shape, *T. pallidum* is also
called a *spirochete*.

TRUTH OR FICTION?

R E V I S I T E D

with people who cannot tolerate ceftriaxone. Since gonorrhea and chlamydia often occur together, persons infected with gonorrhea are usually also treated for chlamydia through the use of another antibiotic, generally *doxycycline* (Moran & Zenilman, 1990)—or *tetracycline* or *erythromycin*—administered orally over a course of seven days. Because there are few treatment failures, routine follow-up tests for gonococcal bacteria are generally unnecessary. Yet some physicians culture samples a month or two later to test for reinfection as well as treatment failure (CDC, 1989b.) (Successful treatment provides no protection against reinfection.) Sex partners of persons with gonorrhea should also be examined.

SYPHILIS

No society wanted to be associated with **syphilis.** In Naples they called it "the French disease"; in France it was "the Neapolitan disease." Many Italians called it "the Spanish disease," but in Spain they called it "the disease of Española" (modern Haiti).

In 1530 the Italian physician Girolamo Fracastoro wrote a poem about Syphilus, a shepherd boy. Syphilus was afflicted with the disease as retribution for insulting the sun god Apollo. In 1905 the German scientist Fritz Schaudinn isolated the bacterium that causes syphilis (Figure 16.1). It is *Treponema pallidum* (*T. pallidum*, for short), a name reflecting Greek and Latin roots meaning a "faintly colored (pallid) turning thread"—a good description of the corkscrewlike shape of the organism, which can be seen under the microscope. Because of the spiral shape, *T. pallidum* is also called a *spirochete*, from Greek roots meaning "spiral" and "hair."

THE ORIGINS OF SYPHILIS   The origins of syphilis are controversial. The Columbian theory holds that Christopher Columbus returned to Spain from his first voyage to the West Indies (1492–1493) with more than beads, blankets, and tobacco. From Spain, or so the Columbian theory has it, Spanish mercenaries may have carried it to Naples when they were imported to protect that city from French invaders. The French army may have contracted syphilis from prostitutes, who also practiced their profession with the Spaniards and Neapolitans. Sailors may have eventually spread syphilis to the East and the Orient.

It is generally accepted that Columbus exhibited symptoms of advanced syphilis when he died in 1506, and investigators have debated whether or not syphilis existed in Europe before the time of Columbus. Evidence reported in 1992 has shed new light on this 500-year-old medical mystery. Investigators unearthed evidence in an Italian cemetery of human skeletal remains dating back hundreds of years before the birth of Christ that showed telltale scars indicating the presence of infections caused by the bacterium that causes syphilis (Wilford, 1992). Investigators also unearthed evidence of a pattern of scarring caused by the syphilitic bacterium in the skeletal remains of two people who lived in England during the fifteenth century ("Disease discovered Europe first?" 1992). These finds, combined with other evidence that the bacterium existed in the New World prior to the time of Columbus, support the view that syphilis existed in some form throughout the world since antiquity. Consequently, researchers now believe that Columbus and his men could not be blamed for introducing syphilis to Europe. Cases of syphilis that occurred in Europe before the time of Columbus were probably misdiagnosed as leprosy. The epidemic of syphilis that erupted in Europe shortly following Columbus's return was probably due to increasing population in urban areas and travel from city to city as well as other demographic factors. It is also possible that warfare played a part in carrying the disease across borders, presumably because military encampments and nearby houses of prostitution can provide an ideal environment for the spread of STDs.

Christopher Columbus brought more than beads, blankets, and tobacco back to Europe from the New World: he brought syphilis. One theory of the origins of syphilis is that Christopher Columbus brought it back to Europe from the New World. New evidence unearthed in the early 1990s refutes this theory, however. •

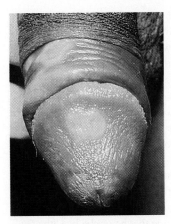

Syphilis Chancre. The first, or primary stage of a syphilis infection is marked by the appearance of a painless sore or chancre at the site of infection.

Chancre
A sore or ulcer.

TRUTH OR *FICTION?*

R E V I S I T E D

Congenital syphilis
A syphilis infection that is present at birth.

The incidence of syphilis decreased markedly in the United States following the introduction of penicillin, an antibiotic that renders a death blow to *T. pallidum* (Zenker & Rolfs, 1990). Yet, despite the availability of penicillin, and the recent emphasis on safer sex, there has been a resurgence of syphilis since the early 1980s (Melvin, 1990; Spark, 1991) (see Figure 16.2). By 1988, the rates of syphilis in the United States had reached their highest levels in 40 years (CDC, 1990a). About 45,000 cases of syphilis are reported annually to public health agencies. Many other cases go unreported.

Researchers believe that the increase in syphilis is linked to increased use of cocaine (Minkoff et al., 1990; Rolfs et al., 1990). Cocaine users may be at greater risk of contracting syphilis than nonusers because they are more likely to engage in risky sexual practices, such as sex with multiple partners or with prostitutes, not because of their cocaine use per se (Rolfs et al., 1990). Syphilis and other STDs are often spread among drug users, prostitutes (many of whom abuse drugs themselves), and their sex partners (Farley et al., 1990) Syphilis is not as widespread as gonorrhea, but its effects can be more harmful and can include heart disease, blindness, gross confusion, and death.

TRANSMISSION   Syphilis, like gonorrhea, is most often transmitted by vaginal or anal intercourse, or oral-genital or oral-anal contact with an infected person. The spirochete is usually transmitted when open lesions on an infected person come into contact with the mucous membranes or skin abrasions of the partner's body during sexual activity. The chance of contracting syphilis from one sexual contact with an infected partner is estimated at one in three (Reinisch, 1990). Syphilis may also be contracted by touching an infectious **chancre,** but, like gonorrhea, not from using the same toilet seat as an infected person.

Gonorrhea and syphilis may be contracted from toilet seats in public restrooms. No, gonorrhea and syphilis may not be contracted from toilet seats in public restrooms. (Pubic lice can be contracted in this manner, however, as we shall see later.) •

Pregnant women may transmit syphilis to their fetuses, because the spirochete can cross the placental membrane. Miscarriage, stillbirth, or **congenital syphilis** may result. Congenital syphilis may impair vision and hearing or deform bones and teeth. Blood tests are administered routinely during pregnancy to diagnose syphilis in the mother so that congenital problems in the baby may be averted. The fetus will probably not be harmed if an infected mother is treated before the fourth month of pregnancy.

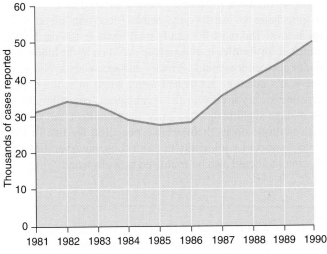

FIGURE 16.2 **Reported Cases of Syphilis in the United States, 1981–1990.** The reported incidence of syphilis increased markedly from the middle-to-late 1980s. (The data indicate cases of primary and secondary stage syphilis.)

Source: CDC, 1991g.

Notes: The incidence of gonorrhea and syphilis declined in the first half of the 1980s, but since 1986 syphilis has increased while gonorrhea has continued to decline. The incidence of gonorrhea decreased 22% in the United States from 1986 to 1989, while syphilis increased 59% during the same time period. (Gershman, K. A. and Rolfs, R. T. Diverging Gonorrhea and Syphilis Trends in the 1980s: Are They Real? *American Journal of Public Health,* 1991, Vol. 81, No. 10, pp. 1263–1267.)

Neurosyphilis
Syphilitic infection of the central nervous system, which can cause brain damage and death.

General paresis
A progressive form of mental illness caused by neurosyphilis and characterized by gross confusion.

TRUTH OR *FICTION?*
R E V I S I T E D

VDRL
The test named after the Venereal Disease Research Laboratory of the U.S. Public Health Service that tests for the presence of antibodies in the blood to *Treponema pallidum.*

Antibodies
Specialized proteins produced by the white blood cells of the immune system in response to disease organisms and other toxic substances. Antibodies recognize and attack the invading organisms or substances.

SYMPTOMS AND COURSE OF ILLNESS   Syphilis develops through several stages. In the first or *primary stage* of syphilis, a painless chancre (a hard, round, ulcerlike lesion with raised edges) appears at the site of infection two to four weeks after contact. When women are infected, the chancre usually forms on the vaginal walls or the cervix. It may also form on the external genitalia, most often on the labia. When men are infected, the chancre usually forms on the penile glans. It may also form on the scrotum or penile shaft. If the mode of transmission is oral sex, the chancre may appear on the lips or tongue. If spread by anal sex, the rectum may serve as the site of the chancre. The chancre disappears within a few weeks, but if the infection remains untreated, syphilis will continue to work within the body.

The *secondary stage* begins a few weeks to a few months later. A skin rash develops, consisting of painless, reddish raised bumps that darken after a while and burst, oozing a discharge. Other symptoms include sores in the mouth, painful swelling of joints, a sore throat, headaches, and fever, so a sufferer may wrongly assume that he or she has "the flu."

These symptoms also disappear, and then syphilis enters the *latent stage* and may lie dormant for one to 40 years. But spirochetes continue to multiply during the latent stage and burrow into the circulatory system, central nervous system (brain and spinal cord), and bones. The person may no longer be contagious to sex partners after several years in the latent stage, but a pregnant woman may pass along the infection to her newborn at any time (Wooldridge, 1991).

In many cases the disease eventually progresses to a late or *tertiary* stage. A large ulcer may form on the skin, digestive organs, lungs, liver, muscle tissue, or other organs. This destructive ulcer can often be successfully treated, but still more serious damage can occur as the infection attacks the central nervous system or the cardiovascular system, which consists of the heart and the major blood vessels. Either outcome can be fatal. **Neurosyphilis** can cause brain damage, resulting in paralysis or the deteriorating form of mental illness called **general paresis.**

The primary and secondary symptoms of syphilis inevitably disappear, so victims may be tempted to believe that they are no longer at risk and fail to see a doctor. This is indeed unfortunate, because failure to eradicate the infection through proper treatment may eventually lead to dire consequences.

If a syphilitic chancre (sore) goes away by itself, the infection does not require medical treatment. The belief that medical treatment is unnecessary if the symptoms of an STD disappear by themselves is unfounded. Both gonorrhea and syphilis, for example, can damage the body even when their symptoms have abated. •

DIAGNOSIS AND TREATMENT   Primary-stage syphilis is diagnosed by clinical examination. If a chancre is found, fluid drawn from it can be examined under a microscope in a dark-field test. The spirochetes are usually quite visible. Blood tests are not definitive until the secondary stage begins. The most frequently used blood test is the **VDRL.** The VDRL tests for the presence of **antibodies** to *Treponema pallidum* in the blood.

Penicillin is the treatment of choice for syphilis. Primary and secondary syphilis, and latent syphilis of less than one year's duration, are treated with a single injection of penicillin (or doxycycline, tetracycline, or erythromycin for nonpregnant, penicillin-allergic patients) (CDC, 1989b). Latent-stage syphilis that has lasted for more than one year and neurosyphilis are treated with multiple doses of injectable penicillin for two or three weeks. Successful treatment does not confer immunity to reinfection, however. Sex partners of persons infected with syphilis should also be evaluated by a physician.

CHLAMYDIA

Although you may be more familiar with gonorrhea and syphilis, another bacterial STD, chlamydia, is actually more common, (CDC, 1993a). Chlamydial infections are caused by

Learning Objective 4:
Discuss the incidence, transmission, symptoms, diagnosis, and treatment of chlamydia.

the *Chlamydia trachomatis* bacterium, a unique parasitic organism that can survive only within cells (Martin, 1990). This bacterium can cause several types of infections, including *nongonococcal urethritis (NGU)* in men and women; *epididymitis* (infection of the epididymis) in men; and *cervicitis* (infection of the cervix), *endometritis* (infection of the endometrium), and PID in women (Martin, 1990; Westrom, 1990; Yarber & Parillo, 1992).

The precise prevalences of chlamydial infections are unknown, since there is no national reporting system for chlamydia as there is for gonorrhea and syphilis (CDC, 1993b). Estimates indicate that as many as four million cases may occur annually (Toomey & Barnes, 1990). The incidence of chlamydial infections is especially high among teenagers and college students. Researchers estimate that between 8 and 40 percent of teenage women become infected (Yarber & Parillo, 1992).

TRANSMISSION *Chlamydia trachomatis* is usually transmitted through sexual intercourse—vaginal or anal. *Chlamydia trachomatis* may also cause an eye infection if a person touches his or her eyes after handling the genitals of an infected partner. A chlamydial infection of the throat can occur if a person performs oral sex on an infected partner (Handsfield, 1988). Newborns can acquire potentially serious chlamydial eye infections as they pass through the cervix of an infected mother during birth. Even newborns delivered by Caesarean section may be infected if the amniotic sac breaks before delivery (Reinisch, 1990). Evidence from several studies suggests that between 2 and 26 percent of pregnant women in the United States carry the *Chlamydia trachomatis* bacterium in the cervix (Reinisch, 1990). Each year more than 100,000 infants are infected with the bacterium during birth (Graham & Blanco, 1990). Of these, about 75,000 develop eye infections and 30,000 develop a form of pneumonia caused by the chlamydial bacterium.

SYMPTOMS Chlamydial infections usually produce symptoms that are similar to, but milder than, those of gonorrheal infections. In men, *Chlamydia trachomatis* can lead to nongonococcal urethritis (NGU). *Urethritis* is an inflammation of the urethra. Nongonococcal urethritis, or NGU, refers to forms of urethritis that are not caused by the gonococcal bacterium. (NGU is generally diagnosed only in men. In women, an inflammation of the urethra caused by *Chlamydia trachomatis* is generally called a chlamydial infection or simply chlamydia.) NGU was formerly called nonspecific urethritis or NSU. Although many organisms can cause NGU, *Chlamydia trachomatis* is the most common cause (Braude et al., 1986), accounting for about half of the cases among men (CDC, 1985b). Oral-genital contact with an infected partner can also result in a throat infection.

NGU in men may give rise to a thin, whitish discharge from the penis and some burning or other pain during urination. These contrast with the yellow-green discharge and more intense pain produced by gonorrhea. There may be soreness in the scrotum and feelings of heaviness in the testes. NGU appears to be about two to three times as prevalent among men in the United States as gonorrhea (CDC, 1989a; Reinisch, 1990). Men in the 20- to 24-year-old age range are most at risk of contracting both gonorrhea and NGU, presumably because of the high level of sexual activity among men in this age group (Bowie, 1990).

Although chlamydia and NGU are usually transmitted sexually, some cases, especially in less countries (Bowie, 1984), have nonsexual origins. The nonsexually transmitted cases are usually communicated by contact with infected fecal matter, by discharges on the fingers or skin of infected people, or by bites by insects carrying the disease-causing organisms. In industrialized countries like the United States and Canada, however, virtually all cases of chlamydial infections in adults involve sexual transmission (Schachter, 1990).

In women, chlamydial infections usually give rise to infections of the urethra or cervix. Women, like men, may experience burning sensations when they urinate, irritation in the genitals, and a mild (vaginal) discharge. Women are also likely to encounter pelvic pain and irregular menstrual cycles. The cervix may look swollen and inflamed.

Despite these symptoms, as many as 25 percent of men and 70 percent of women infected with chlamydia are asymptomatic (Cates & Wasserheit, 1991). For this reason, chlamydia has been dubbed the "silent disease." People with symptom-free cases of chlamydia may go untreated and unknowingly pass along their infections to their part-

Notes: In almost all of the industrialized countries gonorrhea, syphilis and chancroid have nearly disappeared. A steady decline has been observed over the last 15 or 20 years in the incidence of gonorrhea throughout Europe, Australia, New Zealand, and Japan. Yet among members of minority groups in urban centers in the United States these three STDs have been increasing at epidemic rates. (Aral, S. O., and Holmes, K. K. 1991. Sexually transmitted diseases in the AIDS era. *Scientific American*, 264(2), 62–69.)

ners. In women, an untreated chlamydial infection can spread throughout the reproductive system, leading to PID and to scarring of the Fallopian tubes, resulting in infertility (Garland et al., 1990; Hodgson et al., 1990; Holmes et al., 1989). About half of the more than one million annual cases of PID are attributed to chlamydia (Schachter, 1989). Women with a history of exposure to *Chlamydia trachomatis* also stand twice the normal chance of incurring an ectopic (tubal) pregnancy (Sherman et al., 1990). Tubal pregnancies must be surgically removed (aborted) to avoid the rupturing of the tube.

Untreated chlamydial infections can also damage the internal reproductive organs of men. About 50 percent of cases of epididymitis are caused by chlamydial infections (Crum & Ellner, 1985). Yet only about 1 or 2 percent of men with untreated NGU caused by *Chlamydia trachomatis* go on to develop epididymitis (Bowie, 1990). That's no excuse for not seeking treatment, but as far as we know, men stand a much lesser chance of serious complications from chlamydial infections than women. Still, the long-term effects of untreated chlamydial infections in men remain undetermined.

Chlamydial infections also frequently occur together with other STDs, most often gonorrhea. As many as 45 percent of cases of gonorrhea involve coexisting chlamydial infections (CDC, 1985b 1989a).

False positive
An erroneous positive test result or clinical finding.

DIAGNOSIS AND TREATMENT The Abbott Testpack permits physicians to verify a diagnosis of chlamydia in women in about 25 or 30 minutes (Reichart et al., 1990; Reinisch, 1990). The test analyzes a cervical smear (like a Pap smear) and identifies about 75 to 80 percent of infected cases, with relatively few **false positives** (incorrect positive findings). In men, a swab is inserted through the penile opening, and the extracted fluid is analyzed to detect the presence of *Chlamydia trachomatis*.

Antibiotic treatment with a seven-day course of doxycycline, tetracycline, or erythromycin is highly effective in eradicating chlamydial infections (CDC, 1989b; Toomey & Barnes, 1990). (Penicillin, effective in treating gonorrhea, is ineffective against *Chlamydia trachomatis*.) Treatment of sex partners is considered critical regardless of whether the partner shows symptoms, so as to prevent the infection from being passed back and forth (Martin, 1990). But successful treatment does not protect against reinfection. Moreover, a woman whose sex partner develops NGU should be examined for a chlamydial infection herself; at least 30 percent of these women will test positive for chlamydia even though they (and their partners) may be free of symptoms (Stamm & Holmes, 1990). Likewise, men whose sex partners develop urethral or cervical infections should be medically evaluated, whether or not they notice any symptoms themselves. With chlamydia, both partners may be unaware that they are infected, and may be oblivious to the damage the infection is causing internally. Because of the risks posed by untreated chlamydial infections, especially to women, and the high rate of asymptomatic infections, many physicians routinely perform diagnostic tests on young women to detect chlamydia during regular checkups.

Learning Objective 5: Discuss the symptoms and treatments of several less common bacterial STDs.

OTHER BACTERIAL DISEASES

Several other types of bacterial STDs occur less commonly in the United States and Canada. These include chancroid, shigellosis, granuloma inguinale, and lymphogranuloma venereum.

Chancroid
An STD caused by the *Hemophilus ducreyi* bacterium. Also called *soft chancre*.

CHANCROID **Chancroid,** or "soft chancre," is caused by the bacterium *Hemophilus ducreyi*. It is more commonly found in the tropics and Eastern nations than in Western countries. The chancroid sore consists of a cluster of small bumps or pimples on the genitals, perineum (the area of skin that lies between the genitals and the anus), or the anus itself. These lesions usually appear within seven days of infection. Within a few days the lesion ruptures, producing an open sore or ulcer. Several ulcers may merge with other ulcers, forming giant ulcers (Ronald & Albritton, 1990). There is usually an accompanying swelling of a nearby lymph node. In contrast to the syphilis chancre, the chancroid ulcer has a soft rim (hence the name) and is usually quite painful in men. Women frequently do not experience any pain and may be unaware of being infected (Ronald &

Albritton, 1990). The bacterium is typically transmitted through sexual or bodily contact with the lesion or its discharge. Diagnosis is usually confirmed by culturing the bacterium, which is found in pus from the sore, and examining it under a microscope. Antibiotics (erythromycin or ceftriaxone) are usually effective in treating the disease.

SHIGELLOSIS   **Shigellosis** is caused by the *Shigella* bacterium and is characterized by fever and severe abdominal symptoms, including diarrhea and inflammation of the large intestine. About 25,000 cases of shigellosis are reported annually (CDC, 1989a). It is often contracted by oral contact with infected fecal material, which may occur as the result of oral-anal sex. It can be treated with antibiotics, such as tetracycline or *ampicillin*.

GRANULOMA INGUINALE   Rare in the United States, **granuloma inguinale,** like chancroid, is more common in tropical regions. It is caused by the bacterium *Calymmatobacterium granulomatous* and is not as contagious as many other STDs. Primary symptoms are painless red bumps or sores in the groin area that ulcerate and spread. Like chancroid, it is usually spread by intimate bodily or sexual contact with a lesion or its discharge. Diagnosis is confirmed by microscopic examination of tissue taken from the rim of the sore. The antibiotics tetracycline or *streptomycin* are effective in treating this disorder. If left untreated, however, the disease may lead to the development of fistulas (holes) in the rectum or bladder, destruction of the tissues or organs that underlie the infection, or scarring of skin tissue that results in a condition called **elephantiasis,** a condition that afflicted the so-called elephant man in the nineteenth century.

LYMPHOGRANULOMA VENEREUM (LGV)   **Lymphogranuloma venereum (LGV)** is another tropical STD that occurs only rarely in the United States and Canada. Some U.S. soldiers returned home from Vietnam with cases of LGV. It is caused by several strains of the *Chlamydia trachomatis* bacterium. LGV usually enters the body through the penis, vulva, or cervix, where a small, painless sore may form. The sore may go unnoticed, but a nearby lymph gland in the groin swells and grows tender, and other symptoms mimic those of flu: chills, fever, and headache. Other symptoms that may occur include backache, especially in women, and arthritic complaints (painful joints). If LGV is untreated, complications such as growths and fistulas in the genitals and elephantiasis of the legs and genitals may occur. Diagnosis is made by skin tests and blood tests. The antibiotic doxycycline is the recommended treatment; tetracycline, erythromycin, or *sulfisoxazole* are alternatives (CDC, 1989b).

VAGINAL INFECTIONS

Vaginitis is a general term that applies to any kind of vaginal infection or inflammation. Women with vaginitis may encounter genital irritation or itching and burning sensations during urination, but the most common symptom is an odious discharge.

Most cases of vaginitis are caused by organisms that reside in the vagina or by sexually transmitted organisms—which is why we discuss them in this chapter. Organisms that normally reside in the vagina may overgrow and cause symptoms when the environmental balance of the vagina is upset by such factors as birth-control pills, antibiotics, dietary changes, excessive douching, or wearing nylon underwear or pantyhose. (See Chapter 3 for suggestions to help reduce the risk of vaginitis.) Still other cases are caused by specific sensitivities or allergic reactions to various chemicals.

As many as 90 percent of vaginal infections (Friedrich, 1985; Sobel, 1990) involve bacterial vaginosis (BV), candidiasis (commonly called a "yeast" infection), or trichomoniasis ("trich"). Bacterial vaginosis is the most common form of vaginitis, followed by candidiasis, then by trichomoniasis (Reinisch, 1990), but some cases involve combinations of the three.

The microbes causing vaginal infections in women can also infect the man's urethral tract. In some cases, a "vaginal infection" can be passed back and forth between sexual partners.

Shigellosis
An STD caused by the *Shigella* bacterium.

Granuloma inguinale
A tropical STD caused by the *Calymmatobacterium granulomatous* bacterium.

Elephantiasis
A disease characterized by enlargement of parts of the body, especially the legs and genitals, and by hardening and ulceration of the surrounding skin. (From the Greek *elephas,* meaning "elephant," referring to the resemblance of the affected skin areas to elephant hide.)

Lymphogranuloma venereum
A tropical STD caused by the *Chlamydia trachomatis* bacterium.

 STD Increases

Vaginitis
Any type of vaginal infection or inflammation.

Learning Objective 6:
Identify and discuss the symptoms, transmission, and treatment of the most common vaginal infections.

Men too can develop vaginal infections. *Though only women can have vaginal infections (naturally, since only women have vaginas), the microbes causing these infections in women may also cause problems for men.* •

BACTERIAL VAGINOSIS

Bacterial vaginosis
A form of vaginitis usually caused by the *Gardnerella vaginalis* bacterium.

Bacterial vaginosis or BV (formerly called *nonspecific vaginitis*) is most often caused by the bacterium *Gardnerella vaginalis* (Briselden & Hillier, 1990; Platz-Christensen et al., 1989). The bacterium is primarily transmitted through sexual contact. The most characteristic symptom in women is a thin, foul-smelling vaginal discharge, but infected women are often asymptomatic. Accurate diagnosis depends on culturing the bacterium in the laboratory (Reinisch, 1990). Besides causing troublesome symptoms in some cases, medical authorities have raised the possibility that BV may increase the risk of various gynecological problems, including infections of the reproductive tract (Hillier & Holmes, 1990). Oral treatment with *metronidazole* (brand name: Flagyl) for seven days is recommended (CDC, 1989b) and is effective in about 90 percent of cases (Reinisch, 1990). Recurrences are common, however.

Questions remain about whether the male partner should also be treated. The bacterium can usually be found in the male urethra but does not generally cause symptoms (Reinisch, 1990). Lacking symptoms, the male partner may unknowingly transmit the bacterium to others. There is no evidence that treating the male with metronidazole benefits either him or the female patient, however (CDC, 1989b; Moi et al., 1989).

CANDIDIASIS

Candidiasis
A form of vaginitis caused by a yeastlike fungus, *Candida albicans.*

Also known as *moniliasis, thrush,* or, most commonly, a yeast infection, **candidiasis** is caused by a yeastlike fungus, *Candida albicans.* Candidiasis commonly produces soreness, inflammation, and intense (sometimes maddening!) itching around the vulva that is accompanied by a white, thick, curdy vaginal discharge. Yeast generally produces no symptoms when the vaginal environment is normal (Reinisch, 1990). Yeast infections can also occur in the mouth in both men and women and in the penis in men.

Vaginitis is often caused by an overgrowth of infectious organisms that normally reside in the vagina. *Yes, some cases of vaginitis result from organisms that normally are found in the vagina but become infectious when changes in the vaginal environment allow them to multiply and overgrow.* •

Infections most often arise from changes in the vaginal environment that allow the fungus to overgrow. Factors such as the use of antibiotics or birth-control pills, pregnancy, and diabetes may alter the vaginal balance, allowing the fungus that causes yeast infections to grow to infectious levels. Wearing nylon underwear and tight, restrictive, and poorly ventilated clothing may also set the stage for a yeast infection.

Diet may play a role in recurrent yeast infections. Reducing one's intake of substances that produce excessive excretion of urinary sugars (such as dairy products, sugar, and artificial sweeteners) apparently reduces the frequency of recurrent yeast infections (Friedrich, 1985). Recently, researchers reported that the daily ingestion of one pint of yogurt containing active bacterial (*Lactobacillus acidophilus*) cultures actually helped reduce the rate of recurrent infections (Hilton et al., 1992).

The sexual transmission of candidiasis concerns us here. Candidiasis can be passed back and forth between sex partners through vaginal intercourse. It may also be passed back and forth between the mouth and the genitals through oral-genital contact and infect the anus through anal intercourse. However, the role of sexual contact in spreading the infection is believed to be limited (Sobel, 1990). (Most infections in women are believed to be caused by an overgrowth of "yeast" normally found in the vagina, not by sexual transmission.) Still, it is advisable to evaluate both partners simultaneously. Whereas most men with *candida* are asymptomatic (Hillier & Holmes, 1990), some may develop NGU or a genital thrush that is accompanied by sensations of itching and burning during urination, or a reddening of the penis (Hillier & Holmes, 1990; Levy et al., 1987). Candidiasis may also be transmitted by nonsexual means, such as between women who share a damp washcloth (Levy et al., 1987).

About 75 percent of women will experience an episode of candidiasis at some point during their reproductive years (Reinisch, 1990). About half of these women will have recurrent infections. Three days of treatment with vaginal suppositories, creams, or tablets containing miconazole (brand name: Monistat), clotrimazole (brand names: Lotrimin and Mycelex), or terconazole (brand name: Terazol) is usually recommended (CDC, 1989b). Some of these medications are now available without a prescription. Even so, women with vaginal complaints should consult their physicians before taking any medication, to ensure that they receive the proper diagnosis and treatment.

Frequent or persistent vaginal yeast infections are sometimes an early warning sign of HIV infection ("Vaginal yeast infection can be an HIV warning," 1992). Stubborn or repeated cases of vaginal yeast infections are the most common initial symptoms of HIV infection in women. *However, we need to underscore the fact that the great majority of women with recurrent vaginal yeast infections are not infected with HIV.*

TRICHOMONIASIS

Trichomoniasis

A form of vaginitis caused by the protozoan *Trichomonas vaginalis.*

Trichomoniasis ("trich") is caused by *Trichomonas vaginalis. Trichomonas vaginalis* is a parasitic animal that consists of only one cell (technically, a protozoan). Trichomoniasis is the most common parasitic STD (Levine, 1991), accounting for some eight million cases annually among women in the United States (Martens & Faro, 1989). Symptoms in women include burning or itching in the vulva, mild pain during urination or coitus, and an odorous, foamy whitish to yellowish green discharge. Lower abdominal pain is reported by 5 to 12 percent of infected women (Rein & Muller, 1990). Many women notice symptoms appearing or worsening during, or just following, their menstrual periods. Trichomoniasis is also linked to the development of tubal adhesions that can result in infertility (Grodstein et al., 1993). As with many other STDs, about half of infected women are asymptomatic (Reinisch, 1990).

Whereas candidiasis most often reflects an overgrowth of organisms normally found in the vagina, trichomoniasis is almost always sexually transmitted (CDC, 1989b). Because the parasite involved may survive for several hours on moist surfaces outside the body, trich can be communicated from contact with infected semen or vaginal discharges on towels, washcloths, and bedclothes. This parasite is one of the few disease agents that can be picked up from a toilet seat, but it would have to directly touch the penis or vulva (Reinisch, 1990). *Trichomonas vaginalis* can cause NGU in the male, which can be asymptomatic or cause a slight penile discharge that is usually noticeable only upon awakening before one first urinates in the morning. There may be tingling, itching, and other irritating sensations in the urethral tract. Yet, since most infected men are symptom-free (Rein & Muller, 1990), they may unwittingly transfer the organism to their sex partners. Perhaps three or four in ten male partners of infected women are found to harbor *Trichomonas vaginalis* themselves (Reinisch, 1990). Diagnosis is frequently made by microscopic examination of a smear of a woman's vaginal fluids in the physician's office (Levine, 1991). Diagnosis based on examination of cultures grown from the vaginal smear is considered more reliable, however (Thomason & Gelbart, 1989).

TRUTH OR *FICTION?*

R E V I S I T E D

Many men whose partners have "trich" are also infected themselves, often unknowingly. True. *Perhaps three or four men in ten whose partners have "trich" are infected themselves, many without knowing it.* •

Except during the first three months of pregnancy, trichomoniasis is treated in both genders with metronidazole (brand name: Flagyl). Both partners are treated, whether or

What to Do If You Suspect You Have Contracted an STD

First, contact your personal physician right away. If you can't afford your own physician, call your local health department to see if there is a low-cost clinic available in your community that offers STD treatment. This book may make you better aware of the signs and symptoms of various STDs, but it does not qualify you to diagnose yourself. Second, follow your physician's directions or seek a second medical opinion if you have any questions or doubts about the recommended treatment.

If You Are Being Treated for an STD . . .

1. *Take all medication as directed.* Do not skip any doses or combine dosages. If you should inadvertently skip a dose, call your physician for instructions. Discuss any side effects with your physician. Although the medication may relieve symptoms in a day or two, it may be necessary to continue to take the medication for a week or more to ensure that the infection is completely eliminated.

2. *Understand how to use medication correctly.* Some medication calls for you to abstain from alcohol or to avoid certain foods, like dairy products. Some medications should only be taken before or after meals. Check with your physician or pharmacist to determine the correct way to take any medication.

3. *Abstain from sexual contact during an active infection.* Although using a latex condom combined with a spermicidal agent containing the ingredient nonoxynol-9 (which kills many STD-causing organisms) may provide some protection against disease transmission, it is best to abstain from sexual activity until the infection clears. Consult your physician regarding the recommended duration of abstinence.

4. *Contact sexual partners who may have infected you or*

not they report symptoms. When both partners are treated simultaneously, the success rate approaches 100 percent (Thomason & Gelbart, 1989).

VIRAL DISEASES

Viruses are tiny particles of DNA surrounded by a protein coating. They are incapable of reproducing on their own. When they invade a body cell, however, they can direct the cell's own reproductive machinery to spin off new viral particles, which spread to other cells, causing infection. Because they can have worrisome and, in the case of AIDS, life-threatening complications, and because (unlike bacterial STDs like chlamydia and gonorrhea) we as yet have no cure for them, viral infections are among the most troubling and dangerous STDs (McCormack, 1990). In this chapter we discuss several viral STDs: herpes, viral hepatitis, genital warts, and molluscum contagiosum. AIDS is also caused by a virus and is the topic of the following chapter.

HERPES

Learning Objective 7: Discuss the transmission, symptoms, diagnosis, and treatment of the two types of herpes.

The hysteria that surrounded the rapid spread of genital herpes in the 1970s and early 1980s has all but died since the world learned to dread an even more threatening STD: AIDS. Genital herpes was feared because, like AIDS, it is incurable and, at the time, essentially untreatable. Herpes still remains a very real threat. Once you get herpes, it's yours for life. After the initial attack, it remains an unwelcome guest in your body, finding a cozy place to lie low until it stirs up trouble again, causing recurrent outbreaks that usually happen at the worst times, such as around final exams. Not only can't you get rid of the virus, but you can pass it along to whomever else you have sex with for the rest of

whom you may have infected. Suggest that they seek a medical evaluation to see if they too are infected. It is possible that they are infected and are unaware of the problem because of a lack of symptoms. Remember that STDs can cause internal damage and be passed along to others, even if they do not produce any noticeable symptoms.

5. *Return for follow-up visits if your physician instructs you to do so.* Although the symptoms of the infection may be relieved after a few days, return for any requested follow-up visits to ensure that you are free of the infection.

Your physician may also request that your partner be evaluated so that the two of you do not bounce the STD back and forth.

6. *If you have a continuing STD, such as herpes or HIV, share the information with your partner or partners.* Don't keep it a secret. Your sexual partners have a right to know about your infection status before initiating or resuming sexual relations. Make sure that both you and they understand the risks and the necessary precautions that may need to be taken. If you have any doubts about the safety of engaging in sexual relations,

consult your physician before engaging in any sexual contact. It may be helpful for both you and your partner to sit down with your physician and discuss the risks you face and the concerns that either of you may have. Unfounded fears and concerns can often be allayed by receiving corrective information.

---

your life (ugh!). Flare-ups may continue to recur, however, sometimes with annoying frequency over the course of a lifetime. On the other hand, some people, perhaps about 10 percent (Brody, 1992b), have no recurrences; for many others, recurrences are milder and briefer in duration than initial episodes and become less frequent over time.

In the wake of the AIDS epidemic, the threat of genital herpes has been largely ignored (Brody, 1992b). Yet the viruses that cause herpes have hardly disappeared. There are actually different types of herpes that are caused by variants of the *Herpes simplex* virus. The most common type, **Herpes simplex virus type 1,** or HSV-1 virus causes cold sores or fever blisters on the lips or mouth (oral herpes). It can also be transferred to the genitals by the hands or by oral-genital contact and is believed to account for between 10 and 50 percent of the cases of herpetic sores on the genitals (Braude et al., 1986; Kunz & Finkel, 1987). **Genital herpes** is caused by a related but distinct virus, the **Herpes simplex virus type 2** (HSV-2). This virus produces painful shallow sores and blisters on the genitals. HSV-2 can also be transferred to the mouth through oral-genital contact. Since both types of herpes can be transmitted sexually, they are both classified as STDs.

Physicians are not required to report cases of herpes to public health officials, so there are no precise statistics on its prevalence. Estimates are that more than 100 million people in the United States may be infected with oral herpes and perhaps 30 million with genital herpes (Brody, 1993e; CDC, 1989a). Researchers believe that 500,000 new cases of genital herpes occur annually (Brody, 1993e; Leary, 1988).

TRANSMISSION   Herpes can be transmitted through oral, anal, or vaginal sex with an infected person. The herpes viruses can also survive for several hours on toilet seats or other objects, where they can be picked up by direct contact. Oral herpes is easily contracted by drinking from the same cup as an infected person, by kissing, even by sharing towels. But genital herpes is generally spread by coitus or by oral or anal sex. The

Herpes simplex virus type 1
The virus that causes oral herpes, which is characterized by cold sores or fever blisters on the lips or mouth. Abbreviated *HSV-1.*

Genital herpes
An STD caused by the Herpes simplex virus type 2 and characterized by painful shallow sores and blisters on the genitals.

Herpes simplex virus type 2
The virus that causes genital herpes. Abbreviated *HSV-2.*

chance of contracting genital herpes from a single sexual encounter with an infected partner during a flare-up of the disease is estimated at about 50 percent for men and 80 to 90 percent for women (Straus, 1985).

One problem is that many people do not realize that they are infected and so can unknowingly pass along the virus to others through sexual contact. And many of the people who know they are infected don't realize that they can pass along the virus even during times that they have no noticeable outbreak (Brock et al., 1990; Brody, 1992b; Dawkins, 1990; Mertz et al., 1985; Rooney et al., 1986). The unfortunate fact is that any intimate contact with an infected person carries some risk of transmission of the virus, even if the infected person never experiences another outbreak. People may also acquire the virus from sexual contact with an infected partner but never experience outbreaks themselves, yet still be capable of passing along the virus to others (Brody, 1992b).

Genital herpes can only be transmitted during flare-ups of the disease. *Genital herpes may actually be transmitted between flare-ups, although people are most contagious during active outbreaks of the disease.* •

Ocular herpes
A herpes infection of the eye, usually caused by touching an infected area of the body and then touching the eye.

Prodromal symptoms
Warning symptoms that signal the onset or flare-up of a disease. (From the Greek *prodromos,* meaning "forerunner.")

Herpes may also be spread from one part of the body to another by touching the infected area and then touching or rubbing another body part. One potentially serious result is a herpes infection of the eye: **ocular herpes.** Although thorough washing with soap and water after touching an infected area may reduce the risk of spreading the infection to other parts of the body, it is better to avoid touching the infected area altogether, especially if there are active sores.

The miscarriage rate among herpes sufferers is more than three times higher than the rate for the general population (Campbell & Herten, 1981). Women may infect babies with genital herpes during childbirth, which can severely damage or even kill them (Whitley et al., 1991). Obstetricians thus usually perform Caesarean sections if the mother shows an active outbreak at the time of delivery. C-sections are currently recommended for women who show active lesions or **prodromal symptoms** at the time of delivery (Dawkins, 1990; Osborne & Adelson, 1990).

Herpes also appears to place women at greater risk of genital cancers, such as cervical cancer, a potential killer (Graham et al., 1982). All women, not just herpes sufferers, are advised to have regular pelvic examinations, including Pap smears for early detection of cervical cancer.

SYMPTOMS   Genital lesions or sores appear about six to eight days after infection with genital herpes. At first they appear as reddish, painful bumps, or papules, along the penis or the vulva. They may also appear on the thighs or buttocks, or in the vagina or on the cervix. These papules turn into groups of small blisters that are filled with fluid containing infectious viral particles. The blisters are attacked by the body's immune system (white blood cells). They fill with pus, break open, and become extremely painful, shallow sores or ulcers that are surrounded by a red ring. The infected person is especially infectious at this time, as the ulcers shed millions of viral particles. Other symptoms may include headaches and muscle aches, swollen lymph glands, fever, burning urination, and a vaginal discharge. The blisters crust over and heal in from one to three weeks. Internal sores in the vagina or on the cervix may take 10 days longer than external (labial) sores to heal completely, so physicians advise infected women to avoid unprotected intercourse for at least 10 days following the healing of external sores.

Although the symptoms disappear, the disease does not. The virus remains in the body permanently, burrowing into nerve cells in the base of the spine, where it may lie dormant for years or a lifetime. The infected person is least contagious during this dormant stage. For reasons that remain unclear, the virus becomes reactivated and gives rise to recurrences in most cases.

Recurrences may be related to such factors as infections (as in a cold), stress, fatigue, depression, exposure to the sun, and hormonal changes, such as those that occur during pregnancy or menstruation (Kemeny et al., 1989; Kunz & Finkel, 1987; Longo &

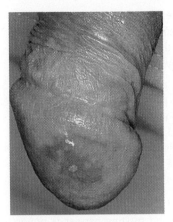

Herpes Lesion on the Male Genitals. Herpes lesions or sores can appear on the genitals in either sex and may be associated with flu-like symptoms.

Clum, 1989). Yet not all researchers have been able to link emotional stress to herpes flare-ups (for example, Rand et al., 1990). Recurrences tend to occur within three to 12 months of the initial episode and to affect the same part of the body.

About 50 percent of people with recurrent herpes experience prodromal symptoms before an active outbreak (Reinisch, 1990). These warning signs may include feelings of burning, itching, pain, tingling, or tenderness in the affected area. These symptoms may be accompanied by sharp pains in the lower extremities, groin, or buttocks. Herpes sufferers may be more infectious when prodromal symptoms appear and so are advised to avoid sex involving direct, unprotected contact until the flare-up is resolved. Infectiousness escalates with the appearance of active sores. Sometimes the symptoms are mild enough to go unnoticed, so that people are unaware of being infectious.

Symptoms of oral herpes include sores or blisters on the lips, the inside of the mouth, the tongue, or the throat. Fever and feelings of sickness may occur. The gums may become red and swollen. The sores heal over in about two weeks, and the virus retreats into nerve cells at the base of the neck, where it lies dormant between flare-ups. About 90 percent of oral herpes sufferers experience recurrences, and about half of these have five or more recurrences during the first two years after the initial outbreak (Reinisch, 1990).

DIAGNOSIS AND TREATMENT   Genital herpes is first diagnosed by clinical inspection of herpetic sores or ulcers in the mouth or on the genitals. A sample of fluid may be taken from the base of a genital sore and cultured in the laboratory to detect the growth of the virus (Mertz, 1990).

There is no cure nor safe and effective vaccine for herpes. Viruses, unlike the bacteria that cause gonorrhea or syphilis, do not respond to antibiotics. The antiviral drug *acyclovir* (brand name: Zovirax) can help relieve pain, speed healing, and reduce the duration of viral shedding (the period of time during which the virus is found in vaginal secretions and semen) in genital herpes when applied directly to sores in ointment form. Acyclovir must be administered orally, in pill form, to be effective against internal lesions in the vagina or on the cervix. Oral administration of acyclovir may reduce the severity of the initial episode and, if taken regularly, the frequency and duration of recurrent attacks of genital herpes (CDC, 1989b; Gold et al., 1988; Goldberg et al., 1993). In a recent study of 389 people who had suffered 12 or more recurrences annually, researchers found that daily doses of acyclovir reduced the number of recurrences, on the average, to 1.7 in the first year, and to less than 1 (0.8) by the fifth year, with few adverse reactions reported (Brody, 1993e; Goldberg et al., 1993). The safety of using acyclovir during pregnancy remains to be established, however (Stone & Whittington, 1990).

Warm baths, loose-fitting clothing, aspirin, and cold, wet compresses may relieve pain during flare-ups of genital herpes. Herpes sufferers are advised to maintain regular sleeping habits, avoid unnecessary stress, and learn to manage unavoidable stress.

COPING WITH GENITAL HERPES   The psychological problems connected with herpes can be more distressing than the physical effects of the illness. The prospects of a lifetime of recurrences and concerns about infecting one's sex partners exacerbate the emotional impact of herpes. A "herpes syndrome" has been described, which involves feelings of anger, depression, isolation, and shame—even self-perceptions of being tainted, ugly, or dangerous (Levy et al., 1987; Mirotznik et al., 1987).

An anonymous survey of Brooklyn College students is suggestive of the enormous emotional toll being exacted by the herpes epidemic. Fifty-five percent of herpes sufferers reported strong emotional responses to it; 28 percent reported moderate reactions; and only 17 percent reported mild reactions (Mirotznik et al., 1987). The majority reported feelings of fear and anger. Half indicated feeling "damaged." Most also felt that herpes had affected their sexual behavior; 75 percent said that they had avoided sex for "a long time" because of herpes. Although most had resumed sexual activity, many sought partners who were similarly infected so that they would not have to explain the disease, or risk transmitting it, to people who were uninfected. Given the consequences of herpes, you might think that students would be concerned about contracting the disease. Yet another survey at Brooklyn College revealed that although most sexually active, uninfected students perceived herpes as having serious consequences, about three of four were not fearful of contracting the disease and nearly half had not changed their dating behavior because of it (Mirotznik, 1991).

Herpes sufferers often feel angry, especially toward those who transmitted the disease to them. The herpes sufferer may feel anxious about making a commitment to a long-term relationship or about bearing children:

> After the first big episode of herpes, I felt distant from my body. When we began love-making again, I had a hard time having orgasms or trusting the rhythm of my responses. I shed some tears over that. I felt my body had been invaded. My body feels riddled with it; I'm somehow contaminated. And there is always that lingering anxiety: is my baby okay? It's unjust that the birth of my child may be affected.
>
> (*The New Our Bodies, Ourselves,* 1984, pp. 276–277)

Discussion Question:
Statistics indicate that upwards of 30 million people in the United States have herpes. Some of you may even have genital herpes. Discuss how people with herpes can approach partners with this information. Should they always inform all partners? Should they inform partners only during a flare-up? How can people with herpes protect their sexual partners from infection?

Most herpes sufferers learn to cope. Some are helped by support groups that share ways of living with the disease (Laskin, 1982). A caring and trusting partner is important. Joanne, a 26-year-old securities analyst, kept her herpes a secret from Jonathan during the first month they were dating. But when they approached the point of becoming sexually intimate, she felt obligated to tell him that she carried the virus:

> "I feared that telling him would scare him off. After all, who wants to have a relationship with someone that can give them herpes? After the first few dates I felt that this was the person I could spend the rest of my life with. I knew he also felt the same way. I had to tell him before things became too intense between us. Believe me, it wasn't easy blurting it out. He wasn't shocked or anything, although he did ask me all kinds of questions about it. I remember telling him that I got recurrences about once a year or so for about a week at a time. I told him that there was always the potential that I could infect him but that we would play it safe and avoid having sex whenever I had an outbreak. I also told him that even at other times I couldn't guarantee that it would be perfectly safe. He said at first that he needed some time to think about it. But later, that very night in fact, he called to tell me that he didn't want this to come between us and that we should try to make our relationship work."

Joanne and Jonathan got married about six months later, and a year after that their daughter Andrea was born. Jonathan remains uninfected and the very occasional outbreaks that Joanne experiences are treated with acyclovir ointment and pass within a week or so.

(From the Authors' Files)

The attitudes of the herpes sufferer also play an important role in adjusting. People who view herpes as a manageable illness or problem, and not as a medical disaster or character deficit, seem to find it easier to cope.

VIRAL HEPATITIS

Learning Objective 8:
Describe the transmission, symptoms, and treatments of the four types of hepatitis.

Hepatitis
An inflammation of the liver. (From the Greek *hepar,* meaning "liver.")

Jaundice
A yellowish discoloration of the skin and the whites of the eyes. (From the Old French *jaune,* meaning "yellow.")

Hepatitis is an inflammation of the liver that may be caused by such factors as chronic alcoholism and exposure to toxic materials. Viral hepatitis refers to several different types of hepatitis caused by related, but distinct, viruses. The major types are *hepatitis A* (formerly called infectious hepatitis), *hepatitis B* (formerly called serum hepatitis), *hepatitis C* (formerly called hepatitis non-A, non-B), and *hepatitis D.*

Most people with acute hepatitis are asymptomatic (CDC, 1989b). When symptoms do appear, they often include **jaundice,** feelings of weakness and nausea, loss of appetite, abdominal discomfort, whitish bowel movements, and brownish or tea-colored urine (Kunz & Finkel, 1987). The symptoms of hepatitis B tend to be more severe and long-lasting than those of hepatitis A or C. In about 10 percent of cases, hepatitis B can lead to chronic liver disease. Hepatitis C tends to have milder symptoms but often leads to chronic liver disease such as cirrhosis or cancer of the liver. Hepatitis D—also called *delta hepatitis* or type D hepatitis—occurs only in the presence of hepatitis B. Hepatitis D, which has symptoms similar to those of hepatitis B, can produce severe liver damage and often leads to death.

The hepatitis A virus is transmitted through contact with infected fecal matter found in contaminated food or water, and by oral contact with fecal matter, as through oral-anal sexual activity (licking or mouthing the partner's anus) (CDC, 1989b; Lemon & Newbold, 1990). (It is largely because of the risk of hepatitis A that restaurant employees

Notes: In 1988, 114 female detainees at Rikers Island (a large New York City jail) agreed to be tested for STDs. Eight percent had abnormal Pap smears, 35 percent had HPV, 7 percent had gonorrhea, and 22 percent had syphilis. The majority did not practice safer sex and 72 percent had not used condoms. (Bickell, N. A., et al. 1991. Human papillomavirus, gonorrhea, syphilis, and cervical dysplasia in jailed women. *American Journal of Public Health, 81(10)*, 1218–1320.)

are required to wash their hands after using the toilet.) Ingesting uncooked infested shellfish is also a frequent means of transmission of hepatitis A (Lemon & Newbold, 1990).

Hepatitis B can be transmitted sexually through anal, vaginal, or oral intercourse with an infected partner; through transfusion with contaminated blood supplies; by the sharing of contaminated needles or syringes; and by contact with contaminated saliva, menstrual blood, nasal mucus, or semen (Lemon & Newbold, 1990). It is also possible that sharing razors, toothbrushes, or other personal articles used by an infected person may result in transmission of hepatitis B. Hepatitis C and hepatitis D may also be transmitted sexually or through contact with contaminated blood. A person can transmit the viruses that cause hepatitis, even if he or she is unaware of having any symptoms of the disease.

Hepatitis is usually diagnosed by testing blood samples for the presence of hepatitis antigens and antibodies. There is no cure for viral hepatitis. Bed rest and intake of plentiful fluids are usually recommended until the acute stage of the infection subsides, generally in a few weeks. Full recovery may take months. Although it is not a cure, the drug alpha interferon has shown promising results in preventing liver damage in victims of hepatitis C (Davis et al., 1989). However, only about one of four patients responds favorably to the drug without later relapsing following drug discontinuation (Kolata, 1992b). A vaccine provides protection against hepatitis B and also against hepatitis D, since hepatitis D can occur only if hepatitis B is present. In 1992, the federal government and the American Academy of Pediatrics recommended that all adolescents and young adults be immunized against hepatitis B. Unfortunately, no vaccine is yet available for hepatitis C or A, although researchers are hopeful that a vaccine against hepatitis A may be developed soon (Lemon & Newbold, 1990).

GENITAL WARTS

Genital warts
An STD that is caused by the *human papilloma* virus and takes the form of warts that appear around the genitals and anus.

The *human papilloma* virus (HPV) causes **genital warts** (formerly termed *venereal warts*). HPV is extremely widespread, possibly infecting as many as 20 to 30 percent of sexually active people in the United States (Blakeslee, 1992). Though the warts may appear in visible areas of the skin, in perhaps seven of 10 cases they appear in areas that cannot be seen, such as on the cervix in women or in the urethra in men (Reinisch, 1990). They occur most commonly among people in the 20-to-24 age range (Reinisch, 1990). Within a few months following infection, the warts are usually found in the genital and anal regions. Women are more susceptible to HPV infection because cells in the cervix divide swiftly, facilitating the multiplication of HPV (Blakeslee, 1992). Women who initiate coitus prior to the age of 18 and who have many sex partners are particularly susceptible to infection (Blakeslee, 1992). A study of University of California at Berkeley women revealed that nearly half—46 percent!—had contracted HPV (Blakeslee, 1992). Similarly, it is estimated that nearly half of the sexually active teenage women in some U.S. cities are infected with HPV (Blakeslee, 1992).

Learning Objective 9:
Discuss the symptoms, transmission, and treatment of genital warts (HPV).

TRUTH OR *FICTION?*

R E V I S I T E D

Most people with genital warts have them on visible parts of the body. *No, actually most people with genital warts have them on areas that cannot be seen, such as on the cervix in women or in the urethra in men.* •

Notes: Fifteen percent of women with HPV develop cervical cancer. (Lilley, L. L., and Schaffer, S. 1990. Human papillomavirus: A sexually transmitted disease with carcinogenic potential. *Cancer Nursing, 13(6)*, 366–372.)

Similar to common plantar warts, genital warts are itchy bumps that vary in their size and shape. Genital warts are hard and yellow-gray when they form on dry skin. They take on pink, soft, cauliflower shapes in moist areas like the lower vagina. In men they appear on the penis, foreskin, scrotum, and within the urethra. They appear on the vulva, along the vaginal wall, and on the cervix in women. They can occur outside the genital area in either gender, for example, in the mouth, on the lips, the eyelids, or the nipples of the breasts, around the anus, or in the rectum.

Genital warts may not cause any symptoms, but those that form on the urethra can cause bleeding or painful discharges. HPV itself is believed to be harmless in most cases (Penn, 1993), but it has been implicated in cancers of the genital organs, particularly cervical cancer and penile cancer (Koutsky et al., 1992; Rando, 1988). Cervical cancer is

Genital Warts. Genital warts are caused by the human papilloma virus (HPV) and often have a cauliflower appearance.

linked to HPV in perhaps as many as 85 to 98 percent of cases (Blakeslee, 1992; Ochs, 1994). Researchers in one study found that women with a history of HPV infection were 11 times more likely than other women to develop cervical cancer during the two-year study period (Koutsky et al., 1992). However, the odds of HPV leading to cervical cancer appear rather slim, as only 13,500 new cases of cervical cancer are reported annually in the United States, compared to perhaps one million new cases of HPV (Penn, 1993). (Penile cancers in men are even rarer.) Even so, it would be wise for women to safeguard themselves from HPV-related cervical cancer by limiting their number of sex partners (to reduce their risk of exposure to HPV) and by having regular Pap smears (to detect cervical cancers in their earliest and most treatable stages) (Blakeslee, 1992).

The virus that causes genital warts can be transmitted sexually through skin-to-skin contact during vaginal, anal, or oral sex (Penn, 1993). It can also be transmitted by other forms of contact, such as touching infected towels or clothing. The incubation period may vary from a few weeks to a couple of years. Freezing the wart (*cryotherapy*) with liquid nitrogen is the preferred treatment (CDC, 1989b). One alternative treatment involves painting the warts over a period of several days with an alcohol-based podophyllin solution that causes them to dry up and fall off. Unfortunately, Though the warts themselves may be removed, treatment does not rid the body of the virus (CDC, 1989b). There may thus be recurrences. Podophyllin is not recommended for use with pregnant women or for treatment of warts that form on the cervix (CDC, 1989b). If necessary, the warts may also be treated (by a doctor!) with electrodes (burning) or surgery (by laser or surgical removal).

Unfortunately, no vaccine against HPV exists or appears to be in the offing. Latex condoms may help reduce the risk of contracting HPV, but cannot eliminate the risk entirely because the virus may be transmitted from areas of the skin not protected by condoms, such as the scrotum (Ochs, 1994). People with active warts should probably avoid any anal or genital sexual contact until the warts are removed and the area heals completely.

MOLLUSCUM CONTAGIOSUM

Molluscum contagiosum
An STD caused by a pox virus that causes painless raised lesions to appear on the genitals, buttocks, thighs, or lower abdomen.

Molluscum contagiosum is caused by a pox virus that may be spread sexually. The virus causes painless raised lesions to appear on the genitals, buttocks, thighs, or lower abdomen. Pinkish in appearance with a waxy or pearly top, they usually appear within two or three months of infection. Most infected people have between 10 and 20 lesions, although the number of lesions may range from 1 to perhaps 100 or more (Douglas, 1990). The lesions are generally not associated with serious complications and often disappear on their own within six months. Or they can be treated by squeezing them (like "popping" a blackhead) to exude the whitish center plug. Freezing with liquid nitrogen may also be used to remove the lesions. However, do not try to treat any lesions on your own. See your doctor.

ECTOPARASITIC INFESTATIONS

Ectoparasites
Parasites that live on the outside of the host's body—as opposed to *endo*parasites, which live within the body. (From the Greek *ektos,* meaning "outside.")

Ectoparasites, as opposed to *endoparasites,* live on the outer surfaces of animals (*ecto* means "outer"). *Trichomonas vaginalis,* which causes trichomoniasis, is an endoparasite that is found within people (*endo* means "inner"). Ectoparasites are larger than the agents that cause other STDs. In this section we consider two types of STDs caused by ectoparasites: pediculosis and scabies.

PEDICULOSIS

Pediculosis
A parasitic infestation by pubic lice (*Pthirus pubis*) that causes itching.

Pediculosis is the name given to an infestation of a parasite whose proper Latin name, *Pthirus pubis* (pubic lice), sounds rather too dignified for these bothersome (dare we say ugly?) creatures that are better known as "crabs." Pubic lice are commonly called "crabs" because they are somewhat similar in appearance to crabs when looked at under a microscope (see Figure 16.3). They belong to a family of insects called biting lice. Another member of the family, the human head louse, is an annoying insect that clings to hair on the scalp and often spreads among children at school.

Pubic lice are of the same family of animals as crabs. Pubic lice are not of the same family of animals as crabs. Under a microscope, however, they are somewhat similar in appearance to crabs. •

Learning Objective 10: Describe the symptoms, methods of transmission, and treatment of pediculosis (pubic lice).

In the adult stage pubic lice are large enough to be seen with the naked eye. Pubic lice are generally spread sexually, but they may also be transmitted by contact with an infested towel, sheet, or—yes—toilet seat. They can survive for only about 24 hours without a human host, but they may deposit eggs that can take up to seven days to hatch in bedding or towels (Reinisch, 1990). Therefore, all bedding, towels, and clothes that have been used by an infested person must be washed and/or dried in hot water or dry-cleaned to ensure that they are safe (CDC, 1989b). A person's fingers may also transmit the lice from the genitals to other hair-covered parts of the body, including the scalp and armpits. Sexual contact should be avoided until the infestation is eradicated.

Itching, ranging from the mildly irritating to the intolerable, is the most prominent symptom of a pubic lice infestation. The itching is caused by the "crabs" attaching themselves to the pubic hair and piercing the skin to feed on the blood of their hosts. (Yecch!) The life span of these insects is only about one month, but they are prolific egg layers and may spawn several generations before they die. An infestation can be treated effectively with a prescription medication, a 1 percent solution of lindane (brand name: Kwell), which is available as a cream, lotion, or shampoo, or with nonprescription medications containing pyrethrins or piperonyl butoxide (brand names: RID, Triple X, and others) (Reinisch, 1990). Kwell is not recommended for use by pregnant or lactating women (CDC, 1989b). A careful reexamination of the body is necessary after four to seven days of treatment to ensure that all mature lice and eggs were killed (Reinisch, 1990).

Learning Objective 11: Describe the symptoms, methods of transmission, and treatment of scabies.

SCABIES

Scabies (short for *Sarcoptes scabiei*) is a parasitic infestation caused by a tiny mite that may be transmitted through sexual contact or by contact with infested clothing, bed linen, towels, and other fabrics. The mites attach themselves to the base of pubic hair and burrow into the skin, where they lay eggs and subsist for the duration of their 30-day life span. Like pubic lice, scabies are often found in the genital region and cause itching and discomfort. They are also responsible for reddish lines (created by their burrowing) and sores, welts, or blisters on the skin. Unlike lice, they are too tiny to be seen by the naked eye, but diagnosis can be made by detecting the mite or its by-products on microscopic examination of scrapings from suspicious-looking areas of skin (Levine, 1991). Scabies are most often found on the hands and wrists, but they may also appear on the genitals, buttocks, armpits, and feet (Reinisch, 1990). But they do not appear above the neck—thankfully!

Scabies
A parasitic infestation caused by a tiny mite (*Sarcoptes scabiei*) that causes itching.

FIGURE 16.3 **Pubic Lice.** Pubic lice are commonly called "crabs" because of their appearance under a microscope.

Scabies, like pubic lice, may be treated effectively with 1 percent lindane (Kwell). The entire body from the neck down must be coated with a thin layer of the medication, which should not be washed off for eight hours (CDC, 1989b). But lindane, as noted, should not be used by women who are pregnant or lactating. To avoid reinfection, sex partners and others who have close bodily contact with infected persons should also be treated. Clothing and bed linen used by the infected person must be washed and dried on the hot cycle or dry-cleaned. As with "crabs," sexual contact should be avoided until the infestation is eliminated.

PREVENTION OF STDs: IT'S MORE THAN SAFER SEX

Learning Objective 12: Cite the many strategies that can be used to decrease one's risk of contracting an STD.

Prevention is the most effective strategy for controlling the spread of STDs (CDC, 1988a), especially viral STDs like herpes and AIDS for which there is no cure or vaccine (Mertz, 1990; McCormack, 1990). Prevention of even one case of an STD may prevent its spread to others, perhaps eventually to you.

Notes: During WWI General Pershing, who headed the American Expeditionary Force in Europe, viewed "venereal" disease as a loss-of-manpower issue. In July 1917 he established venereal disease treatment centers in every command and made failure to report exposure to a venereal disease an offense punishable by court martial. Even so, by late 1917, venereal disease rates had risen 500 percent among soldiers stationed at St.-Nazaire in France. (Brandt, A. M. 1985. *No Magic Bullet: A Social History of Venereal Disease in the United States Since 1880.* New York: Oxford University Press.)

ABSTINENCE AND MONOGAMY   The only fully effective strategies to prevent the sexual transmission of STDs are abstinence or maintaining a monogamous sexual relationship with an uninfected partner (CDC, 1988a). Thus, if you are celibate, or if you and your sex partner are not infected and neither of you engages in sexual activity with anyone else, you have little to be concerned about. Many people are sexually active and have not committed themselves to a monogamous relationship, however. Even for those who seek monogamous relationships, there must always be that "first time."

There are many other things that you can do to lower the risk of contracting STDs. As you will see, safer sex is only one aspect of prevention.

BE KNOWLEDGEABLE ABOUT THE RISKS   Be aware of the risks of STDs. Many of us try to put the dangers of STDs out of our minds (especially in moments of passion), so make a pact with yourself to refuse to play the dangerous game of pretending that the dangers of STDs do not exist or that you are somehow immune.

REMAIN SOBER   Alcohol greatly increases the risk of engaging in riskier sexual behavior (Clapper & Lipsitt, 1991).

INSPECT YOURSELF AND YOUR PARTNER   Inspect yourself for a discharge, bumps, rashes, warts, blisters, chancres, sores, lice, or foul odors. Check out any unusual feature with a physician before you engage in sexual activity.

You may be able to work an inspection of your partner into foreplay—a reason for making love the first time with the lights on. In particular, a woman may hold her partner's penis firmly, pulling the loose skin up and down, as if "milking" it. Then she can check for a discharge at the penile opening. The man may use his fingers to detect any sign of a disturbing vaginal discharge. Other visible features of STDs include herpes blisters, genital warts, syphilitic chancres or rashes, and pubic lice.

If you find anything that doesn't look, feel, or smell right, bring it to your partner's attention. Treat any unpleasant odor as a warning sign. Your partner may not be aware of the symptom and may be carrying an infection that is harmful to him or her as well as to you or others. If you notice any suspicious signs, refrain from further sexual contact until your partner has the chance to seek a medical evaluation. It is advisable to be informed about the common signs and symptoms of STDs, but you need not become a medical expert. Even if your concerns prove groundless, you can resume sexual relations without the uncertainty and anxiety that you would have experienced if you had ignored your concerns.

Of course, your partner may become defensive or hostile if you express a concern that he or she may be carrying an STD. Try to be empathetic and recognize that social stigma attached to people with STDs makes it difficult for people to accept the possibility of infection. It may be appropriate to point out that STDs are quite common (among college students, bank officers, military personnel, or . . . fill in the blanks) and that many people are unaware that they carry them.

But for your sake as well as your partner's, if you are not sure that sex is safe, stop. Think carefully about the risks and seek expert advice.

Teaching Tip: If you did not demonstrate the correct way to use a condom earlier, do so with a banana or a life-like model of a penis. Emphasize the importance of putting on the condom before there is any contact between the penis and the vagina or anus. Emphasize holding onto the condom when withdrawing the penis. Demonstrate how to use spermicides with condoms.

USE LATEX CONDOMS   In the laboratory, latex condoms have been shown to be effective in blocking nearly all sexually transmissible organisms (Liskin et al., 1990). In actual use, however, latex condoms are not perfect and may sometimes leak viral particles (Carey et al., 1992). Even so, condoms can help lower, though not eliminate, the risk of contracting or spreading many STDs. Latex condoms may be even more effective in preventing STDs when used along with spermicides containing the ingredient nonoxynol-9, which kills STD-causing microorganisms, including the viruses that cause AIDS and genital herpes.

Researchers estimate that in regular use, condoms reduce the rate of STD infections by about 50 percent, on the average (Rosenberg et al., 1991). Improper use or inconsistent use is a common reason for failures in using condoms to prevent STD transmission (Rosenberg & Gollub, 1992). Yet, even when used properly, condoms may be of limited or no value against disease-causing organisms that are transmitted externally, such as those causing herpes, genital warts, and ectoparasitic infestations.

AVOID HIGH-RISK SEXUAL BEHAVIORS   Anal penetration by a penis or a partner's hand ("fisting") carries a heightened risk of infection because tears in the anal lining can provide microorganisms a convenient port of entry into the bloodstream. Unless you are absolutely sure that you and your partner are free of STDs, especially of AIDS, such activities are to be avoided. (It is also advisable to avoid any activity that may be physically injurious.) If you do engage in anal-genital sex and are uncertain as to whether you or your partner is infected, use a latex condom and spermicide. Oral-anal sex, or anilingus (sometimes called *rimming*), should be avoided because of the potential of transmitting microbes between the mouth and the anus.

Also avoid sexual contact with people with STDs, people who practice high-risk sexual behaviors, people who inject drugs, and prostitutes or people who frequent prostitutes.

WASH THE GENITALS BEFORE AND AFTER SEX   Washing the genitals before and after sex removes a quantity of potentially harmful agents. Washing together may be incorporated into erotic foreplay. Right after intercourse, a thorough washing with soap and water may help reduce the risk of infection. Do not, however, deceive yourself into believing that washing your genitals is an effective substitute for safer sex. Most STDs are transmitted internally. Washing is of no avail against them and only of limited help in preventing infection of exposed body parts.

There may be some limited benefits to women from douching right after coitus. But frequent douching should be avoided since it may change the vaginal flora and encourage the growth of infectious organisms. Nor is immediate douching possible for women who use a diaphragm and spermicide that must remain in the vagina for at least six to eight hours after intercourse. But such women may profit from washing the external genitals immediately after coitus.

HAVE REGULAR MEDICAL CHECKUPS   A sexually active person should have health examinations regularly, preferably twice a year, and be checked for STDs (Bell, 1980). (Sexually active women are advised to have at least one gynecological examination a year in any case.) Many community clinics and family planning centers set their charges according to the patient's ability to pay. Checkups are a small enough investment to make in one's own health. Recall that a number of people, both women and men, are symptomless carriers of STDs, especially of chlamydial infections. Medical checkups enable the person to learn about and receive treatment for disorders that might otherwise go unnoticed. Many physicians advise routine testing of asymptomatic young women for chlamydial infections to prevent the hidden damage that may occur if the infection goes undetected and untreated (Buhaug et al., 1990).

DISCUSS WHETHER YOU AND YOUR PARTNER SHOULD UNDERGO TESTING BEFORE INITIATING SEXUAL RELATIONS   Some couples reach a mutual agreement to be tested for HIV and other STDs before they initiate sexual relations. (Some people simply insist that their prospective partners be tested before they initiate sexual relations.) But many people resist testing or feel insulted when their partners raise the issue. People usually assume that they are free of STDs if they are symptom-free and have been reasonably "careful" in their choice of partners. STDs happen to the "nicest people," of course, and the absence of symptoms is no guarantee of freedom from infection. Unless you have been celibate or involved in a monogamous relationship with an uninfected partner, you should consider yourself at risk of carrying or contracting an infectious STD.

CONSULT YOUR PHYSICIAN IF YOU SUSPECT THAT YOU HAVE BEEN EXPOSED TO AN STD   Early intervention may prevent the damage of an STD spreading to vital body organs. Be sensitive to any physical changes that may be symptomatic of STDs, and consult a physician when in doubt.

GET TO KNOW YOUR PARTNER BEFORE INITIATING SEXUAL RELATIONS   Be selective in your choice of sex partners. Having sex with multiple partners—especially "one-night stands"—increases your risk of a sexual contact with an infected person. It

A CLOSER LOOK

Sources of Help

Do you have questions about the signs and symptoms of STDs? Do you need assistance in coping with an STD? A number of organizations have established telephone hotlines that provide anonymous callers with information. Some organizations publish newsletters and other material to help sufferers of particular diseases cope more effectively.

National Toll-Free Hotlines for Information About AIDS and Other STDs

These hotlines provide information about AIDS and other STDs, as well as referral sources. You needn't give your name or identify yourself to obtain information.

National AIDS Hotline, Centers for Disease Control AIDS Hotline:

(800) 342-AIDS: Information and referral resources nationwide, 24 hours a day.

National STD Hotline: (800) 227-8922 (in California (800) 982-5883) (A hotline sponsored by the American Social Health Association that dispenses information about STD symptoms and refers callers to local STD clinics that provide confidential, minimum- or no-cost treatment.)

Spanish AIDS/SIDA Hotline: (800) 344-7432

AIDS Hotline for the Hearing Impaired: (800) 243-7889

Canadian Toll-Free Hotline (Toll-free in Canada):

AIDS Committee of Toronto: (800) 267-6600

Where to Obtain Help or Information About Herpes

National Herpes Hotline: (919) 361-8488

The Helper is a newsletter published by HELP (Herpetics Engaged in Living Productively), an organization that helps herpes sufferers cope with the disease. For copies of the newsletter, and for the address of the HELP chapter closest to you, either call the National STD Hotline (800-227-8922) or write to HELP, Herpes Resource Center, P.O. Box 13827, Research Triangle Park, NC 27709.

Herpes Resource Center Box 100, Palo Alto, CA 94302

---

also lessens the opportunity to get to know your partner well enough to know whether he or she has participated in high-risk sexual practices or has had sex partners in the past who themselves practiced high-risk behaviors.

AVOID OTHER HIGH-RISK BEHAVIORS   Avoid contact with bodily substances (blood, semen, vaginal secretions, fecal matter) from other people. Do not share hypodermic needles, razors, cuticle scissors, or other implements that may contain another person's blood. Be careful when handling wet towels, bed linen, or other material that may contain bodily substances.

STD Prevention in China. In response to a rapid increase in STDs during the 1980s, China established a government-sponsored STD hotline—the first of its kind in the country. Here, government nurses counsel a young woman about preventing STDs.

SUMMING UP

AN EPIDEMIC

More than 13 million people in the United States contract a sexually transmitted disease (STD) each year. Although public attention has been riveted on AIDS for a decade, other STDs such as chlamydia and genital warts pose wider threats.

BACTERIAL DISEASES

Bacteria are one-celled microorganisms that cause many illnesses. **Gonorrhea** Gonorrhea is caused by the *gonococcus* bacterium. For men, symptoms include a penile discharge and burning urination. Most women are asymptomatic. If left untreated, gonorrhea can attack the internal reproductive organs and lead to PID in women. Gonorrhea is treated with antibiotics.
Syphilis Syphilis is caused by the *Treponema pallidum* bacterium. Syphilis undergoes several stages of development. Although it may lie dormant for many years, it may also be lethal. Syphilis is treated with antibiotics.
Chlamydia Chlamydia or chlamydial infections are caused by the *Chlamydia trachomatis* bacterium. The symptoms of chlamydial infections resemble those of gonorrhea but tend to be milder. Chlamydial infections also respond to antibiotics.

VAGINAL INFECTIONS

Vaginitis is usually known by a foul-smelling discharge, genital irritation, and burning during urination. Most cases involve bacterial vaginosis, candidiasis, or trichomoniasis.
Bacterial Vaginosis Bacterial vaginosis is usually caused by the *Gardnerella vaginalis* bacterium. Oral treatment with metronidazole is recommended.
Candidiasis Candidiasis is caused by a yeastlike fungus, *Candida albicans*. Infections usually arise from changes in the vaginal environment that allow the fungus to overgrow. Treatment with miconazole, clotrimazole, or terconazole is usually recommended.
Trichomoniasis "Trich" is caused by a protozoan called *Trichomonas vaginalis*. Trichomoniasis is treated with metronidazole.

VIRAL DISEASES

Viruses are particles of DNA that reproduce by invading a body cell and directing the cell's own reproductive machinery to spin off new viral particles.
Herpes Oral herpes is caused by the Herpes simplex virus type 1 (HSV-1). Genital herpes is caused by the Herpes simplex virus type 2 (HSV-2), which produces painful shallow sores and blisters on the genitals. There is no cure or vaccine for herpes, but the antiviral drug acyclovir can relieve pain and speed healing during flare-ups.
Viral Hepatitis There are several types of hepatitis, and they are caused by different hepatitis viruses. Most cases of hepatitis are transmitted sexually or by contact with contaminated blood or fecal matter.
Genital Warts Genital warts are caused by the *human papilloma virus (HPV)*. HPV has been linked to cancers of the genital tract. Freezing the wart is the preferred treatment for removal of the wart, but the virus remains in the body afterwards.

ECTOPARASITIC INFESTATIONS

Pediculosis Pediculosis ("crabs") is caused by pubic lice (*Pthirus pubis*). Pubic lice attach themselves to pubic hair and feed on the blood of their hosts, which often causes itching. Infestations can be treated with a prescription medication, lindane, or with nonprescription medications containing pyrethrins or piperonyl butoxide.
Scabies Scabies (*Sarcoptes scabiei*) is a parasitic infestation caused by a tiny mite that causes itching. Scabies, like pubic lice, is treated with lindane.

PREVENTION OF STDS: IT'S MORE THAN SAFER SEX

Strategies for preventing STDs include abstinence, monogamy, inspecting oneself and one's partner, using latex condoms, avoiding high-risk sex, washing the genitals before and after sex, having regular medical checkups, and getting to know one's partner before engaging in sexual activity.

C H A P T E R

O U T L I N E

_____ By the year 2000, 40 million people around the world are likely to be infected by HIV (the virus that causes AIDS).

_____ Only people in high-risk groups are at serious risk for contracting AIDS.

_____ As you are reading this page, you are engaged in search-and-destroy missions against foreign agents within your body.

_____ AIDS does not kill directly; rather, it kills by disabling the body's ability to fend off other life-threatening diseases.

_____ People can pass along HIV to others even if they have no symptoms of the infection themselves.

_____ Most people who are infected by HIV remain symptom-free and appear healthy for years.

_____ You can be infected by HIV by donating blood.

_____ Only a small proportion of AIDS patients are women.

HIV infection is diagnosed by examination of the virus in the bloodstream.

_____ Awareness of the risks of HIV infection and AIDS leads people to engage in "safe sex."

C H A P T E R **17**

Acquired Immunodeficiency Syndrome (AIDS)

AIDS (AIDS is the acronym for **acquired immunodeficiency syndrome**) is a fatal disease caused by a virus, the *human immunodeficiency virus* (HIV). HIV attacks and disables the immune system, the body's natural line of defense against disease-causing organisms, stripping it of its ability to fend off life-threatening diseases. Although no one knows where HIV originated, it is suspected that it may represent a variant of viruses found in monkeys and chimpanzees that somehow crossed over to humans (Essex & Kanki, 1988; Norman, 1986; Smith et al., 1988).

The first cases in the United States of a mysterious disease that we now call AIDS began to appear in the medical journals in 1981. Physicians reported treating a number of male patients who were suffering from *pneumocystis carinii pneumonia* (PCP). PCP is a rare form of pneumonia that had typically been found among cancer patients whose immune systems were suppressed as a side effect of chemotherapy. Some of these PCP sufferers showed other disorders that were associated with suppressed immune systems—high fevers, weight loss, and candidiasis of the mouth. Although patients with these conditions normally recovered, it was not to be with these patients. All of them died (Gottlieb, 1991).

In the early 1980s, physicians also began to see cases in young men of a rare form of cancer—Kaposi's sarcoma—that leaves purple spots on the body. This illness usually struck only aging Jewish and Italian men. Though aging men usually live with the disease and die later of other causes, the young men quickly deteriorated and died. Some also had PCP.

When this atypical assortment of symptoms and maladies was first reported in the medical journals, the only clear connection among the afflicted patients was that all of them were gay. The syndrome that struck them became known disparagingly as the "gay cancer" or the "gay plague," and some viewed the epidemic as an expression of God's wrath against homosexuals. According to Randy Shilts, who chronicled the early years of the AIDS epidemic in his landmark 1987 book, *And the Band Played On,* the government was slow to respond to the epidemic at first because of prejudice against gays. Not until celebrities such as film star Rock Hudson, choreographer Michael Bennett, and fashion designer Perry Ellis, died from AIDS did the nation take much note of it. Sadly, Shilts himself died of the disease in 1994.

Not until 1982 would the syndrome that first struck gay people be given the name of AIDS. It was not until 1983 that cases of AIDS were discovered among heterosexuals, and not until 1985 that a test for HIV infection was licensed. When the "gay cancer" moved into the heterosexual population, it mainly affected **injecting drug users** (IDUs), who spread the virus from one to another by sharing contaminated needles, and their sex partners. Other common targets included children who were born after their mothers had been infected, and hemophiliacs and others who received transfusions of blood that were contaminated with HIV. It became clear that HIV paid no attention to boundaries related to sexual orientation, race, socioeconomic status, or age.

In 1987, the AIDS Coalition To Unleash Power (ACT-UP) was formed in New York by AIDS activists. ACT-UP has used confrontational tactics in confronting the government and the medical establishment for what they perceive to be an inadequate response to the epidemic. In response to the confrontational stance of ACT-UP, a physician at the University of California at San Francisco Medical School wrote:

> The entry of AIDS activists into the health care scene has added a jarring new dimension to what was previously a genteel dialogue between patient advocates and clinicians, researchers, and policy makers. The activists' unprecedented modus operandi is a study in contrasts: street theater and intimidation on the one

hand, detailed position papers and painstaking negotiation on the other. The effect has been to energize the fight against AIDS with an urgency that has translated into expedited [government] drug approvals, lower prices for medications, and increased funding for AIDS research and care.

(Wachter, 1992, p. 128)

AIDS activists argue that a "genteel dialogue" with the governmental and medical establishments is not of much value when one is facing a death sentence. They contend that vast resources must be poured into the battle against AIDS—now—if the millions of people worldwide who are infected with HIV are not to die. In the early 1990s, a government commission (National Commission on AIDS) and AIDS activists concurred that the government must provide more money for research into the prevention and treatment of AIDS.

The announcement by basketball great Earvin "Magic" Johnson in October 1991 that he was infected with HIV was a watershed event in the short but tragic history of the AIDS epidemic. Johnson, who had led the Lakers to five professional basketball championships, said that he had been infected through heterosexual sex. Johnson's disclosure that he is HIV-positive may help shatter the myth of personal invulnerability held by many people, especially young, vigorous heterosexuals (Specter, 1991). The virus that causes AIDS does not care whether the person it infects is gay or straight, black or white, young or old, or male or female. If someone as physically fit as Johnson could be infected by HIV, any of us are potentially at risk. Johnson's announcement and the resulting publicity may have prompted people to reexamine their personal risk of contracting the AIDS virus and may have led some to reduce unsafe sexual practices (CDC, 1993e; "Publicity about Magic Johnson may have led some to reduce their risky behavior, request HIV testing," 1993). However, it is doubtful that this one event will have significant lasting effects on reducing risk behavior in the general population.

PREVALENCE OF HIV INFECTION AND AIDS

Fewer than 100 Americans had died of AIDS in 1981 when the syndrome was first described in the medical journals (Gottlieb, 1991). By early 1994, more than 360,000 Americans would be diagnosed as having AIDS and more than 220,000 would have died of the disease (AIDS Hotline, April 12, 1994). By 1993, AIDS had become the leading killer in the United States of men ages 25 to 44 and the fourth leading killer of women in that age group ("AIDS is top killer among young men," 1993). By the beginning of the 1990s, one American was dying from AIDS every 12 minutes (Kramer, 1990). The prevalence of AIDS increased steadily in the early 1990s at a rate of about 3 to 5 percent a year. AIDS is increasing most rapidly among women, people of color, people who use injectable drugs, and people who engage in unprotected, heterosexual sex.

Figures 17. 1 and 17.2 (page 522) show, respectively, the geographic distribution of HIV transmission worldwide and of AIDS cases within the United States. The Centers for Disease Control and Prevention (CDC) estimates that one million people in the United States are infected with HIV (Altman, 1991b). It expects that most all of these people will eventually develop AIDS. The World Health Organization (WHO) estimated that 14 million people in the world in 1993 were infected with HIV (Altman, 1993k). Barring any dramatic prevention-oriented efforts by the world community, the head of the WHO AIDS program, Michael Merson, estimated that the number of persons infected with HIV will soar to perhaps 30 to 40 million by the year 2000 (Altman, 1991b). A Harvard University report issued even grimmer projections, with estimates of as many as 110 million infected people worldwide by the year 2000 (Mann et al., 1992). Federal health officials believe that AIDS fatalities will level off in the United States in the mid-1990s at about 50,000 deaths a year, about the same number that are expected to develop AIDS each year (Ekholm, 1992).

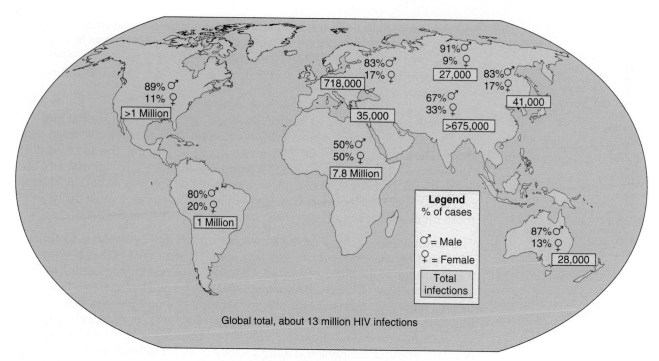

FIGURE 17.1 **Estimated Rates of HIV Transmission Throughout the World.**

Source: Adapted from Mann et al. (1992). *AIDS in the World: A Global Report.* Cambridge, MA: Harvard University Press.

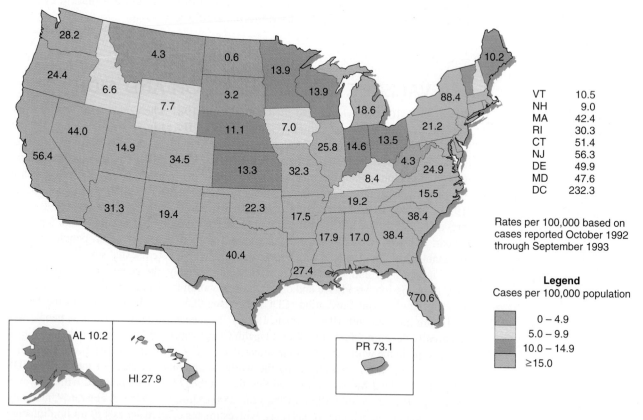

FIGURE 17.2 **AIDS Cases Within the United States.**

Source: Centers for Disease Control and Prevention (1993). *HIV/AIDS Surveillance Report.* 3rd Quarter Edition. Atlanta, GA: Author.

By the year 2000, 40 million people around the world are likely to be infected by HIV (the virus that causes AIDS). According to a leading official with the World Health Organization, some 30 to 40 million people around the world may be infected by HIV by the year 2000, unless the world community takes bold action to stem the epidemic. •

Notes: According to CDC statistics collected from June 1981 through December 1993, the following ten states/territories have the highest cumulative numbers of reported AIDS cases (from highest to lowest): New York, California, Florida, Texas, New Jersey, Puerto Rico, Illinois, Pennsylvania, Georgia, and Massachusetts. (CDC AIDS Hotline personal communication [B. Drinnin], June 16, 1994.)

In the United States, AIDS remains a disease that predominantly affects men who have sex with other men or who use IV drugs (Altman, 1993h; CDC, 1993f). In 1993, 48 percent of AIDS cases involved male-to-male sexual contact and an additional 27 percent involved transmission by injecting drug use (see Figure 17.3a). Yet the rate of new cases of AIDS in gay and bisexual men has been declining steadily—thanks largely to more widespread use of safer sex practices in the gay male community, including increased use of condoms and reductions in the numbers of sexual partners (CDC, 1990d, 1993f; Cowley, 1993; Ehrhardt, 1992). Experts remain concerned, however, about resumptions (relapses) of unsafe sexual practices in older gay men and about younger gay men who may not follow safer sex guidelines (Ehrhardt et al., 1991).

Heterosexual contact is the fastest-growing exposure category and now accounts for 9 percent of cases of AIDS overall (CDC, 1993c; Haverkos, 1993) (see Figure 17.3a). Among women, however, heterosexual contact now accounts for more than one third of cases (see Figure 17.3b). Bear in mind that it is a person's behavior and not the groups to which she or he belongs that determines her or his relative risk of infection. Thus, we speak in terms of high-risk *behaviors* (such as unprotected intercourse) rather than high-risk *groups* (Cochran & Mays, 1989).

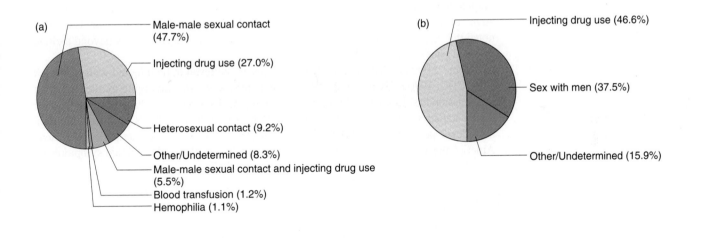

(a)
Male-male sexual contact (47.7%)
Injecting drug use (27.0%)
Heterosexual contact (9.2%)
Other/Undetermined (8.3%)
Male-male sexual contact and injecting drug use (5.5%)
Blood transfusion (1.2%)
Hemophilia (1.1%)

(b)
Injecting drug use (46.6%)
Sex with men (37.5%)
Other/Undetermined (15.9%)

Data reflect cases reported October 1992 through September 1993

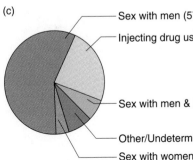

(c)
Sex with men (57.4%)
Injecting drug use (23.9%)
Sex with men & injecting drug use (6.7%)
Other/Undetermined (7.8%)
Sex with women (4.2%)

FIGURE 17.3 AIDS Cases by Exposure Category. Part (a) shows men and women combined; Part (b), women; and Part (c), men. Overall, 9 percent of cases of AIDS in 1993 were believed to have been transmitted by heterosexual contact (a). Among women, however, more than one in three cases (37.5%) of AIDS were attributed to heterosexual contact (b). By contrast, only 4.2 percent of cases of AIDS among men were attributed to sexual contact with women (c).

Only people in high-risk groups are at serious risk for contracting AIDS. It is not true that only people in high-risk groups are at serious risk for contracting AIDS. One's behavior, not one's group membership, places one at risk for AIDS. •

African Americans and Hispanic Americans have suffered disproportionately from the AIDS epidemic (CDC, 1993f; Gayle et al., 1990; Mays, 1993; USDHHS, 1992). Nearly 50 percent of people with AIDS in the United States are African American or Hispanic American, although these groups comprise only about 20 percent of the population (see Figure 17.4). The number of AIDS cases among African Americans and Hispanic Americans has been increasing sharply in recent years, at the same time that the number of cases among whites has declined modestly (Woodard, 1993). Death rates due to AIDS are more than twice as great among African Americans and Hispanic Americans (especially Hispanics of Puerto Rican origin) than among white Americans (CDC, 1991b; 1993i).

Ethnic differences in rates of transmission of HIV appear linked to the use of injectable drugs. Injecting drug users can become infected from using contaminated needles and can transmit the virus to their sexual partners through unprotected sex. Injecting drug users (IDUs) now account for more than one in four AIDS cases (see Figure 17.3a). African Americans constitute about 50 percent of the IDUs with AIDS and Hispanic Americans account for another 29 percent of cases (Woodard, 1993). Since drug abuse and the related problem of prostitution occur disproportionately in poor, urban communities with large populations of people of color, it is not surprising that HIV infection and AIDS have affected these groups disproportionately.

AIDS has ravaged the creative arts, claiming many of its leading talents. The dance world lost the famed ballet star Rudolph Nureyev and the choreographer Michael Bennett, who gave us *A Chorus Line* and *Dreamgirls*. The performing arts lost Liberace, Peter Allen, and Freddie Mercury; the world of fashion, Halston and Perry Ellis; the movie industry, Rock Hudson, Tony Perkins, and Robert Reed; the art world, Robert Mapplethorpe and Keith Haring. In recounting the roster of these and many other creative spirits who have been obliterated by this killer disease, the writers of *Newsweek* noted that though "all lives are irreplaceable, . . . an artist's death echoes beyond a circle of loved ones" (Ansen et al., 1993, p. 17).

Some 2,000 newborns in the United States are believed to be infected with HIV each year (CDC, 1990d; Gwinn et al., 1991). The numbers of cases involving mother-to-infant transmission has been rising in recent years, jumping 13 percent in 1992, the latest year for which statistics were available (Altman, 1993h). More than 5,000 HIV-infected children have developed full-blown AIDS. The great majority of these children are poor and African American or Hispanic. HIV-infected children usually develop AIDS-related symptoms by

Notes: In the United States from June 1981 through the end of December 1993, 5,234 children under the age of 13 were diagnosed with AIDS. Of these children, the transmission route for 4,710 was through a mother with or at risk for HIV infection. (CDC AIDS Hotline, personal communication [B. Drinnin], June 16, 1994.)

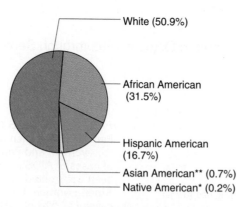

White (50.9%)

African American (31.5%)

Hispanic American (16.7%)

Asian American** (0.7%)

Native American* (0.2%)

*Includes American Indian/Alaskan Native
**Includes Pacific Islander

FIGURE 17.4 **AIDS Cases by Race.**

six months of age and full-blown cases of AIDS by their second birthdays (Fletcher et al., 1991). Some, however, don't develop AIDS until the age of 9 or 11. Some survive into their teens. But most succumb to the disease before the age of 10 (Eckholm, 1992b).

We don't yet know why some children, about one in three (Touchette, 1993), contract the disease from infected mothers while others do not, or why some die by the age of 2 or 5 while others survive into adolescence. Sadly, too, thousands of children are losing their parents to AIDS. Researchers estimate that AIDS will leave some 72,000 to 125,000 children motherless by the end of the decade (Michaels & Levine, 1992; Navarro, 1993; Shahid, 1993).

Researchers fear that worse news lies ahead. The numbers of cases of AIDS and the death toll were expected to rise through at least the early 1990s (CDC, 1990d). What will the future bring? Will we still be in the throes of the AIDS epidemic as we enter the twenty-first century? Have we thus far seen but the tip of the iceberg? Or will efforts to find a vaccine or a cure meet with positive results? Will people engage in effective means of prevention? The answers may be largely up to you.

THE IMMUNE SYSTEM AND AIDS

AIDS is caused by a virus that attacks the body's immune system—the body's natural line of defense against disease-causing organisms. To understand the effects of the AIDS virus, we must first know something about the components and functioning of the immune system.

THE IMMUNE SYSTEM

Given the intricacies of the human body and the rapid advance of scientific knowledge, we tend to consider ourselves dependent on highly trained specialists to contend with illness. Actually we cope with most diseases by ourselves, through the functioning of our **immune systems.**

The immune system combats disease in a number of ways. It produces a trillion white blood cells that systematically envelop and kill **pathogens** like bacteria, viruses, and fungi; worn out body cells; and cells that have become cancerous. White blood cells are referred to as **leukocytes.** Leukocytes engage in microscopic warfare. They undertake search-and-destroy missions; they identify and eradicate foreign agents and debilitated cells.

As you are reading this page, you are engaged in search-and-destroy missions against foreign agents within your body. Yes, the white cells in your immune system continuously engage in search-and-destroy missions against foreign agents (pathogens) within your body. •

Leukocytes recognize foreign agents by their surface fragments to enhance the effectiveness of future combat. The surface fragments are termed **antigens** because the body reacts to their presence by developing specialized proteins, or **antibodies,** that attach to the foreign bodies, inactivating them and marking them for destruction. (Infection by HIV may be determined by examining the blood for the presence of antibodies to the virus. Unfortunately, these antibodies are unable to eradicate the infection.)

Special "memory lymphocytes" are held in reserve, rather than marking pathogens for destruction or going to war against them. They can remain in the bloodstream, sometimes for several years, and they form the basis for a quick immune response to an invader the second time around.[1]

Another function of the immune system is to promote **inflammation.** When you suffer an injury, blood vessels in the region initially contract to check bleeding; then they

Immune system
A term for the body's complex of mechanisms for protecting itself from disease-causing agents such as pathogens.

Pathogen
An agent, especially a microorganism, that can cause a disease. (From the Greek *pathos,* meaning "suffering" or "disease," and *genic,* meaning "forming" or "coming into being.")

Leukocytes
White blood cells that are essential to the body's defenses against infection. (From the Greek *leukos,* meaning "white," and *kytos,* meaning "a hollow," and used in combination with other word forms to mean *cell.*)

TRUTH OR *FICTION?*

R E V I S I T E D

Antigen
A protein, toxin, or other substance to which the body reacts by producing antibodies. (Combined word formed from *anti*body *gen*erator.)

Antibodies
Specialized proteins that attach to foreign substances in the body, inactivating them and marking them for destruction.

---

[1]Vaccination is the placement of a weakened form of an antigen in the body, which activates the creation of antibodies and memory lymphocytes. Smallpox has been annihilated by vaccination, and researchers are trying to develop a vaccine against the virus that causes AIDS.

Inflammation
Redness and warmth that develop at the site of an injury, reflecting dilation of blood vessels that permits the expanded flow of leukocytes to the region.

Learning Objective 4:
Describe how HIV attacks the immune system.

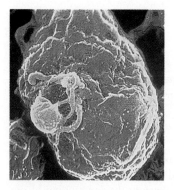

AIDS Virus (HIV) Attacking a White Blood Cell.

TRUTH OR *FICTION?*

R E V I S I T E D

Learning Objective 5:
Identify the symptoms of HIV infection, beginning with the early symptom-free period through the typical opportunistic diseases which characterize full-blown AIDS.

dilate. Dilation expands blood flow to the injured region, causing the redness and warmth that identify inflammation. The elevated blood supply also brings in an army of leukocytes to combat invading microscopic life forms, like bacteria, that would otherwise use the local injury as a beachhead into the body.

EFFECTS OF HIV ON THE IMMUNE SYSTEM

HIV belongs to a class of viruses called *retroviruses* (from the Greek word *retro,* meaning "backward"), thus named because they follow a backward course of reproduction (Kolata, 1992a; Levy, 1993; Temin, 1992). Like other viruses, HIV uses the cells it invades to spin off copies of itself. Scientists have identified the shape of a key enzyme, *reverse transcriptase,* or RT, which HIV uses to cause the genes in the cells it attacks to make certain proteins that the virus needs in order to reproduce. The importance of this discovery is that it may lead to the development of drugs that can, it is hoped, defeat HIV by blocking the function of RT without affecting other proteins needed by the body ("Discovery of shape of key HIV enzyme may lead to new AIDS drugs," 1992).

Scientists have discovered several types of HIV that cause AIDS, including *human immunodeficiency virus type 1 (HIV-1),* the most prevalent form, and a more recently discovered virus, *human immunodeficiency virus type 2 (HIV-2).* HIV-1 appears to be the more virulent form of the virus (Cowley, 1993).

HIV directly attacks the immune system by invading and destroying a particular type of lymphocyte called the CD4 (the so-called helper T-cell[2]), the quarterback (Shilts, 1987) of the immune system. CD4 cells "recognize" invading pathogens and signal B-lymphocytes or B-cells—another kind of white blood cell—to produce antibodies that inactivate pathogens and designate them for annihilation. CD4 cells also signal another class of T-cells, called killer T-cells, to destroy infected cells. By attacking and destroying helper T-cells, HIV disables the very cells that the body relies on to fight off this and other diseases (Reinisch, 1990). As HIV cripples the body's natural defenses, the individual is exposed to serious infections and cancers that would not otherwise take hold. When the immune system is disabled, these diseases proliferate and prove difficult to control, and eventually result in death. Though the CD4 cells appear to be its main target, HIV also attacks other types of white blood cells (Kolata, 1993f).

AIDS does not kill directly; rather, it kills by disabling the body's ability to fend off other life-threatening diseases. True. The AIDS virus (HIV) kills by disabling the immune system and rendering the body vulnerable to life-threatening diseases that it normally would be capable of fending off. •

The blood normally contains about 1,000 CD4 cells per cubic millimeter (Navarro, 1992). The numbers of CD4 cells may remain at about 1,000 per cubic millimeter for several years following HIV infection, and many people show no symptoms and appear healthy while they remain at this level. Then, for reasons that are not clearly understood, the levels of CD4 cells begin to drop off, although symptoms may not appear for perhaps months or years afterwards. As the numbers of CD4 cells decline, however, symptoms generally increase (Palenicek et al., 1993) and people fall prey to the many opportunistic diseases that their weakened immune systems are unable to fight off. People become most vulnerable to opportunistic infections when the level of CD4 cells falls below 200 per cubic millimeter (Hamilton et al., 1992).

PROGRESSION OF HIV INFECTION AND AIDS

HIV follows a complex course once it enters the body.

[2]CD4 cells are also known as T4 cells. The terms are synonymous and completely interchangeable.

CHAPTER 17   ACQUIRED IMMUNODEFICIENCY SYNDROME (AIDS)

Shortly following infection, the person may experience mild flulike symptoms, however—fatigue, fever, headaches and muscle pain, lack of appetite, nausea, swollen glands, and possibly a rash. Such symptoms usually disappear within a few weeks. People may thus dismiss these symptoms as a passing case of flu. People who enter this asymptomatic or carrier state may look and act well and not realize that they are infectious. Thus, they can unwittingly pass along the virus to others.

TRUTH OR *FICTION?*

R E V I S I T E D

People can pass along HIV to others even if they have no symptoms of the infection themselves. *True. You can pass along HIV to your sexual partners even if you have no symptoms yourself.* •

Most HIV-infected people remain asymptomatic carriers of the virus for periods of years. Some enter a symptomatic state (previously labeled *AIDS-related complex* or ARC) that is typically denoted by such symptoms as chronically swollen lymph nodes and intermittent weight loss, fever, fatigue, and diarrhea. The severity of symptomatic HIV infection depends on various factors, such as the person's general health. This symptomatic state does not constitute full-blown AIDS, but shows that HIV is undermining the integrity of the person's immune system. Like asymptomatic carriers, they may unknowingly pass along the virus to others through sexual contact or needle sharing.

TRUTH OR *FICTION?*

R E V I S I T E D

Most people who are infected by HIV remain symptom-free and appear healthy for years. *It is true that most people who are infected by HIV go symptom-free for years and may appear perfectly healthy.* •

Eventually, perhaps a decade or more after the person is infected with HIV, and for reasons that remain unclear, the virus begins to propagate in large numbers, obliterating the cells that house it and spreading to other immune-system cells, eventually destroying or disabling the body's ability to defend itself from disease. About half of the people with HIV develop diagnosable AIDS within 10 years of initial infection. For this reason, people who are infected with HIV may feel as though they carry time bombs within them. AIDS is classified as a *syndrome* because it is characterized by a variety of different symptoms. The beginnings of full-blown cases of AIDS are often marked by such symptoms as swollen lymph nodes, fatigue, fever, "night sweats," diarrhea, and weight loss that cannot be attributed to dieting or exercise.

Opportunistic diseases
Diseases that take hold only when the immune system is weakened and unable to fend them off. Kaposi's sarcoma and pneumocystis carinii pneumonia (PCP) are examples of opportunistic diseases found in AIDS patients.

The diagnosis of AIDS is based on the appearance of various indicator diseases, such as PCP; Kaposi's sarcoma; toxoplasmosis of the brain, which is an infection of parasites; herpes simplex with chronic ulcers; or wasting syndrome (wasting away, that is, as in losing weight without notable dietary changes or expenditure of calories through exercise) (Navarro, 1992). These diseases are termed **opportunistic diseases** because they are not likely to emerge unless a disabled immune system provides them with the opportunity. As AIDS progresses, the person grows thinner and more fatigued, becomes unable to perform ordinary life functions, and falls prey to opportunistic infections, leading eventually to death. As it now stands, AIDS almost always results in death within a few years. The estimated length of survival for the average patient after the onset of full-blown AIDS is little more than a year (Hardy et al., 1986; Lemp et al., 1990). A study of AIDS patients in San Francisco from 1981 to 1987 found that only 3.4 percent survived five years (Lemp et al., 1990).

In 1992, the federal Centers for Disease Control expanded the diagnostic criteria for AIDS (Altman, 1993a; Steinberg, 1993). Three additional diseases were added to the list of 23 other AIDS indicators: tuberculosis of the lungs, recurrent pneumonia, and invasive cervical cancer. These added conditions commonly affect HIV-infected IDUs and women. In addition, the new criteria provides for an AIDS diagnosis when the CD4 cell count in persons infected with HIV falls to fewer than 200 cells per cubic millimeter, about one fifth the normal amount, irrespective of the presence of indicator diseases. The more

HIV Infection and AIDS: A World Epidemic

HIV disease—HIV infection and AIDS—is a worldwide epidemic that shows no signs of ebbing. AIDS respects no boundaries. It is a merciless killer of men, women, children, and people of all nationalities and races. Table 17.1 (see page 530) shows the prevalences of HIV transmission and AIDS around the world, according to a 1992 Harvard University report. The rate of HIV infection is increasing faster in many developing countries in Asia, Latin America, and Africa than in the United States and other industrialized nations. Unless the world community takes effective action in stemming the epidemic, future prospects are indeed harrowing. Consider some facts concerning the spread of HIV and AIDS:

Sub-Saharan Africa has been the region most severely hit by the AIDS epidemic, accounting for about two of three estimated AIDS cases worldwide according to the World Health Organization (Lorch, 1993a). The economic and social costs of AIDS have been staggering, especially to some of the developing nations in Africa where AIDS has struck with devastating effects (Garrett, 1993b). In some countries in the region, one quarter to one third of adults in urban areas are believed to be infected with HIV (Shenon, 1992). By the mid-1990s, an estimated 20 million people in sub-Saharan Africa will be infected with HIV (Lorch, 1993b). In Kenya, 12 percent of young adults in the capital, Nairobi, are believed to be infected (Lorch, 1993b). By the year 2000, two million Kenyans are expected to be infected, or about one tenth of the total population. In Uganda, deaths from AIDS have touched virtually every family, killing mostly the young adults and family breadwinners and leaving other family members to care for the children the disease has orphaned.

The numbers of cases of HIV infection in Asia are skyrocketing (Taylor, 1993a). Asia now ranks as the continent with the second greatest number of cases of HIV infection, after Africa. As in Africa, most cases are spread by heterosexual sex (Taylor, 1993c). Prostitution is a major route of transmission in Asia, especially in large cities such as Bombay and Madras in India and Bangkok in Thailand, where some 30 to 40 percent of the prostitutes are believed to be infected. The World Health Organization estimates that about two million adults in South and Southeast Asia are infected with HIV. Other experts put the figure much higher, at 3.6 million cases, including 2 million in India alone—about twice as many cases as in the United States (Taylor, 1993a). By the end of the decade, the number of cases in Asia may rival or even surpass the number in Africa (Taylor, 1993a). The crisis is most severe in India and Thailand (Shenon, 1992).

Asian governments, like those in the West, have been slow to act to stem the epidemic (Shenon, 1993). In India, for example, the government has only recently begun to address the problem by beginning to screen blood supplies for HIV and launching a national HIV-education and

inclusive definition, which will make more people eligible for AIDS benefits, are intended to better accommodate women infected with HIV, who may develop gynecological conditions, such as persistent and recurrent vaginal yeast infections, that are not seen in men; IDUs; infected children; and unusual cases in which the traditional indicator diseases are not present. The expanded definition of AIDS led to an expected surge in the number of diagnosed cases reported in the first few months following the change in the diagnostic criteria, more than doubling the rate reported under the earlier criteria (Altman, 1993a).

One of the most baffling puzzles is why some people with HIV remain well for years, while others succumb in a relatively short time (Ezzell, 1993). Some people have had HIV for a dozen or more years without developing AIDS (Garrett, 1993d). What distinguishes a long-term survivor of HIV from a short-term survivor remains a mystery (Pfeiffer, 1992). Further study of the immune systems of long-term survivors may shed light on possible protective immunological mechanisms that could help others who are not so fortunate.

prevention campaign (Taylor, 1993a).

The AIDS epidemic in Latin America is well on its way toward surpassing that of the United States (Brooke, 1993). HIV is spreading rapidly through Latin America through heterosexual sex (Eckholm, 1993a). Brazil has about as many people infected with HIV, about one million, as the United States, although it has a population of 150 million as compared to 255 million in the United States. In Mexico, between 225,000 and five million people are believed by government officials to be infected, in a population numbering 85 million. In Haiti, which has the highest rate of HIV in Latin America, infection rates in the largest cities are believed to range between 8 and 10 percent of the population.

After much delay, governments in Latin America are now beginning to fight the epidemic. In Brazil, AIDS education has become part of the national curriculum. Yet Brazilian men, not unlike men elsewhere, are

reluctant to use condoms, in part because they dampen sexual sensations, but also because of their relatively high cost and poor quality. Cost is an especially important factor in Brazil's poorer communities, where condoms are priced out of reach of most people. Moreover, the quality of condoms on the market is poor and foreign companies have been charged with dumping defective or substandard condoms in the market. A more repressive attempt to contain the epidemic is found in Cuba, where HIV infected people are quarantined and where HIV testing for most people is mandatory. Such stiff measures, despite the costs to individual liberties, are credited with having reduced the spread of the AIDS epidemic. A Cuban official estimated that fewer than 1,000 people in the early 1990s were infected with HIV, from a total population of 10 million.

Although still minuscule by comparison with countries like the United States and some other

Asian countries, Japan too is experiencing a rapid rise in the number of AIDS cases (Sterngold, 1992). By 1992, some 274 people in Japan had died from AIDS, the majority of whom were foreigners. Most cases in Japan appear to have been transmitted via heterosexual intercourse involving prostitutes. The government, slow to recognize that HIV and AIDS were affecting its own citizens and not just foreigners, has begun to mount an AIDS prevention program focused on encouraging condom use and encouraging understanding of people infected with the virus. In 1992, a government ministry upheld a ban against oral contraceptives (see Chapter 12) by arguing that approving the pill would discourage condom use and lead to an AIDS epidemic.

TRANSMISSION

Learning Objective 6:
Identify the known routes of HIV transmission.

HIV can be transmitted by contaminated bodily fluids (blood, semen, or vaginal secretions), which enter the body as the result of vaginal, anal, or oral-genital intercourse with an infected partner, sharing a hypodermic needle with an infected person (as is common among IDUs), transfusion with contaminated blood, transplants of organs and tissues that have been infected with HIV, artificial insemination with infected semen, or being stuck by a needle used previously on an infected person (Glasner & Kaslow, 1990; Jones et al., 1992; Perry et al., 1989; Simonds et al., 1992; Spitzer & Weiner, 1989). HIV may enter the body through tiny cuts or sores in the mucosal lining of the vagina, rectum, and even the mouth. These cuts or sores may be so tiny that you may not be aware of them.

Though scientists suspect that transmission of HIV through deep kissing, prolonged kissing, or "French" kissing is theoretically possible, this mode of transmission is consid-

TABLE 17.1 HIV and AIDS: A world epidemic

Region	Infected with HIV			AIDS	
	All Adults '92 (est.)	Women '92 (est.)	All Adults '95 (proj.)	Adults '92 (est.)	Adults '95 (proj.)
North America	1,167	128.5	1,495	257.5	534.0
Western Europe	718	122.0	1,186	99.0	279.5
Australia/ Oceania	28	3.5	40	4.5	11.5
Latin America	995	199.0	1,407	173.0	417.5
Sub-Saharan Africa	7,803	3,901.5	11,449	1,367.0	3,277.5
Caribbean	310	124.0	474	43.0	121.0
Eastern Europe	27	2.5	44	2.5	9.5
Southeast Mediterranean	35	6.0	59	3.5	12.5
Northeast Asia	41	7.0	80	3.5	14.5
Southeast Asia	>675	>223.0	1,220	65.0	240.5
TOTAL	11,799	4,717.0	17,454	2,018.5	4,918.0

Source: Reprinted by permission of the publishers from *AIDS in the World* by Jonathan Mann, Daniel J.M. Tarantola, and Thomas W. Netter, Cambridge, MA: Harvard University Press. Copyright © 1992 by the President and Fellows of Harvard College.

Teaching Tip: Ask students to mention all the ways they have heard people say that HIV can be transmitted. As they do so, write these on the chalkboard. Then examine them one by one for accuracy. Cross out those that are not possible routes of transmission. When the exercise is complete, the verified routes of transmission should remain.

ered unlikely (CDC, 1992b). We have yet to find any confirmed cases of HIV transmission through kissing.

When a person shoots drugs, a small amount of their blood remains inside the needle and syringe. If the person is HIV-infected, the virus may be found in the blood remaining in the needle or syringe. When others use the same needle, they directly inject the infected blood into their bloodstreams. HIV may also be spread by sharing needles used for other purposes, such as injecting steroids, ear piercing, or tattooing. If you are interested in having your ears pierced or getting a tattoo, insist upon seeing a qualified person who uses either brand-new or properly sterilized equipment. Ask questions about the safety measures that are followed before undergoing any such procedure.

Sexual activities may become a means of transmission of HIV only if one of the partners is infected with the virus. *You cannot contract or transmit HIV via sexual activity if neither you nor your partner is infected, no matter what sexual activities you practice.* This is not to say that these activities are entirely free of risk. They may serve as a mode of entry for other STD-causing microorganisms, such as those that cause syphilis, gonorrhea, genital warts, or chlamydia. In addition, anal intercourse may cause injury to sensitive rectal tissue if it is performed too forcefully or without sufficient lubrication. Though it is important to separate fact from fiction regarding the means of transmission of HIV, we do not want to convey the impression that unprotected sexual activities are

AIDS Mom

safe from HIV transmission unless you know that your partner is infected with HIV. Rather, the reverse is true: *You should consider unprotected sex to be unsafe unless you know (not guess, but know!) that your partner is uninfected.*

HIV may also be transmitted from mother to fetus during pregnancy or from mother to child through childbirth or breast-feeding (Glasner & Kaslow, 1990). A recent twins study by James Goedert (1992) of the National Institutes of Health and his colleagues suggests that mother-to-fetus transmission is most likely to occur during the birth process.

Male-to-female transmission through vaginal intercourse is about twice as likely as female-to-male transmission (Allen & Setlow, 1991; deVincenzi et al., 1992; Rosenthal, 1990), partly because more of the virus is found in the ejaculate than in vaginal secretions. A man's ejaculate may also remain for many days in the vagina, providing greater opportunity for infection to occur. The risk of contracting HIV from a single unprotected episode of vaginal intercourse with an infected partner is estimated to be one in 500 for a woman and one in 700 for a man (Turner et al., 1989). Male-female or male-male anal intercourse is especially risky, particularly to the recipient, since it often tears or abrades rectal tissue, facilitating entry of the virus into the bloodstream.

Heterosexual transmission via sexual intercourse is the primary route of HIV infection in Africa, Latin America, and Asia (Altman, 1993e; Quinn, 1990). Worldwide, sexual intercourse between men and women accounts for 75 percent of cases of HIV infection (Novello, 1991). In the United States, heterosexual transmission of HIV accounts for nearly 10 percent of AIDS cases and has become the fastest-growing exposure category, with the numbers of new cases of AIDS in men and women attributable to heterosexual contact more than doubling between 1989 and 1992 (Haverkos, 1993). Though many cases of heterosexual transmission occur within the community of IDUs and their sex partners (Kolata, 1991d), one of two cases of heterosexual transmission in 1993 occurred among people whose partners had risk factors that were either unreported or unknown ("Heterosexual AIDS is no myth," 1994). This raises the concern that HIV infection and the subsequent development of AIDS may be spreading more generally into the population at large through heterosexual activity, as it has in other parts of the world.

In the early years of the AIDS epidemic, HIV spread rapidly among hemophiliacs who had unknowingly been transfused with contaminated blood. Over half of the United States' hemophiliacs were unknowingly infected with HIV in the early 1980s (Fogle, 1991a). In 1985, the test to detect HIV antibodies (revealing the presence of HIV infection) became available, and blood banks began universal screening of donor blood. Tennis great Arthur Ashe, who died of complications from AIDS in 1993, believed that he had contracted HIV during a blood transfusion he received before the blood supply began to be screened for HIV (Altman, 1992b). No hemophiliac in the United States is known to have contracted HIV from a blood transfusion since 1987 (Fogle, 1991a). Blood screening is not yet foolproof, however. Though transmission of HIV in the general population from blood transfusions has become quite rare since routine screening of blood supplies began, a remote possibility of infection continues to exist, with estimates indicating a one in 75,000 chance of contracting the infection during a single transfusion (Altman, 1992b).

HIV may also be spread by donor semen, such as that used in artificial insemination. Surprisingly—no, shockingly!—no federal regulations require sperm banks, which collect and house semen, to test donor semen for HIV and other STDs. Nor is such testing mandated by most states. Though many sperm banks do follow guidelines for STD testing, some apparently do not (Meyer, 1994). Cases have been reported on women who have become infected with hepatitis B, gonorrhea, trichomoniasis ("trich"), chlamydia, and even HIV via insemination with donor semen (Meyer, 1994).

FACTORS AFFECTING THE RISK OF SEXUAL TRANSMISSION

Learning Objective 7:
Identify the factors affecting the risk of sexual transmission of HIV.

Some people are apparently more vulnerable to infection by HIV than others. As a general rule, the probability of sexual transmission rises with the number of coital contacts with an infected partner. Yet there is no predictable connection between the number of episodes of unprotected sex with an infected person and the probability of transmission

(Rosenthal, 1990). Some people seem more likely to communicate the virus, and others seem to be especially vulnerable to contracting it. Why, for instance, are some people infected by one sexual contact with an infected partner, whereas others are not infected during months or years of unprotected coitus (Rosenthal, 1990)?

Some clues have begun to emerge, based on studies in the United States, Europe, and Africa. For one thing, a history of STDs may heighten the risk of infection by HIV. STDs such as genital warts, gonorrhea, trichomoniasis, and chlamydia inflame the genital region, which may heighten the risk of sexual transmission of other STDs. STDs that produce genital ulcers, like syphilis and genital herpes, may heighten vulnerability to HIV infection by allowing the virus to enter the circulatory system through the ulcers (Quinn, 1990).

The probability of transmission is also affected by the type of sexual activity, the amount of HIV in the semen, and circumcision (Rosenthal, 1990). Anal intercourse, for example, is a sexual activity that provides a convenient port of entry for HIV because it often leads to tearing or abrading of the rectal lining. The amount of virus in semen also varies through the course of HIV disease, reaching peaks shortly after initial infection and when full-blown AIDS develops. Circumcised men may have a lower risk of infection because they are less likely to have genital ulcers. Moreover, HIV cannot accumulate under the folds of the foreskin in men who have been circumcised (Holmes, 1988; Simonsen et al., 1988). Cells in the foreskin may be particularly vulnerable to HIV infection as well (Touchette, 1991). Still, more research is necessary to confirm links between circumcision and HIV infection.

Researchers report that alcohol consumption either before, during, or shortly after exposure to HIV can increase the risk of infection (AIDS Update, 1993; Bagasra et al., 1993). Alcohol consumption can also make people more likely to engage in risky sexual practices than if they were cold sober. Researchers also suspect that regular consumption of alcohol may hasten the progression to AIDS among people infected with HIV (Bagasra et al., 1993).

A European study of 563 couples in which one of the partners in each couple was HIV-infected showed that two factors increasing the risk of transmission from the infected female partner to the male partner were unprotected sexual contact during menses and an advanced stage of HIV infection in the female partner (deVincenzi et al., 1992). Among couples in which both of these risk factors were present, 57 percent of the men became infected, as opposed to 1 percent of couples who possessed neither of these risk factors. Factors that increased the likelihood of HIV-infected men transmitting the virus to their female partners were anal intercourse, an advanced stage of HIV infection in the male, and female partners who were older than 45. Among couples with at least two of these risk factors, 54 percent of the women become infected, as compared with 10 percent of the women in couples in which none were present.

A greater risk of transmission from partners in the advanced stage of HIV infection may be due to an increased quantity of viral particles in genital secretions occurring during this stage. Older women may be at increased risk because the genital mucosa becomes more fragile as the woman ages. Sex during menses may increase the likelihood of infection because of a greater concentration of viral particles in the vagina during menstruation. Whatever the particular risk factors, no cases of transmission were reported among partners who regularly used condoms.

HOW HIV IS NOT TRANSMITTED

There is much misinformation about the transmission of HIV. Let us consider some of the ways in which HIV is not transmitted:

1. *HIV is not transmitted from donating blood.* AIDS cannot be contracted by donating blood because needles are discarded after a single use. Unfortunately, many people have avoided donating blood because of unfounded fears of HIV transmission.

TRUTH OR FICTION?
R E V I S I T E D

You can be infected by HIV by donating blood. *You cannot, in fact, be infected by HIV by donating blood because the needles are sterile and are used only once.* •

2. *HIV is not transmitted through casual, everyday contact.* There is no evidence of transmission of HIV through various kinds of casual contact. These include hugging someone, shaking hands, and bumping into strangers on buses and trains; handling money, doorknobs, or other objects that had been touched by infected people; sharing drinking fountains, public telephones, public toilets, or swimming pools; or by trying on clothing that had been worn by an infected person (Gordon & Snyder, 1989; Hatcher et al., 1990). Nor is HIV known to be transmitted by contact with urine, feces, sputum, sweat, tears, or nasal secretions, unless blood is clearly visible in these fluids (Hatcher et al., 1990). (Still, should you need to clean up someone's urine, feces, nasal secretions, and especially blood, it would be wise to use rubber gloves and wash your hands thoroughly immediately afterwards.)

3. *HIV is not transmitted by insect bites.* HIV is not transmitted by mosquito bites or from bites by other insects such as bedbugs, lice, or flies (CDC, 1992b). Nor can you get HIV from contact with animals.

4. *HIV is not transmitted by airborne germs or contact with contaminated food.* People do not contract HIV from contact with airborne germs, as by sneezing or coughing, or by contact with contaminated food or eating food prepared by a person infected with HIV (CDC, 1992b; Cochran & Mays, 1989). (However, other disease-causing organisms, such as the virus that causes hepatitis A, may be transmitted by contact with contaminated food.)

5. *HIV is not transmitted through sharing work or home environments.* HIV has not been shown to be transmitted from infected people to family members or others they live with through any form of casual contact, such as hugging or touching, or through sharing bathrooms, food, or eating utensils, so long as there is no exchange of blood or genital secretions (CDC, 1992b; Hatcher et al., 1990; Holmberg & Curran, 1989). There are some isolated reports of nonsexual transmission of HIV between two children living together in the same household, but investigators suspect that the route of transmission in these rare cases involved blood contact, such as the sharing of razor blades in one of the two reported cases thus far, and possibly sharing a toothbrush in the other (the infected child in this case had bleeding gums) ("AIDS without needles or sex," 1993). No cases of HIV transmission have been documented based on non-sexual contact in schools or in the workplace (Holmberg & Curran, 1990).

Despite the fact that HIV is not transmitted by casual contact, many people keep a distance from people with HIV or AIDS (Mooney et al., 1992). Researchers have found that keeping a distance can involve behaviors such as not talking to someone with AIDS at a party or avoiding a party at which people with AIDS are present (Poling et al., 1990), not taking a course taught by a professor with AIDS (Pryor et al., 1989), and establishing a greater physical distance between oneself and someone with AIDS with whom one is paired in a research laboratory (Mooney et al., 1992). Even physicians and other health care providers are often unwilling to have contact with people with HIV and AIDS (Trinkaus & Chow, 1990) or even to work on an AIDS unit (Dworkin et al., 1991). A recent Canadian study showed that people with more accurate knowledge of AIDS, and those who are more tolerant of homosexuality, are generally more willing to accept a worker who has AIDS (Summers, 1991).

TRANSMISSION VIA MEDICAL OR DENTAL TREATMENT

Though it is theoretically possible for blood to be transferred from health providers to patients, there is only one known case of a health care worker transmitting HIV to a patient or patients during treatment (Taylor, 1993b). The case involved an HIV-infected dentist in Florida who apparently infected six of his patients during dental treatment, including a young woman, Kimberly Bergalis, whose poignant testimony before Congress just before her death in 1991 came to symbolize the debate as to whether or not health providers should be tested for HIV (Lambert, 1991).

Infection can work in the opposite direction as well. For example, health providers risk infection from accidental needle sticks from syringes used on infected patients.

Kimberly Bergalis. Shown here testifying before Congress shortly before her death, Kimberly Bergalis became a public symbol of the public debate over the testing of health care providers for HIV infection.

Although the risks of infection are estimated to be less than half of 1 percent per accident (Kantrowitz, 1991b), the CDC reports that at least 32 people nationwide had become infected with HIV by 1992 on the basis of on-the-job accidents, and some 69 others may possibly have been infected on the job ("32 People got H.I.V. on the job, U.S. says," 1992). Most of these cases involved lab technicians and nurses who accidentally pricked themselves with a needle or were cut by a scalpel that was used previously on an HIV-infected patient. Clearly, health providers need to exercise extra caution to avoid contact with infected blood.

WOMEN AND AIDS

Lily was not supposed to get AIDS. She was heiress to a cosmetics fortune. She had received her bachelor's degree from Wellesley and had been enrolled in a graduate program in art history when she came down with intractable flulike symptoms and was eventually diagnosed as having AIDS.

"No one believed it," she said. "I was never a male homosexual in San Francisco. I never shot up crack in the alleys of The Bronx. My boyfriends didn't shoot up either. There was just Matthew..." Now Lily was 24. At 17, in her senior year in high school, she had had a brief affair with Matthew. Later she learned that Matthew was bisexual. Five years ago, Matthew died from AIDS.

"I haven't exactly been a whore," Lily said ironically. "You can count my boyfriends on the fingers of one hand. None of them caught it from me; I guess I was just lucky." Her face twisted in anger. "You may think this is awful," she said, "but there are times when I wish Jerry and Russ had gotten it from me. Why should they get off?"

Lily's family was fully supportive, emotionally and, of course, financially. Lily had been to fine clinics. Physicians from Europe had been brought in. She was on a regimen of three medicines: two antiviral drugs, which singly and in combination had shown some ability to slow the progress of AIDS, and an antibiotic intended to prevent bacterial infections from taking hold. She took some vitamins—not megavitamin therapy. She exercised almost daily when she felt up to it, and she was doing reasonably well. In fact, there were times when she thought she might get over her illness.

"Sometimes I find myself thinking about children or grandchildren. Or sometimes I find myself looking at all these old pictures [of grandparents and other relatives] and thinking that I'll have silver in my hair, too. Sometimes I really think this is the day the doctors will call me about the new wonder drug that's been discovered in France or Germany."

"I want to tell you about Russ," she said once. "After we found out about me, he went for testing, and he was clear [of antibodies indicative of infection by the AIDS virus]. He stayed with me, you know. When I wanted to do it, we used condoms. A couple of months later, he went for a second test and he was still clear. Then maybe he had second thoughts, because he became impotent—with me. We'd try, but he couldn't do anything. Still he stayed with me, but I felt us drifting apart. After a while, he was just doing the right thing by staying with me, and I'll be damned if anyone is going to be with me because he's doing the right thing."

Lily looked the [interviewer] directly in the eye. "What sane man wants to play Russian roulette with AIDS for the sake of looking like a caring person? And I'll tell you why I eventually sent him away," she added, tears welling, "the one thing I've learned is that you die alone. I don't even feel that close to my parents anymore. Everyone loves you and wishes they could trade places with you, but they can't. You're suddenly older than everyone around you and you're going to go alone. I can't tell you how many times I thought about killing myself, just so that I could be the one who determines exactly where and when I die—how I would be dressed and how I would feel on the final day." Lily died in 1992.

(Adapted from Rathus & Nevid, 1992, pp. 485–486)

Not so long ago, there were a number of erroneous assumptions about HIV and AIDS—assumptions that have had a disproportionately negative impact on women. They included the notions that women were at low risk of HIV infection and that it was difficult to be infected via heterosexual intercourse. It was also assumed that HIV infection

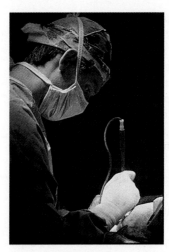

Doctors and AIDS. Despite the controversy concerning the transmission of HIV from infected health care workers to their patients, the dentist who treated Kimberly Bergalis is the only case of a health care worker whom health authorities believe transmitted HIV to a patient or patients during treatment. Still, it is important for health care workers to follow accepted safety protocols when performing invasive procedures such as surgery to prevent transmission of infectious agents.

Learning Objective 9:
Summarize the information about women and AIDS in the United States and worldwide, including the increasing incidence, the risk of infection from heterosexual intercourse with an HIV-positive partner, the course of AIDS in women, and the agonizing choices HIV-positive women must make about motherhood.

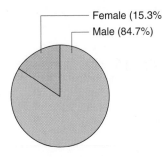

FIGURE 17.5 AIDS Cases by Gender. Women now account for about one in seven AIDS cases.

Female (15.3%
Male (84.7%)

and AIDS would follow the same course in men and women—a belief that may be connected with delayed diagnosis and intervention with women.

ARE WOMEN AT RISK OF AIDS?   Although AIDS was once considered a syndrome that afflicted only gay men, AIDS cases are rising faster among women than among men. Women now account for 15 percent of AIDS cases in the United States (see Figure 17.5). The numbers of reported AIDS cases among women may represent the tip of the iceberg, because symptoms may not develop for years after infection with HIV (Ellerbrock et al., 1991). A leading researcher on AIDS, Alexandra Levine of the University of Southern California Medical Center, notes that:

> We have not begun to see what's going to happen with women. We are now with women at the same situation we were for gay men in 1983 or 1984. It can happen to you or to me or to any of us. This is a sexually transmitted disease. Period. You must think of yourself as potentially at risk. It's the only way we're going to get on top of this epidemic.
>
> (Cited in Parsons, 1991, A14)

AIDS is increasing at a faster rate in the United States among women than among men, with the great majority of cases in women—85 percent—occurring among women of childbearing age. In 1992 alone, the number of AIDS cases in the United States among women jumped nearly 10 percent, as compared to a 2.5 percent increase in men (Altman, 1993i; Mays, 1993). Approximately one in four women with AIDS is 20 to 29 years of age, which indicates that many of them were infected as teenagers (CDC, 1991a). The number of deaths from AIDS is also rising rapidly among women. By 1993, AIDS had become the fourth leading killer of women in the 25 to 44 age range.

Women presently account for about one in three cases of AIDS worldwide. If present trends continue, most new cases of HIV worldwide by the year 2000 will be among women (Altman, 1992b). In some countries, women are already surpassing men in the proportions of new cases. In Uganda, for example, the rate of HIV infection among young women is six times greater than it is among young men (Lorch, 1993b).

Only a small proportion of AIDS patients are women. *Not so. Women now account for nearly one third of AIDS cases worldwide, and the proportion of women among AIDS cases in the United States, now at 15 percent, is on the rise.* •

Teaching Tip: Too often we blame those who acquire AIDS and criticize them for "irresponsible" behavior. Emphasize the real difficulties experienced by poor women who may try to behave responsibly: the cost of condoms and spermicides; transportation difficulties in getting to a clinic; clinic hours that coincide with work hours; lack of access to child care while visiting a clinic; and resistance of male partners to condom use.

Among women in our society, the risks of HIV infection and deaths from AIDS fall most heavily on the least advantaged: poor women, mostly African American or Hispanic who live in depressed urban areas (Chu et al., 1990; Mays & Cochran, 1988). Still, as the case of Lily indicates, HIV infection and AIDS cut across all racial, social, and economic boundaries. Overall, African-American and Hispanic women account for about three of four cases of women with AIDS in the United States, although they constitute only 19 percent of the female population (CDC, 1991a; Ellerbrock et al., 1991; "Toll of American AIDS orphans put at 80,000 by end of decade," 1992).

Though AIDS prevention programs have focused on increasing condom use among sexually active people, health experts recognize that many have difficulty exerting control over use of condoms by their sexual partners (Weinstock et al., 1993). Whereas the latex condoms worn by men are effective barriers to HIV, the one barrier method available to women, the female condom, has yet to be demonstrated to offer protection against HIV and other STDs. Sexual counseling programs stress that men need to take more responsibility for wearing condoms and that both partners should learn how to talk about HIV prevention.

IS IT DIFFICULT TO BE INFECTED WITH HIV VIA HETEROSEXUAL INTERCOURSE?   It was once thought unlikely that HIV could be transmitted through heterosexual intercourse. We now know that heterosexual intercourse accounts for the majority, about 75 percent, of cases of HIV transmission worldwide, and that women stand about twice the risk of infection from engaging in coitus with an infected partner than do men.

A WORLD OF DIVERSITY

Cultural Traditions and the Spread of AIDS in Sub-Saharan Africa

The toll from AIDS in sub-Saharan Africa steadily mounts (see Table 17.2), and many wives have acquired HIV from husbands who engage in extramarital relationships with infected partners (Perlez, 1991). In many African tribal cultures, husbands are permitted to have many sex partners, including secondary wives, mistresses, and concubines, and their extramarital activities are not judged in the same way that they would be in our society. Their wives, however, as in many patriarchal societies, are expected to remain faithful to their husbands. As a result, the wives are vulnerable to HIV infection contracted by their husbands from other sex partners. Charles B. Rwabukwali of Makerere University in Kampala, Uganda, spoke of the threat posed by this sexual double standard:

> This pattern of behavior is creating the greatest havoc in the spread of the disease because if a man is allowed to sleep around, he brings the disease home. It means your culture can put you at the greatest risk in a most unconscious way.

(Perlez, 1991, p. A2)

Moreover, when women in these male-dominated cultures become infected with HIV, their husbands often leave them. Because of their fear of abandonment, women often hide their HIV status from their husbands. One Ugandan woman told an interviewer, "Some women know they are [HIV] positive but don't say because they know the men will run away" (Perlez, 1991, p. A2). Fearful of AIDS, some African wives have summoned the courage to confront their husbands by refusing to engage in sexual activity with them unless they are tested, and by requiring them to use condoms if they are infected with HIV. Cultural traditions that make it more acceptable, even expected, for husbands to take other sex partners may be highly resistant to change, however.

TABLE 17.2 Comparison of the prevalences of HIV infection among population subgroups in selected African countries (percents)

Country and Year	Tested Group	HIV Prevalence (%)
Congo (1985)	Pregnant women	11.0
	Sterility problems patients	16.6
Ghana (1987)	Blood donors and patients	4.7
	Prostitutes	25.2
Ivory Coast (1987)	Pregnant women	2.6
	Prostitutes	17.0
Kenya (1985)	Pregnant women	2.0
	STD clinic patients	7.5
	Prostitutes	51.0
Rwanda (1987)	Married blood donors	6.5
	Single blood donors	10.1
Tanzania (1986)	Pregnant women	3.6
	Barmaids	28.8
Uganda (1986)	Blood donors	10.8
	Pregnant women	13.0
	Prostitutes	80.0
Zaire (1986)	Pregnant women	5.6
	Prostitutes	27.0
Zambia (1985)	Male blood donors and hospital workers	17.2
	Male STD clinic patients	45.4

Source: Quinn, T. C. (1990). Unique aspects of human immunodeficiency virus and related viruses in developing countries. In K. K. Holmes et al. (Eds.), *Sexually Transmitted Diseases* (2nd ed.) (pp. 355–369). New York: McGraw-Hill. Reprinted with permission.

AIDS in Africa. In Kenya about one in eight young adults in the capital, Nairobi, is believed to be infected with HIV.

In the early years of the epidemic, most women in the United States with AIDS had contracted the disease by intravenous drug use. By 1992, heterosexual sex had surpassed intravenous drug use as the primary means of transmission of HIV in women (Altman, 1993h; CDC, 1993f).

Most women who contract HIV live in large metropolitan areas (73%), often in impoverished inner cities where there is widespread drug use. Like syphilis, HIV infection appears higher among women who use cocaine, perhaps because they often engage in high-risk sexual behaviors, such as prostitution or unprotected intercourse with IDUs (Minkoff et al., 1990).

Yet, many women remain unaware that they are at risk of contracting AIDS (CDC, 1991a). Many HIV-infected women go undiagnosed until they develop AIDS or give birth to an HIV-infected baby (CDC, 1991a). Some women feel safe because they are not members of an identified high-risk group. Lily did not belong to any of the groups at high risk, however.

DO HIV INFECTION AND AIDS FOLLOW THE SAME COURSE IN MEN AND WOMEN? Many questions remain about how HIV infection and AIDS affect women. Much of our knowledge about the course of the illness derives from studies of HIV infection and AIDS in homosexual men, and it is not known whether they follow the same course in women. Diagnosis and intervention may be delayed in women because of symptoms that go unrecognized or are misdiagnosed (Kent, 1991; Stephens, 1991b). Moreover, most of the drug trials have been conducted on men, not on women or children, so questions remain about the effectiveness of AIDS drugs on women and children.

We do know that women die faster from AIDS than men do (Cohen, 1990). Women survive an average of only 7 months, whereas men survive for an average of 2 years. Researchers suspect that delayed intervention and treatment of women with AIDS may play a role in this gender difference (Kent, 1991). The fact that AIDS afflicts poor women disproportionately may also in part explain delays in receiving appropriate medical care since disadvantaged women generally have poorer access to medical care (Stephens, 1991b).

DIAGNOSIS OF HIV INFECTION AND AIDS

Seropositive
Having a pathogen or antibodies to that pathogen in the bloodstream

Seronegative
Lacking a pathogen or antibodies to that pathogen in the bloodstream.

The most widely used test for HIV infection is the enzyme-linked immunosorbent assay (ELISA, for short). ELISA does not directly detect HIV in the circulatory system. Instead, it reveals HIV antibodies. People may show an antibody response to HIV long before they develop symptoms of infection (Eckholm, 1991; Jacobsen et al., 1990). A positive (**seropositive**) test result means that antibodies were found, and usually[3] means that the person has HIV in the bloodstream. A negative (**seronegative**) outcome means that antibodies to HIV were not detected (Jacobsen et al., 1990; Reinisch, 1990).

HIV infection is diagnosed by examination of the virus in the bloodstream. Actually, HIV infection is generally diagnosed by examination of HIV antibodies in the bloodstream. •

When people receive positive results on the enzyme-linked immunosorbent assay, the Western blot test can be performed to confirm the findings (Reinisch, 1990). The Western blot test detects a particular pattern of protein bands that are linked to the virus. It may take many months for people who have been exposed to HIV to develop antibodies. For this reason, repeated tests over a six-month or even longer period of time from the date of possible exposure may be in order. A seropositive test result means that HIV antibodies have been found, but does not indicate when, or even if, an individual will develop a full-blown case of AIDS.

[3]But not always! Fetuses, for example, may receive antibodies from infected mothers, but not the virus itself. Some fetuses, however, become infected with the virus.

ISSUES CONCERNING TESTING FOR HIV INFECTION

Activity: *Should You and Your Partner Be Tested for HIV?* This IM exercise encourages students to think about several important factors to consider when deciding whether to be tested for HIV.

It might come as a surprise that although testing for HIV infection is widely available, those at high risk, or those who suspect that they might "test positive," do not necessarily seek information that will confirm or deny their concerns. Why would someone consciously avoid information that might ultimately assist in prolonging life? Clearly, AIDS testing is not a cut-and-dried matter, as suggested by the following comments:

> PHIL, 20: The only change I've made as a result of the AIDS threat is to use condoms as protection. But when I find a girlfriend who is really special, I plan to be tested for AIDS. Hopefully this would alleviate any fears she might have, and it would show her how much I really care.

> MELANIE, 18: How to bring up AIDS with someone you'd like to sleep with confuses me. I mean, what do you say? "Gee, honey, I love you and want to have sex with you, but can you please take an AIDS test today and then lock yourself up for six months so I'm sure you won't sleep with anyone else and then take the test again? Then maybe I'll sleep with you."

> DON, 25: I "came out" just as AIDS hit the media in metro-Boston as the Gay Plague. During the first year or so I did very little to practice safe sex. Now, I will not do anything that is against the safe-sex guidelines. I often fear the days I did not follow these guidelines. I often think of being tested, although I am scared. I would not be able to have sexual relations or even date should I test positive, because I am too moral to pretend that nothing is wrong, and too uncomfortable coming forward with this information to my partners. Sometimes I think it is best not to know and to always behave responsibly; other times I think I should know so that I can make plans for my life and if I test negative, seek a long-term relationship "armed" with this information.

> (Copyright © 1991 by McIntyre, Formichella, Osterhout, and Gresh by arrangement with AVON Books, pp. 145–147)

Concerns and motivations regarding HIV testing can be complex and contradictory. Although all too many of us engage in sexual practices without regard for potential risk, even in the age of AIDS, some people have become more cautious about their sexual intimacies. This vigilance is evident in a broad spectrum of response. People may feel that they need to know more about one another before they proceed with a sexual relationship. Some, however, will not even consider such a relationship in the absence of testing that finds their prospective partner to be clear of HIV infection. Others might even take the initiative to have themselves tested, as a way of assuring a partner that they themselves are safe, or, conversely, to alert their partners that they are indeed infected with HIV. As logical as these measures may seem when weighed against the potential risks, concerned partners may foresee emotional ramifications to such a direct approach. How can one broach such a subject at all? How can a personal relationship get off the

Caring for AIDS Patients. AIDS patients need love and support, but are often rejected by others, even by family members, who fear contracting the disease by touching or hugging them. The AIDS virus can be transmitted through intimate sexual contact or exchange of blood, but it is not contracted by hugging or touching an infected person, or by being in the same room.

Discussion Question: What examples of discrimination against those who are HIV-positive or who have AIDS have you heard about? Consider the workplace, housing, school attendance, insurance company policies, etc. Why do you think people discriminate?

ground with concerns and suspicions at its very start? How do you suggest to someone with whom you would like a sexual relationship that that person be tested for HIV?

And what about obligation? Many believe that people at risk of HIV infection who have not taken steps to determine their HIV status before entering sexual relationships have acted immorally, irresponsibly, and even criminally. A prospective partner has the right, it is argued, to have such information. Its disclosure can lead to appropriate precautions including safer sex practices or the avoidance of needle sharing.

Once again, however, the issues become muddied. Some who are opposed to widespread testing argue that testing is unnecessary and alarmist for people who do not belong to a group that has been hard hit by the epidemic. Such opponents further point out that a person who has been found to be HIV positive is, in effect, "branded," and can soon fall victim to harsh discrimination regarding employment, as represented in the recent film *Philadelphia,* as well as in housing, or medical and life insurance. Moreover, they argue that safe sex guidelines should be practiced as a matter of course in this age of AIDS, regardless of HIV status. Finally, they voice the concern of many that knowledge that one carries HIV antibodies, or has AIDS, can be emotionally devastating and that people may be ill prepared to deal with the enormous stress experienced in the wake of this realization. On the other hand, what they don't know may hurt them, because early detection and intervention may prolong health in infected people.

Discussion Question: How many of you believe that all health care workers should be tested for HIV and be required to inform patients of their HIV status? Health care workers are much more likely to be infected by patients than patients are to be infected by health care workers. Should patients be required to be tested and to inform health care workers of their HIV status before receiving health care? Consider the impact of such a policy on emergency health care services.

DISCLOSURE OF THE IDENTITIES OF HIV-INFECTED HEALTH CARE PROVIDERS

In the wake of the Kimberly Bergalis case, pressure mounted to require mandatory testing of all health care workers. Although Bergalis's death was tragic, health officials believe that the Florida case was an anomaly. No other cases of health care providers transmitting the virus to their patients through medical or dental treatment have been uncovered among more than 20,000 patients who were treated by infected health care providers (CDC, 1993h; Rogers et al., 1993; von Reyn et al., 1993).

Controversy also continues to swirl around the issue of whether health care workers infected with HIV should be prohibited from performing certain procedures, such as surgery. Those favoring restrictions fear that patients might become infected if droplets of blood from tiny cuts in the infected health care worker's skin should enter the patient's bloodstream. Opponents argue that procedures normally followed by health workers to prevent the spread of infection, such as the wearing of gloves and masks, provide sufficient protection for patients. The issue continues to be debated at the state and national levels.

Many health officials argue that regulations requiring massive testings of health care workers are unnecessary and may unfairly affect the careers of health care workers infected with the virus, as well as waste millions of dollars that might otherwise be spent on combating or preventing AIDS (Lambert, 1991). Still, a July 1991 *Newsweek* poll found that more than 90 percent of U.S. residents believe that health care workers who are infected by HIV should be required to inform their patients of the infection.

PARTNER NOTIFICATION The confidentiality of HIV test results is also at issue. Some 15 states now require that doctors, hospitals, and clinics that test for HIV antibodies report the names of people who show positive test results (King, 1991). Reporting may help state officials trace the sexual and needle-sharing contacts of infected people to alert them to the possibility of exposure to the virus.

Through **provider referral** (that is, *health care provider referral,* formerly known as *contact tracing*), public health officials and private health care providers attempt to trace and notify the sex partners of people infected with disease-causing pathogens. Provider referral has apparently reduced the numbers of cases of syphilis and gonorrhea that might otherwise have been expected in the United States (Landis et al., 1992). Yet the mandatory reporting of positive HIV test results could discourage people from coming forward to be tested, especially people in certain high-risk groups such as IDUs who are reluctant to reveal their identities. Some states, like California and New Jersey, have voluntary provider referral. In New Jersey, people can be tested anonymously but are encouraged to have their names sent to the statewide AIDS registry if they test positive for HIV (King, 1991).

Provider referral *(health care provider referral).* Efforts of public health officials and private health care providers to trace and notify the sex (and needle-sharing) partners of people who are infected with disease-causing pathogens. Formerly known as *contact tracing.*

TREATMENT OF HIV INFECTION AND AIDS

Learning Objective 11:
Discuss the current status of treatments for HIV infection and AIDS.

There is neither a cure for HIV infection or AIDS, nor a safe and effective vaccine. The prospects for a cure at this time are grim. On the other hand, a growing number of researchers believe that a vaccine will eventually be developed (American Medical Association, 1991). By 1993, at least 16 experimental AIDS vaccines were being tested on uninfected people, and others were in the stage of animal experimentation (Altman, 1993a). With the number of studies required before a vaccine can be brought to market, none were expected to be available until sometime during the next century. Several vaccines have proved somewhat effective in animal trials (e.g., Hu, 1992). Yet AIDS experts caution that the development of an ideal vaccine against AIDS—one that would be safe, inexpensive, and render lifetime protection against all strains of the disease with a single dose—is perhaps decades away at the earliest (Altman, 1993b).

The mutability of HIV has thus far stymied efforts to find a cure or an effective vaccine. HIV can mutate into forms that are resistant to particular antiviral drugs or vaccines (Cohen, 1993c). The genes making up HIV mutate a million times more rapidly than human genes, leading scientists on wild goose chases as they try to eradicate a killer that keeps changing its form so often (Cowley, 1993). A vaccine that might protect against one strain, or a drug that could render a death blow, may hold no value against another (Altman, 1993j). Consequently, it may be unlikely that any one vaccine will provide a full range of protection against the virus (Cohen, 1993a). Moreover, whenever the body's own immune system or a drug may be initially successful in attacking a particular HIV variant, a mutated form capable of resisting the attack arises and takes its place. Consequently, drugs like AZT, the most widely used HIV/AIDS drug, may ward off the progression of the disease for a time but eventually lose their effectiveness. AZT (*zidovudine*) appears to have only a limited benefit for only a limited period of time (Altman, 1993d; Bartlett, 1993).

A sense of gloom was cast over the fight against AIDS in 1993 when results were reported of a large-scale European study involving the use of AZT in the early asymptomatic stage of HIV infection. The European study, called the Concorde study, which like the airplane of the same name represented an Anglo-French cooperative effort, compared AZT with a placebo over a period of three years in 1,749 symptom-free, HIV-infected people (Aboulker & Swart, 1993). AZT did not effect either the rate of progression to full-blown AIDS or the three-year survival rate. However, an Australian-European study that was reported at about the same time did show some benefits of AZT in delaying the progression of HIV infection from the nonsymptomatic to the symptomatic state (Cooper et al., 1993).

In light of the negative findings reported by the European Concorde study, an expert panel convened by the National Institutes of Health in 1993 concluded that AZT treatment in the early stages of HIV infection should no longer be necessarily recommended as a course of treatment (Altman, 1993e). The panel recommended that physicians and their patients should confer on the need for AZT in the early stages of the infection (Altman, 1993b). The value of AZT in treating people diagnosed with AIDS also continues to be debated.

AZT may produce serious side effects, such as suppression of bone marrow function, which leads to anemia and lowers the white blood count, further reducing the body's ability to combat infections (Yarchoan et al., 1988). Other side effects that are connected with administration of AZT to HIV-infected people who have not developed AIDS include nausea, vomiting, diarrhea, skin rash, and lowering of the number of leukocytes in the bloodstream (Hamilton et al., 1992). Lower-dose formulas of the drug reduce the risk of side effects, however (Fischl et al., 1990).

Scientists are hopeful that a combination of new or current drugs may be found that is effective where single drugs fail (Bartlett, 1993). The use of combination drug treatment is based on the hope that HIV will not be able to mutate quickly enough to develop resistance to a multidrug combination (Cohen, 1993c). So far, though, no combination drug approach has been shown to be effective. A more complicated approach may be needed to combat HIV—one that involves tailoring treatment to the particular strain of the virus, the patient's genetic type, and the particular ways in which the immune system responds to the infection (Garrett, 1993b). A more fine-tuned approach may yield better

Notes: On June 27, 1994 the U.S. Food and Drug Administration approved the use of d4T, one of four drugs now approved for the treatment of HIV and AIDS. It will be prescribed for HIV-infected adult patients who have shown no benefit from or have become intolerant of the other anti-viral drugs. (AIDS anti-viral drug wins FDA approval. *Des Moines Register,* 28 June 1994, 3A.)

results than a blunter approach in which virtually all patients are treated with the same drug or combination of drugs. But unless and until more effective drugs are found, prevention remains the best hope, if not the only hope, of stemming the epidemic.

More promising results are reported in treating some of the opportunistic infections, such as PCP, that take advantage of the AIDS patient's weakened immune system (Altman, 1993a). Shuji Nakamura (1992) of the University of Southern California has also reported some success in stopping the growth of Kaposi's sarcoma in laboratory mice.

Symptom-free carriers of HIV may also be able to prolong health by taking good care of themselves, getting enough sleep, avoiding unnecessary stress, and eating a balanced diet (Antoni et al., 1990, 1991).

With few if any victories to report in the war against AIDS, one genuine breakthrough occurred when researchers found that AZT administered to HIV-infected pregnant women reduced the rate of HIV infection in their newborns by about two thirds (Cowley, 1994). Scientists had suspected that AZT might help prevent AIDS in children of infected mothers by reducing the amount of the virus in the mother's bloodstream. The research focused on 477 pregnant women, all of whom were infected with HIV but were still healthy, in the United States and France. Half took AZT during pregnancy and through labor and delivery, while the other half were given a placebo (a chemically inert pill). After birth, the babies were continued on the treatment the mothers had received for a six-week period. Only 8 percent of the babies born to the AZT-treated women became infected with HIV, as compared to 25 percent of the babies born to women in the placebo group. Mild anemia was the only apparent side effect in the children. These striking results offer the best hope yet that many if not most cases of AIDS in children can be prevented by the use of already available drugs.

PSYCHOLOGICAL ADJUSTMENT OF PERSONS WITH HIV INFECTIONS AND AIDS

Learning Objective 12: Discuss the psychological problems experienced by people who are HIV-positive or have AIDS.

The difficulty of living with HIV and AIDS, their symptoms and suffering, is often compounded by psychological problems. Feelings of uncertainty and thoughts of death are common reactions to being told that one is HIV+ (McCann, 1992). Feelings of hopelessness and anger, guilt about life choices or reckless acts that led to the disease, even suicidal thoughts and feelings like those experienced by Lily, are not uncommon among

AIDS Support Group. In AIDS support groups, people with AIDS receive emotional support and assistance in coping with the devastating effects of the disease.

infected persons. The stress experienced by people with HIV can be overwhelming, and stress may affect the course of the disease by further suppressing the immune system (Goodkin et al., 1992; Kiecolt-Glaser & Glaser, 1988). Not surprisingly, depression in gay men with HIV is higher among those experiencing a greater number of HIV-related symptoms and lower among those expressing greater satisfaction with the social support they received from others (Hays et al., 1992).

Depression, feelings of futility, and feelings of anger and frustration stem from the perception of infected persons that they can do little or nothing to help their situation, and that those who might make a difference—the medical profession, or the political powers that hold the purse strings of medical research funding—have done and intend to do little or nothing. A cure for AIDS has not been found; a vaccine does not exist. And to complicate the general frustration with bureaucracy or politics that burdens persons with AIDS, many experience discrimination, social rejection, or open hostility. Though many have reached out to persons with AIDS, others have made it difficult or impossible for them to proceed with a normal life. Adults and children can be ostracized, or undergo more subtle social rejection—lack of social invitations, parents refusing to set up play dates, and so on.

Asymptomatic carriers of HIV frequently develop serious adjustment problems. There may be an initial tendency upon learning that one is HIV-positive to deny the harsh reality of the disease. And as life continues with the knowledge of HIV, this denial can turn to nagging fears that stem from the uncertainty as to whether or when the virus will lead to AIDS. This state of "suspended animation" can cause feelings of anxiety, depression and hopelessness, fear of death, guilt, and alienation (Catania et al., 1992a; Rundell et al., 1986). The stress that this knowledge can impose, or the stress of having lost a lover or close personal friend to the disease, can further compromise the immune system and hasten the progress of the disease (Martin, 1988).

PREVENTION

Learning Objective 13: Discuss the success rates of programs focused on preventing HIV transmission by blood transfusion, sexual behaviors, and injectable drug use.

What can we do to curb the spread of AIDS, given that there is no vaccine or cure for it? Prevention is our best hope at present for stemming the epidemic. Our discussion of prevention will focus on sexual contact, but other efforts have been made to prevent transmission of HIV through injection of drugs and blood transfusions. The screening of blood supplies and potential donors has reduced the probability of infection through blood transfusions to about one in 75,000 (Altman, 1992b). We have been less successful in reducing the risk of infection through unsafe sexual contact.

Prevention efforts have mainly focused on AIDS education. Sexually active people have been advised to alter their sexual behavior either by practicing abstinence, by limiting their sexual experiences to a lifelong monogamous relationship, or by practicing "safe sex"—which, as we shall see, is more accurately dubbed "safer sex." What impact are prevention programs having?

Prevention programs are apparently raising public awareness of AIDS (CDC, 1988b). Evidence shows that young people are becoming better informed about the means by which HIV is transmitted. A 1993 New York Times/CBS News national poll showed that knowledge about AIDS in the general population is increasing. Seventy-nine percent of respondents correctly recognized that one cannot contract AIDS by sharing a drinking glass with a person with AIDS, up from 34 percent in 1985. Eighty-nine percent recognized that you cannot get AIDS from a toilet seat, up from 49 percent in 1985. Virtually all knew that the AIDS virus can be transmitted by heterosexual sex (96%) and blood transfusions (98%). More people today are also personally acquainted with a person with AIDS. One third of those polled know someone who has died of AIDS or has either HIV infection or AIDS.

Gaps in knowledge about preventing AIDS remain, however. For example, a 1991 national survey of the American public showed that only one in five knew that latex condoms are more effective in preventing the transmission of HIV than natural membrane condoms ("Americans generally well-informed about AIDS, but many lack knowledge about preventive aspects," 1993).

Nor does knowledge about HIV transmission necessarily translate into behavioral change, such as increased use of latex condoms (latex condoms can block the transmission of HIV) and other safer sex practices (DeBuono et al., 1990; Geringer et al., 1993; Kelly et al., 1993; Klepinger et al., 1993; Ruder et al., 1990). In fact, knowledge about transmission of HIV and other STDs appears to be unrelated to condom use (Geringer et al., 1993; Klepinger et al., 1993; Rotheram-Borus & Koopman, 1991). Despite widespread efforts to educate the public about the dangers of unprotected sex, negative attitudes toward using condoms persist, especially among males. Some of the often-heard complaints include "they reduce sexual pleasure . . . they're a nuisance to put on . . . they cost too much . . . they interrupt the sex act," and so on.

Yes, some changes in sexual practices have occurred as the result of people's concerns about the AIDS epidemic. For example, about half of the single respondents, ages 18 to 44, to a 1991 national telephone poll reported that they had changed their sexual behavior because of fear of AIDS (Kagay, 1991). The most frequently cited changes were increased use of condoms and reductions in the numbers of sex partners. Rising sales of condoms in recent years support survey evidence that single people in the United States are making some changes. However, condom use in the United States remains relatively low. By the late 1980s, only about one in five sexually active American women used condoms with their partners (Erhardt et al., 1991; Lewin, 1992b). The results of the National AIDS Behavioral Survey, a large probability sample of the U.S. population based on interviews with 10,630 people, showed that fewer than one in five people (17%) with multiple sexual partners, and only 12.6 percent of those with high-risk sexual partners, reported using condoms all of the time (Catania et al., 1992a; Coates, 1993).

The Battelle survey of more than 3,000 sexually active men found a high incidence of unsafe sexual practices (Barringer, 1993a; Billy et al., 1993; Tanfer et al., 1993). About one in four (23%) of the men reported having vaginal intercourse with 20 or more partners in their lifetimes. About one in five of the single men had four or more partners during the preceding 18-month period; of these men, only one half reported using condoms. Overall, only about one in four sexually active men had used a condom during the four-week period preceding the survey. African-American men were more likely than white men to report using condoms (38% vs. 25%), and men younger than 30 were more likely to do so than older men (36% vs. 19%).

AIDS prevention programs have not been successful in getting their message across to large numbers of at-risk heterosexuals about the dangers of unprotected sex and sex with multiple partners. Yet concerns and fears of HIV infection are widespread. Four in ten of the men in the Battelle survey believe that there is a chance they may be infected with HIV, and nearly one in four worries often about AIDS (Klepinger et al., 1993). Many—more than 40 percent—report having had an HIV blood test; about half of this group had the test specifically to find out if they were infected.

Gay males, the group hardest hit by the AIDS epidemic, have to a large extent adopted safer sexual practices, such as limiting their numbers of sex partners, using latex condoms and spermicides, and decreasing the incidence of anal intercourse (Catania et al., 1991; CDC, 1990c). Researchers find that condoms are used by gay men for anal sex more than 75 percent of the time (USDHHS, 1992). These changes have resulted in major reductions in HIV infections (Coates, 1993). However, substantial proportions of gay males, both HIV+ and HIV-, continue to engage in unsafe sexual practices (Meyer-Bahlburg et al., 1991). In one sample of 219 gay men, more than 40 percent reported having had unprotected sex with three or more men during the preceding year (Gold & Skinner, 1992). Researchers in Seattle find that while unprotected anal intercourse has decreased in their samples of gay and bisexual men, unprotected oral sex has increased (Seattle-King County Department of Public Health, 1991). Moreover, a sizable number of gay and bisexual men who had adopted safer sexual practices are relapsing into riskier behaviors (Schnell & O'Reilly, 1991).

High-risk sexual practices are reported to be especially common among gay youth (Rotheram-Borus & Koopman, 1991). A university investigator found only a few men among 61 gay male students who reported making major changes (such as reducing the number of partners and being more selective when choosing partners) in their sexual behavior because of concerns about HIV (D'Augelli, 1992a). Danish researchers find that a large percentage (43.5%) of the 16- to 19-year-old gay males in their sample had engaged in unsafe sex during the past 12 months (Schmidt et al., 1992).

Researchers in the United States find that frequenting gay bars is associated with greater sexual risk taking among gay men (Ruefli et al., 1992). Alcohol and drug use preceding or during sex is also associated with riskier behavior in gay males (McCusker et al., 1992), as it is among heterosexuals. Risky sexual behavior among gay males may be more prevalent in the cities outside the epicenter of the epidemic (San Francisco, New York, Los Angeles) where the gay community has been better organized in marshalling its efforts to combat HIV/AIDS (Ruefli et al., 1992). This evidence underscores the need for increasing AIDS prevention efforts in the gay male population, especially among younger gay males. Sexual practices of bisexual men are also of special concern because they may be a conduit for heterosexual transmission of HIV (Boulton et al., 1992).

Awareness of the risks of HIV infection and AIDS leads people to engage in "safe sex." *Unfortunately, awareness of the prospects of HIV infection and AIDS is often insufficient to motivate people to engage in "safe sex." Education about HIV infection and AIDS is an indispensable step, however.*
•

Sexual contact between injecting drug users (IDUs) and their sex partners remains the greatest source of heterosexual transmission of HIV in North America and Europe. AIDS prevention programs have led to decreased needle sharing and, occasionally, drug injection altogether, but have had a lesser impact on changing risky sexual behavior in this population (DesJarlais & Friedman, 1988). For instance, a survey of 221 white and 236 African-American heterosexual injecting drug users (IDUs) in California showed that more than two thirds reported that they never use condoms (Lewis & Watters, 1991). Still, some progress toward encouraging safe sex practices has been reported. Researchers in New York City found a sharp increase from 14 percent in 1984 to 60 percent in 1990 of IDUs who report using condoms "at least some of the time" (Kouzi et al., 1992).

A major population group in our society targeted for AIDS-prevention efforts is young people. Let us consider the effects that the AIDS epidemic has had on the sexual behavior of young people today.

COMING OF AGE IN THE AGE OF AIDS

Learning Objective 14: Discuss the knowledge levels, the rates of condom use, and the factors underlying risky sexual behavior among sexually active young people.

Today, for the first time, a generation of young people is becoming sexually active with the threat of a lethal disease hanging over every sexual encounter. How has the threat of AIDS affected the sex lives of young people today? Note these comments:

ERICA, 18: I am terrified of AIDS. When my boyfriend cheated on me while drunk, I was scared. I now use condoms with him every time.

A 23-YEAR-OLD MAN: AIDS is a scary thing that always seems to be nagging away at the back of my mind. I've never been promiscuous, and I've never had casual sex. The frightening thing is that you can't be absolutely sure about your partner. With such a long incubation period, one mistake a long time ago can have fatal results.

RACHEL, 18: AIDS is a definite problem in college because you just don't know. At home, everyone knew who everyone slept with, but here you don't know who[m] they've slept with and they don't know who[m] you've slept with.

(Copyright © 1991 by McIntyre, Formichella, Osterhout, and Gresh by arrangement with AVON Books, pp. 137–139)

 Teen AIDS

Though the number of AIDS cases among teenagers has remained low (Johnson, 1988; Lewin, 1991), about one in five people with AIDS is in his or her twenties, and most of them were probably infected as teens (Curran et al., 1988; Lewin, 1991a; Sonenstein et al., 1989). The impact of HIV and AIDS among young people is disproportionate across ethnic groups. Researchers estimate that African-American and Hispanic adolescents are four to five times more likely to be diagnosed with AIDS than white adolescents (DiClemente, 1991). Homeless youth are at special risk of HIV infection because of the prevalence of unsafe sexual practices and shared drug use in this population group (Goulart & Madover, 1991).

More than three out of four school districts nationwide require some form of AIDS education for grades 6 to 8 (Holtzman et al., 1992). But only about half of the districts require AIDS education at the high school level. Still, evidence shows that AIDS education is having an impact. A recent survey of 197 predominantly African-American students attending an urban high school in the Cleveland area showed that more than half had changed their behavior because of AIDS, such as by reducing the number of sexual partners or reducing their frequency of sexual activity, and/or increasing their use of condoms (Zimet et al., 1992). A 1988 national survey of teenage boys found that exposure to AIDS education was associated with reductions in recent sexual activity (fewer sexual partners and less frequent intercourse) and greater use of condoms (Ku et al., 1992). Instruction in skills needed to resist intercourse had a stronger influence on decreasing sexual activity than did instruction about AIDS. Others report that AIDS education programs in the high schools have increased students' knowledge about AIDS (*Journal of the American Medical Association,* 1993a; Walter & Vaughan, 1993) and more important, have had some impact, albeit to a modest extent, on reducing high-risk sexual behaviors, such as sex with multiple partners, sex with high-risk partners, and inconsistent condom use (Walter & Vaughan, 1993).

The evidence is not all consistent, however. Researchers in Massachusetts find that only one third of sexually active teens reported always using condoms (Hingson et al., 1990). Nationwide, researchers find that one in five high school students polled in a 1990 survey of more than 11,000 students in all 50 states reported having sex with four or more partners, a pattern that puts them at high risk for contracting HIV ("Teen-agers and AIDS: The risk worsens," 1992). Nearly one in three high school seniors (29%) reported having had four or more sexual partners. The percentages were higher among boys than girls, 27 percent versus 12 percent, and among African-American males as compared to white males, 60 percent versus 21 percent. Fewer than half of the students reporting this level of sexual activity sought to protect themselves or their partners against HIV and other infectious agents. "It's like playing Russian roulette and not knowing how many bullets are in the chambers," (p. C3) said an AIDS expert from the CDC about the risks faced by young people having sex with multiple partners. Moreover, about half of the teenage boys and girls sampled in 1988 and 1991 national surveys reported that they had not used a condom the last time they engaged in sexual intercourse (CDC, 1993d; Sonenstein et al., 1989). Clearly, a substantial proportion of young people are engaging in behavior that puts themselves or their partners at risk of HIV.

Evidence also shows that many college students continue to engage in high levels of unsafe sexual behavior that puts them at risk of infection with HIV (Fisher & Misovich, 1991; Miller et al., 1990). Many sexually active college students fail to use condoms consistently if at all, and many continue to have sex with multiple partners. Despite growing awareness of AIDS, a survey of college women who attended a student health service in the Northeast in the 1970s and 1980s found little dropoff in the incidence of coitus with multiple partners (DeBuono et al., 1990). Nor did most of the sexually active women who attended this clinic reliably use condoms. A student survey in an upstate New York college showed that only one in five reported always using condoms (Oswalt & Matsen, 1993). Students in a high-risk category—those with the highest number of partners—used condoms the least often. Fewer than half of a sample of New England college students reported changing their sexual behavior because of AIDS (Carroll, 1988). A survey at a southern California university found that the average student used a condom in fewer than one in three occasions of vaginal intercourse in the previous three-month period (Baldwin et al., 1992). Condoms were used even less frequently (18.5% of the time) during anal intercourse among the 15 percent of the students who engaged in anal sexual activity.

In another college survey, 70 percent of University of Massachusetts students polled reported that they had *not* changed their sexual practices in any way, despite the threat of AIDS (Johnson, 1990). Another survey found that only 35 percent of sexually active stu-

Notes: An anonymous letter sent to the president of Hartwick College begins, "I will leave Hartwick with much guilt. I have recently been tested positive with the HIV virus. I have engaged in unprotected sexual intercourse with six female members of the Hartwick community and regret my horrible mistake." The writer said he lacked the courage to tell the women. The college's president sent every student a memo including the text of the letter and facts about HIV. The president and an AIDS-awareness specialist also held an information session for Hartwick's 1,450 students. (Notebook. *Chronicle of Higher Education,* 1 June 1994, A31.)

dents at two southeastern state universities used condoms reliably (Hernandez & Smith, 1990). A survey of some 5,500 Canadian freshmen at 51 colleges found them to be well aware of the existence of AIDS and the ways in which HIV is transmitted. Nevertheless, only one man in four (24.8%) and one woman in six (15.6%) used condoms regularly (MacDonald et al., 1990). One man in five and one woman in 11 claimed to have had 10 or more sexual partners. In this subgroup, only about 20 percent of the men and 10 percent of the women used condoms reliably.

RISKY SEX: WHY SO PREVALENT IN YOUNG PEOPLE?   At a time when virtually all young people are aware of the sexual transmission of HIV, why does there remain such a high rate of risky sexual behaviors among them? It is clear that informing young people about how HIV is transmitted is not sufficient to induce healthier behaviors (Ting & Carter, 1992). Young people also need to acquire skills to protect themselves from engaging in risky behaviors, such as communication skills for discussing safer sex options with their partners, assertiveness skills for ensuring that their needs and interests are respected by their partners, and social skills to resist peer pressures. Greater efforts are needed to reverse peer norms that discourage condom use, such as by using adolescents themselves to support and teach condom use to their peers (Hodges et al., 1992). Experts advise taking a positive approach to AIDS education that focuses on options, not absolutes, and that emphasizes that intimacy need not involve risky behavior (Ting & Carter, 1992).

Researchers have identified several factors underlying risky sexual behavior among young people, including negative attitudes toward condom use, a low perceived risk of infection, beliefs that one can assess the HIV risk of one's sexual partners by knowing something of their sexual history, and perceptions of personal invulnerability.

1. *Perceived low risk of infection.* One of the major stumbling blocks in promoting safer sex practices is that many young heterosexuals perceive a low risk of contracting HIV (Gold et al., 1992; Nadeau et al., 1993; Oswalt & Matsen, 1993). People who perceive themselves at low risk are less likely to alter their risk behavior. Studies show that most adolescents do not believe themselves to be at risk of acquiring HIV (Gladis et al., 1992).

   Given the current low rate of known infections among heterosexuals who do not inject drugs, many heterosexuals may perceive risky sexual practices to be a reasonable gamble (Pinkerton & Abramson, 1992). Heterosexuals who have never had a friend or relative with HIV or AIDS may dismiss HIV infection and AIDS as problems that affect other types of people. Even gay men may operate under the "I'm not the type" fallacy and underestimate their personal risks. According to Pinkerton & Abramson (1992):

   > ...the frightening picture that emerges is one in which it is only the *other* guy (or gal) who gets AIDS: To the non-drug-injecting heterosexual, it's just gays and "druggies" that get AIDS; to the "average" gay man, it's those gay men who are overly promiscuous; and to the bath house participant, it's those who aren't "careful" (pp. 564–565).

Discussion Question: "I wouldn't wear a condom during sex—it's like showering with a raincoat on." Are you familiar with this attitude? What other reasons do men give for not using condoms? How can we change negative attitudes toward condom use?

2. *Negative attitudes toward condom use.* Use of latex condoms remains the only established method of protection against HIV available to sexually active people. Yet many factors discourage condom use. Some people feel embarrassed to buy them. For others, the risk of being infected with HIV seems to fly out of their minds whenever the opportunity for sex arises. Some claim that a condom dampens romantic ardor in moments of passion by requiring an interruption of the sexual act to apply one. Some people just regard them as too much of a fuss. For many men, beliefs that condoms deprive them of sexual pleasure discourage their use. Until such obstacles to using condoms are overcome, efforts to stem the spread of HIV in the general population may be largely thwarted.

3. *Implicit personality theories.* Heterosexuals who have sexual relations with casual partners are more likely to use condoms than those with steady partners (Champman et al., 1990; Moore & Rosenthal, 1991). Unsafe sexual encounters (vaginal or anal

Implicit personality theories
Our internalized set of assumptions about the personalities of other people, which we use to predict their behavior.

intercourse without use of a latex condom) are more likely to occur in the context of an established intimate relationship. Perhaps love is blind when it comes to condom use. Another factor may be even more important. People tend to construct their own personal theories about other people, called **implicit personality theories,** that they use as a basis for predicting which potential partners are risky and which are not. As one student put it, "When you get to know the person . . . as soon as you begin trusting the person . . . you don't really have to use a condom" (Williams et al., 1992, p. 926). Some (mistakenly) believe that knowing something about the sexual history of their partners frees them of the need to take precautions:

> DONNA, 19: I am very selective with my partners. I know all of their sexual histories. I have never taken any other precautions against AIDS or other STDs.

> GINA, 23: I've discussed AIDS with my partner before deciding to have sex. We tried using a condom the first time and hated it. We felt we knew each other well and trusted each other's judgment about who(m) we had been with in the past.

> (Copyright © 1991 by McIntyre, Formichella, Osterhout, and Gresh by arrangement with AVON Books, pp. 137–139)

A person's implicit personality theory may serve to justify the decision not to use condoms, even though such knowledge of the other person may be based on characteristics that in fact are unrelated to HIV status:

> (Students) . . . tend to assume that risky people are those who dress provocatively, whom one met in bars, who were older than most college students, who are from large cities, or who are overly anxious for sex. . . .

> (Students will use a condom only) . . . with partners they feel they do not know well and whom they perceive might be risky. A typical response was, "If you just met them, you use a condom . . . if it's long-term, you aren't going to worry."

> (Williams et al., 1992, pp. 926–927)

Knowing your partner is not a sufficient basis to evaluate his or her HIV status. You can't know whether your partners are infected with HIV by looking at them, inspecting their genitals, or meeting their folks. The AIDS virus is out there in the general population. You may have a lesser risk of infection than a drug addict in an inner-city neighborhood or a sexually active gay male. You may be at less risk if you have only one or a few sexual partners, don't engage in needle sharing, and don't have sex with partners who themselves have engaged in dangerous sexual or injection practices or have had other partners who did. But how can you be certain that your partners are telling the truth about their own past sexual practices, let alone vouch for the sexual practices of their previous sexual partners? The answer is that you can't. Simply knowing your partner and being monogamous does not constitute safer sex (Williams et al., 1992).

4. *Myth of personal invulnerability.* Another factor underlying risky sexual behaviors is that some people subscribe to a myth of personal invulnerability and believe that they are somehow immune to AIDS and other diseases. Even students who are generally well informed about STDs may perceive themselves as personally immune. One junior at the University of Miami (Ohio) explained to an interviewer why she did not insist that her partners use a condom: "I have an attitude—it may be wrong—that any guy I would sleep with would not have AIDS" (Johnson, 1990, p. A18). The adventurous spirit that we often associate with youth may confer a dangerous sense of immortality and a greater willingness to take risks (Johnson, 1990). Perceptions of personal invulnerability help to explain why AIDS education may not translate into behavior change (Rosenthal et al., 1992).

Some people may not believe themselves to be immune, but may underestimate their perceived vulnerability. People do tend to view themselves as luckier than the norm. (After all, don't you believe that you alone hold the winning lottery ticket?) Moreover, since the transmission of HIV infection through casual heterosexual sexual encounters is an infrequent event, people who regularly engage in risky sexual prac-

Safer Sex. Despite AIDS prevention programs encouraging sexually active people to practice safer sex, many young people, including many college students, continue to engage in unprotected sex.

Discussion Question: What do you think of the following proposals to reduce HIV transmission? 1) Distribute free condoms in high schools. 2) Locate health clinics in high schools to provide STD screening and treatment as well as other health services. 3) Offer high school students free confidential HIV testing with no parental permission or notification. 4) Set up needle exchange programs (whereby any drug user could exchange a dirty needle for a clean one) in areas where there is high injectable drug use. 5) Distribute bleach to injectable drug users and teach them to use it to sterilize any shared equipment.

tices and so far have remained uninfected may be lulled into a false sense of security.

Many young people are deeply concerned about the threat of AIDS, however, and have changed their sexual behavior to reduce their risk of exposure:

> PATRICK, 21: With AIDS here to stay, I would say safe sex is it. The condom can now be a lifesaver. Being alone now poses the problem that if you're down in the dumps, you can no longer look for quick love and warmth in a bar.

> JILL, 26: AIDS has made casual sex out of the question. I take no chances. Sex is not worth dying for. I would only have sex now using a condom and with someone I'm seriously interested in. I would tell others simply that it's life or death. Take precautions or take the consequences.

Even among those who take precautions, feelings of uncertainty may remain:

> CONNIE, 23: Unless your partner has never had sex before, you don't know if you can be totally safe, even if you use rubbers.

> (Copyright © 1991 by McIntyre, Formichella, Osterhout, and Gresh by arrangement with AVON Books, pp. 137–139)

Many college programs have been introduced to educate students about AIDS and what they can do to prevent it (Shulkin et al., 1991). An important part of AIDS prevention programs is to debunk myths about personal invulnerability and to expose the ineffectiveness of implicit personality theories that people use to estimate their potential partners' riskiness (Williams et al., 1991).

There are worrisome signs that concerns about AIDS and perceptions of risk of acquiring AIDS may actually be declining in some population groups, such as among sexually active young men (Pleck et al., 1993). Decreased concerns about AIDS and denial about the seriousness of the threat of AIDS can be expected to lead to a reduced use of condoms.

Inconsistent condom use in young people is not unique to the United States and is even common in Scandinavian countries, in which there is much wider accessibility to sex education and contraceptive services than in the United States. For example, Norwegian researchers found only one in three sexually active adolescents used a condom in their last coital opportunity (Kraft & Rise, 1991). Finnish researchers found a somewhat higher percentage of condom users among sexually active adolescents (Kontula et al., 1992). There, about six of ten reported using condoms. Still, that means that a sizable minority, about four of ten, did not use condoms. The Finnish teens, like many American teens, did not perceive themselves to be at great risk of contracting AIDS.

AIDS PREVENTION: OTHER APPROACHES Information about AIDS, as noted, is often insufficient to produce meaningful behavioral changes. Some AIDS-prevention programs and school districts distribute free condoms in the belief that easier access to condoms will encourage their use and thus reduce the risk of HIV transmission.

Some AIDS experts believe that AIDS prevention programs should be targeted toward the communities that have been hardest hit. It is possible, these experts believe, that the epidemic can be all but wiped out if prevention efforts were focused on the communities, especially poor communities, which have been ravaged by the epidemic (Kolata, 1993e; "Research panel concludes AIDS has small impact on most of U.S.," 1993). A 1993 report issued by the prestigious National Research Council lends support to the targeted approach. The council found that AIDS was devastating a handful of communities while leaving much of the nation virtually untouched. As one of the members of the council committee that drafted the report framed the issue, "If we want to really deal with the epidemic, we have to go where the epidemic is" (p. 26). Proponents of this approach point to the city of Tacoma, Washington, which concentrated its prevention efforts on promoting safer injection and sexual practices in injecting drug users and managed to keep its infection rates in these groups at under 5 percent, as compared to the skyrocketing rates found in other cities like New York, where infection rates in injecting drug users now range between 50 and 80 percent. The belief that AIDS prevention efforts should be narrowly but intensively focused on hard-hit communities is not universally supported by AIDS experts. Some believe that since the virus has spread into the more general population, a broader prevention effort is needed. Health officials also fear that AIDS may become largely ignored by the general public if it becomes perceived as a problem that is endemic to socially disadvantaged groups in our society rather than to the society at large (Woodard, 1993).

Some AIDS researchers argue that IDUs should be given sterile needles as well as easier access to drug treatment programs (e.g., DesJarlais and Friedman, 1988). Canada makes free, clean needles available to addicts, and *may* have suppressed the incidence of new infections by doing so (Reuters, 1991). Many U.S. politicians and religious leaders condemn government distribution of condoms or sterile needles, however. Meanwhile, many drug treatment programs have waiting lists of six months or longer, during which time infected addicts can spread the virus to others through needle sharing and sexual contact. In 1988, a Presidential Commission on AIDS called for expanding the availability of drug treatment programs, but the money to do so has not been forthcoming.

Targeting AIDS prevention efforts within the African-American community has been hampered by the widespread belief among African Americans that a government conspiracy aimed at racial genocide is behind the epidemic and that the AIDS virus was deliberately concocted in a government lab to infect them (Mays, 1993). UCLA psychologist Vickie Mays points out that it is difficult for people to develop trust in their government when they feel disenfranchised from society and believe that government institutions just don't care about them. Many African Americans, especially those in the poorer inner-city neighborhoods, have seen a decline of affordable housing, businesses abandoning their neighborhoods, the spread of the crack epidemic; many believe that a racist government plot must be trying to destroy the African-American community. This distrust translates into lack of involvement in government-sponsored initiatives, such as AIDS education programs. Whether perceptions are true or not, they affect behavior. Consequently, many of the people most at risk of infection may be disinclined to change their behavior or undergo testing (Mays, 1993). To be effective, prevention programs need to focus on community actions, not just changes in individual behavior, and need to address beliefs held in the community that impact health behaviors, including conspiracy theories.

Then there is the issue of how critical a threat HIV and AIDS may seem in the face of other life stresses and threats to personal security. In economically distressed communities, efforts to secure food and decent shelter for one's family, and to protect oneself and one's loved ones from crime, typically hold higher values than practicing safer sex (Airhihenbuwa et al., 1992). These issues highlight the need to develop culturally informed AIDS prevention efforts that are directed toward people in communities already beset with a host of basic survival problems. Prevention efforts that are developed within a community framework and that respect the values of the cultures they serve will likely prove most effective (Airhihenbuwa et al., 1992). So too will programs that make use of community residents themselves in the planning and implementation of prevention efforts (USDHHS, 1992).

The lack of Spanish-language AIDS education materials and bilingual treatment providers has handicapped efforts to stem the spread of AIDS in the Hispanic community (Fuentes, 1993). Recognizing that drug use is often implicated in the transmission of HIV among Hispanic Americans, the National Latino Coalition on AIDS has called for expanding the availability of drug treatment programs and expanding AIDS prevention efforts in the Hispanic (Latino) community.

REDUCING THE RISK OF HIV INFECTION

Learning Objective 15: Identify the ways one can reduce one's risk of HIV infection.

In 1988, Surgeon General C. Everett Koop advised that two assured ways to avert the sexual transmission of AIDS were celibacy or a lifelong monogamous relationship with a person who is free of HIV. These two sexual lifestyles confer safety but are not followed by most people in the United States or Canada. Still, there are many ways in which sexually active people may reduce the risk of transmitting or contracting the AIDS virus. None of these suggestions is guaranteed to make sexual contact perfectly safe, however. Despite the commonly heard buzz words "safe sex," we can speak only of saf*er* sex—not of absolutely safe sex (Rathus & Nevid, 1991).

Sources of Information About HIV Infection and AIDS

We brought you the latest information available on HIV and AIDS when this book went to press. Information about HIV and AIDS, however, changes daily. For the very latest information on HIV infection and AIDS—and for advice on what to do if you are wondering whether or not you have been infected by HIV—contact one or more of the following sources. Many of them, such as the Centers for Disease Control (CDC) AIDS hotline, are toll-free and respect the anonymity of the caller. The CDC, for example, will not ask for your name or attempt to trace the call, even if you inform the listener that you have been involved in illegal drug use. If you or someone to whom you are close is infected by HIV, one of the following groups may be able to lend support. When in doubt, call or write.

Centers for Disease Control AIDS Hotline: (800) 342-AIDS
Information and referral resources nationwide, 24 hours a day

Canadian Toll-Free Hotline (Toll-free in Canada): AIDS Committee of Toronto: (800) 267-6600

If you prefer requesting and receiving your information in Spanish, call: Spanish AIDS/SIDA Hotline: (800) 344-7432

AIDS Hotline for the Hearing Impaired: (800) 243-7889

National AIDS Information Clearinghouse
Education Database Distribution
1600 Research Blvd.
Rockville, Maryland 20850
(800) 458-5231

American Red Cross
AIDS Education Office
1750 K St. NW

Washington, DC 20006
(202) 737-8300

National Association of People with AIDS
1413 K St. NW
Washington, DC 20005
(202) 898-0414

The Henry Nichols Foundation
P.O. Box 621
Cooperstown, New York 13326

Sex Information and Education Council of the United States (SIECUS)
130 West 42nd St., Suite 2500
New York, New York 10036
(212) 819-9770

American Association of Physicians for Human Rights
273 Church St.
San Francisco, California 94114
(415) 255-4547

1. *Avoid high-risk sexual behaviors, unless you are absolutely certain that your partner is not infected* (Reinisch, 1990). Avoid "unprotected" vaginal intercourse (intercourse without the use of a latex condom and a spermicide containing nonoxynol-9 (see item 6). Unprotected anal intercourse is one of the riskiest practices. Other high-risk behaviors include unprotected oral-genital activity, oral-anal activity, insertion of a hand or fist into someone's rectum or vagina, or any activity in which you or your partner would come into contact with the other's blood, semen, or vaginal secretions.

2. *Be careful in your choice of partners.* Choose partners carefully. Avoid sexual contact with someone who is seropositive or has engaged in high-risk sexual or drug-use practices and is not known to be seronegative. Uninfected people cannot transmit HIV, but you probably won't know whether prospective partners are free of HIV infection. It is not enough to ask your partner about past sexual behavior and drug use. You need to know the person well enough to judge the truthfulness of his or her answers. Even then, you cannot be sure that the person is truthful or can completely recall all past sexual experiences, let alone verify the sexual histories of all previous partners. To be safe, it is best to abstain or to practice safer sex techniques with any partner who is not known to be free of HIV.

   You may reduce the risk of HIV transmission by verifying that you and your partner are seronegative for HIV antibodies before engaging in intimate sexual relations involving the exchange of bodily fluids. Since blood tests for HIV antibodies are not foolproof, however, and a person may be infected with the virus for months or perhaps even a year or longer before antibodies can be detected, it may make sense to use condoms until repeated test results are negative.

3. *Limit your number of sex partners.* The more sexual contacts you have, the greater your risk of exposing yourself to a partner with HIV (or another pathogen). Also avoid sex with a partner who has had multiple partners.

4. *Inspect your partner's sex organs.* Do not expect to find telltale signs of an HIV infection, but infected people often have other STDs. You may be able to discreetly inspect your partner's sex organs for lice, discharges, rashes, chancres, warts, and blisters during foreplay. Consider any disagreeable odor a warning sign.

Outercourse

Forms of sexual expression, such as massage, hugging, caressing, mutual masturbation, and rubbing bodies together that do not involve the exchange of body fluids. (Contrast with *intercourse.*)

5. *Engage in noncoital activities.* Other forms of sexual expression, such as hugging, massage, caressing, mutual masturbation, or rubbing bodies together without vaginal, anal, or oral contact, are low-risk ways of finding sexual pleasure, so long as semen or vaginal fluids do not come into contact with mucous membranes or breaks in the skin (Gordon & Snyder, 1989; Reinisch, 1990). Many sexologists refer to such activities as **outercourse** to distinguish them from sexual intercourse. Sharing sexual fantasies can be very titillating, as can taking a bath or shower together. Vibrators, dildos, and other "sex toys" may also be erotically stimulating and carry a low risk of infection, if they are washed thoroughly with soap and water before use and between uses by two people. If used for penetration, they should be used gently and with plenty of lubricant to avoid irritating or breaking vaginal or rectal tissues (Reinisch, 1990).

6. *Use a latex condom with a spermicide containing nonoxynol-9 before engaging in vaginal or anal intercourse.* Latex condoms are an effective barrier against HIV and many other STD-causing organisms and offer highly effective protection against HIV infection and other STDs when used correctly and consistently (CDC, 1993g). (See Chapter 12 for guidelines for using condoms correctly.) Spermicides containing nonoxynol-9 are toxic to the AIDS virus and other STD-causing organisms, as well as to sperm, and may offer an added level of protection (Lourea et al., 1986). Yet no evidence exists showing use of nonoxynol-9 alone without a condom to be effective in preventing HIV transmission (CDC, 1993g).

   Condoms made from animal membranes ("skins") are less effective as barriers against STD-causing organisms (they contain pores that allow tiny microbes, including HIV, to penetrate). Even latex condoms are not 100 percent effective in preventing the transmission of the AIDS virus (CDC, 1988a). Condoms (and the people who use them) are fallible. They can break or slip off.

   New to the market, the female condom (discussed in Chapter 12) has not been shown to be effective against HIV transmission (Altman, 1993b). To date, latex condoms for men are the only form of contraception proven to provide protection against HIV and other STDs (AIDS Update, 1993).

   HIV has been found in the pre-ejaculatory fluid that is emitted before orgasm occurs ("H.I.V. clue supports early use of condom," 1992). This underscores the need for condoms to be used *before* any penile-vaginal or penile-anal contact occurs, not just moments prior to ejaculation.

7. *Use barrier devices when practicing oral sex (fellatio or cunnilingus).* If you do decide to practice oral sex, use a condom before practicing fellatio and a dental dam (a square piece of latex rubber used by dentists during oral surgery) to cover the vagina before engaging in cunnilingus (Reinisch, 1990).

8. *Avoid sexual activity when in doubt.* None of the previous practices guarantees protection. Avoid any sexual activity about which you are in doubt.

Reducing the risk of HIV transmission also involves avoiding contact with blood that may be contaminated. Unsafe injection practices ("sharing needles") are the most risky. But do not share cuticle scissors, razor blades, or other implements that might transmit blood from one person to another.

The advent of AIDS presents the medical, mental-health, and educational communities with an unparalleled challenge in developing programs to contain the spread of AIDS and for compassionate treatment of people with HIV and AIDS. As frightening as AIDS may be, it is preventable.

PREVALENCE OF HIV INFECTION AND AIDS

AIDS has been diagnosed in more than 360,000 people, and has claimed more than 220,000 lives, in the United States. Estimates from health authorities indicate that one million people in the United States, and 14 million people worldwide, are infected with HIV. The number of people infected with HIV may reach 110 million by the year 2000, according to a recent Harvard report.

It is a person's behavior, not the groups to which a person belongs, that determines her or his relative risk of infection.

THE IMMUNE SYSTEM AND AIDS

The Immune System The immune system produces white blood cells (leukocytes) that identify, envelop, and kill disease-causing agents (pathogens) such as bacteria and viruses.

Effects of HIV on the Immune System AIDS is caused by the human immunodeficiency virus (HIV), which attacks the body's immune system. As HIV disables the body's natural defenses, the person becomes vulnerable to opportunistic diseases—such as serious infections and cancers—that are normally held in check.

PROGRESSION OF HIV INFECTION AND AIDS

Shortly following infection, people may experience mild flulike symptoms, which usually disappear within a few weeks. They may then remain symptom-free for years. The beginnings of full-blown cases of AIDS are often marked by such symptoms as fatigue, night sweats, persistent fever, swollen lymph nodes, diarrhea, and unexplained weight loss.

TRANSMISSION

HIV can be transmitted by the exchange of infected blood, semen, and vaginal secretions, through vaginal or anal intercourse, oral-genital contact, transfusion with contaminated blood, sharing a hypodermic needle with an infected person, or childbirth.
Women and AIDS The number of women who are infected with HIV has been growing rapidly. Many women (and men) contract HIV through heterosexual intercourse. HIV infection may progress differently in women and men.

DIAGNOSIS OF HIV INFECTION AND AIDS

HIV infection can be diagnosed by a blood test that detects HIV antibodies in the bloodstream. Until 1992, the diagnosis of AIDS required the appearance of certain so-called indicator diseases, such as Kaposi's sarcoma or PCP, in a person who was seropositive for HIV. In 1992, the CDC revised the definition of AIDS to include several more indicator diseases and to include HIV people whose CD4 cell counts had fallen below 200 per cubic millimeter of blood.
Issues Concerning Testing for HIV Infection Testing for HIV infection raises important emotional, medical, ethical, moral, and lifestyle concerns. Controversy swirls around whether the identities of HIV-infected health care workers should be disclosed, and whether they should be prohibited from performing procedures that might infect patients. There is also the question of whether public officials or health care providers should notify the sex and needle-sharing partners of infected people that they are at risk

TREATMENT OF HIV INFECTION AND AIDS

There is neither a cure for AIDS nor an effective, safe vaccine. The drug AZT appears to have limited benefits for a limited period of time.

PSYCHOLOGICAL ADJUSTMENT OF PERSONS WITH HIV INFECTIONS AND AIDS

People with AIDS often suffer psychological problems, most notably anxiety, depression, guilt about sexual behavior or drug abuse, anger, and suicidal feelings. Those with AIDS often experience rejection and open hostility which can make living a normal life difficult.

PREVENTION

Coming of Age in the Age of AIDS For the first time, a generation of Americans is becoming sexually active when the threat of a lethal disease hangs over every sexual encounter. Yet only a minority of young people have made significant preventative changes in their sexual behavior. **Reducing the Risk of HIV Infection** Methods of prevention include celibacy (or abstention), maintaining a lifelong monogamous relationship with an uninfected partner, and practicing safe(r) sex.

CHAPTER OUTLINE

Truth or Fiction?

Normal Versus Deviant
Sexual Behavior

The Paraphilias
Fetishism
Transvestism
Exhibitionism
Obscene Telephone Calling
Voyeurism
Sexual Masochism
Sexual Sadism
A WORLD OF DIVERSITY:
*Cross-Cultural Perspectives
on Sadomasochism*
Frotteurism
Other Paraphilias

Theoretical Perspectives
Biological Perspectives
Psychoanalytic Perspectives
Learning Perspectives
Sociological Perspectives
An Integrated Perspective:
The "Lovemap"

Treatment of the
Paraphilias
Psychotherapy
Behavior Therapy
Biochemical Approaches

Summing Up

T R U T H   O R   F I C T I O N ?

_____ King Henry III of France insisted on being considered a woman and addressed as "Her Majesty."

_____ Nude sunbathers are exhibitionists.

_____ People who enjoy watching their mates undress are voyeurs.

_____ Exhibitionists and voyeurs are never violent.

_____ Some people cannot become sexually aroused unless they are bound, flogged, or humiliated by their sex partners.

_____ It is considered normal to enjoy some mild forms of pain during sexual activity.

_____ There is a U.S. subculture in which sexual sadists and sexual masochists form liaisons to inflict and receive pain and humiliation during sexual activity.

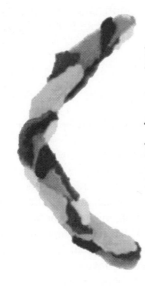

C H A P T E R   18

Atypical Sexual Variations

The following incident took place in New York City. It could have happened anywhere that windows of residences face one another across yards, alleyways, and narrow streets.

> A newly married couple were in their apartment, and the wife walked over to the window, which looked into the window of another apartment, and as she put it when recalling the story, "I just couldn't believe my eyes." The couple across the way, who had not pulled down a shade, and who had no curtain on the window, were relaxing on the bed. At least it seemed as if they were relaxing, but soon they became active and energetic, going through all the motions of discovery and exploration, no doubt precoital. There stood the watcher at the window, safe in a perch where she could remain undetected. "Disgusting," she murmured under her breath, but the spectacle held her in fascination. . . . She could not move herself from the window. She did, however, become fearful that the couple might look up and see her, so she stepped inside, and continued to watch by peering out from behind the wall. Still they continued, still she watched. Finally, she called her husband. He too watched, his eyes glued on what had become by then the primal scene. Then he walked away, went to the bedroom, and returned, a pair of opera glasses in his hand.
>
> "No, you will not look with those glasses," the wife indignantly said. "What are you, anyway, a voyeur?"
>
> "But you've been standing over here, watching, all this time, and you called me over," he protested.
>
> "Yes, I called you to see what's going on, but not to get your glasses. I have a right to look out of my own window, and it's their problem if they don't have the decency to pull down a shade. But when you get a telescope, well, that's going too far!" And she insisted at this point that she and her husband, the peepers, pull down the shades.
>
> (Sagarin, 1973, p. 5)

The incident raises questions about our labels for sexual behavior—particularly about the boundaries of what is normal. One couple clearly created conditions under which their sexual activity might become public. Another couple became spellbound by that activity. The exposed couple were in their own home, but could they be considered *exhibitionists*? And were the observers *voyeurs*? The observing wife became indignant when her husband brought out opera glasses. Perhaps she could justify her own "peeping" by thinking that she had stumbled across the other couple. Using opera glasses would transform her accidental discovery into a purposeful act, however. Then, perhaps, she could no longer regard watching as "normal."

What is normal, and what is abnormal or deviant sexual behavior? In this chapter we explore a number of sexual behaviors that deviate from the norm in one sense or another.

NORMAL VERSUS DEVIANT SEXUAL BEHAVIOR

One common approach to defining normality is based on a statistical norm. From this perspective, rare or unusual sexual behaviors are abnormal or deviant. The statistical approach may seem value-free, since the yardstick of normality is based on the frequency of behavior, not on judgment of its social acceptability. Engaging in coitus while standing, or more than seven times a week, might be considered deviant by this yardstick. The choice of behaviors we subject to statistical comparison is not divorced from our underlying values, however. Sexual practices such as humming tunes from Rogers and Hammerstein musicals while making love may be statistically infrequent (at least for people born after 1960) but would not be considered aberrant. (Your first author, though, draws the line at humming tunes from Andrew Lloyd Webber musicals.) Statistical infrequency, then, is not a sufficient criterion for classifying behavior as abnormal or deviant. We must also consider whether the sexual practice deviates from a social norm.

"Our present concepts (of normality)... cannot be divorced from the value systems of contemporary society," wrote psychiatrist Judd Marmor (1971, p. 165). "Since value systems are always in the processes of evolution and change, we must be prepared to face the possibility that some patterns of sexual behavior currently considered deviant may not always be so regarded."

When Marmor was writing, homosexuality was considered abnormal or deviant and was labeled a mental disorder by the American Psychiatric Association. His writing was prophetic in a sense: By 1973 homosexuality was dropped as a mental disorder from the association's official diagnostic manual. Marmor also recognized that sexual practices and customs have varied widely across cultures and historical periods. What is considered normal in one culture or at a particular time may be considered abnormal in other cultures and at other times. The "normal" behavior of the female adolescent Trobriand islander (see Chapter 1), for example, might be considered deviant—even *nymphomaniacal*—by the standards of Western culture.

In our own culture, sexual practices such as oral sex and masturbation were once considered by people within the mainstream of society to be deviant or abnormal. Today, however, they are practiced so widely in our society that few people would label them as deviant practices. Concepts of "normalcy" and "deviance," then, reflect the mores and customs of a particular culture at a given point in time.

Another basis for determining sexual deviance is to classify sexual practices as deviant when they involve the "habitual and preferential use of nongenital outlets for sexual release" (Marmor, 1971, p. 169). If a man prefers fondling a woman's panties to engaging in sexual relations with her, or prefers to masturbate against her foot rather than engage in coitus, his behavior is likely to be labeled deviant.

Because of the confusing array of meanings of the terms *deviant* and *abnormal,* we prefer to speak about unusual patterns of sexual arousal or behavior as "atypical variations" in sexual behavior rather than as "sexual deviations." Atypical patterns of sexual arousal or behavior that become problematic in the eyes of the individual or society are labeled *paraphilias* by the American Psychiatric Association. Clinicians consider paraphilias to be mental disorders. But milder forms of these behaviors may be practiced by many people and fall within the normal spectrum of human sexuality (Brody, 1990b).

THE PARAPHILIAS

Paraphilias involve sexual arousal in response to unusual stimuli such as children or other nonconsenting persons (such as unsuspecting people whom one watches or to whom one exposes one's genitals), nonhuman objects (such as shoes, leather, rubber, or undergarments), or pain or humiliation. The psychiatric diagnosis of paraphilia requires that the person has acted on the urges or is distinctly distressed by them.

People with paraphilic urges often feel that the urges have an insistent, demanding, or compulsory quality (Money, 1988). They may describe themselves as periodically overcome by these seemingly irresistible urges (Brody, 1990b). Paraphiles tend to experience their urges as beyond their control, much as drug addicts or compulsive gamblers might regard themselves as helpless to avert irresistible urges to gamble or use drugs. For these reasons theorists have speculated that paraphilias may represent a type of sexual compulsion or an addiction.

Paraphilias vary in severity. In some cases the person can function sexually in the absence of paraphilic stimuli and seldom if ever acts upon paraphilic urges. In other cases the person resorts to paraphilic behavior only in times of stress. In more extreme forms the person repeatedly engages in paraphilic behavior and may become preoccupied with thoughts and fantasies about these experiences. In such cases the paraphile may not be able to become sexually aroused without either fantasizing about the paraphilic stimulus or having it present. For some people paraphilic behavior is the only means of attaining sexual gratification.

Paraphilia
A diagnostic category used by the American Psychiatric Association to describe atypical patterns of sexual arousal or behavior that become problematic in the eyes of the individual or society, such as fetishism or exhibitionism. The urges are recurrent and are either acted on or are distressing to the individual. (From Greek roots meaning "to the side of" [*para-*] and "loving" [*philos*].)

Learning Objective 1:
Define the term *paraphilia* and describe the urges and behaviors characteristic of paraphiles.

The paraphile typically replays the paraphilic act in sexual fantasies to stimulate arousal during masturbation or during sexual relations. It is as if he or she is mentally replaying a videotape of the paraphilic scene. The scene grows stale after a while, however. According to sex researcher John Money, "the tape wears out and he has to perform another paraphilic act, in effect, to create a new movie" (quoted in Brody, 1990b, p. C12).

Some paraphilias are generally harmless and victimless, such as *fetishism* and cross-dressing to achieve sexual arousal (*transvestic fetishism*). Even being humiliated by one's partner may be relatively harmless if the partner consents.

Other paraphilic behaviors, such as exposing oneself in public or enticing children into sexual relations, do have victims and may cause harm, sometimes severe physical or psychological harm. They are also against the law. Sexual sadism, in which sexual arousal is connected to hurting or humiliating another person, can be a most harmful form of paraphilia when it is forced upon a nonconsenting person. Some of the most brutal rapes involve elements of sexual sadism.

Except in the case of sexual masochism, paraphilias are believed to occur almost exclusively among men (Money & Wiedeking, 1980). The prevalence of paraphilias in the general population remains unknown, because people are generally unwilling to report these behaviors. Much of what we have learned about paraphilias derives from the reported experiences of paraphiles who have been apprehended for performing illegal acts (such as exposing themselves in public) and the few who have voluntarily sought help. The characteristics of others who have not been identified or studied remain virtually unknown.

We discuss the major types of paraphilia in this chapter, with the exception of *pedophilia*. In pedophilia, children become the objects of sexual arousal. Pedophilia often takes the form of sexual coercion of children, as in incest or sexual molestation. It is discussed in Chapter 19, along with other forms of coerced sexuality.

FETISHISM

The roots of the word *fetish* come from the French *fétiche,* which is thought to derive from the Portuguese *feitico,* meaning "magic charm." The "magic" in this case lies in an object's ability to arouse a person sexually. In **fetishism,** an inanimate object elicits sexual arousal. Articles of clothing (for example, women's panties, bras, lingerie, stockings, gloves, shoes, or boots) and materials made of rubber, leather, silk, or fur are among the more common fetishistic objects. Leather boots and high-heeled shoes are popular fetishistic objects.

The fetishist may act on the urges to engage in fetishistic behavior, such as by masturbating by stroking an object or while fantasizing about it, or he may be distressed about such urges or fantasies but not act upon them. In a related paraphilia, **partialism,** people are excessively aroused by a particular body part, such as the feet, breasts, or buttocks. Fetishism and partialism are believed to occur almost exclusively among males (American Psychiatric Association, 1987).

Most fetishes and partialisms are harmless. Fetishistic practices are almost always private and involve masturbation or are incorporated into coitus with a willing partner. Only rarely have fetishists coerced others into paraphilic activities. Yet some partialists have touched parts of women's bodies in public. And some fetishists have committed burglaries to acquire the fetishistic objects (Sargent, 1988).

TRANSVESTISM

Transvestism may be viewed as a type of fetish. Whereas other fetishists become sexually aroused by handling the fetishistic object while they masturbate, transvestites become excited by wearing articles of clothing—the fetishistic objects—of the opposite gender. A fetishist may find the object itself or sex involving the object erotically stimulating. For the transvestite, the object is sexually alluring only when it is worn. Transvestites, like other fetishists, are almost always males. True transvestism has only been described among heterosexual males, although such men may occasionally engage

Fetishism
A paraphilia in which an inanimate object such as an article of clothing or items made of rubber, leather, or silk elicit sexual arousal.

Partialism
A paraphilia related to fetishism in which sexual arousal is exaggeratedly associated with a particular body part, such as feet, breasts, or buttocks.

Learning Objective 2: Describe the behaviors associated with fetishism and partialism.

Transvestism
A paraphilia in which a person repeatedly cross-dresses to achieve sexual arousal or gratification, or is troubled by persistent, recurring urges to cross-dress. (From the Latin roots *trans-,* meaning "cross," and *vestis,* meaning "garment.") Also known as *transvestic fetishism.*

Fetishism. In fetishism, inanimate objects such as leather underclothes and garter belts, and other sexual paraphernalia come to elicit sexual arousal. Fetishists may derive sexual gratification by fondling, manipulating, or fantasizing about the object during masturbation, or they may insist that the object be present during sex, or be worn by their partners.

Learning Objective 3: Describe the behaviors and characteristics typical of transvestites.

Discussion Question: Why are almost all transvestites male? Could our greater restrictions on what is acceptable male attire play a role?

in homosexual activity. Most are married and otherwise masculine in behavior and style of dress (Wise & Meyer, 1980).

Transvestism is often confused with transsexualism, but there are important differences between them. Transvestites cross-dress because they find it sexually arousing. They have masculine gender identities and do not seek to change their anatomic sex. Transsexuals, by contrast, cross-dress because they are uncomfortable with the attire associated with their anatomic sex.

Like fetishism in general, the origins of transvestism remain obscure. There is no evidence of genetic, hormonal, or other physiological abnormalities in transvestism (Buhrich et al., 1979). Cross-dressing among transvestites typically begins during childhood or early adolescence (American Psychiatric Association, 1987). Transvestites often report a history of "petticoat punishment" during childhood, in which they were humiliated as a form of punishment by being dressed in girls' attire. Some authorities have speculated that the adult transvestite might be attempting psychologically to convert humiliation into mastery by achieving an erection and engaging in sexual activity despite being attired in female clothing (Geer et al., 1984). Transvestism can also be looked at as an attempt by males to escape the narrow confines of the masculine role (Bullough, 1991).

Cross-dressing is common in other cultures and has been reported in historical accounts of such figures as King Henry III of France, a sixteenth-century monarch who wanted to be considered a woman and to be addressed as "Her Majesty" (Geer et al., 1984). But cross-dressing may occur in other cultures for other reasons than sexual arousal, and in the case of King Henry III, it appears that transsexualism, and not transvestism, was involved.

TRUTH OR *FICTION?*
R E V I S I T E D

King Henry III of France insisted on being considered a woman and addressed as "Her Majesty." *True. However, the king appears to have been a transsexual rather than a transvestite.* •

Some men cross-dress for reasons other than sexual arousal and so are not "true transvestites." Some men make a living by impersonating women like Marilyn Monroe and Madonna on stage and are not motivated by sexual arousal. Among some segments of the gay male community, it is fashionable to masquerade as women. Gay men do not usually cross-dress to become sexually stimulated, however.

Transvestism may range from wearing a single female garment when alone to sporting dresses, wigs, makeup, and feminine mannerisms at a transvestite club. Some transvestites become sexually aroused by masquerading as women and attracting the interest of unsuspecting males. They sometimes entice these men or string them along until they find some excuse to back out before their anatomic sex is revealed. The great majority of

Transvestism. Transvestites cross-dress for the purpose of sexual gratification. Some transvestites sport feminine attire in public, others cross-dress only in the privacy of their own homes.

transvestites do not engage in antisocial or illegal behavior. Most practice their sexual predilection in private and would be horrified or deeply embarrassed to be discovered by associates while dressed in female attire.

Although some transvestites persuade their female partners to permit them to wear feminine attire during their sexual activities, most keep their transvestic urges and activities to themselves. A survey of 504 transvestite men showed that most had kept their transvestism a secret from their wives-to-be, hoping that they would not be bothered by their urge to cross-dress once they were married (Weinberg & Bullough, 1986, 1988). The urges continued into their marriages, and the wives eventually discovered their husbands' secrets, however. Seventy of the wives were interviewed (Bullough & Weinberg, 1989). The wives tended to react with confusion, surprise, or shock to discovering their husbands' cross-dressing. Most tried to be understanding at first, and some, however reluctantly, assisted their husbands in their cross-dressing, such as by helping them apply makeup. Yet the longer the women were married, the more negative their attitudes tended to become toward their husbands' cross-dressing. Over time, wives generally learned to be tolerant, though not supportive, of their husbands' cross-dressing.

EXHIBITIONISM

Exhibitionism
A paraphilia characterized by persistent, powerful urges and sexual fantasies involving exposing one's genitals to unsuspecting strangers for the purpose of achieving sexual arousal or gratification.

Learning Objective 4:
Describe the behaviors associated with exhibitionism, the effects on the victims, and the characteristics of exhibitionists.

Exhibitionism ("flashing") involves persistent, powerful urges and sexual fantasies involving exposing one's genitals to unsuspecting strangers for the purpose of achieving sexual arousal or gratification. The urges are either acted upon or are disturbing to the individual. Exhibitionists are almost always males. Only three cases of female exhibitionism have been reported in the scientific literature (Freund & Blanchard, 1986).

What we know of exhibitionists, as with most other paraphiles, is almost entirely derived from studies of men who have been apprehended or treated by mental health professionals. Such knowledge may yield a biased picture of exhibitionists (Cox, 1988). Although about one in three arrests for sexual offenses involves exhibitionism, relatively few reported incidents result in apprehension and conviction (Cox, 1988). Studies in England (Gittleson et al., 1978), Guatemala (Rhoads & Borjes, 1981), the United States, and Hong Kong (Cox et al., 1982) show that fewer than 20 percent of occurrences are reported to the police (Cox, 1988). The characteristics of most perpetrators may thus differ from those of people who have been available for study (Cox, 1988).

The prevalence of exhibitionism in the general population is unknown, but a survey of 846 college women at nine randomly selected U.S. universities found exposure to exhibitionism to be widespread. A third of the women reported that they had run into a "flasher" (Cox, 1988). A majority of the victimized women had been approached for the first time (some had been approached more than once) by 16 years of age. Only 15 of the women had reported these incidents to the police. The clinical definition of exhibitionism involves exposure to a *stranger,* but about a third (36%) of the incidents among the college women were committed by acquaintances, relatives, or "good friends" of the victim.

A Case of Transvestism

Most transvestites are married and engage in sexual activity with their wives. Yet they seek additional sexual gratification through dressing as women, as in the case of Archie:

Archie was a 55-year-old plumber who had been cross-dressing for many years. There was a time when he would go out in public as a woman, but as his prominence in the community grew, he became more afraid of being discovered in public. His wife Myrna knew of his "peccadillo," especially since he borrowed many of her clothes, and she also urged him to stay at home, offering to help him with his "weirdness." For many years his paraphilia had been restricted to the home.

The couple came to the clinic at the urging of the wife. Myrna described how Archie had imposed his will on her for 20 years. Archie would wear her undergarments and masturbate while she told him how disgusting he was. (The couple also regularly engaged in "normal" sexual intercourse, which Myrna enjoyed.) The cross-dressing situation had come to a head because a teenaged daughter had almost walked into the couple's bedroom while they were acting out Archie's fantasies.

With Myrna out of the consulting room, Archie explained how he grew up in a family with several older sisters. He described how underwear had been perpetually hanging all around the one bathroom to dry. As an adolescent Archie experimented with rubbing against articles of underwear, then with trying them on. On one occasion a sister walked in while he was modeling panties before the mirror. She told him he was a "dredge to society" and he straightaway experienced unparalleled sexual excitement. He masturbated when she left the room, and his orgasm was the strongest of his young life.

Archie did not think that there was anything wrong with wearing women's undergarments and masturbating. He was not about to give it up, regardless of whether his marriage was destroyed as a result. Myrna's main concern was finally separating herself from Archie's "sickness." She didn't care what he did any more, so long as he did it by himself. "Enough is enough," she said.

That was the compromise the couple worked out. Archie would engage in his fantasies by himself. He would choose times when Myrna was not at home, and she would not be informed of his activities. He would also be very, very careful to choose times when the children would not be around.

Six months later the couple were together and content. Archie had replaced Myrna's input into his fantasies with transvestic-sadomasochistic magazines. Myrna said, "I see no evil, hear no evil, smell no evil." They continued to have sexual intercourse. After a while, Myrna even forgot to check to see which underwear had been used.

(From Nevid et al., 1994, pp. 385–386)

The archetypal exhibitionist is young, unhappily married, and sexually repressed. An exhibitionist may claim that marital coitus is reasonably satisfactory, but that he also experiences the compulsion to expose himself to strangers. Many exhibitionists are single, however. They typically have difficulties relating to women and have been unable to establish meaningful heterosexual relationships.

Exhibitionism usually begins before age 18 (American Psychiatric Association, 1987). The urge to exhibit oneself, if not the actual act, usually begins in early adolescence, generally between the ages of 13 and 16 (Freund et al., 1988). The frequency of exhibitionism declines markedly after the age of 40 (American Psychiatric Association, 1987). The typical exhibitionist does not attempt further sexual contact with the victim and so does not usually pose a physical threat (American Psychiatric Association, 1987).

The police may sometimes trivialize exhibitionism as a "nuisance crime," but the psychological consequences among victims, especially young children, indicate that exhibitionism is not a victimless crime. Victims may feel violated and be bothered by recurrent images or nightmares for months or years. They may harbor misplaced guilt that they had unwittingly enticed the exhibitionist. They may blame themselves for reacting excessively or for failing to apprehend the perpetrator. They may also develop fears of venturing out on their own.

Exhibitionism. Exhibitionists seek sexual arousal or gratification by exposing their genitals to unsuspecting strangers. Most of the 238 exhibitionists in a recent Canadian study masturbated while exhibiting themselves or while fantasizing about it.

Geer and his colleagues (1984) see exhibitionism as an indirect means of expressing hostility and aggression toward women. Exposure may be an attempt by the exhibitionist to strike back at women because of a belief that women have wronged him in the past or have damaged his self-esteem by having failed to notice him or take him seriously. The direct expression of anger may be perceived as too risky, so the exhibitionist vents his rage by humiliating a defenseless stranger. Geer and his colleagues note that the urge to expose oneself almost always follows a conflict or a situation in which the exhibitionist feels that his masculinity has been insulted. Some evidence suggests that exhibitionists may be attempting to assert their masculinity by evoking a response from their victims. A number of exhibitionists have reported that they hoped that the women would enjoy the experience and be impressed with the size of their penises (Langevin et al., 1979).

Other studies show exhibitionists to be shy, dependent, passive, lacking in sexual and social skills, even inhibited (e.g., Dwyer, 1988). They tend to be self-critical, to have doubts about their masculinity, and to suffer from feelings of inadequacy, inferiority, and poor self-esteem (Blair & Lanyon, 1981; Dwyer, 1988). Many have had poor relationships with their fathers and over-protective mothers (Dwyer, 1988). Exhibitionists who are socially shy or inadequate may be using exhibitionism as a substitute for the intimate relationships they cannot otherwise develop (Freund, 1978; Kolarsky et al., 1978).

Discussion Question: How many of you have been victims of exhibitionists? How did you react? Would you react differently if this happened to you again?

Studies of apprehended exhibitionists show that the preferred victims are typically girls or young women (Freund & Blanchard, 1986). The typical exhibitionist drives up to, or walks in front of, a stranger and exposes his penis. In one sample of 130 exhibitionists, about 50 percent reported that they always or nearly always had erections when they exposed themselves (Langevin et al., 1979). After his victim has registered fear, disgust, confusion, or surprise, an exhibitionist will typically cover himself up and flee. He usually masturbates, either while exposing himself or shortly afterwards while thinking about the act and the victim's response (American Psychiatric Association, 1987; Blair & Lanyon, 1981). Some exhibitionists ejaculate during the act of exposure. Most of the 238 exhibitionists in a Canadian study reported masturbating to orgasm while exposing themselves or afterwards while fantasizing about it (Freund et al., 1988).

Exhibitionists may also need to risk being caught to experience a heightened erotic response (Stoller, 1977). The exhibitionist may even situate himself to increase the risk, as by repeatedly exposing himself in the same location or exposing himself while sitting in his own, easily identifiable car.

Courts nowadays tend to be hard on exhibitionists, partly because of evidence that shows that some exhibitionists progress to more serious crimes of sexual aggression. In one sample, about 10 percent of rapists and child molesters had begun their "sexual careers" by exposing themselves to strangers (Abel et al., 1984). This does not mean that exhibitionists inevitably become rapists and child molesters. Most do not.

Definitions of exhibitionism also bring into focus the boundaries between normal and abnormal behavior. Are exotic dancers (stripteasers) or nude sunbathers exhibitionists? After all, aren't they also exposing themselves to strangers? Exotic dancers—male

How to Respond to an Exhibitionist

It is understandable for an unsuspecting woman who is exposed to an exhibitionist to react with shock, surprise, or fear. Unfortunately, her display of shock or fear may reinforce the flasher's tendencies to expose himself. She may fear that the flasher, who has already broken at least one social code, is likely to assault her physically as well. Fortunately, most exhibitionists are physically harmless. They usually do not seek actual sexual contact with their victims and run away before they can be apprehended by the police or passersby.

Some women may respond with anger, insults, even arguments that the offender should feel ashamed. A display of anger may reinforce exhibitionism. We do not recommend that the victim insult the flasher, lest it provoke a violent response. Although most exhibitionists are nonviolent, about one in ten has considered or attempted rape (Gebhard et al., 1965). As a general rule, the closer an exhibitionist is, the more likely it is that he may become violent.

When possible, showing no reaction at all or simply continuing on one's way may be the best response. If women do desire to respond to the flasher, they might calmly say something like, "You really need professional help. You should see a professional to help you with this problem." Afterwards they should promptly report the incident to police, so that authorities can apprehend the offender.

or female—usually remove their clothes to sexually excite or entertain an expectant audience, not themselves. Their motive is to earn a living or (arguably) to express themselves in dance. Sunbathers in their "birthday suits" may also seek to sexually arouse others, not themselves. Of course, they may also be seeking an all-over tan or trying to avoid feeling encumbered by clothing. In any case, stripteasers and sunbathers do not expose themselves to unsuspecting others. Thus these behaviors are not regarded as exhibitionistic.

TRUTH OR *FICTION?*
R E V I S I T E D

Nude sunbathers are exhibitionists. *Nude sunbathers are not exhibitionists, at least not in terms of the clinical definition of the disorder. Exhibitionists seek to become sexually aroused by exposing themselves to unsuspecting victims, not to show off their physical attractiveness.* •

It is also normal to become sexually excited while stripping before one's sex partner. Such stripping is done to elicit a positive response from one's partner, not surprise or shock from a stranger.

OBSCENE TELEPHONE CALLING

Telephone scatologia
A paraphilia characterized by the making of obscene telephone calls. (From the Greek *skatos,* meaning "excrement.")

Learning Objective 5:
Describe the behaviors typical of obscene telephone callers.

Like the exhibitionist, obscene phone callers (almost all of whom are male) are motivated to become sexually aroused by shocking their victims. Whereas an exhibitionist exposes his genitals to produce the desired response, the obscene phone caller exposes himself verbally by using the telephone to utter obscenities and sexual provocations to a nonconsenting person. Because of such similarities, obscene telephone calling is sometimes considered a subtype of exhibitionism. The American Psychiatric Association (1987) labels this type of paraphilia **telephone scatologia** (lewdness).

Relatively few obscene callers are women (Matek, 1988). Women who are charged with such offenses are generally motivated by rage for some actual or fantasized rejection rather than the desire for sexual arousal. They use the phone to hurl sexual invectives against men whom they feel have wronged them. By contrast, male obscene phone callers are generally motivated by a desire for sexual excitement and usually choose their victims randomly from the phone book or by chance dialing. They typically masturbate during the phone call or shortly afterwards. Despite the offensiveness of their actions, most obscene phone callers are not dangerous. Nor do most make repeat calls to the same person (Reinisch, 1990).

There are many patterns of obscene phone calling (Matek, 1988). Some callers limit themselves to obscenities; others make sexual overtures. Some just breathe heavily into the receiver; others describe their masturbatory activity to their victims. Some profess to have previously met the victim at a social gathering or through a mutual acquaintance. Some even present themselves as "taking a sex survey," and ask a series of personally revealing questions.

The typical obscene phone caller is a socially inadequate heterosexual male who has had difficulty forming intimate relationships with women. The relative safety and anonymity of the telephone may shield him from the risk of rejection he would face from direct contacts with women. A reaction of shock or fright from his victims may fill him with feelings of power and control that are lacking in his life, especially in his relationships with women. The obscenities may vent the rage that he holds against women who have rejected him or failed to notice him.

Obscene phone calls are illegal, but it has been difficult for legal authorities to track down perpetrators (Matek, 1988). A new telephone service, *call tracing,* which is now available in some communities, can help police track obscene or offending phone callers. Call tracing works in different ways in different locales. Another new service that is also available in some communities, *Caller ID,* shows the caller's telephone number on a display panel on the receiving party's telephone. Though this service may deter some obscene callers, others may opt to use public phones instead of their home phones. Callers may also be able to electronically block the display of their telephone numbers. Check with your local telephone company if you are interested in these services.

What should a woman do if she receives an obscene phone call? Advice generally parallels that given to women who are victimized by exhibitionists. Above all, women are advised to remain calm and not reveal shock or fright, since such reactions tend to reinforce the caller and increase the probability of repeat calls. Women may be best advised to say nothing at all and gently hang up the receiver. A woman might alternatively offer a brief response that alludes to the caller's problems before hanging up, such as suggesting that he seek professional help (Matek, 1980). She might say in a calm but strong voice, "It's unfortunate you have this problem. I think you should seek professional help." If she should receive repeated calls, the woman might request an unlisted number or contact the police about tracing the calls. Many women list themselves only by their initials in the phone directory so as to disguise their gender. But since this practice is so widespread, obscene callers may surmise that people listed by initials are women living alone. Women have also been advised by some police officials to blow a whistle in the caller's ear to discourage repeated obscene calls. But Powell (1991) cautions against employing tactics that might anger an obscene caller, lest they provoke a violent response. After all, the caller may have the woman's name and address. Retaliation by an obscene caller is apparently rare, however (Powell, 1991).

VOYEURISM

Voyeurism involves strong, repetitive urges to observe unsuspecting strangers who are naked, disrobing, or engaged in sexual relations (American Psychiatric Association, 1987). The voyeur becomes sexually aroused by the act of watching and typically does not seek sexual relations with the observed person. Like fetishism and exhibitionism, voyeurism is found almost exclusively among males. It usually begins before the age of 15 (American Psychiatric Association, 1987).

The voyeur may masturbate while "peeping" or afterward while "replaying" the incident in his imagination or engaging in voyeuristic fantasies. The voyeur may fantasize about making love to the observed person but have no intention of actually doing so.

Are people who become sexually aroused by the sight of their lovers undressing voyeurs? What about people who enjoy watching pornographic films or stripteasers? No,

Learning Objective 6:
Describe the behaviors and
characteristics typical of
voyeurs.

no, and no. For one thing, in these cases the people being observed are not unsuspecting strangers. The lover knows that his or her partner is watching. Porn actors and strippers know that others will be viewing them. They would not be "performing" if they did not expect or have an audience.

It is also perfectly normal for men and women to be sexually stimulated by the sight of other people who are nude, undressing, or engaged in sexual relations. Voyeurism is characterized by urges to "peep" on *unsuspecting* strangers.

TRUTH OR *FICTION?*
R E V I S I T E D

People who enjoy watching their mates undress are voyeurs. *People who enjoy watching their partners undress are* not *voyeurs. In these cases the undresser is knowingly and willingly being observed, and the watcher's enjoyment is completely normal. Voyeurs target unsuspecting victims.* •

Voyeurs are also known as "peepers," or *peeping Toms*. Why "peeping Toms"? According to an old English legend, Lady Godiva asked the townspeople not to look upon her while she rode horseback in the nude to protest the oppressive tax that her husband, a landowner, had imposed on them. A tailor named Tom of Coventry was the only townsperson not to grant her request.

Voyeurs often put themselves in risky situations in which they face the prospect of being discovered or apprehended. They may risk physical injury by perching themselves in trees or otherwise assuming precarious positions to catch a preferred view of their target. They will occupy rooftops and fire escapes in brutal winter weather. Peepers can be exceedingly patient in their outings, wait hour after hour, night after night, for a furtive glimpse of an unsuspecting person. One 25-year-old, recently married man secreted himself in his mother-in-law's closet, waiting for her to disrobe. Part of the sexual excitement seems to stem from the risks voyeurs run. The need for elements of risk in their voyeurism may explain why voyeurs are not known to frequent nude beaches or nudist camps where it is acceptable to look (though not to stare) at others (Tollison & Adams, 1979).

Although most voyeurs are nonviolent, some go on to commit violent crimes like assault and rape (Langevin et al., 1985). Voyeurs who break into and enter homes or buildings, or who tap at windows to gain the attention of victims, are among the more dangerous.

TRUTH OR *FICTION?*
R E V I S I T E D

Exhibitionists and voyeurs are never violent. *It is incorrect to say that exhibitionists and voyeurs are* never *violent. Exhibitionistic and voyeuristic activities per se do not involve outright violence, but some exhibitionists and voyeurs have been known to be violent, and they may, if provoked or angered, react violently.* •

Compared to other types of sex offenders, voyeurs tend to be less sexually experienced and are less likely to be married (Gebhard et al., 1965). Like exhibitionists, voyeurs tend to harbor feelings of inadequacy and poor self-esteem and to lack social and sexual skills (Dwyer, 1988). They may thus have difficulty forming romantic relationships with women. For this shy and socially inadequate type of voyeur, "peeping" affords sexual gratification without risk of rejection. Yet not all voyeurs are socially awkward and inept with women.

Sexual masochism
A paraphilia characterized by the desire or need for pain or humiliation to enhance sexual arousal so that gratification may be attained. (From Leopold von Sacher-Masoch.)

SEXUAL MASOCHISM

Although pleasure and pain may seem like polar opposites, some people experience sexual pleasure through having pain or humiliation inflicted on them by their sex partners. People who associate the receipt of pain or humiliation with sexual arousal are called **sexual masochists.** A sexual masochist either acts upon or is distressed by persistent urges and sexual fantasies involving the desire to be bound, flogged, humiliated, or made to suffer in some way by a sexual partner so as to achieve sexual excitement. In extreme cases the person is incapable of becoming sexually aroused unless pain or humiliation is incorporated into the sexual act.

TRUTH OR *FICTION?*

R E V I S I T E D

Some people cannot become sexually aroused unless they are bound, flogged, or humiliated by their sex partners. *It is true that some sexual masochists cannot become sexually aroused unless they are bound, flogged, or humiliated by their sex partners.* •

Learning Objective 7:
Describe the behaviors and characteristics typical of masochists and sadists and discuss the S&M subculture.

Bondage
Ritual restraint, as by shackles, as practiced by many sexual masochists.

Sexual sadists
People who become sexually aroused by inflicting pain or humiliation on others.

Sexual masochism is the only paraphilia that is found among women with some frequency (American Psychiatric Association, 1987). Even sexual masochism is much more prevalent among men than women, however. Male masochists may outnumber females by a margin of 20 to 1 (American Psychiatric Association, 1987).

Masochism is named after the Austrian storyteller Leopold von Sacher-Masoch (1835–1895). He wrote tales of men who derived sexual satisfaction from having a female partner inflict pain on them, typically by flagellation (beating or whipping).

Sexual masochists may derive pleasure from various types of punishing experiences, including being restrained (a practice known as **bondage**), blindfolded (*sensory* bondage), spanked, whipped, or made to perform humiliating acts, such as walking around on all fours and licking the boots or shoes of the sex partner, or being subjected to vulgar insults. Some masochists have their partners humiliate them by urinating or defecating on them. Some masochists prefer a particular source of pain. Others seek an assortment. But we should not think that sexual masochists enjoy other types of pain that are not connected with their sexual practices. Sexual masochists are no more likely than anyone else to derive pleasure from the pain they experience when they accidentally stub their toes or touch a hot appliance. Pain only has erotic value within a sexual context. It must be part of an elaborate sexual ritual.

Sexual masochists and **sexual sadists** often form sexual relationships to meet each other's needs. Some sexual masochists enlist the services of prostitutes, or obtain the cooperation of their regular sexual partners, to enact their masochistic fantasies.

It may seem contradictory for pain to become connected with sexual pleasure. The association of sexual arousal with mildly painful stimuli is actually quite common, however. Kinsey and his colleagues (1953) reported that perhaps as many as one person in four has experienced erotic sensations from being bitten during lovemaking. The eroticization of mild forms of pain (love bites, hair pulls, minor scratches) may fall within the normal range of sexual variation. Pain from these sources increases overall bodily arousal, which may enhance sexual excitement. Some of us become sexually excited when our partners "talk dirty" to us or call us vulgar names. When the urge for pain for purposes of sexual arousal becomes so persistent or strong that it overshadows other sources of sexual stimulation, or when the masochistic experience causes physical or psychological harm, we may say that the boundary between normality and abnormality has been breached.

TRUTH OR *FICTION?*

R E V I S I T E D

It is considered normal to enjoy some mild forms of pain during sexual activity. *It is, in fact, considered normal to enjoy some mild forms of pain during sexual activity. Love bites, hair pulls, and minor scratches are examples of sources of pain that are considered to fall within normal limits.* •

Baumeister (1988a) proposes that sexual masochism may represent an escape from one's normal level of self-awareness. Our ordinary sense of independent and responsible selfhood may become burdensome or stressful at times when we are pressured to make difficult decisions or are fearful that our actions may hurt others or meet with social disapproval. Sexual masochism, in this view, provides a temporary reprieve from the responsibilities of independent selfhood, a kind of blunting of one's ordinary level of self-awareness that is achieved by "...focusing on immediate sensations (both painful and pleasant) and on being a sexual object" (Baumeister, 1988a, p. 54).

Hypoxyphilia
A practice in which a person seeks to enhance sexual arousal, usually during masturbation, by becoming deprived of oxygen. (From the Greek root meaning "under" [*hypo*-].)

Sexual masochism can range from relatively benign practices to some that are potentially lethal, like **hypoxyphilia.** People who practice hypoxyphilia may place plastic bags over their heads or nooses around their necks during sexual acts to enhance their sexual arousal by being temporarily deprived of oxygen. Or they may apply pressure to their chests. Oxygen deprivation is usually accompanied by sexual fantasies of being strangled by a lover. People usually discontinue oxygen deprivation before they lose consciousness, but some miscalculations result in death due to suffocation (Blanchard & Hucker, 1991; Cosgray et al., 1991).

SEXUAL SADISM

Sexual sadism
A paraphilia characterized by the desire or need to inflict pain or humiliation on others to enhance sexual arousal so that gratification is attained. (From the Marquis de Sade.)

Sadism is named after the infamous Marquis de Sade (1774–1814), a Frenchman who wrote tales of becoming sexually aroused by inflicting pain or humiliation on others. The virtuous Justine, the heroine of his best-known novel of the same name, endures terrible suffering at the hands of fiendish men. She is at one time bound and spread-eagled so that bloodhounds can savage her. She then seeks refuge with a surgeon who tries to dismember her. Later she falls into the clutches of a saber-wielding mass murderer, but Nature saves her with a timely thunderbolt.

Sexual sadism is characterized by persistent and powerful urges and sexual fantasies involving the inflicting of pain and suffering on others to achieve sexual excitement or gratification. The urges are acted on or are disturbing enough to cause personal distress. Some sexual sadists cannot become sexually aroused unless they make their sex partners suffer. Others can become sexually excited without such acts.

Some sadists hurt or humiliate willing partners, such as prostitutes or sexual masochists. Others—clearly a small minority—stalk and attack nonconsenting victims. When sexual sadism is inflicted on a nonconsenting person, it is a form of sexual assault or rape.

Sadomasochism
A mutually gratifying sexual interaction between consenting sex partners in which sexual arousal is associated with the infliction and receipt of pain or humiliation. Commonly known as *S&M*.

SADOMASOCHISM Sadomasochism (or *S&M*) involves *mutually gratifying sexual interactions between consenting partners.* Occasional S&M is quite common among the general population. Couples may incorporate mild or light forms of S&M in their lovemaking now and then, such as mild dominance and submission games or gentle physical restraint. It is also not uncommon for lovers to scratch or bite their partners to heighten their mutual arousal during coitus. They generally do not inflict severe pain or damage, however.

Twenty-two percent of the men and 12 percent of the women surveyed by Kinsey and his colleagues (1953) reported at least some sexual response to sadomasochistic stories. Janus and Janus (1993) reported that 14 percent of the men in their national sample, and 11 percent of the women, had some experience with sadomasochism. Although some milder forms of sadomasochism may fall within the boundaries of normal sexual variation, sadomasochism becomes pathological when such fantasies are acted upon in ways that become destructive, dangerous, or distressing to oneself or others, as we find in the following case example:

> A 25-year-old female graduate student described a range of masochistic experiences. She reported feelings of sexual excitement during arguments with her husband when he would scream at her or hit her in a rage. She would sometimes taunt him to make love to her in a brutal fashion, as though she were being raped. She found the brutality and sense of being punished to be sexually stimulating. She had also begun having sex with strange men and enjoyed being physically punished by them during sex more than any other type of sexual stimulus. Being beaten or whipped produced the most intense sexual experiences she had ever had. Although she recognized the dangers posed by her sexual behavior, and felt somewhat ashamed about it, she was not sure that she wanted treatment for "it" because of the pleasure that it provided her.
>
> (Adapted from Spitzer et al., 1989, pp. 87–88)

In one subculture, sadomasochism is the preferred or even the exclusive form of sexual gratification. People in this subculture seek one another out through mutual contacts, S&M social organizations, or personal ads in S&M magazines. The S&M subculture has spawned magazines and clubs catering to people who describe themselves as "into

A WORLD OF DIVERSITY

Cross-Cultural Perspectives on Sadomasochism

The use of painful stimulation to heighten sexual excitement is not unique to our culture or species. Ford and Beach (1951) suggest that all men and women can respond erotically to mild pain. The particular culture in which a person is reared shapes this capacity from early childhood. Use of painful stimulation during coitus is absent in some cultures but widespread in others:

> Choroti women spit in their lovers' face during coitus, and the Apinaye woman may bite off bits of her partner's eyebrows, noisily spitting them to one side. Ponapean men usually tug at the woman's eyebrows, occasionally yanking out tufts of hair. Trukese women customarily poke a finger into the man's ear when they are highly aroused.

Women of many societies bite the skin of the partner's neck, shoulder, or chest when sexual excitement is at its height. The red marks left on the skin may be a subject of jest; the Toda greet any person who is so marked with the quip, "you have been bitten by a tiger."[1]

(Ford and Beach, 1951, p. 56)

In consensual sexual relations in these cultures the infliction of pain is invariably mutual, or bilateral: the man bites, scratches, or pulls his partner's hair and she does the same to him. Ford and Beach found no evidence for exclusively masochistic or sadistic sexual behavior.

Ford and Beach also note that the association between painful stimulation and sexual arousal is common only in sexually permissive societies. In cultures in which painful stimulation is used during sex, women usually play an active, assertive role in sexual relations, are accorded equal rights in initiating sexual activity, and are expected to achieve orgasm through coitus. We might conjecture that the use of milder forms of painful stimulation to heighten sexual arousal became more commonplace in our own society with the liberalization of sexual attitudes and the lessening of restrictive gender roles that occurred during the 1950s and 1960s. The development of an institutionalized S&M subculture appears to be unique to Western society, however (Weinberg, 1987).

[1]The Choroti and Apinaye people live in South America. The Ponapean and Trukese people live in the South Pacific. The Toda people live in India.

S&M," as well as sex shops that sell sadomasochistic paraphernalia. These include leather restraints and leather face masks that resemble the ancient masks of executioners.

There is a U.S. subculture in which sexual sadists and sexual masochists form liaisons to inflict and receive pain and humiliation during sexual activity. *True. It is called the* S&M *subculture and is catered to by sex shops and magazines.* •

Participants in sadomasochism often engage in highly elaborate rituals involving dominance and submission. Rituals are carefully staged, as if they were scenes in a stage play (Weinberg et al., 1984). In the "master and slave" game, the sadist humiliates the masochist by leading the masochist around by a leash. The masochist follows orders from the sadist and performs degrading or menial acts. In "bondage and discipline" (B&D), the dominant partner restrains the submissive partner and then flagellates (spanks or whips) or sexually stimulates the submissive partner. The erotic appeal of bondage seems connected with physically controlling another person or being controlled.

Various types of stimulation may be used to administer pain during S&M encounters, but pain is not always employed. When it is, it is usually mild or moderate. Psychological pain, or humiliation, may be as common a part of the S&M ritual as physical pain (Mosher & Levitt, 1987). Pain may also be used symbolically, as in the case of a sadist

S&M Paraphernalia. People who participate in S&M often incorporate handcuffs and other paraphernalia into their sadomasochistic encounters.

who uses a harmless, soft rubber paddle to spank the masochist. So the erotic appeal of pain for some S&M participants may derive from its use within a ritual that symbolizes the complete control of one person over another, rather than from the pain itself (Weinberg, 1987).

Extreme forms of pain, such as torture or severe beatings, are rarely reported by sadomasochists (Breslow et al., 1985). Masochists may seek pain, but they carefully avoid serious injury and avoid partners who are known within the S&M subculture to injure their lovers (Baumeister, 1988b).

S&M participants may be heterosexual, gay, or bisexual (Breslow et al., 1986). They may assume either the masochistic or the sadistic role, or may alternate roles depending on the sexual script that they are enacting. Persons who seek sexual excitement by enacting both sadistic and masochistic roles are known as *sadomasochists*. In heterosexual relationships the partners may reverse traditional gender roles. The man may assume the submissive or masochistic role and the woman may take the dominant or sadistic role (Reinisch, 1990).

A survey of S&M participants drawn from ads in S&M magazines found that about three out of four were male and about one in four female (Breslow et al., 1985). Most were married. Women respondents engaged in S&M more frequently and had a greater number of different partners than men. (Apparently a greater number of men than women seek partners for S&M.) A listing of the sadomasochistic sexual preferences reported by male and female respondents is shown in Table 18.1.

TABLE 18.1 Sexual preferences of male and female participants in S&M encounters (percentages)

Interest	Male	Female
Spanking	79	80
Master-slave relationships	79	76
Oral sex	77	90
Masturbation	70	73
Bondage	67	88
Humiliation	65	61
Erotic lingerie	63	88
Restraint	60	83
Anal sex	58	51
Pain	51	34
Whipping	47	39
Rubber/leather	42	42
Boots/shoes	40	49
Verbal abuse	40	51
Stringent bondage	39	54
Enemas	33	22
Torture	32	32
Golden showers (urination)	30	37
Transvestism	28	20
Petticoat punishment	25	20
Toilet activities	19	12

Source: Breslow et al. (1986). Comparisons among heterosexual, bisexual and homosexual male sadomasochists. *Journal of Homosexuality, 13,* 83–107. Copyright © 1986 by the Haworth Press, Inc. All rights reserved. Reprinted with permission.

The causes of sexual masochism and sadism, as of other paraphilias, are unclear. Ford and Beach (1951) speculated that humans may possess a physiological capacity to experience heightened sexual arousal from the receipt or infliction of pain (which may explain the prevalence of love bites). Mild pain may heighten physiological arousal both in the aggressor and victim, adding to the effects of sexual stimulation. Yet intense pain is likely to decrease rather than increase sexual arousal. We should not be surprised, then, that most sadomasochists limit the amount of pain they inflict or receive. Still, we do not know why pain becomes highly eroticized for some people (Weinberg, 1987).

Beyond its ability to heighten arousal, pain may have more direct biological links to pleasure. Natural chemicals called *endorphins*, similar to opiates, are released in the brain in response to pain messages and produce feelings of euphoria and general well-being. Perhaps, then, pleasure is derived from pain during sadomasochistic encounters due to the release or augmentation of these pleasure-inducing chemicals in the brain (Weinberg, 1987). This theory fails to explain the erotic appeal of sadomasochistic encounters that involve minimal or symbolic pain, however. Nor does it explain the erotic appeal to the sadist of inflicting pain.

Whatever their causes, the roots of sexual masochism and sadism apparently date to childhood. Sadomasochistic behavior commonly begins in early adulthood, but sadomasochistic fantasies are likely to have been present during childhood (American Psychiatric Association, 1987; Breslow et al., 1986).

FROTTEURISM

Frotteurism (also known in slang as "mashing") involves rubbing against or touching a nonconsenting person. As with other paraphilias, a diagnosis of frotteurism requires either acting upon these urges or being distressed by them. Frotteurism has been reported exclusively among males (Spitzer et al., 1989).

Most frotteuristic acts take place in crowded places, such as buses, subway cars, or elevators. The man finds the rubbing or the touching to be sexually stimulating, not the coercive nature of the act. While rubbing against a woman, he may fantasize a consensual, affectionate sexual relationship with her. Typically the man incorporates images of his mashing within his masturbation fantasies. Frotteurism also incorporates a related practice, **toucherism:** the persistent urge to fondle nonconsenting strangers.

Frotteuristic contact may be so fleeting and furtive that the woman victim may not realize what has happened or protest very much (Spitzer et al., 1989). Frotteurs thus stand little chance of being apprehended. Consider the case of a man who victimized a thousand or so women within a decade but was arrested only twice:

> Charles, 45, was seen by a psychiatrist following his second arrest for rubbing against a woman in the subway. He would select as his target a woman in her 20s as she entered the subway station. He would then position himself behind her on the platform and wait for the train to arrive. He would then follow her into the subway car and when the doors closed would begin bumping his penis against her buttocks, while fantasizing that they were enjoying having intercourse in a loving and consensual manner. About half of the time he would ejaculate into a plastic bag that he had wrapped around his penis to prevent staining his pants. He would then continue on his way to work. Sometimes when he hadn't ejaculated he would change trains and seek another victim. While he felt guilty for a time after each episode, he would soon become preoccupied with thoughts about his next encounter. He never gave any thought to the feelings his victims might have about what he had done to them. While he was married to the same woman for 25 years, he appears to be rather socially inept and unassertive, especially with women.
>
> (Adapted from Spitzer et al., 1989, pp. 106–107)

Although this frotteur was married, many have difficulties forming relationships with women and are handicapped by fears of rejection. Frotteurism provides sexual contact in a relatively nonthreatening context.

Frotteurism
A paraphilia which is characterized by recurrent, powerful sexual urges and related fantasies involving rubbing against or touching a nonconsenting person. (From the French *frottage*, which refers to a technique that artists use to make a drawing by rubbing a pencil, chalk, etc., on a paper laid over a raised object.)

Toucherism
A practice related to frotteurism and characterized by the persistent urge to fondle nonconsenting strangers.

Learning Objective 8:
Describe the behaviors associated with frotteurism, zoophilia, necrophilia, and other less common paraphilias.

Paraphilias as Sexual Addictions

In his book *The Sexual Addiction* (1983), Patrick Carnes suggests that some paraphiles suffer from a sexual addiction, a nonchemical form of addiction. Sexual addicts ("sexaholics") may feel unable to resist their sexual urges and may act upon them indiscriminately, remaining oblivious to resultant harm or damage they cause. Carnes argues that sexual addicts use sex in much the same way that drug addicts and alcoholics use drugs or alcohol: to alter their moods and temporarily relieve psychological states of discomfort, such as depression or anxiety. In the end, however, the destructive nature of the paraphilia reinforces feelings of shame and worthlessness.

Carnes identifies a four-step cycle through which sexual addictions progress and gather strength. Let us apply this model to exhibitionism:

1. *Preoccupation.* The person enters a trancelike state characterized by a preoccupation with thoughts about exposing himself, leading to a strong craving to commit the act.
2. *Ritualization.* The person begins t o act upon the exhibitionistic urge. He engages in rituals that precede the act in order to increase his level of sexual arousal, such as driving a route through a park frequented by women walking alone.
3. *Compulsive sexual behavior.* The person exposes himself, while feeling that he cannot control or prevent the act.
4. *Despair.* Whereas most people feel pleasure and a release from sexual tension following sex, the exhibitionist sinks into feelings of hopelessness and despair over his inability to control his exhibitionistic urges. Such feelings may be temporarily offset by recurrent preoccupation with the paraphilia, leading to the completion of a new cycle. But the completion of each cycle provides further confirmation of personal unworthiness.

The concept of sexual addiction may not apply to all paraphilias or all paraphiles. Fetishists and transvestites, for example, may feel in control of their sexual urges, not controlled by them. They may not become preoccupied with paraphilic thoughts and fantasies or experience irresistible cravings to perform paraphilic acts.

The view of paraphilias as addictions has met with controversy within the scientific community. Some authorities believe that paraphilias are forms of sexual compulsion, which are more akin to compulsive behaviors such as compulsive hand-washing or compulsive gambling than to chemical addictions (Coleman, 1986; Goldberg, 1987). The model of sexual addiction may hold some promise in the development of treatment approaches for paraphilias, however. Treatment might be modeled after approaches for the chemical addictions and alcoholism, such as Alcoholics Anonymous (AA), in which people with chemical dependencies are encouraged to confront their addictions and learn to cope with their urges. Self-help groups in this mold, such as Sexaholics Anonymous and Sex Addicts Anonymous, have been formed in some communities to help people who feel unable to control their sexual urges. It will be interesting to see whether evidence supports the utility of this approach.

OTHER PARAPHILIAS

Let us consider some other less common paraphilias.

Zoophilia
A paraphilia involving persistent or repeated sexual urges and related fantasies involving sexual contact with animals.

ZOOPHILIA A person with **zoophilia** experiences repeated, intense urges and related fantasies involving sexual contact with animals. As with other paraphilias, the urges may be acted upon or cause personal distress. A child or adolescent who shows some sexual response to an occasional episode of rough-and-tumble play with the family pet is thus not displaying zoophilia.

The term *bestiality* applies to actual sexual contact with an animal. Human sexual contact with animals, mythical and real, has a long history. Michelangelo's painting *Leda and the Swan* depicts the Greek god Zeus taking the form of a swan to mate with a woman, Leda. Zeus was also portrayed as taking the form of a bull or serpent to mate

Hypersexuality and Gender

Is a woman who enjoys a hearty sexual appetite and engages in a series of brief sexual encounters a "nymphomaniac"? What about a man with a similarly active sexual lifestyle? What term might we use to describe him? How might the labels we use to describe men and women with heightened sexual drives reflect underlying sexist biases or double standards in our society? Where should we draw the line separating normal from excessive sexual drives?

Consider the following case description:

> Sarah R., a never-married, 39-year-old artist became sexually active in her junior year in high school and has rarely been without at least one or two lovers ever since. Whenever she has not had an opportunity for sexual intercourse for several weeks or longer, for one reason or another, she has felt quite uncomfortable, or as she put it, "horny and hard-up." She has had two unwanted pregnancies, both of which resulted in abortions and has contracted gonorrhea on three separate occasions and has suffered several times from infestations of pubic lice. She continues to be troubled with recurrent episodes of genital herpes. She generally limits her sexual relationships to one or two partners, but has on occasion maintained sexual relationships at the same time with three or four men. She engages in sexual intercourse two or three times a week, on the average, and engages in masturbation to relieve her sexual urges when intercourse is not possible.
>
> Both her family practitioner and gynecologist, who have treated her for years, consider her to be a nymphomaniac. Her gynecologist says of her, "Of course she has herpes. What can you expect with the kind of sexual excesses she indulges in? She's a real nympho."
>
> (Goldberg, 1987, p. 204)

Would you have reached the same conclusion as the woman's physicians? Why or why not? What criteria would you use to define **nymphomania**? Perhaps most readers have heard of nymphomania, but only a few are likely to be acquainted with the term describing the same condition in men, **satyriasis. Don Juanism** is another term for the condition.

The fact that nymphomania is more commonly used in our society than the male counterpart underscores the traditional double standard in Western society. Greater sexual liberties are accorded to men than women. A man who has a number of flings is likely to be labeled a "playboy," a "Casanova," or even a "stud." A woman who does so is likely to be branded with labels which carry more negative connotations, such as "nympho," "slut," or "whore," however.

Clinicians prefer to use the term **hypersexuality** to refer to nymphomania in women and satyriasis in men, thereby avoiding disparaging connotations. No absolute criteria exist for determining hypersexuality or establishing the boundary between normal sexuality and hypersexuality, however. Some people might consider a person who requires a sexual release through masturbation or coitus more than once daily to be hypersexual, whereas others draw the line at two, three, or perhaps six or ten or more times daily. Among some couples, the partner desiring less frequent sexual activity may label the other as "oversexed." But what defines "oversexed" in one relationship may be considered normal, even subnormal, in another.

Nymphomania

An excessive, insatiable sexual appetite or drive in women. (From the Greek roots *nymphe,* meaning "a bride," and *mania,* which means "madness.")

Satyriasis

An excessive, insatiable sexual appetite or drive in men. (After *satyr,* a sexually insatiable, goat-legged crea-

with humans. In the Old Testament, God is said to have put to death people who had relations with animals. The Greek historian Herodotus notes that goats at the Egyptian temple at Mendes were trained to copulate with people.

Although the prevalence of zoophilia in the general population is unknown, Kinsey and his colleagues (1948, 1953) found that about 8 percent of male and 3 to 4 percent of female subjects admitted to sexual contacts with animals. Men more often had sexual contact with farm animals, such as calves and sheep, whereas women more often reported sexual contacts with household pets. Men were more likely to masturbate or copulate with the animals. Women more often reported general body contact. Both sexes reported encouraging the animals to lick their genitals. A few women reported that they had

Clinicians may weigh the compulsivity or self-defeating nature of the behavior in determining the boundaries of hypersexuality, not the sheer frequency of sexual activity. Hypersexual people may use sex as a means of buttressing a flagging sense of self-esteem. They may feel driven to a series of sexual conquests or brief encounters to reassure themselves that they are desirable, or masculine or feminine enough. Because they lack true intimacy, however, the encounters leave them feeling empty and sexually unfulfilled. Such relationships provide only a temporary salve for relieving feelings of self-doubt or unworthiness. The person quickly loses sexual interest in the new partner once the conquest or brief encounter has occurred and begins searching for another. Partners are treated like objects to be used and discarded.

Hypersexuality should not be confused with promiscuity. People who are promiscuous are in control of their actions and can exercise discrimination in their choice of sexual partners, even though they may be more liberal in their sexual mores and behavior than the general society. The hyper-sexual person feels driven or compelled to engage in sexual acts with little if any regard to consequences of choice of partners, however. Another difference is that promiscuous people typically find sexual satisfaction in their sexual activity, whereas hypersexual people seldom if ever feel satisfied.

Hypersexuality is sometimes likened to a sexual addiction. Like drug addicts who have cravings for addictive substances that they feel unable to control, hypersexual people may feel "addicted" to or controlled by their sexual urges and desires.

Return to Sarah. Do the facts of her case suggest hypersexuality? Did Sarah feel a lack of control over her sexual urges? Did she feel compelled to engage in sexual behaviors that put herself at risk of incurring unwanted pregnancies or sexually transmitted diseases?

Goldberg (1987) argues that Sarah's physicians labeled her as a nymphomaniac because her behavior did not meet social expectations of female sexuality. Goldberg (1987) comments, "In all likelihood, a 39-year-old man living the sort of life that Sarah is living would not be regarded as suffering from satyriasis or, indeed, as being sexually abnormal in any way" (p. 204). Does the label of nymphomania represent a sexist tendency to judge women by a different set of social standards than men?

Satyr. The satyr is a figure in Greek mythology depicted as part man, part goat, and described as having an insatiable sexual appetite. The word is the root of the term *satyriasis,* which refers to an excessive, uncontrollable sexual desire in men. It may reflect upon the cultural double standard in our society that the equivalent term for women, *nymphomania,* is much more widely known than its male counterpart.

ture with pointed ears and short horns in Greek mythology.

Don Juanism
An excessive, insatiable sexual appetite or drive in men. (After the fictional Spanish nobleman who was unable to obtain true sexual gratification despite numerous affairs.)

trained a dog to engage in coitus with them. Urban-rural differences also emerged. Rates of bestiality were higher among boys reared on farms. Compared to only a few city boys, 17 percent of farm boys had reached orgasm at some time through sexual contact with dogs, cows, and goats. These contacts were generally restricted to adolescence, when human outlets were not available. Still, adults sometimes engage in sexual contacts with animals, generally because of curiosity, novelty, or for a sexual release when human partners are unavailable (Tollison & Adams, 1979). Whether or not such contacts constitute zoophilia depends upon their frequency and intensity or whether they cause the person distress. In most cases true zoophilia is associated with deep-seated psychological problems and difficulties developing intimate relationships with people.

Hypersexuality

An excessive or apparently insatiable sex drive that disrupts the person's ability to concentrate on other needs or leads to self-defeating behavior, such as indiscriminate sexual contacts.

Necrophilia

A paraphilia characterized by desire for sexual activity with corpses. (From the Greek *nekros,* meaning "dead body.")

Klismaphilia

A paraphilia in which sexual arousal is derived from use of enemas.

Coprophilia

A paraphilia in which sexual arousal is attained in connection with feces. (From the Greek *copros,* meaning "dung.")

Urophilia

A paraphilia in which sexual arousal is associated with urine.

Notes: In his book *The Evolution of Human Sexuality* (1979), Symons suggests that the "sexually insatiable woman is to be found primarily, if not exclusively, in the ideology of feminism, the hopes of boys, and the fears of men" (p. 92).

Learning Objective 9: Discuss the role of biological factors in paraphilic behavior.

NECROPHILIA In **necrophilia,** a rare paraphilia, a person desires sex with corpses. Three types of necrophilia have been identified (Rosman & Resnick, 1989). In *regular necrophilia,* the person has sex with a deceased person. In *necrophilic homicide,* the person commits murder to obtain a corpse for sexual purposes. In *necrophilic fantasy,* the person fantasizes about sex with a corpse but does not actually carry out necrophilic acts. Necrophiles often obtain jobs that provide them with access to corpses, such as working in cemeteries, morgues, or funeral homes. The primary motivation for necrophilia appears to be the desire to sexually possess a completely nonresistant and nonrejecting partner (Rosman & Resnick, 1989). Many necrophiles are clearly mentally disturbed.

LESS COMMON PARAPHILIAS In **klismaphilia,** sexual arousal is derived from use of enemas. Klismaphiles generally prefer the receiving role to the giving role. Klismaphiles may have derived sexual pleasure in infancy or childhood from the anal stimulation provided by parents giving them enemas.

In **coprophilia,** sexual arousal is connected with feces. The person may desire to be defecated on or to defecate on a sex partner. The association of feces with sexual arousal may also be a throwback to childhood. Many children appear to obtain anal sexual pleasure by holding in and then purposefully expelling feces. It may also be that the incidental connection between erections or sexual arousal and soiled diapers during infancy eroticizes feces.

In **urophilia,** sexual arousal is associated with urine. As with coprophilia, the person may desire to be urinated upon or to urinate upon a sexual partner. Also like coprophilia, urophilia may have childhood origins. Stimulation of the urethral canal during urination may become associated with sexual pleasure. Or urine may have become eroticized by experiences in which erections occurred while the infant was clothed in a wet diaper.

THEORETICAL PERSPECTIVES

The paraphilias are among the most fascinating and perplexing variations in sexual behavior. We may find it difficult to understand how people can become sexually excited by fondling an article of clothing or by cross-dressing. It may also be difficult to identify with people who feel compelled to exhibit their genitals or to rub their genitals against unsuspecting victims in crowded places. Perhaps we can recognize some voyeuristic tendencies in ourselves, but we cannot imagine peeping through binoculars while perched in a nearby tree or, for that matter, risking the social and legal consequences of being discovered in the act. Nor might we understand how people can become sexually turned on by inflicting or receiving pain.

Let us consider the explanations that have been advanced from the major theoretical perspectives.

BIOLOGICAL PERSPECTIVES

Little is known about the role of biological factors in paraphilic behavior. Efforts to date to find concrete evidence of brain damage or abnormalities among paraphiles have failed (for example, Langevin et al., 1989). Because testosterone is linked to sexual drive, researchers have also focused on differences in testosterone levels between paraphiles and comparison groups of nonparaphilic people. A recent study found evidence of some hormonal differences between a group of 16 male exhibitionists and controls (Lang et al., 1989). Although no differences in overall levels of testosterone were found, researchers reported significantly elevated levels among the exhibitionists of the measure of testosterone believed to be most closely linked to sexual drive. This difference suggests that exhibitionists may have biologically elevated sex drives. The significance of the finding is limited by the fact that hormone levels among many of the paraphiles studied fell within the normal range. Clearly, more work is needed to explore biological underpinnings of the paraphilias.

PSYCHOANALYTIC PERSPECTIVES

Learning Objective 10: Present the psychoanalytic explanations for various paraphilias.

Classical psychoanalytic theory suggests that paraphilias are psychological defenses, usually against unresolved castration anxiety dating back to the Oedipus complex of early childhood (Fenichel, 1945). To the transvestic man, the sight of a woman's vagina threatens to arouse castration anxiety. It reminds him that women do not have penises and that he might suffer the same fate. Sequestering his penis beneath women's clothing symbolically asserts that women do in fact have penises, which provides some unconscious reassurance against his own fears of castration.

By exposing his genitals, the exhibitionist unconsciously seeks reassurance that his penis is secure. It is as if he were asserting, "Look! I have a penis!" Shock or surprise on the victim's face provides an acknowledgment that his penis still exists, temporarily relieving unconscious castration anxiety.

Masturbation with a fetishistic object (a shoe, for example) allows the fetishist to gratify his sexual desires while keeping a safe distance from the fantasized dangers that he unconsciously associates with sexual contact with women. Or the fetishistic object itself—the shoe—may unconsciously symbolize the penis. Stroking a woman's shoe during sexual relations, or fantasizing about one, may unconsciously provide reassurance that the man's own penis, symbolically represented by the fetishistic object, is secure.

In one psychoanalytic view of voyeurism, the man is unconsciously denying castration by searching for a penis among women victims. Other psychoanalytic views suggest that the voyeur is identifying with the man in the observed couple as he had identified with his own father during childhood observations of the parental coitus—the so-called *primal scene*. Perhaps he is trying to "master" the primal scene by compulsively reliving it.

Psychoanalytic explanations of sadism commonly suggest that sadists are attempting to defend themselves against unconscious feelings of impotence and powerlessness by inflicting pain on others. The recipients' shouts of pain or confessions of unworthiness make sadists feel masculine and powerful.

Psychoanalytic theory suggests that masochism in the male may be the turning inward of aggressive impulses originally aimed toward the powerful, threatening father. The flagellation or bondage may also be unconsciously preferred to castration as a form of punishment for having unacceptable sexual feelings. Like the child who experiences relief when punishment is over, the sexual masochist willingly accepts immediate punishment in the form of flagellation or bondage in place of the future punishment of castration. Or a woman who witnessed her parents having coitus at an early age may have misperceived the father to be assaulting the mother. Her masochism then represents her unconscious reliving of her mother's (imagined) role with her father. Sexual masochists of either gender may also have such high levels of sex guilt that they can only permit themselves to experience sexual pleasure if they are adequately punished for it during sex.

The paraphilias have provided a fertile ground for psychoanalytic theories. There is a lack of evidence to support the role of such unconscious processes as unresolved castration anxiety, however. The basic shortcoming of psychoanalytic theory is that many of its key concepts involve unconscious mechanisms that cannot be directly observed or measured. So psychoanalytic theories remain interesting but speculative hypotheses about the origins of these unusual sexual behavior patterns.

LEARNING PERSPECTIVES

Learning Objective 11: Discuss learning theory explanations of paraphilic behavior.

Learning theorists believe that fetishes and other paraphilias are learned behaviors that are acquired through experience. An object may acquire sexually arousing properties through association with sexual arousal or orgasm. Early proponents of the learning theory viewpoint were Alfred Kinsey and his colleagues, who wrote in *Sexual Behavior in the Human Female* (1953):

> Even some of the most extremely variant types of human sexual behavior may need no more explanation than is provided by our understanding of the processes of learning and conditioning. Behavior which may appear bizarre, perverse, or unthinkably unacceptable

to some persons, and even to most persons, may have significance for other individuals because of the way in which they have been conditioned (pp. 645–646).

Like Pavlov's dogs, who learned to salivate to the ringing of a bell that had been repeatedly paired with food, "an animal may become conditioned to respond not only to particular stimuli, but to objects and other phenomena which were associated with the original experience. . . . In the laboratory, male animals may respond to particular dishes, to particular boards, or to particular pieces of furniture with which some female has had contact" (Kinsey et al., 1953, p. 647).

According to the conditioning model, a boy who catches a glimpse of his mother's stockings hanging on the towel rack while he is masturbating may go on to develop a fetish for stockings (Breslow, 1989). Orgasm in the presence of the object would reinforce the erotic connection, especially if the experience occurs repeatedly.

In an early experimental test of the conditioning model, Rachman (1966) showed normal (nonfetishistic) males slides of nude women interspersed with slides of women's boots. After numerous repetitions, the men showed a sexual response to the boots alone. This "fetish" was weak and short-lived, however. It could still be argued that more persistent fetishes might be learned if pairings of such stimuli were to occur repeatedly during childhood. If fetishes were mechanically acquired by association, however, we might expect fetishists to be more attracted to objects that are inadvertently (and often repeatedly) associated with sexual activity, such as pillows, bedsheets, and even ceilings (Breslow, 1989). Yet we do not find this to be the case. The *meaning* of the object also seems to play a role. The development of fetishes may depend on the ability to eroticize the object or stimulus and incorporate it within one's erotic fantasies and sexual arousal system, not merely on its incidental pairing with sexual excitement.

Along these lines, Breslow (1989) proposed a learning theory explanation that describes the development of paraphilias in terms of the gradual acquisition of sexual arousal to an unusual object or activity through its incorporation in masturbatory fantasies. A transvestite, for example, may have achieved an erection while trying on his mother's panties in childhood. The paraphilic object or activity is then incorporated within masturbatory fantasies and is reinforced by orgasm. The paraphilic object or activity is then repeatedly used as a masturbatory aid, further strengthening the erotic bond.

We can also consider a role for parental approval as a reinforcing agent in the early development of transvestism. Parents who really wanted to have a girl have been known to occasionally dress their little boys in girls' clothing. The reinforcement of parental approval for cross-dressing may lead the boy to experiment with cross-dressing himself, which may then become eroticized if it is combined with masturbation or sexual fantasies and reinforced by sexual arousal or orgasm.

Fetishistic interests can often be traced to early childhood. Some rubber fetishists, for example, recall erotic interests in rubber objects since early childhood. Reinisch (1990) speculates that for some rubber fetishists, the earliest awareness of sexual arousal or response (such as erection) may have been associated with the presence of rubber pants, diapers, and so forth, such that a connection was formed between the two. Or perhaps the sexual attraction to objects associated with infancy may derive from their association with feelings of being completely loved and cared for. The fetishistic act may represent an attempt to recapture sexual or loving feelings from early childhood.

McGuire and his colleagues (1965) report a case that provides some support for the role of learning in the development of exhibitionism. Two young males were surprised by an attractive woman while urinating. Although embarrassed at the time, their memories of the incident were sexually stimulating, and they masturbated repeatedly while fantasizing about it. The fantasies persisted, possibly reinforced by frequent orgasms. After a while, the young men purposely began to expose themselves to rekindle the high level of sexual excitement. Still, we should caution that only a very small percentage of men who have accidentally been discovered exposed have become exhibitionists.

Blair and Lanyon (1981) suggest that modeling may play a role in some cases. Parents may have obviously or inadvertently modeled exhibitionistic behavior to their young sons, which could have led the sons to eroticize the act of exposing themselves.

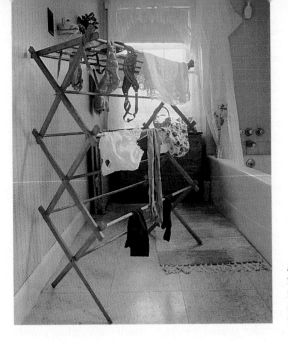

Mother's Stockings. According to the conditioning model of fetishism, boys who repeatedly masturbate in the presence of feminine undergarments may develop an erotic attraction to the undergarments themselves. Incorporation of the object within one's erotic fantasies and sexual arousal system may also play a role.

Learning explanations of sexual masochism focus on the pairing of sexual excitement with punishment. For example, a child may be punished when discovered masturbating. Or a boy may reflexively experience an erection if his penis accidentally rubs against the parent's body as he is being spanked. With repeated encounters like these, pain and pleasure may become linked in the person's sexual arousal system. Another learning explanation focuses on the association of pain with parental affection (Breslow, 1989; Sue et al., 1981). A child with cold and indifferent parents is hugged only following a spanking. The pain or humiliation associated with the spanking becomes associated with the affection of the hug, which leads in later life to pain becoming a prerequisite for sexual pleasure. One limitation of these learning approaches is that they fail to account for how sexual masochism develops within a larger and more complex sadomasochistic lifestyle (Breslow, 1989).

Learning theories of the origins of paraphilias also fail to consider the predisposing factors that may explain why some people who are exposed to early conditioning experiences develop paraphilic interests and others do not. Such predisposing factors may include poor self-esteem and difficulties forming intimate relationships (Tollison & Adams, 1979). Many exhibitionists, voyeurs, frotteurs, and other paraphiles have few interpersonal skills in relating to women. They may avoid customary social interactions with women for fear of rejection. Their furtive, paraphilic behaviors may provide a sexual release with minimal risks of rejection or apprehension and be maintained because they represent the only available source of sexual gratification or reinforcement. Some paraphilias, such as voyeurism, exhibitionism, and frotteurism, may also be conceptualized as *courtship disorders,* involving an exaggeration or distortion of the steps normally taken during courtship in identifying, approaching, and becoming more intimate with new sexual partners (Freund & Blanchard, 1986).

Although paraphilias may be learned, perhaps in early childhood, they are not "catching" (Reinisch, 1990). That is, one does not become a fetishist or another kind of paraphile by reading about one in books, or by observing such behavior in others or in movies or television shows.

SOCIOLOGICAL PERSPECTIVES

Learning Objective 12: Discuss sociological explanations of paraphilic behaviors.

Most paraphiles engage in paraphilic behavior privately. Sexual masochists and sadists require a partner, however, save for those few masochists who practice only autoerotic forms of masochism and the few sadists who stalk nonconsenting partners. Most sadomasochists also relate in one way or another to the sadomasochistic subculture. It is within the S&M subculture—the loosely connected network of S&M clubs, specialty shops, organizations, magazines, and so on—that S&M rituals are learned, sexual contacts are made, sadomasochistic identities are confirmed, and sexual paraphernalia is acquired. But the S&M subculture exists in the context of the larger society, and the rituals it invents mirror the social and gender roles that exist in the larger society.

Martin Weinberg (1987) proposes a sociological model that focuses on the social context of sadomasochism. Weinberg notes that S&M rituals generally involve some form of dominance and submission and attributes their erotic appeal to the opportunity to reverse the customary power relationships that exist between the genders and social classes in society at large. Within the confines of the carefully scripted S&M encounter, the meek can be powerful and the powerful meek (Geer et al., 1984). People from lower social classes or in menial jobs may be drawn to S&M by the opportunities it affords to enact a dominant role. They may have the opportunity to bark orders and commands that are followed unquestioningly. Those who customarily hold high status positions that require them to be in control and responsible may be attracted by the opportunity to surrender control to another person. Dominance and submission games also allow opportunities to accentuate or reverse the gender stereotypes that identify masculinity with dominance and femininity with submissiveness.

Individual sadomasochistic interests may become institutionalized as an S&M subculture in societies (like ours) that have certain social characteristics: (1) dominance-submission relationships are embedded within the culture and aggression is socially valued; (2) there is an unequal distribution of power between people from different gender or social class categories; (3) there are enough affluent people to enable them to participate in such leisure-time activities; and (4) imagination and creativity, important elements in the development of S&M scripts and fantasies, are socially valued and encouraged (Weinberg, 1987).

AN INTEGRATED PERSPECTIVE: THE "LOVEMAP"

Learning Objective 13: Discuss Money's theory of "lovemaps" and its application to the development of paraphilias.

Like other sexual patterns, the paraphilias may have multiple biological, psychological, and sociocultural origins. According to John Money and his colleagues, they may be best approached from a theoretical framework that incorporates multiple perspectives.

Money and Lamacz (1989) trace the origins of paraphilias to childhood. They believe that childhood experiences etch a pattern in the brain, called a "lovemap," that determines the types of stimuli and activities that become sexually arousing to the individual. In the case of paraphilias, these lovemaps become distorted or "vandalized" by early traumatic experiences, such as incest, overbearing antisexual upbringings, and physical abuse or neglect.

Discussion Question: Which of the five explanations for the development of paraphilias makes the most sense to you?

Research suggests that voyeurs and exhibitionists often were the victims of childhood sexual abuse (Dwyer, 1988). Not all children exposed to such influences develop paraphilic compulsions, however. For reasons that remain unknown, some children exposed to such influences appear to be more vulnerable to developing distorted lovemaps than are others. A genetic predisposition, hormonal factors, brain abnormalities, or a combination of these and other factors may play a role in determining one's vulnerability to vandalized lovemaps (Brody, 1990). Future research may help us to uncover the complex web of factors that account for the development of the paraphilias.

Learning Objective 14: Describe the psychoanalytic, behavioral, and biochemical approaches to treatment of paraphilias.

TREATMENT OF THE PARAPHILIAS

The treatment of these atypical patterns of sexual behavior raises several issues. First, paraphiles usually do not want or seek treatment, at least not voluntarily. They often deny that they are offenders, even after they are apprehended and convicted (Dwyer,

1988). They are generally seen by mental health workers only when they come into conflict with the law or at the urging of family members or sexual partners who have discovered them performing paraphilic behavior or found evidence of paraphilic interests.

Paraphilic behavior is a source of pleasure, so it is not surprising that people may not be motivated to give it up. The paraphile typically perceives his or her problems as stemming from society's intolerant response to the variation, not from feelings of guilt or shame. Thus, although some paraphiles may be pressured to undergo therapy, most would prefer to retain their atypical patterns of sexual excitement (Money, 1980).

Second, helping professionals may encounter ethical problems when they are asked to contribute to a judicial process by trying to persuade a sex offender that he (virtually all are male) *ought* to change his behavior. Helping professionals traditionally help clients clarify or meet their own goals; it is not their role to impose societal goals on the individual. Many helping professionals believe that the criminal justice system, and not they, ought to enforce social standards.

The third issue is a treatment problem. Therapists realize that they are generally less successful with resistant or recalcitrant clients. Unless the motivation to change is present, therapeutic efforts may be wasted.

The fourth problem is the issue of perceived responsibility. Sex offenders almost invariably claim that they are unable to control their urges and impulses. Such claims of uncontrollability are often self-serving and may lead others to treat offenders with greater sympathy and understanding. Most therapies, however, are based on the belief that whatever causes may have led to the problem behavior, and however difficult it may be to resist these unusual sexual urges, accepting personal responsibility for one's actions is a prelude to change. Thus, if therapy is to be constructive, it is necessary to break through the client's personal mythology that he is powerless to control his behavior.

Despite these issues, many offenders are referred for treatment by the courts. A few seek therapy themselves because they have come to see how their behavior harms themselves or others. Let us consider some of the ways in which therapists treat people with these atypical sexual behavior patterns.

PSYCHOTHERAPY

Psychoanalysis focuses on resolving the unconscious conflicts that are believed to originate in childhood and to give rise in adulthood to pathological problems such as paraphilias. The aim of therapy is to help bring unconscious conflicts, principally Oedipal conflicts, into conscious awareness so that they might be worked through in light of the individual's adult personality.

Although some favorable case results have been reported (e.g., Rosen, 1967), psychoanalytic therapy of the paraphilias has not been subjected to experimental analysis. We thus do not know whether successes are due to the psychoanalytic treatment itself or to other factors, such as spontaneous improvement or a client's willingness to change.

BEHAVIOR THERAPY

Behavior therapy
The systematic application of the principles of learning to help people modify problem behavior.

Whereas traditional psychoanalysis tends to be a lengthy process of exploration of the childhood origins of problem behaviors, **behavior therapy** is relatively briefer and focuses directly on changing the problem behaviors themselves. Behavior therapy has spawned a number of techniques to help eliminate paraphilic behaviors and strengthen appropriate sexual behaviors. These techniques include systematic desensitization, aversion therapy, social skills training, covert sensitization, and orgasmic reconditioning, to name a few.

Systematic desensitization attempts to break the link between the sexual stimulus (such as a fetishistic stimulus) and the inappropriate response (sexual arousal). The client is first taught to relax selected muscle groups in the body. Muscle relaxation is then paired repeatedly with each of a series of progressively more arousing paraphilic images or fantasies. Relaxation comes to replace sexual arousal in response to each of these

Systematic desensitization
A method for terminating the connection between a stimulus (such as a fetishistic object) and an inappropriate response (such as sexual arousal to the paraphilic stimulus). Muscle relaxation is practiced in connection with each stimulus in a series of increasingly arousing stimuli, so that the person learns to remain relaxed (and not become sexually aroused) in their presence.

Aversion therapy
A method for terminating undesirable sexual behavior in which the behavior is repeatedly paired with an aversive stimulus, such as electric shock, so that a conditioned aversion develops.

Covert sensitization
A form of aversion therapy in which thoughts of engaging in undesirable behavior are paired repeatedly with imagined aversive stimuli.

Pedophiles
Persons with pedophilia, a paraphilia involving sexual interest in children.

Social skills training
Behavior therapy methods for building social skills which rely on a therapist's coaching and practice.

Orgasmic reconditioning
A method for strengthening the connection between sexual arousal and appropriate sexual stimuli (such as fantasies about an adult of the opposite gender) by repeatedly pairing the desired stimuli with orgasm.

stimuli, even the most provocative. In one case study, a fetishistic transvestite who had become attracted to his mother's lingerie at age 13 was taught to relax and presented with audiotaped scenes representing transvestite or fetishistic themes (Fensterheim & Kantor, 1980). He played such tapes daily while remaining relaxed. He later reported a complete absence of transvestite thoughts or activities.

In **aversion therapy,** the undesirable sexual behavior (for example, masturbation to fetishistic fantasies) is paired repeatedly with an aversive stimulus (such as a harmless but painful electric shock or a nausea-inducing chemical) in the hope that the client will develop a conditioned aversion toward the paraphilic behavior.

Covert sensitization is a variation of aversion therapy in which paraphilic fantasies are paired with an aversive stimulus in imagination. In a broad-scale application, 38 **pedophiles** and 62 exhibitionists, more than half of whom were court-referred, were treated by pairing imagined aversive odors with fantasies of the problem behavior (Maletzky, 1980). Clients were instructed to fantasize pedophiliac or exhibitionistic scenes. Then,

> at a point . . . when sexual pleasure is aroused, aversive images are presented. . . . Examples might include a pedophiliac fellating a child, but discovering a festering sore on the boy's penis, an exhibitionist exposing to a woman but suddenly being discovered by his wife or the police, or a pedophiliac laying a young boy down in a field, only to lie next to him in a pile of dog feces.
>
> (Maletzky, 1980, p. 308)

Maletzky used this treatment weekly for six months, then followed it with "booster sessions" every three months over a three-year period. The procedure resulted in at least a 75 percent reduction of the deviant activities and fantasies for over 80 percent of the subjects at follow-up periods of up to 36 months.

Social skills training focuses on helping the paraphile improve his ability to relate to the opposite gender. The therapist might first model a desired behavior, such as how to ask a woman out on a date or how to handle a rejection. The client might then practice the behavior in a role-playing exercise with the therapist playing the part of the woman. Following the role-play enactment, the therapist would provide feedback and additional guidance and modeling to help the client improve his skills. This process would be repeated until the client achieved mastery of the particular skill.

Orgasmic reconditioning aims to increase sexual arousal to socially appropriate sexual stimuli by pairing culturally appropriate imagery with orgasmic pleasure (Adams et al., 1981). The paraphile is instructed to become sexually aroused by masturbating to paraphilic images or fantasies. But as he approaches the point of orgasm, he switches to appropriate imagery and focuses on it during orgasm. In a case example, Davison (1977) reports reduction of sadistic fantasies in a 21-year-old college man. The client was instructed to attain an erection in any way he could, even through the use of the sadistic fantasies he wished to eliminate. But once erection was achieved, he was to masturbate while looking at photos of *Playboy* models. Orgasm was thus paired with nonsadistic images. These images and fantasies eventually acquire the capacity to elicit sexual arousal. Orgasmic reconditioning is often combined with other techniques, such as social skills training, so that more desirable social behaviors can be strengthened as well (Adams et al., 1981).

Although behavior therapy techniques tend to have higher reported success rates than most other methods, they too are limited by reliance on uncontrolled case studies. Without appropriate controls we cannot isolate the effective elements of therapy or determine that the results were not due merely to the passage of time or other factors unrelated to the treatment. It is possible that clients who are highly motivated to change may succeed in doing so with any systematic approach.

BIOCHEMICAL APPROACHES

There is no biologically based "cure" for the paraphilias, no drug or surgical technique that eliminates paraphilic urges and behavior. Yet some progress has recently been reported in using a popular antidepressant, Prozac (fluoxetine hydrochloride) in treating voyeurism and fetishism (Emmanuel et al., 1991; Lorefice, 1991; Peilstein et al., 1991). Why Prozac? In addition to treating depression, Prozac has been helpful in treating obsessive-compulsive disorder, a type of emotional disorder involving recurrent obsessions (intrusive ideas) and/or compulsions (urges to repeat a certain behavior or thought). Researchers speculate that paraphilias may be linked to obsessive-compulsive disorder (Kruesi et al., 1992). Paraphiles often experience intrusive, repetitive thoughts or images of the paraphilic object or stimulus, such as mental images of young children. Many also report feeling compelled to repeatedly carry out the paraphilic acts. Paraphilias may belong to what researchers have dubbed an obsessive-compulsive spectrum of behaviors (Kruesi et al., 1992).

Antiandrogen drug
A chemical substance that reduces the sex drive by lowering the level of testosterone in the bloodstream.

Paraphiles who experience such intense urges that they are at risk of committing sexual offenses may be helped by **antiandrogen drugs,** which reduce the level of testosterone circulating in the bloodstream (Marshall et al., 1991). Testosterone is closely linked to sexual drive and interest. *Medroxyprogesterone acetate* (MPA) (trade name: Depo-Provera), which is administered in weekly injections, is the antiandrogen that has been used most extensively in the treatment of sex offenders. In men, antiandrogens like Depo-Provera reduce testosterone to a level that is typical of a prepubertal boy (Money, 1987b) and consequently reduce sexual desire and frequency of erections and ejaculations (Cooper, 1986; Money, 1987b).

Depo-Provera suppresses the sexual appetite in men. It can lower the intensity of sexual drives and erotic fantasies and urges so that the man may feel less compelled to act upon them (Berlin, 1989). Antiandrogens do not, however, eliminate paraphilic urges or behavior. As an analogy, consider the relationship between the accelerator pedal and the steering wheel of a car. The accelerator pedal controls the car's speed but not its direction. In much the same way releasing pressure on the accelerator pedal slows the car, the use of antiandrogens reduces the intensity of sexual drives and desires. The types of stimuli that have erotic value are not affected by antiandrogens, however, any more than easing up on the accelerator alters the direction of a car.

The use of antiandrogens is sometimes incorrectly referred to as *chemical castration.* Surgical castration, the surgical removal of the testes, has sometimes been performed on convicted rapists and violent sex offenders (see Chapter 19). Actual castration eliminates testicular sources of testosterone. Antiandrogens suppress, but do not eliminate, testicular production of testosterone. Also, unlike surgical castration, the use of antiandrogens can be reversed when the treatment is terminated (Money, 1987b).

Evidence suggests that antiandrogens may be helpful to some paraphiles when they are used in conjunction with psychological treatment (Marshall et al., 1991; Murray, 1988). The value of antiandrogens has been limited by high refusal and dropout rates, however (Marshall et al., 1991). Questions also remain concerning potential side effects (Money, 1987b). Since the effects of antiandrogens are reversible when the use of the drugs is discontinued, such therapy does little for men who terminate its use after a short trial period. The use of antiandrogens also raises ethical questions (Melella et al., 1989), especially when they are administered to convicted offenders who are offered the option of receiving these drugs in return for a lighter sentence and who thus may not be in a position to exercise full voluntary consent.

Although we have amassed a great deal of research on atypical variations in sexual behavior, our understanding of them and our treatment approaches to them remain largely in their infancy.

SUMMING UP

NORMAL VERSUS DEVIANT SEXUAL BEHAVIOR

What is considered normal in one culture or at a particular time may be considered abnormal in other cultures and at other times. Atypical patterns of sexual arousal or behavior that become problematic in the eyes of the individual or society are labeled *paraphilias*.

THE PARAPHILIAS

Paraphilias involve sexual arousal in response to unusual stimuli such as children or other nonconsenting persons, nonhuman objects, or pain or humiliation. The psychiatric diagnosis of paraphilia requires that the person has acted on these persistent urges or is distinctly distressed by them. Except in the case of sexual masochism, paraphilias are believed to occur almost exclusively among men.

Fetishism In fetishism, an inanimate object comes to elicit sexual arousal. In partialism, people are inordinately aroused by a particular body part, such as the feet.

Transvestism Whereas other fetishists become sexually aroused by handling the fetishistic object while they masturbate, transvestites become excited by wearing articles of clothing—the fetishistic objects—of the opposite gender.

Exhibitionism An exhibitionist experiences the compulsion to expose himself to strangers. The typical exhibitionist does not attempt further sexual contact with the victim and so does not usually pose a physical threat.

Obscene Telephone Calling The obscene phone caller is motivated to become sexually aroused by shocking his victim. Such callers typically masturbate during the phone call or shortly afterwards.

Voyeurism Voyeurs become sexually aroused by watching, and do not seek sexual relations with the target. The voyeur may masturbate while "peeping," or afterward while engaging in voyeuristic fantasies. Like exhibitionists, voyeurs tend to harbor feelings of inadequacy and poor self-esteem and to lack social and sexual skills.

Sexual Masochism Sexual masochists associate the receipt of pain or humiliation with sexual arousal. Sexual masochists and sexual sadists may form liaisons to meet each other's needs.

Sexual Sadism Sexual sadism is characterized by persistent and powerful urges and sexual fantasies involving the inflicting of pain and suffering on others to achieve sexual excitement or gratification. Sadomasochists enjoy playing both sadistic and masochistic roles.

Frotteurism Most frotteuristic acts take place in crowded places, such as buses, subway cars, or elevators.

Other Paraphilias Zoophiles desire to have sexual contact with animals. Necrophiles desire to have sexual contact with dead bodies.

THEORETICAL PERSPECTIVES

Biological Perspectives The links between paraphilias and biological factors have yet to be fully explored in research.

Psychoanalytic Perspectives Classical psychoanalytic theory suggests that paraphilias in males are psychological defenses against castration anxiety.

Learning Perspectives Some learning theorists have argued that unusual stimuli may acquire sexually arousing properties through association with sexual arousal or orgasm. Another possibility is that unusual stimuli gradually acquire sexually arousing properties through incorporation in masturbatory fantasies.

Sociological Perspectives According to Weinberg's sociological model, the erotic appeal of S&M rituals may result from the opportunity to reverse the customary power relationships that exist between different gender and social class categories in society at large.

An Integrated Perspective: The "Lovemap" Money and Lamacz suggest that childhood experiences etch a pattern in the brain—a "lovemap"—that determines the types of stimuli and activities that become sexually arousing. In the case of paraphilias, these lovemaps become distorted by early traumatic experiences.

TREATMENT OF THE PARAPHILIAS

Paraphiles may be motivated to seek help because of fears of exposure, criminal prosecution, or humiliation, but they seldom desire to surrender their sexual preferences.

Psychotherapy Psychoanalysis aims to bring unconscious Oedipal conflicts into awareness so that they can be worked through in adulthood.

Behavior Therapy Behavior therapy employs techniques to eliminate paraphilic behaviors such as systematic desensitization, aversion therapy, social skills training, covert sensitization, and orgasmic reconditioning.

Biochemical Approaches The antidepressant Prozac has shown some promise in treating paraphilias. By reducing sexual drives, antiandrogen drugs may help paraphiles who have difficulty combatting intense paraphilic urges. They may be most helpful when used in conjunction with psychological treatment.

CHAPTER OUTLINE

_____ A woman is raped every five minutes in the United States.

_____ The prevalence of rape is 20 times greater in the United States than in Japan.

_____ The majority of rapes are committed by strangers in deserted neighborhoods or darkened alleyways.

_____ Men who rape other men are gay.

_____ A healthy woman can resist a rapist if she really wants to.

_____ In India, accused rapists were acquitted by a judge who concluded that the complainants were so poor that they _might have been_ bribed to file false charges.

_____ Most rapists are mentally ill.

_____ Women who encounter a rapist should attempt to fight off the assailant.

_____ Father-daughter incest is the most common type of incest.

C HAPTER 19

Sexual Coercion

In recent years the airwaves have been flooded with allegations of sexual assault and sexual harassment involving celebrities, highly placed politicians, and even members of the armed services. In late 1991 and early 1992, media sharks went on a feeding frenzy in covering the rape trials of William Kennedy Smith and Mike Tyson, and the Senate confirmation hearings of Supreme Court nominee Clarence Thomas, who faced charges of sexual harassment leveled by a former assistant, law professor Anita Hill.

The Senate hearings failed to determine the truthfulness of the allegations against Clarence Thomas. William Kennedy Smith, a nephew of Senator Edward Kennedy, was acquitted of the rape charges brought against him, but former heavyweight boxing champion Mike Tyson was found guilty and sentenced to prison. Some observers of the media frenzy surrounding these cases claimed that *all* men, not just these three, were being judged. Other critics charged that rapes or claims of sexual harassment rarely receive much media coverage unless the accused party is a celebrity, a highly placed official, or a member of a prominent family.

The media frenzy has since focused on two other highly publicized cases, the so-called Tailhook incident and the charges of sexual harassment by more than a dozen women against a prominent U.S. Senator, Robert Packwood of Oregon. The Tailhook Association, an organization representing U.S. Navy aviators, held its annual convention in 1991 at a hotel in Las Vegas. It is alleged that during the convention, scores of male aviators sexually harassed and assaulted a number of women, including several fellow aviators. Some women were literally forced to run a gauntlet of drunken male officers along a hotel corridor, where they were fondled, molested, and subjected to sexual insults by many of the men ("Deepening shame," 1992). An internal report commissioned by the Navy secretary was highly critical of the way the higher echelons of the Navy handled the charges brought against the male officers reportedly involved in the incident, who have yet to be brought to trial. As of this writing, Senator Packwood faces ethics charges against him in the Senate and has refused the request of his fellow senators to turn over to them his personal diaries.

A team of professional writers could not have tickled the public's fancy more, but the plots and the characters in these media series were very real. Many observers to this media frenzy winced as they saw aspects of ourselves— either as aggressors or victims—being laid bare before the nation.

This chapter is about sexual coercion, which includes rape, but also encompasses other forms of sexual pressure, including the use of lies and deceit to seduce one's partner and, of course, sexual harassment. Sexual coercion also includes *any* sexual activity between an adult and a child. Even when children cooperate, sexual relations with children are by definition a form of sexual coercion because children are legally below the age of consent. Although sexual coercion is most often perpetrated by men, we shall see that some offenders are women.

Robert Packwood. Senator Robert Packwood of Oregon faced ethics charges following complaints of sexual harassment lodged against him by more than a dozen women.

RAPE

Learning Objective 1: Discuss the historical and current definitions of rape and the incidence of rape.

I wanted to knock the woman off her pedestal, and I felt rape was the worst thing I could do to her.

She wanted it, she was asking for it. She just said "no" so I wouldn't think she was easy. The only reason she yelled rape was she got home late and her husband knew she hadn't been out with her girlfriend.

I found myself having sexual fantasies that would put women in precarious positions. I was thinking about this more and more, like devising a rack, perhaps, that would spread her legs as wide open as they could possibly be spread—something of this nature. I acted tough with them. The first one and the last pleaded for their virginity. I told them to do what they were told and they wouldn't get hurt. I said that if they didn't do what they were told, they would be sorry. I don't know if I actually threatened to kill them or not, but I very strongly feel that I never would have. The only thing is, perhaps if I continued on and hadn't been caught this time, seeing what happened from the first three times to the second three times—I just wonder—maybe in the next set of three somebody would have gotten hurt, you know, somebody would have really gotten hurt.

Rape
Sexual intercourse that takes place as a result of force or threats of force rather than consent. (The legal definition of rape varies from state to state.) See also *forcible rape* and *statutory rape*.

Forcible rape
Sexual intercourse with a nonconsenting person obtained by the use of force or the threat of force.

Statutory rape
Sexual intercourse with a person who is below the age of consent. Sexual intercourse under such conditions is considered statutory rape even though the person attacked may cooperate.

These statements made by rapists in *Men who Rape* (Groth & Birnbaum, 1979) express the theme that **rape** involves the subjugation of women by men by force or threat of force. Many social scientists view rape as an act of violence that is associated with domination, control, power, and sadism, not as a crime of passion or sexual desire. Although sexual motivation plays a role in many rapes, the use of sex as the instrument to express aggression, anger, and power is more central to our understanding of rape.

For the first few thousand years of recorded history, the only rapes that were punished were those that defiled virgins, and those were classified as crimes against property (virgins being the property of their fathers)—not as crimes against persons (Gibbs, 1991). In ancient Babylonia, rape laws applied to married women as well, but the law required the woman who was raped and her assailant to be bound and thrown into a river. As the injured party (after all, *his* property had been damaged), the husband could choose to let his wife drown or draw her from the water alive. The historical record bears witness to the age-old tradition, carried regrettably to the present day, that stigmatizes rape survivors and ascribes some degree of guilt to them. The ancient Hebrews stoned a married woman who was raped and her assailant to death. In both the ancient Babylonian and Hebrew cultures, the wife was seen as guilty of adultery. Virgins who were raped within the protection of the city gates would also be stoned by the Hebrews. It was believed that they could have maintained their purity simply by crying out.

Today the definition of rape varies from state to state. **Forcible rape** is usually defined, however, as sexual intercourse with a nonconsenting person by the use of force or the threat of force. **Statutory rape** refers to sexual intercourse with a person who is below the age of consent, even though the person may cooperate.

Traditionally, a man could not be convicted for raping his wife, though he might have forced her to submit to sexual activity by physical power or threats (Estrich, 1987). This marital exclusion was derived from the English common law that held that a woman "gives herself over" to her husband when she becomes his wife and cannot then retract her consent (Dixon, 1991). Today, however, more than 30 states (the list is growing) and the District of Columbia have rape statutes that permit the prosecution of husbands who

Forcible Rape. Forcible rape involves the use of force or threats of force to compel a person into sexual intercourse. A rapist's motives typically have more to do with the desire to control, abuse, or punish the victim than with sexual gratification.

Sexual assault

Any sexual activity that involves the use of force or the threat of force.

rape their wives. Many states have also broadened the scope of rape laws to include forced sexual acts other than coitus, such as anal intercourse and oral-genital relations, and to apply rape laws to men who rape other men or women who coerce men into sexual activity or assist men in raping other women. Forcible rape is a form of **sexual assault.** Even when a sexual attack does not meet the legal definition of rape, as in the case of forced penetration of the anus by an object such as a bottle or a broom handle, it can be classified and prosecuted as a sexual assault (Powell, 1991).

INCIDENCE OF RAPE

FBI records reveal that 102,555 forcible rapes were reported in the United States in 1990—more rapes than had ever been recorded in the United States (FBI, 1991; U.S. Senate Committee on the Judiciary, 1991). One woman was reported to be raped about every five minutes on the average in 1990. The numbers of reported rapes have swelled alarmingly, faster than the population. In 1960 the FBI reported over 17,000 cases; in 1975, 56,000; in 1980, more than 75,000. The numbers of reported rapes increased to 90,000 in 1986 and then jumped another 10 percent by 1990 (Uniform Crime Reports, 1990). The vast majority of rapes—as many as 90 percent—are believed to go unreported, however (Gibbs, 1991). Authorities believe that unreported rapes are increasing even faster than reported rapes (U.S. Senate Committee on the Judiciary, 1991).

TRUTH O R *FICTION?*

R E V I S I T E D

A woman is raped every five minutes in the United States. *Based on the number that are* reported, *in the United States a woman is raped every five minutes on the average. Because only the minority of U.S. rapes are reported, a woman is probably raped at least once every minute.* •

CNN Rape Reporting

Statistics concerning reported crimes thus underestimate the prevalence of rape. *Victimization surveys,* which ask random samples of people whether they have ever been sexually assaulted, provide information about both reported and unreported rapes (Harney & Muehlenhard, 1991). Victimization surveys reveal that the numbers of reported rapes are but the tip of the iceberg. A national study of 4,000 women found five times the number of rapes occurred during 1990 as were reported by the Justice Department in the same year ("Unsettling report on an epidemic of rape," 1992). Perhaps the most shocking finding from the study (see Figure 19.1) was that 61 percent of women who were raped were less than 18 years of age when attacked. Nearly three of 10 were 10 years of age or younger. In four of five cases, the woman knew her attacker.

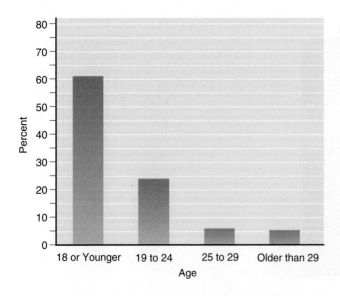

FIGURE 19.1 **Age of Rape Survivors and Percentages Who Knew Their Assailants.**

Source: Adapted from "Rape victim's age . . . and relationship to rapist." 1992. *TIME,* 4 May, p. 15.

Other surveys report the following prevalences of rape or sexual assaults: 21 percent of a sample of more than 5,000 female members of a health maintenance plan (Koss, 1989); 18.5 percent of a sample of women clients of 257 psychotherapists in North Carolina (Dye & Roth, 1990); 13 percent of a sample of 542 female college students and employees at Duke University (Roth et al., 1989). In a 1980s survey of a national sample of more than 6,000 college students (3,187 women and 2,972 men) on 32 campuses across the United States, 15 percent of the women reported that they had been raped. An additional 12 percent reported that they had been victims of an attempted rape (Koss et al., 1987). A survey of undergraduate students in New Zealand revealed similar results: 25 percent reported having been victims of rape or attempted rape (Gavey, 1991).

Although precise statistics concerning the frequency of rape remain elusive, the weight of the evidence leads researchers to estimate that between 14 and 25 percent of women in United States are raped at some point during their lifetimes (Calhoun & Atkeson, 1991; Koss, 1993). The prevalence of reported rapes in the United States is 13 times greater than that in Great Britain and more than 20 times greater than that in Japan (*Newsweek*, 1990). Later we shall consider some of the cultural influences that make our society such a breeding ground for rape.

The prevalence of rape is 20 times greater in the United States than in Japan. *Yes, the prevalence of reported rape is more than 20 times greater in the United States than in Japan.* •

Women of all ages, races, and social classes risk encountering a rapist. Young women, however, are at greater risk than older women. Women ages 16 to 24 are two to three times more likely to be raped than are women in general (U.S. Department of Justice, 1985). Although a disproportionate number of *reported* rapes involve women from lower socioeconomic classes, this difference may partly reflect the tendency of more affluent rape survivors to forgo reporting attacks to avoid dealing with the legal system and publicity (Hall & Flannery, 1985).

TYPES OF RAPES

Learning Objective 2:
Discuss the types of rapes, the incidence of each, and the characteristics of the perpetrators.

One of the central myths about rape in our culture is that most rapes are perpetrated by strangers lurking in dark alleyways or by intruders who climb through open windows in the middle of the night. Most women, about 80 percent, are raped by men they know, however—often by men they have come to trust. The types of rapes include stranger rape, acquaintance rape, marital rape, male rape, and rape by females.

The majority of rapes are committed by strangers in deserted neighborhoods or darkened alleyways. *Actually, most women are raped by men they know, not by strangers.* •

Stranger rape
Rape that is committed by an assailant previously unknown to the person who is assaulted.

STRANGER RAPES **Stranger rape** refers to a rape that is committed by an assailant (or assailants) who is not previously known to the person attacked. The stranger rapist often selects targets who seem vulnerable—women who live alone, are older or retarded, who are walking down deserted streets, or who are asleep or intoxicated. After choosing a target the rapist may search for a safe time and place to commit the crime—a deserted, run-down part of town, a darkened street, a second-floor apartment without window bars or locks. One quarter of the persons attacked by strangers in a Denver study of 300 rapes had responded to the assailant's feigned requests for help (Hursch, 1977).

Acquaintance rape
Rape by an acquaintance of the person who is assaulted.

ACQUAINTANCE RAPES Women are more likely to be raped by men they know, such as classmates, fellow office workers, and even their brothers' friends, than by strangers (Gibbs, 1991). **Acquaintance rapes** are much less likely than stranger rapes to be reported to the police (Koss, 1988). One reason is that rape survivors may not perceive sexual assaults by acquaintances as rapes. Only 27 percent of the women in the national college survey who had been sexually assaulted saw themselves as rape victims (Koss et al., 1987). Despite the increased public awareness of acquaintance rape, the belief is still common that rapists are strangers lurking in shadows and that a woman should be able to resist a sexual advance unless the man uses a weapon (Calhoun & Atkeson, 1991). Acquaintance rapists tend to believe in myths that serve to legitimize their behavior to themselves, such as the traditional view that men are expected to assume a sexually aggressive role in dating relationships and the belief that rapists are strangers (Lewin, 1985). Even when acquaintance rapes are reported to police, they are often treated as "misunderstandings" or lovers' quarrels rather than as violent crimes (Estrich, 1987).

Discussion Question: A popular saying for buttons and T-shirts reads, "What part of 'No' don't you understand?" Do you think that men really don't understand that when women say no, they mean no?

DATE RAPE   Date rape is a form of acquaintance rape that occurs in a dating situation. Several recent studies of college women show a consistent trend: about 15 percent of women report that a date had raped them or attempted to rape them (Koss, 1988; Muehlenhard & Linton, 1987; Sherman, 1985). In one college study, most reported date rapes were not committed by recent acquaintances or by "blind dates" but by men whom the women had known for a length of time, nearly a year on the average (Muehlenhard & Linton, 1987). Rapes were more likely to occur when the couple had too much to drink and then parked in the man's car or went back to his residence. The man tended to perceive his partner's willingness to return home with him as a signal of sexual interest, even if she resisted his advances. Most of the men ignored women's protests and overcame their resistance by force. None used a weapon, and only a few used threats of violence.

Men who commit date rape may believe that acceptance of a date indicates willingness to engage in coitus, or that women should reciprocate with coitus if they are taken to dinner. Others assume that women who frequent settings such as singles bars are expressing tacit agreement to engage in coitus with men who show interest in them. Some date rapists believe that a woman who resists their advances is merely "protesting too much" so that she will not look "easy." They interpret resistance as coyness—a ploy in the cat and mouse game that, to them, typifies the "battle of the sexes." They may believe that when a woman says no, she means maybe; that when she says maybe, she means yes. They may thus not see themselves as committing rape. But they are.

The issue of consent lies at the heart of determining whether an act of sexual intercourse is a rape. Unlike cases of stranger rape, date rape occurs within a context in which sexual relations may occur voluntarily, so the issue of consent can become murky. Juries and judges are often faced with a woman complainant who alleges that the male defendant, who may appear neatly dressed and looking like the boy next door, forced her into sexual relations against her will. As in the William Kennedy Smith and Mike Tyson trials, the defendant may concede that sexual intercourse took place but

Rape on Campus. Many colleges and universities have instituted rape awareness programs to combat the problem of rape on campus.

A CLOSER LOOK

Anatomy of a Date Rape: Ann and Jim

Date rape is a pressing concern on college campuses, where thousands of women have been raped by men they knew or had dated, and where there is much controversy as to what exactly constitutes date rape (Gibbs, 1991). Consider the case of Ann (Trenton State College, 1991):

> I first met him at a party. He was really good looking and he had a great smile. I wanted to meet him but I wasn't sure how. I didn't want to appear too forward. Then he came over and introduced himself. We talked and found we had a lot in common. I really liked him. When he asked me over to his place for a drink, I thought it would be OK. He was such a good listener, and I wanted him to ask me out again.
>
> When we got to his room, the only place to sit was on the bed. I didn't want him to get the wrong idea, but what else could I do? We talked for a while and then he made his move. I was so startled. He started by kissing. I really liked him so the kissing was nice. But then he pushed me down on the bed. I tried to get up and I told him to stop. He was so much bigger and stronger. I got scared and I started to cry. I froze and he raped me.

It took only a couple of minutes and it was terrible, he was so rough. When it was over he kept asking me what was wrong, like he didn't know. He had just forced himself on me and he thought that was OK. He drove me home and said he wanted to see me again. I'm so afraid to see him. I never thought it would happen to me.

College men on dates frequently perceive their dates' protests as part of an adversarial sex game. One male undergraduate said "Hell, no" when asked whether a date had consented to sex. He added, " . . . but she didn't say no, so she must have wanted it, too. . . . It's the way it works" (Celis, 1991). Consider the comments of Jim, the man who raped Ann (Trenton State College, 1991):

> I first met her at a party. She looked really hot, wearing a sexy dress that showed off her great body. We started talking right away. I knew that she liked me by the way she kept smiling and touching my arm while she was speaking. She seemed pretty relaxed so I asked her back to my place for a drink. . . . When she said yes, I knew that I was going to be lucky!

When we got to my place, we sat on the bed kissing. At first, everything was great. Then, when I started to lay her down on the bed, she started twisting and saying she didn't want to. Most women don't like to appear too easy, so I knew that she was just going through the motions. When she stopped struggling, I knew that she would have to throw in some tears before we did it.

She was still very upset afterwards, and I just don't understand it! If she didn't want to have sex, why did she come back to the room with me? You could tell by the way she dressed and acted that she was no virgin, so why she had to put up such a big struggle I don't know.

Accepting a date is not the equivalent of consenting to coitus. Accompanying a man to his room or apartment is not the equivalent of consenting to coitus. Kissing and even petting are not the equivalent of consenting to coitus. Let us reiterate a point worth restating: When the woman says no, the man is obligated to take no for an answer.

---

claim that it was consensual. Judges and juries face the task of discerning subtle shadings in meaning regarding the issue of consent, and attorneys on both sides vie to persuade them to see things their way.

Charges of date rape often come down to a case of his word against hers. Her word often becomes less persuasive in the eyes of the jury if it was clear that she had consented to a series of consensual acts beforehand, such as sharing dinner, attending the movies together, accompanying him to his home, sharing a drink alone, and perhaps kissing or even petting. Let us state in no uncertain terms, however, that it does not matter whether the woman wore a "sexy" outfit, was "on the pill," or shared a passionate kiss or embrace with the man. If the encounter ended with the woman being forcibly violated, then it is rape (Gibbs, 1991). When a woman says no, a man is obligated to take no for an answer.

The problem of date rape has been brought within closer public scrutiny in recent years. "Take Back the Night" marches have become a common form of student protest

Notes: The president of Antioch College, Alan Guskin, says that despite criticism from various sources, ". . . more than 210 educational institutions have called, faxed, or written to us requesting copies of our policy. . . We have received hundreds of requests from lawyers, think tanks, social workers, and guidance counselors." (Mélange. 1994. *Chronicle of Higher Education,* June 1, B3.)

Notes: A study of 524 women and 337 men on one campus found that of the women, 34 percent had experienced unwanted sexual contact, 20 percent unwanted attempted intercourse, and 10 percent unwanted completed intercourse. In over 75 percent of the incidents the women reported that the man had consumed alcohol; in over half of the incidents the women themselves had done so. (Ward, S. K. et al., 1991. Acquaintance rape and the college social scene. *Family Relations, 40,* 65–71.)

on college campuses against the sexual misconduct of men (Gross, 1993). Many colleges have mandated date rape seminars and workshops. Antioch College, a small, traditionally liberal college in Ohio, has gone even further by instituting a sexual offense policy that requires that "willing and verbal consent" be given for every sexual act, from petting to coitus. If you want to hold your partner's hand, you need to ask first. To kiss your partner on the lips, you first have to ask. To put your tongue in your partner's mouth, you have to ask. To touch your partner's breast, you have to ask. To take your partner's blouse or shirt off, you have to ask. To touch your partner's genitals, you have to ask. This policy was developed by the students themselves, but the sanctions for violating the policy can be severe, including expulsion from the school. The policy is not without its critics. Though supporters claim that it is a way of improving communication and ensuring that sexual activity is consensual, others claim that it makes sexual relations mechanical and lacking in spontaneity.

Some observers have argued that concerns about date rape are overblown and even border on public hysteria (Crichton, 1993). In a controversial 1993 book, *The Morning After: Sex, Fear and Feminism on Campus,* writer Katie Roiphe, a Princeton University student, argued that date rape is more hype than reality. Roiphe suggests that date rape statistics are exaggerated because the label of rape is now being inappropriately applied to many situations in which verbal pressure but no force or threat of force was used to induce women to have sex. She maintains that broadening the definition of date rape in this way serves to reduce women to the role of helpless victims in need of protection against sexually avaricious men. Roiphe has her critics, some of whom argue that she is uninformed about the extent of the problem and that she relies on an unscientific sampling of her circle of friends as the basis for her belief that the prevalence of date rape is overblown (Faludi, 1993).

THE GANG RAPE   Groth and Birnbaum (1979) relate the story of Kurt, a 23-year-old white, married father of three who was involved in a number of rapes with a friend, Pete:

> I always looked up to Pete and felt second-class to him. I felt I owed him and couldn't chicken out on the rapes. I worshipped him. He was the best fighter, lover, water-skier, motorcyclist I knew. Taking part in the sexual assaults made me feel equal to him. . . . I didn't have any friends and felt like a nobody. . . . He brought me into his bike club. He made me a somebody.

> I'd go to a shopping center and find a victim. I'd approach her with a knife or a gun and then bring her to him. He'd rape her first and then I would. . . . We raped about eight girls together over a four-month period (p. 113).

By participating in a gang rape, the follower, like Kurt, appears to be attempting to conform his behavior to that of the sex-role stereotype of the tough, competent, "masculine" he-man. Followers, however, appear to provide the instigator of the act with additional courage in committing the rape. One of Groth and Birnbaum's planners of such an assault remarks: "Having a partner is like having something to drink. I felt braver. I felt stronger. This gave me the courage to do something I might not have done on my own" (1979, p. 112).

Exercise of power appears to be the major motive behind gang rapes, although some attackers may also be expressing anger against the women they rape or women in general. Gang members often believe that once women engage in coitus they are "whores." Thus, each offending gang member may become more aggressive as he takes his turn.

The Koss college survey (Koss et al., 1987) showed that sexual assaults involving a group of assailants tend to be more vicious than assaults perpetrated by individual assailants (Gidycz & Koss, 1990). As compared to survivors of individual assaults, group assault survivors felt more afraid, offered greater resistance (such as by running away, hitting, pushing, or crying or sobbing), were more suicidal afterwards, and were less likely to have known the offenders beforehand. Relatively few survivors of either type of assault reported the attack to police or sought support from a crisis center.

MALE RAPE   The prevalence of male rape is unknown because most assaults are never reported. Some estimates suggest that perhaps one in 10 rape survivors is a man, however (Gibbs, 1991). Most men who rape other men are heterosexual. Their motives tend to include domination and control, revenge and retaliation, sadism and degradation, and (when the rape is carried out by a gang member) status and affiliation (Groth & Birnbaum, 1979). Sexual motives are generally absent.

Men who rape other men are gay. *Most men who rape other men are actually heterosexual, not gay.* •

Most male rapes occur in prison settings, but some occur outside prison walls. Male rape survivors tend to suffer greater physical injury than female survivors (Kaufman et al., 1980). Males are more often attacked by multiple assailants, are held captive longer, and are more often reluctant to reveal the assault to authorities (Kaufman et al., 1980). Male survivors are also less likely to disclose a sexual assault to others (Gerrol & Resick, 1988; Groth & Burgess, 1980; Myers, 1989). After all, victimization does not fit the male stereotype of capacity for self-defense. Men are expected to be not only strong but silent. Male rape survivors may suffer traumatic effects similar to those suffered by female rape survivors, however (Calhoun & Atkeson, 1991).

Most male rape survivors are raped by other men, but some men have been raped by women (Sarrel & Masters, 1982; Struckman-Johnson, 1988). Sarrel and Masters reported 11 cases of men who were sexually assaulted by women, including one case of a 37-year-old man who was coerced into sexual intercourse by two women who accosted him at gunpoint. In another case, a 27-year-old man fell asleep in his hotel room with a woman he had just met in a bar and then awakened to find that he was bound to his bed, gagged, and blindfolded. He was then forced into sexual intercourse with four different women, who threatened him with castration if he did not perform satisfactorily. Rape of a man may not be recognized as rape in states that adhere to a legal definition that requires forced vaginal penetration of a woman by a man. In such cases, the assailant or assailants may be charged under other statutes governing physical or sexual assaults.

MARITAL RAPE

The typical marital rapist is a man who still believes that husbands are supposed to "rule" their wives. This extends, he feels, to sexual matters. When he wants her, she should be glad, or at least willing. If she isn't, he has the right to force her. But in forcing her he gains far more than a few minutes of sexual pleasure; he humbles her and reasserts, in the most powerfully emotional way possible, that he is the ruler and she is the subject.

(Hunt, 1979, p. 38)

Discussion Question:
Think about the immense contrast between our culture views of "ideal" wedded bliss and the statistic that one wife in seven is likely to be raped by her husband. What explanations can you offer for the contrast?

As late as 1979, most states had legal protections that prevented husbands from being prosecuted for even the most violent of rapes (Gibbs, 1991). A number of recent legal changes have made it possible for sexually assaultive husbands to be convicted on rape charges, however.

Marital rapes are probably more common than date rapes because a sexual relationship has already been established. A husband may believe that he is entitled to sexual access to his wife any time he desires it. He may be less willing to accept a rebuff. He may believe it is his wife's duty to satisfy his sexual needs even when she is uninterested. Although there are no precise statistics on marital rape, a committee of the U.S. Congress estimated that one wife in seven is likely to be raped by her husband (Gibbs, 1991).

Marital rape goes largely unreported and unrecognized by survivors as rape (Russell, 1982). Women may fail to report marital rape because of fear that no one will believe them. Although 20 states have completely removed preferential treatment for assaultive husbands, in many other states husbands are still afforded the benefit of the doubt unless there is evidence of gross brutality (Gibbs, 1991).

Motives for marital rape vary. Some men use sex to dominate their wives. Others degrade their wives through sex, especially after arguments. Sexual coercion often occurs within a context of a pattern of marital violence, battering, and physical intimidation (Finkelhor & Yllo, 1982; Gibbs, 1991; Russell, 1982). In some cases, though, violence is limited to the sexual relationship (Finkelhor & Yllo, 1982). Some marital rapists

Notes: Women in relationships characterized by domestic violence have good reason to be fearful for their safety. According to The Women's Center, a Washington resource center, 4 to 6 million women are battered each year. "That means once every 5 seconds, somewhere in the United States, a woman is punched or kicked or thrown against a wall or held down and pummeled." According to the Department of Justice, about 29 percent of all female murder victims in 1992 were killed by their husbands or boyfriends. That compares with 4 percent of male victims killed by wives or girl friends. (Spotlight is now on domestic violence. 1994. *Des Moines Register,* June 22, 1A–2A.)

use sex to "teach" their spouses a "lesson" (Groth & Birnbaum, 1979, p. 179). Some men see sex as the solution to all marital disputes. They think that if they can force their wives into coitus, "everything will be OK."

Survivors of marital rape may be as fearful as survivors of stranger rape of serious injury or death (Kilpatrick et al., 1987). The long-term effects of marital rape on survivors are also similar to those experienced by survivors of stranger rape (Calhoun & Atkeson, 1991), including fear, depression, and sexual dysfunctions (Kilpatrick et al., 1987). Moreover, the woman who is raped by her husband usually continues to live with her assailant, and may fear repeated attacks.

RAPE BY WOMEN   Rape by women is rare. When it does occur, it often involves aiding or abetting men who are attacking another woman. Rape by women may occur in gang rape in which women follow male leaders to gain their approval. In such cases, a woman may be used to lure another woman to a reasonably safe place for the rape. Or the woman may hold the other woman down while she is assaulted.

SOCIAL ATTITUDES AND MYTHS THAT ENCOURAGE RAPE

Many people believe a number of myths about rape, such as "only bad girls get raped," "any healthy woman can resist a rapist if she really wants to," and "women 'cry rape' only when they've been jilted or have something to cover up" (Burt, 1980, p. 217). Another myth is that rapists are not responsible for their actions but were driven to rape by uncontrollable sexual urges that were aroused by sexually provocative women. Yet another myth is that deep down inside, women want to be raped. Although many women report experiencing rape fantasies within the safe and secure confines of their own minds, this does not mean that they wish to have the fantasy enacted in real life. The belief that women desire to be overpowered and forced by men into sexual relations is a rationalization for violence (Gordon & Snyder, 1989).

TRUTH OR *FICTION?*

R E V I S I T E D

A healthy woman can resist a rapist if she really wants to. The belief that a healthy woman can (successfully) resist a rapist—if she "really" wants to—is actually a cultural myth that has the effect of encouraging rape. •

Learning Objective 3: Discuss the myths, social attitudes, and sociocultural factors that encourage rape in the United States.

Rape myths create a social climate that legitimizes rape and increases the potential for rape. Though both men and women are susceptible to rape myths, researchers find that college men show greater acceptance of rape myths than do college women (Brady et al., 1991; Margolin et al., 1989). Men also cling more stubbornly to myths about date rape than do women, following exposure to date rape education classes specifically designed to challenge these views (Lenihan et al., 1992). College men who endorse rape myths are more likely to see themselves as likely to commit rape (Malamuth, 1981, 1989). Such myths do not occur in a social vacuum. Burt (1980) found that they are related to other social attitudes, including gender-role stereotyping, the perception of sex as adversarial, and the acceptance of violence in interpersonal relationships.

SOCIOCULTURAL FACTORS IN RAPE

Many observers contend that our society breeds rapists by socializing males into socially and sexually dominant roles (Burt, 1980; Lisak, 1991). Men in our society are often reinforced from early childhood for stereotypical aggressive and competitive behaviors (Lisak, 1991). Gender typing may also lead men to reject or repress attributes that might restrain sexual aggression but are associated with the feminine gender role, such as tenderness and empathy (Lisak, 1991).

Research with college students supports the connection between stereotypical masculine identification and tendencies to rape or condone rape. In one study, college men who adhered more strictly to stereotypical gender-role beliefs expressed a greater likelihood of committing rape, were more accepting of violence against women, were more

Activity: *Cultural Myths That Support Rape* This 13-item self-scoring questionnaire in the IM allows students to measure how much they believe the cultural myths associated with rape.

likely to blame rape survivors, and were more aroused by depictions of rape than were men holding less rigid attitudes (Check & Malamuth, 1983). Other researchers studied college men at a Midwestern university. They found that men who more closely identified with the traditional masculine gender role more often reported having engaged in verbal sexual coercion and forcible rape (Muehlenhard & Falcon, 1990).

Women, too, may be socialized into assuming the helpless role. The stereotypical feminine gender role includes such characteristics as submissiveness, passivity, cooperativeness, even obedience to male authority. Such qualities may make it difficult for a woman to suddenly overcome her socialization and resist when faced with the possibility of rape. A woman may thus be unprepared to cope with an assailant. She may lack aggressive skills and may believe that physical resistance is inappropriate or that she is incapable of resisting. Women are also taught that it is important to be sexually attractive to men. Women may thus unfairly blame themselves for the assault, believing that they somehow enticed the assailant, failed to exercise due caution, or failed to fend off the attack.

Notes: In a study of 262 undergraduate males, fraternity members were more likely than nonmembers to associate with men who engage in violent or coercive sexual activities, to be reinforced by their friends for engaging in such activities, and to use drugs or alcohol to obtain intercourse. (Boeringer, S. B. et al., 1991. Social contexts and social learning in sexual coercion and aggression: Assessing the contribution of fraternity membership. *Family Relations, 40,* 58–64.)

Social influences may reinforce themes that may underlie rape, such as the belief that a truly masculine man is expected to be sexually aggressive and overcome a woman's resistance until she "melts" in his arms (Stock, 1991). The popular belief that women fantasize about being overpowered sanctions coercive tactics to "awaken" a woman's sexual desires. Images from popular books and movies reinforce these themes, such as that of Rhett Butler in *Gone with the Wind* carrying a protesting Scarlett O'Hara up the stairs to her bedroom. Violent pornography, which fuses violence and erotic arousal, may also serve to legitimize rape (Stock, 1991).

Young men may come to view dates not as chances to get to know their partners but as opportunities for sexual conquest in which the object is to overcome their partners' resistance by whatever means are necessary. In one study, male college students expressed support for a man's right to kiss his female partner even if she resists (Margolin et al., 1989). Malamuth (1981) found that 35 percent of the college men in his sample said they would force a woman into sexual relations if they knew they could get away with it.

The social philosopher Myriam Miedzian (cited in Levy, 1991) suggests that lessons learned in competitive sports may also predispose U.S. youth to sexual violence. Boys are often exposed to coaches who emphasize winning at all costs. They are taught to be dominant and to vanquish their opponents, even if winning means injuring or "taking out" the opposition. This philosophy, Miedzian argues, may be carried from the playing field into relationships with women. Some athletes can distinguish between sports and dating relationships, but others cannot. Evidence shows that student athletes commit a disproportionate number of sexual assaults (Eskenazi, 1990). Many of these are gang rapes committed by groups of student athletes who live together and "bond" so strongly that they even share sexual experiences. Few schools, however, have rape-prevention programs or sensitivity training aimed at male athletes (Eskenazi, 1990).

Sexual behavior and competitive sports in our culture are linked through common idioms. A young man may be taunted by his friends after a date with a woman with such questions as, "Did you score?" or more bluntly, "Did you get in?" Consider, for example, the aggressive competitiveness with which this male college student views dating relationships between men and women:

> A man is supposed to view a date with a woman as a premeditated scheme for getting the most sex out of her. Everything he does, he judges in terms of one criterion—"getting laid." He's supposed to constantly pressure her to see how far he can get. She is his adversary, his opponent in a battle, and he begins to view her as a prize, an object, not a person. While she's dreaming about love, he's thinking about how to conquer her.
>
> (Powell, 1991, p. 55)

PSYCHOLOGICAL CHARACTERISTICS OF RAPISTS

Learning Objective 4:
Examine the characteristics of rapists and discuss their motives for rape.

Although sexual aggressiveness may be embedded within our social fabric, not all men are equally vulnerable to such cultural influences (Burkhart & Fromuth, 1991). Not all men become rapists. Personal factors are thus also involved. What are they? Are rapists mentally disturbed? Retarded? Driven by insatiable sexual urges?

Much of our knowledge of the psychological characteristics of rapists derives from studies of samples of incarcerated rapists (Harney & Muehlenhard, 1991). One conclusion that emerges from these studies is that there is no single type of rapist. Rapists vary widely in their psychological characteristics, family backgrounds, mental health, and criminal histories (Prentky & Knight, 1991). As a group, rapists are no less intelligent or more likely to be mentally ill than comparison groups (Renzetti & Curran, 1989; Wolfe & Baker, 1980). Many rapists show no evidence of psychological disturbance (Dean & de Bruyn-Kops, 1982). The great majority of rapists are in control of their behavior, and they know that it is illegal.

Most rapists are mentally ill. *Actually, most rapists have* not *been found to be mentally ill, even though their crimes might strike observers as being "sick."* •

Some rapists feel socially inadequate and report that they cannot find willing partners. Some lack social skills and avoid social interactions with women (Overholser & Beck, 1986). Others are no less skillful socially than nonrapists in the same socioeconomic group, however (Segal & Marshall, 1985). Some rapists are basically antisocial and have long histories of violent behavior (Knight et al., 1991). They tend to act upon their impulses regardless of the cost to the person they attack. Some were sexually victimized or physically assaulted as children (Groth, 1979; Sack & Mason, 1980) and may as adults be identifying with the aggressor role in interpersonal relationships. For some rapists violence and sexual arousal become enmeshed, so that they seek to combine sex and violence to enhance their sexual arousal (Quinsey et al., 1984). The use of alcohol may also dampen self-restraint and spur sexual aggressiveness.

Some evidence shows that rapists, as a group, are more sexually aroused (as measured by the size of erections) by verbal descriptions, films, or audiotapes that portray themes of rape than are normal controls (Abel et al., 1977; Barbaree et al., 1989). Other researchers, however, have failed to find deviant patterns of arousal in rapists (Baxter et al., 1986; Hall, 1989). These researchers find that as a group, rapists, like normal control subjects, are more aroused by stimuli depicting mutually consenting sexual activity than by rape stimuli.

Studies of incarcerated rapists may be criticized on grounds that the samples may not represent the total population of rapists. It is estimated that fewer than 4 percent of rapists are caught and eventually imprisoned (Gibbs, 1991). Most rapes are committed by acquaintances, and acquaintance rapists are even less likely than stranger rapists to be arrested, and if arrested, to be convicted and incarcerated.

To offset this methodological concern, researchers have turned to the survey method to study men who anonymously report that they have engaged in sexually coercive behaviors, including rape, but have not been identified by the criminal justice system.

Koss and her colleagues (1987) found that about one man in thirteen (7.7%) in their national college sample of nearly 3,000 college men admitted to committing or attempting rape. Sexually aggressive men reported greater hostility toward women, had more accepting attitudes toward the use of violence in interpersonal relationships, and tended to belong to peer groups that viewed women as sexual objects. They were likely to become sexually active at a younger age, to view sexually violent pornography, and to use alcohol frequently. Other researchers also found that self-reported rapists or attempted rapists among a sample of college men were more likely than nonviolent college men to hold hypermasculine attitudes and interests and to relate to women in angry, power-oriented ways (Lisak & Roth, 1990). Harney and Muehlenhard (1991) summarized research findings on self-identified sexually aggressive men. They are more likely than other men to condone rape and violence against women, hold traditional gender role attitudes, be sexually experienced, and be hostile toward women. They also are more likely than other men to engage in sexual activity in order to express social dominance, be sexually aroused by depictions of rape, be irresponsible and lack a social conscience, and have peer groups, such as fraternities, that pressure them into sexual activity.

Rapists. Despite the fact that most incarcerated rapists and other sex offenders will eventually be released, the great majority receive little if any psychological treatment in prison. Here a group of teenage sex offenders at a state school engage in a role-playing exercise during a therapy session.

Rape-Prone and Rape-Free Societies: Whither the United States?

Cross-cultural studies suggest that sexual violence is not unique to our culture. It may in fact be culturally sanctioned in some societies. Rape is more common in violent cultures, especially in the minority of cultures in which violence toward women is legitimized (Ember & Ember, 1990; Powell, 1991). Among the Yanomamö people of the Amazon jungle, a tribe known to be among the fiercest and most aggressive people in the world, men often raid neighboring villages and literally carry away the women to keep as their wives (Ember & Ember, 1990). Wives are often savagely beaten, stabbed with sticks, or burned with glowing firewood by husbands as punishment for misbe-havior (Harris, 1974). Wives come to accept punishment as part of their marital role. They may also come to regard the scars as signs that their husbands must care deeply for them to have beaten them so badly.

Sanday (1981) characterized 18 percent of the 156 cultures she studied as *rape-prone.* These rape-prone societies or "cultures of violence" tended to treat women as property. By contrast, Sanday found 45 "rape-free" cultures in which rape was entirely absent or occurred only rarely. Rape-free societies were characterized by sexual equality in which both genders shared power and were deemed to make important contributions, albeit in different ways, to the welfare of the society. In such societies women were not economically dependent on men and were able to control their own resources. Such societies also rear their children to be nurturant and to shun interpersonal violence. It thus appears that sexual violence occurs within the cultural context of interpersonal violence and male dominance (Stock, 1991).

Such cultural factors may help to explain the high rate of rape in our own culture (Renzetti & Curran, 1989), which is characterized by both a high level of violent behavior (the United States, for example, has the highest homicide rate among the industrialized nations) and unequal gender relations.

In another study of self-identified date rapists, Kanin (1985) found that men who admitted to committing date rape were nearly twice as likely to have engaged in a consensual coital experience in the year preceding the rape than did a reference group of nonrapists. These results do not indicate that date rapists, as a group, are unable to find willing partners. The self-identified date rapists believed that sexual coercion was justified with a "loose" woman or a "tease." Other researchers also find that sexually coercive college men have a greater frequency of coital experiences (Mahoney et al., 1986).

THE MOTIVES OF RAPISTS: THE SEARCH FOR TYPES Although sexual arousal is an obvious and important element of most rapes (Barbaree & Marshall, 1991), some researchers argue that sexual desire is not the basic motivation for rape (Gebhard et al., 1965; Groth & Birnbaum, 1979). Other researchers believe that sexual motivation plays a key role in at least some rapes (Hall & Hirschman, 1991). Based on their clinical work with more than 1,000 rapists, Groth and Birnbaum believe that there are three basic kinds of rapes: anger rape, power rape, and sadistic rape.

The **anger rape** is a vicious, unplanned attack that is triggered by anger and resentment toward women. The anger rapist usually employs more force than is needed to obtain compliance. The person who is raped is often coerced into performing degrading and humiliating acts, fellatio, or anal intercourse. Typically, the anger rapist reports that he had suffered humiliations at the hands of women and used the rape as a means of revenge.

The man who commits a **power rape** is motivated by the desire to control and dominate the woman he rapes. Sexual gratification is secondary. The power rapist uses rape as

Anger rape
A vicious, unplanned rape that is triggered by feelings of intense anger and resentment toward women.

Power rape
Rape that is motivated by the desire to control and dominate the person assaulted.

an attempt "to resolve disturbing doubts about [his] masculine identity and worth, [or] to combat deep-seated feelings of insecurity and vulnerability" (Groth & Hobson, 1983, p. 165). Only enough force to subdue the woman is used.

The **sadistic rape** is a highly ritualized, savage attack. Sadistic rapists often carefully plan their assaults and use a "con" or pretext to approach their targets, such as asking for directions or offering or requesting assistance (Dietz et al., 1990). Some sadists bind their victims and subject them to humiliating and degrading experiences and threats. Some torture or murder their victims (Dietz et al., 1990). Mutilation of the victim is unfortunately common. Groth and Birnbaum (1983) suggest that sadistic rapists are often preoccupied with violent pornography, but have little or no interest in nonviolent (consensual) pornography. Groth (1979) estimated that about 40 percent of rapes are anger rapes; 55 percent, power rapes; and 5 percent, sadistic rapes.

ADJUSTMENT OF RAPE SURVIVORS

Women who are raped almost always report that they feared for their lives during the attack (Calhoun & Atkeson, 1991). Whether or not weapons or threats were used, the experience of being dominated by an unpredictable and threatening assailant is terrifying, especially since the woman does not know whether she will survive and may feel helpless to do anything about it. Afterwards, many survivors enter a state of **crisis.**

Many survivors are extremely distraught in the days and weeks following the rape (Calhoun & Atkeson, 1991; Koss, 1993). They have trouble sleeping and cry frequently. They tend to report eating problems, cystitis, headaches, irritability, mood changes, anxiety and depression, and menstrual irregularity (Norris & Feldman-Summers, 1981). They may become withdrawn, sullen, and mistrustful (McArthur, 1990). Because of society's tendency to believe that women who are raped are at least partly to blame for the assault (Gordon & Snyder, 1989), some survivors experience feelings of guilt and shame (McArthur, 1990). Some, however, show few negative effects in the aftermath of the assault (Calhoun & Atkeson, 1991). Emotional distress tends to peak in severity by about three weeks following the assault and generally remains high for about a month before beginning to abate about a month or two later (Koss, 1993). About one survivor in four encounters emotional problems that linger beyond a year (Calhoun & Atkeson, 1991; Hanson, 1990).

CNN Comfort Women in the Philippines

According to a community survey of sexual assault survivors (both women and men) from Los Angeles, the most frequent emotional reactions to sexual assault were anger (59%), sadness (43%), and anxiety (40%) (see Table 19.1). A total of 447 persons from the sample of more than 3,000 adults reported that they had suffered a sexual assault, which included a range of coercive acts from fondling of the breasts or sex organs to sexual intercourse (Siegel et al., 1990). As shown in Table 19.1, women were significantly more likely to report 12 of 14 listed reactions. Survivors who were physically threatened by their assailants reported greater fear and anxiety, depression, and sexual distress (reduced interest and pleasure, fear of sex). Attacks that resulted in forced intercourse were more distressing than those that did not.

Rape survivors may also suffer physical injuries and sexually transmitted diseases, even AIDS, as a result of a sexual assault. In one study, unsolicited concerns about contracting AIDS were spontaneously reported by about one in four survivors interviewed within three months of a rape or sexual assault (Baker et al., 1990).

Rape survivors may also be at risk for long-term health complications. In one study, survivors reported more current physical complaints, including gynecological problems, when they were assessed *two or more years* following the attack than did a reference group matched on demographic variables such as race and age (Waigandt et al., 1990).

Survivors may also encounter problems at work, such as problems relating to co-workers or bosses or difficulties in concentrating. Work adjustment, however, usually returns to normal levels within a year (Calhoun & Atkeson, 1991). Relationships with spouses or partners may also be impaired. Disturbances in sexual functioning are common, and may last for years or a lifetime. Survivors often report a lack of sexual desire, fears of sex, and difficulty becoming sexually aroused (Becker et al., 1986). Even in the

TABLE 19.1 Prevalence of emotional and behavioral reactions to sexual assault in Los Angeles community sample (in percentages)

Reaction	Women	Men	Total
Fearful	45.5	15.9*	35.1
Stopped doing things	31.8	15.2*	25.9
Fearful of sex	21.6	7.9*	16.8
Less sexual interest	32.5	6.9*	23.5
Less sexual pleasure	27.1	8.0*	20.4
Felt dishonored or spoiled	33.9	20.0*	29.1
Guilt	35.0	25.9*	31.8
Sad, blue, or depressed	50.6	28.8*	43.0
Anger	72.0	34.8*	59.0
Tense, nervous, or anxious	49.9	22.9*	40.4
Insomnia	25.2	11.6*	20.4
Loss/increase in appetite	15.8	8.4	13.2
Alcohol/drug use	5.1	5.9	5.4
Fearful of being alone	23.0	2.2*	15.7

*Indicates that the differences between men and women were statistically significant at the .05 level of significance; that is, that there is less than a 5 percent chance that the differences between men and women were due to chance fluctuations.

Source: Siegel, J. M. et al. (1990). Reactions to sexual assault: A community study. *Journal of Interpersonal Violence, 5,* 229–246. Reprinted by permission of Sage Publications, Inc.

absence of a clearly identified dysfunction, a woman may not experience the level of sexual enjoyment she found before the assault (Calhoun & Atkeson, 1991).

SURVIVORS' REACTIONS TO THE ASSAULT: WHOM TO TELL?   About two thirds (65%) of the 447 sexual assault survivors in the Los Angeles survey reported they had told someone about the assault (Golding et al., 1989). The person was usually a friend or a relative. Only one in 10 reported the assault to the police, however, and only 16 percent consulted mental health professionals. Survivors were more likely to inform police or physicians of attacks by strangers than by acquaintances.

Most women fail to report sexual assaults to police. Why? Some of the reasons women commonly report for not informing the authorities include fears of retaliation, the social stigma attached to the survivors of rape, doubts that others will believe them, feelings that it would be hopeless to try to bring charges against the perpetrator, concerns about negative publicity, and fears about the emotional distress to which they would be subjected if the case were to go to trial.

RAPE TRAUMA AND PSYCHIATRIC DISORDERS   Rape survivors are at higher than average risk of developing psychiatric problems such as depression, alcohol and substance abuse disorders, and anxiety disorders (Koss, 1993). Investigators in the United States (Moscarello, 1990) and Norway (Dahl, 1989) report that rape survivors often develop or show signs of **post-traumatic stress disorder** (PTSD), a type of anxiety disorder that is brought on by exposure to a traumatic event and most commonly seen in soldiers who were in combat. Typical features of PTSD include flashbacks of the traumatic experience in the form of disturbing dreams or intrusive recollections, emotional numbing, and heightened arousal. PTSD may persist for years. The person may also develop fears of situations that are connected with the traumatic event. For example, a woman who was raped on an elevator may develop a fear of riding elevators by herself.

Post-traumatic stress disorder

A type of stress reaction brought on by a traumatic event and characterized by flashbacks of the experience in the form of disturbing dreams or intrusive recollections, a sense of emotional numbing or restricted range of feelings, and heightened body arousal. Abbreviated *PTSD*.

Researchers also report that women who blame themselves for the rape tend to suffer more severe depression and adjustment problems in the immediate aftermath of the rape (Frazier, 1990) and more lasting sexual problems (Wyatt et al., 1990).

Rape trauma syndrome
A two-phase reaction to rape that is characterized by disruption of the survivor's life-style (the acute phase) and reorganization of the survivor's life (the long-term phase).

RAPE TRAUMA SYNDROME Ann Burgess and Lynda Holmstrom (1974) identified some common response patterns in rape survivors, which they labeled the **rape trauma syndrome.** Through emergency room interviews with 92 women at Boston City Hospital, and telephone or in-person follow-up interviews, Burgess and Holmstrom found two phases in rape trauma syndrome: an acute phase that is characterized by disruption of the woman's lifestyle and a long-term process of reorganization.

The acute phase: disorganization. The first stage, called the acute phase, typically lasts for several weeks following the attack. Many survivors are disorganized during this time and may benefit from conversation with rape-trauma counselors. The woman may cry uncontrollably and experience feelings of anger, shame, fear, and nervousness.

Other women present a calm, composed face to the world, but inwardly have not yet come to terms with the traumatic experience. Calmness often gives way to venting of feelings later on.

The long-term process: reorganization. The second phase, or long-term reorganization phase, may last for years. The woman gradually comes to deal with her feelings and to reorganize her life (Sales et al., 1984). Lingering fears may lead rape survivors to move to safer surroundings to help put the incident out of mind. Women who informed the police may have continuing fears of retaliation by the rapist. They may change their phone numbers, often to unlisted numbers. Some take out-of-state trips, often visiting parents, although they do not necessarily tell them of the rape. Many survivors continue to be bothered by frightening dreams.

Burgess and Holmstrom noted two variations of the rape trauma syndrome, the compounded reaction and the silent rape reaction.

COMPOUNDED REACTION Survivors with histories of psychiatric or medical problems sometimes became more severely depressed than other survivors, or became suicidal or psychotic. They required attention for these problems as well as for the rape trauma.

SILENT RAPE REACTION Survivors who do not disclose their attacks to anyone are said to suffer a silent rape reaction. Unfortunately, concealing the rape may prevent them from receiving social support. If survivors are children or adolescents when assaulted, their feelings may go unresolved for many years. They may avoid men or develop sudden panic reactions—like fear of being alone or of going out. They may have frightening dreams and lose self-confidence.

When these survivors seek assistance for other problems, they may show anxiety when the discussion comes around to sexuality. They may even stutter or be silent for long periods. Under these circumstances an empathic interviewer may suspect a silent reaction to a past rape.

Not all survivors, however, suffer a lengthy or predictable struggle of readjustment (Gordon & Snyder, 1989). For reasons that are not clear, some are able to put the rape behind them with little disruption of their regular lives. Each survivor is an individual, however, and copes with crisis in her own way (Gordon & Snyder, 1989).

Elizabeth Powell (1991, p. 239) offers the following suggestions if you should be raped yourself:

1. Don't change anything about your body—don't wash or even comb your hair. Leave your clothes as they are. Otherwise you could destroy evidence.
2. Strongly consider reporting the incident to police. You may prevent another woman from being assaulted, and you will be taking charge, starting on the path from victim to survivor.
3. Ask a relative or friend to take you to a hospital, if you can't get an ambulance or a police car. If you call the hospital, tell them why you're requesting an ambulance, in case they are able to send someone trained to deal with rape cases.

Rape Crisis Center. Rape crisis centers provide rape victims with emotional support to help them cope with the traumatic effects of rape. They also assist victims in obtaining medical, legal, and psychological services.

4. Seeking help is an assertive way to show your self-worth. Seek medical help. Injuries you are unaware of may be detected. Insist that a written or photographic record be made to document your condition. You may decide that you're going to file charges, and the prosecutor may need this evidence to obtain a conviction.

5. You have medical rights. Ask questions. Ask what treatments are available to you. Ask for whatever would help make you comfortable. You are calling the shots now. Ask for confidentiality if that's what you want. Refuse what you don't want.

You may also wish to call a rape hotline or rape crisis center for advice, if one is available in your area. A rape crisis volunteer may be available to accompany you to the hospital and help see you through the medical evaluation and police investigation if you report the attack. It is not unusual for rape survivors to try to erase the details of the rape from their minds, but trying to remember details clearly will permit you to provide an accurate description of the rapist to the police, including his clothing, type of car, and so on. This information may help police apprehend the rapist and assist in the prosecution.

TREATMENT OF RAPE SURVIVORS

Treatment of rape survivors typically involves a two-stage process of helping the woman (the vast majority are female) through the crisis period following the attack and then helping to foster long-term adjustment. Crisis intervention typically provides the survivor with support and information to help her express her feelings in the immediate aftermath of the rape and develop strategies for coping with the trauma (Resick & Schnicke, 1990). Psychotherapy, involving group or individual approaches, can be used to help the survivor cope with the emotional consequences of rape, avoid self-blame, improve self-esteem, validate the welter of feelings surrounding the experience, and help her establish or maintain loving relationships. Therapists also recognize the importance of helping the rape survivor identify supportive social networks (Ledray, 1990). One's family, friends, religious leaders, and health care specialists are all potential sources of help in coping with rape trauma. There are also "outside" support systems. In major cities and many towns, concerned men and women have formed rape crisis centers and hotlines, peer counseling groups, and referral agencies geared to assessing and treating survivors' needs after the assault. Some counselors are even trained to mediate between survivors of rape and their loved ones—husbands, lovers, and so forth. These counselors help people to discuss and work through the often complex emotional legacy of rape. Phone numbers for these services can be obtained from feminist groups (for example, your local office of the National Organization for Women [NOW], the police department, or the telephone directory.

Learning Objective 6: List specific precautions women can take to reduce the risk of rape and strategies women can use if confronted by a rapist.

RAPE PREVENTION

The elimination of rape would probably require massive changes in cultural attitudes and socialization processes. Educational intervention on a smaller scale may reduce its incidence, however. A study of 276 undergraduates at Pitzer College in California showed that college men who were more knowledgeable about the trauma caused by rape were less likely to report that they might commit a rape in the future (Hamilton & Yee, 1990). Many colleges and universities offer educational programs about date rape. The University of Washington, for example, offers students lectures and seminars on date rape (and also provides women with escorts to their homes or dorms after dark). Brown University requires all first-year students to attend orientation sessions on rape (Celis, 1991). The point of such programs is for men to learn that "no" means "no," despite the widespread belief that some women like to be "talked into" sex.

Until the basic cultural attitudes that support rape change, however, "rape prevention" will require that women take a number of precautions. Why, a reader may wonder, should women be advised to take measures to avoid rape? Is not the very listing of such measures a subtle way of blaming the woman if she should fall prey to an attacker? No, providing the information does not blame the person who is attacked. The rapist is *always* responsible for the assault. Women can take precautions, however, that might lower their risk of being assaulted. *The New Our Bodies, Ourselves* (1984) lists several suggestions that may help prevent rape:

1. Establish a set of signals with other women in the building or neighborhood.
2. List yourself in the phone directory and on the mailbox by your first initials only.
3. Use dead-bolt locks.
4. Lock windows and install iron grids on first-floor windows.
5. Keep doorways and entries well lit.
6. Keep your keys handy when approaching the car or the front door.
7. Do not walk by yourself after dark.
8. Avoid deserted areas.
9. Do not allow strange men into your house or apartment without first checking their credentials.
10. Keep your car doors locked and the windows up.
11. Check out the back seat of your car before entering.
12. Don't live in a risky building. (We realize that this suggestion may be of little use to women who are poor and have relatively little choice as to where they live.)
13. Don't give rides to hitchhikers (including women hitchhikers).
14. Don't converse with strange men on the street.
15. Shout "Fire!" not "Rape!" People are likely to flock to fires but to avoid scenes of violence.

Powell (1991) adds the following suggestions for avoiding date rape:

1. *Communicate your sexual limits to your date.* Tell your partner how far you would like to go so that he will know what the limits are. For example, if your partner starts fondling you in ways that make you uncomfortable, you might say, "I'd prefer if you didn't touch me there. I really like you, but I prefer not getting so intimate at this point in our relationship."
2. *Meet new dates in public places and avoid driving with a stranger or a group of people you've met.* When meeting a new date, drive in your own car and meet your date at a public place. Don't drive with strangers or offer rides to strangers or groups of people. In some cases of date rape, the group disappears just prior to the assault.
3. *State your refusal definitively.* Be firm in refusing a sexual overture. Look your partner straight in the eye. The more definite you are, the less likely your partner is to misinterpret your wishes.
4. *Become aware of your fears.* Take notice of any fears of displeasing your partner that might stifle your assertiveness. If your partner is truly respectful of you, you need not fear an angry or demeaning response. But if your partner is not respectful, it is best to become aware of it and end the relationship right there.
5. *Pay attention to your "vibes."* Trust your "gut-level feelings." Many victims of acquaintance rape said afterward that they had had a "strange" feeling about the man but failed to pay attention to it.

Self Defense Against Rape. Many women take self-defense classes to become better prepared to fend off an assailant. Yet no one strategy is likely to be effective in all situations.

6. *Be especially cautious if you are in a new environment, such as college or a foreign country.* You may be especially vulnerable to exploitation when you are becoming acquainted with a new environment, different people, and different customs.

7. *If you have broken off a relationship with someone you don't really like or feel good about, don't let him into your place.* Many so-called date rapes are committed by ex-lovers and ex-boyfriends.

Discussion Question: At some colleges and universities women have begun posting the names of date rapists on bulletin boards, often located in womens' restrooms. Should the administration intervene in any way to prevent these actions? Why or why not?

CONFRONTING A RAPIST: SHOULD YOU FIGHT, FLEE, OR PLEAD?   What if you are accosted by a rapist? Should you try to fight him off, flee, or try to plead with him to stop? Some women have thwarted attacks by pleading or crying. Yet research has shown that less forceful forms of resistance, such as pleading, begging, or reasoning, can be dangerous strategies. They may not fend off the attack and may heighten the probability of injury (Bart & O'Brien, 1985; Ullman & Knight,1992). Screaming may be particularly effective in warding off some attacks (Byers & Lewis, 1988). No suggestion is likely to be helpful in all rape cases, however. Running away is sometimes an effective strategy for avoiding a rape (Bart & O'Brien, 1985), for example, but running may not be effective if the woman is outnumbered by a group of assailants (Gidycz & Koss, 1990).

Self-defense training may help women become better prepared to fend off an assailant. Yet law enforcement officials caution that physical resistance may spur some rapists to become more aggressive (Powell, 1991). Federal statistics show that women who resist increase their chances of preventing the completion of a rape by 80 percent. However, resistance increases the odds of being physically injured by as much as threefold (Brody, 1992c). A study of 116 rapes showed that women were more likely to physically resist if the attacker was a friend or relative, if the attacker made verbal threats, and if the attacker physically restrained her or injured her (Atkeson et al., 1989).

It is difficult, if not impossible, for people to think through their options clearly and calmly when they are suddenly attacked. Rape experts recommend that women rehearse alternative responses to a rape attack. The Boston Police Department recommends that whatever form of self-defense a woman intends to use, she should carefully think through how it is used and practice using it (Brody, 1992c). Thompson (1991) suggests that effective self-defense is built upon the use of multiple strategies, ranging from attempts to avoid potential rape situations (such as by installing home security systems or by walking only in well-lit areas) to acquiescence when active resistance would seem too risky, to the use of more active verbal or physical forms of resistance in some low-risk situations.

TRUTH OR *FICTION?*
R E V I S I T E D

Women who encounter a rapist should attempt to fight off the assailant. *There is no one answer here. Women must make their own decisions about whether to physically resist a rapist, based on their assessment of the rapist, the situation, and their own ability to resist.* •

Sexual Pressure Lines

Rape is an extreme form of sexual pressure that involves the use of threats or force to coerce an unwilling person into a sexual act. But sexual pressure may take a more subtle form, such as persistent verbal pressure or the use of seduction "lines" that aim to manipulate, by deception or trickery, another person into having sexual relations.

Powell (1991) lists the following examples of sexual pressure lines and some possible replies that may help a person resist them:

	Sexual Pressure Lines	Sample Responses
Lines that reassure you about the negative consequences	"Don't worry, I'm sterile."	"I know you want to make me feel safer, but . . . well, I'm just not comfortable having sex without a condom. I've known a few people who were more fertile than they thought."
	"You can't get pregnant the first time." (This is not true)	"Hey, where did you get your sex education? People can get pregnant any time they have intercourse, even if it's just for one second."
	"Don't worry—I'll pull out." (Withdrawal before ejaculation may not prevent pregnancy—see Ch. 12.)	"I know you want to reassure me, but people can get pregnant that way, even without ejaculating."
Lines that threaten you with rejection	"If you don't have sex, I'll find someone who will."	"I can't believe you are making a threat like this. I'm furious that you would treat lovemaking like some kind of a job, as if anyone will do."
Lines that put down the refuser	"Are you frigid?"	"It's hard to believe you want to make love to me, and you think calling me names will put me in the mood. I need to leave, now."
		"I resent being called names just because I tell you what I want to do with my body."
Lines that stress the beautiful experience being missed	"Our relationship will grow stronger."	"I know you really would like to get more involved right now. But I need to wait. And lots of people have had their relationship grow stronger without intercourse."
Lines that imply that one might settle for less	"I don't want to do anything. I just want to lie next to you."	"The way we're attracted to each other, I don't think that would be a good idea. As much as I care about you, I'd better not spend the night."
Lines to make you prove yourself	"If you loved me, you would."	"You know I care a lot about you. But I feel very pressured when you try to get me to do something I'm not ready for. It's not fair to me. Please consider my feelings."
Lines that attempt to be logical, but aren't	"You're my girlfriend—it's your obligation."	"If you think sex is an obligation, we need to think about this relationship right now." (*Watch out* for any such talk—it is very common in abusers and rapists. At best, it's an irrational comment by an immature person.)
Lines that are totally transparent	"I'll say I love you after we do it."	"Bye, now." (There is no way to deal with a person who would say such a thing.)

Though these countering statements may be helpful in resisting specific pressure lines, Powell recognizes that "saying no" to sexual pressure is not a privilege you earn by out-debating your partner, but a basic right you have in controlling your body. Remember, it's your right to determine how, when, where, and with whom you will share a sexual experience. You may think it is appropriate to offer an explanation in a particular situation. But, as Powell recognizes, "you don't *have* to explain." Your body is not debatable. You don't have to say anything except, "I don't want to."

Now it's your turn. How would you respond to the following pressure lines? Ask yourself how you would reply.

"Why not? We both need it."

"We'll use protection; it's okay."
"But I thought you loved me!"
"Are you a child or a woman?" or, "Are you a man or a boy?"
"Is something wrong with me? Aren't you attracted to me?"
"But I have needs!"
"It's only a natural act; it doesn't mean anything."
"Grow up!"
"Let me show you how much I love you."
"Now you have me all hot and bothered."
"Don't worry, honey. I'm on the pill," or, "Don't worry, honey. I'll use protection."
"I know you're attracted to me. What's wrong?"

Source: Adapted from Powell, 1991.

VERBAL SEXUAL COERCION

Verbal sexual coercion is persistent verbal pressure or the use of seduction "lines" to manipulate a person into sexual activity. A study of 194 male undergraduates in a southeastern university showed that 42 percent admitted to verbally coercing a female partner into sex (Craig et al., 1989). In a survey of 325 college undergraduates from a northwestern state university, about one in five of the men reported having said things to women they didn't mean to engage in sexual intercourse (Lane & Gwartney-Gibbs, 1985). Women were more likely than men to have been pressured into sexual relations. One in four of the women respondents reported that they engaged in sexual intercourse with someone they would otherwise have rejected because they had "felt pressured by his continual arguments" (p. 56). About one in fifteen of the *men* reported engaging in sexual intercourse unwillingly as a result of sexual pressure.

The use of verbal pressure and seduction "lines" is so common in dating relationships that they are seldom recognized as forms of sexual coercion. Consider the man who deceives his partner into believing that he really loves her in order to persuade her to have sex with him. His use of lies or deception can be considered a form of sexual coercion because it employs devious means to exploit his partner's emotional needs to curry sexual favors. Note, however, that the use of the statement "I love you" is not a coercive tactic, sexual pressure, or a seduction line if it is spoken honestly and is not used for purposes of manipulation (Powell, 1991).

SEXUAL ABUSE OF CHILDREN

Deep inside, there is a wound that can never be healed.

(Diary entry of a 13-year-old girl who suffered sexual abuse)

Learning Objective 7: Define child sexual abuse and examine the incidence of the problem.

Many view child sexual abuse as among the most heinous of crimes. Children who are sexually assaulted often suffer social and emotional problems that impair their development and persist into adulthood, affecting their self-esteem and their ability to form intimate relationships.

No one knows how many children are sexually abused. The number of reported cases, some 45,000 annually, may represent the tip of the iceberg (Finkelhor & Hotaling, 1984). Like rape, child sexual abuse is greatly underreported. Perhaps only one in three or four cases becomes known to authorities (Alter-Reid et al., 1986).

Although most sexually abused children are girls (Knudsen, 1991), one quarter to one third are boys (Finkelhor, 1990). A randomized national telephone survey of more than 2,600 U.S. adults, conducted in 1990, showed that 9.5 percent of the men and 14.6 percent of the women reported having been sexually abused (a completed or attempted act of sexual intercourse) prior to age 19 (Finkelhor et al., 1990). These estimates may underrepresent the actual prevalences, as people may fail to report such incidents due to faulty memories or because of shame or embarrassment. In addition, about one in four people refused to participate in the survey, casting some doubt on the sample's representativeness. Other researchers estimate that the prevalence of sexual abuse among boys ranges from 4 to 16 percent (Genuis et al., 1991; Janus & Janus, 1993; Kohn, 1987) and among girls exceeds 20 percent (Janus & Janus, 1993; Kohn, 1987). Whatever the actual prevalences, sexual abuse of children cuts across all racial, ethnic, and economic boundaries (Alter-Reid et al., 1986).

WHAT IS CHILD SEXUAL ABUSE?

Sexual abuse of children may range from exhibitionism, kissing, fondling, and sexual touching to oral sex and anal intercourse and, in the case of girls, vaginal intercourse (Knudsen, 1991). By definition, any form of sexual contact between an adult and a child is abusive, even if force or physical threat is not used, since children are deemed incapable of voluntarily consenting to sexual activity with adults (Finkelhor, 1979). Although the age of consent varies among the states, sexual relations between adults and children under the age of consent are criminal offenses in every state, even when children consent.

Voluntary sexual activity between children of similar ages, however, is not generally considered sexual abuse (Gordon & Snyder, 1989). Children often engage in consensual sex play with peers or even with siblings of similar ages, as in "playing doctor" and in mutual masturbation. Although such experiences may be recalled in adulthood with feelings of shame or guilt, they are not typically as harmful as adult-child sexual contact. When the experience involves coercion, however, or when the other person is significantly older than the child or is in a position of power or control over the child, the sexual contact may be considered sexual abuse rather than sexual play.

PATTERNS OF ABUSE

Children from stable, middle-class families appear to be generally at lower risk of encountering sexual abuse than children from poorer, less cohesive families (Finkelhor, 1984). In most cases, children who are sexually abused are not accosted by the proverbial stranger lurking in the school yard. In perhaps 75 to 80 percent of cases, instead, the molesters are people who are close to them: relatives, step-relatives, family friends, and neighbors (Waterman & Lusk, 1986). Estimates of the percentage of sexually molested children who are abused by family members have ranged from 10 to 50 percent of cases (Waterman & Lusk, 1986). In a random survey of 521 Boston parents, 55 percent of the respondents who said they had been sexually abused as children reported that the perpetrator was a family member or acquaintance (Finkelhor, 1984).

Parents who discover that their child has been abused by a family member are often reluctant to notify authorities. Some may feel that such problems are "family matters" that are best kept private. Others may be reluctant to notify authorities for fear that it may shame the family or that they may be held accountable for failing to protect the child. The decision to report the abuse to the police depends largely on the relationship between the abuser and the person who discovers the abuse (Finkelhor, 1984). In the Boston community survey, none of the parents whose children were sexually abused by family members notified the authorities. By contrast, 23 percent of the parents whose children had been abused by acquaintances notified the authorities; 73 percent of the parents whose children were abused by strangers did so (Finkelhor, 1984).

Typically, the child initially trusts the abuser. Physical force is seldom needed to gain compliance, largely because of the child's helplessness, gullibility, and submission to

So there really was a monster in her bedroom.

For many kids, there's a real reason to be afraid of the dark.

Last year in Indiana, there were 6,912 substantiated cases of sexual abuse. The trauma can be devastating for the child and for the family. So listen closely to the children around you.

If you hear something you don't want to believe, perhaps you should. For helpful information on child abuse prevention, contact the LaPorte County Child Abuse Prevention Council, 7451 Johnson Road, Michigan City, IN 46360. (219) 874-0007

LaPorte County Child Abuse Prevention Council

So There Really Was a Monster in Her Bedroom. Not all monsters are make-believe. Some, like incest perpetrators, are even family members.

adult authority. Whereas most sexually abused children are abused only once, those who are abused by family members are more likely to suffer repeated acts of abuse (Briere & Runtz, 1987; Dube & Hebert, 1988). Genital fondling is the most common type of abuse of both boys and girls (Knudsen, 1991). In one sample of women who had been molested in childhood, most of the contacts involved genital fondling (38% of cases) or exhibitionism (20% of cases). Intercourse occurred in only 4 percent of cases (Knudsen, 1991). Repeated abuse by a family member, however, commonly follows a pattern that begins with affectionate fondling during the preschool years, progresses to oral sex or mutual masturbation during the early school years, and then to sexual penetration (vaginal or anal intercourse) during preadolescence or adolescence (Waterman & Lusk, 1986).

Abused children rarely report the abuse, often because of fear of retaliation from the abuser or because they believe they will be blamed for it. Adults may suspect abuse if a child shows sudden personality changes or develops fears, problems in school, or eating or sleeping problems (Finkelhor, 1979). A pediatrician may discover physical signs of abuse during a medical exam.

The average age at which most children are first sexually abused ranges from 6 to 12 years for girls and 7 to 10 years for boys (Knudsen, 1991). Boys are relatively more likely to be abused in public places and by strangers and non-family members (Faller, 1989a; Knudsen, 1991). Boys are also more likely to be threatened and physically injured during the incident.

TYPES OF ABUSERS Researchers find that the overwhelming majority of perpetrators of child sexual abuse of both boys and girls are males (Thomlison et al., 1991). Experts estimate that men account for perhaps 95 percent of the abusers of young girls and 80 percent of the abusers of young boys (Finkelhor & Russell, 1984). Contrary to assumptions that some people may hold, gay males and lesbians account for but a small percentage of abusers (Groth, 1979). Although most sexual abusers are adults, some are adolescents. Researchers are only now beginning to focus on this subgroup of offenders. One finding is that male adolescent sexual offenders are more likely than nonoffenders to have been molested themselves as young boys (Becker et al., 1989; Muster, 1992). This suggests that some adolescent sexual offenders may be imitating their own victimization. Adolescent child molesters also tend to feel socially inadequate and to be fearful of social interactions with age-mates of the opposite gender (Katz, 1990).

Although the great majority of sexual abusers are male, the number of female sexual abusers may be greater than has been generally believed (Banning, 1989). Many female sexual abusers may go undetected because society accords women a much freer range of physical contact with children than it does men. A woman who fondles a child might be seen as affectionate, or at worst seductive, whereas a man would be more likely to be perceived as a child molester (Banning, 1989).

What motivates a woman to sexually abuse children, and in some cases, her own children? Little research has been done to explore this question, but some factors have begun to emerge (Matthews et al., 1990). Some female abusers have histories of becoming dependent on, or rejected by, abusive males. Some appear to have been manipulated into engaging in sexual abuse by their husbands. Others appear to have unmet emotional needs and low self-esteem and may have been seeking acceptance, closeness, and attention through sexual acts with children. Some, motivated by unresolved feelings of anger, revenge, powerlessness, or jealousy, may view their own and others' children as safe targets for venting these feelings. Some view their crimes as expressions of love.

Males account for a disproportionate number of child molesters. Why? Banning (1989), arguing from a sociocultural framework, suggests that males in our culture are socialized into seeking partners who are younger and weaker than they, partners whom they can easily dominate. This pattern of socialization may take the extreme form of development of sexual interest in children and adolescent girls, who because of their age are more easily dominated than adult women. Yet sexual interest in children may also be motivated by unusual patterns of sexual arousal in which children become the objects of sexual desire, sometimes to the exclusion of more appropriate (adult) stimuli. This brings us to pedophilia.

Notes: A recent Justice Department study of 11 states and the District of Columbia found that 10,000 women under 18 were raped in these jurisdictions in 1992. At least 3,800 were children under the age of 12. "Although females under age 18 made up only 25 percent of the nation's total female population in 1992, in the 12 reporting jurisdictions, they made up 51 percent of the rape victims, according to the report and Census Bureau statistics." (Alarming incidence of child rape seen. 1994. *Des Moines Register,* June 23, 1A–2A.)

PEDOPHILIA

The prevalence of **pedophilia** in the general population is unknown (Ames & Houston, 1990). Some pedophiles are so distressed by their urges that they never act on them. Many, however, molest young children and adolescents, often repeatedly. Some pedophiles appear to be responsible for a large number of sexual assaults on children. One study of 232 convicted pedophiles showed that they had each molested an average of 76 children (Abel et al., 1987). Incarcerated pedophiles have usually committed many more offenses than those for which they were convicted (Ames & Houston, 1990).

Although pedophiles are sometimes called child molesters, not all child molesters are pedophiles. Pedophilia involves persistent or recurrent sexual attraction to children. Some molesters, however, may seek sexual contacts with children only when they are under unusual stress or lack other sexual outlets and so do not meet the clinical definition of pedophilia.

Pedophiles are almost exclusively male, although some isolated cases of female pedophiles have been reported (Cooper et al., 1990). Some pedophiles are only sexually attracted to children, whereas others are sexually attracted to adults as well. Some pedophiles limit their sexual interest in children to incestuous relationships with family members. Others abuse children to whom they are not related. Some pedophiles limit their sexual interest in children to looking at them or undressing them, whereas others fondle them or masturbate in their presence. Some manipulate or coerce children into oral sex or anal or vaginal intercourse.

Children tend not to be worldly-wise and can often be "taken in" by pedophiles who tell them that they would like to "show them something," "teach them something," or do something with them that they would "like." The pedophile may seek to gain the child's affection and discourage the child from disclosing the sexual activity by showering the child with attention and gifts. Some pedophiles threaten the child or the child's family to prevent disclosure, however.

There is no consistent personality profile of the pedophile (Okami & Goldberg, 1992). Most pedophiles do not fit the common stereotype of the "dirty old man" in the trenchcoat who hangs around school yards. Most are otherwise law-abiding, well-respected citizens, generally in their thirties and forties. Many are married or divorced and have children of their own.

Mild paraphilic behavior may be found within the normal spectrum of human sexuality (see Chapter 18). What about pedophilia, however? Is pedophilia so aberrant that it is restricted to a deviant subgroup of the population? A recent research study suggests that sexual attraction to children may be more common than is generally believed. The researchers administered an anonymous survey to a sample of 193 college men (Briere & Runtz, 1989). A surprisingly high percentage of the students—21 percent—admitted to having been sexually attracted to some small children. Nine percent reported sexual fantasies involving young children; 5 percent reported masturbating to such fantasies; and 7 percent reported that there was some likelihood that they would have sex with a young child if they knew they could avoid detection and punishment. If these findings are repeated in other samples, it would suggest that sexual interest in young children is not as variant as we may think, although the level of sexual interest may not reach the level associated with pedophilia. Fortunately, most people with such erotic interests never act upon them.

Pedophilia may have complex and varied origins. Some pedophiles who are lacking in social skills may turn to children after failing to establish gratifying relationships with adult women (Overholser & Beck, 1986; Tollison & Adams, 1979). Research generally supports the stereotype of the pedophile as a weak, passive, shy, socially inept, and isolated man who feels threatened by mature relationships and turns to children for sexual gratification (Ames & Houston, 1990; Wilson & Cox, 1983). Pedophiles who engage in incestuous relationships with their own children tend to present a somewhat different picture, however. Incestuous pedophiles tend to fall on either end of the dominance spectrum; some are very dominant, others are very passive. Few are found between these extremes (Ames & Houston, 1990).

Some pedophiles were sexually abused as children and may be attempting to establish feelings of mastery by reversing the situation (De Young, 1982). Cycles of abuse may be perpetuated from generation to generation as children who are sexually abused become victimizers or partners of victimizers as adults.

INCEST

Incest

Marriage or sexual relations between people who are so closely related (by "blood") that sexual relations are prohibited and punishable by law. (From the Latin *in-*, meaning "not" and *castus*, meaning "chaste.")

Learning Objective 9: Discuss the incidence of incest, the most common types, and the characteristics of incest perpetrators and their families.

True **incest** applies only to people who are related by blood, or *consanguineally*. The law may also proscribe coitus between, say, a stepfather and stepdaughter, however. Although a few societies have permitted incestuous pairings among royalty, all known cultures have some form of an incest taboo. Incest between an adult family member and a child is, by definition, a form of child sexual abuse, since the child is deemed incapable of giving voluntary consent.

PERSPECTIVES ON THE INCEST TABOO   Speculations about the origin of incest taboos abound. One explanation holds that the incest taboo developed because it was adaptive for ancient humans to develop this social prohibition to prevent the harmful effects of inbreeding that may result when genetic defects or diseases are carried within family bloodlines (Leavitt, 1990). Although our ancient ancestors lacked knowledge of the mechanisms of genetics, perhaps they observed that certain diseases or defects tended to run in families. Evidence does show that marriage between close relations is associated with an increased rate of genetic diseases, mental retardation, and other physical abnormalities (Ames & Houston, 1990). Inbreeding may also be counterproductive to survival because by reducing the amount of genetic variation in the gene pool, it can reduce the ability of the population to adapt to changes in the environment (Van den Berghe, 1983).

Other theorists explain the incest taboo in terms of the role that it may play in maintaining stability in the family and establishing kinship ties within the larger social grouping (Ember & Ember, 1990). The anthropologist Bronislaw Malinowski (1927), for example, argued that the incest taboo serves to reduce sexual competition within the family, which if left uncontrolled would create such rivalry and hostility that the family would be unable to function effectively as a social unit. Since the functioning of the family is necessary for a society to survive, the incest taboo may have developed as a means of keeping the family intact by reducing sexual competition within the family.

Cooperation theory emphasizes the importance to the survival of the society of promoting cooperative ties between family groups (Ember & Ember, 1990). Society is complex and requires the working together of large numbers of people if it is to survive. Marriage establishes kinship ties that help break down suspiciousness and hostility between family groups and promotes cooperation. So, according to cooperation theory, the incest taboo was established to help ensure that people would marry outside their own families, and so help the community hold together. Still, it remains an open question whether the origins of the incest taboo reflect these biological or social factors.

Teaching Tip: Present information on local programs (if any) for incest perpetrators. In some programs the perpetrator must live away from the family after charges are filed and attend counseling regularly. If he fails to comply, a trial date is set.

TYPES OF INCEST   Most of our knowledge of incestuous relationships concerns father-daughter incest, because most identified cases involve fathers who were eventually incarcerated. About 1 percent of a sample of women in five American cities reported a sexual encounter with a biological father or stepfather (Cameron et al., 1986). Brother-sister incest, not parent-child incest, is the most common type of incest, however (Waterman & Lusk, 1986). Brother-sister incest is also believed to be greatly underreported (Waterman & Lusk, 1986), probably due to the fact that it tends to be transient and is apparently less harmful than parent-child incest (Dixen & Jenkins, 1981). Finkelhor (1979, 1980) found that 21 percent of the college men in his sample, and 39 percent of the college women, reported incestuous relationships with a sibling of the opposite gender, as compared to 4 percent who reported an incestuous relationship with their fathers. Incest between siblings of the same gender is considered to be rare (Waterman & Lusk, 1986). Mother-daughter incest is considered the rarest form of incest (Waterman & Lusk, 1986).

TRUTH OR *FICTION?*
———————————
R E V I S I T E D

***Father-daughter incest is the most common type of incest.** Father-daughter incest may be the most highly publicized variety of incest, but brother-sister incest is actually more common.* •

Effects of Childhood Sexual Abuse in African-American and White Women: The Wyatt Survey

Gail Wyatt (1990) examined similarities and differences in the effects of childhood sexual abuse among her sample of 126 African-American and 122 white women from Los Angeles County. The groups were balanced on such factors as education, marital status, and the presence and number of children. Sexual abuse during childhood (under age 18) was defined broadly, ranging from solicitations to engage in sexual behavior and exhibitionism to actual body contact, such as fondling, coitus, and oral sex.

The prevalence of child sexual abuse was similar for both groups; about one in two women reported an incident of abuse. About 40 percent of the incidents for both groups went unreported.

Abuse that involved contact was more likely to be concealed than other forms of abuse. African-American women were slightly less likely to report incidents to immediate family members or the police. African-American women were about twice as likely to have reported the incident to extended family members, however, which is suggestive of the importance of the extended family among African Americans. African-American women were more likely than their white peers (35% versus 22%) to cite fear of repercussions as their reason for not reporting the incident. White women more often cited a fear of being blamed (36%) than did African-American women (23%). Perhaps African-American women were more vulnerable to

the financial hardships that their family would incur if the perpetrator, often a household member, were forced to leave the house.

African-American and white women were similarly affected by the abuse. Women in both groups were likely to feel violated and to experience emotions such as disgust, anger, and fear. Both groups were likely to encounter sexual problems in adulthood. The African-American women were more likely to report that the abusive experience affected their attitudes toward men; they especially tended to avoid men who reminded them of the perpetrator. All in all, the similarities of the effects of childhood sexual abuse on the two ethnic groups overshadowed the differences, however.

Let us further consider the two most common incest patterns, father-daughter incest and brother-sister incest.

FATHER-DAUGHTER INCEST Father-daughter incest often begins with affectionate cuddling or embraces and then progresses to teasing sexual play, lengthy caresses, hugs, kisses, and genital contact, even penetration. In some cases genital contact occurs more abruptly, usually when the father has been drinking, or arguing with his wife. Force is not typically used to gain compliance, but daughters are sometimes physically overcome by their fathers and may suffer physical injuries.

BROTHER-SISTER INCEST In sibling incest, the brother usually initiates sexual activity and assumes the dominant role (Meiselman, 1978). Some brothers and sisters may view their sexual activity as natural and not know that it is taboo (Knox, 1988).

Evidence on the effects of incest between brothers and sisters is mixed. A study of college undergraduates who reported childhood incest with siblings did not reveal greater evidence of sexual adjustment problems among them than among undergraduates who reported no sibling sexual experience or no sexual experience at all before the age of 13 (Greenwald & Leitenberg, 1989). Sibling incest may be harmful for some children, however (Sorrenti-Little et al., 1984). Sibling incest is most likely to be harmful when it is recurrent, when it involves force or coercion, when it consists of more intrusive sexual acts such as coitus (as opposed to "playing doctor"), and when parents respond harshly upon discovery (Knox, 1988; Laviola, 1989).

Notes: One study of incestuous fathers and stepfathers referred for outpatient treatment revealed that 18 percent of those studied were raping adult women and 49 percent were abusing children outside the family at the same time they were sexually abusing their own children. (Abel, G. G. 1988. Multiple paraphiliac diagnoses among sex offenders. *Bulletin of Psychiatry and the Law, 16,* 153–168.)

FAMILY FACTORS IN INCEST   Incest frequently occurs within the context of general family disruption, as in families in which there is spouse abuse, dysfunctional marriages, or alcoholic or physically abusive parents (Alter-Reid et al., 1986; Sirles & Franke, 1989; Waterman, 1986a). Stressful events in the father's life, such as the loss of a job or problems at work, often precede the initiation of incest (Waterman, 1986a).

Fathers who abuse older daughters tend to be domineering and authoritarian with their families (Waterman, 1986a). Fathers who abuse younger, preschool daughters are more likely to be passive and dependent and low in self-esteem. As Waterman (1986a) notes:

> [The fathers] may need soothing and comforting, and may feel especially safe with preschool children: "I felt safe with her . . . I didn't have to perform. She was so little that I knew she wouldn't and couldn't hurt me" (p. 215).

Marriages in incestuous families tend to be characterized by an uneven power relationship between the spouses, with the abusive father usually the one who is dominant. Another thread that frequently runs through incestuous families is a troubled sexual relationship between the spouses, often involving a pattern in which the wife rejects the husband sexually (Waterman, 1986a).

Gebhard and his colleagues (1965) found that many fathers who committed incest with their daughters were religiously devout, fundamentalist, and moralistic. Perhaps such men, when sexually frustrated, are less likely to seek extramarital and extrafamilial sexual outlets or to turn to masturbation as a sexual release. In many cases the father is under stress but does not find adequate emotional and sexual support from his wife (Gagnon, 1977). He turns to a daughter as a wife surrogate, often when he has been drinking alcohol (Gebhard et al., 1965). The daughter may become, in her father's fantasies, the "woman of the house," which may become his justification for continuing the incestuous relationship. In some incestuous families, a role reversal occurs in which the abused daughter assumes many of the mother's responsibilities for managing the household and caring for the younger children (Waterman, 1986a).

Incestuous abuse is often repeated from generation to generation. Parents who were sexually abused as children often victimize their own children. One study found that in 154 cases of children who were sexually abused within the family, more than a third of the male offenders and about half of the mothers had either been abused themselves or were exposed to abuse as children (Faller, 1989b).

Sociological factors, such as poverty, overcrowded living conditions, and social or geographical isolation may contribute to incest in some families (Waterman, 1986a). Finkelhor (1979), for example, finds that an unusually high percentage of college students revealing incestuous experiences were raised on farms. Sibling incest may be encouraged by the crowded living conditions and open sexuality that occur among some economically disadvantaged families (Sagarin, 1977a; Waterman, 1986a).

EFFECTS OF CHILD SEXUAL ABUSE

Learning Objective 10:
Describe the short-term and long-term effects on victims of child sexual abuse.

Child sexual abuse often inflicts great psychological harm on the developing child, whether the abuse is perpetrated by a family member, acquaintance, or stranger. Children who are sexually abused may suffer from a litany of short- and long-term psychological complaints, including anger, depression, anxiety, eating disorders, inappropriate sexual behavior, aggressive behavior, self-destructive behavior, sexual promiscuity, drug abuse, suicide attempts, post-traumatic stress disorder, low self-esteem, sexual dysfunction, mistrust of others, and feelings of detachment, among others (Beitchman et al., 1992; Finkelhor, 1990; Goodwin et al., 1990; Harrison et al., 1989; McLaren & Brown, 1989). Child sexual abuse may also have physical effects such as genital injuries and cause psychosomatic problems such as stomachaches and headaches.

Abused children commonly "act out," displaying aggressive or antisocial behavior, delinquency, tantrums, and, in older children, substance abuse (alcohol and drugs) (Finkelhor, 1990; Lusk & Waterman, 1986). Some abused children become withdrawn and retreat into fantasy or refuse to leave the house. Regressive behaviors, such as thumb sucking, fear of the dark, and fear of strangers are also common among sexually abused children. On the heels of the assault and in the ensuing years, many survivors of childhood sexual abuse—like many rape survivors—show signs of post-traumatic stress disorder such as flashbacks, nightmares, numbing of emotions, and feelings of estrangement from others (Finkelhor, 1990).

Sexual development of abused children may also become shaped in inappropriate or dysfunctional ways; for example, the survivor may become prematurely sexually active or promiscuous in adolescence and adulthood (Finkelhor, 1988; Lusk & Waterman, 1986; Tharinger, 1990). Researchers find that adolescent girls who are sexually abused tend to engage in consensual coitus at earlier ages than nonabused peers (Wyatt, 1988).

Researchers generally find more similarities than differences between the genders with respect to the effects of sexual abuse in childhood (Finkelhor, 1990). For example, both abused boys and girls tend to suffer fears and sleep disturbance. There are some gender differences, however. The most consistent gender difference appears to be that boys more often "externalize" their problems, perhaps by becoming more physically aggressive, whereas girls more often "internalize" their difficulties, perhaps by becoming depressed (Finkelhor, 1990; Gomez-Schwartz et al., 1990).

There has been comparatively little research comparing child survivors of sexual abuse from different ethnic groups. In one of the few reported studies, researchers compared Asian-American children who had been sexually abused with random samples of African-, white-, and Hispanic-American sexually abused children drawn from the same child sex-abuse clinic (Rao et al., 1992). As compared to the other groups, Asian children were more likely to become suicidal though less likely to exhibit anger and sexual acting-out.

The long-term consequences of sexual abuse in childhood tend to be greater for children who were abused by their fathers or stepfathers, who experienced penetration, who were subjected to force or threat of force, and who suffered more prolonged and severe abuse (Beitchman et al., 1992; Waterman & Lusk, 1986; Wyatt & Newcomb, 1990). Children who suffer incest often feel a deep sense of betrayal by the offender and, perhaps, by other family members, especially their mothers, whom they perceive as failing to protect them (Finkelhor, 1988). Incest survivors may feel powerless to control their bodies or their lives.

Late adolescence and early adulthood seem to pose especially difficult periods for survivors of childhood sexual abuse. Studies of women in these age groups reveal more psychological and social problems in abused women than are found among nonabused reference groups (Jackson et al., 1990; Roland et al., 1989).

Effects of childhood sexual abuse are often long-lasting. In one study, researchers found evidence of greater psychological distress in a group of 54 adult women, ranging from 23 to 61 years of age, who had been sexually abused as children than in a matched group of nonabused women (Greenwald et al., 1990). Women who blame themselves for the abuse apparently have relatively lower self-esteem and more depression than those who do not (Hoagwood, 1990).

PREVENTION OF CHILD SEXUAL ABUSE

Many of us were taught by our parents never to accept a ride or an offer of candy from a stranger, but many instances of child sexual abuse are perpetrated by familiar adults, often a family member or family friend. A number of prevention programs have been developed to help children understand what sexual abuse is and how they can avoid it. A recent national survey showed that two of three children in the United States have participated in school-based sex-abuse prevention programs (Goleman, 1993). In addition to learning to avoid strangers, children need to recognize the differences between acceptable touching, as in an affectionate embrace or pat on the head, and unacceptable or "bad" touching. Trainers need to be aware, however, that teaching children to distinguish between "good touching and bad touching" may leave some of them confused about what acts of touching are to be avoided (Durfee, 1989). Still, researchers find that even elementary-school-age children are capable of learning basic concepts about sexual abuse prevention (Tutty, 1992). Moreover, a national study showed that the better school-based programs were generally helpful in preparing children to handle an actual encounter with a potential molester (Goleman, 1993). Not only are children who receive

Anatomically Correct Dolls. Therapists and investigators often use anatomically correct dolls to assist sexually abused children in describing their experiences. Through manipulating the dolls, children can describe experiences, such as oral molestation and masturbation, that they are reluctant or unable to put into words. Controversy persists, however, over the reliability of the information obtained by use of this method.

comprehensive training more likely to use strategies like running away, yelling, or saying no when they are threatened by an abuser, but they are also more likely to report any such incidents to adults. Yet many programs are inadequate and need to be improved.

Researchers recognize that children can easily be intimidated or overpowered by adults or older children and may be unable to say no in a sexually abusive situation, even though they would like to and know that it is the "right thing" to do (Waterman et al., 1986). Although children may not be able to prevent abuse in many cases, they can nevertheless be encouraged to tell someone about the experience. Most prevention programs emphasize teaching children messages such as "It's not your fault," "Never keep a bad or scary secret," and "Always tell your parents about this, especially if someone says you shouldn't tell them" (Waterman et al., 1986). Children also need to be alerted to the types of threats they might receive for disclosing the abuse to others. They are more likely to resist threats if they are reassured that they will be believed if they disclose the abuse, that their parents will continue to love them, and that they and their families will be protected from the molester.

School-based prevention programs tend to focus on protecting the individual child. In most states teachers and helping professionals are required to report suspected abuse to authorities. Tighter controls and better screening are needed to monitor the hiring of day care employees. Administrators and teachers in preschool and day care facilities also need to be educated to recognize the signs of sexual abuse and to report suspected cases (Waterman et al., 1986). Treatment programs are also needed to help people who recognize that they are sexually attracted to children *before* they commit abusive acts.

TREATMENT OF SURVIVORS OF CHILD SEXUAL ABUSE

Since 75 percent or more of cases of child sexual abuse go unreported, psychotherapy in adulthood often becomes the first opportunity for survivors to confront leftover feelings of pain, anger, and, perhaps, misplaced guilt (Alter-Reid et al., 1986; Ratican, 1992). Group or individual therapy can help improve their self-esteem and ability to develop intimate relationships. Confronting the trauma within a supportive therapeutic relationship may also help prevent the cycle of abuse from perpetuating itself from one generation to another (Alter-Reid et al., 1986).

Although many survivors of child sexual abuse may not obtain treatment until adulthood, specialized programs have begun to appear that provide therapeutic services to abused children and adolescents. Most therapists recommend a multicomponent treatment approach, which may involve individual therapy for the child, mother, and father; group therapy for the adolescent or even preadolescent survivor; art therapy or play therapy for the younger child (e.g., using drawings or puppets to express feelings); marital counseling for the parents; and family therapy for the entire family unit (de Luca et al., 1992; Waterman, 1986b).

Notes: Insensitivity to the female victims of incest reached a new high in a reply by a state representative to the question of why he opposed abortion in cases of incest: "Inbreeding is how we get championship horses" (p. 15). (1990: The Year That Was. 1991. *Ms.*, *1(4)*, 14–15.)

Teaching Tip: Obtain a list of community services for survivors of child sexual abuse. Distribute copies to your students.

TREATMENT OF RAPISTS AND CHILD MOLESTERS

Learning Objective 12: Describe treatment programs for rapists and child molesters and evaluate their effectiveness.

When applied to sex offenders, the term *treatment* may suggest helping them "adjust" to feelings of inadequacy or deficiencies in social skills that may be the basis of their crimes. It must be understood first and foremost, however, that rapists and child molesters are criminals, not patients. Most convicted rapists and child molesters are incarcerated as a form of punishment, not treatment. They may receive psychological treatment or rehabilitation in prison to help prepare them for eventual release and reentry into society, however. The most common form of treatment is group therapy, which is based on the belief that though offenders may fool counselors, they cannot so easily fool one another (Kaplan, 1993). Yet the great majority of incarcerated sex offenders receive little or no treatment in prison (Goleman, 1992b). In California, for example, which has 15,000 incarcerated sex offenders, treatment has been provided in but one experimental program for only 46 rapists and child molesters (Goleman, 1992b).

The results of prison-based treatment programs have been mixed at best. A Canadian study of 54 rapists who participated in a treatment program showed that following release from prison, 28 percent were later convicted of a sexual offense and 43 percent were convicted of a subsequent violent offense (Rice et al., 1990). Treatment also failed to deter recidivism among a sample of 136 child molesters (Rice et al., 1991). More promising findings were reported in 1992 based on innovative programs in prison facilities in California and Vermont (Goleman, 1992b). In Vermont, the average rate of recommission of sex crimes following release was reduced by at least half in a group of sex offenders who received a treatment program compared to a control group who did not. These innovative programs used a variety of techniques. Empathy training was used to increase the offender's sensitivity to his victims, such as by writing about his crimes from what he imagines is the victim's perspective. Another technique designed to help offenders resist deviant sex fantasies involved having the offender associate in his imagination scenes involving rape and molestation with negative outcomes, a technique called *covert sensitization* (described in Chapter 18). An exhibitionist, for example, might be asked to practice imagining that he is about to expose himself and is discovered in the act by his parents. A child molester might fantasize about sexually approaching a child, only to find himself confronted by police officers.

Other approaches to "treating" rapists and other sex offenders have focused on medical interventions aimed at reducing their sexual drives. In a few European countries, some rapists and other sex offenders who claimed they were unable to control their sexual drives have been castrated to reduce these urgings (Heim & Hursch, 1979; Wille & Beier, 1989). The effects of castration are mixed. Many castrated rapists report markedly lowered sex drives, as might be expected from the reductions in testosterone production that result from the removal of the testes (Wille & Beier, 1989). They may retain sexual interest and remain capable of erection, however, and some have repeated their crimes (Heim, 1981). Other researchers report lower recidivism rates among castrated offenders than among noncastrated offenders (Wille & Beier, 1989). In any event, the use of castration with sex offenders appears to be declining. In Germany, for example, the number of sex-offender castrations fell from about 40 per year during the 1970s to about 5 per year by the late 1980s (Wille & Beier, 1989).

Castration is an extreme measure. It is controversial and raises serious ethical concerns because of its invasive character and irreversibility. Antiandrogen drugs such as Depo-Provera lower the testicular production of testosterone, which reduces the sex drive and offers a means of temporarily controlling urges to offend (Bradford, 1985; Cooper, 1986; Hucker et al., 1988; Ingersoll & Patton, 1991). Unlike castration, antiandrogen drugs are reversible, but compliance in taking the drugs is a major obstacle to their use (Hucker et al., 1988). Nor do drugs help rapists resolve their hostility toward women or the needs for dominance and power that so often underlie attacks on women. Drugs do not provide offenders with social skills that may help them form consensual sexual relationships. Evidence from carefully controlled studies of therapeutic outcomes is also lacking (Cooper, 1986). We thus do not know whether drugs curb recidivism.

SEXUAL HARASSMENT

Learning Objective 13: List the EEOC guidelines for defining workplace sexual harassment and discuss the research on its incidence.

Sexual harassment
Deliberate or repeated unsolicited verbal comments, gestures, or physical contact of a sexual nature that is considered to be unwelcome by the recipient.

Notes: In 1992, the Equal Employment Opportunity Commission reported a total of 10,532 sexual harassment complaints, up from 6,883 in 1991. Ninety percent of the charges were made by women. (Clippings. 1993. *Ms., 4(1),* 87.)

For a few days in October 1991, the United States was held spellbound by the Senate confirmation hearings on Judge Clarence Thomas's nomination to the Supreme Court, during which a former assistant, Anita Hill, charged that Thomas had sexually harassed her. One result of the Thomas hearings was a sharp rise in the number of sexual harassment complaints filed with the Equal Employment Opportunity Commission (EEOC) (Gross, 1992). The number of complaints rose by 50 percent in the first half of 1992 as compared to the same period a year earlier. Though more people are talking about sexual harassment and more complaints are being filed, the incidence of sexual harassment does not appear to have lessened (Ingrassia, 1993).

What *is* **sexual harassment**? Definitions of sexual harassment vary, but the definition of sexual harassment in the workplace as the "deliberate or repeated unsolicited verbal comments, gestures, or physical contact of a sexual nature that is considered to be unwelcome by the recipient" has been widely adopted (U.S. Merit Systems Protection Board, 1981, p. 2). Sexual harassment can range from unwelcome sexual jokes, overtures, suggestive comments, and sexual innuendos to outright sexual assault, and may include such behaviors as the following (Powell, 1991, p. 110):

Verbal harassment or abuse
Subtle pressure for sexual activity
Remarks about a person's clothing, body, or sexual activities
Leering or ogling at a person's body
Unwelcome touching, patting, or pinching
Brushing against a person's body
Demands for sexual favors accompanied by implied or overt threats concerning
    one's job or student status
Physical assault

Both men and women can commit, and be subject to, sexual harassment, although the great majority of cases are perpetrated by men against women. Charges of sexual harassment are often ignored or trivialized by co-workers and employers, however. The complainant may hear, "Why make a big deal out of it? It's not like you were attacked in the street." Evidence shows, however, that persons subjected to sexual harassment do suffer from it. In one study, 75 percent of people who were sexually harassed reported physical or emotional reactions such as anxiety, irritability, lowered self-esteem, and anger (Gruber & Bjorn, 1986; Loy & Stewart, 1984). Some find harassment on the job so unbearable that they feel forced to resign. College women have been forced to drop courses, switch majors, change graduate programs, or even change colleges because they were unable to stop persistent sexual harassment from professors (Dziech & Weiner, 1984; Fitzgerald, 1992, 1993).

One reason that sexual harassment is so stressful is that, as with so many other forms of sexual exploitation or coercion, the blame tends to fall on the survivor (Powell, 1991). Harassers may sincerely believe that charges of harassment were exaggerated or that the person bringing the charges "overreacted" or "took me too seriously." In our society, women are expected to be "nice"—to be passive and not "make a scene." The woman who assertively protects her rights may be seen as "strange" and disturbing, or a "troublemaker." "Women are damned if they assert themselves and victimized if they don't" (Powell, 1991, p. 114).

Sexual harassment may have more to do with the abuse of power than with sexual desire (Goleman, 1991). Relatively few cases of sexual harassment involve outright requests for sexual favors. Most involve the expression of power as a tactic to control or frighten someone, usually a woman. The harasser usually holds a dominant position in relation to the harassed person and abuses that position by taking advantage of the other's vulnerability. Sexual harassment may be used as a tactic of social control—a means of keeping women "in their place," especially in work settings that are traditional male preserves, such as the firehouse, the construction site, or the military academy. Sexual

Activity: *Thinking Critically About Where to Draw the Line on Sexual Harassment* This IM activity encourages students to examine ten situations and decide if they constitute sexual harassment.

Notes: An article examining sexual abuse by the clergy cited cases involving Catholics, Presbyterians, Jews, Buddhists, Methodists, Lutherans, etc. Some Catholic dioceses and major protestant denominations have recently developed guidelines for handling cases of sexual harassment and abuse by clergy members. (Bonavoglia, A. 1992. The sacred secret. *Ms., 2*(5), 40–45.)

Notes: As of March 1992, six states (Minnesota, Wisconsin, North Dakota, Colorado, Florida, and Iowa) had made it a felony for a psychotherapist to have sex with a client, even if the client appears to consent.

Discussion Question: How many of you have been subject to workplace behavior that you think meets the EEOC definition of sexual harassment? How did you handle the situation? If this happened again, would you react differently?

harassment in the workplace can be seen as an expression of the resentment and hostility directed at women who venture beyond the boundaries of the traditional feminine role to enter the masculine workplace (Bularzik, 1978; Fitzgerald, 1993).

Sexual harassment is not confined to the workplace or the university. Sexual harassment may also occur between patients and doctors and between therapists and clients. Therapists may use their power and influence over clients to pressure them into having sexual relations. The harassment may be disguised, expressed in terms of the "therapeutic benefits" of sexual activity to the client. The great majority of mental-health professionals, however, believe that any sexual intimacy between a client and therapist is an abuse of the therapist's power and therapeutic role (Burgess & Hartman, 1986). Two of the most common settings in which sexual harassment occurs are the workplace and the university.

SEXUAL HARASSMENT IN THE WORKPLACE

Harassers in the workplace can be employers, supervisors, co-workers, or clients of a company. In some cases clients make unwelcome sexual advances to employees that are ignored or approved of by the boss. If a worker asks a co-worker for a date and is refused, it is not sexual harassment. If the co-worker persists with unwelcome advances and does not take no for an answer, the behavior crosses the line from a social invitation and becomes harassment, however.

Perhaps the most severe form of sexual harassment, short of an outright assault, involves an employer or supervisor who demands sexual favors from an employee as a condition of employment or job advancement. In 1980, the Equal Employment Opportunity Commission, the agency Clarence Thomas was later to direct, drafted a set of guidelines that expanded the definition of sexual harassment in the workplace to include any behavior of a sexual nature that interferes with an individual's work performance or creates a *hostile,* intimidating, or offensive work environment.

In 1986, the U.S. Supreme Court recognized sexual harassment as a form of sex discrimination under Title VII of the Civil Rights Act of 1964. The Supreme Court held that employers could be held accountable if such behavior was deemed to create a hostile or abusive work environment or to interfere with an employee's work performance. A 1993 Supreme Court ruling held that a person need not suffer psychological damage to sue an employer on grounds of sexual harassment ("Court, 9–0, makes sex harassment easier to prove," 1993). Moreover, employers can be held responsible not only for their own actions, but also for sexual harassment by their employees when they either knew *or should have known* that harassment was taking place and failed to eliminate it promptly (McKinney & Maroules, 1991). To protect themselves, many companies and universities have developed antiharassment programs to educate workers about sexual harassment, established mechanisms for dealing with complaints, and imposed sanctions against harassers.

Under the law, persons subjected to sexual harassment can obtain a court order to have the harassment stopped, have their jobs reinstated (when they have lost them by resisting sexual advances), receive back pay and lost benefits, and obtain monetary awards for the emotional strain imposed by the harassment. However, proving charges of sexual harassment is generally difficult because there are usually no corroborating witnesses or evidence. As a result, relatively few persons who encounter sexual harassment in the workplace file formal complaints or seek legal remedies.

One survey found that most people who were sexually harassed handled the harassment either by ignoring the harasser (32%) or by saying something directly to the harasser (39%) (Loy & Stewart, 1984). Seventeen percent sought job transfers or quit their jobs. Relatively few, 2 percent, sought legal help. Only about 3 percent of women who have been sexually harassed actually file a formal complaint (Goleman, 1991). Like people subjected to other forms of sexual coercion, persons experiencing sexual harassment often do not report the offense for fear that they will not be believed or will be subjected to retaliation. Some fear that they will be branded as "troublemakers" or that they will lose their jobs (Goleman, 1991).

Sexual Harassment. According to the U.S. government, sexual harassment in the workplace involves behavior of a sexual nature that interferes with the individual's ability to work effectively or that creates a hostile, intimidating, or offensive work environment. Do you believe that the man's reaching over and holding the woman's chair constitutes sexual harassment? Why or why not? What other information might assist you in reaching a decision?

Notes: Some staffers on Capitol Hill believe that they work in the "sexual harassment capital of the country" (p. 28). An informal network of women staffers warn other women about the worst harassers; some say about 50 offices should definitely be avoided. (Sharpe, R. 1992. Capitol Hill's Worst Kept Secret: Sexual Harassment. *Ms., 2 (4),* 28–31.)

How common is sexual harassment in the workplace? Although two thirds of the men interviewed by the *Harvard Business Review* said that reports of sexual harassment in the workplace were exaggerated (Castro, 1992), a survey by *Working Woman* magazine showed that more than 90 percent of the Fortune 500 companies had received complaints of sexual harassment from their employees. More than one third of the companies had been sued on charges of sexual harassment (Sandross, 1988). Complaints of sexual harassment in the workplace rose about 50 percent from 1980 to 1990 (Ladd & Wechsler, 1991). Sexual harassment against women is more common in workplaces where women have traditionally been underrepresented (Fitzgerald, 1993), such as the construction site or the shipyard. A survey of federal employees by the United States Merit System Protection Board found that 42 percent of females and 14 percent of males reported instances of sexual harassment (DeWitt, 1991). A 1991 *New York Times*/CBS News poll found that 38 percent of the U.S. women sampled reported that they had been the object of sexual advances or remarks from supervisors or other men in positions of power (Kolbert, 1991). Janus and Janus (1993) report that 19 percent of the men and 45 percent of the women in their nationwide sample reported experiencing sexual harassment on the job. Overall, experts estimate that as many as one in two women in the United States encounters some form of sexual harassment on the job or in college, making sexual harassment the most common form of sexual victimization (Fitzgerald, 1993b). Research overseas finds that about 70 percent of the women who work in Japan and 50 percent of those who work in Europe have encountered sexual harassment (Castro, 1992).

SEXUAL HARASSMENT ON CAMPUS

Learning Objective 14: Discuss the incidence of sexual harassment in schools and on college campuses and list suggestions for resisting sexual harassment.

Estimates of the frequency of sexual harassment of undergraduate and graduate students vary widely across studies, from 7 to 27 percent of men and from 12 to 65 percent of women (McKinney & Maroules, 1991). Overall, about 25 to 30 percent of students report at least one incident of sexual harassment in college. In 1992, the U.S. Supreme Court ruled that the federal law prohibiting sex discrimination in academic institutions permits students to sue their schools for monetary damages for sexual harassment (Greenhouse, 1992).

Sexual harassment on campus usually involves the less severe forms of harassment, such as sexist comments and sexual remarks, as well as come-ons, suggestive looks, propositions, and light touching (McKinney & Maroules, 1991). Relatively few acts involve the use of direct pressure for sexual intercourse. Harassers are typically (but not always) male. Most students who encounter sexual harassment do not report the incident, but if they do, it is usually to a confidant and not a person in authority.

Notes: For more information on the implications of sexual harassment law for sexual relations in academe and a review of the legal decisions relevant to higher education, see the 1992 article "Sexual Harassment: Faculty, Student Considerations" by Doric Little. (NEA *Higher Education Journal, 8(1)*, 5–12.)

Although most forms of harassment involve unequal power relationships between the harasser and the person harassed, some cases occur between people who are equal in power, as in the cases of repeated sexual taunts from fellow employees, students, or colleagues. Such harassment has been labeled *peer harassment* (Benson, 1984). In some cases, the harasser may even have less formal power than the person harassed. For example, women professors have been sexually harassed by students (Grauerholz, 1989). Here, of course, the traditional social dominance of the male may override the academic position of the woman—at least in the mind of the offender.

The most common form of harassment by students, reported by nearly one third of the female professors polled in a recent survey, involved sexist remarks. Other forms of harassment were also relatively common, such as obscene phone calls from callers who were believed to be students, undue attention, and written or verbal sexual remarks. Outright sexual advances were reported by a few professors, and one professor reported being sexually assaulted by a student (Grauerholz, 1989).

Male faculty and staff members may also be subject to harassment. Six percent of 235 male faculty members polled at one university reported being sexually harassed by a student. Nearly double that percentage (11%) reported that they had attempted to stroke, caress, or touch a student, however (Fitzgerald et al., 1988).

SEXUAL HARASSMENT IN THE SCHOOLS

CNN Sexual Harassment in Schools

Sexual harassment in the schools is not limited to colleges and universities. Though playful antics have long been a behavior pattern associated with adolescence, unwelcome sexual advances and lewd comments go beyond customary playfulness and have become a troubling concern to many of America's teens. A 1993 nationwide survey of high school and junior high school students found that many boys and girls had encountered harassment in the form of others grabbing or groping them or subjecting them to sexually explicit put-downs when walking through school hallways (Henneberger, 1993).

The picture that emerges from a 1993 Louis Harris nationwide poll of teenagers in grades 8 through 11 indicates that sexual taunts and advances have become part of an unwelcome ritual for many students, especially girls, in trying to make their way through the hallways and stairwells of junior and senior high schools (Barringer, 1993b; Henneberger, 1993). More than two out of three girls, and more than four out of ten boys, reported being touched, grabbed, or pinched at school. Two of three boys and about one in two girls reported harassing other students. Many of the harassers (41 percent of the boys and 31 percent of the girls) viewed their actions as "just part of school life" and "no big deal." Unwelcome sexual comments and advances had a negative impact on both boys and girls, but especially on girls. One in three girls who experienced sexual harassment at school reported that it made them feel that they didn't want to go to school. Twenty-eight percent said that it made it more difficult to pay attention in class, and 20 percent said that it lowered their grades.

One problem is that teachers tend to tolerate sexually harassing behavior by male students against female classmates, according to a 1992 report by the American Association of University Women Education Foundation (Chira, 1992). Most of the harassment (about 80%) reported in the Harris survey was committed by other students, but some students reported being harassed by teachers, coaches, custodians, and other adults.

Though sexual harassment and outright sexual assaults among teens and even some subteens may not be new, it appears to be increasing. In 1993, several incidents of groups of boys sexually molesting young girls in public swimming pools in inner-city areas of New York prompted the mayor to initiate a campaign with the slogan "Don't Dis Your Sis." Rap lyrics, favored by white and African-American adolescents alike, are seen by many adults and by adolescents themselves as a factor promoting demeaning attitudes toward women. The boys in the New York incidents chanted rap lyrics as they harassed the female swimmers. Rap music, and other forms of popular youth culture that depict women in demeaning terms and that treat them as sexual objects, such as many music videos seen on MTV, may well play a part in creating a culture that legitimizes sexual violence and harassment.

HOW TO RESIST SEXUAL HARASSMENT

What would you do if you were sexually harassed by an employer or a professor? How would you handle it? Would you try to ignore it and hope that it would stop? What actions might you take? We offer some suggestions, adapted from Powell (1991), that may be helpful. Recognize, however, that responsibility for sexual harassment always lies with the perpetrator and the organization that permits sexual harassment to take place, not with the person subjected to the harassment.

1. *Convey a professional attitude.* Harassment may be stopped cold by responding to the harasser with a businesslike, professional attitude.

2. *Discourage harassing behavior and encourage appropriate behavior.* Harassment may also be stopped cold by shaping the harasser's behavior. Your reactions to the harasser may encourage businesslike behavior and discourage flirtatious or suggestive behavior. If a harassing professor suggests that you come back after school to review your term paper so that the two of you will be undisturbed, set limits assertively. Tell the professor that you'd feel more comfortable discussing the paper during regular office hours. Remain task-oriented. Stick to business. The harasser should quickly get the message that you wish to maintain a strictly professional relationship. If the harasser persists, do not blame yourself. You are only responsible for your own actions. When the harasser persists, a more direct response may be appropriate: "Professor Jones, I'd like to keep our relationship on a purely professional basis, okay?"

3. *Avoid being alone with the harasser.* If you are being harassed by your professor but need some advice about preparing your term paper, approach him or her after class when other students are milling about, not privately during office hours. Or bring a friend to wait outside the office while you consult the professor.

4. *Maintain a record.* Keep a record of all incidents of harassment as documentation in the event you decide to lodge an official complaint. The record should include the following: (1) where the incident took place; (2) the date and time; (3) what happened, including the exact words that were used, if you can recall them; (4) how you felt; and (5) the names of witnesses. Some people who have been subjected to sexual harassment have carried a hidden tape recorder during contacts with the harasser. Such recordings may not be admissible in a court of law, but they are persuasive in organizational grievance procedures. A hidden tape recorder may be illegal in your state, however. It is thus advisable to check the law.

5. *Talk with the harasser.* It may be uncomfortable to address the issue directly with a harasser, but doing so puts the offender on notice that you are aware of the harassment and want it to stop. It may be helpful to frame your approach in terms of a description of the specific offending actions (e.g., "When we were alone in the office, you repeatedly attempted to touch me or brush up against me"); your feelings about the offending behavior ("It made me feel like my privacy was being violated. I'm very upset about this and haven't been sleeping well"); and what you would like the offender to do ("So I'd like you to agree never to attempt to touch me again, okay?"). Having a talk with the harasser may stop the harassment. If the harasser denies the accusations, it may be necessary to take further action.

6. *Write a letter to the harasser.* Set down on paper a record of the offending behavior, and put the harasser on notice that the harassment must stop. Your letter might (1) *describe what happened* ("Several times you have made sexist comments about my body"); (2) *describe how you feel* ("It made me feel like a sexual object when you talked to me that way"); and (3) *describe what you would like the harasser to do* ("I want you to stop making sexist comments to me").

7. *Seek support.* Support from people you trust can help you through the often trying process of resisting sexual harassment. Talking with others allows you to express your feelings and receive emotional support, encouragement, and advice. In addition, it may strengthen your case if you have the opportunity to identify and talk with other people who have been harassed by the offender.

8. *File a complaint.* Companies and organizations are required by law to respond reasonably to complaints of sexual harassment. In large organizations, a designated

Teaching Tip: Inform your students about your institution's procedure for filing sexual harassment complaints.

official (sometimes an ombudsman, affirmative action officer, or sexual harassment advisor) is usually charged to handle such complaints. Set up an appointment with this official to discuss your experiences. Ask about the grievance procedures in the organization and your right to confidentiality. Have available a record of the dates of the incidents, what happened, how you felt about it, and so on.

The two major government agencies that handle charges of sexual harassment are the Equal Employment Opportunity Commission (look under the government section of your phone book for the telephone number of the nearest office) and your state Human Rights Commission (listed in your phone book under state or municipal government). These agencies may offer advice on how you can protect your legal rights and proceed with a formal complaint.

9. *Seek legal remedies.* Sexual harassment is illegal and actionable. If you are considering legal action, consult an attorney familiar with this area of law. You may be entitled to back pay (if you were fired for reasons arising from the sexual harassment), job reinstatement, and punitive damages.

In closing, perhaps the question we should ask is not what persons who suffer rape, incest, and sexual harassment will do to redress the harm that has been done to them, but what all of us will do to reshape our society so that sex is no longer used as an instrument of power, coercion, and violence.

SUMMING UP

RAPE

Although sexual motivation plays a role in many rapes, the use of sex to express aggression, anger, and power is more central to our understanding of rape. The definition of rape varies from state to state but usually refers to obtaining sexual intercourse with a nonconsenting person by the use of force or the threat of force.

Incidence of Rape More than 100,000 forcible rapes were reported in the United States in 1990, but it is believed that the vast majority of rapes go unreported to authorities.

Types of Rapes The types of rapes include stranger rape, acquaintance rape, marital rape, gang rape , male rape, and rape by females. Women are more likely to be raped by men they know than by strangers. Most male rapes occur in prison settings. Husbands who rape their wives can now be prosecuted under the rape laws in many states.

Social Attitudes and Myths That Encourage Rape Social attitudes such as gender-role stereotyping, seeing sex as adversarial, and acceptance of violence in interpersonal relationships all help create a climate that encourages rape.

Sociocultural Factors in Rape Many observers contend that our society breeds rapists by socializing males to be socially and sexually dominant.

Psychological Characteristics of Rapists Incarcerated rapists vary in their psychological characteristics. Self-identified sexually aggressive men are more likely than other men to condone rape and violence against women, have traditional gender role attitudes, be hostile toward women, engage in sexual activity to express social dominance, be sexually aroused by rape, lack a social conscience, and have peer groups such as fraternities that pressure them into sexual activity. Groth and

Birnbaum identified three basic kinds of rapes: anger rape, power rape, and sadistic rape.

Adjustment of Rape Survivors Rape survivors are often in a state of crisis afterward. Burgess and Holmstrom identified some common response patterns in rape survivors that they labeled the rape trauma syndrome.

Treatment of Rape Survivors Treatment of rape survivors typically involves helping them through the crisis period following the attack and then helping to foster long-term adjustment.

Rape Prevention Rape prevention involves education of society at large and the taking of a number of precautions that are available to women. Whether or not women take precautions to prevent rape, however, the rapist is always the one responsible for the assault.

VERBAL SEXUAL COERCION

Verbal sexual coercion involves the use of verbal pressure or seduction lines to manipulate a person into having sexual relations.

SEXUAL ABUSE OF CHILDREN

Like rape, child sexual abuse is greatly underreported.

What Is Child Sexual Abuse? Any form of sexual contact between an adult and a child is abusive, even if force or physical threat is not used, since children are incapable of voluntarily consenting to sexual activity with adults.

Patterns of Abuse Child sexual abuse, like rape and other forms of sexual coercion, cuts across all socioeconomic classes. In most cases, the molesters are close to the children they abuse—relatives, step-relatives, family friends, and neighbors. Genital fondling is the most common type of abuse.

Pedophilia Pedophilia is a type of paraphilia in which adults are sexually attracted to children. Pedophiles are almost exclusively male.

Incest Incest is marriage or sexual relations between people who are so closely related that sex is prohibited and punished by virtue of the kinship tie. Several theories have been expounded to explain the development of the incest taboo, including theories based on the dangers of inbreeding, the role played by the taboo in maintaining stability in the family, and cooperation theory. Father-daughter incest is most likely to be reported and prosecuted, but brother-sister incest is the most common type of incest. Incest frequently occurs within the context of general family disruption.

Effects of Child Sexual Abuse Children who are sexually abused often suffer social and emotional problems that impair their development and persist into adulthood, affecting their self-esteem and their formation of intimate relationships.

Prevention of Child Sexual Abuse In addition to learning to avoid strangers, children need to learn the difference between acceptable touching, such as an affectionate embrace or pat on the head, and unacceptable or "bad" touching. Children who may not be able to prevent abuse may nevertheless be encouraged to tell someone about the experience.

Treatment of Survivors of Child Sexual Abuse Psychotherapy may help adult survivors of child sexual abuse improve their self-esteem and ability to develop intimate relationships. Specialized programs provide therapeutic services to abused children and adolescents.

TREATMENT OF RAPISTS AND CHILD MOLESTERS

The effectiveness of prison-based rehabilitation programs and antiandrogen drugs in curbing repeat offenses requires further empirical support.

SEXUAL HARASSMENT

Sexual Harassment in the Workplace Sexual harassment in the workplace involves "deliberate or repeated unsolicited verbal comments, gestures, or physical contact of a sexual nature that [are] unwelcome [to] the recipient." Sexual harassment may be used as a tactic to keep women "in their place," especially in work settings that are traditional male preserves. The most severe form of sexual harassment, short of physical assault, may involve an employer or supervisor who requests sexual favors from an employee as a condition of employment or job advancement.

Sexual Harassment on Campus About 25 to 30 percent of students report at least one incident of sexual harassment in college. Professors may also be harassed by students.

Sexual Harassment in Schools Sexual harassment in school has become an unwelcome ritual that many junior and senior high school students are forced to endure.

How to Resist Sexual Harassment There is no guaranteed way to put an end to sexual harassment, but some suggestions that have helped many individuals include conveying a professional attitude, avoiding being alone with the harasser, keeping a record of incidents, and seeking legal remedies.

_____ Prostitution is illegal throughout the United States.

_____ The massage and escort services advertised in the yellow pages are fronts for prostitution.

_____ Most female prostitutes were sexually abused as children.

_____ Typical customers of prostitutes have difficulty forming sexual relationships with other women.

_____ Most prostitutes take precautions to avoid becoming infected by or transmitting the AIDS virus.

_____ Only males are sexually aroused by pornography.

_____ If advertisements are too sexy, consumers may forget what the product is.

C H A P T E R 20

Commercial Sex, Obscenity, and Censorship

In the caverns of Wall Street, the brokers and traders sell the stocks and other financial instruments that drive the nation's commercial enterprises. On the floor of Chicago's Board of Trade, they trade commodities—soybeans, corn, wheat, and other goods. Prices go up, prices go down, responding to the law of supply and demand. On street corners a few short blocks from these financial institutions another sort of commerce takes place. In New York and Chicago, as in other big cities and in smaller towns and villages, prostitutes engage in commerce of their own, exchanging sex for money or for goods such as drugs. For prostitutes hawking their bodies on the sidewalk, as for producers and distributors of pornographic movies and magazines, sex is a form of commerce.

The commercial aspects of sexuality, however, are not restricted to the selling of sexual goods or services. Sex is also used as a vehicle for selling other goods and services. "Sex sells" is a common catchphrase that has driven the imaginations of countless copywriters to create advertising campaigns projecting a "sexy" image for products ranging from automobiles to blue jeans, and from beer to breadsticks.

THE WORLD OF COMMERCIAL SEX: A DISNEYLAND FOR ADULTS

Sex as commerce runs the gamut from "adult" movie theaters and book shops to live sex shows, sex toy shops, "erotic" hotels and motels, escort/outcall services and massage parlors (typically fronts for prostitution), among others (Edgley, 1989). One of the newer wrinkles in the commerce of sex is the proliferation of "900" telephone services, by which callers can hear prerecorded erotic messages or have a "one-on-one" conversation with "lonely housewives who are just dying to hear from you," "party girls who give you the best time," or "beach bunnies who can fulfill all your desires." Calls can be billed directly to the caller's phone bill. Legislation enacted by Congress in 1988 is intended to clamp down on telephone sex services by prohibiting the commercial use of indecent or obscene telephone messages or conversations.

All in all, the "world of commercial sex," notes sociologist Charles Edgley (1989), "is a kind of X-rated amusement park—Disneyland for Adults" (p. 372).

In this chapter, we discuss three commercial aspects of sexuality: prostitution, pornography, and the use of sex in advertising. Though the streetwalker, the purveyor of "adult" movies, and the Madison avenue copywriter may otherwise have little else in common, they all have learned to use sex to make a profit. We also compare and contrast the concepts of pornography and obscenity. We shall see that what impresses one person as obscene may be a work of art to another person.

Male Strippers. Male strip clubs have become very popular in recent years.

Prostitution
The sale of sexual activity for money or goods of value, such as drugs. (From the Latin *prostituere,* meaning "to cause to stand in front of." The implication is that one is offering one's body for sale.)

PROSTITUTION

In the United States, **prostitution** is illegal everywhere except for some rural counties in Nevada, where it is restricted to state-licensed brothels.

TRUTH OR *FICTION?*

R E V I S I T E D

Prostitution is illegal throughout the United States. *Prostitution is actually legal in some counties in the state of Nevada, although it is restricted to regulated, state-licensed brothels.* •

Learning Objective 1:
Summarize the cross-cultural history of prostitution and the changing incidence of prostitution in the United States.

Discussion Question: What social factors account for the large number of arrests of female prostitutes and the small number of arrests of "johns," when both are committing criminal offenses?

Although legal definitions of prostitution vary, prostitution is generally recognized as sexual activity in which a person exchanges sexual services for money or other items of value such as drugs. Soliciting the services of a prostitute is also illegal in many states. Police rarely crack down on customers or "johns," however. The few who are arrested are usually penalized with a small fine. On occasion, the names of convicted "johns" are published in local newspapers, which may deter men who fear similar publicity. Although prostitutes and their clients can be male or female, most prostitutes are female and virtually all customers are male.

Prostitution is often called "the world's oldest profession," and for good reason. Its history can be traced at least as far back as ancient Mesopotamia, where temple prostitution flourished. The Greek historian Herodotus noted that all women in the city were expected to put in some time at the temple. They would offer their bodies to passing strangers, who would then make a "religious" donation (Bullough, 1976).

Prostitution flourished in medieval Europe and during the sexually repressive Victorian period in the nineteenth century. Then, as now, the major motive for prostitution was economic. Young women from impoverished backgrounds, with limited means of support, were drawn to prostitution as one of the few means of survival available to them. Although prostitution did not receive official favor in Victorian England, it was widely regarded as a necessary outlet for men to satisfy their sexual appetites. In an era when it was widely held that women lack the potential to enjoy sex, it was commonly believed that it was better for a man to visit a prostitute than to "soil" his wife with his carnal passions.

In the nineteenth-century United States, married and unmarried men frequented prostitutes regularly, and use of prostitution cut across all economic and social boundaries (Gagnon, 1977). Prostitution most often occurred within two contexts, sexual initiation for young males and regular brothel visitation (Edgley, 1989).

INCIDENCE OF PROSTITUTION IN CONTEMPORARY U.S. SOCIETY

No one knows how many people in the United States engage in prostitution or frequent prostitutes. Census takers do not ask people if they have engaged in the practice. What little we know of prostitution derives from sex surveys that make inquiries about prostitution.

Almost two thirds of the white males in Kinsey's sample (Kinsey et al., 1948) reported visiting a prostitute at least once. About 15 to 20 percent visited them regularly. The use of prostitutes varied with educational level, however. By the age of 20, about 50 percent of Kinsey's noncollege single males, but only 20 percent of his college males, had visited a prostitute. By the age of 25, the figures swelled to about two thirds for noncollege males but only slightly above 25 percent for college men.

Activity: *Thinking Critically About Whether Prostitution Should Be Legalized* This IM exercise encourages students to examine the pros and cons of legalizing or decriminalizing prostitution.

Kinsey's data foreshadowed a falling off of experience with prostitutes that seems linked to the decay of the sexual double standard among subsequent generations of young people. Kinsey found that 20 percent of his college-educated men had been sexually initiated by prostitutes, but this figure was more than cut in half among generations who came of age in the 1960s and 1970s (Hunt, 1974). In more liberated recent times, the educational difference also appears to have largely evaporated. Less than 10 percent of the college *and* noncollege males in the *Playboy* survey (Hunt, 1974) of the 1970s reported being sexually initiated by a prostitute.

Why has there been such a falling off in the use of prostitutes' services by younger men? For one thing, young men in recent generations were more likely to become sexually initiated with their girlfriends than were their predecessors in earlier generations (see Chapter 13). As Edgley (1989) put it, "An old and hallowed economic principle was at work; those who charge for a service cannot compete with those who give it away" (p. 392). Moreover, increased concerns about the spread of sexually transmitted diseases, especially AIDS, has been another limiting factor on the use of prostitution. Despite such downturns in their potential pool of clients, prostitution continues to flourish not only in large metropolitan areas but also in smaller hamlets across the country, although in less obvious ways.

TYPES OF FEMALE PROSTITUTION

Streetwalkers
Prostitutes who solicit customers on the streets.

Pimps
Men who serve as agents for prostitutes and live off their earnings. (From the Middle French *pimper,* meaning "to dress smartly.")

The types of female prostitutes—commonly called *hookers, whores,* or *working girls*—are usually classified according to the settings in which the women work. The major types of prostitutes today are streetwalkers, brothel or "house" prostitutes, many of whom work in massage parlors and for "escort services" (many prostitutes today have their customers "Let [their] fingers do the walking through the yellow pages"), and call girls. Traditional brothel prostitution is much less common today than before World War II.

STREETWALKERS   Most prostitutes are **streetwalkers.** Streetwalkers hold the lowest status and typically earn the lowest incomes of the different types of prostitutes. They also incur the greatest risk of abuse by customers and **pimps.** Streetwalkers tend to come from impoverished backgrounds and to have had unhappy childhoods (Edgley, 1989). Perhaps as many as 80 percent were survivors of rape, sexual abuse, or incest (Gordon & Snyder, 1989). Many were teenage runaways who became initiated into prostitution in order to survive on their own.

Since streetwalkers operate out in the open, they are more likely than other prostitutes to draw attention to themselves and risk arrest. In an effort to avoid police action, streetwalkers may be indirect about their services, asking passersby if they are interested in a "good time" or some "fun" rather than directly offering to sell sex. In many cities, streetwalkers dress in revealing or provocative fashions, which change somewhat with the seasons and the times.

There is the stereotype of the prostitute as a sexually unresponsive woman who feigns sexual arousal during sex with johns while she keeps one eye glued to the clock. Most street prostitutes in a recent sample from Philadelphia, however, reported that some forms of sex with customers were "very satisfying" (Savitz & Rosen, 1988). More than 60 percent of the prostitutes reported achieving orgasm with customers at least occasionally.

Far from being sexually unresponsive, most prostitutes reported that they had enjoyable sexual relationships in their private lives and were regularly orgasmic. Not surprisingly, prostitutes report more sexual enjoyment in their personal relationships than in their work.

In most locales, penalties for prostitution involve small fines or short jail terms. Many police departments, besieged by crimes such as drug peddling and violent crimes, consider prostitution a "minor" or "nuisance" crime. Many prostitutes find the criminal justice system a revolving door. They pay the fine. They spend a night or two in jail. They return to the streets.

A bar prostitute is a variation of the streetwalker. She approaches men in a bar she frequents, rather than on the streets. Payoffs to bar owners or managers secure their cooperation, although the women are sometimes tolerated because they draw customers to the bar (Prus & Irini, 1980). Some streetwalkers work X-rated or "adult" movie houses and may service their patrons in their seats with manual or oral sex. Payoffs may be used to secure the cooperation of the management.

Many streetwalkers support a pimp, a man who acts as lover-father-companion-master. He provides them with protection, bail money, and sometimes room and board, in exchange for a high percentage of their earnings, often more than 90 percent. As Chris, a streetwalker explains, a prostitute cannot expect to survive long on the streets without a pimp:

> CHRIS: You can't really work the streets for yourself unless you got a man—not for a long length of time . . . 'cause the other pimps are not going to like it because you don't have anybody to represent you. They'll rob you, they'll hit you in the head if you don't have nobody to take up for you. Yea, it happens. They give you a hassle . . . [The men] will say, "Hey baby, what's your name? Where your man at? You got a man?"
>
> INTERVIEWER: So you can't hustle on your own?
>
> CHRIS: Not really, no. You can, you know, but not for long.
>
> (Romenesko & Miller, 1989, pp. 116–117)

Prostitutes are often physically abused by their pimps, who may use threats and beatings as a means of control. In a study of young streetwalkers in Boston, Virginia Ann

Streetwalkers. Streetwalkers or street prostitutes earn the lowest wages and have the lowest status among the various types of prostitutes. They are also at greatest risk of arrest and of being abused by pimps and customers.

Brothel Prostitutes. In this Nevada brothel, customers typically select their sex partners from among a group of women who assemble in a central area.

Price (1989) observed that as the relationship progressed, the beatings became more vicious. As Kim Romenesko and Eleanor Miller (1989), who studied streetwalkers in Milwaukee, commented, "Clearly, 'men' are the rulers of the underworld" (p. 117).

Streetwalkers do not tend to remain in the business (sometimes referred to as "the life") very long (Edgley, 1989). Some make the transition to a more traditional life or simply get married. Others die prematurely from drug abuse, disease, suicide, or physical abuse from pimps or customers. Those who survive become less marketable with age.

Streetwalkers who work hotels and conventions generally hold a higher status than those that work the streets or bars. Clients are typically conventioneers or businessmen traveling away from home. The hotel prostitute must be skilled in conveying subtle messages to potential clients without drawing the attention of hotel management or security. They usually provide sexual services in the client's hotel room. Some hotel managers will tolerate known prostitutes (usually for a payoff "under the table"), so long as the woman conducts herself discreetly.

BROTHEL PROSTITUTION   Brothel prostitutes occupy a middle status in the hierarchy of prostitutes, between streetwalkers on one end and call girls on the other (Edgley, 1989). They work in a brothel, or, more commonly today, in a massage parlor or for an escort service.

The life of the brothel (or "house") prostitute is neither as lucrative as that of the call girl nor as degrading as that of the streetwalker. Brothel prostitutes in massage parlors or working for escort services may not consider themselves to be "real prostitutes" because they do not walk the streets and because they work for businesses that present a legitimate front (Edgley, 1989). *Cathouse, bordello, cat wagon, parlor house, whorehouse, joy house, sport house, house of ill repute*—these are but a handful of the names given to houses in which prostitutes work. The heyday of the brothel is all but over in the United States. Formal brothels today are rare, except in Nevada, where they are legal but regulated.

Brothel prostitutes may attempt to maintain a traditional life apart from their prostitution activities. Ricker (1980) tells the story of one dual-world prostitute:

> Jan has been married 15 years and is the mother of three children—her earnings help keep them in a snooty Northern California boarding school. A relative newcomer [at the Chicken Ranch, a licensed Nevada brothel], she tried massage parlors, escort services, and other forms of "the business" [earlier]. Jan got into this line of work because she needed extra money. . . . Jan feels her home relationship has been improved by her job. "Before I went to work, my husband and I were always entertaining, trying to keep up that affluent suburban image. Now, when we're together we just enjoy each other and the children." She also feels her work has made her more interesting to her husband. "I've had to learn to relate to all kinds of different people. And I've learned how to play a variety of roles—I can be nurse, sophisticated companion, psychologist, temptress. . . . " No, Jan doesn't tell her children what she does (p. 282).

Jan, like other brothel prostitutes, splits her fees with the management. In addition to her "split," she receives free room and board. They are on duty three weeks a month and on call 24 hours a day during that time. When a customer arrives, they step into the living room "lineup." After one has been chosen, they wait again, resting, reading, or watching television.

THE MASSAGE PARLOR   "Massage parlors" have sprung up from coast to coast to fill the vacuum left by the departure of the brothels. Many massage parlors are legitimate establishments that provide massage, and only massage, to customers. Masseuses and masseurs are licensed in many states, and laws restrict them from offering sexual services (Rasmussen & Kuhn, 1976). Many localities have specified that the masseuse or masseur must keep certain parts of her or his body clothed and not extend the massage to the client's genitals.

Many massage parlors serve as fronts for prostitution, however. In these establishments, clients typically pay standard fees for massages, which is not against the law, and then make additional illegal arrangements for sexual services.

Massage-parlor prostitutes generally offer to perform manual stimulation of the penis ("a local"), oral sex, or less frequently, coitus. Massage-parlor prostitutes are generally better-educated than streetwalkers and brothel workers. Many massage-parlor prostitutes would not work in these other venues in which prostitution occurs.

ESCORT SERVICES   Today, conventioneers and businessmen are more likely to turn to the listings for "massage" and "escort services" in the telephone directory yellow pages or under the personal ads in local newspapers than to seek hotel prostitutes. Services that provide "outcall" send masseuses (or masseurs) or escorts to the hotel room.

Escort services are typically (but not always) fronts for prostitution. Escort services are found in every major American city and present themselves as legitimate businesses providing escorts for men (Edgley, 1989). Indeed, one will find female companionship for corporate functions and for unattached men traveling away from home under "escort services." Many escort services provide only prostitution, however, and clients of other escort services sometimes negotiate sexual services after formal escort duties are completed—or in their stead (Edgley, 1989).

TRUTH OR *FICTION?*
_____

R E V I S I T E D

The massage and escort services advertised in the yellow pages are fronts for prostitution. *Some, but not all, of the massage and escort services advertised in the yellow pages are fronts for prostitution. (Legitimate masseuses and masseurs often advertise that they are state-licensed.)* •

Discussion Question: Compare your views of street prostitutes to your views of prostitutes who are paid by a business to entertain out-of-town businessmen. How similar or different are your views of the men who have sex with these prostitutes?

Prostitutes who work for escort services often come from middle-class backgrounds and are well-educated—so much the better to help prepare them to hold their own in social conversation. Escort services may establish arrangements with legitimate companies to provide "escorts" for visiting customers or potential clients. Escort services also provide female escorts to "entertain" at conventions. Because of her high-society background, Sidney Biddle Barrow, the so-called Mayflower Madam, attracted a great deal of publicity when it was discovered that she ran an exclusive "escort service" in New York in the 1980s.

Call girls
Prostitutes who arrange for their sexual contacts by telephone. *Call* refers both to telephone calls and to being "on call."

CALL GIRLS   **Call girls** occupy the highest status on the social ladder of female prostitution (Greenwald, 1970). Call girls tend to be the most attractive and well-educated prostitutes and tend to charge more for their services than other types of prostitutes. Many come from middle-class backgrounds (Edgley, 1989). Unlike other types of prostitutes, call girls usually work on their own, so they need not split their income with a pimp, escort service, or massage parlor. Consequently they can afford to lead a luxurious lifestyle when business is good, living in expensive neighborhoods and wearing stylish clothes, and to be more selective about the customers they will accept. Yet they incur expenses for answering services and laundry services, and for payoffs to landlords, doormen, and sometimes to police to maintain their livelihood and avoid arrest.

Call girls often escort their clients to dinner and social functions, and are expected not only to provide sex but also charming and gracious company and conversation (Edgley, 1989). Call girls often give clients the feeling that they are important and attractive. They may effectively simulate pleasure and orgasm and can create the illusion that time does not matter. It does, of course. To the call girl, as to other entrepreneurs, time is money.

Call girls sometimes affiliate with madams who steer clients in their direction, but clientele usually grow by personal reference or "word of mouth." Some call girls are even carried on the payroll of corporations for tax purposes (Edgley, 1989). Call girls are sometimes hired by lonely men for social companionship rather than sexual services.

Call girls may receive clients in their apartments or make "outcalls" to clients' homes and hotels. Call girls may trade or sell "black books" that list clients and their sexual preferences. To protect themselves from police and abusive clients, call girls may insist on reviewing a client's business card before personal contact is made. They may investigate whether the customer is in fact the person he purports to be.

CHARACTERISTICS OF FEMALE PROSTITUTES

Learning Objective 3:
Describe the economic and family influences characteristic of most prostitutes.

Although no single factor explains entry into female prostitution, poverty and sexual and/or physical abuse figure prominently in the backgrounds of many prostitutes. Female prostitutes often come from conflict-ridden or one-parent homes in poor urban areas or rural farming communities.

For young women of impoverished backgrounds and marginal skills, the life of the prostitute may seem an alluring alternative to the menial and dismal work opportunities that are otherwise available (Romenesko & Miller, 1989). Based on their studies of streetwalkers in Milwaukee, Romenesko and Miller concluded that

> . . . poverty, and the many concomitants of poverty manifest in American society, were the factors pushing these women into the world of illicit work. Conversely, the bright lights, money, and independence that the street seemingly offered—things that were largely absent from these women's lives prior to their entrance into street life—were enticements that drew women to street life (p. 112).

Researchers also find a high level of psychological disturbance among streetwalkers. In New York, Exner and his colleagues (1977) found that call girls and brothel prostitutes could not be distinguished from nonprostitutes on their psychological characteristics. Streetwalkers and drug-addicted prostitutes showed higher rates of psychological disturbance than comparison groups, however.

Cross-cultural evidence from a study of 41 prostitutes in Belgium showed similar patterns of psychopathology (De Schampheleire, 1990). Compared to a group of nonprostitutes (women flight attendants), streetwalkers in the Belgian study were more fearful, anxious, resentful, and depressed. They also had poorer relationships with their families and were in poorer health. In a study in the United States, teenage female prostitutes were more likely than normal female adolescents or delinquents who did not engage in prostitution to show signs of psychological disturbance and to have been placed in special-education classes in school (Gibson et al., 1988).

Poverty accounts for the entry of young women into prostitution in many countries. In some third world nations, such as Thailand, rural, impoverished parents may in effect sell daughters to recruiters who place them in brothels in cities (Erlanger, 1991). Many of the women send home whatever money they can and also work hard to try to pay off the procurers and break free of their financial bonds.

In the United States and Canada, many initiates into prostitution are teenage runaways. The family backgrounds of teenage runaways vary in socioeconomic status (some come from middle-class or affluent homes, whereas others are reared in poverty), but a consistent pattern of family discord and dysfunction apparently sets the stage for their entry to street life and prostitution (Price, 1989). Many teenage runaways perceive life on the street to be the only possible escape from family strife and conflict, or from the physical, emotional, or sexual abuse they suffer at home. Despite its dangers, life on the streets appears more attractive than remaining in the troubled family environment. A study of teenage prostitutes in Boston found that a majority had come from broken homes and were reared by single parents or in reconstituted families consisting of half siblings and stepsiblings (Price, 1989). Those who came from intact families nevertheless reported high levels of family conflict.

Teenage runaways are at particularly high risk of unsafe sexual practices, such as sex with multiple partners and lack of condom use. The average male teenage runaway in a New York City study reported having had 11 female sexual partners in his lifetime (Rotheram-Borus et al., 1992). Only 8 percent of the teenage boys reported using condoms consistently.

Teenage runaways with marginal skills and limited means of support may find few alternatives to prostitution. Adolescent prostitution results from the "necessities of street life—it is survival behavior more than it is sexual behavior" (Seng, 1989, p. 674). It is not long before the teenage runaway is approached by a pimp or a john. A study of 149 teenage runaways in Toronto found that 67 percent of the boys and 82 percent of the girls who had been away from home for more than a year had been offered money to engage in sexual activity with an adult (Hartman et al., 1987).

Studies of teenage prostitutes in the United States show that perhaps as many as one half to two thirds of female prostitutes had been sexually abused as children (Seng, 1989). One sample of 45 former prostitutes in Canada showed that 73 percent had been sexually abused in childhood (Bagley & Young, 1987).

TRUTH OR *FICTION?*

R E V I S I T E D

Most female prostitutes were sexually abused as children. *It appears that the majority of female prostitutes were in fact sexually abused as children.* •

Some teenagers who have endured sexual abuse or incest may have learned how to detach themselves emotionally from sex in order to survive unwanted sexual experiences. The transition to prostitution may represent an extension of this unfortunate learning experience. Though teenage prostitutes may turn to prostitution primarily for money, Price (1989) recognizes that survivors of sexual abuse or incest may also be attracted to prostitution because they have learned that it is through their sexuality that they can obtain attention or love from adults:

> For a lonely adolescent, attention from tricks or a sugar daddy is not all that different from the attention he or she received at home. In fact, it may be preferable, as there may not be any physical abuse involved (p. 84).

Not all sexually abused children become prostitutes, of course. Only 12 percent of one sample of predominantly female 16- to 18-year-olds who had been sexually abused became involved in prostitution (Seng, 1989). Abused children who run away from home are much more likely to become involved in prostitution than those who do not (Seng, 1989). Runaways are also more likely to become drug and alcohol abusers.

Nor do all teenage runaways become prostitutes. Though information on prevalences of prostitution among runaways is scarce, a Boston study of homeless street youth in the mid-1980s found that fewer than 20 percent had engaged in prostitution (Price, 1989). Though most had been approached for prostitution within a few days of living on the streets, the overwhelming majority refused.

In sum, evidence suggests that most female prostitutes are survivors of sexual abuse or incest. Running away from home appears to funnel many survivors of childhood sexual abuse into prostitution, yet not all survivors of sexual abuse, nor all teenage runaways, become prostitutes.

Teenage runaways are in need of outreach programs that provide support services to help them meet their needs for shelter, emotional support, counseling, and education. Far too often, however, troubled youth fall between the cracks of the social support system and are placed at risk for homelessness, drug abuse, emotional problems, unemployment, and prostitution (Raychaba, 1989).

CUSTOMERS OF FEMALE PROSTITUTES

The world of commerce has its consumers, and the consumers of prostitutes are often referred to as "johns" or "tricks." Terms like patron, meatball, sucker, and beefbuyer are also heard. Men who use female prostitutes come from all walks of life and represent all socioeconomic and racial groups (Turner et al., 1989). Many, perhaps most, are married men of middle-class background. A study of the address listings of customers (seized by the local police) of an "escort service" in a southern city showed that most of the clients lived in relatively affluent neighborhoods consisting of a high percentage of well-educated, largely white and married residents (Adams, 1987).

Most patrons are "occasional johns," such as traveling salesmen or military personnel who are stopping over in town and away from their regular sex partners. One study of 30 occasional johns showed that all had regular sex partners. They used prostitutes because they desired novelty or sexual variety, not because they lacked other sexual outlets (Holzman & Pines, 1982).

"Habitual johns," however, use prostitutes as their major or exclusive sexual outlet. Some habitual johns have never established an intimate sexual relationship. Some wealthy men who wish to avoid intimate relationships habitually patronize call girls.

Discussion Question: If the early family lives of so many prostitutes are characterized by sexual abuse, why don't people demand a massive program to eliminate child sexual abuse instead of periodically demanding that the police crack down on prostitution? Does prostitution serve such an important function in American society that we are not really committed to its elimination?

Learning Objective 4: Discuss the demographic profiles and motives of customers of female prostitutes.

Whore-madonna complex
A rigid stereotyping of
women as either sinners or
saints.

"Compulsive johns" feel driven to prostitutes to meet some psychological or sexual need. They may repeatedly resolve to stop using prostitutes but feel unable to control their compulsions. Some compulsive johns feel compelled to engage in acts of fetishism or transvestism with prostitutes but would not inform their wives or girlfriends of their variant interests. Some men who are compulsive users of prostitutes suffer from a **whore-madonna complex** in which they see women as either sinners or saints. They can only permit themselves to enjoy sex with prostitutes or would only ask prostitutes to engage in acts such as fellatio, and they see marital coitus as a duty or obligation.

MOTIVES FOR USING PROSTITUTES   Though the reasons for using prostitutes vary, researchers have identified six of the most common motives (Edgley, 1989; Gagnon, 1977):

1. *Sex without negotiation.* Prostitution may be attractive to men who do not want to spend the time, effort, and money involved in dating and getting to know someone simply to obtain sex. As Edgley comments, the customer "gives [the prostitute] money for sex, she gives sex in return. The entire matter is simple, direct, and sure" (p. 393).
2. *Sex without commitment.* Prostitutes require no commitment from the man other than payment for services rendered. The prostitute will not call him at home or expect to be called in return. The relationship is virtually anonymous as well as impersonal.
3. *Sex for eroticism and variety.* Many prostitutes offer "something extra" in the way of novel or kinky sex, for example, use of special costumes (e.g., leather attire), and S&M rituals (such as bondage and discipline or spanking). Men may desire such activity but not obtain it with their regular partners; they may even be afraid to mention the idea. Since 90 percent or so of today's young married couples use fellatio and cunnilingus (see Chapter 9), desire for oral sex may have slackened off as a motive for visiting prostitutes. Prostitution may also be attractive to men who seek additional sex partners for the sake of variety or novelty.
4. *Prostitution as sociability.* In the nineteenth and early twentieth centuries, the brothel served not only as a place to obtain sex, but also as a kind of "stopping off" place between home and work—referred to by some writers as a "third place" (Oldenberg & Brissett, 1980). The local tavern or pool hall are nonsexual examples of "third places." At times, sex was secondary to the companionship and amiable conversation that men would find in brothels, especially in the days of the "bawdy houses" of the pioneer West. Today, however, such brothels are more likely to exist in nostalgia than reality. Sociability is more likely to be found among call girls and escort prostitutes who offer social companionship, with or without sex. The discovery that sex is not always part of the deal may come as a surprise. As Edgley notes, "Sometimes companionship and sociability is all the client wants for his money" (p. 396).
5. *Sex away from home.* The greatest contemporary use of prostitution occurs among men who are away from home, such as businessmen attending conventions and sports fans attending out-of-town sporting events. In these typical all-male preserves, there is often intense peer pressure to engage in sexual adventures.

Notes: According to the *International Children's Rights Monitor,* there were 6,000 women working as prostitutes in Cambodia in 1991; by the end of the United Nations peacekeeping operation there in 1992, the number had risen to 20,000. This publication also documented a sharp rise in prostitution involving children. In December, 1993 the International Save the Children Alliance charged U.N. military personnel in Mozambique with buying sex from hundreds of girls, some as young as 12. In February, 1994, a U.N. report concluded that the increase in prostitution in Mozambique generated by the U.N. contingent "has negatively affected the quality of urban public life and apparently generated some ill feelings toward troops in some areas." (Kirshenbaum, G. 1994. Who's watching the peacekeepers?: *Ms., 4(6),* 10–15.)

TRUTH OR *FICTION?*

R E V I S I T E D

Typical customers of prostitutes have difficulty forming sexual relationships with other women. *Most customers of prostitutes today have in fact formed sexual relationships with other women. Such men often turn to prostitution for sexual variety or because they seek sexual attentions when they are away from home.* •

6. *Problematical sex.* Persons with physical disabilities or disfiguring conditions sometimes seek the services of prostitutes because of difficulty attracting other partners or because of fears of rejection. (One prostitute at a Nevada brothel said that she was a favorite of the management because she accepted johns with cerebral palsy.) Though some prostitutes are selective about the clients they will accept, others will accept virtually any client who is willing to pay. Men with sexual dysfunctions may also turn to prostitutes to help them overcome their problems. Some lonely men who lack sex partners may seek prostitutes as substitutes.

MALE PROSTITUTION

Male prostitution includes both homosexual and heterosexual activities. Male prostitutes who service female clients—*gigolos*—are rare. Their clients are typically older, wealthy, unattached women. Gigolos may serve as escorts or as surrogate sons for women, and may or may not offer sexual services. Many gigolos are struggling actors or models.

The overwhelming majority of male prostitutes service other men in homosexual liaisons. Men who engage in male prostitution are called **hustlers.** Their patrons are typically called **scores.** Hustlers average 17 to 18 years of age and become initiated into prostitution at an average age of 14 or so (Coleman, 1989). They typically have less than eleventh-grade educations and few if any marketable skills. The majority come from working-class and lower-class backgrounds. Many male prostitutes, like many female prostitutes, come from families troubled by conflict, alcoholism, or abuse (Coleman, 1989). More than four of five (83%) of a sample of 47 male prostitutes in Seattle, Washington, had been survivors of sexual abuse (Boyer, 1989). Two of three are survivors of rape or attempted rape. In another study, the factor that most clearly distinguished juvenile male prostitutes and male delinquent street youth was the absence of sexual victimization in the histories of the delinquents (Janus et al., 1984).

Hustlers may be gay, bisexual, or heterosexual in orientation. Most researchers find that at least half of the male prostitutes they study are gay (e.g., Allen, 1980; Fisher et al., 1982). Seventy percent of the male prostitutes in the Seattle study identified themselves as gay or bisexual. Only 30 percent identified themselves as heterosexual (Boyer, 1989).

The major motive for male prostitution, like female prostitution, is money. In one study, 69 percent of male prostitutes cited money as their principal motive (Fisher et al., 1982). Running away from home typically serves as an entry point for male as well as female prostitution. In one study, three of four male prostitutes had run away by an average age of 15 (Weisberg, 1985). Some had run away because of family problems; others, because of a desire for adventure or independence (Coleman, 1989). Some gay male prostitutes are literally thrown out because their families cannot accept their homosexual orientation (Coleman, 1989; Kruks, 1991). Researcher Debra Boyer (1989) comments:

> The responses of families to the homosexuality of their sons ranged from strong condemnation to total rejection, for example, "it's disgusting"; "we refuse to accept it"; "we don't want to talk about it"; "that's it, you are leaving." These young men suffered outright rejection from their families and were often literally thrown away as sullied human beings (pp. 168–169).

For many of these gay "throwaways," prostitution may represent a way of obtaining adult acceptance, albeit within the context of exchanging sex for money. Another distinguishing characteristic of the gay prostitutes in the Seattle study was the lack of a network of gay friends. These young gay males became initiated into the gay subculture in the life of the street. Their only contacts with other gay men were through turning tricks or "hanging out" with other young hustlers. The ability to attract clients and the money they received inflated their self-esteem. As Boyer puts it, they were "no longer outcasts, but stars" (p. 177). Many hoped to find companionship or a meaningful relationship through prostitution. Some would fall in love with "tricks," only to be disappointed when the encounter or relationship fizzled.

Heterosexual hustlers may try to psychologically detach themselves from male clients by refusing to kiss or hug them or to perform fellatio. Gagnon (1977) writes that, "As long as the [client's] head is below the [hustler's] belly button and contact is on the penis, it is the other person who is homosexual" (p. 264). To become aroused, heterosexual hustlers may fantasize about women while the "score" is fellating them. Many heterosexual male prostitutes maintain heterosexual relationships in their private lives while "turning tricks" with men to earn money.

Most hustlers are part-timers who continue some form of educational or vocational activity as they support themselves through prostitution (Allen, 1980). Drug dealing and drug use are also common among hustlers (Coleman, 1989). In one study, about three in four male prostitutes used drugs while they were hustling (Fisher et al., 1982).

'Tis a Puzzlement: On AIDS and Prostitution in Thailand

"'Tis a puzzlement," sang the king in the Broadway musical *The King and I*. The king of nineteenth-century Thailand was referring to the import of Western values and culture. Today it could be considered a puzzlement that so many Thais continue high-risk sexual behavior in the face of AIDS, which may be another import from the West.

HIV may have been brought to Thailand by gay Thais who lived for a while in the West (Erlanger, 1991). Through the 1980s, HIV was spread in Thailand mostly via gay male sexual activity and injectable drug use. In the 1990s, however—in a progression that is found in many other nations—the central route of infection has become heterosexual intercourse.

AIDS may be spiraling out of control in Thailand. In 1991, more than 300,000 of this nation of 56 million were infected. Given the rate of infection, however, the Population and Community Development Association of Thailand estimated that more than five million could be infected by the year 2000, with more than a million dead.

The high-risk sexual behavior in question involves prostitution. Whereas only a minority of Westerners visit (or admit to visiting)

prostitutes, prostitution is a way of life in Thailand. About three in four Thai men—at a rate of 450,000 a day—avail themselves of prostitutes. In many brothels in northwest Thailand, such as in the city of Chiang Mai, where the epidemic is most advanced, 80 percent of the "working women" test positive for HIV antibodies (Erlanger, 1991). In populous Bangkok, the figure now exceeds 20 percent. Fourteen percent of the male army recruits from the northwest region test positive. HIV is leapfrogging from prostitutes to customers to the customers' wives, lovers, and—through pregnancy, childbirth, or breast-feeding—to their children.

Printed on the glass "showcase" of one brothel in Chiang Mai is the legend, "We welcome only guests using condoms." Yet 59 percent of Thai men report that they never wear them (and more than 80 percent do not consider AIDS a threat). Do the prostitutes insist on condoms? As says Daeng, a Bangkok bar girl, "If the man seems clean and healthy, I say, OK. If the man comes to me often and is nice to me, I say, OK. If he offers me more money, I say, OK" (Erlanger, 1991, p. 49). 'Tis a puzzlement.

Bangkok Sex Tours

AIDS in Thailand. In many brothels in northwest Thailand, four out of five prostitutes carry HIV.

Unlike female prostitutes, hustlers typically are not attached to a pimp (Luckenbill, 1985). They generally make contacts with clients in gay bars and social clubs, or by working the streets in areas frequented by gay men. They typically learn to hustle through their interactions with other hustlers and by watching other hustlers ply their trade (Luckenbill, 1985).

Coleman (1989) identifies several subtypes of male prostitutes. *Kept boys* hold the highest status. They develop a relationship with an older, economically secure male who provides them with access to an affluent lifestyle. The older male, or "sugar daddy," often assumes a parental role. *Call boys,* like call girls, may work on their own or through an agency or escort service. *Punks* are prison inmates who are used sexually by other inmates and rewarded with protection or such goods as cigarettes or drugs. A *drag prostitute* is a transvestite or a (presurgery) male-to-female transsexual who impersonates a female prostitute and has sex with men who are unaware of his anatomic gender. The drag prostitute generally limits himself to the fellating role so as to conceal his true biological gender. *Brothel prostitutes* are even rarer than their female counterparts; even fewer male prostitution houses exist. *Bar hustlers* and *street hustlers,* like their female counterparts, occupy the lowest status and ply their trade in gay bars or on streets frequented by gay passersby. Street hustlers are the most common and typically the youngest subtype. They are also the most visible and consequently the ones most likely to draw the attention of the police.

Male prostitutes typically have much shorter careers than their female counterparts (Price, 1989). By and large, male prostitution is an adolescent enterprise. The younger the hustler, the higher the fee he can command and the more tricks he can turn. By the time he reaches his mid-twenties, he may be forced to engage in sexual activities he might have rejected when younger or to seek clients in sleazier places.

HIV, AIDS, AND PROSTITUTION

Learning Objective 6:
Examine the dangers to prostitutes and to society posed by the AIDS virus.

Concerns about the spread of sexually transmitted diseases by prostitution is nothing new. In the 1960s, two of three prostitutes surveyed by Gebhard (1969) had contracted gonorrhea or syphilis. Though prostitutes are still exposed to a heightened risk of contracting or spreading these and other sexually transmitted diseases, such as chlamydia, today the risk of AIDS poses a more deadly threat. The risk of HIV transmission has been linked to both male and female prostitution (Bloor et al., 1990; Campbell, 1991; Van den Hoek et al., 1990; Yates et al., 1991).

Sex with prostitutes is considered the most important factor in the heterosexual transmission of HIV in Africa, where the infection is spread predominantly via heterosexual intercourse (Holmes & Kreiss, 1988). A Florida study showed that regular contact with female street prostitutes was a risk factor in the transmission of HIV in U.S. men (Castro et al., 1988). Prostitutes incur a greater risk of HIV transmission because they have sexual relations with a great many partners, often without any form of protection (Quadagno et al., 1991). Moreover, many prostitutes and their clients and other sex partners are injectable drug users who share contaminated needles (Bloor et al., 1990; Freund et al., 1989). HIV may be spread by unprotected sex from prostitutes to customers, then to the customers' wives or lovers (Adams, 1987). Nationwide, about 12 percent of the prostitutes tested in the late 1980s were seropositive for HIV (Lambert, 1988). In Thailand, the transmission of HIV by prostitution seems even more widespread, as noted in the A World of Diversity box on page 633.

Men who frequent male prostitutes may represent a vector or conduit for heterosexual transmission of HIV, since the rate of HIV infection is high among male prostitutes, and many if not most of their male customers describe themselves as either bisexual or heterosexual (Morse et al., 1992). Some of these men may be exposing their wives and girlfriends to HIV that they contracted from male prostitutes.

Despite the obvious dangers of HIV transmission, many U.S. prostitutes, like many Thai prostitutes, have not altered either their sexual behavior or their patterns of drug use to any large extent. Only 30 percent of a sample of 20 street prostitutes in Camden, New Jersey, reported always using condoms (Freund et al., 1989). A recent study of 72 heroin-addicted female street prostitutes in southern California showed a high level of knowledge and fear about AIDS but a failure to change patterns of sexual behavior or drug use (Bellis, 1990). The prostitutes sampled did nothing to protect themselves or their clients from HIV. Their need for money led them to deny the risks to which they were exposing themselves. Surveys of adolescent prostitutes show a similar pattern of denial, as Price (1989) observes:

Some [adolescent prostitutes] simply believe it will not happen to them, while others say they are willing to take the risk. Still others do not care whether they live or die, and expect their lives to end shortly anyway (p. 86).

Some changes in prostitution practices have taken place. Brothel owners in Nevada, for example, now require customers to wear condoms. But prostitutes who are bent on denial or are so filled with despair that they care nothing about their own or clients' lives may be most resistant to change.

TRUTH OR FICTION?

R E V I S I T E D

Most prostitutes take precautions to avoid becoming infected by or transmitting the AIDS virus. Actually it appears that most street prostitutes in the United States, and many brothel workers in foreign nations, do not take precautions against becoming infected by or transmitting HIV. •

PORNOGRAPHY AND OBSCENITY

Learning Objective 7:
Discuss the continuing social debate over the definition of pornography.

The production and distribution of sexually explicit materials has become a boom industry in the United States. In the United States, 20 million "adult" magazines are sold each month. X-rated or adult movies (also called *porn* movies) have moved from sleazy adult theaters to the living rooms of middle America in the form of videocassette rentals and sales. According to a Gallup poll, X-rated films account for about one in five video sales (Linsley, 1989).

Pornography is indeed popular, but also highly controversial. Many people in our society are opposed to pornography on moral grounds. Feminists oppose pornography on the grounds that it portrays women in degrading and dehumanizing roles, as sexual objects who are subservient to men's sexual wishes, as sexually insatiable nymphomaniacs, or as sexual masochists who enjoy being raped and violated (Blakely, 1985; Elshtain, 1984; Faust, 1980). Moreover, feminists hold that depictions of women in sexually subordinate roles may encourage men to treat them as sex objects and may increase the potential for rape (Scott & Schwalm, 1988). Yet feminists are split on the issue of legal suppression of pornography. For example, the feminist writer Kate Millett argues that "We're better off hanging tight to the First Amendment so that we have freedom of speech" (Press et al., 1985). But what is pornography? How is it defined? Why is it used? How does it affect people who are exposed to it?

WHAT IS PORNOGRAPHIC?

Pornography
Written, visual, or audio-taped material that is sexually explicit and produced for purposes of eliciting or enhancing sexual arousal. (From Greek roots meaning "to write about prostitutes.")

Prurient
Tending to excite lust; lewd. (From the Latin *prurire,* meaning "to itch" in the sense of "to long for.")

Webster's Deluxe Unabridged Dictionary defines **pornography** as "writing, pictures, etc., intended to arouse sexual desire." The inclusion of the word *intended* places the determination of what is pornographic in the mind of the person composing the work. Applying this definition makes it all but impossible to determine what is pornographic. If a filmmaker admits that he or she wanted to arouse the audience sexually, we may judge the work to be pornographic, even if no naked bodies or explicit sex scenes are shown. On the other hand, explicit representations of people engaged in sexual activity would not be pornographic if the work was intended as an artistic expression, rather than created for its **prurient** value. Many works that were once prohibited in this country because of explicit sexual content, like the novels *Tropic of Cancer* by Henry Miller, *Lady Chatterley's Lover* by D. H. Lawrence, and *Ulysses* by James Joyce, are now generally considered literary works rather than excursions into pornography. Even Mark Twain's *Huckleberry Finn,* John Steinbeck's *The Grapes of Wrath,* and Ernest Hemingway's *For Whom the Bell Tolls* have been banned from place to place because local citizens found them to be offensive, obscene, or morally objectionable (Linsley, 1989).

There is thus a subjective element in the definition of pornography. An erotic statue that sexually arouses viewers may not be considered pornographic if the sculptor's intent was artistic. A grainy photograph of a naked body that was intended to excite sexually may be pornographic. One alternative definition finds material pornographic when it is judged to be offensive by others. This definition, too, relies on the subjective judgment of the person exposed to the material. In other words, one person's pornography is another person's work of art.

Legislative bodies usually write laws about **obscenity** rather than pornography. Even the Supreme Court, however, has had a difficult time defining obscenity and determining where, if anywhere, laws against obscenity do not run afoul of the Bill of Rights' guarantee of free speech. In the case of *Miller v. California* (1973), Supreme Court Justice William Brennan wrote that obscenity is "incapable of definition with sufficient clarity to withstand attack on vagueness grounds." Such vagueness did not deter Supreme Court Justice Potter Stewart from quipping that although he could not define obscenity in objective terms, he knew it when he saw it. Recall that *Huckleberry Finn* was once considered obscene, however.

Let us follow Mosher (1988) and define pornography as written, visual, or audio-taped material that is sexually explicit or graphic and produced for purposes of eliciting or enhancing sexual arousal. **Erotica** may be as sexually explicit as pornography is, but many writers use the term to refer to sexual materials that are artistically produced or motivated. Although some people find any erotic material to be offensive or obscene, we agree with Gordon and Snyder (1989) that artistic expressions of erotic themes and "hard-core" pornography should not be lumped together.

Pornography is often classified as either "hard-core" (X-rated) or "soft-core" (R-rated). Hard-core pornography typically includes graphic and sexually explicit depictions of sex organs and sexual acts. Soft-core porn, as represented by photographs found in magazines like *Playboy* or *Penthouse,* features more stylized nude photos and suggestive (or simulated) rather than explicit depictions of sexual acts. Soft-core porn films typically include simulated sexual acts with partial or full nudity but without close-ups of genitalia.

PORNOGRAPHY AND THE LAW

Laws against obscenity provide the legal framework for outlawing the dissemination of pornography. Since the definition of obscenity relies on offending people or running afoul of community standards, that which is deemed obscene may vary from person to person and from culture to culture. Going topless on a public beach may be deemed obscene in some locales but not along beaches on the French Riviera or Rio de Janeiro, where this style of (un)dress is customary and broadly accepted. The word *obscene* extends beyond sexual matters. One could judge TV violence or some beer commercials to be obscene because they are personally offensive or are offensive to women, even if such depictions do not meet legal standards of obscenity.

In the United States, legal prohibition of pornography as a form of obscenity dates to the nineteenth century. In 1873, an antiobscenity bill, the Comstock Act, was passed by Congress. One effect of the bill was to outlaw the dissemination of information about birth control (see Chapter 12). The Comstock Act and similar laws made it a felony to mail obscene books, pamphlets, photographs, drawings, or letters. But what is obscene?

A landmark case in 1957 helped establish the legal basis of obscenity in the United States. In *Roth v. United States,* the U.S. Supreme Court ruled that portrayal of sexual activity was protected under the First Amendment to the Constitution unless its dominant theme dealt with "sex in a manner appealing to prurient interest" (*Roth v. United States,* 1957, p. 487). In a 1973 case, *Miller v. California,* the U.S. Supreme Court held that obscenity is based upon a determination of

> ...(a) whether the average person, applying contemporary community standards, would find that the work, taken as a whole, appeals to the prurient interest...; (b) whether the work depicts or describes, in a patently offensive way, sexual conduct specifically defined by the applicable state law; and (c) whether the work, taken as a whole, lacks serious literary, artistic, political, or scientific value.
>
> (*Miller v. California,* 1973, p. 24)

Courts have since had to grapple with the *Miller* standard in judging whether material is obscene. *Miller* recognizes that judgments of obscenity may vary with "community

Obscenity

That which offends people's feelings or goes beyond prevailing standards of decency or modesty. (From the Latin *caenum,* meaning "filth.")

Erotica

Books, pictures, and so on that have to do with sexual love (from the Greek *eros,* meaning "love"). Many contemporary writers use *erotica* to refer to sexual material that is artistically produced or motivated by artistic intent.

standards." As a result, the same material may be considered obscene in one community but not in another. The *Miller* standard raises some obvious and unresolved questions. For example, who is the *average* person who can speak for a community? Many of us live in ethnically, racially, and religiously diverse communities. Can one viewpoint in *any* community truly represent the community? Even in relatively homogeneous communities, a diversity of opinion may exist on particular issues. Moreover, what is a *community*? Is it one's neighborhood, police precinct, municipality, county, or a larger political unit? What does "patently" offensive mean? Who judges "serious" literary, artistic, political, or scientific value? An attempt to clarify this last question was made in a 1987 case, *Pope v. Illinois,* in which the Supreme Court held that

> The proper inquiry is not whether an ordinary member of any given community would find serious literary, artistic, political, or scientific value in allegedly obscene material, but whether a reasonable person would find such value in the material, taken as a whole (p. 445).

In this ruling, the court held that sexually explicit material could not be declared obscene if many or most people in a particular community held it to lack serious literary, artistic, political, or scientific value, unless a "reasonable" person were to reach the same judgment. Whether the concept of a "reasonable" person will provide the courts with a clearer standard than that of an "average" or "ordinary" person for adjudicating obscenity cases remains to be seen.

Child pornography, and violent and degrading or dehumanizing pornography complicate matters further. People who do not find depictions, however explicit, of consensual sexual activity between adults to be obscene may regard child pornography or violent pornography to be obscene. Child pornography is clearly psychologically harmful to the juvenile actors (Silbert, 1989). Many people also object to sexually explicit material that portrays women as "sex objects" or in a position subordinate to men—one serving no function other than gratifying the sexual appetites of ravenous men.

Some footnotes: The U.S. Supreme Court ruled (in *Stanley v. Georgia,* 1969) that the mere possession of obscene material in one's home cannot be made a criminal act (Sears, 1989). However, states may make it illegal to possess child pornography (Sears, 1989). Some communities (such as Indianapolis, Indiana) have sought to ban pornography on the grounds that it represents a form of sex discrimination. Pornography, that is, was held to damage women's opportunities for equal rights by perpetuating stereotypes of women as subservient to men. However, the Indianapolis ordinance was later overturned by a federal court on the grounds that it represented an unconstitutional infringement of free speech (Lewin, 1992a). However, in a 1992 ruling, the Supreme Court of Canada redefined obscenity as involving sexually explicit material containing violence toward women or that degrades or dehumanizes women (Lewin, 1992a). The court ruled that such material may be outlawed under tha nation's obscenity law.

Porn Movies. Some cities have established so-called red light districts to limit the proliferation of strip clubs and movie theaters featuring X-rated movies.

Learning Objective 9:
Discuss the current use of
pornography in the United
States, the people who use
it, and the gender differences in attitudes and
responses.

PREVALENCE AND USE OF EROTICA AND PORNOGRAPHY

Nearly all of us have been exposed to sexually explicit materials, whether in the form of a novel, an article in *Playboy* or *Playgirl* (purchased, no doubt, for its literary value), or an X-rated film. A survey of more than 2,000 randomly selected Canadian adults found that more than one in three (38%) had viewed an explicit scene of sexual intercourse on film (Peat et al., 1984). A 1986 *Roper* poll in the United States showed that 25 percent of respondents had seen an X-rated movie in the previous year, as compared to 16 percent in 1980 (Smith, 1987). A 1985 *Newsweek*/Gallup poll found that 13 percent of the respondents had attended an X-rated movie, and 40 percent of those who owned a VCR had either bought or rented an X-rated videocassette during the past year (Press et al., 1985). According to the same poll, people in the United States were about equally divided as to whether or not they wanted stricter laws concerning the sale of pornography. Forty-three percent felt that the laws should be tightened, whereas 48 percent wanted to leave them alone.

People in the United States are typically introduced to pornography by their high school years, often by peers (Bryant & Brown, 1989). Females are more likely to have been exposed to pornography by their boyfriends than the reverse (Bryant & Brown, 1989). A randomized telephone survey of 600 Midwesterners showed that more than 90 percent of the men and women had been exposed to *Playboy, Playgirl,* or similar magazines (Bryant, 1985). Ninety-four percent of respondents had seen "at least one sexually oriented R-rated film" (p. 45). Sixty-nine percent of both males and females had seen an X-rated film.

Pornography is typically used to elicit or enhance sexual arousal, often as a mastur-bation aid. Pornographic materials may also be used by couples to enhance sexual arousal during lovemaking. Couples may find that running a soft- or hard-core video on the VCR, or reading an erotic story aloud, enlivens their sexual appetite or suggests novel sexual techniques. Despite earlier beliefs that women were not sexually aroused by explicit sexual material, researchers have found that both men and women are physiolog-ically sexually aroused by pornographic pictures, movies, or audiotaped passages (e.g., Schmidt & Sigusch, 1970; Schmidt et al., 1973; Wincze et al., 1976). Men and women tend to respond to pornographic stimuli in similar ways, physiologically speaking—with vasocongestion of the genitals and myotonia (muscle tension) (Athanasiou, 1980; Heiman, 1975). Moreover, repeated exposure to the same pornographic materials pro-gressively lessens the sexual response to them (Meuwissen & Over, 1990; Zillmann, 1989). People may become aroused by the familiar materials again if some time is allowed to go by; novel materials are also likely to reactivate a sexual response (Meuwissen & Over, 1990; Zillmann, 1989).

Notes: The editor of a book
by Anthony Comstock (first
published in 1883), Robert
Bremner, lists some of
Comstock's "accomplish-
ments" in his introduction.
In 1875 alone, Comstock's
efforts as an unpaid postal
inspector resulted in 47
arrests, 27 convictions,
and 9,100 fines for mailing
obscene material. Also, in
1875 the New York Society
for the Suppression of Vice
seized 1,200 pounds of
books and destroyed over
29,000 sexually explicit cir-
culars, rubber goods, leaflets,
songs, and photos. (Com-
stock, A. 1967. *Traps for
the Young.* Robert Bremner
(Ed.). Cambridge, MA:
Belknap Press.)

TRUTH OR FICTION?

R E V I S I T E D

Only males are sexually aroused by pornography. *It is not true that only males are sexually aroused by erotica. Most male and female subjects are sex-ually aroused by erotica, physiologically speaking. As we see in the follow-ing section, however, their interest in, and subjective responses to, pornogra-phy may differ quite a bit.* •

GENDER DIFFERENCES IN RESPONSE TO PORNOGRAPHY   Although both gen-ders can become physiologically aroused by erotic materials, men and women do not necessarily share the same subjective response to them or level of interest in them. Visual pornography (sexually explicit pictures or films) is actually largely a male pre-serve (Symons, 1979; Winick, 1985). The majority of erotic visual materials are pro-duced by men for men. Attempts to market visual materials to females have been largely unsuccessful (Symons, 1979). Women may read erotic romance novels, but they show little interest in acquiring erotic pictures, films, or videotapes (Lawrence & Herold, 1988). Women respondents to the Bryant (1985) survey were twice as likely to be dis-gusted by their initial exposure to X-rated material as to enjoy it. Men, by contrast, were twice as likely to report a positive response.

Cybersex: From Computer Porn to Virtual Sex

In the computer industry, a "killer app" is a software program or application that makes the hardware appealing to users. Word processing and spreadsheet programs were among the first generation of "killer apps" that popularized the personal computer. In the mid-1990s, however, a potentially new killer app began to appear: CD-ROM disks that play X-rated interactive videos (Tierney, 1994). In some versions, nude female models appear on the computer screen and respond sexually to commands input by the user on a keyboard or by use of a computer mouse. We should not be surprised by this development, as pornography has crept into virtually every other form of popular media, from books and magazines to videotapes. Like other forms of pornography,

X-rated CD-ROMs have been criticized for projecting an image of women as sexual objects or playthings who are always readily available to satisfy a man's every whim and fancy (virtually all users of these products are men).

X-rated interactive CD-ROMs may represent the first volleys in a technological revolution that might be limited only by the imaginations and libidos of computer engineers and programmers. Futurists can envision a world of *virtual sex* in which developments in technology will allow people to have simulated sexual encounters even if they are hundreds or thousands of miles apart. In one version of this cybersexual future, people will be able to link their computers electronically and then don wired body suits and virtual-reality helmets that allow them to have

simulated sexual encounters with one another in a virtual-reality environment. The suits may be fitted with miniature tactile detectors coupled to simulators that allow them to experience sounds, sights, and the sensations of touching and being touched. The images projected in this virtual world are conceivably endless, with the participants taking on the appearance of their favorite movie stars or even engaging in gender-bending transformations. These cybersexual encounters might involve rapid scene changes, from a medieval castle to a Roman bath house to the surface of an alien planet. We have only to wonder whether this "brave new world" of virtual sex might one day vie for popularity with "the real thing."

The reasons for these gender differences remain unclear (Bryant & Brown, 1989). Women may find erotica a "turn-off" when it portrays women in unflattering roles, as "whorish," as subservient to the sexual demands of men, and as sexually aroused by male domination and coercion. Symons (1979), a sociobiologist, believes that a basic evolutionary process is at work. He argues that ancestral men who were more sexually aroused by the sight of a passing female may have had reproductive advantages over their less arousable peers:

> The male's desire to look at female genitals, especially genitals he has not seen before, and to seek out opportunities to do so, is part of the motivational process that maximizes male reproductive opportunities (p. 181).

Women, however, have fewer mating opportunities than men and must make the most of any reproductive opportunity by selecting the best possible mate and provider. To be sexually aroused by the sight of male genitalia might encourage random matings, which would undermine their reproductive success.

Learning Objective 10: Summarize the results of research that has investigated the link between pornography and sexual coercion.

PORNOGRAPHY AND SEXUAL COERCION

Is pornography a harmless diversion or an impetus to sexual violence or other antisocial acts? Let us consider several sources of evidence in examining these highly charged questions, beginning with the findings of a 1970 government commission impaneled to review the evidence that was available at the time.

THE COMMISSION ON OBSCENITY AND PORNOGRAPHY   In the 1960s, Congress created the Commission on Obscenity and Pornography to study the effects of pornography. Upon reviewing the existing research, the commission (Abelson et al., 1970) concluded that there was no evidence that pornography led to crimes of violence or sexual offenses such as exhibitionism, voyeurism, or child molestation. Some people were sexually aroused by pornography and increased the frequency of their usual sexual activity, such as masturbation or coitus with regular partners, following exposure. They did not engage in antisocial behavior, however. Studies carried out during the 1970s with participants ranging from middle-aged married couples to college students showed similar results (Brown et al., 1976; Hatfield et al., 1978; Heiby & Becker, 1980; Herrell, 1975; Schmidt et al., 1973). Shortly after exposure to pornography, there was a slight increase in observers' usual sexual behaviors (Byrne, 1977).

The commission found no causal link between pornography and delinquent behavior or sexual violence against women. The commission noted, for example, that when pornographic materials became widely available in Denmark following its legalization in the late 1960s, there was no corresponding increase in the incidence of sex crimes. Finding pornography basically harmless (Edgley, 1989), the commission recommended that "federal, state, and local legislation should not seek to interfere with the right of adults who wish to read, obtain, or view explicit sexual materials" (Abelson et al., 1970, p. 58). Congress and then-president Richard Nixon rejected the commission's findings and recommendation, however, on moral and political—not scientific—grounds.

PORNOGRAPHY AND SEX OFFENDERS   Another approach to examining the role of pornography in crimes of sexual violence involves comparing the experience of sex offenders and nonoffenders with pornographic materials. A recent review of the research literature found little or no difference in the level of exposure to pornography between incarcerated sex offenders and comparison groups of felons who were incarcerated for nonsexual crimes (Marshall, 1989).

Yet evidence also shows that as many as one in three rapists and child molesters use pornography to become sexually aroused immediately preceding, and during the commission of, their crimes (Marshall, 1989). These findings suggest that pornography may stimulate sexually deviant urges in certain subgroups of men who are predisposed to commit crimes of sexual violence (Marshall, 1989).

THE MEESE COMMISSION REPORT   In 1985, President Ronald Reagan appointed a committee headed by Attorney General Edwin Meese to reexamine the effects of pornography. In 1986, the United States Attorney General's Commission on Pornography, known as the Meese Commission, issued a report that reached very different conclusions than the 1970 commission. The Meese Commission claimed to find a causal link between sexual violence and exposure to violent pornography (U.S. Department of Justice, 1986). The commission asserted that a substantial increase in the proliferation of violent pornography had occurred since the earlier commission had been convened. Moreover, the report concluded that exposure to pornography that portrayed women in degrading or subservient roles increased acceptability of rape in the minds of viewers. The commission found no evidence linking exposure to nonviolent, nondegrading pornography (consensual sexual activity between partners in equal roles) and sexual violence but noted that only a small fraction of the pornographic materials on the market was of this type.

The commission issued 92 recommendations for tighter enforcement of obscenity laws and greater restrictions on the dissemination of pornography. Some recommendations focused on the enforcement and prosecution of existing child pornography laws. Others encouraged states that had not already done so to make the knowledgeable possession of child pornography a felony.

Notes: A 1992 book entitled *Arresting Images: Impolitic Art and Uncivil Actions* examines the social, political, and psychological influences on attempts to censor visual art, photography, and film in the United States from 1988 to 1992. The book contains 27 photographs of the works that were at the center of the controversies. (Dubin, Steven C. 1992. *Arresting Images: Impolitic Art and Uncivil Actions.* New York: Routledge.)

The commission's findings are controversial. Critics suggest that although the Meese Commission did not blatantly falsify the data, its conclusions reflected an over-generalization of laboratory-based findings (Wilcox, 1987). Two of the leading researchers in the area, Edward Donnerstein and Daniel Linz (1987), contended that the Meese Commission failed to distinguish between the effects of sexually explicit materials per se and the effects of violent materials. Evidence is lacking that links exposure to sexually explicit materials without violent content to sexual aggression. Donnerstein and Linz concluded that "It is not sex, but violence that is an obscenity in our society" (1986, p. 56). Nor do researchers confirm the Meese Commission's belief in the rising incidence of violent pornography. Evidence does not show depictions of violence in sexually explicit media such as in the magazines *Playboy* and *Hustler,* or in X-rated movies and videos, to have increased in recent years (Scott & Cuvelier, 1993). In fact, X-rated movies and videos contain less violence than do general release movies.

If nothing else, the Meese Commission raised awareness about different types of pornography and their potential effects on viewers' behaviors and attitudes. Let us take a look at the scientific evidence on the effects of violent and nonviolent pornography.

VIOLENT PORNOGRAPHY   Laboratory-based studies have shown that men exposed to violent pornography are more likely to become aggressive against females and to show less sensitivity toward women who have been sexually assaulted. In one study (Donnerstein, 1980), 120 college men interacted with a male or female confederate (accomplice) of the experimenter, who treated them in either a neutral or hostile manner. The subjects were then shown neutral, nonviolent pornographic, or violent pornographic films. In the latter, a man forced himself into a woman's home and raped her. Subjects were then given the opportunity to aggress against the male or female confederate by delivering electric shock, presumably to assist the confederate in learning a task. The measure of aggression was the intensity of the shock chosen by the subject. No shock was actually delivered, but subjects did not know that the shock apparatus was fake. Nonprovoked men who viewed violent pornographic films showed greater aggression toward the women than did nonprovoked men who viewed nonviolent films, however. Provoked men who were shown violent pornography selected the highest shock levels of all. The film may have served as a model for retaliation.

In another study, aggression by male subjects against female confederates following exposure to violent pornography (a rape scene) was increased by depictions of the woman being raped as either enjoying the experience or becoming sexually aroused during the rape (Donnerstein & Berkowitz, 1981). These findings suggest that depictions of women enjoying or becoming aroused by their victimization may legitimize violence against women in the viewer's mind, reinforcing the cultural myth that some women need to be dominated and are sexually aroused by an overpowering male.

Other research has shown that exposure to violent pornography leads men to become more accepting of rape, less sensitive to women survivors of rape, and more accepting of the use of violence in interpersonal relationships (Donnerstein & Linz, 1984; Linz, 1985; Malamuth, 1984).

Yet recent research suggests that it is the violence in violent pornography, and not sexual explicitness, that hardens men's attitudes toward rape survivors. In one study (Donnerstein et al., 1986), college men were exposed to films consisting of either violent pornography, nonviolent pornography (a couple having consensual intercourse), or a violent film that was not sexually explicit. The violent pornographic and nonpornographic films both showed a woman being tied up and slapped at gunpoint, but the nonpornographic version contained no nudity or explicit sexual activity. The subjects had first been either angered or treated in a neutral manner by a female confederate of the experimenter. The results showed that, in comparison with nonviolent pornography, both violent pornographic films and violent *non*pornographic films produced greater acceptance of rape myths, reported increased willingness to force a woman into sexual activity, and reported greater likelihood of engaging in rape (if the man also knew that he could get away with it). These effects occurred regardless of whether the man was angered by the woman or not.

A CLOSER LOOK

Are the Obscenities of Today the Classics of Tomorrow? An Essay on Art, Pornography, and Censorship —Lois Fichner-Rathus

> Man's drive for self-expression, which over the centuries has built his monuments, does not stay within set bounds; the creations which yesterday were the detested and the obscene become the classics of today.
>
> (California Supreme Court Justice Matthew Tobriner, in ruling that Henry Miller's *Tropic of Cancer* was not pornographic (*Wall Street Journal.* 1964, February 3.)

We are about to delve into some works of art that have been considered to inhabit the gray areas between pornography and art. Given that contemporary Western culture is inundated with images of performers such as Madonna and Michael Jackson engaging in pelvic thrusting in concert (Figure 20.1), you may chuckle at those who would have censored the first two of them. But you might rather have kept others under wraps yourself. As you wend your way through these works and the commentaries, you will see that I am biased in favor of free expression. The issues surrounding censorship are not always cut and dried, however.

On the one hand, we have been reared to value free speech, which is protected by the U.S. Constitution. Free speech would seem to extend to unfettered expression of artistic impulses. On the other hand, when people are shocked or offended by things that seem obscene to them, they sometimes rethink their devotion to freedom. They may focus, instead, on matters related to the effects of pornography. It is almost impossible to argue that *nothing* is pornographic and that material of this sort is in no way harmful to innocent people. How can we ignore the evidence that violent pornography stimulates many men to behave aggressively toward women?—and violence against women strikes me as obscene. How can we ignore evidence that child pornography is harmful to the actors and, perhaps, other children who might be vic-

timized by people who gather in this material?—especially when hurting children, in my eyes, is the ultimate obscenity.

It is also difficult to argue that taxpayers must support the exhibition of artworks, or indeed the creative efforts of an artist, whom they find obscene or hurtful toward other human beings. Yet because of the history of almost arbitrary censorship, it is difficult to align oneself with the notion that select forms of artistic expression should be censored. When the ideal of free expression comes into conflict with the demonstrated potential to harm society's most vulnerable people, it is difficult to lightly ignore either value.

It is not my purpose here to arrive at final answers as to where art ends and pornography and obscenity begin. I shall illustrate, however, that many works in the history of art—from different periods and cultures—have been labeled as obscene or pornographic. You will also see that many artists, art professionals such as gallery directors, and the public have suffered from censorship.

The depictions of genitalia and explicit sex in the visual arts and literature are not recent developments. We find relief carvings depicting acts of sexual intercourse as early as 7000 B.C. and in modern Zaire (Figure 20.2). Sculptures depicting exaggerated female genitalia can be dated back even further, and similar sculptures, sometimes referred to as "vulva goddesses," are created by modern Nigerians (Figure 20.2). Grecian urns and cups were often decorated with explicit heterosexual and homosexual activity (see Chapter 1). The Indian sex manual of the third century, the *Kama Sutra,* had graphic illustrations, and statues of idealized men and women in erotic acts grace the facades of

FIGURE 20.1 In Concert. Madonna is certainly not the only contemporary performer who engages in pelvic thrusting on stage. Is this behavior obscene? Should the government ban them, or would you rather cast your vote by buying or not buying tickets, tapes, and the products they promote?

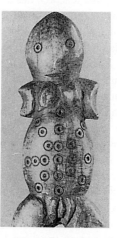

FIGURE 20.2 Nigerian Vulva Goddess. Artworks have shown human genitalia for thousands of years. Is the exhibition of nudity obscene? Do artists (and other people) have the right to express themselves as they wish? Where, if anywhere, is the line to be drawn between art and obscenity?

FIGURE 20.3 *Maya Desnuda* **and** *Maya Vestida.* An oil-on-canvas painting executed circa 1796 by Francisco Goya, 37 3/8 x 74 3/4 inches. Museo del Prado, Madrid. Although it may be hard to imagine, given contemporary community standards, paintings such as this one (left) by Goya were once considered obscene and resulted in clothed Maya paintings such as the "vestida" by Goya.

many Hindu temples (Fichner-Rathus, 1992). Chinese novels of the early seventeenth century contained explicit sexual narratives. Genitalia, often of exaggerated size, were commonly depicted in Japanese art from 1600 through 1900 (Brewer, 1982).

As there have been nude and erotic works in various cultures, so too has there been censorship—and the threat of censorship (Schneemann, 1991). You may have noticed in museums that many later copies of some of the classical sculptures of ancient Greece, a culture that exalted the human body, sport strategically placed fig leaves. In spite of centuries of so-called enlightenment, censorship could not be kept at bay. The Spaniard Francisco Goya (1746–1828) is considered to be one of the greatest painters of the neoclassical and romantic periods (Fichner-Rathus, 1992). Yet at the time of its appearance in about 1796, his *Maya desnuda* ("Nude Maya," Figure 20.3) was quite controversial because of the way the model displayed her nudity and confronted the viewer with her direct gaze. In an article entitled "Burn It, Hide It, Flaunt It," Tomlinson (1991) describes the official Spanish attitude toward nudity at the time:

> In 1762 King Carlos III ordered the First Court Painter, Anton Rafael Mengs, to assemble all the paintings in the royal collection that showed "too much nudity" so that they might be burned. Since these included five paintings by Titian . . . as well as works by Rubens, we may be thankful that Mengs suggested an alternative solution of moving the paintings to his studio. . . . The incendiary passion seems to have been hereditary, for in 1792 Carlos IV sought once again to burn the paintings (p. 61).

In part because of this oppressive atmosphere, Goya also painted a number of draped Mayas.

The French painter Edouard Manet (1832–1883) was a pivotal figure in the rise of the impressionist movement (Fichner-Rathus, 1992). Manet's work is known for its luminosity; its duplication of natural light; its broad, flat application of pigments; and its capturing of the fleeting moment. Manet's artistic innovations and, in this case, his sassy brush, aroused the ire of the French critics and public alike. His masterpiece, *Le Déjeuner sur l'Herbe* (Figure 20.4), a contemporary reinterpretation of a painted passage by Renaissance master Raphael, aroused the public for more than stylistic reasons:

> What was so alarming to the Parisian spectator, and remains so to this day, is that there is no explanation for the behavior of the picnickers. Why are the men clothed and the women undraped to varying degrees? Why are the men chatting among themselves, seemingly unaware of

FIGURE 20.4 *Le Déjeuner sur l'Herbe.* An 1863 oil-on-canvas painting by Edouard Manet, 7' x 8' 10", Musée d'Orsay, Galerie du Jeu de Paume. This work aroused the ire of the public and critics alike at a Parisian exhibition.

the women? The public was quite used to the painting of nudes, . . . but they were not prepared to witness one of their fold—an ordinary citizen—displayed so shamefully on such a grand scale [the painting is 7 feet high and almost 9 feet wide]. The painting was further intolerable because the seated woman meets the viewer's stare, as if the viewer had intruded on their gathering in a voyeuristic fashion.

(Fichner-Rathus, 1992, p. 387)

Today, prudish reactions to the works of Goya and Manet seem unjustified or downright silly. But in their time, these works posed moral dilemmas for their observers.

Today, the issue of where the lines are to be drawn between art and pornography may be most clearly embodied in the photographs of Robert Mapplethorpe, who died of AIDS in 1989. Philadelphia's Institute of Contemporary Art compiled a traveling retrospective exhibition of the artist's work from the late 1960s to 1988, just shortly before his death, entitled: "Robert Mapplethorpe: The Perfect Moment." As noted by Judith Tannenbaum (1991), however,

. . . what started out to be a "normal" exhibition turned into something quite different—a national cause célèbre, the impetus for intense congressional debate about federal funding of the arts, and, ultimately, the focus of an obscenity trial in Cincinnati (p. 71).

In 1989, the Corcoran Gallery of Art in Washington, D.C., canceled its scheduled installation of the exhibition. When shown in Philadelphia and Cincinnati, the exhibition was accompanied by warnings that there were sexually explicit photographs and that the content might be inappropriate for children. The obscenity trial involved Dennis Barrie, the director of the Contemporary Arts Center of Cincinnati, Ohio. He was indicted and subsequently acquitted, in October 1990, on charges of pandering to obscenity and the illegal use of a minor in the exhibition.

The "illegal use of a minor" charge referred to photographs of children that showed frontal nudity. Since nudity itself is hardly ever considered the criterion for obscenity in Western culture these days, it is hard to imagine that these photographs stirred members of the public or government officials. But they did. The reason may be in part because other sections of the exhibition, such as the *X Portfolio,* contained photographs such as *X Portfolio, Patrice* (Figure 20.5). Though *Patrice* may distress some readers in its barely contained sexual power, other photographs portrayed explicit homoerotic sex acts, such as fisting (see Chapter 10). The nudes of the children, in the larger context, did disturb people at the exhibition. The "larger context," by the way, also included lovely, uncontroversial photographs of flowers and a number of more familiar sorts of adult female nudes.

Treating Dennis Barrie and the works of art by critically acclaimed photographer Robert Mapplethorpe according to the letter of the law as it applies to obscenity and abuse of minors—rather than interpreting the case according to the spirit of the law, raises serious questions. For example, can the government serve as a competent final judge as to what is pornographic or obscene? Can the government serve as art critic and aesthetician? Artists and advocates of free expression have the greatest of fears in the face of these prospects. Their concerns are rooted in ghastly historical events affecting the arts, such as Hitler's denouncing of, and his overt threats to, German expressionists and abstract artists whom he labeled as degenerate.

The artists discussed up to this point have been men. Women artists are no less immune to being considered pornographers, however, or at least of exceeding the bounds of community standards of decency. Artist Sue Coe was commissioned by *Boston* magazine to illustrate the reportage of a highly publicized rape trial in New Bedford (MA). A group of men were accused of the gang rape of a woman on a pool table in a bar. The result was *Gray Rape* (Figure 20.6). Carol Jacobsen (1991) reports that Coe discovered that the magazine had printed the drawing *with the bottom half—the part showing the rape—cut off.* This "editing" was carried out without the artist's prior knowledge or permission. Jacobsen (1991) notes that

more significant is the fact that rape itself—both a national disgrace and a glaring symptom of our misogynist public

FIGURE 20.5 X Portfolio, Patrice. A 1977 gelatin silver print by Robert Mapplethorpe, 7¾ x 7¾ inches. Estate of Robert Mapplethorpe. Photographs from Mapplethorpe's *X Portfolio* stimulated authorities in Cincinnati, Ohio, to indict a gallery director for "pandering to obscenity." The gallery director was subsequently acquitted, however.

FIGURE 20.6 *Gray Rape.* A 1983 charcoal-on-paper drawing by Sue Coe, 30 x 40 inches. The bottom half of this drawing, commissioned by a news magazine, was cut off when it was printed, without the artist's prior knowledge or permission.

FIGURE 20.7 *Seduction III.* A 1984 acrylic-on-canvas painting by Joan Lyon, 58 x 44 inches. Collection of the artist, Glencoe, Illinois. This painting was censored by a university president.

policies and laws—has so far been addressed in only one major art exhibition: the 1985 show titled "Rape," organized by Stephanie Blackwood at Ohio State University (1991, p. 49).

Nor are our great U.S. cathedrals of learning—our universities—safe from censorship. In 1987, the Perkison Gallery at Illinois's Millikin University invited a Chicago artists' cooperative to present a group exhibition. The exhibition included Joan Lyon's painting, *Seduction III* (Figure 20.7), which shows some nudes interacting in a suggestively erotic but not sexually explicit manner. As noted by Lyon, the university president removed the painting from the gallery after it had been on display for a week. The president asserted that the painting was "not appropriate for a general, nonselective audience" (Lyon, 1991, p. 81). The other artists in the exhibition withdrew their works in protest, and some other artists have since declined offers to have solo exhibitions at the university.

Carolee Schneemann has been creating erotic drawings, paintings, photographs, films, installations, and performances since the 1960s. She may be considered one of the founders of the sexual revolution in the arts. One source of the controversy that has surrounded her work is that she is the artist and the subject of so many of her works. Her film *Fuses,* for example, shows her engaging in explicit sexual activity with a partner (Figure 20.8). She performed in the nude in *Body Collage* (Figure 20.9). Schneemann (1991) discusses her motives for creating *Fuses* and considers society's response to it:

Since my deepest expressive and responsive life core was considered obscene, I thought I had better see what it looked like in my own vision. I had never seen any erotica or pornography that approached what lived sexuality felt like. . . . My film *Fuses* has been subject to constant censorship despite its special awards in Cannes in 1968 and at the Yale Film Festival in 1972. . . .

FIGURE 20.8 *Fuses* and a Sculpture from Zaire. In her 1965 film *Fuses,* artist Carolee Schneemann engaged in sexual activity with a partner to depict her "deepest expressive and responsive life core." Here, Schneemann juxtaposes a film still from *Fuses* with a sculpture on the same theme from Zaire to show that people from many cultures have responded to their sexuality through artistic expression. Judgments as to what is obscene are made within a cultural context.

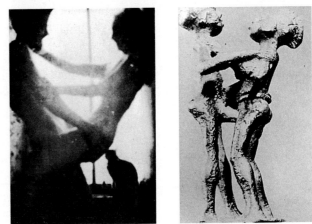

If my paintings, photographs, film, and enacted works have been judged obscene, the question arises: is this because I use the body in its actuality—without contrivance, fetishization, displacement? Is this because my photographic works are usually self-shot, without an external, controlling eye? And are these works obscene because I posit my female body as a locus of autonomy, pleasure, desire; and insist that as an artist I can be both image and image maker, merging two aspects of a self deeply fractured in the contemporary imagination? (pp. 31, 33).

What of it? What are the limits? May artists, as Schneemann states, make any image that they wish? If their "deepest expressive and responsive life core [is] considered obscene," may they nevertheless express themselves without being fettered by the government? Can the U.S. public in the 1990s tolerate the right to free expression and allow—to paraphrase Justice Tobriner—that some of the creations that today are the detested and the obscene may become the classics of tomorrow?

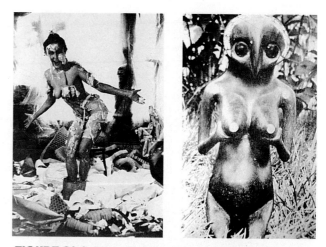

FIGURE 20.9 *Body Collage* **and an Owl Goddess from New Guinea.** Here, artist Carolee Schneemann juxtaposes an image of herself in a 1968 performance with an "owl goddess" from New Guinea that also celebrates the female form.

Notes: An analysis of 56 slasher films (with 474 victims) found that females *were not* more likely than males to be victims and females *were* more likely to survive an attack. The survival of female victims was strongly associated with the relative absence of sexual behavior. "In slasher films, the message appears to be that sexual women get killed and only the pure women survive" (p. 194). (Cowan, G., and O'Brien, M. 1990. Gender and survival vs. death in slasher films: A content analysis. *Sex Roles, 23(3/4),* 187–196.)

In another study, Linz, Donnerstein, and Penrod (1988) assigned college men, at random, to watch five feature-length films over a two-week period. One group saw X-rated nonviolent films. A second group watched R-rated "slasher-type" violent films such as *Friday the 13th, Part 2.* ("Slasher films" show graphic violence, primarily directed at women, intermingled with mild erotic scenes.) A third group saw R-rated, nonviolent, "teenage sex films" such as *Porky's.* Afterwards, subjects viewed a videotaped reenactment of a trial in which a woman accused a man of raping her. Men who had watched the R-rated slasher films showed less sensitivity toward the woman complainant than did subjects who had been exposed to either the R- or the X-rated nonviolent films. Exposure to sexually explicit material *without violence,* whether soft-core (R-rated) or hard-core (X-rated), did not reduce sympathy toward the woman complainant.

Based upon a review of the research literature, Linz (1989) concluded that short-term and prolonged exposure to sexual violence, whether sexually explicit or not, lessens sensitivity toward survivors of rape and increases acceptance of the use of force in sexual encounters. "Slasher" films are connected with the strongest antisocial effects. Such films, however, are regularly shown over commercial television, although some of the more gruesome parts may be edited. (They are uncut on pay cable channels.) Donnerstein and Linz (1986) arrived at the

> . . . inescapable conclusion that it is violence, whether or not accompanied by sex, that has the most damaging effect upon those who view it, hear it or read about it. . . . The most clear and present danger, well documented by the social science literature, is all violent material in our society, whether sexually explicit or not, that promotes violence against women (p. 59).

Research on the effects of pornography should be interpreted with caution, however. Most of it has employed college students, whose behavior may or may not be typical of people in general or of people with propensities toward sexual violence. On the other hand, research discussed in Chapter 19 shows that a large percentage of college men have either engaged in rape, attempted rape, or engaged in some form of sexual coercion. Another issue is that most studies in this area are laboratory-based experiments that involve simulated aggression or judgments of sympathy toward hypothetical women who have been portrayed as rape victims. None measured *actual* violence against women outside the lab. We are still bereft of evidence that normal men have been, or would be, spurred to rape or to sexually violate women because of exposure to violent pornography or other forms of violent media.

NONVIOLENT PORNOGRAPHY Nonviolent pornography may not contain scenes of sexual violence, but it typically portrays women in degrading or dehumanizing roles—as sexually promiscuous, insatiable, and subservient. Might such portrayals of women reinforce traditional stereotypes of women as sex objects? Might they lead viewers to condone acts of rape by suggesting that women are essentially promiscuous? Might the depiction of women as readily sexually accessible inspire men to refuse to "take no for an answer" on dates?

Most of the research on the effects of pornography has focused on violent pornography (Linz, 1989), so we cannot respond to these questions with certainty. The evidence nevertheless raises concerns that nonviolent pornography may also affect male sensitivity toward women who are sexually victimized (Zillmann & Weaver, 1989). Zillmann and Bryant (1982, 1984), for example, exposed male and female subjects to six sessions of pornography over six consecutive weeks. Subjects were exposed to either a massive dose of pornography, consisting of six nonviolent pornographic films ("Swedish Erotica") during each weekly session; to an intermediate dose consisting of three pornographic and three neutral films each session; or to a no-dose control, consisting of six nonsexual films each session. When later tested in a purportedly independent study, both males and females who received extended exposure to pornography, especially those receiving the massive dose, gave more lenient punishments to a rapist who was depicted in a newspaper article. Moreover, males became more callous in their attitudes toward women.

Zillmann and Weaver (1989) argue that making women appear sexually permissive and promiscuous increases men's callousness toward women who have been sexually assaulted. Once men brand women as promiscuous, they lose respect for them and see them as "public property" who have forfeited their rights to exercise choice in sex partners.

Not all researchers, however, find exposure to nonviolent pornography to increase callousness toward women. Some report finding that nonviolent pornography did not reduce the sensitivity of male (Linz et al., 1988) and female subjects (Krafka, 1985) to female victims of sexual assault. Others report that nonviolent pornography did not increase men's aggression toward women in laboratory studies (Malamuth & Ceniti, 1986). Still others did not find repeated exposure to nonviolent pornography to make men adopt more callous attitudes toward women or increase their acceptance of rape myths (Padgett & Brislin-Slütz, 1987; Padgett et al., 1989).

Given the inconsistencies in the research findings, and the limited amount of research on nonviolent pornography, Linz (1989) concludes that

> ... the data, *overall,* do not support the contention that exposure to nonviolent pornography has significant adverse effects on attitudes toward rape as a crime or more general evaluations of rape victims (p. 74).

Moreover, if nonviolent pornography can be connected with negative attitudes toward women, Linz (1989) suggests that such attitudes may result from the demeaning portrayals of women as sexual playthings who are valued only for their physical attributes and sexual availability, rather than from sexual explicitness per se.

Yet another concern is the possible effect of nonviolent pornography on the viewer's sexual and family values. Nonviolent pornography typically features impromptu sexual encounters between new acquaintances. Might repeated exposure to such material alter viewers' attitudes toward traditional sexual and family values? Zillmann (1989) reports intriguing evidence that repeated exposure to this type of nonviolent pornography loosens traditional sexual and family values. When compared to control subjects who viewed nonsexual films, men and women who were exposed to weekly, hour-long sessions involving scenes of explicit sexual encounters between new acquaintances over a six-week period showed attitudinal changes including greater acceptance, in comparison to controls who viewed nonsexual films, of premarital and extramarital sex and of simultaneous sexual relationships with multiple partners. Men and women who viewed such pornography also reported desiring fewer children than control subjects and were relatively less committed to marriage as an "essential institution."

Zillmann (1989) argues that nonviolent pornography loosens traditional, family values by projecting an image of sexual enjoyment without responsibility or obligations. Prolonged exposure to such pornography may also foster dissatisfaction with the physical appearance and sexual performance of one's intimate partners (Zillmann, 1989).

In sum, research on the effects of nonviolent pornography does not permit definite conclusions. The effects of nonviolent pornography may be more connected with whether or not women are presented in a dehumanizing manner than with sexual explicitness per se. No research has yet linked sexual explicitness itself with undesirable effects. It is of interest to note that only a minority of people in the United States support legislation making sexually explicit materials illegal, yet three out of four favor the criminalization of *violent* pornography (Harris, 1988).

SEX IN ADVERTISING

In the 1980s a coquettish Brooke Shields was featured in a TV commercial that showed her spreading her denim-clad legs, smiling coyly at the camera, and murmuring that nothing came between her and her Calvins (Calvin Klein jeans, that is) (*Time*, 1980). The advertising campaign evoked a storm of complaints from viewers who felt that it was vulgar and obscene. Meanwhile, the sales of Calvin Klein jeans went through the roof. In short, sex sells.

The use of sexual imagery in advertising ranges from more subtle uses of innuendo and double entendre, such as in slogans like "take it off, take it all off" (for Noxema shave cream) and "*It's* better in the Bahamas," to the use of an attractive woman who says her men wear "English Leather or they wear nothing at all."

Sex in Advertising. Advertisers often use sexual imagery to promote their products. Sexy ads can sometimes backfire, however, if they are perceived as offensive or if viewers attend only to the sexual imagery and not to the product itself.

Sex in advertising operates according to the principle of association (Hefzallah & Maloney, 1979). Advertisers hope that people will link the product with the sexual imagery that is incorporated within the advertisement. Perhaps the use of a sexy ad will make consumers think that the product will make them more sexually alluring or enhance their sexual arousal, which, in turn, will prompt them to purchase the product rather than that of a competitor.

Researchers caution, however, that sexy ads can backfire. Viewers may pay such careful attention to the sexy imagery that they tune out the advertising message or product claims, or even forget what the product is (Edgley, 1989; LaChance et al., 1978; Severn, 1990). Sexy advertising may not only be distracting; it may even turn people off to the advertisement and, by extension, to the product, especially if the sexual image is unrelated to the nature of the product.

TRUTH OR FICTION?

R E V I S I T E D

If advertisements are too sexy, consumers may forget what the product is.
It is true that sexy ads may cause consumers to focus on the sexual content of the advertisements and thus forget the products.

Advertisers may also need to consider the gender of the target audience. Researchers find that men tend to react more positively and women more negatively toward various forms of sexual content in advertising, whether it be sexual innuendos uttered by female models in TV commercials (Bello et al., 1983) or female nudity in print advertising (LaTour, 1990).

ADVERTISING AND GENDER-ROLE STEREOTYPES

Learning Objective 12: Discuss the common gender-role stereotypes found in advertisements.

The frequent use of sexy female models in advertisements raises broader concerns about the depiction of women in advertising. As Edgley notes, "Despite years of feminist consciousness-raising about the issue, commercials still tend to depict women in stereotypical ways" (Edgley, 1989). What Komisar said of advertising in 1971 may be as true today as it was then:

> If television commercials are to be believed, most American women go into uncontrollable ecstasies at the sight and smell of tables and cabinets that have been lovingly caressed with long-lasting, satin-finish, lemon-scented, spray-on furniture polish. Or they glow with rapture at the blinding whiteness of their wash—to the green-eyed envy of their neighbors . . . it is an amazing feat of hocus-pocus worthy of Tom Sawyer and P. T. Barnum to lovingly declare that domestic labor is the true vocation of women wearing wedding bands (p. 209).

Studies of TV commercials in the United States, Canada, the United Kingdom, and Italy show a consistent pattern: Females are more likely to be portrayed visually on screen, while males are more likely to be featured in the role of the off-camera "voice of authority" (Ferrante et al., 1988; Furnham & Voli, 1989; Lovdal, 1989). A recent study of 320 U.S. TV commercials employing voice-overs showed that 91 percent used male voices; only 9 percent, female voices (Lovdal, 1989).

Teaching Tip: Have students bring to class magazines they usually read. Have them analyze advertisements in small groups.

Teaching Tip: *Ms* magazine often reserves the back cover of each issue for reprinting examples of print advertisements showing women as sex objects or in demeaning ways. (For example, see the following issues: Nov/Dec 1993, Jan/Feb 1994, March/April 1994, and May/June 1994.) Show these (or similar) ads to students and then discuss the content and the possible effects of these ads on the intended audience.

TV commercials also tend to portray men in a wider variety of occupational roles than women (Bretl & Cantor, 1988; Lovdal, 1989). Despite increased awareness of gender-role stereotypes, the image of women in TV commercials has not changed much in recent years (Lovdal, 1989). Women's roles are still generally stereotyped in traditional roles as wives, mothers, brides, waitresses, actresses, and so on. Rarely are they photographers, athletes, or businesswomen. Still, we can report some signs of change, at least with respect to the portrayal of men's roles. Men today are increasingly represented in commercials as spouses and parents (Bretl & Cantor, 1988). Women, however, are still more likely to be seen in domestic settings, advertising products that they can use in the home (Bretl & Cantor, 1988).

Why should we be concerned about how women are portrayed in advertising? For one thing, stereotypic advertising may serve to perpetuate traditional gender-role expectations by portraying women primarily in domestic roles or as sex objects. TV commercials (and programs), for example, may influence viewers' perceptions of acceptable gender-role behaviors (Lovdal, 1989). Girls and young women who are continually exposed to images of women in domestic roles may perceive themselves as having fewer career options than their male counterparts. Not surprisingly, researchers have found that heavier TV viewing is linked to the adoption of more traditional gender-role attitudes among children (Gross & Jeffries-Fox, 1978).

SUMMING UP

THE WORLD OF COMMERCIAL SEX: A DISNEYLAND FOR ADULTS

Commercial sex runs the gamut from "adult" movie theaters and book shops to strip shows, sex toy shops, brothels, escort services, massage parlors, "900" telephone services, and the use of sex in advertising.

PROSTITUTION

In the United States, prostitution is illegal everywhere except rural counties in Nevada.

Incidence of Prostitution in Contemporary U.S. Society

Fewer young men in the United States use prostitutes than in Kinsey's day, apparently because of the liberalizing trends of the sexual revolution.

Types of Female Prostitution

The major types of female prostitutes today are streetwalkers, brothel prostitutes—many of whom work in massage parlors and for "escort services," and call girls. Streetwalkers often support, and are abused by, pimps.

Characteristics of Female Prostitutes No single factor explains entry into female prostitution, but poverty and sexual and/or physical abuse figure prominently in the backgrounds of many prostitutes. Teenage runaways with marginal skills and limited means of support may find few alternatives to prostitution.

Customers of Female Prostitutes The consumers of prostitutes are often referred to as "johns" or "tricks." Most patrons are "occasional johns" with regular sex partners. Some people use prostitutes habitually or compulsively, however.

Male Prostitution Most male prostitutes are "hustlers" who service male clients. Hustlers typically begin selling sex in their teens and may be homosexual or heterosexual in orientation.

HIV, AIDS, and Prostitution

Prostitutes are at greater risk of HIV transmission because they have sexual relations with many partners, often without protection. Many prostitutes and their clients and other sex partners also inject drugs and share contaminated needles. HIV may be spread by unprotected sex from prostitutes to customers, then to the customers' wives or lovers. Despite the dangers of HIV transmission, many U.S. prostitutes have not altered either their sexual behavior or their patterns of drug use.

PORNOGRAPHY AND OBSCENITY

What Is Pornographic? Pornography is "writing, pictures, etc., intended to arouse sexual desire." Erotica, by contrast, refers to sexual materials that are artistically produced or motivated. The judgment as to what is pornographic or obscene varies from person to person and culture to culture.

Pornography and the Law

In *Miller v. California,* the U.S. Supreme Court held that obscenity is based upon a determination of "whether the average person, applying contemporary community standards, would find that the work . . . appeals to the prurient interest . . . ; whether the work depicts [sexual behavior] in a patently offensive way, [and] whether the work, taken as a whole, lacks serious literary, artistic, political, or scientific value." *Miller* recognizes that judgments of obscenity may vary with "community standards."

Prevalence and Use of Erotica and Pornography People in the United States are typically introduced to pornography by their high school years. Although both genders can become physiologically aroused by erotic materials, men are relatively more interested in sexually explicit pictures and films.

Pornography and Sexual Coercion A 1970 government commission found no harmful effects of pornographic material on normal people. A later government commission, the Meese Commission, issued a report in 1986 linking exposure to violent pornography with sexual aggression and exposure to degrading but nonviolent pornography with increased acceptability of rape in the minds of viewers. Research evidence suggests that exposure to pornography may stimulate sexually deviant urges in some men who are predisposed to commit crimes of sexual violence. Research evidence in laboratory settings also suggests that violent pornography may stimulate college men to act more aggressively toward women. Some researchers argue that it is the violence in violent pornography and not sexual explicitness per se that promotes violence against women. The effects of nonviolent pornography on normal populations remain unclear.

SEX IN ADVERTISING

Sex in advertising operates according to the principle of association. Advertisers hope that people will link the product with the sexual imagery that is incorporated within the advertisement. Sexy ads can backfire, however, by diverting attention from the product or turning people off to the product.

Advertising and Gender-Role Stereotypes Women in TV commercials are still generally stereotyped as wives, mothers, brides, waitresses, actresses, and so on.

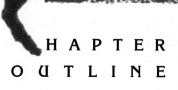

CHAPTER OUTLINE

C H A P T E R *21*

Making Responsible
Sexual Decisions—
An Epilogue

Making choices is deeply intertwined with our sexual experience. Although sex is a natural function, the ways in which we express our sexuality are matters of personal choice. We choose how, where, and with whom to become sexually involved. We may face a wide array of sexual decisions: Whom should I date? When should my partner and I become sexually intimate? Should I initiate sexual relations or wait for my partner to approach me? Should my partner and I practice contraception? If so, which method? Should I use a condom to protect against sexually transmitted diseases (or insist that my partner does)? Should I be tested for HIV? Should I insist that my partner be tested for HIV before we engage in sexual relations?

CHOICES, INFORMATION, AND DECISION MAKING

Learning Objective 1: Examine the role information can play in sexual decision making when one's choices involve value conflicts.

We have presented you with information you will need to make responsible sexual decisions. Information alone cannot determine whether the options you consider are morally acceptable to you, however. Many of these issues raise moral concerns, especially issues such as premarital and extramarital sex, contraception, and abortion. Gathering information and weighing the scientific evidence will alert you to what is possible in the contemporary world, but only you can determine which of your options are compatible with your own moral values. We all have unique sets of moral values—as Americans, as members of one of America's hundreds of subcultures, as individuals. No single value system defines us all. Indeed, the world of diversity in which we live is a mosaic of different moral codes and cultural traditions and beliefs.

CONFLICT

The most difficult decisions involve choices between alternatives that each have positive and negative aspects or that each have compelling negative features. Consider contraceptive techniques. The pill is effective and does not interfere with sexual spontaneity, but it is costly and has side effects. The condom has no side effects (for the great majority of users), but some people find that it disrupts lovemaking and reduces sexual sensations. It is also not as effective as the pill. Or consider the plight of Kim, a college student who becomes pregnant as a result of date rape: Should she have an abortion, which may be morally offensive to her, or bear an unwanted child? Then, too, should she report the crime and hope the criminal-justice system will successfully prosecute her assailant, or should she try to swallow her bitter feelings and protect her anonymity? Or consider the college student who feels morally committed to remaining a virgin until marriage but fears earning the disapproval of dating partners or having no dates at all.

Discussion Question: Do you experience ethical conflicts when making sexual decisions? What are some of the most common ethical dilemmas? What ethical standards guide your sexual decision making?

When we are pulled in different directions at the same time, we are in a state of psychological conflict. Conflict can be extremely stressful, especially if it is prolonged. People in conflict often feel "damned if they do and damned if they don't." They may also vacillate—take tentative steps in one direction and then in the other. Kim, a survivor of date rape, takes a bus to an abortion clinic across town and gets off at the next stop. She checks the telephone number of the police, then hesitates to pick up the telephone. She is obsessed with the question of what is the right thing to do.

Part of Kim's conflict is over a moral issue. She would very much like to terminate her unwanted pregnancy by having an abortion, but she holds back because she firmly believes that the embryo within is a precious, human life. Her conflict over whether or not to report her assailant is in part moral, in part practical. It is morally proper to report him, but what if she is not believed? What if the incident becomes widely known on campus and to her family? Moreover, she realizes that the longer she waits, the more it may appear that she is making up the story.

DECISIONS, DECISIONS, DECISIONS . . .

Making decisions involves choosing among various courses of action. The act of not making a formal decision may itself represent a type of tacit decision. For example, we may vacillate about whether to use a particular form of birth control but continue to engage in unprotected sex. Is this because we have not made a decision or because we have decided to let happen what will happen?

Gathering information helps us predict the outcomes of the decisions we make. This textbook provides you with a broad database concerning scientific developments and ways of relating to other people—including people who come from other cultures. By talking to people who have had similar questions or been in similar conflicts, you can also learn which decisions worked for them, which did not, and, perhaps, why. Or you may be able to learn what happens when people do not make decisions but simply hope for the best. You can also talk to your parents, friends, religious counselors, course instructors, psychologists, and other helping professionals. Regarding which contraceptive method to use, you may wish to discuss the information in this book with a physician, nurse, or other health counselor.

VALUE SYSTEMS

Our value systems provide another framework for judging the moral acceptability of sexual options. We often approach sexual decisions by determining whether the choices we face are compatible with our moral values. Our value systems do not necessarily determine the outcomes of all of our sexual decisions, however—any more than laws strictly determine people's behavior. Some of us adhere more strictly to moral values. Some people make choices that bend or violate their values but try not to focus on the discrepancies too closely. Many of us also act on impulse, especially sexual impulses, without thinking through the consequences of our actions. Afterward, we may regret our decisions or feel guilty if our behavior was inconsistent with our values.

Our value systems—our sexual standards—have many sources: parents, peers, religious training, ethnic subcultures, the larger culture, and our appraisal of all these influences. Several value systems that provide a guiding framework to determine the moral acceptability of sexual choices include legalism, situation ethics, hedonism, asceticism, utilitarianism, and rationalism.

Learning Objective 2: Describe the basis for decision making that defines each of the seven value systems discussed in this chapter.

LEGALISM

The legalistic approach formulates ethical behavior on the basis of a code of moral laws derived from an external source, such as the creed of a particular religion (Knox, 1988). The Bible contains many examples of the moral code of the Jewish and Christian religions. In the book of Leviticus (20:10–17) in the Old Testament we find many of the biblical prohibitions against adultery, incest, homosexuality, and bestiality:

> And the man that committeth adultery with another man's wife, even he that committeth adultery with his neighbor's wife, both the adulterer and the adulteress shall surely be put to death. And the man that lieth with his father's wife . . . both of them shall surely be put to death; their blood shall be upon them. . . . And if a man lie with mankind, as with womankind, both of them have committed abomination: they shall surely be put to death; . . . And if a man lie with a beast, he shall surely be put to death; and ye shall slay the beast. . . . And if a man shall take his sister, . . . and see her nakedness, and she sees his nakedness: it is a shameful thing; and they shall be cut off in the sight of the children of their people. . . .

Leviticus also proscribes intercourse during menstruation and the forcing of daughters into prostitution.

Throughout the centuries, many Christians and Jews have adhered to religious laws that are intended to promote the solidarity of the family and the community by minimizing interpersonal jealousies and frictions. Adultery, for example, could set neighbor against neighbor. Religious laws have also directed followers to be "fruitful and multiply" so as to ensure that an ample number of progeny would be available to meet the needs for labor and defense of the family and the community of religious followers.

Many religious followers today accept the moral codes of their religions as a matter of faith and commitment, not necessarily because they can logically or rationally derive them from contemporary societal needs. Some people find it reassuring to be informed by religious authorities or scripture that a certain course of action is right or wrong. Others, however, have questioned how closely one must adhere to religious teachings if one is to be ethical. A number of fundamentalist Protestants, conservative Catholics, and orthodox Jews would argue that the Bible is to be followed to the letter, not just "in spirit." They see every detail of the Bible as the revealed word of God.

Other Christians and Jews take a more liberal view. They say that the Bible was inspired by God but that it was written or transcribed by fallible humans and is subject to various interpretations. They may also assert that the Bible reflects the social setting of the time in which it was written, not only divine inspiration. At a time of burgeoning population growth in many parts of the world, biblical injunctions to be fruitful and multiply may no longer be socially and environmentally sound. Prohibitions, such as that against coitus during menstruation, may have been based on prescientific perceptions of danger. Thus religious teachings may be viewed as a general framework for decision making rather than as a set of absolute rules.

SITUATION ETHICS

Episcopal theologian Joseph Fletcher (1966, 1967) argued that ethical decision making should be guided by genuine love for others rather than by rigid moral rules. Fletcher advocated that sexual decision making should be based on the context of the particular situation that the person faces. For this reason, his view is termed *situation ethics.* According to Fletcher, a Roman Catholic woman will have been taught that abortion is the taking of a human life. Her situation, however—her love for her existing family and her recognition of her limited resources for providing for another child—might influence her to decide in favor of an abortion.

Fletcher argues that one's rules for conduct should not be inflexible. Rather they should be general guidelines. "The situationist is prepared in any concrete case to suspend, ignore, or violate any principle if by doing so he can effect more good than by following it" (1966, p. 34).

Note that situation ethics is not an excuse for selfishness. The moral situation ethicist acts in a manner that he or she believes will lead to the greater good. Now and then, such an act may be frustrating, painful, or difficult. Situation ethicists also may find it difficult, as psychologist David Knox (1988) points out, to make sexual decisions on a case-by-case basis:

> "I don't know what's right anymore" reflects the uncertainty of a situation ethics view. Once a person decides that mutual love is the context justifying intercourse, how often and how soon should the person fall in love? Can love develop after two hours of conversation? How does one know that her or his own love feelings and those of a partner are genuine? The freedom that situation ethics brings to sexual decision making requires responsibility, maturity, and judgment. In some cases, individuals may deceive themselves by believing they are in love so they will not feel guilty about having intercourse.
>
> (Knox, 1988, p. 97. Reprinted by permission.)

ETHICAL RELATIVISM

Ethical relativism rests on the belief that a diversity of values is a fundamental aspect of human existence. Ethical relativists reject the idea that there is a single correct moral view. One person may believe that premarital sex is unacceptable under any circumstances, whereas another may hold that "being in love" makes it acceptable. Still another person may believe that premarital sex is morally permissible without an emotional commitment between the partners.

The ethical relativist believes that there is no objective way of justifying one set of moral values over another. In this view, the essence of human morality is to derive one's own principles and apply them according to one's own conscience. From this perspective, whatever a person believes is right is right for him or her. Subscribing to ethical relativism does not free us of the need to develop moral beliefs. It challenges us, instead, to take responsibility for our decisions and to live up to them.

Opponents of ethical relativism believe that allowing people free rein to determine what is right or wrong may bring about social chaos and decay.

One form of ethical relativism is cultural relativism. From this perspective, what is right or wrong must be understood in terms of the cultural beliefs that effect sexual decision making. In some cultures, premarital sex is tolerated or even encouraged, whereas in others it is considered immoral. Cultural relativism, like ethical relativism, does not ascribe moral superiority to one cultural tradition over another.

HEDONISM

The hedonist is guided by the pursuit of pleasure, not by whether a particular behavior is morally or situationally justified (Knox, 1988). "If it feels good, do it" expresses the hedonistic ethic. The hedonist believes that sexual desires, like hunger or thirst, do not invoke moral considerations.

Of course, one could make the case that there are two kinds of hedonism: short-sighted and long-term hedonism. Basing decisions upon what feels good at the moment may fail to account for the long-term consequences of one's actions. The short-sighted hedonist may risk becoming so driven by the pursuit of pleasure that sex becomes a form of "addiction" in which sexual pleasure overshadows other important aspects of life.

On the other hand, taking a long-term hedonistic view, one can attempt to make responsible sexual decisions that can lead to a lifetime of sexual pleasure. Choosing to do what is necessary to maintain our sexual health, for instance, can help us lead long lives and to enjoy our bodies throughout our spans of years.

ASCETICISM

Religious celibates, such as Roman Catholic priests and nuns, choose asceticism (self-denial of material and sexual desires) in order to devote themselves to spiritual pursuits. Many ascetics in Eastern and Western religions seek to transcend physical and worldly desires.

UTILITARIANISM

Some people believe that it is necessary to adhere to specific religious principles or teachings if one is to be a moral or ethical person, but others believe that ethical guidelines can be based on principles other than religious ones. The English philosopher John Stuart Mill (1806–1873), for example, proposed an ethical system based on utilitarianism.

The core ethic of utilitarianism is that moral conduct is based on that which will bring about "the greatest good for the greatest number" (Mill, 1863). The utilitarian characterizes behavior as ethical when it does the greatest good and causes the least harm. This is not license. Utilitarians may come down hard in opposition to premarital sex and bearing children out of wedlock, for example, if they believe that these behavior patterns jeopardize a nation's health and social fabric. Mill's ethics generally require that we treat one another justly and honestly, because it serves the greater good for people to be true to their word and just in their dealings with others.

RATIONALISM

Rationalism involves the use of reason as the means of determining a course of action (Knox, 1988). The rationalist believes that decisions should be based on intellect and reasoning, rather than emotions or blind obedience to a particular faith. The rationalist attempts to assess the facts in a sexual situation and then logically weigh the consequences of each course of action before making a decision. The rationalist shares with the utilitarian the belief that reasoning can lead to a course of ethical behavior. The rationalist is not bound to the utilitarian code that makes choices on the basis of the greatest good for the greatest number, however. The rationalist may contend that personal needs and desires outweigh the needs of the many.

The utilitarian may decide, for example, to prolong an unhappy marriage because of the belief that the greater good (of the family and the community) is better served by maintaining an unhappy marriage than by dissolving it. The rationalist might decide that the personal consequences of continuing an unhappy marriage outweigh the consequences to the family or the community at large. The religious follower, adopting a legalistic view, might decide that divorce is or is not acceptable depending on the tenets of the person's religion. The situation ethicist might interpret religious principles in light of how the greater good would be served in a particular situation.

Teaching Tip: Have students divided into pairs. Students should take turns identifying the value system which most closely resembles their own. Students should then explain to their partners how they came to hold this value system and how they use it to guide their decision making.

These ethical systems represent general frameworks of moral reasoning or pathways for judging the moral acceptability of sexual and nonsexual behavior. Whereas some of us may adopt one or another of these systems in their purest forms, others adopt a system of moral reasoning that involves some combination or variation of these ethical systems. Some also shift from one ethical system to another from time to time, sometimes reasoning legalistically and sometimes adopting a more flexible situationist approach. Despite these variations, understanding these general guidelines of moral reasoning assists our understanding of how people approach questions of moral acceptability of sexual choices.

THE BALANCE SHEET FOR DECISION MAKING

In their book *Decision-Making,* Janis and Mann (1977) suggested using a balance sheet to help weigh the pluses and minuses of alternatives when making decisions. Rosa, a Mexican-American student at a California state college, has been involved in a sexual relationship for several weeks and is contemplating going on the pill. Rosa uses the balance sheet (Table 21.1) to list the projected gains and losses for herself and her partner according to five criteria:

Experiential: How will it feel? What is its effect on sexual relations? How does it affect sexual sensations and spontaneity?

Biological: How do contraceptive methods work? What are the side effects of birth-control methods? What are the risks involved? What are its effects on preventing STDs?

Financial: Can I afford it—literally? For example, how much do pills cost? How much do babies cost?

Ethical: Is what I am considering consistent with my religious and parental teachings? Is that important to me? Will I experience guilt, anxiety, or shame? Is the course of behavior consistent with my ideas concerning sex roles and who takes the responsibility for the decision? (For example, should the responsibility for birth control be placed on the woman's shoulders only?)

Legal: Am I contemplating something that is against the law? What could happen to my partner and me?

As shown in Table 21.1, Rosa filled in some of the spaces on the sheet to indicate the following pieces of information:

Sex can be spontaneous.

TABLE 21.1 Rosa's balance sheet for deciding whether or not to use birth-control pills

		Positive Anticipations	Negative Anticipations
Experiential gains and losses	For self	Sex would be spontaneous	(Possible side effects: nausea, bloating, etc.)
	For partner	Sex would be spontaneous	None
Biological gains and losses	For self	High effectiveness	Probably no negative impact on health; (useless against STDs)
	For partner	High effectiveness	None
Financial gains and losses	For self	(Needn't worry about the cost of a child)	Expensive!
	For partner	(Needn't worry about the cost of a child)	(None!)
Ethical gains and losses	For self	Would not risk bearing unwanted child or having to decide whether to have an abortion if became pregnant	Moderate concern about using artificial means of birth control; responsibility for birth control would be all mine
	For partner	Would not have to worry about causing pregnancy	None!
Legal factors	For self		None
	For partner		None

For all practical purposes, the pill can be considered 100 percent effective (I'm assuming I'll take them as directed).

I'm 20 years old (young enough and healthy enough not to be too worried about the pill's potential effect on my health).

The pill is kind of expensive—about $20 per month.

I have some moral concerns about using the pill.

The pill is legal.

The remaining blank spaces prompted Rosa to consider other issues. For example, she realized that she forgot to think about the side effects of the pill and the fact that it is useless against STDs. The information prompted by using the balance sheet is placed in parentheses.

Rosa decided not to go on the pill for several reasons: (1) she was concerned about side effects; (2) she did not want to spend the money; and (3) she felt that by taking the pill, she was assuming all responsibility for birth control and that she would rather share it with her partner. Her periods were regular, and she decided (1) to use the rhythm method (to abstain from intercourse for a week in the middle of her cycle), and (2) to have her partner use condoms (and spermicide containing nonoxynol-9) every time they made love. The condoms and spermicide would also afford protection against STDs.

After completing a balance sheet as shown in Table 21.1, Rosa might fill out a similar one for the alternative of using the condom before making a decision. The balance sheet does not automatically lead to one "correct" choice. You might, for example, reach a different decision than Rosa did if you were faced with the same situation. Rather, it is a means of organizing one's perceptions of the positive and negative features of each alternative for oneself and one's partner. Research has shown that balance sheet users hold fewer regrets about the road not taken and are more likely to stick with their decisions.

BACK TO YOU

Activity: *Balance Sheet for Decision Making* The IM contains a Balance Sheet which allows students to weigh the positives and negatives of alternative decisions.

What decisions are you facing in your own sex life? What sexual decisions are you likely to face in the future? As we return to our worlds of diversity, what value systems will you draw upon in making these decisions? What kinds of conflicts may be engendered if your partner comes from another cultural background and holds different values? What role can be played by the information presented in this textbook? Will you use this information to critically examine stereotypes and folklore, or will you think "Oh, it's just another textbook" and toss it aside at the end of the term?

We have come a long way together, and we wish you well. Perhaps we have helped you to phrase the most important questions and to find some answers. We also hope that we have encouraged you to try to understand other people's sexual beliefs and values in light of their cultural backgrounds. Understanding is an essential stopping point on the pathway to respect, and respect is vital to resolving conflicts and establishing healthful relationships.

A P P E N D I X   A

SCORING KEYS FOR SELF-SCORING QUESTIONNAIRES

SCORING KEY FOR THE LOVE ATTITUDES SCALE
(CHAPTER 7, pp. 206–207)

First add your scores on the 30 items of the scale to yield a total score.

Write down your total score here: _____

Note that each of the items is keyed so that lowered numbered responses represent more romantic responses; higher numbered responses represent more realistic responses. The lower your total score (30 is the lowest possible score), the more you identify with a romantic view of love. The higher your score (150 is the highest possible score), the more realistic you are in your love attitudes. A score of 90 places you at the midpoint on the romantic-realist dimension. You may wish to compare your score with your partner's score to see who is more the romantic or more the realist.

SCORING KEY FOR STERNBERG'S TRIANGULAR LOVE SCALE
(CHAPTER 7, pp. 210–211)

First add your scores for the items on each of the three components—Intimacy, Passion, and Decision/Commitment—and divide each total by 15. This will yield an average rating for each subscale. An average rating of 5 on a particular subscale indicates a moderate level of the component represented by the subscale. A higher rating indicates a greater level. A lower rating indicates a lower level. Examining your ratings on these components will give you an idea of the degree to which you perceive your love relationship to be characterized by these three components of love. For example, you might find that passion is stronger than decision/commitment, a pattern that is common in the early stages of an intense romantic relationship. You might find it interesting to complete the questionnaire a few months or perhaps a year or so from now to see how your feelings about your relationship change over time. You might also ask your partner to complete the scale so that the two of you can compare your respective scores. Comparing your ratings for each component with those of your partner will give you an idea of the degree to which you and your partner see your relationship in a similar way.

Sternberg (1988) reports the results of administering the scale to a sample of 50 men and 51 women (average age of 31 years) from the New Haven (CT) area who were either married or presently involved in a close relationship. Average scores for the three components were 7.39 for intimacy, 6.51 for passion, and 7.20 for commitment. High scores (scores representing approximately the top 15 percent of scores) were 8.6 for intimacy, 8.2 for passion, and 8.7 for commitment. Low scores, representing the bottom 15 percent of scores, were 6.2, 4.9, and 5.7 for the three components, respectively. Since romantic ardor may be more difficult to maintain over time, the lower average scores for passion may reflect the length of the relationships in which the people in the sample were involved, which averaged 6.3 years in length. Although you may want to compare your scores with those from this sample, we caution that the Sternberg sample was small and most likely does not accurately represent the general population.

SCORING KEY FOR REASONING ABOUT ABORTION SCALE
(CHAPTER 12, p. 377)

First tally your scores for the following items: 1,3,7,8,9,11,13,14,17,20. This score represents your support for a pro-choice point of view:_____.

Now tally your scores for the remaining items: 2,4,5,6,10,12,15,16,18,19. This score represents your support for a pro-life point of view:_____.

Now subtract your *pro-choice* score from your *pro-life* score. Write the difference, including the sign, here:_____. A positive score indicates agreement with a pro-life philosophy. A negative score indicates agreement with a pro-choice philosophy. The higher your score, the more strongly you agree with the philosophy you endorsed. Scores may range from -40 to +40.

One sample of 230 undergraduate students (115 of each gender) obtained a mean score of -7.48 and a median score of -13.33 (Parsons et al., 1990). This indicates that the students tended to be pro-choice in their attitudes. Another sample of 38 graduate students (31 women and 7 men) obtained mean scores of -11 to -12 and median scores of -17 to -18 on two separate occasions. Scores for other samples may vary.

SCORING KEY FOR STD ATTITUDE SCALE
(CHAPTER 16, pp. 492–493)

Scores on this scale are interpreted in terms of a predisposition to high-risk sexual behavior. The scale is composed of three subscales, which measure your predisposition to high-risk behavior on the basis of your *beliefs* about STDs (items 1-9), your *feelings* about STDs (items 10-18), and your *intentions* to act (items 19-27). Calculate a total for each subscale and for the total scale by using the point values below.

For items 1, 10-14, 16, 25:

Strongly Agree	= 5 points
Agree	= 4 points
Undecided	= 3 points
Disagree	= 2 points
Strongly Disagree	= 1 point

For items 2-9, 15, 17-24, 26, 27:

Strongly Agree	= 1 point
Agree	= 2 points
Undecided	= 3 points
Disagree	= 4 points
Strongly Disagree	= 5 points

Subtotal for Beliefs subscale (items 1-9):_____

Subtotal for Feelings subscale (items 10-18):_____

Subtotal for Intentions to Act subscale (items 19-27):_____

Total score (based on all items):_____

The higher your subscale and total scores, the greater the likelihood that your attitudes, feelings, and intentions put you at risk of contracting an STD. The lower your scores, the less risk you are likely to incur. Although we have no norms at present, we suggest that subscale scores higher than 27 and total scores higher than 81 indicate that your responses are weighted more toward risky than safe behavior. We suggest that you weigh your particular risk by examining not only your scores but your responses to the individual scale items as well. Ask yourself, "How do my responses to these items increase or decrease my risk of contracting an STD?" Then ask yourself, "How might I change my attitudes to reduce my chances of contracting an STD?"

ADDITIONAL READINGS: BOOKS ON HUMAN SEXUALITY AND RELATED TOPICS

Barbach, L. G. (1975). *For yourself: The fulfillment of female sexuality.* Garden City, NY: Doubleday & Co., Inc. A popular self-help book for women who have difficulty achieving orgasm.

Barbach, L. (1984). *For each other.* New York: Signet. Suggestions for enhancing communication and sexual satisfaction in relationships.

Barrett, M. B. (1990). *Invisible lives: The truth about millions of women-loving women.* New York: Morrow. Based upon interviews with 125 lesbians, this book reveals what it is like to be a lesbian in contemporary America and seeks to bridge an understanding between lesbians and parents, children, and friends.

Beck, A. (1988). *Love is never enough.* New York: Harper & Row. Aaron Beck, a leading psychiatrist and originator of cognitive therapy, examines the factors that underlie relationship problems and presents specific techniques that couples can use to resolve conflicts and improve their relationships.

Blumstein, P., & Schwartz, P. (1983) *American couples. New York: Morrow.* A major study of relationships in contemporary America, based on a sample of heterosexual and homosexual couples.

Bornoff, N. (1991). *Pink samurai: Love, marriage & sex in contemporary Japan.* New York: Pocket Books. An enlightening account of sexual customs and practices in modern Japan.

Boston Women's Health Book Collective (1984). *The New Our Bodies, Ourselves.* New York: Simon & Schuster. A highly popular repository of information concerning women's health care and sexuality.

Bridge, T. P., Mirsky, A. F., & Goodwin, F. K. (Eds.) (1988). *Psychological, neuropsychiatric, and substance abuse aspects of AIDS.* New York: Raven Press. A scholarly compendium of information about the medical, behavioral, and legal aspects of AIDS.

Butler, R., & Lewis, M. (1988). *Love and sex after 60.* (Rev. ed.). New York: Harper & Row. Practical information about adjusting to sexual changes in later life.

Calderone, M. S., & Johnson, E. W. (1989). *Family book about sexuality.* (Rev. ed.) New York: Harper & Row. A straightforward and balanced compendium of information and advice about sexual development through the life cycle.

Calderone, M. S., & Ramey, J. (1982). *Talking with your child about sex.* New York: Random House. A practical guide to parents raising sexually healthy children. Provides parents with answers to questions that children frequently ask about sex.

Cass, V. (1988). *There's more to sex than AIDS: The A to Z guide to safe sex.* Richmond, Victoria, Australia: Greenhouse Publications. A comprehensive guide to safer sexual techniques.

Coles, R., & Stokes, G. (1985). *Sex and the American teenager.* New York: Harper & Row. Findings of a survey of the sexual attitudes and practices of a national sample of 1,067 teenagers in the United States.

Cook, E. P. (1985). *Psychological androgyny.* New York: Pergamon. An examination of psychological androgyny that compares and contrasts androgyny to traditional masculine and feminine gender roles.

Donnerstein, E., Linz, D., & Penrod, S. (1987). *The question of pornography.* New York: The Free Press. A comprehensive review of scientific knowledge of the effects of exposure to pornography and legal issues in the debate over pornography.

Eisenberg, A., Murkoff, H., & Hathaway, S. E. (1989). *What to expect the first year.* New York: Workman Publishing. A comprehensive guide to infant development during the first year of life.

Ford, C. S., & Beach, F. A. (1951). New York: Harper. *Patterns of sexual behavior.* A classic study of sexuality from a cross-cultural and cross-species perspective.

Gilligan, C. (1982). *In a different voice.* Cambridge, MA: Harvard University Press. An influential book that examines the differences between men and women with respect to issues of autonomy and intimacy.

Grauerholz, E., & Koralewski, M. A. (Eds.) (1991). *Sexual coercion: A sourcebook on its nature, causes, and prevention.* Lexington, MA: D.C. Heath and Company. A number of leading scholars address the nature, causes, and prevention of sexual coercion.

Greenburg, M. (1985). *The birth of a father.* New York: Continuum. A first-hand account of the experience of fatherhood.

Griffin, C., Wirth, M., & Wirth, A. (1986). *Beyond acceptance.* Englewood Cliffs, NJ: Prentice-Hall. Written by parents of gay and lesbian children for parents of gay and lesbian children, this book sensitively discusses issues and conflicts that arise in the context of discovering that one's child is homosexual.

Hatcher, R. A., et al. (1994). (16th rev. ed.). *Contraceptive technology.* New York: Irvington. The authoritative guide to the most recent developments in contraception.

Hatfield, E. & Sprecher, S. (1986). *Mirror, mirror...The importance of looks in everyday life.* Albany, NY: SUNY Press. An examination of the role of physical appearance in interpersonal attraction and relationships.

Heiman, J., & LoPiccolo, J. (1988). *Becoming orgasmic: A sexual and personal growth program for women.* Englewood Cliffs, NJ: Prentice Hall. A self-help guide to women to learn to become orgasmic and enhance their sexual pleasure in masturbation and lovemaking.

Holmes, K. K., et al. (1990). *Sexually transmitted diseases.* (2nd Ed.). New York: McGraw-Hill Information Services Company. A scholarly, technical resource book on sexually transmitted diseases.

Janus, S. S., & Janus, C. L. (1993). *The Janus Report on sexual behavior.* New York: Wiley. The findings of a new nationwide survey of sexual behavior in the U.S. Conducted from 1988 to 1992, the Janus Report was based on a survey of 2,765 adults who anonymously completed written questionnaires assessing a wide range of sexual behaviors and attitudes.

Kaplan, H. S. (1979). *Disorders of sexual desire.* New York; Brunner/Mazel. Kaplan, a leading sex therapist, examines the causes and treatments of sexual desire disorders.

Kaplan, H. (1987). *The illustrated manual of sex therapy.* New York: Brunner/Mazel. A well-illustrated manual that clearly describes the steps involved in sex therapy for various sexual dysfunctions in men and women.

Kinsey, A. C., Pomeroy, W., Martin, C., (1948). *Sexual behavior in the human male.* Philadelphia, PA: W. B. Saunders Co., _____, _____, _____, & Gebhard, P. (1953). *Sexual behavior in the human female.* Philadelphia, PA: W. B. Saunders Co. The classic "Kinsey reports" containing statistical tables and data describing the sexual behavior patterns of men and women in the U.S., based on interviews of nearly 12,000 people.

Langston, D. (1983). *Living with herpes.* Garden City, NY: Doubleday & Co. A sensitive, practical guide that will be useful to people coping with herpes and to their sexual partners.

Leach, P. (1989). *Your baby & child: From birth to age five.* (Rev. ed.). New York: Knopf. A comprehensive, clearly presented, and well-illustrated guide to child care.

MacFarlane, K., Waterman, J., and others (Eds.) (1986). *Sexual abuse of young children: Evaluation and treatment.* This edited volume features a compilation of clinical and research findings on the problem of child sexual abuse.

Madaras, L. (1983). *The what's happening to my body? Book for girls: A growing up guide for parents and daughters.* New York: Newmarket Press._____(1984). *The what's happening to my body? Book for boys: A growing up guide for parents and sons.* New York: Newmarket Press. Down-to-earth guides about the changes of puberty and adolescence.

Margulis, L., & Sanga, D. (1991). *Mystery dance: On the evolution of human sexuality.* New York: Summit Books. An exploration of the ancestral origins of human sexuality

Marshall, D., & Suggs, R. (1971) (Eds.). *Human sexual behavior: Variations in the ethnographic spectrum.* Englewood Cliffs, NJ: Prentice-Hall. A splendid compendium of ethnographic accounts of sexual behavior and customs in various cultures around the world.

Masters, W. H., & Johnson, V. (1970). *Human sexual inadequacy.* This classic book describes the treatment protocol and results of Masters and Johnson's sex therapy program.

Masters, W., & Johnson, V. (1966). *Human sexual response.* Boston: Little, Brown. An account of the classic scientific studies of sexual arousal and response in men and women by Masters and Johnson. Must reading for students seeking more detailed knowledge of sexual physiology and functioning.

McNaught, B. (1988). *On being gay.* New York: St. Martin's Press. The author discusses various aspects of the experience of being gay, including the coming-out process, dealing with conflicts with family members, developing gay relationships, and confronting the AIDS crisis.

McWhirter, D. P., Sanders, S. A., & Reinisch, J. M. (Eds.) (1990). *Homosexuality/heterosexuality: Concepts of sexual orientation.* The Kinsey Institute Series, Volume II. New York: Oxford University Press. A compendium of scholarly articles on the classification and understanding of sexual orientation.

Millet, K. (1976). *The prostitution papers.* New York: Ballantine Books. A leading feminist examines the role of prostitutes in our society and argues for decriminalization, but not legalization, of prostitution.

Money, J. (1988). *Gay, straight, and in-between: The sexology of erotic orientation.* New York: Oxford University Press. Written by a leading researcher, this is a scholarly treatise on the biological and psychosocial factors underlying sexual orientation.

Money, J., & Ehrhardt, A. (1972). *Man and woman, boy and girl.* Baltimore: Johns Hopkins Press. A comprehensive analysis of the biological and psychosocial factors that determine gender identity.

Nillson, L. (1977). *A child is born.* New York: Dell. Breathtaking pictures of fetal development with accompanying text.

Peters, B. (1988). *Terrific sex in fearful times.* New York: St. Martin's Press. A guide to safer sex in the age of AIDS.

Pomeroy, W., Flax, C., & Wheeler, C. (1982). *Taking a sex history: Interviewing and recording.* New York: Free Press. The authors review the interviewing methods used in the original Kinsey research and discuss contemporary issues in conducting sex surveys.

Reinisch, J., & Rosenblum, L. (Eds.) (1987). *Masculinity-femininity: Basic perspectives.* New York: Oxford University Press. A compendium of scientific articles that address issues of gender differences from multiple perspectives, including the biological, psychosocial, and developmental perspectives.

Reinisch, J. (1990). *The Kinsey Institute new report on sex: What you must know to be sexually literate.* New York: St. Martin's Press. The findings of a national survey of sexual knowledge, along with a comprehensive and well-researched compendium of information on contraception, sexually transmitted diseases, sexual development, sexual health, and problems with sexual functioning.

Rubin, L. B. (1983). *Intimate strangers: Men and women together.* New York: Harper & Row. A sensitive and probing study of the struggles of men and women, both with themselves and with their partners, to establish intimate relationships.

Samuels, M., & Samuels, N. (1986). *The well pregnancy book.* A comprehensive and sensitive guide to pregnancy and childbirth. New York; Harper & Row.

Shilts, R. (1987). *And the band played on: Politics, people, and the AIDS epidemic.* New York: Viking Penguin. A national best-seller, investigative reporter Randy Shilts provides a compelling account of the chronology of the AIDS epidemic and the lack of governmental response to the AIDS crisis.

Spark, R. F. (1991). *Male sexual health: A couple's guide.* Mount Vernon, NY: Consumer Reports Books. A concise up-to-date guide to male sexual problems ranging from infertility to erectile dysfunction.

Starr, B., & Weiner, M. (1981). *The Starr-Weiner report on sex and sexuality in the mature years.* New York: Stein & Day. Findings of a survey of the sexual interests and practices of a sample of more than 800 people from 60 to 91 years of age.

Stephenson, L. (1987). *Give us a child: Coping with the personal crisis of infertility.* New York: Harper & Row. A sensitive guide to couples coping with infertility.

Sternberg, R. J., & Barnes, M. L. (Eds.) (1988). *The psychology of love.* New Haven, CT: Yale University. Modern scholars examine the concept of love from a scientific standpoint.

Symons, D. (1979). *The evolution of human sexuality.* New York: Oxford University Press. A provocative exploration of the evolutionary roots of human sexuality.

Tannahill, R. (1980). *Sex in history.* New York: Stein & Day. A highly readable and entertaining account of the history of sexual practices and customs in Western and Eastern societies.

Tannen, D. (1990). *You just don't understand: Women and men in conversation.* New York: Morrow. Written by a linguistics professor, this down-to-earth, best-selling book shows how gender-based differences in conversational styles lead to misunderstandings in relationships between men and women.

Tennov, D. (1979). *Love and limerence: The experience of being in love.* New York: Stein & Day. A clearly written book describing the experience of love.

Warshaw, R. (1988). *I never called it rape.* New York: Harper & Row. A probing review of the problem of acquaintance rape and date rape.

Zilbergeld, B. (1992). *The new male sexuality: A guide to sexual fulfillment.* New York: Bantam. A thorough updating of this informative guide to male sexuality.

Abarbanel, G. (1986). Rape and resistance. *Journal of Interpersonal Violence, 1,* 1010–1015.

Abbey, A. (1982). Sex differences in attributions for friendly behavior. *Journal of Personality and Social Psychology, 42,* 830–838.

ABC News. (1992, April 2). *Prime Time Live.*

'Abd Allah, M. M. (1917). Siwan customs. *Harvard African Studies, 1,* 7, 20.

Abel, G. G. (1985, September). *Use of pornography and erotica by sex offenders.* Paper presented to the United States Attorney General's Commission on Pornography, Houston, Texas.

Abel, G. G., et al. (1989). The measurement of the cognitive distortions of child molesters. *Annals of Sex Research, 2,* 135–152.

Abel, G. G., et al. (1977). The components of rapists' sexual arousal. *Archives of General Psychiatry, 34,* 895–903.

Abel, G., Becker, J., & Cunningham-Rather, J. (1984). Complications, consent, and cognitions in sex between children and adults. *International Journal of Law and Psychiatry, 7,* 89–103.

Abelson, H., et al. (1970). Public attitudes toward and experience with erotic materials. In *Technical Reports of the Commission on Obscenity and Pornography, Vol. 6.* Washington, DC: U.S. Government Printing Office.

Abou-David, K. (1967). Epidemiology of carcinoma of the cervix uteri in Lebanese Christians and Moslems. *Cancer, 20,* 1706–1714.

Aboulker, J. P., & Swart, A. M. (1993). Preliminary analysis of the Concorde trial. *Lancet, 341,* 889–890.

Abramowitz, S. (1986). Psychosocial outcomes of sex reassignment surgery. *Journal of Consulting and Clinical Psychology, 54,* 183–189.

Acker, M., & Davis, M. H. (1992). Intimacy, passion and commitment in adult romantic relationships: A test of the triangular theory of love. *Journal of Social and Personal Relationships, 9,* 21–50.

Ackerman, D. (1991). *The moon by whale light.* New York: Random House.

Ackerman, D. (1990). *A natural history of the senses* (1st ed.). New York: Random House.

Adams, R. (1987). The role of prostitution in AIDS and other STDs. *Medical Aspects of Human Sexuality, 21,* 27–33.

Adams, V. (1980, August). Sex therapists in perspective. *Psychology Today,* pp. 35–36.

Adams, G. R. (1977). Physical attractiveness research: Toward a developmental social psychology of beauty. *Human Development, 20,* 217–239.

Adams, E. H., Gfroerer, J. C., & Rouse, B. A. (1989). Epidemiology of substance abuse including alcoholism and cigarette smoking. *Annals of the New York Academy of Sciences, 62,* 14–20.

Adams, H. E., et al. (1981). Behavior therapy with sexual deviations. In S. M. Turner, K. S. Calhoun, & H. E. Adams (Eds.), *Handbook of clinical behavior therapy,* (pp. 318–346). New York: Wiley.

Adams, R.A., et al. (1992). Components of a model adolescent AIDS/drug abuse prevention program: A delphi study. *Family Relations, 41,* 312–317.

Addiego, F., et al. (1981). Female ejaculation: A case study. *Journal of Sex Research, 17,* 13–21.

Ade-Ridder, L. (1985). Quality of marriage: A comparison between golden-wedding couples and couples married less than fifty years. *Lifestyles, 7,* 224–237.

Adelman, M. R. (1977). A comparison of professionally employed lesbians and heterosexual women on the MMPI. *Archives of Sexual Behavior, 6,* 193–202.

Adelson, A. (1990, November 19). Study attacks women's roles in TV. *The New York Times,* p. C18.

Adler, J. (1993, April 26). Sex in the snoring '90s. *Newsweek,* pp. 55, 57.

Adler, J., et al. (1991, November 18). Living with the virus: When–and–how–HIV turns into AIDS. *Newsweek,* pp. 33–34. A flock with changing views. (1993, August 1). *The New York Times,* p. A26

Ageton, S. (1983). *Sexual assault among adolescents.* Lexington, MA: D. C. Heath.

Ahmed, R.A. (1991). Women in Egypt and the Sudan. In L. L. Adler (Ed.), *Women in cross-cultural perspective.* (pp. 107-134). New York: Praeger.

AIDS cases seen leveling off in next 5 years, (1991, July 5) *The New York Times.* p. A10.

AIDS, violence grow as top killers in U.S. (1993, April 13). *New York Newsday,* p. 67.

AIDS update. (1993, July/August). *American Health,* p. 8.

AIDS without needles or sex. (1993, December 20). *Newsweek,* pp. 106-107.

Airhihenbuwa, C. O., & Pineiro, O. (1988). Cross-cultural health education: A pedagogical challenge. *Journal of School Health, 58,* 240-242.

Akhtar, S. (1988). Four culture-bound psychiatric syndromes in India. *The International Journal of Social Psychiatry, 34,* 70–74.

Alan Guttmacher Institute. (1991). *Facts in brief.* New York: Author.

Albrecht, S. L., Bahr, H. M., & Goodman, K. L. (1983). *Divorce and remarriage: Problems, adaptations, and adjustments.* Westport, CT: Greenwood Press.

Alexander, C. J., Sipski, M. L., & Findley, T. W. (1993). Sexual activities, desire, and satisfaction in males pre- and post-spinal cord injury. *Archives of Sexual Behavior, 22,* 217-228.

Alexander, M. W., & Judd, B. B. (1986). Differences in attitudes toward nudity in advertising. *Psychology: A Quarterly Journal of Human Behavior, 23,* 26–29.

Alexander, P. C., et al. (1989). A comparison of group treatments of women sexually abused as children. *Journal of Consulting and Clinical Psychology, 57,* 479–483.

Allen, H. (1990, December 31). Gender games in the gulf: In anonymity of the military, sex does a vanishing act. *Washington Post,*

Allen, D. M. (1980). Young male prostitutes: A psychosocial study. *Archives of Sexual Behavior, 9,* 399–426.

Allen, J. R., & Setlow, V. P. (1991). Heterosexual transmission of HIV: A view of the future. *Journal of the American Medical Association, 266,* 1695–1696.

Allgeier, A. R. (1981). Ideological barriers to contraception. In D. Byrne & W. A. Fisher (Eds.), *Adolescents, sex, and contraception.* New York; McGraw-Hill.

Allgeier, E. (1981). The influence of androgynous identification on heterosexual relations. *Sex Roles, 7,* 321–330.

Allon, N., & Fishel, D. (1979). Single bars. In N. Allon (Ed.), *Urban life styles,* Dubuque, IA: Brown.

Alter, M. J., et al. (1989). The importance of heterosexual activity and intravenous drug use in the transmission of hepatitis B and non-A, non-B hepatitis. *Journal of the American Medical Association, 262,* 1201–1205.

Alter-Reid, K., et al. (1986). Sexual abuse of children: A review of the empirical findings. *Clinical Psychology Review, 6,* 249–266.

Althof, S. E., et al. (1989). Why do so many people drop out from autoinjection therapy for impotence? *Journal of Sex and Marital Therapy, 15,* 121–129.

Althof, S. E., et al. (1991). Sexual, psychological, and marital impact of self-injection of papaverine and phentolamine: A long-term prospective study. Special Issue: The treatment of male erectile disorders.*Journal of Sex & Marital Therapy, 17,* 101-112.

Altman, I., & Taylor, D. A. (1973). *Social penetration: The development of interpersonal relationships.* New York: Holt, Rinehart and Winston.

Altman, L. K. (1988, January 26). Cocaine's many dangers: The evidence mounts. *The New York Times,* p. C3.

Altman, L. K. (1989, April 24). Experts on AIDS, citing new data, push for testing. *The New York Times,* pp. A1, B8.

Altman, L. K. (1991a, April 15). Study challenges federal research on risks of IUD's. *The New York Times,* p. A1.

Altman, L. K. (1991b, June 18). W.H.O. says 40 million will be infected with AIDS virus by 2000. *The New York Times*, p. C3.

Altman, L. K. (1992a, July 24). AIDS-like illness to get close look. *The New York Times*, D.16.

Altman, L. K. (1992b, April 9). Ashe received a transfusion before blood supply was tested for H.I.V. *The New York Times*, p. B15.

Altman, L. K. (1992c, May 15). Study sees no new transmission of H.I.V. by health-care workers. *The New York Times*, p. A18.

Altman, L. K. (1992d, July 21). Women worldwide nearing higher rate for AIDS than men. *The New York Times*, p. C3.

Altman, L. K. (1993a, June 6). At AIDS talks, science confronts daunting maze. *The New York Times*, p. A20.

Altman, L. K. (1993b, June 15). Conference ends with little hope for AIDS cure. *The New York Times*, pp. C1, C3.

Altman, L. K. (1993c, February 18). Drug mixture halts H.I.V. in lab, doctors say in a cautious report. *The New York Times*, pp. A1, B9.

Altman, L. K. (1993d, June 27). Experts change guide on using H.I.V. drugs. *The New York Times*, p. A23.

Altman, L. K. (1993e, June 29). Government panel on H.I.V. finds the prospect for treatment bleak. *The New York Times*, p. C3.

Altman, L. K. (1993f, June 12). Little progress seen in effort to crack AIDS puzzle. *The New York Times*, p. A5.

Altman, L. K. (1993g, February 21). New caution, and some reassurance, on vasectomy. it>The New York Times, Section 4, p. 2.

Altman, L. K. (1993h, July 23). Sex is leading cause of AIDS in women. *The New York Times*, p. A12.

Altman, L. K. (1993i, December 22). Study suggests high rate of impotence. *The New York Times*, p. C13.

Altman, L. K. (1993j, February 17). 2 new studies link vasectomy to higher prostate cancer risk. *The New York Times*, p. C12.

Altman, L. K. (1993k, April 30). Widened definition of AIDS leads to more reports of it. *The New York Times*, p. A18.

Altman, L. K. (1993l, June 8). World health official says AIDS spread could be controlled. *The New York Times*, p. C6.

Alzate, H., & Londono, M. L. (1984). Vaginal erotic sensitivity. *Journal of Sex and Marital Therapy, 10*, 49–56.

Alzate, H. (1989). Sexual behavior of unmarried Colombian university students: A follow-up. *Archives of Sexual Behavior, 18*, 239–250.

Alzate, H., & Hoch, Z. (1986). The "G-spot" and "female ejaculation": A current appraisal. *Journal of Sex and Marital Therapy, 12*, 211–220.

Alzate, H. (1985). Vaginal eroticism: A replication study. *Archives of Sexual Behavior, 14*, 529–537.

American College of Obstetricians and Gynecologists. (1985, January). *Dysmenorrhea*. New York: Author.

American Humane Association. (1988). *Highlights of official child neglect and abuse reporting 1986*. Denver: Author.

American Cancer Society. (1991). *Cancer facts and figures*. New York: Author.

American Psychiatric Association. (1987). *Diagnostic and statistical manual of mental disorders* (3rd ed., rev.). Washington, DC: Author.

American Medical Association. (1991). AIDS vaccines inch closer to useful existence. *Journal of the American Medical Association, 265*, 1356.

American Cancer Society (1990). *For men only: Testicular cancer and how to do TSE (a self exam) (rev. ed.)*. Atlanta: Author.

American Cancer Society. (1987). *Cancer facts and figures–1987*. New York: Author.

American Civil Liberties Union. (1986). *Polluting the censorship debate*. Washington, DC: Author.

American Cancer Society. (1986). *Cancer facts and figures*. New York: Author.

American Social Health Association. (1991). *STD (VD)*. Research Triangle Park, NC: Author. Americans generally well-informed about AIDS, but many lack knowledge about preventive aspects. (1993). Family Planning Perspectives, 25, 139-140.

Ames, M. A., & Houston, D. A. (1990). Legal, social, and biological definitions of pedophilia. *Archives of Sexual Behavior, 19*, 333–342.

Amir, M. (1971). *Patterns in forcible rape*. Chicago: University of Chicago Press.

Ammar, H. (1954). *Growing up in an Egyptian village*. London:

Anderson, V. N. (1992). For whom is this world just? Sexual orientation and AIDS. *Journal of Applied Social Psychology, 22*, 248-259.

Anderson, B. J., & Wold, F. M. (1986). Chronic physical illness and sexual behavior. *Journal of Consulting and Clinical Psychology, 54*, 168–175.

Anderson, P. B., & Aymami, R. (1993). Reports of female initiating of sexual contact: Male and female differences. *Archives of Sexual Behavior, 22*, 335-343.

Anderson, J. E., & Dahlberg, L. L. (1992). High-risk sexual behavior in the general population: Results from a national survey, 1988-1990. *Sexually Transmitted Diseases, 19*, 320-325.

Anderson, J. L., et al. (1992). Was the Duchess of Windsor right? A cross-cultural review of the socioecology of ideals of female body shape. *Ethology and Sociobiology, 13,*,197-227.

Anderson, S. A., Russell, C. S., & Schumm, W. R. (1983). Perceived marital quality and family life cycle categories: A further analysis. *Journal of Marriage and the Family, 45*, 127–139.

Angell, M. (1990). New ways to get pregnant. *The New England Journal of Medicine, 323*, 1200–1202.

Angier, N. (1991, August 30). Zone of brain linked to men's sexual orientation. *The New York Times*, A1, D18.

Angier, N. (1990, July 19). Scientists say gene on Y chromosome makes a man a man. *The New York Times*, pp. A1, 19.

Angier, N. (1992a). A male menopause? Jury is still out. *The New York Times*, p. C14.

Angier, N. (1992b, January 30). Odor receptors discovered in sperm cells. *The New York Times*, p. A19.

Angier, N. (1993b, January 30). Future of the pill may lie just over the counter. *The New York Times*, Section 4, p. 5.

Angier, N. (1993a). Report suggests homosexuality is linked to genes. *The New York Times*, pp. A12, D21.

Annas, G. J. (1988). Fairy tales surrogate mothers tell [Special Issue: Forum on surrogate motherhood: Politics and privacy]. *Law, Medicine and Health Care, 16*, 27–33.

Annas, G., & Elias, S. (1990). Legal and ethical implications of fetal diagnosis and gene therapy. *American Journal of Medical Genetics, 35*, 215–218.

Annon, J. (1974). *The behavioral treatment of sexual problems* (Vol. I). Honolulu: Enabling Systems.

Ansen, D., with others. (1993, January 18). A lost generation. *Newsweek*, pp. 16-23.

Antill, J. K. (1983). Sex role complementarity versus similarity in married couples. *Journal of Personality and Social Psychology, 52*, 260–267.

Antonarakas, S. E., et al. (1991). Prenatal origin of the extra chromosome in trisomy 21 as indicated by analysis of DNA polymorphisms. *The New England Journal of Medicine, 324*, 872-876.

Antonarakas, S. E., et al. (1991). Prenatal origin of the extra chromosome in trisomy 21 as indicated by analysis of DNA polymorphisms. *The New England Journal of Medicine, 324*, 872-876.

Antoni, M. H., et al. (1990). Psychoneuroimmunology and HIV-1. *Journal of Consulting and Clinical Psychology, 58*, 38–49.

Antoni, M. H., et al. (1991). Cognitive-behavioral stress management intervention buffers distress responses and immunologic changes following notification of HIV-1 seropositivity. *Journal of Consulting and Clinical Psychology, 59*, 906–915.

Apfelbaum, B. (1988). An ego-analytic perspective on desire disorders. In S. Leiblum & R. Rosen (Eds.), *Sexual desire disorders*, New York: Guilford Press.

Apfelbaum, B. (Ed.) (1980). *Expanding the boundaries of sex therapy* (rev. ed.). Berkeley, CA: Berkeley Sex Therapy Group.

Apgar, V. (1953). A proposal for a new method of evaluation of the newborn infant. *Current Research in Anesthesia and Analgesia, 32*, 260–267.

Appell, R. A. (1986). Importance of the neurological examination in erectile dysfunction. *Medical Aspects of Human Sexuality, 20*, 32–36.

Araji, S., & Finkelhor, D. (1986). Abusers: A review of the research. In D. Finkelhor & Associates (Eds.), *Sourcebook on child sexual abuse* (pp. 89–118). Beverly Hills, CA: Sage.

Archer, R. P., & Cash, T. F. (1985). Physical attractiveness and maladjustment among psychiatric patients. *Journal of Social and Clinical Psychology, 3*, 170–180.

Armsworth, M. W. (1991). Psychological response to abortion. *Journal of Counseling and Development, 69*, 377-379.

Asch, A., & Rousso, H. (1985). Therapists with disabilities: Theoretical and clinical issues. *Psychiatry, 48*, 1–12.

Asso, D., & Magos, A. (1992). Psychological and physiological changes in severe premenstrual syndrome. *Biological Psychology, 33*, 115-132.

Associated Press. (1991, November 1). Girls twice as likely as boys to think themselves fat, study finds. *The Hartford Courant*, p. A3.

Astley, S. J., et al. (1992). Analysis of facial shape in children gestationally exposed to marijuana, alcohol, and/or cocaine. *Pediatrics, 89*, 67–77.

Athanasiou, R., Shaver, P., & Tavris, C. (1970, July). Sex. *Psychology Today*, pp. 39–52.

Atkeson, B. M., Calhoun, K. S., & Morris, K. T. (1989). Victim resistance to rape: The relationship of previous victimization, demographics, and situational factors. *Archives of Sexual Behavior, 18*, 497–507.

Atwater, L. (1982). *The extramarital connection: Sex, intimacy and identity*. New York: Irvington Publishers.

Atwood, J. D., & Gagnon, J. (1987). Masturbatory behavior in college youth. *Journal of Sex Education and Therapy, 13*, 35–42.

Austin, C. R., & Short, R. V. (1972). *Reproduction in mammals.* London: Cambridge University Press.

Austrom, D., & Hanel, K. (1985). Psychological issues of single life in Canada. *International Journal of Women's Studies, 8,* 12–23.

Avery, M. E., & Merritt, T. A. (1991). Surfactant-replacement therapy. *The New England Journal of Medicine, 324,* 910–912.

Axinn, W. G. (1991). The influence of interviewer sex on responses to sensitive questions in Nepal. *Social Science Research, 20,* 303-318.

Bach, G. R., & Deutsch, R. M. (1970). *Pairing.* New York: Peter H. Wyden.

Bachmann, G., & Gill, J. (1988, February). Endocrine and metabolic changes of menopause. *Medical Aspects of Human Sexuality, 74,* 81.

Bachmann, G., Moeller, T., & Bennett, J. (1988). Childhood sexual abuse and the consequences in adult women. *Obstetrics and Gynecology, 71,* 631–642.

Bachrach, C. A. (1984). Contraceptive practice among American women: 1973–1982. *Family Planning Perspectives, 16,* 253–259.

Bachu, A. (1991, December 4). Cited in Pear, R. Larger number of new mothers are unmarried. *The New York Times,* p. A20.

Baggett, C. R. (1992). Sexual orientation: Should it affect child custody rulings?. *Law & Psychology Review, 16,* 189-200.

Bagley, C. (1985). Child abuse and juvenile prostitution: A commentary on the Bagley report on sexual offenses against children and youth in Canada. *Journal of Public Health, 76,* 65–66.

Bagley, C., & Young, L. (1987). Juvenile prostitution and child sexual abuse: A controlled study. *Canadian Journal of Community Mental Health, 6,* 5–26.

Bailey, M., & Pillard, R. (1991, December 17). Are some people born gay? *The New York Times,* p. A21.

Bailey, J. M., & Pillard, R. C. (1991). A genetic study of male sexual orientation. *Archives of General Psychiatry, 48,* 1089–1096.

Baker, J. N. (1990, Summer/Fall). Coming out, (Special Issue). *Newsweek,* pp. 60–61.

Baker, S., Thalberg, S., & Morrison, D. (1988). Parents' behavioral norms as predictors of adolescent sexual activity and contraceptive use. *Adolescence, 23,* 278–281.

Baker, T. C., et al. (1990). Rape victims' concerns about possible exposure to HIV infection. *Journal of Interpersonal Violence, 5,* 49–60.

Bakwin, H. (1973). Erotic feelings in infants and young children. *American Journal of Diseases of Children, 126,* 52–54.

Baldwin, J. D., & Baldwin, J. I. (1989). The socialization of homosexuality and heterosexuality in a non-Western society. *Archives of Sexual Behavior, 18,* 13–29.

Baldwin, J. D., Whiteley, S., & Baldwin, J. I. (1992). The effect of ethnic group on sexual activities related to contraception and STDs. *Journal of Sex Research, 29,* 189-205.

Bancroft, J. (1984). Hormones and human sexual behavior. *Journal of Sex and Marital Therapy, 10,* 3–21.

Bancroft, J., et al. (1983). Mood, sexuality, hormones, and the menstrual cycle. III: Sexuality and the role of androgens. *Psychosomatic Medicine, 45,* 509–516.

Bancroft, J. (1974). *Deviant sexual behavior: Modification and assessment.* New York: Oxford University Press.

Bancroft, J. (1990). Commentary: Biological contributions to sexual orientation. In D. P. McWhirter, S. A. Sanders, & J. M. Reinisch (Eds.), *Homosexuality/heterosexuality: Concepts of sexual orientation* (pp. 101–111). New York: Oxford University Press.

Bandura, A. (1986). *Social foundations of thought and action: A social-cognitive theory.* Englewood Cliffs, NJ: Prentice-Hall.

Banmen, J., & Vogel, N. (1985). The relationship between marital quality and interpersonal sexual communication. *Family Therapy, 12,* 45–58.

Banning, A. (1989). Mother-son incest: Confronting a prejudice. *Child Abuse and Neglect, 13,* 563–570.

Bar-Tal, D., & Saxe, L. (1976). Perceptions of similarly and dissimilarly physically attractive couples and individuals. *Journal of Personality and Social Psychology, 33,* 772–781.

Barbach, L. G. (1975). *For yourself: The fulfillment of female sexuality.* New York: Doubleday.

Barbaree, H. E., Baxter, D. J., & Marshall, W. L. (1989). Brief research report: The reliability of the rape index in a sample of rapists and nonrapists. *Violence and Victims, 4,* 299–306.

Barbaree, H. E., & Marshall, W. L. (1991). The role of male sexual arousal in rape: Six models. *Journal of Consulting and Clinical Psychology, 59,* 621–630.

Bard, L., et al. (1987). A descriptive study of rapists and child molesters: Developmental, clinical and criminal characteristics. *Behavioral Sciences and the Law, 5,* 203–220.

Bardwick, J. (1971). *Psychology of women: A study of bio-cultural conflicts.* New York: Harper & Row.

Barlow, D. H. (1986). Causes of sexual dysfunction: The role of anxiety and cognitive interference. *Journal of Consulting and Clinical Psychology, 54,* 140–148.

Barlow, D. H., et al. (1974). Sex role motor behavior: A behavioral checklist. *Behavioral Assessment, 1,* 119–138.

Barnard, C.P. (1989). Alcoholism and sex abuse in the family: Incest and marital rape [Special Issue: Aggression, family violence and chemical dependency]. *Journal of Chemical Dependency Treatment, 3,* 131–144.

Barnes, A., et al. (1980). Fertility and outcome of pregnancy in women exposed in utero to diethylstilbestrol. *The New England Journal of Medicine, 302,* 609–613.

Barnes, D. M. (1991). AIDS in court. *The Journal of NIH Research, 3,* 8.

Barrett, M. B. (1990). *Invisible lives: The truth about millions of women-loving women.* New York: Harper & Row (Perennial Library).

Barringer, F. (1990, August 17). After long decline, teen births are up. *The New York Times,* p. A14.

Barringer, F. (1991, June 7). Changes in family patterns: Solitude and single parents. *The New York Times,* pp. A1, A18.

Barringer, F. (1992a, November 8). Making birth control easier raises touchy political issues. *The New York Times,* p. E6.

Barringer, F. (1992b, July 19). More Americans are saying, "I don't." *The New York Times,* p. E2.

Barringer, F. (1992c, July 17). Rate of marriage continues decline. *The New York Times,* p. A20.

Barringer, F. (1993a, April 25). Polling on sexual issues has its drawbacks. *The New York Times,* p. A23.

Barringer, F. (1993b, June 2). School hallways as gantlets of sexual taunts. *The New York Times,* p. B7.

Barringer, F. (1993c, April 18). Sex, lies and statistics. *The New York Times,* Section 4, p. 1.

Barringer, F. (1993d, April 15). Sex survey of American men finds 1% are gay. *The New York Times,* p. A1.

Barringer, F. (1993e, April 1). Viral sexual diseases are found in 1 of 5 in U.S. *The New York Times,* pp. A1, B9.

Barry, H., II, & Schlegel, A. (1984). Measurements of adolescent sexual behavior in the Standard Sample of Societies. *Ethnology, 23,* 315–329.

Bart, P. B., & O'Brien, P. B. (1985). *Stopping rape: Successful survival strategies.* Elmsford, NY: Pergamon Press.

Bartel, G. D. (1971). *Group sex: A scientific eyewitness report on the American way of swinging.* New York: Wyden.

Bartell, G. (1970). Group sex among mid-Americans. *Journal of Sex Research, 6,* 113–131.

Bartlett, J. G. (1993). Zidovudine now or later? *The New England Journal of Medicine, 329,* 351-352. (Editorial)

Basgara, O., et al. (1993). Alcohol intake increases human immunodeficiency virus type 1 replication in human peripheral blood mononuclear cells. The Journal of Infectious Diseases, 167, 789-797.

Bassoff, E. S., & Glass, G. V. (1982). The relationship between sex roles and mental health: A meta-analysis of twenty-six studies. *Counseling Psychologist, 10,* 105–112.

Bateson, G., & Mead, M. (1942). *A photographic analysis.* New York: The New York Academy of Sciences.

Baucom, D. H., & Danker-Brown, P. (1979). Influence of sex roles on the development of learned helplessness. *Journal of Consulting and Clinical Psychology, 47* 928–936.

Baum, A., & Nesselhof, S. E. A. (1988). Psychological research and the prevention, etiology, and treatment of AIDS. *American Psychologist, 3,* 900–906.

Bauman, K. E., & Wilson, R. R. (1976). Premarital sexual attitudes of unmarried university students. *Archives of Sexual Behavior, 5,* 29–37.

Baumeister, R. F. (1988a). Gender differences in masochistic scripts. *Journal of Sex Research, 25,* 478–499.

Baumeister, R. F. (1988b). Masochism as escape from self. *Journal of Sex Research, 25,* 28–59.

Baxter, D. J., Barbaree, H. E., & Marshall, W. L. (1986). Sexual responses to consenting and forced sex in a large sample of rapists and nonrapists. *Behaviour Research and Therapy, 17,* 215–222.

Beach, S. R. H., Jouriles, E. N., & O'Leary, K. D. (1985). Extramarital sex: Impact on depression and commitment in couples seeking marital therapy. *Journal of Sex and Marital Therapy, 11,* 99–108.

Beach, F. A. (1976). Cross-species comparisons and the human heritage. *Archives of Sexual Behavior, 5,* 469–485.

Beck, J. G., & Barlow, D. H. (1984). Current conceptualizations of sexual dysfunction: A review and an alternative perspective. *Clinical Psychology Review, 4,* 363–378.

Beck, A. (1988). *Love is never enough.* New York: Harper & Row.

Beck, J. G. (1993). Vaginismus. In W. O'Donohue & J. H. Geer (Eds.), *Handbook of sexual dysfunctions: Assessment and treatment.* (pp. 381-397). Boston: Allyn & Bacon.

Beck, J. G., & Davies, D. K. (1987). Teen contraception: A review of perspectives on compliance. *Archives of Sexual Behavior, 16,* 337–368.

Beck, J. G., et al. (1984, August). *A cognitive processing account of anxiety and sexual arousal: The role of selective attention, thought content, and affective states.* Paper presented at the annual convention of the American Psychological Association, Toronto, Ontario, Canada.

Becker, J. V., et al. (1989). Factors associated with erection in adolescent sex offenders. *Journal of Psychopathology and Behavioral Assessment, 11,* 353–362.

Becker, J. V. (1990). Treating adolescent sexual offenders. *Professional Psychology: Research and Practice, 21,* 362–365.

Becker, J. V., et al. (1989). Factors associated with erection in adolescent sex offenders. *Journal of Psychopathology and Behavioral Assessment, 11,* 353–362.

Becker, J. V., et al. (1986). Level of postassault sexual functioning in rape and incest victims. *Archives of Sexual Behavior, 15,* 37–49.

Becker, J. V., & Skinner, L. J. (1984). Behavioral treatment of sexual dysfunctions in sexual assault survivors. In I. R. Stuart & J. G. Greer (Eds.), *Victims of sexual aggression* (pp. 211–233). New York: Van Nostrand Reinhold.

Beckwith, C. (1983, October). Niger's Wodaabe: People of the taboo. *National Geographic Magazine,* 482–509.

Begley, S. (1993, July 26). Does DNA make some men gay? *Newsweek,* p. 59.

Behrens, D. (1990, September 21). Test-tube baby in tug-of-war. *New York Newsday,* pp. 3, 23.

Beitchman, J. H., et al. (1992). A review of the long-term effects of child sexual abuse. *Child Abuse and Neglect, 16,* 101-118.

Belcastro, P. A. (1985). Sexual behavior differences between black and white students. *Journal of Sex Research, 21,* 56–67.

Belch, M. A., Belch, G. E., & Hollgerson, B. E. (1982). Psychophysiological and cognitive responses to sex in advertising. In A. Mitchell (Ed.), *Advances in Consumer Research, IX* (pp. 424–427). Ann Arbor, MI: Association for Consumer Research.

Bell, A. P., & Weinberg, M. S. (1978). *Homosexualities: A study of diversity among men and women.* New York: Simon & Schuster.

Bell, A. P., Weinberg, M. S., & Hammersmith, S. K. (1981). *Sexual preference: Its development in men and women.* Bloomington, IN: University of Indiana Press.

Bell, R. (1980). *Changing bodies, changing lives.* New York: Random House.

Bellis, D. J. (1990). Fear of AIDS and risk reduction among heroin-addicted female street prostitutes: Personal interviews with 72 Southern California subjects. *Journal of Alcohol and Drug Education, 35,* 26-37.

Bello, D. C., Pitts, R. E., & Etzel, M. J. (1983). The communications effects of controversial sexual content in television programs and commercials. *Journal of Advertising, 12, (3),* 32–42.

Belsky, J. (1984). The determinants of parenting: A process model. *Child Development, 55,* 83–96.

Belzer, E. (1981). Orgasmic expulsions of women: A review and heuristic inquiry. *Journal of Sex Research, 17,* 1–12.

Belzer, E. G., Jr., Whipple, B., & Moger, W. (1984). On female ejaculation. *Journal of Sex Research, 20,* 403–406.

Bem, S. L. (1975). Sex role adaptability: One consequence of psychological androgyny. *Journal of Personality and Social Psychology, 31,* 634–643.

Bem, S. L. (1974). The measurement of psychological androgyny. *Journal of Consulting and Clinical Psychology, 42,* 151-162.

Bem, S. L. (1985). Androgyny and gender schema theory: A conceptual and empirical integration. In T. B. Sonderegger (Ed.), *Nebraska symposium on motivation, 1984: Psychology and gender.* Lincoln: University of Nebraska Press.

Bem, S. L. (1983). Gender schema theory and its implications for child development: Raising gender-aschematic children in a gender-schematic society. *Signs, 8,* 598–616.

Bem, S. L. (1981). Gender schema theory: A cognitive account of sex typing. *Psychological Review, 88,* 354–364.

Bem, S. L., & Bem, D. J. (1973). Training the woman to know her place: The power of a nonconscious ideology. In L. S. Wrightsman & J. C. Brigham (Eds.), *Contemporary issues in social psychology* (2nd ed.) Monterey, CA: Brooks/Cole.

Bem, S. L., & Lenney, E. (1976). Sex typing and the avoidance of cross-sexed behaviors. *Journal of Personality and Social Psychology, 33,* 48–54.

Bem, S. L., Martyna, W., & Watson, C. (1976). Sex typing and androgyny: Further explorations of the expressive domain. *Journal of Personality and Social Psychology, 34,* 1016–1023.

Benedek, E., & Vaughn, R. (1982). Voluntary childlessness. In M. Kirkpatrick (Ed.), *Women's sexual experience* New York: Plenum Press.

Benedict, R. (1934). *Patterns of culture.* Boston: Houghton Mifflin.

Benet, S. (1974). *Abkhasians: The long living people of the Caucasus.* New York: Holt, Rinehart & Winston.

Bennett, N. G., Blanc, A. K., & Bloom, D. E. (1988). Commitment and the modern union: Assessing the link between premarital cohabitation and subsequent marital stability. *American Sociological Review, 53,* 127–138.

Benson, K. A. (1984). Comment on Crocker's "An analysis of university definitions of sexual harassment". *Signs, 9,* 516–519.

Bentler, P. M. (1976). A typology of transsexualism: Gender identity theory and data. *Archives of Sexual Behavior, 5,* 567–584.

Bentler, P. M., & Newcomb, M. D. (1978). Longitudinal study of marital success and failure. *Journal of Consulting and Clinical Psychology, 46,* 1053–1070.

Bentler, P. M., & Abramson, P. R. (1981). The science of sex research: Some methodological considerations. *Archives of Sexual Behavior, 10,* 225–252.

Berelson, B. (1979). The value of children: A taxonomical essay. In J. G. Wells (ed.), *Current issues in marriage and the family* (2nd ed.). New York: Macmillan.

Berg, J. H., & Peplau, L. A. (1982). Loneliness: The relationship of self-disclosure and androgyny. *Personality and Social Psychology Bulletin, 8,* 624–630.

Berger, C. R., & Calabrese, R. J. (1975). Some explorations in initial interaction and beyond: Toward a developmental theory of interpersonal communication. *Human Communication Research, 1,* 99–112.

Berger, C. R., et al. (1976). Perceptions of information sequencing in relationship development. *Human Communication Research, 3,* 29–46.

Berger, J. (1991, November 27). Matter-of-factly, New York City begins school condom program. *The New York Times,* pp. A1, B2.

Berger, K. S. (1988). *The developing person through the life span.* New York: Worth Publishers, Inc.

Berkowitz, W. R., Nebel, J. C., & Reitman, J. W. (1971). *Height and interpersonal attraction: The 1960 mayoral election in New York City.* Paper presented to the American Psychological Association, Washington, DC.

Berlin, F. S. (1989). The paraphilias and Depo-provera: Some medical, ethical and legal considerations. *Bulletin of the American Academy of Psychiatry and the Law, 17,* 233–239.

Berlin, F. (1983). Sex offenders: A biomedical perspective and a status report of biomedical treatment. In J. G. Greer & I. R. Stuart (Eds.), *The sexual aggressor* (pp. 83–123). New York: Van Nostrand Reinhold.

Berlin, F. S., & Meinecke, C. F. (1981). Treatment of sexual offenders with antiandrogenic medication: Conceptualization, review of treatment modalities, and preliminary findings. *American Journal of Psychiatry, 138,* 601.

Bernard, J. (1975). Notes on changing lifestyles, 1970–1974. *Journal of Marriage and the Family, 37,* 582–593.

Bernstein, S. J., et al. (1993). The appropriateness of hysterectomy: A comparison of care in seven health plans. *Journal of the American Medical Association, 269,* 2398-2402.

Bernstein, W. M., et al. (1983). Causal ambiguity and heterosexual affiliation. *Journal of Experimental Social Psychology, 19,* 78–92.

Berscheid, E., & Walster, E. (1978). *Interpersonal attraction.* Reading, MA: Addison-Wesley.

Berscheid, E. (1988). Some comments on love's anatomy: Or, whatever happened to old-fashioned lust? In R. J. Sternberg & M. L. Barnes (Eds.), *The psychology of love* (pp. 359–374). New Haven: Yale University Press.

Berscheid, E., et al. (1971). Physical attractiveness and dating choice: A test of the matching hypothesis. *Journal of Experimental Social Psychology, 7,* 173–189.

Berscheid, E., & Walster, E. H. (1974). Physical attractiveness. In L. Berkowitz (Ed.), *Advances in Experimental Social Psychology,* (Vol. 7). New York: Academic Press.

Berzins, J. I., Welling, M. A., & Wetter, R. E. (1977). *The PRF ANDRO scale: User's manual.* Unpublished manuscript, University of Kentucky.

Bess, B. E., & Janus, S. S. (1976). Prostitution. In B. J. Sadock, et al. (Eds.), *The sexual experience* Baltimore: Williams & Wilkins.

Beutler, L. E., et al. (1986). Inflatable and noninflatable penile prostheses: Comparative follow-up evaluation. *Urology, 28,* 136–143.

Bezanson, R. P. (1988). Solomon would weep: A comment on "In the matter of Baby M" and the limits of judicial authority [Special Issue: Forum on surrogate motherhood: Politics and privacy]. *Law, Medicine and Health Care, 16,* 126–130.

Bieber, I. (1975). Biosocial roots of childhood sexuality. In E. Adelson (Ed.), *Sexuality and Psychoanalysis.* New York: Brunner/Mazel.

Bieber, I. (1976). A discussion of "Homosexuality: The ethical challenge." *Journal of Consulting and Clinical Psychology, 44,* 163–166.

Bieber, I., et al. (1962). *Homosexuality.* New York: Basic Books.

Biggar, R. J., & Melbye, M. (1992). Responses to anonymous questionnaires concerning sexual behavior: A method to examine potential biases. *American Journal of Public Health, 82,* 1506-1512.

Billingham, R. E., & Sack, A. R. (1986). Gender differences in college students' willingness to participate in alternative marriage and family relationships. *Family Perspectives, 20,* 37–44.

Billings, E. L., & Billings, J. J. (1974). *Atlas of the ovulation method.* Collegeville, MN: The Liturgical Press.

Billy, J. O. G., et al. (1993). The sexual behavior of men in the United States. *Family Planning Perspectives, 25,* 52-60.

Bing, E. D. (1983). *Dear Elizabeth Bing: We've had our baby.* New York: Pocket Books.

Binion, V. J. (1990). Psychological androgyny: A Black female perspective. *Sex Roles, 22,* 487–507.

Birk, L., et al. (1973). Serum testosterone levels in homosexual men. *New England Journal of Medicine, 289,* 1236–1238.

Bitter, R. G. (1986). Late marriage and marital instability: The effects of heterogeneity and inflexibility. *Journal of Marriage and the Family, 48,* 631–640.

Bixler, R. H. (1981). The incest controversy. *Psychological Reports, 49,* 267–283.

Bixler, R. H. (1989). Diversity: A historical/comparative perspective. *Behavioral and Brain Sciences, 12,* 15–16.

Blader, J. C., & Marshall, W. L. (1989). Is assessment of sexual arousal in rapists worthwhile? A critique of current methods and the development of a response compatability approach. *Clinical Psychology Review, 9,* 569-587.

Blair, C. D., & Lanyon, R. I. (1981). Exhibitionism: A critical review of the etiology and treatment. *Psychological Bulletin, 89,* 439–463.

Blakeley, M. K. (1985). Is one woman's sexuality another woman's pornography? The question behind a major legal battle. *Ms.,* pp. 37–47, 120–123.

Blakeslee, S. (1992, January 22). An epidemic of genital warts raises concern but not alarm. *The New York Times,* p. C12.

Blakeslee, S. (1993, June 2). New therapies are helping men to overcome impotence. *The New York Times,* p. C12.

Blakeslee, S. (1988, September 8). New groups aim to help parents face grief when a newborn dies. *The New York Times,* p. B13.

Blanc, A. K. (1987). The formation and dissolution of second unions: Marriage and cohabitation in Sweden and Norway. *Journal of Marriage and the Family, 49,* 391–400.

Blanchard, R. (1989). The classification and labeling of nonhomosexual gender dysphorias. *Archives of Sexual Behavior, 18,* 315–334.

Blanchard, R., & Hucker, S. J. (1991). Age, transvestism, bondage, and concurrent paraphilic activities in 117 fatal cases of autoerotic asphyxia. *British Journal of Psychiatry, 159,* 371-377.

Blanchard, R., Steiner, B.W., & Clemmensen, L.H. (1985). Gender dysphoria, gender reorientation, and the clinical management of transsexualism. *Journal of Consulting and Clinical Psychology, 53,* 295-304.

Blanchard, E. B., et al. (1985). Behavioral treatment of 250 chronic headache patients: A clinical replication series. *Behavior Therapy, 16,* 308–327.

Blau, P., Beeker, C., & Fitzpatrick, K. M. (1984). Intersecting social affiliations and intermarriage. *Social Forces, 62,* 585–606.

Blenner, J. L. (1992). Stress and mediators: Patients' perceptions of infertility treatment. *Nursing Research, 41,* 92-97.

Blood test's value in early prostate cases. (1993, August 25). *The New York Times,* p. C10.

Bloom, B. J., Asher, S. J., & White, S. W. (1978). Marital disruption as a stressor: A review and analysis. *Psychological Bulletin, 85,* 867–894.

Bloom, D. E., & Bennett, N. G. (1986). Childless couples. *American Demographics, 8,* 22–25.

Bloom, B. L., & Kindle, K. R. (1985). Demographic factors in the continuing relationship between former spouses. *Family Relations, 34,* 375–381.

Bloor, M., McKeganey, N., & Barnard, M. (1990). An ethnographic study of HIV-related risk practices among Glasgow rent boys and their clients: Report of a pilot study. *AIDS Care, 2,* 17–24.

Blum, H. P. (1976). Masochism, the ego ideal, and the psychology of women. *Journal of the American Psychoanalytic Association, 24,* 157–191.

Blumstein, P. & Schwartz, P. (1990). Intimate relationships and the creation of sexuality. In D. P. McWhirter, S. A. Sanders, & J. M. Reinisch (Eds.), *Homosexuality/heterosexuality: Concepts of sexual orientation* (pp. 307–320). New York: Oxford University Press.

Blumstein, P. W., & Schwartz, P. (1977). Bisexuality: Some social psychological issues. *Journal of Social Issues, 3,* 30–45.

Blumstein, P., & Schwartz, P. (1983). *American couples: Money, work, sex.* New York: William Morrow.

Bohannan, P. (1971). The six stations of divorce. In P. Bohannan (Ed.), *Divorce and after* (pp. 33–62). New York: Anchor Books.

Bohlen, C. (1987, April 4). In Moscow and Warsaw, the press begins to report on the hidden side of life. *Washington Post.*

Bolling, D. R., & Voeller, B. (1987). AIDS and heterosexual anal intercourse. *Journal of the American Medical Association, 258,* 474.

Bonavoglia, A. (1991). *The choices we made.* New York: Random House, 137–141.

Bond, S., & Mosher, D. (1986). Guided imagery of rape: Fantasy, reality, and willing victim myth. *Journal of Sex Research, 22,* 162–183.

Boodman, S. (1993, April 8). A doctor's story: A firm belief that "What goes around comes around." *Washington Post,* p. A16.

Booth, A., & Johnson, D. (1988). Premarital cohabitation and marital success. *Journal of Family Issues, 9,* 255–272.

Booth, A., & Edwards, J. N. (1985). Age at marriage and marital instability. *Journal of Marriage and the Family, 47,* 67–75.

Bornoff, N. (1991). *Pink samurai: Love, marriage & sex in contemporary Japan.* New York: Pocket Books.

Boston Women's Health Book Collective. (1979). *Our Bodies, ourselves.* New York: Simon & Schuster.

Boston Women's Health Book Collective. (1984). *The new our bodies, ourselves.* New York: Simon & Schuster.

Boswell, J. (1990). Sexual and ethical categories in premodern Europe. In D. P. McWhirter, S. A. Sanders, & J. M. Reinisch (Eds.) *Homosexuality/Heterosexuality: Concepts of sexual orientation* (pp. 15–31). New York: Oxford University Press.

Both-Orthman, B., et al. (1988). Menstrual cycle phase: Related changes in appetite in patients with premenstrual syndrome and in control subjects. *American Journal of Psychiatry, 145,628–631.*

Boulton, M., Hart, G., & Fitzpatrick, R. (1992). The sexual behaviour of bisexual men in relation to HIV transmission *AIDS Care, 4,* 165-175.

Bowe, C. (1986, May). What are men like today? *Cosmopolitan,* p. 263 et passim.

Bowie, W. (1990). Approach to men with urethritis and urological complications of sexually transmitted diseases. *Medical Clinics of North America, 74,* 1543-1557.

Bowie, W. R. (1990). Approach to men with urethritis and urologic complications of sexually-transmitted diseases. *Medical Clinics of North America, 74,* 1543–1557.

Bowie, W. (1984). Epidemiology and therapy of chlamydia trachomatis infections. *Drugs, 27,* 459–468.

Bowlby, J. (1969). *Attachment and loss,* (Vol. 1). New York: Basic Books.

Boyer, D. (1989). Male prostitution and homosexual identity. [Special Issue: Gay and lesbian youth: I]. *Journal of Homosexuality, 17,* 151–184.

Bradbard, M.R., & Endsley, R.C. (1983). The effects of sex typed labeling on preschool children's information-seeking and retention. *Sex Roles, 9.* 247-261.

Bradford, J. (1985). Organic treatment for the male sexual offender. *Behavioral Sciences & the Law, 3/4,* 355–375.

Brady, E. C., et al. (1991). Date rape: Expectations, avoidance strategies, and attitudes toward victims. *Journal of Social Psychology, 131,* 427-429.

Bram, S. (1984). Voluntarily childless women: Traditional or nontraditional? *Sex Roles, 10,* 195–206.

Branden, N. (1981). *The psychology of romantic love.* New York: Bantam.

Braude, A. I., Davis, C. E., & Fierer, J. (Eds.). (1986). *Infectious diseases and medical microbiology* (2nd ed.) Philadelphia: W. B. Saunders.

Breakwell, G. M., & Fife-Schaw, C. R. (1992). Sexual activities and preferences in a United Kingdom sample of 16- to 20-year-olds. *Archives of Sexual Behavior, 21,* 271-293.

Breast fears fade. (1993, November). *Prevention,* pp. 19-20.

Brecher, E. M, and the Editors of Consumer Reports Books. (1984). *Love, sex, and aging.* Boston: Little, Brown.

Breiman, K. (1991, February 6). Debate over plan to distribute condoms in New York City Public schools [Recording]. Brooklyn, NY: Department of Education.

Breslow, N. (1989). Sources of confusion in the study and treatment of sadomasochism. *Journal of Social Behavior and Personality, 4,* 263–274.

Breslow, N., Evans, L., & Langley, J. (1986). Comparisons among heterosexual, bisexual and homosexual male sadomasochists. *Journal of Homosexuality, 13,* 83–107.

Breslow, N., Evans, L., & Langley, J. (1985). On the prevalence and roles of females in the sadomasochistic subculture: Report on an empirical study. *Archives of Sexual Behavior, 14,* 303–317.

Bretl, D. J., & Cantor, J. (1988). The portrayal of men and women in U.S. television commercials: A recent content analysis and trends over 15 years. *Sex Roles, 18,* 595–609.

Bretschneider, J., & McCoy, N. (1988). Sexual interest and behavior in healthy 80- to 102-year olds. *Archives of Sexual Behavior, 17,* 109.

Brewer, J. J. (1982). A history of erotic art as illustrated in the collectors of the Institute for Sex Research (The "Kinsey Institute"). In A. Hoch & H. I. Lief (Eds.), *Sexology: Sexual biology, behavior and therapy* (pp. 318–321). Amsterdam, The Netherlands: Excerpta Medica.

Brewer, J. S. (1981). Duration of intromission and female orgasm rates. *Medical Aspects of Human Sexuality, 15,* 70–71.

Briddell, D. W., & Wilson, G. T. (1976). Effects of alcohol and expectancy set on male sexual arousal. *Journal of Abnormal Psychology, 85,* 225–234.

Briere, J., & Runtz, M. (1989). University males' sexual interest in children: Predicting potential indices of "pedophilia" in a nonforensic sample. *Child Abuse and Neglect, 13,* 65–75.

Briere, J., & Runtz, M. (1987). Post sexual abuse trauma: Data and implications for clinical practice. *Journal of Interpersonal Violence, 2,* 367–379.

Brigham, J. C. (1980). Limiting conditions of the "physical attractiveness stereotype": Attributions about divorce. *Journal of Research in Personality, 14,* 365–375.

Brigman, W. (1986). Pornography as political expression. *Journal of Popular Culture, 17(2),* 129–134.

Briselden, A. M., & Hillier, S. L. (1990). Longitudinal study of the biotypes of Gardnerella vaginalis. *Journal of Clinical Microbiology, 28,* 2761–2764.

Brock, B. V., et al. (1990). Frequency of asymptomatic shedding of herpes simplex virus in women with genital herpes. *Journal of the American Medical Association, 263,* 418–420.

Brodbar-Nemzer, J. Y. (1986). Divorce and group commitment: The case of the Jews. *Journal of Marriage and the Family, 48,* 329–340.

Broderick, C. B. (1966). Sexual development among preadolescents. *The Journal of Social Issues, 22,* 6–21.

Brody, J. (1982). *Jane Brody's The New York Times guide to personal health.* New York: Times Books.

Brody, J. E. (1988, May 5). Sifting fact from myth in the face of asthma's growing threat to American children. *The New York Times,* p. B19.

Brody, J. E. (1989, January 5). How women can begin to cope with premenstrual syndrome, a biological mystery. *The New York Times,* p. B12.

Brody, J.E. (1990a, August 2). In fight against breast cancer, mammograms are a crucial tool, but not foolproof. *The New York Times,* p. B5.

Brody, J. E. (1991, January 3). Hysterectomies, the second-most frequent operation, need not be so common, some say. *The New York Times,* p. B5.

Brody, J. E. (1984, March 27). Autoerotic death of youths causes widening concern. *The New York Times,* pp. 17, 20.

Brody, J. E. (1992b, August 12). Genital herpes thrives on ignorance and secrecy. *The New York Times,* p. C12.

Brody, J. E. (1991, June 5). The value and limits of the mammogram and exams. *The New York Times,* p. C10.

Brody, J. E. (1986, December 16). Boyhood effeminacy and later homosexuality. *The New York Times,* pp. C1, C8.

Brody, J. E. (1990, January 23). Scientists trace aberrant sexuality. *The New York Times,* pp. C11, C12.

Brody, J. E. (1993c, December 8). Deciding how, or whether, to treat menopause. *The New York Times,* p. C. 16.

Brody, J. E. (1992e, November 11). PMS is a worldwide phenomenon. *The New York Times,* p. C14.

Brody, J. E. (1992a, April 29). How to outwit a rapist: Rehearse. *The New York Times,* p. C13.

Brody, J. E. (1992d, October 7). Living with a diagnosis of H.I.V. infection. *The New York Times,* p. C13.

Brody, J. E. (1989, July 27). Research casts doubt on need for many Caesarean births as their rate soars. *The New York Times,* p. B5.

Brody, J. E. (1993g, October 6). Study ties prostate deaths to animal fat. *The New York Times,* p. C13.

Brody, J. E. (1993a, August 4). A new look at an old quest for sexual stimulants. *The New York Times,* p. C12.

Brody, J. E. (1993e, July 7). Genital herpes drug found safe for daily use. *The New York Times,* p. C11

Brody, J. E. (1993b, December 14). Breast cancer screening under 50: Some radiologists asay the evidence will emerge in time. *The New York Times,* pp. C1, C16.

Brody, J. E. (1992a, May 20). Alternatives to hormone therapy after menopause. *The New York Times,* p. C14.

Brody, J. E. (1993f, June 2). Ovary cancer: Still working toward early diagnosis. *The New York Times,* p. C12.

Broman, S. H. (1981). Long-term development of children born to teenagers. In K. Scott, T. Field, & E. G. Robertson (Eds.), *Teenage parents and their offspring* (pp. 194–224). New York: Grune & Stratton.

Bronfenbrenner, U. (1960). Freudian theories of identification and their derivatives. *Child Development, 31,* 15–40.

Brooke, J. (1993, January 25). In deception and denial, an epidemic looms: AIDS in Latin America. *The New York Times,* pp. A1, A6.

Brookmeyer, R. (1991). Reconstruction and future trends of the AIDS epidemic in the United States. *Science, 253,* 37–42.

Brooks, J., Ruble, D. N., & Clarke, A. E. (1977). College women's attitudes and expectations concerning menstrual-related changes. *Psychosomatic Medicine, 39,* 288.

Brooks, V. R. (1982). Sex differences in student dominance behavior in female and male professors' classrooms. *Sex Roles, 8,* 683–690.

Brooks-Gunn, J., Boyer, C. B., & Hein, K. (1988). Preventing HIV infection and AIDS in children and adolescents. *American Psychologist, 43,* 958–964.

Brooks-Gunn, J., & Furstenberg, F. F. (1989). Adolescent sexual behavior. *American Psychologist, 44,* 249–257.

Brooks-Gunn, J., & Ruble, D. (1983). Dysmenorrhea in adolescence. In S. Golub (Ed.), *Menarche.* Lexington, MA: Lexington Books.

Brooks-Gunn, J., & Matthews, W. S. (1979). *He and she: How children develop their sex-role identity.* Englewood Cliffs, NJ: Spectrum.

Brooks-Gunn, J., et al. (1986). Physical similarity of and disclosure of menarchal status to friends: Effects of grade and pubertal status. *Journal of Early Adolescence, 6,* 3–14.

Broude, G. J., & Greene, S. J. (1976). Cross-cultural codes on twenty sexual attitudes and practices. *Ethnology, 15,* 409–429.

Broverman, I. K., et. al. (1972). Sex-role steretypes: A current appraisal. *Journal of Social Issues, 28(2),* 59–78.

Brown, D., & Bryant, J. (1989). The manifest content of pornography. In D. Zillmann & J. Bryant (Eds.), *Pornography: Research advances and policy considerations* (pp. 3–24). Hillsdale, NJ: Lawrence Erlbaum Associates.

Brown, J. B., et al. (1987). Natural family planning. *American Journal of Obstetrics and Gynecology, 157,* 1082–1089.

Brown, M., Amoroso, D., & Ware, E. (1976). Behavioral aspects of viewing pornography. *Journal of Social Psychology, 98,* 235–245.

Brown, N. A., Goulding, E. H., & Fabros, S. (1979). Ethanol embryotoxicity: Direct effects on mammalian embryos in vitro. *Science, 206,* 573–575.

Brown, Z. A., et al. (1991). Neonatal herpes simplex virus infection in relation to asymptomatic maternal infection at the time of labor. *The New England Journal of Medicine, 324,* 1247–1252.

Brownmiller, S. (1975). *Against our will: Men, women, and rape.* New York: Simon & Schuster.

Brozan, N. (1984, January 9). Helping to heal the scars left by incest. *The New York Times.*

Brozan, N. (1991, March 7). Rise in anti-gay crimes is reported in New York. *The New York Times,* p. B3.

Bruce, K. E. M., & Bullins, C. G. (1989). Students' attitudes and knowledge about genital herpes. *Journal of Sex Education and Therapy, 15,* 257–270.

Bryant, J., & Brown, D. (1989). Uses of pornography. In D. Zillmann & J. Bryant (Eds.), *Pornography: Research advances and policy considerations* (pp. 25–55). Hillsdale, NJ: Lawrence Erlbaum Associates.

Buchanan, M., & Robbins, C. (1990). Early adult psychological consequences for males of adolescent pregnancy and its resolution. *Journal of Youth and Adolescence, 19,* 413–424.

Buffum, J. (1985). Pharmacosexology update: Yohimbine and sexual function. *Journal of Psychoactive Drugs, 17,* 131–132.

Buhaug, H., et al. (1990). Should asymptomatic patients be tested for Chlamydia trachomatis in general practice? *British Journal of General Practice, 40,* 142–145.

Buhrich, N., et al. (1979). Plasma testosterone, serum FSH, and serum LH levels in transvestism. *Archives of Sexual Behavior, 8,* 49–54.

Bularzik, M. (1978). Sexual harassment at the workplace: Historical notes. *Radical America, 12,* 25-43.

Bulcroft, K., & O'Connor-Roden, M. (1986, June). The importance of dating relationships on quality of life for older persons. Never too late. *Psychology Today,* pp. 66–69.

Bullough, V. (1990). The Kinsey Scale in historical perspective. In D. P. McWhirter, S. A. Sanders, & J. M. Reinisch (Eds.) *Homosexuality/heterosexuality: Concepts of sexual orientation* (pp. 3–14). New York: Oxford University Press.

Bullough, V. L. (1991). Transvestism: A reexamination. *Journal of Psychology and Human Sexuality, 4,* 53-67.

Bullough, V. L. (1976). *Sexual variance in society and history.* New York: Wiley & Sons.

Bullough, V. L. (1984). Weighing the shift from sexual identity to sexual relationships. *Journal of Homosexuality, 10(3/4),* 3–14.

Bullough, V. L., & Weinberg, T. S. (1989). Women married to transvestites: Problems and adjustments. *Journal of Psychology & Human Sexuality, 1,* 83–104.

Bumiller, E. (1990, October 25). Japan's abortion agony: In a country that prohibits the pill, reality collides with religion. *Washington Post.*

Bumpas, L. L. (1991, December 4). Cited in Pear, R. Larger number of new mothers are unmarried. *The New York Times,* p. A20.

Bumpas, L., Sweet, J., & Castro, T. (1988, August). *Changing patterns of remarriage.* Paper presented at the meeting of the American Sociological Association, Atlanta, Georgia.

The bum's rush in advertising: Some turn-on commercials appear to be turn-offs. p. 52. *Time,* (1980, December 1).

Burden, D. S. (1986). Single parents and the work setting: The impact of multiple job and home-life responsibilities. *Family Relations, 35,* 37–44.

Burgess, A. W., & Hartman, C. R. (1986). *Sexual exploitation of patients by health professionals.* New York: Praeger.

Burgess, A. W., & Holmstrom, L. L. (1974). Rape trauma syndrome. *American Journal of Psychiatry, 131,* 981–986.

Burgess, A. W., & Holmstrom, L. L. (1978). Recovery from rape and prior life stress. *Research in Nursing and Health, 1,* 165–174.

Burgess, A. W., & Holmstrom, L. L. (1979). *Rape: Crisis and recovery.* New York: Brady Communications.

Burke, D. S., et al. (1988). Measurement of the false positive rate in a screening program for human immunodeficiency virus infections. *New England Journal of Medicine, 319,* 961–964.

Burkhart, B., & Fromuth, M. E. (1991). Individual psychological and social psychological understandings of sexual coercion. In E. Grauerholz & M. A. Koralewski (Eds.), *Sexual coercion: A sourcebook on its nature, causes, and prevention* (pp. 7–89). Lexington, MA: Lexington Books.

Burkman, R.T. (1981). The Women's Health Study: Association between intrauterine device and pelvic inflammatory disease. *Obstetrics & Gynecology, 57,* 269.

Burnam, M. A., et al. (1988). Sexual assault and mental disorders in a community population. *Journal of Consulting and Clinical Psychology, 56,* 843–850.

Burnell, G. M., & Norfleet, M. A. (1987). Women's self-reported responses to abortion. *The Journal of Psychology, 121,* 71–76.

Burns, G. L., & Farina, A. (1987). Physical attractiveness and self-perception of mental disorder. *Journal of Abnormal Psychology, 96,* 161–163.

Burr, C. (1993, August 2). The search for sexual identity: Genes vs. hormones. *The New York Times,* p. A15.

Burt, M. R. (1980). Cultural myths and supports for rape. *Journal of Personality and Social Psychology, 38,* 217–230.

Busch, M. P., et al. (1991). Evaluation of screened blood donations for HIV-1 infection by culture and DNA amplification of pooled cells. *The New England Journal of Medicine, 325,* 1–5.

Buss, D. M., & Barnes, M. (1986). Preferences in human mate selection. *Journal of Personality and Social Psychology, 50,* 559–570.

Buss, D. M. (1985). Human mate selection. *American Scientist, 73,* 47–51.

Buss, D. M. (1984). Toward a psychology of person-environment (PE) correlation: The role of spouse selection. *Journal of Personality and Social Psychology, 47,* 361–377.

Buss, D. M. (1989). Sex differences in human mate preferences: Evolutionary hypotheses tested in 37 cultures. *Behavioral and Brain Sciences, 12,,* 1–49.

Bustillo, M., et al. (1984). Delivery of a healthy infant following nonsurgical ovum transfer. *Journal of the American Medical Association, 251,* 889.

Byers, E. S., & Lewis, K. (1988). Dating couples' disagreements over the desired level of sexual intimacy. *Journal of Sex Research, 24,* 15–29.

Byrne, D. (1977). The imagery of sex. In Money, J., & Musaph, H. (Eds.), *Handbook of sexology* (pp. 327–350). New York: Elsevier/North Holland.

Byrne, D. (1982). Predicting human sexual behavior. In A. G. Kraut, *The G. Stanley Hall Lecture Series* (Vol. 2). Washington, DC: American Psychological Association.

Byrne, D., & Buehler, J. A. (1955). A note on the influence of propinquity upon acquaintanceships. *Journal of Abnormal and Social Psychology, 51,* 147–148.

Byrne, D., Ervin, C. R., & Lamberth, J. (1970). Continuity between the experimental study of attraction and real-life computer dating. *Journal of Personality and Social Psychology, 16,* 157–165.

Cable News Network. (1991, July). *AIDS issues: Policy for health care providers* [Television series: Blackline Master I Segments, 1, 2, 5, 9, 10]. New York: CNN.

Cado, S., & Leitenberg, H. (1990). Guilt reactions to sexual fantasies during intercourse. *Archives of Sexual Behavior, 19,* 49–64.

Cahill, L. S. (1988). The ethics of surrogate motherhood: Biology, freedom, and moral obligation. [Special Issue: Forum on surrogate motherhood: Politics and privacy] *Law, Medicine and Health Care, 16,* 65–71.

Calderone, M. S. (1983). Fetal erection and its message to us. *SIECUS Report, 11,* 9–10.

Calderone, M. S., & Johnson, E. W. (1989). *Family book about sexuality* (rev. ed.). New York: Harper & Row.

Calhoun, A. W. (1945). *A social history of the American family.* New York: Barnes & Noble.

Calhoun, K. S., & Atkeson, B. M. (1991). *Treatment of rape victims: Facilitating social adjustment.* New York: Pergamon Press.

Cameron, P., et al. (1986). Child molestation and homosexuality. *Psychological Reports, 58,* 327–337.

Campbell, A. (1975, December). The American way of mating: Marriages, children only maybe. *Psychology Today,* pp. 37–43.

Campbell, M. (1970). Anomalies of the genital tract. In M. Campbell & J. Harrison (Eds.), *Urology,* (Vol. 2). Philadelphia: W. B. Saunders Co.

Campbell, C. A. (1991). Prostitution, AIDS, and preventive health behavior. *Social Science and Medicine, 32,* 1367-1378.

Campbell, C. E., & Herten, R. J. (1981). VD to STD: Redefining venereal disease. *American Journal of Nursing, 81,* 1629–1635.

Campbell, F. L., Townes, B. D., & Beach, L. R. (1982). Motivational bases of childbearing decisions. In G. L. Fox (Ed.), *The childbearing decision.* Beverly Hills, CA: Sage.

Campbell, M. F., & Harrison, J. H. (1970). *Urology* (Vol. 1). Philadelphia: W. B. Saunders Co.

Campbell, S. B., & Cohn, J. F. (1991). Prevalence and correlates of postpartum depression in first-time mothers. *Journal of Abnormal Psychology, 100,* 594–599.

Cann, A., & Newbern, S. R. (1984). Sex stereotype effects in children's picture recognition. *Child Development, 55,* 1085–1090.

Caplow, T., & Forman, R. (1950). Neighborhood interaction in a homogeneous community. *American Sociological Review, 15,* 357–366.

Cappella, J. N., & Palmer, M. T. (1990). Attitude similarity, relational history, and attraction: The mediating effects of kinesic and vocal behaviors. *Communication Monographs, 5,* 161–183.

Carani, C., et al. (1990). Effects of androgen treatment in impotent men with normal and low levels of free testosterone. *Archives of Sexual Behavior, 19,* 223–234.

Cardell, M., Finn, S., & Marecek, J. (1981). Sex-role identity, sex-role behavior, and satisfaction in heterosexual, lesbian, and gay male couples. *Psychology of Women Quarterly, 5,* 488–494.

Carey, et al. (1992). Effectiveness of latex condoms as a barrier to human immunodeficiency virus-sized particles under conditions of simulated use. *Sexually Transmitted Diseases, 19,* 230-234.

Carlile, T. (1981). Breast cancer detection. *Cancer, 47,* 1164–1169.

Carlson, M. (1990, July 9). Abortion's hardest cases. *Time,* pp. 22–26.

Carlson, N. R. (1988). *Foundations of physiological psychology.* Boston: Allyn & Bacon.

Carmignani, G., et al. (1987). Cavernous artery revascularization in vasculogenic impotence: New simplified technique. *Urology* (Vol. 30), pp. 23–26.

Carnegie, D. (1937). *How to win friends and influence people.* New York: Simon & Schuster.

Carnes, P. (1983). *The sexual addiction.* Minneapolis: CompCare Publications.

Carpenter, C. R. (1942). Sexual behavior of free-ranging rhesus monkeys *(Macaca Mulatta). Journal of Comparative and Physiological Psychology, 33,* 113–162.

Carper, A. (1993, October 19). Questions about safety. *New York Newsday,*p. 15.

Carrera, M. (1981). *Sex: The facts, the acts and your feelings.* New York: Crown.

Carrier, J. M. (1980). Homosexual behavior in cross-cultural perspective. In J. Marmor (Ed.), *Homosexual behavior: A modern reappraisal* (pp. 100–122). New York: Basic Books.

Carrier, J. M. (1986). Childhood cross-gender behavior and adult homosexuality. *Archives of Sexual Behavior, 15,* 89–93.

Carroll, L. (1988). Concern with AIDS and the sexual behavior of college students. *Journal of Marriage and the Family, 50,* 405–411.

Carson, S. (1988). Sex selection: The ultimate in family planning. *Fertility and Sterility, 50,* 16–19.

Carter, D. B., & Levy, G. D. (1988). Cognitive aspects of early sex-role development: The influence of gender schemas on preschoolers' memories and preferences for sex-typed toys and activities. *Child Development, 59,* 782–792.

Carter, D. L., et al. (1987). Use of pornography in the criminal and developmental histories of sexual offenders. *Journal of Interpersonal Violence, 2,* 196–211.

Cartwright, R. D., et al. (1983). The traditional-liberated woman dimension: Social stereotype and self-concept. *Journal of Personality and Social Psychology, 44,* 581-588.

Cash, T. F., & Duncan, N. C. (1984). Physical attractiveness stereotyping among black American college students. *Journal of Social Psychology, 122,* 71–77.

Cass, V. C. (1979). Homosexual identity formation: A theoretical model. *Journal of Homosexuality, 4,* 219–235.

Cass, V. C. (1983/1984). Homosexual identity: A concept in need of definition. *Journal of Homosexuality, 9,* 105–126.

Cass, V. C. (1990). The implications of homosexual identity formation for the Kinsey Model and Scale of Sexual Preference. In D. P. McWhirter, S. A. Sanders, & J. M. Reinisch (Eds.), *Homosexuality/Heterosexuality: Concepts of sexual orientation* (pp. 239–266). New York: Oxford University Press.

Castro, J. (1992, January 20). Sexual harassment: A guide. *Time magazine,* p. 37.

Castro, K. G., et al. (1988). Transmission of HIV in Belle Glade, Florida: Lessons for other communities in the United States. *Science, 239,* 193–197.

Catalan, J., Hawton, K., & Day, A. (1990). Couples referred to a sexual dysfunction clinic: Psychological and physical morbidity. *British Journal of Psychiatry, 156,* 61–67.

Catalona, W. J., et al. (1991). Measurement of prostate-specific antigen in serum as a screening test for prostate cancer. *The New England Journal of Medicine, 324,* 1156–1161.

Catalona, W. J., et al. (1993). Detection of organ-confined prostate cancer is increased through prostate-specific antigen-based screening. *Journal of the American Medical Association, 270,* 948-954.

Catania, J. A., et al. (1991). Changes in condom use among homosexual men in San Francisco. *Health Psychology, 10,* 190–199.

Catania, J. A., et al. (1992a). Coping with death anxiety: Help-seeking and social support among gay men with various HIV diagnoses. *AIDS, 6,* 999-1005.

Catania, J. A., et al. (1992b). Prevalence of AIDS-related risk factors and condom use in the United States. *Science, 258,* 1101-1106.

Cates, W., & Stone, K. M. (1992a). Family planning, sexually transmitted diseases, and contraceptive choice: A literature update. *Family Planning Perspectives, 24,* 75-84.

Cates, W., Jr., & Stone, K. M. (1992b). Family planning, sexually transmitted diseases, and contraceptive choice: A literature update—Part II. *Family Planning Perspectives, 24,* 122-127

Cates, W., Jr., & Wasserheit, J. N. (1991). Genital chlamydial infections: Epidemiology and reproductive sequelae. *American Journal of Obstetrics and Gynecology, 164,* 1171-1181.

CBS News. (1991, May 22). *48 hours: For better or worse.*

CDC AIDS Hotline Communication. (1992a). January 8, 1992.

CDC AIDS Hotline Communication. (1992b). March 31, 1992.

Celis, W. (1991, January 2). Students trying to draw line between sex and an assault. *The New York Times,* pp. 1, B8.

Centers for Disease Control. (1985a). Abortion Surveillance Report, 1981. Center for Health Promotion and Education, Division of Reproductive Health, Pregnancy Epidemiology Branch. Washington, DC: U.S. Department of Health and Human Services.

Centers for Disease Control. (1985b). *Chlamydia trachomatis* infections. *Morbidity and Mortality Weekly Report, 34,* 53.

Centers for Disease Control. (1987). Public Health Service guidelines for counseling and antibody testing to prevent HIV infection and AIDS. *Morbidity and Mortality Weekly Report, 36,* 509–515.

Centers for Disease Control. (1988a). Leads from the MMWR/Morbidity and Mortality Weekly Report (Vol 37/No.7, 9, 1988): Condoms for prevention of sexually transmitted diseases. *Journal of the American Medical Association, 259,* 1925–1927.

Centers for Disease Control. (1988b). Leads from the MMWR/Morbidity and Mortality Weekly Report (Vol 37/717–727): HIV-related beliefs, knowledge, and behaviors among high school students. *Journal of the American Medical Association, 260,* 3567, 3570.

Centers for Disease Control. (1988c, April). Prevalence of human immunodeficiency virus antibody in U.S. active military personnel. *Morbidity and Mortality Weekly Report, 37,* 461.

Centers for Disease Control. (1989a). Summaries of identifiable diseases in the United States.

Centers for Disease Control. (1989b). Treatment guidelines for sexually transmitted diseases. *Morbidity and Mortality Weekly Report, 38,* No. S-8.

Centers for Disease Control. (1990a). Estimates of HIV prevalence and projected AIDS cases: Summary of a workshop, October 31–November 1, 1989. *Morbidity and Mortality Weekly Report, 39,* 110–119.

Centers for Disease Control. (1990b). Heterosexual behaviors and factors that influence condom use among patients attending a sexually transmitted disease clinic—San Francisco. *Morbidity and Mortality Weekly Report, 39,* 685–689.

Centers for Disease Control. (1990c). HIV/AIDS surveillance. Washington, D.C.: U.S. Department of Health and Human Services.

Centers for Disease Control. (1990d). HIV prevalence estimates and AIDS case projections for the United States: Report based on a workshop. *Morbidity and Mortality Weekly Report, 39,* (No. RR-16), 30.

Centers for Disease Control. (1990e). Progress toward achieving the 1990 objectives for the nation for sexually transmitted diseases. *Morbidity and Mortality Weekly Report 39,* 53–57.

Centers for Disease Control. (1990f). Update: Acquired Immunodeficiency Syndrome—

United States, 1989. *Journal of the American Medical Association, 263,* 1191–1192.

Centers for Disease Control. (1990g). Update: Serologic testing for HIV-1 antibody–United States, 1988 and 1989. *Morbidity and Mortality Weekly Report, 39,* 380–383.

Centers for Disease Control. (1991a). AIDS in women—United States. *Journal of the American Medical Association, 265,* 23.

Centers for Disease Control, Division of Sexually Transmitted Diseases/HIV Prevention. (1991b). *Annual Report.* Atlanta, GA: Centers for Disease Control.

Centers for Disease Control. (1991c). Characteristics of, and HIV infection among, women served by publicly funded HIV counseling and testing services—United States, 1989–1990. *Journal of the American Medical Association, 265,* 2051.

Centers for Disease Control. (1991d, June 15). Cited in Quarter of newborns in U.S. were born to single women. *The New York Times,* p. 9.

Centers for Disease Control. (1991e). Mortality attributable to HIV infection/AIDS—United States, 1981–1990. *Journal of the American Medical Association, 265,* 848.

Centers for Disease Control. (1991f). Premarital sexual experience among adolescent women—United States, 1970-1988. *Mortality and Morbidity Weekly Report, 39,* 929-932.

Centers for Disease Control. (1991g). Summary of notifiable diseases, United States 1990. *Morbidity and Mortality Weekly Report, 39,* 1–53.

Centers for Disease Control. (1991h). Update: Acquired immunodeficiency syndrome—United States, 1991–1990. *Morbidity and Mortality Weekly Report, 40,* 358–369.

Centers for Disease Control. (1992a). Abortion surveillance—United States, 1989. *Mortality and Morbidity Weekly Report, 41,* 955, 966.

Centers for Disease Control. (1992b, January). *HIV infection and AIDS: Are you at risk?* Atlanta: Centers for Diseases Control.

Centers for Disease Control. (1993a). Abortion surveillance: Preliminary data—United States, 1990. *Mortality and Morbidity Weekly Report, 41,* 936-938.

Centers for Disease Control. (1993b). Evaluation of surveillance for *Chlamydia trachomatis* infections in the United States, 1987 to 1991. *Mortality and Morbidity Weekly Report, 42 (SS-3),* 21-27.

Centers for Disease Control. (1993c). Projections of the number of persons diagnosed with AIDS and the number of immunosuprressed HIV-infected persons—United States, 1992-1994. Abortion surveillance—United States, 1989. *Mortality and Morbidity Weekly Report, 42,* 217-218.

Centers for Disease Control. (1993d). Selected behaviors that increase risk for HIV infection, other sexually transmitted diseases, and unintended pregnancy among high school students—United States, 1991. *Mortality and Morbidity Weekly Report, 41,* 945-950.

Centers for Disease Control. (1993e). Sexual risk behaviors of STD clinic patients before and after Earvin "Magic" Johnson's HIV-infection announcement—Maryland, 1991-1992. *Mortality and Morbidity Weekly Report, 42,* 46-48.

Centers for Disease Control. (1993f). Update: Acquired immunodeficiency syndrome—United States, 1992. *Mortality and Morbidity Weekly Report, 42 (No. 28),* pp. 547-557.

Centers for Disease Control. (1993g). Update: Barrier protection against HIV infection and other sexually transmitted diseases. Atlanta: Centers for Disease Control and Prevention. *Mortality and Morbidity Weekly Report, 42,* 589-591; 597.

Centers for Disease Control. (1993h). Update: Investigations of persons treated by HIV-infected health-care workers—United States. *Mortality and Morbidity Weekly Report, 42,* 329-331, 337.

Centers for Disease Control. (1993i). Update: Mortality attributable to HIV infection/AIDS among persons aged 25-44 years—United States, 1990 and 1991. *Mortality and Morbidity Weekly Report, 42,* 481-486.

Centers, R. (1949). Marital selection and occupational strata. *American Journal of Sociology, 54,* 530–535.

Chadda, R. K., & Ahuja, N. (1990). Dhat syndrome: A sex neurosis of the Indian subcontinent. *British Journal of Psychiatry, 156,* 577–579.

Chan, D. W. (1990). Sex knowledge, attitudes, and experiences of Chinese medical students in Hong Kong. *Archives of Sexual Behavior, 19,* 73-93.

Chance of breast cancer is figured at 1 in 8. (1992, September 27). *The New York Times,* p. A30.

Chasnoff, I. J., et al. (1985). Cocaine use in pregnancy. *The New England Journal of Medicine, 313,* 666–669.

Chateau, D., & Aron, C.L. (1988). Heterotypic sexual behavior in male rats after lesions in different amygdaloid nuclei. *Hormones and Behavior, 22* 379-387.

Cheating going out of style but sex is popular as ever. (October 19, 1993). *Newsday,* p. 2.

Check, J. V. P. (1985). *The effects of violent and nonviolent pornography.* Report to the Department of Justice, Ottawa, Ontario, Canada.

Check, J. V. P., & Guloien, J. (1989). Reported proclivity for coercive sex following repeated exposure to sexually violent pornography, nonviolent dehumanizing pornography, and erotica. In D. Zillmann & J. Bryant (Eds.), *Pornography: Research advances and policy considerations* (pp. 159–184). Hillsdale, NJ: Lawrence Erlbaum Associates.

Check, J. V. P., & Malamuth, N. M. (1983). Sex-role stereotyping and reactions to depictions of stranger versus acquaintance rape. *Journal of Personality and Social Psychology, 45,* 344–356.

Chelune, G. A. (1976). A multidimensional look at sex and target differences in disclosure. *Psychological Reports, 39,* 259–263.

Cherlin, A. J. (1981). *Marriage, divorce, remarriage.* Cambridge, MA: Harvard University Press.

Cherlin, A. J., & McCarthy, J. (1985). Remarried couple households: Data from the June 1980 Current Population Survey. *Journal of Marriage and the Family, 47,* 23–30.

Chevalier-Skolnikoff, S. (1976). Homosexual behavior in a laboratory group of stumptail monkeys (*Macaca arctoides*). *Archives of Sexual Behavior, 5* 511–528.

Chiazze, L., Jr., et al. (1968). The length and variability of the human menstrual cycle. *Journal of the American Medical Association, 203,* 6.

Chideya, F., et al. (1993, August 30). Endangered family. *Newsweek,* pp. 17-27.

Children's Defense Fund (1988, September/October). *What about the boys: Teenage pregnancy prevention strategies.* In SIECUS Report, No. 17.

Chilman, C. (1979). *Adolescent sexuality in a changing American society.* (NIH Pub. 79–1426). Bethesda, MD: U.S. Department of Health, Education, and Welfare.

Chilman, C. S. (1983). *Adolescent sexuality in a changing American society* (2nd ed.). New York: Wiley.

Chira, S. (1992, February 12). Bias against girls is found rife in schools, with lasting damage. *The New York Times,* pp. A1, A23.

Choi, P. Y. (1992). The psychological benefits of physical exercise: Implications for women and the menstrual cycle. Special issue: The menstrual cycle. *Journal of Reproductive and Infant Psychology, 10,* 111-115.

Christensen, H. T. (1973). Attitudes toward marital infidelity: A nine-cultural sampling of university student opinion. *Journal of Comparative Family Studies, 4,* 197–214.

Chu, S. Y., Buehler, J. W., & Berkelman, R. L. (1990). Impact of the human immunodeficiency virus epidemic on mortality in women of reproductive age, United States. *Journal of the American Medical Association, 264,* 225–229.

Chumlea, W. C. (1982). Physical growth in adolescence. In B. B. Wolman (Ed.), *Handbook of developmental psychology* Englewood Cliffs, NJ: Prentice-Hall.

Clanton, G., & Smith, L. (1977). *Jealousy.* Englewood Cliffs, NJ: Prentice-Hall, Inc.

Clapper, R. L., & Lipsitt, L. P. (1991). A retrospective study of risk-taking and alcohol-mediated unprotected intercourse. *Journal of Substance Abuse, 3,* 91-96.

Clark, S. D., Jr., Zabin, L. S., & Hardy, J. B. (1984). Sex, contraception and parenthood: Experience and attitudes among urban black young men. *Family Planning Perspectives, 16,* 77–82.

Clark, M. S., Mills, J. R., & Corcoran, D. M. (1989). Keeping track of needs and inputs of friends and strangers. *Personality and Social Psychology Bulletin, 15,* 533–542.

Clark, P. G., Siviski, R. W., & Weiner, R. (1986). Coping strategies of widowers in the first year. *Family Relations, 35,* 425–430.

Clay, W. (1992). Perspectives on international sex practices and American family sex communication relevant to teenage sexual behavior in the United States. *Health-Communication, 4,*121-136.

Clayton, R. R., & Voss, H. L. (1977). Shacking up: Cohabitation in the 1970s. *Journal of Marriage and the Family, 39,* 273–283.

Cleary, P. D., et al. (1988). Sociodemographic and behavioral characteristics of HIV antibody-positive blood donors. *American Journal of Public Health, 78,* 953–957.

Cleek, M., & Pearson, T. (1985). Perceived causes of divorce: An analysis of interrelationships. *Journal of Marriage and the Family, 47,* 179–183.

Clement, U., & Schmidt, G. (1983). The outcome of couple therapy for sexual dysfunction using three different formats. *Journal of Sex and Marital Therapy, 9,* 67–78.

Clore, G. L., & Byrne, D. (1974). A reinforcement-affect model of attraction. In T. L. Juston (Ed.), *Foundations of interpersonal attraction* New York: Academic Press.

Clore, G. L., Wiggins, N. H., & Itkin, S. (1975). Gain and loss in attraction: Attributions from nonverbal behavior. *Journal of Personality and Social Psychology, 31,* 706–712.

Clore, G. L., & Byrne, D. (1977). The process of personality interaction. In R. B. Cattell & R. M. Dreger (Eds.), *Handbook of modern personality theory.* Washington, DC: Hemisphere.

Cobb, M., & Jallon, J. M. (1990). Pheromones, mate recognition and courtship stimulation in the Drosophila melanogaster species subgroup. *Animal Behaviour, 39,* 1058–1067.

Cochran, S. D. (1988, August). *Risky behavior and disclosure: Is it safe if you ask?* Paper presented at the meeting of the American Psychological Association, Atlanta, GA.

Cochran, S. D., & Mays, V. M. (1990). To the editor: Sex, lies, and HIV. *The New England Journal of Medicine, 322,* 774–775.

Cochran, S. D., & Mays, V. M. (1989). Women and AIDS-related concerns: Roles for psychologists in helping the worried well. *American Psychologist, 44,* 529–535.

Cochran, S. D, & Peplau, L. A. (1989). *Sexual risk reduction behaviors among young heterosexual adults.* Unpublished manuscript.

Cochran, W. G., Mosteller, F., & Tukey, J. W. (1953). Statistical problems of the Kinsey Report. *Journal of the American Statistical Association, 48,* 673–716.

Cockrum, J., & White, P. (1985). Influences on the life satisfaction of never-married men and women. *Family Relations, 34,* 551–556.

Cocores, J., & Gold, M. (1989, February). Substance abuse and sexual dysfunction. *Medical Aspects of Human Sexuality,* 22–31.

Cohen, J. B. (1990, December 13). *A crosscutting perspective on the epidemiology of HIV infection in women.* Paper presented at the Women and AIDS Conference, Washington, DC (abstract).

Cohen, M. W., & Friedman, S. B. (1975). Nonsexual motivation of adolescent sexual behavior. *Medical Aspects of Human Sexuality, 9 (9),* 9–31.

Cohen, J. (1993a). AIDS research: The mood is uncertain. *Science, 260,* 1254-1255.

Cohen, J. (1993b). Can combination therapy overcome drug resistance? *Science, 260,* 1258.

Cohen, J. (1993c). What causes the immune system collapse seen in AIDS? *Science, 260,* 1256-1257.

Colditz, G. A., et al. (1993). Family history, age, and risk of breast cancer: Prospective data from the nurses' health study. *Journal of the American Medical Association, 270,* 338-343.

Cole, D. (1987, July). It might have been: Mourning the unborn. *Psychology Today,* pp. 64–65.

Cole, H. M. (Ed.). (1989). Intrauterine devices. *Journal of the American Medical Association, 261,* 2127–2130.

Cole, S. S. (1988). Women's sexuality, and disabilities. *Women and Therapy, 7,* 277–294.

Coleman, E. (1986, July). Sexual compulsion vs. sexual addiction: The debate continues. *SIECUS Report,* 7–10.

Coleman, E. (1987). Bisexuality: Challenging our understanding of sexual orientation. *Sexuality and Medicine, 1,* 225–242.

Coleman, E. (1989). The development of male prostitution activity among gay and bisexual adolescents [Special Issue: Gay and lesbian youth]. *Journal of Homosexuality, 17,* 131–149

Coleman, E., Hoon, P., & Hoon, E. (1983). Arousability and sexual satisfaction in lesbian and heterosexual women. *Journal of Sex Research, 19,* 58–73.

Coleman, M., & Ganong, L. H. (1985). Love and sex role stereotypes: Do macho men and feminine women make better lovers? *Journal of Personality and Social Psychology, 49,* 170–176.

Coles, R., & Stokes, G. (1985). *Sex and the American teenager.* New York: Harper & Row.

Collins, G., & Kinder, B. (1984). Adjustment following surgical implantation of a penile prosthesis: A critical overview. *Journal of Sex and Marital Therapy, 10,* 255–271.

Comfort, A. (1974). *More joy of sex.* New York: Simon & Schuster.

Commission on Obscenity and Pornography. (1970). *The technical report of the Commission on Obscenity and Pornography.* Washington, DC: U.S. Government Printing Office.

Condon, J. W., & Crano, W. D. (1988). Inferred evaluation and the relation between attitude similarity and interpersonal attraction. *Journal of Personality and Social Psychology, 54,* 789–797.

Conerly, S. (1986). Assessment of suspected child sexual abuse. In K. MacFarlane, et al. (Eds.), *Sexual abuse of young children: Evaluation and treatment* (pp. 30–51). New York: Guilford.

Conn, P. M., & Crowley, W. F., Jr. (1991). Gonadotropin-releasing hormone and its analogues. *The New England Journal of Medicine, 324,* 93–103.

Connelly, S. (1981, March). Contraceptives: The latest news on how to choose. *Ladies Home Journal,* pp. 56–62.

Connor, J. (1972). Olfactory control of aggressive and sexual behavior in the mouse. *Psychonomic Science, 27,* 1–3.

Constantine, L., & Constantine, J. (1973). *Group marriage.* New York: Macmillan.

Conte, H. R. (1986). Multivariate assessment of sexual dysfunction. *Journal of Consulting and Clinical Psychology, 54,* 149–157.

Cook, E. P. (1985). *Psychological androgyny.* New York: Pergamon Press.

Cooper, A. J. (1978). Neonatal olfactory bulb lesions: Influences on subsequent behavior of male mice. *Bulletin of the Psychonomic Society, 11,* 53–56.

Cooper, A. J. (1986). Progestogens in the treatment of male sex offenders: A review. *Canadian Journal of Psychiatry, 31,* 73–79.

Cooper, A. J. (1987). Preliminary experience with a vacuum constriction device (VC) as a treatment for impotence. *Journal of Psychosomatic Research, 31,* 413–418.

Cooper, A. J., et al. (1990). A female sex offender with multiple paraphilias: A psychologic, physiologic (laboratory sexual arousal) and endocrine case study. *Canadian Journal of Psychiatry, 35,* 334–337.

Cooper, D. A., et al. (1993). Zidovudine in persons with asymptomatic HIV infection and CD4 cell counts greater than 400 per cubic millimeter. *The New England Journal of Medicine, 329,* 297-303.

Cooper, H. M. (1979). Statistically combining independent studies: A meta-analysis of sex differences in conformity research. *Journal of Personality and Social Psychology, 37,* 131–146.

Corby, N. H., et al. (1991). AIDS knowledge, perceptions of risk and behaviors among female sex partners of injection drug users. *AIDS Education and Prevention, 3,* 353-366.

Corey, L., & Fleming, T. R. (1992). Treatment of HIV infection—Progress in perspective. *The New England Journal of Medicine, 326,* 484–486.

Cormier, W. H., & Cormier, L. S. (1985). *Interviewing strategies for helpers.* Monterey, CA: Brooks/Cole.

Cosgray, R. E., et al. (1991). Death from auto-erotic asphyxiation in a long-term psychiatric setting. *Perspectives in Psychiatric Care, 27,* 21-24.

Court, 9-0, makes sex harassment easier to prove. (1993, November 10). *The New York Times,* pp. A1, A22.

Cowley, G. (1993, March 22). The future of AIDS. *Newsweek,* pp. 46-52.

Cowley, G., & Hager, M. (1992, February 24). For users of AZT, some sobering news. *Newsweek,* p. 63.

Cox, D. J. (1980). Exhibitionism: An overview. In D. J. Cox & R. J. Daitzman (Eds.), *Exhibitionism: Description, assessment and treatment* (pp. 3–10). New York: Garland.

Cox, D. J. (1988). Incidence and nature of male genital exposure behavior as reported by college women. *Journal of Sex Research, 24,* 227–234.

Cox, D. J., Tsang, K., & Lee, A. (1982). A cross cultural comparison of the incidence and nature of male exhibitionism among female college students. *Victimology: An International Journal, 7,* 231–234.

Cozby, P. C. (1973). Self-disclosure: A literature review. *Psychological Bulletin, 79,* 73–91.

Craig, M. E., Kalichman, S. C., & Follingstad, D. R. (1989). Verbal coercive sexual behavior among college students. *Archives of Sexual Behavior, 18,* 421–434.

Crepault, C., et al. (1977). Erotic imagery in women. In R. Gemme & C. C. Wheeler (Eds.), *Progress in sexology* (pp. 267–283). New York: Plenum.

Crews, D., & Moore, M. C. (1986). Evolution of mechanisms controlling mating behavior. *Science, 231,* 121–125.

Crichton, S. (1993, October 25). Sexual correctness: Has it gone too far? *Newsweek,* pp. 52-56.

Cronin, A. (1993, June 27). Two viewfinders, two views of Gay America. *The New York Times,* Section 4, p. 10.

Crowe, L. C., & George, W. H. (1989). Alcohol and human sexuality: Review and integration. *Psychological Bulletin, 105,* 374–386.

Crown, S., & D'Ardenne, D. (1982). Symposium on sexual dysfunction: Controversies, methods, results. *British Journal of Psychiatry, 140,* 70–77.

Crowne, D. P., & Marlowe, D. A. (1960). A new scale of social desirability independent of pathology. *Journal of Consulting Psychology, 24.*

Crum, C., & Ellner, P. (1985). Chlamydia infections: Making the diagnosis. *Contemporary Obstetrics and Gynecology, 25,* 153–159, 163, 165, 168.

Cunningham, F. G., & Gilstrap, L. C. (1991). Maternal serum alpha-fetoprotein screening. *The New England Journal of Medicine, 325,* 55–57.

Cunningham, G., Cordero, E., & Thornby, J. (1989). Testosterone replacement with transdermal therapeutic systems. *Journal of the American Medical Association, 261,* 2525–2531.

Curran, J. W., et al. (1988). Epidemiology of HIV infection and AIDS in the United States. *Science, 239,* 610–616.

Curtis, R. C., & Miller, K. (1986). Believing another likes or dislikes you: Behavior making the beliefs come true. *Journal of Personality and Social Psychology, 51,* 284–290.

Cutler, N. E., & Harootyan, R. A. (1975). Demography of the aged. In D. S. Woodrull & J. E. Birren (Eds.), *Aging: Scientific perspectives and social issues.* New York: Van Nostrand Reinhold.

Cutler, W. B., & Preti, G., (1986). Human axillary secretions influence women's menstrual cycles: The role of donor extract from men. *Hormones and Behavior, 20,* 463–473.

Cutrona, C. E. (1982). Transition to college: Loneliness and the process of social adjustment. In L. A. Peplau & D. Perlman (Eds.), *Loneliness: A sourcebook of current theory, research, and therapy* (pp.). New York: Wiley.

Cutrona, C. E. (1983). Causal attributions and perinatal depression. *Journal of Abnormal Psychology, 92,* 161–172.

Cutrona, C. E., & Troutman, B. R. (1986). Social support, infant temperament, and parenting self-efficacy: A mediational model of postpartum depression. *Child Development, 57,* 1507–1518.

D'Augelli, A. R. (1992a). Lesbian and gay male undergraduates' experiences of harassment and fear on campus. *Journal of Interpersonal Violence, 7,* 383-395.

D'Augelli, A. R. (1992b). Sexual behavior patterns of gay university men: Implications for preventing HIV infection. *Journal of American College Health, 41,* 25-29.

Dabbs, J. M., Jr., & Morris, R. (1990). Testosterone, social class, and antisocial behavior in a sample of 4,462 men. *Psychological Science, 1,* 1–3.

Dahl, S. (1989). Acute response to rape: A PTSD variant. [Special Issue: Traumatic stress: Empirical studies from Norway]. *Acta Psychiatrica Scandinavica, 80 (355, Suppl.),* 56–62.

Daling, J. R., et al. (1992). The intrauterine device and primary tubal infertility. *The New England Journal of Medicine, 326,* 203–204.

Dalton, K. (1960). The effect of menstruation on schoolgirls' weekly grades. *British Medical Journal, 1,* 326–328.

Dalton, K. (1961). Menstruation and crime. *British Medical Journal, 2,* 1752–1753.

Dalton, K. (1980). Cyclical criminal acts in premenstrual syndrome. *Lancet, 2,* 1070–1071.

Dalton, K. (1968). Menstruation and examinations. *Lancet, 2,* 1386–1388.

Dalton, K. (1972). *The menstrual cycle.* New York: Warner Books.

Daly, M., & Wilson, M. (1978). *Sex, evolution & behavior.* North Scituate, MA: Duxbury Press.

Dan, A. J. (1976, August). *Behavioral variability and the menstrual cycle*. Paper presented at the meeting of the American Psychological Association, Washington, DC. Dancing nurses dumped, *Advertising Age*, (1986, March 10). p. 36.

Daniel, H. J., III, et al. (1985). Values in mate selection: A 1984 campus survey. *College Student Journal, 19*, 44–50.

Daniels, P., & Weingarten, K. (1982). *Sooner or later: The timing of parenthood in adult lives*. New York: Norton.

Darabi, K. F., Dryfoos, J., & Schwartz, D. (1986). Hispanic adolescent fertility. *Hispanic Journal of Behavioral Sciences, 8*, 157–171.

Darling, C. A., Davidson, J. K., & Passarello, L. C. (1992). The mystique of first intercourse among college youth: The role of partners, contraceptive practices, and psychological reactions. *Journal of Youth and Adolescence, 21*, 97–117.

Darling, C. A., Davidson, J. K., & Jennings, D. A. (1991). The female sexual response revisited: Understanding the multiorgasmic experience in women. *Archives of Sexual Behavior, 20*, 527–540.

Darling, C. A., & Davidson, J. K., Sr. (1986). Coitally active university students: Sexual behaviors, concerns, and challenges. *Adolescence, 21*, 403–419.12.

Darrow, W. W. (1987, February). *Condom use and use-effectiveness in high*-risk populations. Paper presented at the Conference on Condoms in the Prevention of Sexually Transmitted Diseases, Centers for Disease Control, Atlanta, GA.

DATTA (Diagnostic and Theapeutic Technology Assessment). (1988). Questions and answers: Penile implants for erectile impotence. *Journal of the American Medical Association, 260*, 997–1000.

Davenport, W. (1965). Sexual patterns and their regulation in a society of the Southwest Pacific. In F. A. Beach (Ed.), *Sex and behavior*. New York: Wiley.

Davenport, W. (1977). Sex in cross-cultural perspective. In F. Beach (Ed.), *Human sexuality in four perspectives*. Baltimore: Johns Hopkins University Press.

Davenport, W. H. (1976). Sex in cross-cultural perspective. In F. A. Beach (Ed.), *Human sexuality in four perspectives* (pp. 115–163). Baltimore: Johns Hopkins University Press.

David, H. P. (1978). Abortion: A continuing debate. *Family Planning Perspectives, 10*, 313–316.

Davidson, J. K. (1985). The utilization of sexual fantasies by sexually experienced university students. *Journal of American College Health, 34*, 24–32.

Davidson, B., Balswick, J., & Halverson, C. (1983). Affective self-disclosure and marital adjustment: A test of equity theory. *Journal of Marriage and the Family, 45*, 93–102.

Davidson, J. K., & Hoffman, L. E. (1986). Sexual fantasies and sexual satisfaction: An empirical analysis of erotic thought. *Journal of Sex Research, 22*, 184–205.

Davidson, K. J., Darling, C., & Conway-Welch, C. (1989). The role of the Grafenberg spot and female ejaculation in the female orgasmic response: An empirical analysis. *Journal of Sex and Marital Therapy, 15*, 102–119.

Davis, D. L., & Whitten, R. G. (1987). The cross-cultural study of human sexuality. *Annual Review of Anthropology, 16*, 69–98.

Davis, S. (1990). Men as success objects and women as sex objects: A study of personal advertisements. *Sex Roles, 23*, 43–50.

Davis, J. A., & Smith, T. (1987). *General Social Surveys, 1972–1987: Cumulative data*. Storrs, CT: University of Connecticut, Roper Center for Public Opinion Research.

Davis, G. L., et al. (1989). Treatment of chronic hepatitis C with recombinant interferon alfa. *New England Journal of Medicine, 321*, 1501–1506.

Davison, G. C. (1977). Elimination of a sadistic fantasy by a client-controlled counterconditioning technique. In J. Fischer & H. Gochios (Eds.), *Handbook of behavior therapy with sexual problems*. New York: Pergamon Press.

Davison, G. C. (1978). Not can but ought: The treatment of homosexuality. *Journal of Consulting and Clinical Psychology, 46*, 170–172.

Dawes, R. M. (1989). Statistical criteria for establishing a truly false consensus effect. *Journal of Experimental Social Psychology, 25*, 1–17.

Dawkins, R. (1976). *The selfish gene*. Oxford: Oxford University Press.

Dawkins, B. J. (1990). Genital herpes simplex infections. *Primary Care: Clinics in Office Practice, 17*, 95–113.

de Young, M. (1982). *The sexual victimization of children*. Jefferson, NC: McFarland & Company.

de Raad, B., & Doddema-Winsemius, M. (1992). Factors in the assortment of human mates: Differential preferences in Germany and the Netherlands. *Personality and Individual Differences, 13*, 103-114.

de Schampheleire, D. (1990). MMPI characteristics of professional prostitutes: A cross-cultural replication. *Journal of Personality Assessment, 54*, 343–350.

de Luca, R. V., et al. (1992). Group treatment for child sexual abuse. Special Issue: Violence and its aftermath. *Canadian Psychology, 33*,168-179.

De Casper, A. J., & Fifer, W. P. (1980). Of human bonding: Newborns prefer their mothers' voices. *Science, 208*, 1174–1176.

De Moja, C. A. (1986). Anxiety, self-confidence, jealousy, and romantic attitudes toward love in Italian undergraduates. *Psychological Reports, 58*, 138.

Dean, C. W., & Bruyn-Kops, E. (1982). *The crime and consequences of rape*. Springfield, IL: Charles C. Thomas.

Deaux, K. (1985). Sex and gender. *Annual Review of Psychology, 36*, 49–81.

Deaux, K. (1984). From individual differences to social categories: Analysis of a decade's research on gender. *American Psychologist, 39*, 105–116.

Deaux, K., & Lewis, L. L. (1983). Assessment of gender stereotypes: Methodology and components. *Psychological Documents, 13*, 25 (Ms. No. 2583).

DeBuono, B. A., et al. (1990). Sexual behavior of college women in 1975, 1986, and 1989. *The New England Journal of Medicine, 322*, 821–825.

Decline in abortions reported. (1987, August 25). *The New York Times*.

Deepening shame: A Newsweek investigation into the scandal that is rocking the navy. (1992, August 10). *Newsweek*, pp. 30-36.

Defense dept. suspends its policy on homosexuals. (1993, October 8). The New York Times, p. A.25.

DeHaan, C. B., & Wallander, J. L. (1988). Self-concept, sexual knowledge and attitudes, and parental support in the sexual adjustment of women with early- and late-onset physical disability. *Archives of Sexual Behavior, 17*, 145–161.

Dekker, J. (1993). Inhibited male orgasm. In W. O'Donohue & J. H. Geer (Eds.), *Handbook of sexual dysfunctions: Assessment and treatment* (pp. 279-301). Boston: Allyn & Bacon.

DeLamater, J., & MacCorquodale, P. (1979). *Premarital sexuality: Attitudes, relationships, behavior*. Madison, WI: University of Wisconsin.

Delany, J., Lupton, M. J., & Toth, E. (1976). *The curse: A cultural history of menstruation*. New York: E. P. Dutton.

Delgado, J. (1969). *Physical control of the mind*. New York: Harper & Row.

Demar, D., Briere, J., & Lips, H. M. (1988). Violent pornography and self-reported likelihood of sexual aggression. *Journal of Research in Personality, 22*, 140–153.

DeMaris, A., & Leslie, G. R. (1984). Cohabitation with the future spouse: Its influence upon marital satisfaction and communication. *Journal of Marriage and the Family, 46*, 77–84.

Dement, W. (1965). An essay on dreams. In F. Barron (Ed.), New directions in psychology, Vol. II. New York: Holt, Rinehart & Winston.

Denfeld, D. (1974). Dropouts from swinging. *The Family Coordinator, 23*, 45–49.

Denny, N., Field, J., & Quadagno, D. (1984). Sex differences in sexual needs and desires. *Archives of Sexual Behavior, 13*, 233–245.

DeParle, J. (1993, July 14). Big rise in birth outside wedlock. *The New York Times*, pp. A1, A14.

Department of Health and Human Services. (1991). *Faculty member's handbook:* Strategies for preventing alcohol and other drug problems. Public Health Service, Alcohol, Drug Abuse, and Mental Health Administration, Office for Substance Abuse Prevention. (DHHS Publication No. ADM 91-1843). Rockville, MD: Author.

DePaulo, B. M., et al. (1978). Decoding discrepant nonverbal cues. *Journal of Personality and Social Psychology, 38*, 313–323.

Dermer, M., & Thiel, D. L. (1975). When beauty may fail. *Journal of Personality and Social Psychology, 31*, 1168–1176.

Derogatis, L. R. (1980). Etiologic factors in premature ejaculation. *Medical Aspects of Human Sexuality, 14*, 32–47.

DeRougemont, D. (1940). *Love in the Western world*. New York: Harcourt, Brace.

DesJarlais, D. C., & Friedman, S. R. (1988). The psychology of preventing AIDS among intravenous drug users: A social learning conceptualization. *American Psychologist, 43*, 865–871.

Desmond, M. M., & Wilson, G. S. (1975). Neonatal abstinence syndrome: Recognition and diagnosis. *Addictive Diseases: An International Journal, 2*, 113–121.

Deutsch, F. M., LeBaron, D., & Fryer, M. M. (1987). What is in a smile? *Psychology of Women Quarterly, 11*, 341–352.

DeWitt, K. (1991, October). The evolving concept of sexual harassment. *The New York Times*.

Diagnostic and Therapeutic Technology Assessment (DATTA). (1988). Questions and answers: Penile implants for erectile impotence. *Journal of the American Medical Association, 260*, 997–1000.

Diamond, M. (1977). Human sexual development: Biological foundations for social development. In F. Beach (Ed.), *Human sexuality in four perspectives.* Baltimore: Johns Hopkins University Press.

Diamond, M. (1982). Sexual identity, monozygotic twins reared in discordant sex roles and a BBC follow-up. *Archives of Sexual Behavior, 11,* 181–186.

Diamond, M. (1993). Homosexuality and bisexuality in different populations. *Archives of Sexual Behavior, 22,* 291-310.

Diamond, M. (1993). Homosexuality and bisexuality in different populations. *Archives of Sexual Behavior, 22,* 291-310.

Diamond, S. (1981, March). Spanish fly. *Omni,* p. 42.

Diana, L. (1985). *The prostitute and her clients: Your pleasure is her business.* Springfield, IL: Thomas.

Diaz-Guerrero, R. (1975). *Psychology of the Mexican.* Austin: University of Texas Press.

DiClemente, R. J. (1992). Epidemiology of AIDS, HIV prevalence, and HIV incidence among adolescents. *Journal of School Health, 62,* 325-330.

Dick-Read, G. (1944). *Childbirth without fear: The principles and practices of natural childbirth.* New York: Harper & Bros.

Dietz, P. E., Hazelwood, R. R., & Warren, J. (1990). The sexually sadistic criminal and his offenses. *Bulletin of the American Academy of Psychiatry and the Law, 18,* 163–178.

Dimont, M. I. (1962). *Jews, God, and history.* New York: Signet Books.

Dindia, K., & Allen, M. (1992). Sex differences in self-disclosure: A meta-analysis. *Psychological Bulletin, 112,* 106-124.

Dion, K. K., Berscheid, E., & Walster, E. H. (1972). What is beautiful is good. *Journal of Personality and Social Psychology, 24,* 285-290.

Dion, K. K., & Dion, K. L. (1975). Self-esteem and romantic love. *Journal of Personality, 43,* 39-57.

Dionne, E. J., Jr. (1989, July 4). On both sides, advocates predict a 50-state battle. *The New York Times,* pp. A1, A11.

Disease discovered Europe first? (1992, November 24). *New York Newsday,* p. 49.

Dixen, J., & Jenkins, J. O. (1981). Incestuous child sexual abuse: A review of treatment strategies. *Clinical Psychology Review, 1,* 211–222.

Dixon, J. (1991). Feminist reforms of sexual coercion. In E. Grauerholz & M. A. Koralewski (Eds.), *Sexual coercion: A sourcebook on its nature, causes, and prevention* (pp. 161–171). Lexington, MA: Lexington Books.

Doerr, P., et al. (1973). Plasma testosterone, estradiol, and semen analysis in male homosexuals. *Archives of General Psychiatry, 29,* 829–833.

Donnerstein, E. (1980). Aggressive erotica and violence against women. *Journal of Personality and Social Psychology, 39,* 269–277.

Donnerstein, E. (1983). Erotica and human aggression. In R. G. Green & E. I. Donnerstein (Eds.), *Aggression: Theoretical and empirical reviews* (pp. 127–154). New York: Academic Press.

Donnerstein, E., & Berkowitz, L. (1981). Victim reactions in aggressive erotic films as a factor in violence against women. *Journal of Personality and Social Psychology, 41,* 710–724.

Donnerstein, E. I., & Linz, D. G. (1986). The question of pornography. *Psychology Today, 20,* pp. 56-59.

Donnerstein, E., Berkowitz, L., & Linz, D. (1986). *Role of aggressive and sexual images in violent pornography.* Unpublished manuscript, University of Wisconsin-Madison.

Donnerstein, E. I., & Linz, D. G. (1987). *The question of pornography.* New York: The Free Press.

Donnerstein, E., & Linz, D. Sexual violence in the media: A warning. Psychology Today 18, 14–15.

Donnerstein, E., Linz, D., & Penrod, S. (1988). *The question of pornography: Research findings and policy implications.* New York: Free Press.

Dormont, P. (1989, April). Life events that predispose to erectile dysfunction. *Medical Aspects of Human Sexuality,* 17–19.

Dorner, G. (1988). Neuroendocrine response to estrogen and brain differentiation in heterosexuals, homosexuals, and transsexuals. *Archives of Sexual Behavior, 17,* 57–75.

Douglas, A. R., Matson, I. C., & Hunter, S. (1989). Sex therapy for women incestuously abused as children. *Sexual and Marital Therapy, 4,* 143–159.

Douglas, R. G. (1987). Infectious disease. *Journal of the American Medical Association, 258,* 2252–2254.

Douglas, J. M., Jr. (1990). Molluscum contagiosum. In K. K. Holmes, P. Mardh, P. F. Sparling, & P. J. Wiesner (Eds.), *Sexually transmitted diseases (2nd ed.) (pp. 443-448). New York: McGraw-Hill.*

Dover, K. J. (1978). *Greek homosexuality.* Cambridge, MA: Harvard University Press.

Dow, M. G. T., & Gallagher, J. (1989). A controlled study of combined hormonal and psychological treatment for sexual unresponsiveness in women. *British Journal of Clinical Psychology, 28,* 201–212.

Drapers, P. (1975). !Kung women: Contrasts in sexual egalitarianism in foraging and sedentary contexts. In R. R. Reiter (Ed.), *Toward an anthropology of women* (pp. 77–109). New York: Monthly Review Press.

Driscoll, R., Davis, K. E., & Lipetz, M. E. (1972). Parental interference and romantic love. *Journal of Personality and Social Psychology, 24,* 1–10.

Drucker, E. (1991, June 5). AIDS—the second decade: Families need the most help. *New York Times,* p. A29.

Dryfoos, J. (1985). School-based health clinics: A new approach to preventing adolescent pregnancy? *Family Planning Perspectives, 17,* 70–75.

Dryfoos, J. G. (1982). Contraceptive use, pregnancy intentions, and pregnancy outcomes among U.S. women. *Family Planning Perspectives, 16,* 193–195.

Dube, R., & Hebert, M. (1988). Sexual abuse of children 12 years of age: A review of 511 cases. *Child Abuse and Neglect, 12,* 321–330.

Duffy, S. M., & Rusbult, C. E. (1985/1986). Satisfaction and commitment in homosexual and heterosexual relationships. *Journal of Homosexuality, 12,* 1–24.

Dullea, G. (1988, February 7). Gay couples' wish to adopt grows, along with increasing resistance. *The New York Times,* p. 26.

Dunn, M. E., & Trost, J. E. (1989). Male multiple orgasms: A descriptive study. *Archives of Sexual Behavior, 18,* 377–387.

DuRant, R. H., & Sanders, J. M. (1989). Sexual behavior and contraceptive risk taking among sexually active adolescent females. *Journal of Adolescent Health Care, 10,* 1-19.

DuRant, R. H., Seymore, C., Pendergrast, R., & Beckman, R. (1990). Contraceptive behavior among sexually active Hispanic adolescents. *Journal of Adolescent Health Care,* 11, 490-496.

Durden-Smith, J. (1980, November/December). How to win the mating game by a nose. *Next,* pp. 85–89.

Durfee, M., Heger, A. H., & Woodling, B. (1986). Medical evaluation. In K. MacFarlane et al. (Eds.), *Sexual abuse of young children: Evaluation and treatment.* (pp. 52–66). New York: Guilford.

Durfee, M. (1989). Prevention of child sexual abuse. *Psychiatric Clinics of North America, 12,* 445–453.

Dusenbury, L., et al. (1991). AIDS risk knowledge, attitudes, and behavioral intentions among multi-ethnic adolescents. *AIDS Education and Prevention, 3,* 367-375.

Dutton, D. G., & Aron, A. P. (1974). Some evidence for heightened sexual attraction under conditions of high anxiety. *Journal of Personality and Social Psychology, 30,* 510–517.

Dworkin, J., Albrecht, G., & Cooksey, J. (1991). Concern about AIDS among hospital physicians, nurses and social workers. *Social Science Medicine, 33,* 239-248.

Dwyer, M. (1988). Exhibitionism/voyeurism. *Journal of Social Work and Human Sexuality, 7,* 101–112.

Dye, E., & Roth, S. (1990). Psychotherapists' knowledge about and attitudes toward sexual assault victim clients. *Psychology of Women Quarterly, 14,* 191–212.

Dziech, B. W., & Weiner, L. (1984). *The lecherous professor: Sexual harassment on campus.* Boston: Beacon Press.

Earle, J. R., & Perricone, P. J. (1986). Premarital sexuality: A ten-year study of attitudes and behavior on a small university campus. *Journal of Sex Research, 22,* 304–310.

Earls, C. M., & David, H. (1989a). Male and female prostitution: A review. *Annals of Sex Research, 2,* 5–28.

Earls, C. M., & David, H. (1989b). A psychosocial study of male prostitution. *Archives of Sexual Behavior, 18,* 401–419.

Easier way found for abortion pill. (1993, May 27). *The New York Times,* p. B9.

Eckert, E. D., et al. (1986). Homosexuality in monozygotic twins reared apart. *British Journal of Psychiatry, 148,* 421–425.

Eckholm, E. (1992a, June 28). Homosexuality, AIDS, fatally steady in the U.S., accelerates worldwide. *The New York Times,* Section 4, p. 5.

Eckholm, E. (1992b, June 28). Illness can be delayed but no cure's in sight. *The New York Times,* p. E5.

Eckholm, E. (1991, November 17). Facts of life: More than inspiration is needed to fight AIDS. *The New York Times,* pp. E1, E3.

Edeiken, S. (1987). Mammography and palpable cancer of the breast. *Cancer, 61,* 263-265.

Edelman, D. A., McIntyre, S. L., & Harper, J. (1984). A comparative trial of the contraceptive sponge and diaphragm: A preliminary report. *Journal of Reproductive Medicine, 28,* 781–784.

Edgley, C. (1989). Commercial sex: Pornography, prostitution, and advertising. In K. McKinney & S. Sprecher (Eds.), *Human sexuality: The societal and interpersonal context* (pp. 370–424). Norwood, NJ: Ablex Publishing Corporation.

Edmonson, B. (1988). Disability and sexual adjustment. In V. B. Van Hasselt, P. S. Strain, & M. Hersen (Eds.), *Handbook of developmental and physical disabilities* (pp. 91–106). New York: Pergamon Press.

Edwards, L. E., Steinman, M. E., & Hakanson, E. Y. (1977). An experimental comprehensive high school clinic. *American Journal of Public Health, 67,* 765–766.

Edwards, L. E., et al. (1980). Adolescent pregnancy prevention services in high school clinics. *Family Planning Perspectives, 12,* 6–14.

Eggert, A. K., & Muller, J. K. (1989). Mating success of pheromone-emitting necrophorus males: Do attracted females discriminate against resource owners? *Behaviour, 110,* 248–257.

Ehrhardt, A. A. (1992). Trends in sexual behavior and the HIV pandemic. *American Journal of Public Health, 82,* 1459-1461. (Editorial)

Ehrhardt, A. (1985). The psychobiology of gender. In A. Rossi (Ed.), *Gender and life course.* New York: Aldine.

Ehrhardt, A. A., et al. (1985). Sexual orientation after prenatal exposure to exogenous estrogen. *Archives of Sexual Behavior, 14,* 57–77.

Ehrhardt, A. A., Grisanti, G., & McCauley, E. A. (1979). Female-to-male transsexuals compared to lesbians: Behavioral patterns of childhood and adolescent development. *Archives of Sexual Behavior, 8,* 481–490.

Ehrhardt, A. A., Ince, S. E., & Meyer-Bahlburg, H. F. L. (1981). Career aspiration and gender role development in young girls. *Archives of Sexual Behavior, 10,* 281–300.

Ehrlich, G. (1988, March). Sexual concerns of patients with arthritis. *Medical Aspects of Human Sexuality,* 104–107.

Eisen, M. & Zellman, G. (1987). Changes in incidence of sexual intercourse of unmarried teenagers following a community-based sex education program. *The Journal of Sex Research, 23,* 527–544.

Elias, S., & Annas, G. (1986). Social policy considerations in noncoital reproduction. *Journal of the American Medical Society, 255,* 62–68.

Eliasson, R., & Lindholmer, C. (1976). Functions of male accessory genital organs. In E. Hafez (Ed.), *Human semen and fertility regulations in men.* St. Louis: Mosby.

Ellerbrock, T. V., et al. (1991). Epidemiology of women with AIDS in the United States, 1981 through 1990: A comparison with heterosexual men with AIDS. *Journal of the American Medical Association, 265,* 2971–2975.

Ellis, A. (1962). *Reason and emotion in psychotherapy.* New York: Lyle Stuart.

Ellis, A. (1977). The basic clinical theory of rational-emotive therapy. In A. Ellis & R. Grieger (Eds.), *Handbook of rational-emotive therapy.* New York: Springer.

Ellis, L. (1989–1990). Sex differences in criminality: An explanation based on the concept of R/K selection. *Mankind Quarterly, 30,* 17–37, 399–417.

Ellis, L. (1991). A synthesized (biosocial) theory of rape. *Journal of Consulting and Clinical Psychology, 59,* 631–642.

Ellis, L. (1990). Prenatal stress may affect sex-typical behaviors of a child. *The Brown University Child Behavior and Development Letter, 6(1),* 1–3.

Ellis, L., & Ames, M. A. (1987). Neurohormonal functioning and sexual orientation: A theory of homosexuality-heterosexuality. *Psychological Bulletin, 101,* 233–258.

Ellis, L., Burke, D., & Ames, M. A. (1987). Sexual orientation as a continuous variable: A comparison between the sexes. *Archives of Sexual Behavior, 16,* 523–529.

Ellsworth, P. C., & Langer, E. J. (1976). Staring and approach: An interpretation of the stare as a nonspecific activator. *Journal of Personality and Social Psychology, 33,* 117–122.

Elmer-Dewitt, P. (1991, September 30). Making babies. *Time,* pp. 56–63.

Elshtain, J. M. (1984, June 25). The new porn wars. *New Republic,* 15–20.

Elwin, V. (1968). *The kingdom of the young.* Oxford: Oxford University Press.

Ember, M. (1974). Warfare, sex ratio, and polygyny. *Ethnology, 13,* 197–206.

Ember, M. (1984–1985). Alternative predictors of polygyny. *Behavior Science Research, 19,* 1–23.

Ember, C. R., & Ember, M. (1990). *Anthropology.* (6th ed., Instructor's Edition). Englewood Cliffs, NJ: Prentice-Hall, Inc.

Emmanuel, N. P., Lydiard, R. B., & Ballenger, J. C. (1992). Fluoxetine treatment of voyeurism. *American Journal of Psychiatry, 148,* 950.

English, P. B., & Eskenazi, B. (1992). Reinterpreting the effects of maternal smoking on infant birthweight and perinatal mortality: A multivariate approach to birthweight standardization. *International Journal of Epidemiology, 21,* 1097-1105.

Enright, S. J. (1989). Paedophilia: A cognitive/behavioural treatment approach in a single case. *British Journal of Psychiatry, 155,* 399–401.

Erikson, E. H. (1963). *Childhood and society.* New York: W. W. Norton.

Erlanger, S. (1991, July 14). A plague awaits. *The New York Times Magazine,* pp. 24, 26, 49, 53.

Eskenazi, G. (1990, June 3). The male athlete and sexual assault. *The New York Times,* pp. L1, L4.

Essex, M., & Kanki, P. (1988, October). The origins of the AIDS virus. *Scientific American,* 64–71.

Estrich, S. (1987). *Real rape.* Boston: Harvard University Press.

Ettinger, B. (1988). Prevention of osteoporosis: Treatment of estradiol deficiency. *Obstetrics and Gynecology, 72,* 12s-17s.

Evans, R. B. (1969). Childhood parental relationships of homosexual men. *Journal of Consulting and Clinical Psychology, 33,* 129–135.

Evans, H. J. (1981). Abnormalities and cigarette smoking. *Lancet, 1,* 627–634.

Everaerd, W. (1993). Male erectile disorder. In W. O'Donohue & J. H. Geer (Eds.), *Handbook of sexual dysfunctions: Assessment and treatment* (pp. 201-224). Boston: Allyn & Bacon.

Everett, G. M. (1975). Amyl nitrate ("poppers") as an aphrodisiac. In M. Sandler & G. L. Gessa (Eds.), *Sexual behavior: Pharmacology and biochemistry.* New York: Raven Press.

Everitt, B. J. (1990). Sexual motivation: A neural and behavioural analysis of the mechanisms underlying appetitive and copulatory responses of male rats. *Neuroscience and Biobehavioral Reviews, 14,* 217-232.

Everson, M. D., & Boat, B. W. (1989). False allegations of sexual abuse by children and adolescents. *Journal of the American Academy of Child and Adolescent Psychiatry, 28,* 230–235.

Everson, M. D., & Boat, B. W. (1990). Sexualized doll play among young children: Implications for the use of anatomical dolls in sexual abuse evaluations. *Journal of the American Academy of Child and Adolescent Psychiatry, 29,* 736–742.

Exner, J. E., et al. (1977). Some psychological characteristics of prostitutes. *Journal of Personality Assessment, 41,* 474–485.

Ezzell, C. (1993, July). On borrowed time: Long-term survivors of HIV-1 infection. *The Journal of NIH Research,* pp. 77-82.

Fagot, B. I. (1985a). Beyond the reinforcement principle: Another step toward understanding sex role development. *Developmental Psychology, 21,* 1097–1104.

Fagot, B. I. (1985b). Changes in thinking about early sex role development. *Developmental Review, 5,* 83–98.

Fagot, B. I. (1974). Sex differences in toddlers' behavior and parental reaction. *Developmental Psychology, 10,* 554–558.

Faich, G., et al. (1986). Toxic shock syndrome and the vaginal contraceptive sponge. *Journal of the American Medical Association, 255,* 216–218.

Falk, J., et al. (1983). Primary and secondary amenorrhea in anorexia nervosa. In S. Golub (Ed.), *Menarche.* Lexington, MA: Lexington Books.

Faller, K. C. (1989a). The role relationship between victim and perpetrator as a predictor of characteristics of intrafamilial sexual abuse. *Child and Adolescent Social Work Journal, 6,* 217–229.

Faller, K. C. (1989b). Why sexual abuse? An exploration of the intergenerational hypothesis. *Child Abuse and Neglect, 13,* 543–548.

Fallon, A. E., & Rozin, P. (1985). Sex differences in perceptions of desirable body shape. *Journal of Abnormal Psychology, 94,* 102–105.

Faludi, S. (1993, October 25). Whose hype? *Newsweek,* p. 61.

Farina, A., et al. (1986). The role of physical attractiveness in the readjustment of discharged psychiatric patients. *Journal of Abnormal Psychology, 95,* 139–143.

Farkas, G. M., & Rosen, R. C. (1976). Effect of alcohol on elicited male sexual response. *Journal of Studies on Alcohol, 37,* 265–272.

Farley, A. U., Hadler, J. L., & Gunn, R. A. (1990). The syphilis epidemic in Connecticut: Relationship to drug use and prostitution. *Sexually Transmitted Diseases, 17,* 163–168.

Faulstich, M. E. (1987). Psychiatric aspects of AIDS. *American Journal of Psychiatry, 144,* 551–556.

Faust, B. (1980). *Women, sex and pornography.* New York: Basic Books.

Fausto-Sterling, A. (1985). *Myths of gender.* New York: Basic Books.

Faux, M. (1989). *Roe v. Wade.* New York: Mentor Books.

Faux, M. (1984). *Childless by choice.* Garden City, NY: Doubleday/Anchor Press.

Fay, R. E. et al. (1989). Prevalence and patterns of same-gender sexual contact among men. *Science, 243,* 338–348.

Fear of AIDS reflected in study, p. 1. *San Jose Mercury News* . (1991, August 17).

Feder, H. H. (1984). Hormones and sexual behavior. *Annual Review of Psychology, 35,* 165–200.

Federal Bureau of Investigation. (1990). *Uniform crime reports.* Washington, D.C.: U.S. Department of Justice.

Federal Bureau of Investigation (FBI). (1991). *Uniform crime reports.* Washington, D.C.: U.S. Department of Justice.

Feinauer, L. L. (1989). Sexual dysfunction in women sexually abused as children. *Contemporary Family Therapy: An International Journal, 11,* 299–309.

Feingold, A. (1988). Cognitive gender differences are disappearing. *American Psychologist, 43,* 95–103.

Feingold, A. (1991). Sex differences in the effects of similarity and physical attractiveness on opposite-sex attraction. *Basic and Applied Social Psychology, 12,* 357-367.

Feldman, S. S., et al. (1983). Antecedents of fathering. *Child Development, 54,* 1628-1636.

Feldman-Summers, S., Gordon, P. E., & Meagher, J. R. (1979). The impact of rape on sexual satisfaction. *Journal of Abnormal Psychology, 88,* 101–105.

Felsman, D., Brannigan, G., & Yellin, P. (1987). Control theory in dealing with adolescent sexuality and pregnancy. *Journal of Sex Education and Therapy, 13,* 15–16.

Feng, T. (1993). Substance abuse in pregnancy. *Current Opinions in Obstetrics and Gynecology, 5,* 16-23.

Fenichel, O. (1945). *The psychoanalytic theory of neurosis.* New York: W. W. Norton & Co.

Fensterheim, H., & Kantor, J. S. (1980). Behavioral approach to sexual disorders. In B. Wolman & J. Money (Eds.), *Handbook of human sexuality.* Englewood Cliffs, N.J.: Prentice-Hall.

Ferguson, J. H., Kreshel, P. J., & Tinkham, S. F. (1990). In the pages of Ms.: Sex role portrayals of women in advertising. *Journal of Advertising, 19,* 40–51.

Ferrante, C. L., Haynes, A. M., & Kingsley, S. M. (1988). Image of women in television advertising. *Journal of Broadcasting and Electronic Media, 32,* 231–237.

Fichner-Rathus, L. (1992). *Understanding art* (3d ed.). Englewood Cliffs, NJ: Prentice Hall.

Filsinger, E. E., Braun, J. J., & Monte, W. C. (1985). An examination of the effects of putative pheromones on human judgments. *Ethology and Sociobiology, 6,* 227–236.

Finkelhor, D. (1988). The trauma of child sexual abuse: Two models. In G. E. Wyatt & G. J. Powell (Eds.), *The lasting effects of child sexual abuse* (pp. 61–82). Newbury Park, CA: Sage.

Finkelhor, D. (1984). *Child sexual abuse: Theory and research.* New York: Free Press.

Finkelhor, D. (1979). *Sexually victimized children.* New York: Free Press.

Finkelhor, D. (1990). Early and long-term effects of child sexual abuse: An update. *Professional Psychology: Research and Practice, 21,* 325–330.

Finkelhor, D., & Hotaling, G. T. (1984). Sexual abuse in the National Incidence Study of Child Abuse and Neglect: An appraisal. *Child Abuse and Neglect, 8,* 22–33.

Finkelhor, D., & Yllo, K. (1982). Rape in marriage: A sociological view. In D. Finkelhor, R. J. Gelles, G. T. Hotaling, & M. A. Straus (Eds.), *The dark side of families: Current family violence research* (pp. 119–130). Beverly Hills, CA: Sage.

Finkelhor, D., et al. (1990). Sexual abuse in a national survey of adult men and women: Prevalence, characteristics, and risk factors. *Child Abuse and Neglect, 14,* 19–28.

Finkelhor, D., & Russell, D. (1984). Women as perpetrators: Review of the evidence. In D. Finkelhor (Ed.), *Child sexual abuse: Theory and research.* New York: The Free Press.

Fischl, M. A., et al. (1990). A randomized controlled trial of a reduced daily dose of zidovudine in patients with acquired immunodeficiency syndrome. *New England Journal of Medicine, 323,* 1009–1014.

Fish, V., & Faynik, C. (1989). Treatment of incest families with the father temporarily removed: A structural approach [Special Issue: Childhood sexual abuse]. *Journal of Strategic and Systemic Therapies, 8,* 53–63.

Fisher, J. (1992, January 11). Cited in Associated Press, Boy beaver foils experts. *The New York Times,* p. 6.

Fisher, S. (1973). *The female orgasm.* New York: Basic Books.

Fisher, T. D., & Hall, R. H. (1988). A scale for the comparison of the sexual attitudes of adolescents and their parents. *The Journal of Sex Research, 24,* 90–100.

Fisher, S. (1973). *The female orgasm.* New York: Basic Books.

Fisher-Thompson, D. (1990). Adult sex typing of children's toys. *Sex Roles, 23,* 291–303.

Fisher, B., Weisberg, D. K., & Marotta, T. (1982). *Report on adolescent male prostitution.* San Francisco: Urban and Rural Systems Associates.

Fisher, C., Gross, J., & Zuch, J. (1965). Cycle of penile erection synchronous with dreaming. *Archives of General Psychiatry, 12,* 29-45.

Fisher, H. E. (October, 1987). The four-year itch. *Natural History, 96 (10),* 22–33.

Fisher, J. D., & Misovich, S. J. (1991). *1990 technical report on undergraduate students' AIDS-preventive behavior, AIDS-knowledge, and fear of AIDS.* Storrs, CT: University of Connecticut, Department of Psychology.

Fisher, J. D., & Fisher, W. A. (1992). Changing AIDS-risk behavior. *Psychological Bulletin, 111,* 455-474.

Fisher, L. E. (1980). Relationships and sexuality in contexts and culture: The anthropology of eros. In B. B. Wolman & J. Money (Eds.), *Handbook of human sexuality.* Englewood Cliffs, NJ: Prentice-Hall.

Fitzgerald, L. F. (1993b). Sexual harassment: Violence against women in the workplace. *American Psychologist, 48,* 1070-1076.

Fitzgerald, L. F. (1992). *Sexual harassment in higher education: Concepts and issues.* Washington, D.C.: National Education Association.

Fitzgerald, L. F., et al. (1988). Academic harassment: Sex and denial in scholarly garb. *Psychology of Women Quarterly, 12,* 329–340.

Flaceliere, R. (1962). *Love in Ancient Greece* (James Cleugh Trans.). New York: Crown.

Flaherty, J. F., & Dusek, J. B. (1980). An investigation of the relationship between psychological androgyny and components of self-concept. *Journal of Personality and Social Psychology, 38,* 984–992.

Flavell, J. H. (1985). *Cognitive development* (2nd ed.). Englewood Cliffs, NJ: Prentice-Hall.

Fletcher, J. (1966). *Situation ethics.* Philadelphia: Westminster Press.

Fletcher, J. (1967). *Moral responsibility: Situation ethics at work.* Philadelphia: Westminster Press.

Fletcher, J. M., et al. (1991). Neurobehavioral outcomes in diseases of childhood: Individual change models for pediatric human immunodeficiency viruses. *American Psychologist, 46,* 1267–1277.

Floyd, F. J., & Markman, H. J. (1984). An economical observational measure of couples' communication skill. *Journal of Consulting and Clinical Psychology, 52,* 97–103.

Floyd, R. L., Rimer, B. K., Giovino, G. A., Mullen, P. D., & Sullivan, S. E. (1993). A review of smoking in pregnancy: Effects on pregnancy outcomes and cessation efforts. *Annual Review of Public Health, 14,* 379-411.

Fogle, S. (1991a). The advent of AIDS. *The Journal of NIH Research, 3,* 88–91.

Fogle, S. (1991b). AIDS hemophiliacs in tough court battles. *The Journal of NIH Research, 3,* 46–47.

Folkes, V. S. (1982). Forming relationships and the matching hypothesis. *Personality and Social Psychology Bulletin, 8,* 631–636.

Foltz, K. R., Partin, J. S., & Lennarz, W. J. (1993). Sea urchin egg receptor for sperm: Sequence similarity of binding domain and hsp 70. *Science, 259,* 1421-1425.

For high school girls, Norplant debate hits home. (1993, March 7) *The New York Times,* p. 28.

Ford, C. S., & Beach, F. A. (1951). *Patterns of sexual behavior.* New York: Harper & Row.

Forrest, J. D., & Fordyce, R. R. (1993). Women's contraceptive attitudes and use in 1992. *Family Planning Perspectives, 25,* 175-179.

Forrest, J. D., & Singh, S. (1990). The sexual and reproductive behavior of American women, 1982–1988. *Family Planning Perspectives, 22,* 206-224.

Forsyth, C. J., & Fournet, L. (1987). A typology of office harlots: Mistresses, party girls, and career climbers. *Deviant Behavior, 8,* 319–328.

Forward, S., & Buck, C. (1978). *Betrayal of innocence: Incest and its devastation.* New York: J. P. Tarcher.

Fox, M. (1985, December). Interfering with herpes. *Today's Health,* 22.

Fox, R., et al. (1979). Stereopsis in human infants. *Science, 207,* 323–324.

Fox, R., et al. (1987). Effect of antibody test disclosure on subsequent sexual activity in homosexual men. *AIDS, 1,* 241–246.

Frank, E., Anderson, C., & Rubenstein, D. (1978). Frequency of sexual dysfunction in "normal" couples. *New England Journal of Medicine, 299,* 111–115.

Frank, E., & Anderson, P.A. (1987). Psychiatric disorders in rape victims: Past history and current symptomatology. *Comprehensive Psychiatry, 28,* 77–82.

Frank, E., & Stewart, B. D. (1983). Treatment of depressed rape victims: An approach to stress-induced symptomatology. In P. J. Clayton & J. E. Barrett (Eds.), *Treatment of depression: Old controversies and new approaches* (pp. 307–330). New York: Raven Press.

Franklin, D. (1984). Rubella threatens unborn in vaccine gap. *Science News, 125,* 186.

Franzoi, S. L., & Herzog, M. E. (1987). Judging physical attractiveness: What body aspects do we use? *Personality and Social Psychology Bulletin, 13,* 19–33.

Frayser, S. (1985). *Varieties of sexual experience: An anthropological perspective on human sexuality.* New Haven, CT: Human Relations Area Files Press.

Frazier, P. A. (1990). Victim attributions and post-rape trauma. *Journal of Personality and Social Psychology, 59,* 298–304.

Freeman, E. W., et al. (1982). Never-pregnant adolescents and family planning programs: Contraception, continuation, and pregnancy risk. *American Journal of Public Health, 72,* 815–822.

Freud, S. (1922). *Group psychology and the analysis of the ego* (James Strachey, Ed. & Trans.). London: Hogarth Press.

Freud, S. (1959). Analysis of a phobia in a 5-year-old boy. In A. & J. Strachey (Ed. & Trans.), *Collected papers* (Vol. 3). New York: Basic Books. (Original work published 1909.)

Freud, S. (1943). *A general introduction to psychoanalysis.* (Translation from German edition of 1917). Garden City, NY: Garden City Publishing Co.

Freud, S. (1933/1964). New introductory lectures. In *The Standard Edition of the Complete Works of Sigmund Freud (Vol. 22).* London: Hogarth Press.

Freud, S. (1961). Instincts and their vicissitudes. *The Standard Edition of the Complete Psychological Works of Sigmund Freud* (Vol. 14). London: Hogarth Press.

Freund, K. (1978). *Analysis of disorders of courtship phases.* Unpublished manuscript, Clarke Institute of Psychiatry, Toronto.

Freund, K., Watson, R., & Rienzo, D. (1988). The value of self-reports in the study of voyeurism and exhibitionism. *Annals of Sex Research, 1,* 243–262.

Freund, K., Watson, R., & Dickey, R. (1990). Does sexual abuse in childhood cause pedophilia: An exploratory study. *Archives of Sexual Behavior, 19,* 557–568.

Freund, K., & Blanchard, R. (1986). The concept of courtship disorder. *Journal of Sex and Marital Therapy, 12,* 79–92.

Freund, M., Leonard, T. L., & Lee, N. (1989). Sexual behavior of resident street prostitutes with their clients in Camden, New Jersey. *Journal of Sex Research, 26,* 460–478.

Frey, K. S., & Ruble, D. N. (1992). Gender constancy and the "cost" of sex-typed behavior: A test of the conflict hypothesis. *Developmental Psychology, 28,* 714-721.

Friday, N. (1973). *My secret garden.* New York: Trident.

Fried, P. A. (1986). Marijuana use in pregnancy. In I. J. Chasnott (Ed.), *Drug use in pregnancy: Mother and child.* Boston: MTP Press.

Fried, P. A., Watkinson, B., & Willan, A. (1984). Marijuana use during pregnancy and decreased length of gestation. *American Journal of Obstetrics and Gynecology, 150,* 23–27.

Friedman, R. C., et al. (1980). Behavior and the menstrual cycle. *Signs, 5,* 719–738.

Friedman, S. R., et al. (1987). AIDS and self-organization among intravenous drug uses. *International Journal of Addictions, 22,* 201–220.

Friedrich, E. (1985). Vaginitis. *American Journal of Obstetrics and Gynecology, 152,* 247–251.

Frisch, R. E. (1972). Weight at menarche. *Pediatrics, 50,* 445-450.

Frisch, R. E. (1983). Fatness, puberty and fertility: The effects of nutrition and physical training on menarche and ovulation. In J. Brooks-Gunn & A. C. Petersen (Eds.), *Girls at puberty: Biological and psychosocial aspects.* New York: Plenum.

Frisch, R. (1988, March). Fatness and fertility. *Scientific American,* pp. 88-95.

Frodi, A. M., Macauley, J., & Thome, P. R. (1977). Are women always less aggressive than men? A review of the experimental literature. *Psychological Bulletin, 84,* 634-660.

Fuentes, A. (1993, June 30). AIDS rising among Latinos. *New York Daily News,* p. 21.

Fundudis, T. (1989). Children's memory and the assessment of possible child sex abuse. *Journal of Child Psychology and Psychiatry and Allied Disciplines, 30,* 337–346.

Furby, L., Weinrott, M. R., & Blackshaw, L. (1989). Sex offender recidivism: A review. *Psychological Bulletin, 105,* 3–30.

Furby, L., Fischhoff, B., & Morgan, M. (1989). Judged effectiveness of common rape prevention and self-defense strategies. *Journal of Interpersonal Violence, 4,* 44–64.

Furnham, A., & Voli, V. (1989). Gender stereotypes in Italian television advertisements. *Journal of Broadcasting and Electronic Media, 33,* 175–185.

Furstenberg, F. (1984). Family communication and teenagers' contraceptive use. *Family Planning Perspectives, 16,* 163–170.

Furstenberg, F. F., Jr., Moore, K. A., & Peterson, J. L. (1985). Sex education and sexual experience among adolescents. *American Journal of Public Health, 75,* 1221–1222.

Furstenberg, F. F., Jr., Brooks-Gunn, J., Chase-Lansdale, L. (1989). Teenaged pregnancy and childbearing. *American Psychologist, 44,* 313–320.

Furstenberg, F., Brooks-Gunn, J., & Morgan, S. (1987). *Adolescent mothers in later life.* Cambridge, MA: Cambridge University Press.

Furstenberg, F. F., Jr. (1976). *Unplanned parenthood: The social consequences of teenage childbearing.* New York: Free Press.

Furstenberg, F. F., et al. (1982). Parental involvement: Selling family planning clinics short. *Family Planning Perspectives, 14,* 140–144.

Gaddis, A., & Brooks-Gunn, J. (1985). The male experience of pubertal change. *Journal of Youth and Adolescence, 14,* 61.

Gagnon, J. H. (1965). Sexuality and sexual learning in the child. *Psychiatry, 28,* 212–228.

Gagnon, J. H. (1977). *Human sexualities.* Glenview, IL: Scott, Foresman.

Gagnon, J. H. (1990). Gender preferences in erotic relations: The Kinsey scale and sexual scripts. In D. P. McWhirter, S. A. Sanders, & J. M. Reinisch (Eds.), *Homosexuality/Heterosexuality: Concepts of sexual orientation* (pp. 177–207). New York: Oxford University Press.

Gagnon, J. H., & Simon, W. (1987). The sexual scripting of oral genital contacts. *Archives of Sexual Behavior, 16,* 1–25.

Gagnon, J. H., & Simon, W. (1973). *Sexual conduct: The social origins of human sexuality..* Chicago: Aldine.

Gagnon, J. H., & Simon, W. (Eds.). (1967). *Sexual deviance.* New York: Harper & Row.

Galizio, M., & Hendrick, C. (1972). Effect of musical accompaniment on attitude: The guitar as a prop for persuasion. *Journal of Applied Social Psychology, 2,* 350–359.

Ganitsch, C. (1991, December 27). Personal communication.

Ganitsch, C. (1992, January 14). Personal communication.

Garber, D., et al. (1992, January 30). Cited in Angier, N. Odor receptors discovered in sperm cells. *The New York Times,* p. A19.

Garcia, L. T. (1986). Exposure to pornography and attitudes about women and rape: A correlational study. *Journal of Sex Research, 22,* 378–385.

Gardiner, H. W., & Gardiner, O. S. (1991). Women in Thailand. In L. L. Adler (Ed.), *Women in cross-cultural perspective* (pp. 175–187). New York: Praeger.

Garland, S. M., Lees, M. I., & Skurrie, I. J. (1990). Chlamydia trachomatis: Role in tubal infertility. *Australian and New Zealand Journal of Obstetrics and Gynaecology, 30,* 83–86.

Garner, B., & Smith, R. W. (1977). Are there really any gay male athletes? An empirical survey. *Journal of Sex Research, 13,* 22–34.

Garraty, J. A., & Gay, P. (Eds.). (1972). *The Columbia history of the world.* New York: Harper & Row.

Garrett, L. (1993a, June 7). Does AZT extend life? Big AIDS debate. *New York Newsday,* p. A16.

Garrett, L. (1993d, June 15). Why some survive. *New York Newsday,* pp. 61, 66.

Garrett, L. (1993c, June 15). The AIDS epidemic's financial toll. *New York, Newsday,* p. A67.

Garrett, L. (1993b, June 9). Experts: Tailor AIDS treatment: Strains need different tactics. *New York Newsday,* p. 21.

Garry, R. F., et al. (1988). Documentation of an AIDS virus infection in the United States in 1968. *Journal of the American Medical Association, 260,* 285–287.

Gartrell, N. K. (1982). Hormones and homosexuality. In W. Paul, J. D. Weinrich, J. C. Gonsiorek, & M. E. Hotvedt (Eds.), *Homosexuality: Social, psychological and biological issues.* Beverly Hills, CA: Sage.

Garwood, S. G., et al. (1980). Beauty is only "name deep": The effect of first name in ratings of physical attraction. *Journal of Applied Social Psychology, 10,* 431–435.

Gavey, N. (1991). Sexual victimization prevalence among New Zealand university students. *Journal of Consulting and Clinical Psychology, 59,* 464–466.

Gay, P. (1984). *The bourgeois experience: Victoria to Freud.* New York: Oxford University Press.

Gayle, H. D., et al. (1990). Prevalence of human immunodeficiency virus among university students. *The New England Journal of Medicine, 323,* 1538–1541.

Gayle, J., Selik, R., & Ccu, S. (1990). Surveillance for AIDS and HIV infection among Black and Hispanic children and women of child-bearing age, 1981-1989. *Morbidity and Mortality Weekly Report: Progress in Chronic Disease Prevention, 39,* 23-29. Washington, D.C.: U.S. Department of Health and Human Services.

Gebhard, P. H. (1977). *Memorandum on the incidence of homosexuals in the United States.* Bloomington, IN: Indiana University Institute for Sex Research.

Gebhard, P. H., et al. (1965). *Sex offenders: An analysis of types.* New York: Harper & Row.

Gebhard, P. H. (1976a). Fetishism and sadomasochism. In M. S. Weinberg (Ed.), *Sex Research: Studies from the Kinsey Institute* (pp. 156–166). New York: Oxford University Press.

Gebhard, P. H. (1976b) The institute. In M. S. Weinberg (Ed.), *Sex research: Studies from the Kinsey Institute.* New York: Oxford University Press.

Gebhard, P. H. (1969). Misconceptions about female prostitutes. *Medical Aspects of Human Sexuality, 3,* 24–26.

Geer, J., Heiman, J., & Leitenberg, H. (1984). *Human sexuality.* Englewood Cliffs, NJ: Prentice-Hall.

Geer, J., Morokoff, P., & Greenwood, P. (1974). Sexual arousal in women: The development of a measurement device for vaginal blood volume. *Archives of Sexual Behavior, 3,* 559–564.

Geiger, R. (1981). Neurophysiology of sexual response in spinal cord injury. In D. Bullard & S. Knight (Eds.), *Sexuality and physical disability: Personal perspectives.* St. Louis: C. V. Mosby.

Gelbard, M. (1988). Dystropic penile calcification in Peyronie's disease. *Journal of Urology, 139,* 738–740.

Gelles, R. J., & Cornell, C. P. (1985). *Intimate violence in families.* Beverly Hills, CA: Sage.

Gelman, D., with P. Kandell. (1993, January 18). Isn't it romantic? *Newsweek,* pp. 60-61.

Genuis, M., Thomlison, B., & Bagley, C. (1991, Fall). Male victims of child sexual abuse: A brief overview of pertinent findings. Special issue: Child sexual abuse. *Journal of Child and Youth-Care,* 1-6.

George, L.K., & Weiler, S.J. (1981). Sexuality in middle and late life: The effects of age cohort and gender. *Archives of General Psychiatry, 38* 919-923.

Geringer, W. M., et al. (1993). Knowledge, attitudes, and behavior related to condom use and STDs in a high risk population. *Journal of Sex Research, 30,* 75-83.

Gerrard, M. (1987). Sex, sex guilt, and contraceptive use revisited: The 1980s. *Journal of Personality and Social Psychology, 52,* 975–980.

Gerrol, R., & Resick, P. A. (1988, November). *Sex differences in social support and recovery from victimization.* Paper presented at the meeting of the Association for Advancement of Behavior Therapy, New York, NY.

Gerson, M. (1980). The lure of motherhood. *Psychology of Women Quarterly, 5,* 207–218.

Gerson, M. (1984). Feminism and the wish for a child. *Sex Roles, 11,* 389–399.

Geshwind, N. (1972). Language and the brain. *Scientific American, 226,* 76-83.

Gibbs, N. (1991, June 3). When is it rape? *Time,* pp. 48–54.

Gibson, A. I., et al. (1988). Adolescent female prostitutes. *Archives of Sexual Behavior, 17,* 431–438.

Gibson, J. W., & Kempf, J. (1990). Attitudinal predictors of sexual activity in Hispanic adolescent females. *Journal of Adolescent Research, 5,* 414–430.

Gidycz, C. A., & Koss, M. P. (1990). A comparison of group and individual sexual assault victims. *Psychology of Women Quarterly, 14,* 325–342.

Gilbert, H. W., & Gingell, J. C. (1991). The results of an intracorporeal papaverine clinic. *Sexual and Marital Therapy,* 649-56.

Gilgun, J. F., & Connor, T. M. (1989, May). How perpetrators view child sexual abuse. *Social Work,* 249–251.

Gill, W. B., Schumacher, G. F. B., & Bibbo, M. (1977). Pathological semen and anatomical abnormalities of the genital tract in human male subjects exposed to diethylstilbestrol in utero. *Journal of Urology, 117,* 477–480.

Gillespie, M. W., ten Vergert, E. M., & Kingma, J. (1988). Secular trends in abortion attitudes: 1975–1980–1985. *Journal of Psychology, 122,* 323–341.

Gillis, J. S., & Avis, W. E. (1980). The male-taller norm in mate selection. *Personality and Social Psychology Bulletin, 6,* 396–401.

Gilmartin, B. G. (September 1975). That swinging couple down the block. *Psychology Today,* 54.

Giovannucci, E., et al. (1993a). A prospective cohort study of vasectomy and prostate cancer in U.S. men. *Journal of the American Medical Association, 269,* 873-877.

Giovannucci, E., et al. (1993b). A retrospective cohort study of vasectomy and prostate cancer in U.S. men. *Journal of the American Medical Association, 269,* 878-882.

Gitlin, M. J., & Pasnau, R. O. (1989). Psychiatric syndromes linked to reproductive function in women: A review of current knowledge. *American Journal of Psychiatry, 146,* 1413-1422.

Gittelson, N. (1980, January). Marriage: What women expect and what they get. *McCall's,* pp. 87–89.

Gittes, R. F. (1991). Carcinoma of the prostate. *The New England Journal of Medicine, 324,* 236–245.

Gittleson, N. L., Eacott, S. E., & Mehta, B. M. (1978). Victims of indecent exposure. *British Journal of Psychiatry, 132,* 61–66.

Glasner, P. D., & Kaslow, R. A. (1990). The epidemiology of human immunodeficiency virus infection. *Journal of Consulting and Clinical Psychology, 58,* 13–21.

Glass, S. P., & Wright, T. L. (1992). Justifications of extramarital relationships: The association between attitudes, behaviors, and gender. *Journal of Sex Research, 29,* 361-387.

Glass, R. H., & Ericsson, R. (1982). *Getting pregnant in the 1980s.* Berkeley: University of California Press.

Glenn, N. (1981). The well-being of persons remarried after divorce. *Journal of Family Issues, 2,* 61–75.

Glenn, N. D. (1982). Interreligious marriage in the United States: Patterns and recent trends. *Journal of Marriage and the Family, 44,* 556–566.

Glenn, N. D., & Kramer, K. B. (1985). The psychological well-being of adult children of divorce. *Journal of Marriage and the Family, 47,* 905–912.

Glenn, N. D., & Weaver, C. N. (1988). The changing relationship of marital status to reported happiness. *Journal of Marriage and the Family, 50,* 317–324.

Glick, P. C., & Lin, S. (1986). Recent changes in divorce and remarriage. *Journal of Marriage and the Family, 48,* 737–747.

Goedert, J. J., et al. (1992, January 7). Cited in Leary, W. E. Study of H.I.V. transmission at birth. *The New York Times,* p. C3.

Gold, A. R., & Adams, D. B. (1981). Motivational factors affecting fluctuations of female sexual activity at menstruation. 670–680.

Gold, A. R., & Adams, D. B. (1978). Measuring the cycles of female sexuality. *Contemporary Obstetrics and Gynecology, 12,* 147–156.

Gold, D., et al. (1988). Chronic-dose acyclovir to suppress frequently recurring genital herpes simplex virus infection: Effect on antibody response to herpes simplex virus type 2 proteins. *Journal of Infectious Diseases, 158,* 1227–1234.

Gold, R. B. (1990). *Abortion and women's health.* New York: Alan Guttmacher Institute.

Gold, R. S., & Skinner, M. J. (1992). Situational factor and thought processes associated with unprotected intercourse in young gay men. *AIDS, 6,* 1021-1030.

Gold, S. R., & Gold, R. G. (1993). Sexual aversions: A hidden disorder. In W. O'Donohue & J. H. Geer (Eds.), *Handbook of sexual dysfunctions: Assessment and treatment.* (pp. 83-102). Boston: Allyn & Bacon.

Goldberg, M. (1987). Understanding hypersexuality in men and women. In G. R. Weeks and Larry Hof (Eds.), *Integrating sex and marital therapy: A clinical guide* (pp. 202–220). New York: Brunner/Mazel.

Goldberg, L. H., et al. (1993). Longterm suppression of recurrent genital herpes with acyclovir. *Archives of Dermatology, 129,* 582-587.

Goldberg, S., & Lewis, M. (1969). Play behavior in the year-old infant: Early sexual differences. In U. Bronfenbrenner (Ed.), *Influences on Human Development.* Hinsdale, IL: Dryden Press.

Goldberg, D. C., et al. (1983). The Grafenberg spot and female ejaculation: A review of initial hypotheses. *Journal of Sex and Marital Therapy, 9,* 27–37.

Golden, N. (1985). Treating the adolescent with Chlamydia trachomatis infection. *Medical Aspects of Human Sexuality, 19,* 80.

Goldenring, J. D., & Purtell, E. (1984). Knowledge of testicular cancer risk and need for self-examination in college students: A call for equal time for men in teaching of early cancer detection techniques. *Pediatrics,* 1093–1096.

Goldfoot, D. A., Essock-Vitale, S. M., Asa, C. S., Thornton, J. E., & Leshner, A. I. (1978). Anosmia in male rhesus monkeys does not alter copulatory activity with cycling females. *Science, 199,* 1095–1096.

Golding, J. M., et al., (1989, January). Social support sources following sexual assault. *Journal of Community Psychology, 17(1)*, 92–107.

Goldman, L., & Tosteson, A. N. A. (1991). Uncertainty about post-menopausal estrogen: Time for action, not debate. *The New England Journal of Medicine, 325*, 800–802.

Goldman, W., & Lewis, P. (1977). Beautiful is good: Evidence that the physically attractive are more socially skillful. *Journal of Experimental Social Psychology, 13*, 125–130.

Goldsmith, M. F. (1987). Sex in the age of AIDS calls for common sense and condom sense. *Journal of the American Medical Association, 257*, 2261–2266.

Goldsmith, M. F. (1989). Medical news and perspectives: "Silent epidemic" of "social disease" makes STD experts raise their voices. *Journal of the American Medical Association, 261*, 3509–3510.

Goldsmith, M. F. (1991). Costs in dollars and lives continue to rise. *Journal of the American Medical Association, 266*, 1055.

Goldstein, I. (1987). Penile revascularization. *Urologic Clinics of North America, 14*, 805–813.

Goldstein, A. M., & Clark, J. H. (1990). Treatment of uncomplicated gonococcal urethritis with single-dose ceftriaxone. *Sexually Transmitted Diseases, 17*, 181–183.

Goleman, D. (1991, October 22). Sexual harassment: It's about power, not lust. *The New York Times*, pp. C1, C12.

Goleman, D. (1992a, December 2). Studies find no disadvantage in growing up in a gay home. *The New York Times*, p. C14.

Goleman, D. (1993, October 6). Abuse-prevention efforts aid children. *The New York Times*, p. C13.

Goleman, D. (1991, December 10). New studies map the mind of the rapist. *The New York Times*, pp. C1, C10.

Goleman, D. (1988, October 18). Chemistry of sexual desire yields its elusive secrets. *The New York Times*, pp. C1, C15.

Goleman, D. (1992b). Therapies offer hope for sex offenders. *The New York Times*, pp. C1, C11.

Golub, S. (1983). Menarche: The beginning of menstrual life. In S. Golub (Ed.), *Lifting the curse of menstruation*. New York: Haworth.

Gomez-Schwartz, B., Horowitz, J., & Cardarelli, A. (1990). *Child sexual abuse: The initial effects*. Newbury Park, CA: Sage.

Gonsiorek, J. (1988). Mental health issues of gay and lesbian adolescents. *Journal of Adolescent Health Care, 9*, 114-122.

Gonsiorek, J. (1982). Results of psychological testing on homosexual populations, In W. Paul, J. D. Weinrich, J. C. Gonsiorek, & M. E. Hotvedt (Eds.), *Homosexuality: Social, psychological and biological issues* (pp. 71–81). Beverly Hills, CA: Sage.

Goodall, J. (1963, August). My life among wild chimpanzees. *National Geographic*, pp. 272–308.

Goodenough, W. H. (1949). Premarital freedom on Truk: Theory and practice. *American Anthropologist, 54*, 615–620.

Goodkin, K., et al. (1992). Life stressors and coping style are associated with immune measures in HIV-1 infection: A preliminary report. *International Journal of Psychiatry in Medicine, 22*, 155-172.

Goodman, M. J., et al. (1985). The compatibility of hunting and mothering among the Agta hunter-gatherers of the Philippines. *Sex Roles, 12*, 199–209.

Goodwin, J.M., Cheeves, K, & Connell, V. (1990). Borderline and other severe symptoms in adult survivors of incestuous abuse. *Psychiatric Annals, 20*, 22–32.

Goodwin, M., Gooding, K. M., & Regnier, F. (1979). Sex pheromone in the dog. *Science, 203*, 559-561.

Gordis, R. (1978). *Love and sex: A modern Jewish perspective*. New York: Farrar, Straus, & Giroux.

Gordon, M. (1978). *The American family: Past, present and future*. New York: Random House.

Gordon, M. (1989). The need for physicians to recognize sexual abuse in children. *New York State Journal of Medicine, 89*, 131–132.

Gordon, P. H., & DeMarco, L. J. (1984). Reproductive health services for men: Is there a need? *Family Planning Perspectives, 16*, 44–46.

Gordon, S. & Snyder, C. W. (1989). *Personal issues in human sexuality: A guidebook for better sexual health*. (2nd ed.). Boston: Allyn & Bacon.

Gosselin, C., & Wilson, G. (1980). *Sexual variations*. New York: Simon & Schuster.

Gostin, L, (1988). A civil liberties analysis of surrogacy arrangements [Special Issue: Forum on surrogate motherhood: Politics and privacy]. *Law, Medicine and Health Care, 16*, 7–17.

Gotfried, F. (1992, August). Personal communication.

Gottlieb, M. S. (1991, June 5). AIDS–the second decade: Leadership is lacking. *The New York Times*, p. A29.

Gottman, J. M., et al. (1976). *A couple's guide to communication*. Champaign, IL: Research Press.

Gouaux, C. (1971). Induced affective states and interpersonal attraction. *Journal of Personality and Social Psychology, 20*, 37–43.

Goulart, M., & Madover, S. (1991). An AIDS prevention program for homeless youth. *Journal of Adolescent Health, 12*, 573-575.

Gould, R. L. (1981, July 12). Men's desires: The Hite report on male sexuality. *The New York Times Book Review*, pp. 8–9, 19.

Goy, R. W., & Goldfoot, D. A. (1976). Neuroendocrinology: Animal models and problems of human sexuality. In E. A. Rubinstein, R. Green, & E. Brecher (Eds.), *New Directions in Sex Research*. New York: Plenum.

Graber, B. (1993). Medical aspects of sexual arousal disorders. In W. O'Donohue & J. H. Geer (Eds.), *Handbook of sexual dysfunctions: Assessment and treatment* (pp. 103-156). Boston: Allyn & Bacon.

Graca, L. M., Cardoso, C. G., Clode, N., & Calhaz-Jorge, C. (1991). Acute effects of maternal cigarette smoking on fetal heart rate and fetal body movements felt by the mother. *Journal of Perinatal Medicine, 19*, 385-390.

Grafenberg, E. (1950). The role of the urethra in female orgasm. *International Journal of Sexology, 3*, 145–148.

Graham, J. M., & Blanco, J. D. (1990). Chlamydial infections. *Primary Care: Clinics in Office Practice, 17*, 85–93.

Graham, N. M. H. et al. (1992). The effects on survival of early treatment of human immunodeficiency virus infection. *New England Journal of Medicine, 326*, 1037–1042.

Graham, S. (1848). *Lecture to young men, on chastity, intended also for the serious consideration of parents and guardians* (10th ed.). Boston: C. H. Pierce.

Graham, S. et al. (1982). Sex patterns and herpes simplex virus type 2 in the epidemiology of cancer of the cervix. *American Journal of Epidemiology, 115*, 729–735.

Grauerholz, E. (1989). Sexual harassment of women professors by students: Exploring the dynamics of power, authority, and gender in a university setting. *Sex Roles, 21*, 789–301.

Grauerholz, E., & Koralewski, M. A. (1991). What is known and not known about sexual coercion. In E. Grauerholz & M. A. Koralewski (Eds.), *Sexual coercion: A sourcebook on its nature, causes, and prevention* (pp. 187–197). Lexington, MA: Lexington Books.

Gray, P. (1993, February 15). What is love? *Time*, pp. 47-49.

Graziano, W., Brothen, T., & Berscheid, E. (1978). Height and attraction: Do men and women see eye-to-eye? *Journal of Personality, 46*, 128–145.

Green, D. S., & Green, B. (1965, March). Double sex. *Sexology*, 561–563.

Green, L. W., & Horton, D. (1982). Adolescent health: Issues and challenges. In J. T. Coates, A. C. Petersen, and C. Perry (Eds.), *Promoting adolescent health: A dialogue on research and practice*. New York: Academic Press.

Green, R. (1985). Gender identity in childhood and later sexual orientation. *American Journal of Psychiatry, 143(3)*, 339–341.

Green, R. (1979). Childhood cross-gender behavior and subsequent sexual preference. *American Journal of Psychiatry, 136*, 106–108.

Green, R. (1978). Sexual identity of 37 children raised by homosexual or transsexual parents. *American Journal of Psychiatry, 135*, 692–697.

Green, R. (1974). *Sexual identity conflict in children and adults*. Baltimore: Penguin, 1974.

Green, R. et al. (1986). Lesbian mothers and their children: A comparison with solo parent heterosexual mothers and their children. *Archives of Sexual Behavior, 15*, 167–184.

Green, R. (1987). *The "sissy boy syndrome" and the development of homosexuality*. New Haven, CT: Yale University Press.

Green, S. K., Buchanan, D. R., & Heuer, S. K. (1984). Winners, losers, and choosers: A field investigation of dating initiation. *Personality and Social Psychology Bulletin, 10*, 502–511.

Greenbaum, P., & Rosenfeld, H. M. (1978). Patterns of avoidance in response to interpersonal staring and proximity: Effects of bystanders on drivers at a traffic intersection. *Journal of Personality and Social Psychology, 36*, 575–587.

Greenberg, E. R. et al. (1984). Breast cancer in mothers given diethylstilbestrol in pregnancy. *New England Journal of Medicine, 311*, 1393–1398.

Greenberg, J. S., Bruess, C. E, & Sands, D. W. (1986). *Sexuality: Insights and issues*. Dubuque, IA: William C. Brown.

Greenblatt, C. S. (1983). The salience of sexuality in the early years of marriage. *Journal of Marriage and the Family, 4*, 289–299.

Greenglass, E. R. (1985). A social-psychological view of marriage for women. *International Journal of Women's Studies, 8*, 24–31.

Greenhouse, L. (1992, February 27). Court opens path for student suits in sex-bias cases. *The New York Times*, pp. A1, A16.

Greenwald, E., & Leitenberg, H. (1989). Long-term effects of sexual experiences with siblings and non-siblings during childhood. *Archives of Sexual Behavior, 18,* 389–399.

Greenwald, E., et al. (1990). Childhood sexual abuse: Long-term effects on psychological and sexual functioning in a nonclinical and nonstudent sample of adult women. *Child Abuse and Neglect, 14,* 503–513.

Greenwald, H. (1970). *The call girl.* New York: Ballantine Books.

Greer, W. R. (1986, November 23). Violence against homosexuals rising, groups seeking wider protection say. *The New York Times,* p. 36.

Griffeth, R. W., Vecchio, R. P., & Logan, J. W. (1989). Equity theory and interpersonal attraction. *Journal of Applied Psychology, 74,* 394–401.

Griffin, E., & Sparks, G. G. (1990). Friends forever: A longitudinal exploration of intimacy in same-sex friends and platonic pairs. *Journal of Social and Personal Relationships, 7,* 29–46.

Grimes, D. A. (1987). Intrauterine devices and pelvic inflammatory disease: Recent developments. *Contraception, 36,* 97–109.

Grodstein, F., Goldman, M. G., & Cramer, D. W. (1993). Relation of tubal infertility to history of sexually transmitted diseases. *American Journal of Epidemiology, 137,* 577-584.

Grogger, J., & Bronars, S. (1993). The socioeconomic consequences of teenage childbearing: Findings from a natural experiment. *Family Planning Perspectives, 25,* 156-161.

Gross, J. (1992, July 13). Suffering in silence no more: Fighting sexual harassment. *The New York Times,* pp. A10, D10.

Gross, J. (1991, February 11). New challenge of youth: Growing up in gay home. *The New York Times,* pp. A1, B7.

Gross, J. (1993, September 25). Combating rape on campus in a class on sexual consent. *The New York Times,* pp. 1, 9.

Gross, L., & Jeffries-Fox, S. (1978). What do you want to be when you grow up, little girl? In G. Tuchman et al. (Eds.), *Hearth and home: Images of women in the mass media.* New York: Oxford University Press.

Grosskopf, D. (1983). *Sex and the married woman.* New York: Wallaby Books.

Grossman, C. J., & Wilson, E. J. (1992). The immune system. *Alcohol World: Health & Research, 16,* National Institute on Alcohol Abuse and Alcoholism, NIH Publication No. 93-3466.

Grossman, S. (1991, December 22). Undergraduates drink heavily, survey discloses. *The New York Times,* p. 46.

Groth, A. N. (1982). The incest offender. In S. M. Sgroi (Ed.), *Handbook of clinical intervention in child sexual abuse.* Lexington, MA: Lexington Books.

Groth, A. N. (1978). Patterns of sexual assault against children and adolescents. In A. W. Burgess, A. N. Groth, L. L. Holmstrom, & S. M. Sgroi (Eds.), *Sexual assault of children and adolescents.* Toronto: Lexington Books.

Groth, A. N. *Men who rape.* New York: Plenum Press.

Groth, A. N., & Birnbaum, H. J. (1979). *Men who rape: The psychology of the offender.* New York: Plenum Press.

Groth, A. N., & Burgess, A. W. (1980). Male rape: Offenders and victims. *American Journal of Psychiatry, 137,* 806–810.

Groth, A., & Hobson, W. (1983). The dynamics of sexual assault. In L. Schlesinger & E. Revitch (Eds.), *Sexual dynamics of antisocial behavior.* Springfield, IL: Thomas.

Group W Video Services, *America's Black Forum.* (1991, November 24). Washington, DC: Uniworld Inc.

Grover, K. J., et al. (1985). Mate selection processes and marital satisfaction. *Family Relations, 34,* 383–386.

Gruber, J. E., & Bjorn, L. (1986). Women's responses to sexual harassment: An analysis of sociocultural, organizational, and personal resource models. *Social Science Quarterly, 67,* 814-826.

Gruber, V. A., & Wildman, B. G. (1987). The impact of dysmenhorrea on daily activities. *Behaviour Research and Therapy, 25,* 123–128.

Grush, J. E., & Yehl, J. G. (1979). Marital roles, sex differences, and interpersonal attraction. *Journal of Personality and Social Psychology, 37,* 116–123.

Guerrero, R. (1975). Type and time of insemination within the menstrual cycle and the human sex ratio. *Studies in Family Planning, 6,* 367–371.

Guinan, M. E. (1992, February 1). W. E. U.S. panel backs approval of first condom for women. *The New York Times,* p. 7.

Gupta, C., Yaffe, S. J., & Shapiro, B. H. (1982) Prenatal exposure to phenobarbital permanently decreases testosterone and causes reproductive dysfunction. *Science, 216,* 640–642.

Gustavson, A. R., Dawson, M. E., & Bonett, D. G. (1987). Androstenol, a putative human pheromone, affects human (Homo sapiens) male choice performance. *Journal of Comparative Psychology, 101,* 210–212.

Gutek, B. A., Morasch, B., & Cohen, A. G. (1983). Interpreting social-sexual behavior in a work setting. *Journal of Vocational Behavior, 22,* 30–48.

Gutek, B. A., et al. (1980). Sexuality and the workplace. *Basic and Applied Social Psychology, 1,* 255–265.

Guttmacher, A. F., & Kaiser, I. H. (1986). The genesis of liberalized abortion in New York: A personal insight. In J. D. Butler & D. F. Walbert (Eds.), *Abortion, medicine, and the law* (3rd ed.) (pp. 229–246). New York: Facts on File Publications.

Gwinn, M., et al. (1991). Prevalence of HIV infection in childbearing women in the United States: Surveillance using newborn blood samples. *Journal of the American Medical Association, 265,* 1704–1708.

Haas, A. (1979). Male and female spoken language differences: Stereotypes and evidence. *Psychological Bulletin, 86,* 616–626.

Haas-Hawkings, G., et al. (1985). A study of relatively immediate adjustment to widowhood in late life. *International Journal of Women's Studies, 8,* 158–165.

Haffner, D. (1993, August). *Sex education: Trends and issues.* Paper presented at the meeting of the American Psychological Association, Toronto, Canada.

Haglund, B., & Cnattingius, S. (1990). Cigarette smoking as a risk factor for sudden infant death syndrome: A population based study. *American Journal of Public Health, 80,* 29-32.

Hall, C. S. (1984). "A ubiquitous sex difference in dreams" revisited. *Journal of Personality and Social Psychology, 46,* 1109–1117.

Hall, E. J., & Ferree, M. M. (1986). Race differences in abortion attitudes. *Public Opinion Quarterly, 50,* 193–207.

Hall, E. J., & Flannery, P. J. (1985). Prevalence and correlates of sexual assault experiences in adolescents. *Victimology: An International Journal, 9,* 398–406.

Hall, G., et al. (1986). The utility of the MMPI with men who have sexually assaulted children. *Journal of Consulting and Clinical Psychology, 54,* 493–496.

Hall, G. C. N. (1989). Sexual arousal and arousability in a sexual offender population. *Journal of Abnormal Psychology, 98,* 145–149.

Hall, G. C. N., & Hirschman, R. (1991). Toward a theory of sexual aggression: A quadripartite model. *Journal of Consulting and Clinical Psychology, 59,* 662–669.

Hall, J. A., & Taylor, M. C. (1985). Psychological androgyny and the masculinity-femininity interaction. *Journal of Personality and Social Psychology, 49,* 429–435.

Hall, N. R. S. (1988). The virology of AIDS. *American Psychologist, 43,* 907–913.

Halleck, S. L. (1981). The ethics of antiandrogen therapy. *American Journal of Psychiatry, 138,* 642–643.

Halpern, D. F. (1986). *Sex differences in cognitive abilities.* Hillsdale, NJ: Erlbaum.

Halpern, S. (1978). *Rape: Helping the victim.* Oradell, NJ: Medical Economics Company.

Halverson, H. (1940). Genital and sphincter behavior of the male infant. *Journal of Genetic Psychology, 56,* 95–136.

Hamer, D. H., et al. (1993, July 16). A linkage between DNA markers on the X chromosome and male sexual orientation. *Science, 261,* 321-327.

Hamilton, E. (1942). *Mythology.* New York: New American Library.

Hamilton, J. D., et al. (1992). A controlled trial of early versus late treatment with zidovudine in symptomatic human immunodeficiency virus infection. *The New England Journal of Medicine, 326,* 437–443.

Hamilton, M., & Yee, J. (1990). Rape knowledge and propensity to rape. *Journal of Research in Personality, 24,* 111–122.

Hand, J. R. (1970). Surgery of the penis and urethra. In M. F. Campbell & J. H. Harrison (Eds.), *Urology* (Vol. 3). Philadelphia: W. B. Saunders Co.

Handler, A. (1990). The correlates of the initiation of sexual intercourse among young urban Black females. *Journal of Youth and Adolescence, 19,* 159–170.

Handsfield, H. (1984). Gonorrhea and uncomplicated gonococcal infection. In K. K. Holmes, et al. (Eds.), *Sexually transmitted diseases* (pp. 205–220). New York: McGraw-Hill.

Handsfield, H. H. (1988). Questions and answers: "Safe sex" guidelines: Mycoplasma and chlamydia infections. *Journal of the American Medical Association, 259,* 2022.

Handyside, A., et al. (1989, February 18). Biopsy of human implantation embryos and sexing by DNA amplification. *Lancet,* 347–349.

Hankins, C. A. (1990). Issues involving women, children, and AIDS primarily in the developed world. *Journal of Acquired Immune Deficiency Syndrome, 3,* 443-448.

Hanrahan, J. P., et al. (1992). The effect of maternal smoking during pregnancy on early infant lung function. *American Review of Respiratory Disease, 145,* 1129-1135.

Hansen, G. L. (1983). Marital satisfaction and jealousy among men. *Psychological Reports, 52,* 363–366.

Hanson, S. L., Morrison, D. R., & Ginsburg, A. L. (1989). The antecedents of teenage fatherhood. *Demography, 26,* 579–596.

Hanson, J. W., Streissguth, A. P., & Smith, D. W. (1978). The effects of moderate alcohol consumption during pregnancy on growth and morphogenesis. *The Journal of Pediatrics, 92,* 457–460.

Hanson, R. K., & Slater, S. (1988). Sexual victimization in the history of sexual abusers: A review. *Annals of Sex Research, 1,* 485–499.

Hanson, R. K. (1990). The psychological impact of sexual assault on women and children: A review. *Annals of Sex Research, 3,* 187-232.

Harahap, M., & Siregar, A. (1988). Circumcision: A review and a new technique. *Journal of Dermatology and Surgical Oncology, 14,* 383–386.

Harcourt, A. H., Stewart, K. J., & Fossey, D. (1981). Gorilla reproduction in the wild. In C. E. Graham (Ed.), *Reproductive biology of the great apes* (pp. 265–279). New York: Academic Press.

Harding, J. J. (1989). Postpartum psychiatric disorders: A review. *Comprehensive Psychiatry, 30,* 109–112.

Hardy, A. M., et al. (1986). The economic impact of the first 10,000 cases of acquired immune deficiency syndrome in the United States. *Journal of the American Medical Association, 225,* 209–211.

Hare-Mustin, R. T., & Broderick, P. C. (1979). The myth of motherhood: A study of attitudes toward motherhood. *Psychology of Women Quarterly, 4,* 114–128.

Hariton, E. B. (October 1973). The sexual fantasies of women. *Psychology Today,* pp. 39–44.

Hariton, E. B., & Singer, J. L. (1974). Women's fantasies during sexual intercourse: Normative and theoretical implications. *Journal of Consulting and Clinical Psychology, 42,* 313–322.

Harlap, S., & Shiono, P. H. (1980). Alcohol, smoking, and incidence of spontaneous abortions in the first and second trimester. *Lancet, 2,* 173–176.

Harlow, H. F. (1959). Love in infant monkeys. *Scientific American, 200,* 68–86.

Harlow, H. F. (1965). Sexual behavior in the rhesus monkey. In F. Beach (Ed.), *Sex and behavior.* New York: Wiley.

Harney P. A., & Muehlenhard, C. L. (1991). Rape. In E. Grauerholz & M. A. Koralewski (Eds.), *Sexual coercion: A sourcebook on its nature, causes, and prevention* (pp. 3–16). Lexington, MA: Lexington Books.

Harris, L. (1988). *Inside America.* New York: Vintage.

Harris, M. (1981). *America now: The anthropology of a changing culture.* New York: Simon & Schuster.

Harris, M. (1974). *Cows, pigs, wars and witches: The riddles of culture.* New York: Vintage Books.

Harris, R. E., et al. (1990). Changes in AIDS risk behavior among intravenous drug abusers in New York City. *New York State Journal of Medicine, 90,* 123–126.

Harris, G. W., & Levine, S. (1965). Sexual differentiation of the brain and its experimental control. *Journal of Physiology, 181,* 379–400.

Harris, M. B., Harris, R. J., & Bochner, S. (1982). Fat, four-eyed, and female: Stereotypes of obesity, glasses, and gender. *Journal of Applied Social Psychology, 12,* 503–516.

Harry, J. (1983). Defeminization and adult psychological well-being among male homosexuals. *Archives of Sexual Behavior, 12,* 1–19.

Harry, J., & Lovely, R. (1979). Gay marriages and communities of sexual orientation. *Alternative Lifestyles, 2,* 177–200.

Hart, J., et al. (1991). Sexual behavior in pregnancy: A study of 219 women. *Journal of Sex Education and Therapy, 17,* 86-90.

Hart, B.L. (1986). Medial preoptic-anterior hypothalamic lesions and sociosexual behavior of male goats. *Physiology and Behavior, 36* 301-305.

Hart, C. W. M., & Pilling, A. R. (1979). *The Tiwi of North Australia.* New York: Holt, Rinehart & Winston.

Hartman, C. R., Burgess, A. W., & McCormack, A. (1987). Pathways and cycles of runaways: A model for understanding repetitive runaway behavior. *Hospital and Community Psychiatry, 38,* 292–299.

Hartman, W. E., & Fithian, M. (1974). *Treatment of sexual dysfunction.* New York: Jason Aronson.

Hartman, W. E., & Fithian, M. (1984). *Any man can: The multiple orgasmic technique for every loving man.* New York: St. Martin's Press.

Harvey, S. (1987). Female sexual behavior: Fluctuations during the menstrual cycle. *Journal of Psychosomatic Research, 31,* 101–110.

Hass, A. (1979). *Teenage sexuality.* New York: Macmillan.

Hassett, J. (1978). Sex and smell. *Psychology Today, 12(10),* pp. 40–42, 45.

Hatcher, R. A., et al. (1988). *Contraceptive technology: 1988-1989* (14th rev. ed.). New York: Irvington Publishers.

Hatcher, R. A., et al. (1994). *Contraceptive technology 1992-1994* (16th rev. ed.). New York: Irvington Publishers.

Hatcher, R. A., et al. (1990). *Contraceptive technology 1990-1992* (15th rev. ed.). New York: Irvington Publishers.

Hatfield, E. (1988). Passionate and companionate love. In R. J. Sternberg & M. L. Barnes (Eds.), *The psychology of love* (pp. 191–217). New Haven, CT: Yale University Press.

Hatfield, E., & Rapson, R. L. (1987). Passionate love/sexual desire: Can the same paradigm explain both? *Archives of Sexual Behavior, 16,* 259–278.

Hatfield, E., & Sprecher, S. (1986). Measuring passionate love in intimate relationships. *Journal of Adolescence, 9,* 383–410.

Hatfield, E., & Walster, G. W. (1978). *A new look at love.* Lantham, MA: University Press of America.

Hatfield, E., Sprecher, S., & Traupman, J. (1978). Men's and women's reaction to sexually explicit films: A serendipitous finding. *Archives of Sexual Behavior, 7,* 583–592.

Havemann, E., & Lehtinen, M. (1990). *Marriages and families: New problems, new opportunities* (2nd ed.). Englewood Cliffs, N J: Prentice-Hall, Inc.

Haverkos, H. W. (1993). Reported cases of AIDS: An update. *The New England Journal of Medicine, 329,* 511.

Hawton, K. (1991). Sex therapy. Special issue: The changing face in behavioural psychotherapy. *Behavioural Psychotherapy, 19,* 131-136.

Hawton, K., et al. (1986). Long-term outcome of sex therapy. *Behaviour Research and Therapy, 24,* 665–675.

Hawton, K., & Catalan, J. (1990). Sex therapy for vaginismus: Characteristics of couples and treatment outcomes. *Sexual and Marital Therapy, 5,* 39–48.

Hawton, K., & Catalan, J. (1986). Prognostic factors in sex therapy. *Behaviour Research and Therapy, 24,* 377–385.

Hayes, C. D. (Ed.). (1987). *Risking the future* (Vol. 1). Washington, DC: National Academy Press.

Hayes, M. P., Stinnett, N., & DeFrain, J. (1981). Learning about marriage from the divorced. *Journal of Divorce, 4,* 23–29.

Hays, R. B., Turner, H., Coates, T. J. (1992). Social support, AIDS-related symptoms, and depression among gay men. *Journal of Consulting and Clinical Psychology, 60,* 463-469.

Hazan, C., & Shaver, P. (1987). Love conceptualized as an attachment process. *Journal of Personality and Social Psychology, 52,* 511-524.

Hazelwood, R. R., Deitz, P. E., & Burgess, A. W. (1983). *Autoerotic fatalities.* Lexington, MA: Lexington Books.

Hazelwood, R. R., Reboussin, R., & Warren, J. I. (1989). Serial rape: Correlates of increased aggression and the relationship of offender pleasure to victim resistance. *Journal of Interpersonal Violence, 4,* 65–78.

Hearst, N., & Hulley, S. B. (1988). Preventing the heterosexual spread of AIDS: Are we giving our patients the best advice? *Journal of the American Medical Association, 259,* 2428–2432.

Heath, R. (1972). Pleasure and brain activity in man. *Journal of Nervous and Mental Disease, 154,* 3–18.

Hebert, Y., et al. (1989). Factors related to the use of condoms among French-Canadian university students. *The Journal of Social Psychology, 129,* 707–709.

Hechtman, L. (1989). Teenage mothers and their children: Risks and problems: A review. *Canadian Journal of Psychiatry, 34,* 569–575.

Hefzallah, I. M., & Maloney, W. (1979). Are there only six kinds of TV commercials? *Journal of Advertising Research, 19(4),* 57–62.

Hegeler, S., & Mortensen, M. (1977). Sexual behavior in elderly Danish males. In R. Gemme & C. Wheeler (Eds.), *Progress in sexology* (pp. 285–292). New York: Plenum Press.

Heiby, E., & Becker, J. D. (1980). Effect of filmed modeling on the self-reported frequency of masturbation. *Archives of Sexual Behavior, 9,* 11–20.

Heilbrun, A. B., Jr., & Seif, D. T. (1988). Erotic value of female distress in sexually explicit photographs. *Journal of Sex Research, 24,* 47–57.

Heim, N. (1981). Sexual behavior of castrated sex offenders. *Archives of Sexual Behavior, 10,* 11–19.

Heim, N., & Hursch, C. J. (1979). Castration for sex offenders: Treatment or punishment? A review & critique of recent European literature. *Archives of Sexual Behavior, 8,* 281–304.

Heiman, J. R. (1978). Uses of psychophysiology in the assessment and treatment of sexual dysfunction. In J. LoPiccolo & L. LoPiccolo (Eds.), *Handbook of sex therapy* (pp. 123–135). New York: Plenum Press.

Hein, K., DiGeronimo, T. F., & the Editors of Consumer Reports Books. (1989). *AIDS: Trading fears for facts.* Mount Vernon, NY: Consumers Union.

Heller, J., & Gleich, P. (1988). Erectile impotence: Evaluation and management. *Journal of Family Practice, 26,* 321–324.

Helmreich, R. L., Spence, J. T., & Holahan, C. J. (1979). Psychological androgyny and sex-role flexibility: A test of two hypotheses. *Journal of Personality and Social Psychology, 37,* 1631–1644.

Hendrick, C., & Hendrick, S. (1986). A theory and method of love. *Journal of Personality and Social Psychology, 50,* 392–402.

Hendrick, S. S. (1981). Self-disclosure and marital satisfaction. *Journal of Personality and Social Psychology, 40,* 1150–1159.

Hendrick, S. S., Hendrick, C., & Adler, N. L. (1988). Romantic relationships, love, satisfaction, and staying together. *Journal of Personality and Social Psychology, 54,* 980-988.

Henneberger, M. (with M. Marriott). For some, rituals of abuse replace youthful courtship. *The New York Times,*, pp. A1, A33.

Henry, J. (1963). *Culture against man.* New York: Random House.

Henry, W. A. III. (1993, July 26). Born gay? *Time,* pp. 36-39.

Henshaw, S. K., & Silverman, J. (1988). The characteristics and prior contraceptive use of U.S. abortion patients. *Family Planning Perspectives, 20,* 158-168.

Henshaw, S. K., & Singh, S. (1986). Sterilization regret among U.S. couples. *Family Planning Perspectives, 18,* 238–240.

Hensley, W. E. (1992). Why does the best-looking person in the room always seem to be surrounded by admirers? *Psychological Reports, 70,* 457-458.

Herberg, L. J. (1963). Seminal ejaculation following positively reinforcing electrical stimulation of the rat hypothalamus. *Journal of Comparative and Physiological Psychology, 56,* 679.

Herbst, A. (1979). Coitus and the fetus. *New England Journal of Medicine, 301,* 1235–1236.

Herdt, G. (1987). *The Sambia: Ritual and gender in New Guinea.* New York: Holt, Rinehart & Winston.

Herdt, G. H. (1981). *Guardians of the flutes: Idioms of masculinity.* New York: McGraw-Hill

Herdt, G. H. (1984). Semen transactions in Sambia culture. In G. H. Herdt (Ed.), *Ritualized homosexuality in Melanesia* (pp. 167–210). Berkeley: University of California Press.

Herdt, G. H., & Stoller, R. J. (1989). Commentary to "The socialization of homosexuality and heterosexuality in a non-Western society." *Archives of Sexual Behavior, 18,* 31–34.

Herek, G. (1988). Heterosexuals' attitudes toward lesbians and gay men: Correlates and gender differences. *Journal of Sex Research, 25,* 451–477.

Hernandez, J. T., & Smith, F. J. (1990). Inconsistencies and misperceptions putting college students at risk of HIV infection. *Journal of Adolescent Health Care, 11,* 295–297.

Herrel, J. M. (1975). Sex differences in emotional responses to "erotic literature." *Journal of Consulting and Clinical Psychology, 43,* 921.

Herzog, L. (1989). Urinary tract infections and circumcision. *American Journal of Diseases of Children, 143,* 348–350.

Herzog, R. (1957). *Die Nubier.* Berlin.

Hess, B. B., Markson, E. W., & Stein, P. J. (1993). *Sociology* (4th ed.). New York: MacMillan.

Hetherington, E. M., Camara, K. A., & Featherman, D. L. (1983). Achievement and intellectual functioning of children from one-parent households. In J. Spence (ED.), *Achievement and achievement motives.* San Francisco: Freeman.

Hetherington, E. M., Cox, M., & Cox, R. (1982). Effects of divorce on parents and children. In M. E. Lamb (Ed.), *Nontraditional families; Parenting and child development.* Hillsdale, NJ: Erlbaum.

Hicks, J. M., & Iosefsohn, M. (1989). Reliability of home pregnancy-test kits in the hands of laypersons. *New England Journal of Medicine, 320,* 320–321.

High court lets Pentagon put gay policy into effect. (1993, October 30). *The New York Times,* p. 6.

Higham, E. (1980). Sexuality in the infant and neonate: Birth to two years. In B. Wolman & J. Money (Eds.), *Handbook of human sexuality* Englewood Cliffs, N J: Prentice-Hall.

Hill, C. T., Rubin, Z., & Paplau, L. A. Breakups before marriage: The end of 103 affairs. *Journal of Social Issues, 32,* 147–168.

Hillier, S., & Holmes, K. K. (1990). Bacterial vaginosis. In K. K. Holmes, P. Mardh, P. F. Sparling, & P. J. Wiesner (Eds.), *Sexually transmitted diseases (2nd ed.)* (pp. 547-560). New York: McGraw-Hill.

Hilton, E., et al. (1992). Ingestion of yogurt containing *Lactobacillus acidophilus* as prophylaxis for candidal vaginitis. *Annals of Internal Medicine, 116,* 353-357.

Hilts, P. J. (1992, December 2). Federal agency start of human tests of AIDS vaccines. *The New York Times,*, p. B9.

Hilts, P. J. (1993, February 25). Door may be open for abortion pill to be sold in U.S. *The New York Times,* pp. A1, D23.

Hilts, P. J. (1992, January 18). Strange history of silicone held many warning signs. *The New York Times,* pp. 1, 8.

Hinds, M. D. (1981, June 15). The child victim of incest. *The New York Times,* B9.

Hingson, R. W., et al. (1990). Beliefs about AIDS, use of alcohol and drugs, and unprotected sex among Massachusetts adolescents. *American Journal of Public Health, 80,* 295-298.

Hinsz, V. B. (1989). Facial resemblance in engaged and married couples. *Journal of Social and Personal Relationships, 6,* 223–229.

Hite, S. (1987). *Women and love, a cultural revolution in progress.* New York: Knopf.

Hite, S. (1981). *The Hite report on male sexuality.* New York: Knopf.

Hite, S. (1977). *The Hite report: A nationwide study of female sexuality.* New York: Dell.

Hite, S. (1976). *The Hite report.* New York: Macmillan.

H.I.V. clue supports early use of condom. (1992, December 18). *The New York Times,* p.C9.

Hoagland, J. (1988, February 13). Sexual politics, Islamic style. *Washington Post,*

Hoagwood, K. (1990). Blame and adjustment among women sexually abused as children. *Women and Therapy, 9,* 89–110.

Hobbins, J. C. (1991). Diagnosis and management of neural-tube defects today. *The New England Journal of Medicine, 324,* 690–691.

Hochman, D. (1992, November 29). A safe-sex product in need of a marketing plan. *The New York Times,* p. F10.

Hock, Z. (1983). The G Spot. *Journal of Sex and Marital Therapy, 9,* 166–167.

Hodges, B. C., et al. (1992). Gender-differences in adolescents' attitudes toward condom use. *Journal of School Health, 62,* 103-106.

Hodgson, R., et al. (1990). Chlamydia trachomatis: The prevalence, trend and importance in initial infertility management. *Australian and New Zealand Journal of Obstetrics and Gynaecology, 30,* 251–254

Hodgson, et al. v. Minnesota, et al. (1990). 110 S. Ct. 2926.

Hofferth, S. L., & Hayes, C. D. (Eds.). (1987). *Risking the future: Adolescent sexuality, pregnancy, and childbearing: Vol. 2. Working papers and statistical reports.* Washington, DC: National Academy Press.

Hofferth, S. L., Kahn, J. B., & Baldwin, W. (1987). Premarital sexual activity among teenage American women over the past three decades. *Family Planning Perspectives, 19,* 46–53.

Hoffman, L. W., & Manis, J. D. (1978). Influences of children on marital interaction and parental satisfaction and dissatisfaction. In R. M. Lerner & G. B. Spanier (Eds.), *Child influences on marital and family interaction.* New York: Academic Press.

Hoffman, M. (1972). Homosexuality. In F. A. Beach (Ed.), *Human sexuality in four perspectives* Baltimore: Johns Hopkins University Press.

Hoffman, J. (1993, January 10). The morning after pill: A well-kept secret. *The New York Times Sunday Magazine,* p. 12.

Hogan, D. P., & Kitigawa, E. M. (1985). The impact of social status, family structure and neighborhood on the fertility of black adolescents. *Family Planning Perspectives, 17,* 165–169.

Hogbin, I. (1970). *The island of menstruating men: Religion in Wogeo, New Guinea.* Scranton, PA: Chandler.

Holder, A. R. (1988). Surrogate motherhood and the best interests of children [Special Issue: Forum on surrogate motherhood: Politics and privacy]. *Law, Medicine and Health Care, 16,* 51–56.

Holeman, R. E., & Winokur, G. (1965). Effeminate homosexuality: A disease of childhood. *American Journal of Orthopsychiatry, 35,* 48–56.

Hollestedt, C., Dahlgren, L., & Rydbert, U. (1983). Outcome of pregnancy in women treated at an alcohol clinic. *Acta Psychiatrica Scandinavica, 67,* 236–248.

Holman, T. B., & Jacquart, M. (1988). Leisure-activity patterns and marital satisfaction: A further test. *Journal of Marriage and the Family, 50,* 69–77.

Holmberg, S. D., & Curran, J. W. (1989). The epidemiology of HIV infection in industrialized countries. In K. K. Holmes, et al. (Eds.), *Sexually transmitted diseases* (pp. 343–354). New York: McGraw-Hill, Inc.

Holmes, K. K., & Kreiss, J. (1988). Heterosexual transmission of human immunodeficiency virus: Overview of a neglected aspect of the AIDS epidemic. *Journal of Acquired Immune Deficiency Syndromes, 1,* 602–610.

Holmes, K. K., et al. (Eds.). (1989). *Sexually transmitted diseases* (2nd ed.). New York: McGraw-Hill.

Holtzman, D., et al. (1992). HIV education and health education in the United States: A national survey of local school district policies and practices. *Journal of School Health, 62,* 421-427.

Holzman, H. R, & Pines, S. (1982). Buying sex: The phenomenology of being a john. *Deviant Behavior, 4*, 89–116.

Hong, L. K. (1974). The instability of teenage marriage in the United States: An evaluation of the socio-economic status hypothesis. *International Journal of Sociology of the Family, 4*, 201–212.

Hong, L. K. (1984). Survival of the fastest: On the origin of premature ejaculation. *Journal of Sex Research, 20*, 109–122.

Honig, A. S. (1978). What we need to know to help the teenage parent. *Family Coordinator, 27*, 113–119.

Hooker, E. (1957). The adjustment of the male overt homosexual. *Journal of Projective Techniques, 21*, 18–31.

Hooker, E. (1965). An empirical study of some relations between sexual patterns and gender identity in male homosexuals. In J. Money (Ed.), *Sex research: New developments.* New York: Holt, Rinehart and Winston.

Hoorwitz, A. N. (1992). *The clinical detective: Techniques in the evaluation of sexual abuse.* New York: Norton.

Horney, K. (1967). *Feminine psychology.* New York: Norton.

Horowitz, M. (1976). *Stress response syndromes.* New York: Aronson.

Horowitz, R. (1983). *Honor and the American dream: Culture and identity in a Chicano community.* New Brunswick, NJ: Rutgers University Press.

Horvath, T. (1981). Physical attractiveness: The influence of selected torso parameters. *Archives of Sexual Behavior, 10*, 21–24.

Hott, L. R., & Hott, J. R. (1980). Sexual misunderstandings. *Medical Aspects of Human Sexuality, 14*, 13–31.

Howard, J. L., Reifler, C. B., & Liptzin, M. B. (1971). Effects of exposure to pornography. *Technical Report of The Commission on Obscenity and Pornography* (Vol. 8, pp. 97–132). Washington, DC: U.S. Government Printing Office.

Howard, M., & McCabe, J. B. (1990). Helping teenagers postpone sexual involvement. *Family Planning Perspectives, 22*, 21–26.

Howard, M. C. (1989). *Contemporary cultural anthropology.* (3rd ed.). Glenview, IL: Scott, Foresman and Company.

Hu, S. (1992, January 24). Cited in Immune deficiency vaccine for monkeys succeeds. *The New York Times*, p. A17.

Huang, K., & Uba, L. (1992). Premarital sexual behavior among Chinese college students in the United States. *Archives of Sexual Behavior, 21*, 227–240.

Hubbard, R., & Wald, E. (1993). *Exploding the gene myth.* Boston: Beacon Press.

Hubbard, R. (1993, August 2). The search for sexual identity: False genetic markers. *The New York Times*, p. A15.

Hucker, S., Langgevin, R., & Bain, J. (1988). A double blind trial of sex drive reducing medication in pedophiles. *Annals of Sex Research, 1*, 227–242.

Hull, J.G., et al. (1983). Self-awareness-reducing effects of alcohol consumption. *Journal of Personality and Social Psychology, 44*, 461–473.

Humphreys, L. (1970). *Tearoom trade: Impersonal sex in public places.* Chicago: Aldine.

Hunt, M. (1979). Legal rape. *Family Circle*, January 9.

Hunt, M. (1974). *Sexual behavior in the 1970's.* New York: Dell Books.

Hunt, M., & Hunt, B. (1977). *The divorce experience.* New York: Signet.

Hunter, J., et al. (1990). An examination of variables differentiating clinical subtypes of incestuous child molesters. *International Journal of Offender Therapy and Comparative Criminology, 34*, 95–104.

Hursch, C. (1977). *The trouble with rape.* Chicago: Nelson-Hall.

Huston, A. C. (1983). Sex-typing. In P. H. Mussen (Ed.), *Handbook of child psychology, Vol. 4: Socialization, personality, and social development.* New York: Wiley.

Hyde, J. S. (1981). How large are cognitive gender differences? *American Psychologist, 36*, 892–901.

Hyde, J. S., & Linn, M. C. (1988). Gender differences in verbal ability: A meta-analysis. *Psychological Bulletin, 104*, 53-69.

Hyde, J. S., Fennema, E., & Lamon, S. J. (1990). Gender differences in mathematics performance: A meta-analysis. *Psychological Bulletin, 107*, 139–155.

Ibsen, H. H., et al. Treatment of nongonococcal urethritis: Comparison of olfoxacin and erythromycin. *Sexually Transmitted Diseases, 16*, 32–35.

Ickovics, J. R., & Rodin, J. (1992). Women and AIDS in the United States: Epidemiology, natural history, and mediating mechanisms. *Health Psychology, 11*, 1-16.

Ikafor, N. A. O. (1991). Some traditional aspects of Nigerian women. In L. L. Adler (Ed.), *Women in cross-cultural perspective* (pp. 135–141). New York: Praeger.

Imperato-McGinley, J., et al. (1974). Steroid 5 reductase deficiency in man: An inherited form of male pseudohermaphroditism. *Science, 186*, 1213–1215.

Inazu, J. K., & Fox, G. L. (1980). Maternal influence on the sexual behavior of teenage daughters. *Journal of Family Issues, 1*, 81–102.

Ingersoll, S. L, & Patton, S. O. (1991). *Treating perpetrators of sexual abuse.* Lexington, MA: Lexington Books.

Ingrassia, M. (1993, October 25). Abused and confused. *Newsweek*, pp. 57-58.

Intons-Peterson, M. J., & Roskos-Ewoldsen, B. (in press). Mitigating the effects of violent pornography. In S. Gubar & J. Hoff-Wilson (Eds.), *For adult users only: The dilemma of violent pornography.* Bloomington, IN: Indiana University Press.

Isay, R. A. (1986). The development of sexual identity in homosexual men. *Psychoanalytic Study of the Child, 41* 467–489.

Isay, R. A. (1990). Psychoanalytic theory and the therapy of gay men. In D. P. McWhirter, S. A. Sanders, & J. M. Reinisch (Eds.) *Homosexuality/Heterosexuality: Concepts of sexual orientation* (pp. 283–303). New York: Oxford University Press.

Isay, R. A. (1993, April 23). Sex survey may say most about society's attitudes to gays. *The New York Times*, Section 4, p. 16. (Letter)

Ison, C. A. (1990). Laboratory methods in genitourinary medicine: Methods of diagnosing gonorrhoea. *Genitourinary Medicine, 66*, 453–459.

Ivey, M. E., & Bardwick, J. M. (1968). Patterns of affective fluctuation in the menstrual cycle. *Psychosomatic Medicine, 30*, 336–345.

Jacklin, C. N, DiPietro, J. A., & Maccoby, E. E. (1984). Sex-typing behavior and sex-typing pressure in child-parent interaction. *Archives of Sexual Behavior, 13*, 413–425.

Jackson, B. B., Taylor, J., & Pyngolil, M. (1991). How age conditions the relationship between climacteric status and health symptoms in African American women. *Research in Nursing and Health, 14*, 1-9.

Jackson, L. A., & Ervin, K. S. (1992). Height stereotypes of women and men: The liabilities of shortness for both sexes. *Journal of Social Psychology, 132*, 433-445.

Jackson, T. L. (1991). A university athletic department's rape and assault experiences. *Journal of College Student Development, 32*, 77-78.

Jackson, J., et al. (1990). Young adult women who report childhood intrafamilial sexual abuse: Subsequent adjustment. *Archives of Sexual Behavior, 19*, 211–221.

Jacobsen, C. (1991). Redefining censorship: A feminist view. *Art Journal, 50, (4)*, 42–55.

Jacobsen, P. B., Perry, S. W., & Hirsch, D. (1990). Behavioral and psychological responses to HIV antibody testing. *Journal of Consulting and Clinical Psychology, 58*, 31–37.

Jacobson, N. S. (1984). A component analysis of behavioral marital therapy: The relative effectiveness of behavior exchange and communcation/problem-solving training. *Journal of Consulting and Clinical Psychology, 52*, 295–305.

James, W. H. (1971). The distribution of coitus within the human intermenstruum. *Journal of Biosocial Science, 3*, 159–171.

Jamison, P. L., & Gebhard, P. H. (1988). Penis size increase between flaccid and erect states. An analysis of the Kinsey data. *Journal of Sex Research, 24*, 177–183.

Jancin, B. (1988). Prenatal gender selection appears to be gaining acceptance. *Obstetrical and Gynecological News, 23*, 30.

Janda, L. H., & O'Grady, E. E. (1980). Development of a sex anxiety inventory. *Journal of Consulting and Clinical Psychology, 48*, 169–175.

Janis, I. L., Kaye, D., & Kirschner, P. (1965). Facilitating effects of "eating while reading" on responsiveness to persuasive communications. *Journal of Personality and Social Psychology, 1*, 181–186.

Janis, I., & Mann, L. (1977). *Decision-making.* New York: Free Press.

Jankowiak, W. R., & Fischer, E. F. (1992). A cross-cultural perspective on romantic love. *Ethnology, 31*, 149-155.

Jankowski, L. (1985). Marriage satisfying, 65% say. *USA Today*, p. A1.

Janus, M. D., Scanlon, B, & Prince, V. (1984). Youth prostitution. In A. W. Burgess (Ed.), *Sex rings and child pornography.* Lexington, MA: Heath.

Janus, S. S., & Janus, C. L. (1993). *The Janus Report on Sexual Behavior.* New York: Wiley.

Jasso, G. (1985). Marital coital frequency and the passage of time: Estimating the separate effects of spouses' ages and marital duration, birth and marriage cohorts, and period influences. *American Sociological Review, 50*, 224–241.

Jay, K., & Young, A. (1979). *The gay report.* New York: Summit Books.

Jehu, D., Gazan, M., & Klassen, C. (1985, Spring). Common therapeutic targets among women who were sexually abused in childhood. *Journal of Social Work and Human Sexuality, 3*, 25–45.

Jellison, J. M., & Oliver, D. F. (1983). Attitude similarity and attraction: An impression management approach. *Personality and Social Psychology Bulletin, 9*, 111–115.

Jencks, C., & Mayer, S. E. (1990). Residential segregation, job proximity, and Black job opportunities. In L. E. Lynn and M. McGeary (Eds.), *Inner-city poverty in the United States*. Washington, D.C.: National Academy Press.

Jenks, R. (1985). Swinging: A replication and test of a theory. *The Journal of Sex Research, 21*, 199–210.

Jessor, R., & Jessor, R. (1977). *Problem behavior and psychosocial development*. New York: Academic Press.

Jiao, S., Ji, G., & Jing, Q. (1986). Comparative study of behavioral qualities of only children and sibling children. *Child Development, 57*, 357–361.

Jick, H. (1981). Vaginal spermicides and congenital disorders. *Journal of the American Medical Association, 245*, 1329–1332.

Jimenez, M. A., & Jimenez, D. R. (1992). Latinos and HIV disease: Issues, practice and policy implications. *Social Work in Health Care, 17*, 41-51.

Job rights for homosexuals backed in poll. (1992, September 7). *The New York Times*, p. L10.

Johnson, A. M., et al. (1992). Sexual lifestyles and HIV risk. *Nature, 360*, 420-426.

Johnson, D. (1990, March 8). AIDS clamor at colleges muffling older dangers. *The New York Times*, p. A18.

Johnson, K. (1988). *Teens and AIDS: Opportunities for prevention*. Washington, DC: Children's Defense Fund.

Johnson, K. A., & Williams, L. (1993). Risk of breast cancer in the nurses' health study: Applying the Gail model. *Journal of the American Medical Association, 270*, 2925-2926.

Johnson, J. E., & McGillicuddy-Delisi, A. (1983). Family environment factors and children's knowledge of rules and conventions. *Child Development, 54*, 218-226.

Johnson, R. C., & Nagoshi, C. T. (1986). The adjustment of offspring of within-group and interracial/intercultural marriages: A comparison of personality factors. *Journal of Marriage and the Family, 48*, 279–284.

Johnson, R. E., et al. (1989). A seroepidemiologic survey of the prevalence of herpes simplex virus type 2 infection in the United States. *New England Journal of Medicine, 321*, 7–12.

Jones, C. C., et al. (1987). Persistence in high risk sexual activity among homosexual men in an area of low incidence of acquired immunodeficiency syndrome. *Sexually Transmitted Diseases, 14*, 79–82.

Jones, D. S., et al. (1992). Epidemiology of transfusion-associated acquired immunodeficiency syndrome in children in the United States, 1981 through 1989. *Pediatrics, 89*, 123–127.

Jones, E. F., et al. (1985). Teenage pregnancy in developed countries: Determinants and policy implications. *Family Planning Perspectives, 17*, 53–62.

Jones, H. W., & Toner, J. P. (1993). The infertile couple. *The New England Journal of Medicine, 329*, 1710-1715.

Jones, J. C., & Barlow, D. H. (1990). Self-reported frequency of sexual urges, fantasies and masturbatory fantasies in heterosexual males and females. *Archives of Sexual Behavior, 19*, 269–279.

Jones, R.T. (1976). Human effects. In R. C. Petersen (Ed.), *Marihuana research findings; 1976*. (pp. 128-178). National Institute of Drug Abuse (ADM 78-501). Washington, D.C.: U.S. Government Printing Office.

Jones, W. H. (1982). Loneliness and social behavior. In L. A. Peplau & D. Perlman (Eds.), *Loneliness: A sourcebook of current theory, research, and therapy*. New York: Wiley.

Jones, W. H., Freeman, J. A., & Goswick, R. A. (1981). The persistence of loneliness: Self and other determinants. *Journal of Personality, 49*, 27–48.

Jorgensen, S. R., & Gaudy, J. C. (1980). Self-disclosure and satisfaction in marriage: The relation examined. *Family Relations, 29*, 281–288.

Jorgensen, S. R., et al. (1980). Dyadic and social network influences on adolescent exposure to pregnancy risk. *Journal of Marriage and the Fmaily, 42*, 141–155.

Jourard, S. M. (1971). *The transparent self (2nd ed.)*. New York: Van Nostrand.

Journal of the American Medical Association. (1993a). Preventing HIV/AIDS among adolescents; Schools as agents of behavior change. *Journal of the American Medical Association, 269*, 760-762. (Editorial)

Journal of the American Medical Association. (1993b). Rising HIV-related mortality in young Americans. *Journal of the American Medical Association, 269*, 3034-3035. (Editorial)

Joyce, T., Racine, A. D., & Mocan, N. (1992). The consequences and costs of maternal substance abuse in New York City: A pooled time-series, cross-section analysis. *Journal of Health Economics, 11*, 297-314.

Judson, F. N. (1990). Gonorrhea. *Medical Clinics of North America, 74*, 1353–1366.

Justice, B., & Justice, R. (1979). *The broken taboo: Sex in the family*. New York: Human Science Press.

Kagan, J. (1964). Acquisition and significance of sex-typing and sex-role identity. In M. L. Hoffman & L. W. Hoffman (Eds.), *Review of child development research*, (Vol. 1). New York: Russell Sage.

Kagay, M. R. (1993, June 8). Poll finds knowledge about AIDS increasing. *The New York Times*, p. C5.

Kagay, M. R. (1991, June 19). Poll finds AIDS causes single people to alter behavior. *The New York Times*, p. C3.

Kalick, S. M. (1988). Physical attractiveness as a status cue. *Journal of Experimental Social Psychology, 24*, 469-489.

Kallmann, F. J. (1952). Comparative twin study on the genetic aspects of male homosexuality. *Journal of Nervous and Mental Disease, 115*, 283–298.

Kammeyer, K. C. W. (1987). *Marriage and family: A foundation for personal decisions*. Boston: Allyn & Bacon, Inc.

Kammeyer, K. C. W. (1990). *Marriage and family: A foundation for personal decisions*. (2nd ed.). Boston: Allyn & Bacon, Inc.

Kammeyer, K. C. W., Ritzer, G., & Yetman, N. R. (1990). *Sociology: Experiencing changing societies*. Boston: Allyn & Bacon.

Kanekar, S., & Kolsawalla, M. B. (1980). Responsibility of a rape victim in relation to her respectability, attractiveness, and provocativeness. *Journal of Social Psychology, 112*, 153–154.

Kanin, E. J. (1985). Date rapists: Differential sexual socialization and relative deprivation. *Archives of Sexual Behavior, 14*, 219–231.

Kanin, E. J., Davidson, K. R., & Scheck, S. R. (1970). A research note on male-female differentials in the experience of heterosexual love. *Journal of Sex Research, 6*, 64–72.

Kantner, J. F., & Zelnik, M. (1972). Sexual experience of young unmarried women in the United States. *Family Planning Perspectives, 4*, 9–18.

Kantrowitz, B. (1992, December 14). A "silver bullet" against teen pregnancies? Baltimore offers Norplant at school. *Newsweek*, p. 43.

Kantrowitz, B. et al. (1991a, April 29). Naming names. *Newsweek*, pp. 26-32.

Kantrowitz, B. (1990b, Summer/Fall Special Issue). The push for sex education. *Newsweek*, p. 52.

Kantrowitz, B.(1990a, Summer/Fall Special Issue). High school homeroom. *Newsweek*, pp. 50–54.

Kantrowitz, B. et al. (1991b, July 1). Doctors and AIDS. *Newsweek*, pp. 48–57.

Kaplan, D. (1993, January 18). The incorrigibles. *Newsweek*, pp. 48-50.

Kaplan, D. A. (1993, December 20). Is it torture or tradition? *Newsweek*, p. 124.

Kaplan, H. (1987). *The illustrated manual of sex therapy*. New York: Brunner/Mazel.

Kaplan, H. S. (1974). *The new sex therapy: Active treatment of sexual dysfunctions*. New York: Brunner/Mazel.

Kaplan, H. S. (1979a). *Disorders of sexual desire*. New York: Simon and Schuster.

Kaplan, H. S. (1979b). Inhibited sexual desire. *Medical Aspects of Human Sexuality, 13*, 26–47.

Kaplan, H. S., & Sager, C. J. (1971). Sexual patterns at different ages. *Medical Aspects of Human Sexuality, 5 (6)*, 10–23.

Kaplan, H. S. (1990). Sex, intimacy, and the aging process. *Journal of the American Academy of Psychoanalysis, 18*, 185–205.

Kaplan, H. S. (1987). *Sexual aversion, sexual phobias, and panic disorder*. New York: Brunner/Mazel.

Kaplowitz, L. G., et al. (1991). Prolonged continuous acyclovir treatment of normal adults with frequently recurring genital herpes simplex virus infection. *Journal of the American Medical Association, 265*, 747–751.

Karacan, I. (1978). Advances in the psychophysiological evaluation of male erectile incompetence. In J. LoPiccolo & L. LoPiccolo (Eds.), *Handbook of sex therapy*, New York: Plenum.

Karacan, I. (1970). Clinical value of nocturnal erection in the prognosis and diagnosis of impotence. *Medical Aspects of Human Sexuality, 4*, 27–34.

Karacan, I. (1982) Nocturnal penile tumescence as a biological marker in assessing erectile dysfunction. *Psychosomatics, 23*, 349–360.

Karlen, A. (1971). *Sexuality and homosexuality: A new view*. New York: Norton.

Karraker, K. H., Vogel, D. A., & Evans, S. (1987, August). *Responses of students and pregnant women to newborn physical attractiveness*. Paper presented at the annual meeting of the American Psychological Association, New York.

Kasper, A. (1985). Health and public policy. *Women and Health, 10*, 109–127.

Katchadourian, H. A. (1987). *Fifty: Midlife in perspective.* New York: Freeman.

Katz, J. (1976). *Gay American history.* New York: Avon.

Katz, R. C. (1990). Psychosocial adjustment in adolescent child molesters. *Child Abuse and Neglect, 14,* 567–575.

Kaufman, A., et al. (1980). Male rape victims: Noninstitutionalized assault. *American Journal of Psychiatry, 137,* 221–223.

Kawar, S. (1987, June 16). Evolution and revolution change lives of Islamic women: Saudi feminists emerge from behind the veil. *Washington Post.*

Kay, D. S. (1992). Masturbation and mental health: Uses and abuses. *Sexual and Marital Therapy, 7,* 97-107.

Kaya, N., Moore, C., & Karacan, I. (1979). Nocturnal penile tumescence and its role in impotence. *Psychiatric Annals, 9,* 426–431.

Kedia, K. (1983). Ejaculation and emission: Normal physiology, dysfunction, and therapy. In R. J. Krane, M. B. Siroky, & I. Goldstein (Eds.), *Male sexual dysfunction* (pp. 37–54). Boston: Little, Brown.

Keen, S., & Zur, O. (1989). Who is the new ideal man? *Psychology Today, 23, (11),* pp. 54–60.

Kegel, A. H. (1952). Sexual functions of the pubococcygeus muscle. *Western Journal of Surgery, 60.* 521-524.

Kegeles, S. M., Alan, M. E., & Irwin, C. (1988). Sexually active adolescents and condoms: Changes over one year in knowledge, attitudes, and use. *American Journal of Public Health, 78,* 460–461.

Keith, J. B., et al. (1991). Sexual activity and contraceptive use among low-income urban Black adolescent females. *Adolescence, 26,* 769-785.

Kellerman, J., Lewis, J., & Laird, J. D. (1989). Looking and loving: The effects of mutual gaze on feelings of romantic love. *Journal of Research in Personality, 23,* 145–161.

Kelley, K. (1981). Adolescent sexuality: The first lessons. In D. Byrne & W. A. Fisher (Eds.), *Adolescents, sex, and contraception.* New York: McGraw-Hill.

Kelley, K., Dawson, L, & Musialowski, D. M. (1989). Three faces of sexual explicitness: The good, the bad, and the useful. In D. Zillmann & J. Bryant (Eds.), *Pornography: Research advances and policy considerations* (pp. 57–91). Hillsdale, NJ: Lawrence Erlbaum Associates.

Kelley, K., & Musialowski, D. (1986, April). *Female sexual victimization and effects of warning about violent pornography.* Paper presented at the meeting of the Eastern Psychological Association, New York.

Kelly, J. A., Brasfield, T. L., & St. Lawrence, J. S. (1991). Predictors of vulnerability to AIDS risk behavior relapse. *Journal of Consulting and Clinical Psychology, 59,* 163–166.

Kelly, J. A., & St. Lawrence, J. S. (1988). AIDS prevention and treatment: Psychology's role in the health crisis. *Clinical Psychology Review, 8,* 255–284.

Kelly, J. A., et al. (1989). Behavioral intervention to reduce AIDS risk activities. *Journal of Consulting and Clinical Psychology, 57,* 60–67.

Kelly, J. A., et al. (1993). Psychological interventions to prevent HIV infection are urgently needed. *American Psychologist, 48,* 1023-1034.

Kelly, M. P., Strassberg, D. S., & Kircher, J. R. (1990). Attitudinal and experiential correlates of anorgasmia. *Archives of Sexual Behavior, 19,* 165–177.

Kemeny, M. E., Cohen, F., Zegans, L. S., & Conant, M. A. (1989). Psychological and immunological predictors of genital herpes recurrence. *Psychosomatic Medicine, 51,* 195–208.

Kempe, R. S., & Kempe, C. H. (1984). *The common secret: Sexual abuse of children and adolescents.* New York: W. H. Freeman.

Kemper, T. D. (1983). Predicting the divorce rate: Down? *Journal of Family Issues, 4,* 507–524.

Kenney, A. M., Guardad, S., & Brown, L. (1989). Sex education and AIDS education in the schools. *Family Planning Perspectives, 21,* 56–64.

Kent, M. R. (1991). Women and AIDS. *New England Journal of Medicine, 324,* 1442.

Kermis, M. D. (1984). *The psychology of human aging: Theory, research, and practice.* Boston: Allyn & Bacon.

Kessler, R. (1992, January 9). Cited in Blakeslee, S. Chemical a factor in male impotence. *The New York Times,* pp. 1, B10.

Kessner, D. M. (1973). *Infant death: An analysis by maternal risk and health care.* Washington, DC: National Academy of Sciences.

Kettl, P. et al. (1991). Female sexuality after spinal cord injury. *Sexuality and Disability, 9,* 287-295.

Kiecolt-Glaser, J. K., & Glaser, R. (1988). Psychological influences on immunity: Implications for AIDS. *American Psychologist, 43,* 892–898.

Kiecolt-Glaser, J. K., et al. (1984). Stress and the transformation of lymphocytes in Epstein-Barr virus. *Journal of Behavioral Medicine, 7,* 1–12.

Kiely, E. A., Williams, G., & Goldie, L. (1987). Assessment of the immediate and long-term effects of pharmacologically induced penile erections in the treatment of psychogenic and organic impotence. *British Journal of Urology, 59,* 164–169.

Kiernan, K. E. (1988). Who remains celibate? *Journal of Biosocial Science, 20,* 253–263.

Kiersch, T. A. (1990). Treatment of sex offenders with Depo-Provera. *Bulletin of the American Academy of Psychiatry and the Law, 18,* 179–187.

Kilbourne, B. W., Buehler, J. W., & Rogers, M. F. (1990). AIDS as a cause of death in children, adolescents, and young adults. *American Journal of Public Health, 80,* 499-500.

Killmann, P. R., & Auerbach, R. (1979). Treatments of premature ejaculation and psychogenic impotence: A critical review of the literature. *Archives of Sexual Behavior, 8,* 81–100.

Killmann, P. R., et al. (1984). The sexual interaction of women with secondary orgasmic dysfunction and their partners. *Archives of Sexual Behavior, 13,* 41–49.

Killmann, P. R., et al. (1987). The treatment of secondary orgasmic dysfunction II. *Journal of Sex and Marital Therapy, 13,* 93–105.

Kilpatrick, D. G., et al. (1987, January). *Rape in marriage and dating relationships: How bad are they for mental health?* Paper presented at the meeting of the New York Academy of Science, New York, NY.

Kilpatrick, D. G., & Best, C. L. (1990, April). *Sexual assault victims: Data from a random national probability sample.* Paper presented at the meeting of the Southeastern Psychological Association, Atlanta.

Kilpatrick, D. G., Veronen, L. J., & Resick, P. A. (1982). Psychological sequelae to rape: Assessment and treatment strategies. In D. M. Doleys, R. L. Meredith, & A. R. Ciminero (Eds.), *Behavioral medicine: Assessment and treatment strategies* (pp. 473–498). New York: Plenum Publishing Corp.

Kimlicka, T., Cross, H., & Tarnai, J. (1983). A comparison of androgynous, feminine, masculine, and undifferentiated women on self-esteem, body satisfaction, and sexual satisfaction. *Psychology of Women Quarterly, 1,* 291–294.

Kinard, E., & Reinherz, H. (1987). School aptitude and achievement in children of adolescent mothers. *Journal of Youth and Adolescence, 16,* 69–78.

Kinder, B. N., & Curtiss, G. (1988). Specific components in the etiology, assessment, and treatment of male sexual dysfunctions: Controlled outcome studies. *Journal of Sex and Marital Therapy, 14,* 40–48.

King, L. (1988). Editorial comment in response to Wisell et al., 1987. *Journal of Urology, 139,* 883.

King, W. (1991, December 4). Registry of AIDS-virus carriers is begun. *The New York Times,* p. B3.

Kinsey, A. C., Pomeroy, W. B., & Martin, C. E. (1948). *Sexual behavior in the human male.* Philadelphia: W. B. Saunders Co.

Kinsey, A. C., Pomeroy, W. B., Martin, C. E., & Gebhard, P. H. (1953). *Sexual behavior in the human female.* Philadlphia: W. B. Saunders Co.

Kirby, D., et al. (1993). The effects of school-based health clinics in St. Paul on school-wide birthrates. *Family Planning Perspectives, 25,* 12-16.

Kirby, D., Waszak, C., & Ziegler, J. (1992). School-based clinics: Their reproductive health services and impact on sexual behavior. *Family Planning Perspectives, 23,* 6-16.

Kirkham, G. L. (1971). Homosexuality in prison. In J. M. Henslin (Ed.), *Studies in the sociology of sex.* New York: Appleton-Century-Croft.

Kite, M. E. (1992). Individual differences in males' reactions to gay males and lesbians. *Journal of Applied Social Psychology, 22,* 1222-1239.

Kite, M. S. (1984). Sex differences in attitudes toward homosexuals. *Journal of Homosexuality, 10,* 69–81.

Kitson, G. C., & Sussman, M. B. (1982). Marital complaints, demographic characteristics, and symptoms of mental distress in divorce. *Journal of Marriage and the Family, 44,* 87–101.

Kjersgaard, A., et al. (1989). Male or female sterilization: A comparative study. *American Fertility Society, 51,* 439–443.

Klagsbrun, G. (1985). *Married people: Staying together in the age of divorce.* New York: Bantam Books.

Kleeman, J. (1965). A boy discovers his penis. *Psychoanalytic Study of the Child, 20,* 239–266.

Kleinke, C. L., & Staneski, R. A. (1980). First impressions of female breast size. *Journal of Social Psychology, 110,* 123–134.

Kleinman, S., et al. (1988). Follow-up testing and notification of anti-HIV Western blot atypical (indeterminant) donors. *Transfusion, 28,* 280–282.

Kleinman, P. H., et al. (1990). Knowledge about and behaviors affecting the spread of AIDS: A street survey of intravenous drug users and their associates in New York City. *International Journal of the Addictions, 25,* 345-361.

Klepinger, D. H., et al. (1993). Perceptions of AIDS risk and severity and their association with risk-related behavior among U.S. men. *Family Planning Perspectives, 25,* 74-82.

Kluver, H., & Bucy, P. C. (1939). Preliminary analysis of functions of the temporal lobes in monkeys. *Archives of Neurology and Psychiatry, 42,* 979.

Knapp, M. L. (1978). *Social intercourse: A behavioral approach to counseling.* Champaign, IL: Research Press.

Knapp, J. (1976). An exploratory study of seventeen sexually open marriages. *Journal of Sex Research, 12,* 206–219.

Knaub, P. K., Eversoll, D. B., & Voss, J. H. (1983). Is parenthood a desirable adult role? An assessment of attitudes held by contemporary adult women. *Sex Roles, 9,* 355–362.

Knight, R. A., et al. (1991). *Antisocial personality disorder and Hare assessments of psychopathy among sexual offenders.* Manuscript in preparation.

Knight, S. E. (1989). Sexual concerns of the physically disabled. In B. W. Heller, L. M. Flohr, & L. S. Zegans (Eds.), *Psychosocial interventions with physically disabled persons* (pp. 183–199). New Brunswick, NJ: Rutgers University Press.

Knox, D. (1982). *What kind of love is yours?* Unpublished study, East Carolina University, Department of Sociology, Anthropology, and Economics, Greenville, NC.

Knox, D. (1983). *The love attitudes inventory* (rev. ed.). Saluda, NC: Family Life Publications.

Knox, D. (1988). *Choices in relationships: An introduction to marriage and the family.* St. Paul, MN: West Publishing Co.

Knox, D., & Sporakowski, M. J. (1968). Attitudes of college students toward love. *Journal of Marriage and the Family, 30,* 638–642.

Knox, D., & Wilson, K. (1983). Dating problems of university students. *College Student Journal, 17,* 225–228.

Knudsen, D. D. (1991). Child sexual coercion. In E. Grauerholz & M. A. Koralewski (Eds.), *Sexual coercion: A sourcebook on its nature, causes, and prevention* (pp. 17–28). Lexington, MA: Lexington Books.

Knussman, R., Christiansen, K., & Couwenbergs, C. (1986). Relations between sex hormone levels and sexual behavior in men. *Archives of Sexual Behavior, 15,* 429–445.

Knutson, D. C. (1980). Homosexuality and the law: Introduction. *Journal of Homosexuality, 5,* 5–23.

Kockott, G., et al. (1980). Psychophysiological aspects of male sexual inadequacy: Results of an experimental study. *Archives of Sexual Behavior, 9,* 477–493.

Kockott, G., & Fahrner, E. (1988). Male-to-female and female-to-male transsexuals: A comparison. *Archives of Sexual Behavior, 17,* 539–545.

Kockott, G., & Fahrner, E. (1987). Transsexuals who have not undergone surgery: A follow-up study. *Archives of Sexual Behavior, 16,* 511–522.

Koenig, M. A., & Zelnick, M. (1982). The risk of premarital first pregnancy among metropolitan-area teenagers: 1976 and 1979. *Family Planning Perspectives, 14,* 239–247.

Kogan, B. A. (1973). *Human sexual expression.* New York: Harcourt Brace Jovanovich.

Kohlberg, L. (1966). A cognitive-developmental analysis of children's sex-role concepts and attitudes. In E. E. Maccoby (Ed.), *The development of sex differences.* Stanford, CA: Stanford University Press.

Kohn, A. (1987, February). Shattered innocence. *Psychology Today,* pp. 54–58.

Kolarsky, A., et al. (1978). Stimuli eliciting sexual arousal in males who offend adult women: An experimental study. *Archives of Sexual Behavior, 7,* 79–87.

Kolata, G. (1988, February 16). Drug combination gains support as alternative to surgical abortion. *The New York Times,* p.C3.

Kolata, G. (1990, July 26). A breakthrough on evolution as guppies change behavior. *The New York Times,* pp. A1, B6.

Kolata, G. (1991a, November 9). For heterosexuals, diagnosis of AIDS is often unmercifully late. *The New York Times,* p. 32.

Kolata, G. (1991b, November 8). Studies cite 10.5 years from infection to illness. *The New York Times,* pp. B12.

Kolata, G. (1991c, June 4). 10 years of AIDS battle: Hopes for success dim. *The New York Times,* p. A14.

Kolata, G. (1991d, November 28). Theory links AIDS to malaria experiments. *The New York Times,* p. B14.

Kolata, G. (1991e, July 20). U.S. panel backs sale of experimental AIDS drug. *The New York Times,* pp. A1, 13.

Kolata, G. (1991f, November 10). Young women offer to sell their eggs to infertile couples. *The New York Times,* pp. A1, A30.

Kolata, G. (1992a, March 17). How AIDS smolders: Immune system studies follow the tracks of H.I.V. *The New York Times,* pp. C1,11.

Kolata, G. (1992b, December 31). Hepatitis C may be hidden epidemic, studies show. *The New York Times,* p. A20.

Kolata, G. (1993a, December 14). Breast cancer screening under 50: Experts disagree if benefit exists: Statisticians find no proof that screening saves lives. *The New York Times,* pp. C1, C17.

Kolata, G. (1993b, November 24). Mammograms before 50? A hung jury. *The New York Times,* p. C8.

Kolata, G. (1993c, March 9). New theory suggests cell regulator may hold the key to fighting AIDS. *The New York Times,* p. C3.

Kolata, G. (1993d, Feburary 26). Studies say mammograms fail to help many women. *The New York Times,* pp. A1, A15.

Kolata, G. (1993e, March 7). Targeting urged in attack on AIDS. *The New York Times,* pp. A1, A26.

Kolata, G. (1993f, January 5). Tests show infection by AIDS virus affects greater share of cells. *The New York Times,* p. C3.

Kolata, G. (1993g, June 23). Whether positive or negative, result of prostate cancer test can create maze of questions. *The New York Times,* p. C12.

Kolata, G. (1994, January 11). Reproductive revolution is jolting old views. *The New York Times,* pp. A1, C12.

Kolbert, E. (1991, October 11). Sexual harassment at work is pervasive, survey suggests. *The New York Times,* pp. A1, A17.

Kolodny, R. C. (1981). Evaluating sex therapy: Process and outcome at the Masters & Johnson Institute. *Journal of Sex Research, 17,* 301-318.

Kolodny, R. C., et al. (1974). Depression of plasma testosterone levels after chronic intensive marijuana use. *New England Journal of Medicine, 290,* 873.

Kolodny, R. C., et al. (1971). Plasma testosterone and semen analysis in male homosexuals. *New England Journal of Medicine, 285,* 1170–1174.

Kolodny, R. C., et al. (1979). *Textbook of human sexuality for nurses.* Boston: Little, Brown.

Komisar, L. (1971). The image of women in advertising. In V. Gornick & B. Moran (Eds.), *Women in sexist society.* New York: Basic Books.

Kondo, Y., et al. (1990). Role of septum and preoptic area in regulating masculine and feminine sexual behavior in male rats. *Hormones and Behavior, 24,* 21-34.

Kontula, O., Rimpela, M., & Ojanlatva, A. (1992). Sexual knowledge, attitudes, fears and behaviors of adolescents in Finland (the KISS study). *Health Education Research, 7,* 69-77.

Koonin, L. M. (1992). Abortion surveillance—United States, 1989. *Morbidity and Mortality Weekly Report, 41,* Special Supplement 5.

Koop, C. E. (1987, March 25). Cited in Koop urges AIDS test before getting pregnant. *New York Times,* p. B4.

Koop. C. E. (1988). *Understanding AIDS.* HHS Publication No. HHS–88–8404. Washington, D.C.: U.S. Government Printing Office.

Kornblum, W. (1988). *Sociology in a changing world.* New York: Holt, Rinehart & Winston.

Koss, L. (1989). The papanicolaou test for cervical cancer detection. *The Journal of Sex Research, 261,* 737.

Koss, M. P. (1988). Stranger and acquaintance rape: Are there differences in the victim's experience? *Psychology of Women Quarterly, 12,* 1–24.

Koss, M. P. (1993). Rape: Scope, impact, interventions, and public policy responses. *American Psychologist, 48,* 1062-1069.

Koss, M. P., Gidycz, C. A., & Wisniewski, N. (1987). The scope of rape: Incidence and prevalence of sexual aggression and victimization in a national sample of higher education students. *Journal of Consulting and Clinical Psychology, 55,* 162–170.

Koutsky, L. A., et al. (1992). A cohort study of the risk of cervical intraepithelial neoplasia Grade 2 or 3 in relation to papillomarvirus infection. *New England Journal of Medicine, 327,* 1272.

Kouzi, A. C., et al. (in press). Contraceptive behavior among intravenous drug users at risk for AIDS. *Psychology of Addictive Behaviors.*

Krafka, C. L. (1985). Sexually explicit, sexually violent, and violent media: Effects of multiple naturalistic exposures and debriefing on female viewers. Unpublished doctoral dissertation, University of Wisconsin-Madison.

Kramer, L. (1990, July 16). A "Manhattan Project" for AIDS. *The New York Times,* A15.

Krane, R. J. (1986). Surgical implants for impotence: Indications and procedures. In R. J. Santen & K. S. Swerdloff (Eds.), *Male reproductive dysfunction* (pp. 563–576). New York: Marcel Dekker.

Kresin, D. (1993). Medical aspects of inhibited sexual desire disorder. In W. O'Donohue & J. H. Geer (Eds.), *Handbook of sexual dysfunctions: Assessment and treatment* (pp. 15-52). Boston: Allyn & Bacon.

Kristof, N. D. (1991a, June 17). A mystery from China's census: Where have young girls gone? *The New York Times,* pp. A1, A8.

Kristof, N. D. (1991b, November 5). Stark data on women: 100 million are missing. *The New York Times*, pp. C1, C12.

Kristof, N. D. (1993, April 25). China's crackdown on births: A stunning, and harsh, success. *The New York Times*, pp. 1, 12.

Kroger, F. (1991, December 7). Cited in Sims, C. H.I.V. tests up 60% since the disclosure from Magic Johnson. *The New York Times*, pp. 1, 28.

Kroll, J., Smith, V., & Murr, A. (1991, June 10). A black-white affair is the catalyst for Spike Lee's panoramic view of a culture in a color bind. *Newsweek*,.

Kronmal, R. A., Whitney, C. W., & Mumford, S. D. (1991). The intrauterine device and pelvic inflammatory disease: The Women's Health Study reanalyzed. *Journal of Clinical Epidemiology, 44*, 109-122.

Kruesi, M. J. P., et al. (1992). Paraphilias: A double-blind cross-over comparison of clomipramine versus desipramine. *Archives of Sexual Behavior, 21*, 587-594.

Krug, R. S. (1989). Adult male report of childhood sexual abuse by mothers: Case descriptions, motivations and long-term consequences. *Child Abuse and Neglect, 13*, 111–119.

Kruks, G. (1991). Gay and lesbian homeless/street youth: Special issues and concerns. Special issue: Homeless youth. *Journal of Adolescent Health, 12*, 515-518.

Krulewitz, J. E., & Nash, J. E. (1980). Effects of sex role attitudes and similarity on men's rejection of male homosexuals. *Journal of Personality and Social Psychology, 38*, 67–74.

Ku, L. C., Sonenstein, F. L., & Pleck, J. H. (1992). The association of AIDS education and sex education with sexual behavior and condom use among teenage men. *Family Planning Perspectives, 24*, 100-106.

Kuhn, D., et al. (1978). Sex-role concepts of two- and three-year olds. *Child Development, 49* 445-451.

Kuiper, B., & Cohen-Kettenis, P. (1988). Sex reassignment surgery: A study of 141 Dutch transsexuals. *Archives of Sexual Behavior, 17*, 439–457.

Kulin, H., et al. (1989). The onset of sperm production in pubertal boys. *American Journal of Diseases of Children, 143*, 190–193.

Kumar, U. (1991). Life stages in the development of the Hindu woman in India. In L. L. Adler (Ed.), *Women in cross-cultural perspective* (pp. 143–158). New York: Praeger.

Kunkel, L. E., & Temple, L. L. (1992). Attitudes towards AIDS and homosexuals: Gender, marital status, and religion. *Journal of Applied Social Psychology, 22*, 1030-1040.

Kunz, J. R. M., & Finkel, A. J. (Eds.). (1987). *The American Medical Association family medical guide: Revised and updated*. New York: Random House.

Kurdek, L. A, & Schmitt, J. P. (1986a). Relationship quality of gay men in closed or open relationships. *Journal of Homosexuality, 12(2)*, 85–99.

Kurdek, L. A, & Schmitt, J. P. (1986b). Relationship quality of partners in heterosexual married, heterosexual cohabiting, gay, and lesbian relationships. *Journal of Personality and Social Psychology, 51*, 711–720.

Kushner, M. (1977). The reduction of a longstanding fetish by means of aversive conditioning. In J. Fischer & H. Gochros (Eds.), *Handbook of behavior therapy with sexual problems*. New York: Pergamon Press.

Kutchinsky, B. (1976). Deviance and criminality: The case of a voyeur in a peeper's paradise. *Disease of the Nervous System, 37*, 145–151.

Kutchinsky, B. (1973). The effect of easy availability of pornography on the incidence of sex crimes. *Journal of Social Issues, 29*, 163–182.

Kuvin, S. F. (1991, June 25). Test for virus also [Letter]. *The New York Times*, p. A24.

Lacayo, R. (1993, March 22). One doctor down, how many more? *Time*, p. 47.

LaChance, C. C., Chestnut, R. W., & Lubitz, A. (1978). The "decorative" female model: Sexual stimuli and the recognition of advertisements. *Journal of Advertising, 8*, 231-235.

Ladas, A. K., Whipple, B., & Perry, J. D. (1982). *The G spot and other recent discoveries about human sexuality*. New York: Holt, Rinehart & Winston.

Lader, L. (1970, July). A national guide to legal abortion. *Ladies Home Journal*, p. 73.

Ladner, J. A. (1971). *Tomorrow's tomorrow: The black woman*. Garden City, NY: Doubleday & Co.

Lamaze, F. (1981). *Painless childbirth*. New York: Simon & Schuster.

Lamb, M. E. (1981). The development of father-infant relationships. In M. E. Lamb (Ed.), *The role of the father in child development*. New York: Wiley.

Lambert, B. (1991, December 9). Kimberly Bergalis is dead at 23; symbol of debate over AIDS tests. *The New York Times*, p. D9.

Lambert, B. (1988, September 20). AIDS among prostitutes not as prevalent as believed, studies show. *The New York Times*, p. B1.

Lambert, B. (1990, July 11). AIDS in black women seen as leading killer. *The New York Times*, B3.

Lamke, L. K. (1982a). Adjustment and sex-role orientation. *Journal of Youth and Adolescence, 11*, 247-259.

Lamke, L. K. (1982b). The impact of sex-role orientation on self-esteem in early adolescence. *Child Development, 53*, 1530-1535.

Landesman, S. H., et al. (1989). HIV disease in reproductive age women: A problem of the present. *Journal of the American Medical Association, 261*, 1326–1327.

Landesman-Dwyer, S., & Emanuel, I. (1979). Smoking during pregnancy. *Teratology, 19*, 119–126.

Landis, S. E., et al. (1992). Results of a randomized trial of partner notification in cases of HIV infection in North Carolina. *The New England Journal of Medicine, 326*, 101–106.

Landry, M., & Zibello, T. (1988). Ability of herpes simplex virus (HSV) types 1 and 2 to induce clinical disease and establish latency following previous genital infection with the heterologous HSV type. *Journal of Infectious Diseases, 158*, 1382–1385.

Landy, D., & Sigall, H. (1974). Beauty is talent: Task evaluation as a function of the performer's physical attractiveness. *Journal of Personality and Social Psychology, 30*, 299–304.

Lane, K. E., & Gwartney-Gibbs, P. A. (1985). Violence in the context of dating and sex. *Journal of Family Issues, 6*, 45–59.

Lang, A. R. (1985). The social psychology of drinking and human sexuality. *Journal of Drug Issues, 15*, 273–289.

Lang, A. R., et al. (1980). Expectancy, alcohol, and sex guilt as determinants of interest in and reaction to sexual stimuli. *Journal of Abnormal Psychology, 89*, 644–653.

Lang, R. A., et al. (1989). An examination of sex hormones in genital exhibitionists. *Annals of Sex Research, 2*, 67–75.

Langevin, R. (1983). *Sexual strands: Understanding and treating sexual anomalies in men*. Hillsdale, NJ: Lawrence Erlbaum Associates.

Langevin, R., et al. (1988). Pornography and sexual offenses.*Annals of Sex Research, 1*, 335–362.

Langevin, R., & Russon, A. (1985). Voyeurism: Does it predict sexual aggression or violence in general? In R. Langevin (Ed.), *Erotic preference, gender identity, and aggression in men: New research studies*. Hillsdale, NJ: Erlbaum.

Langevin, R., Paitich, D., & Steiner, B. (1977). The clinical profile of male transsexuals living as females vs. those living as males. *Archives of Sexual Behavior, 6*, 143–154.

Langevin, R., Wright, P., & Handy, L. (1989). Characteristics of sex offenders who were sexually victimized as children. *Annals of Sex Research, 2*, 227–253.

Langevin, R., et al. (1989). An examination of brain damage and dysfunction in genital exhibitionists. *Annals of Sex Research, 2*, 77–87.

Langevin, R., et al. (1979). Experimental studies of the etiology of genital exhibitionism. *Archives of Sexual Behavior, 8*, 307–332.

Lansky, D., & Wilson, G. T. (1981). Alcohol, expectations, and sexual arousal in males: An information-processing analysis. *Journal of Abnormal Psychology, 90*, 35–45.

Largen, M. A. (1988). Rape reform law: An analysis. In A. W. Burgess (Ed.), *Rape and sexual assault* (pp. 271–292). New York: Garland.

Laskin, D. (1982, February 21). The herpes syndrome. *The New York Times Sunday Magazine*, pp. 94–108.

LaTour, M. S. (1990). Female nudity in print advertising: An analysis of gender differences in arousal and ad response. *Psychology and Marketing, 7*, 65–81.

Laviola, M. (1989). Effects of older brother–younger sister incest: A review of four cases. *Journal of Family Violence, 4*, 259–274.

Lavrakas, P. J. (1975). *Female preferences for male physiques*. Paper presented to the Midwestern Psychological Association, Chicago.

Lawrence, K., & Herold, E. S. (1988). Women's attitudes toward and experience with sexually explicit materials. *Journal of Sex Research, 24*, 161–169.

Lawson, C. (1993, August 5). Single but mothers by choice: "Who is my daddy?" can be answered in different ways. *The New York Times*, pp. C1, C9.

Layde, P. M., Ory, H. W., & Schlesselman, J. J. (1982). The risk of myocardial infarction in former users of oral contraceptives. *Family Planning Perspectives, 14*, 78–80.

Lazarus, A. A. (1989). Dyspareunia: A multimodal psychotherapeutic perspective. In S. R. Leiblum & R. C. Rosen (Eds.), *Principles and practice of sex therapy* (2nd. ed.) (pp. 89–112). New York: Guilford Press.

Lazarus, A. A., & Davison, G. C. (1971). Clinical innovation in research and practice. In A. E. Bergin & S. L. Garfield (Eds.), *Handbook of psychotherapy and behavior change: An empirical analysis*. New York: Wiley.

Lear, M. (1987, December 20). The pain of loneliness. *The New York Times Magazine*, pp. 47–48.

Leary, W. E. (1988, July 14). Sharp rise in rare sex-related diseases. *The New York Times*, p. B6.

Leary, W. E. (1989, May 23). AIDS risk among college students is real but not rampant, tests find. *The New York Times*, pp.

Leary, W. E. (1990, September, 13). New focus on sperm brings fertility successes. *The New York Times*, p. B11.

Leary, W. E. (1991, October 22). Vaginal infection tied to low birth weight. *The New York Times*, p. C3.

Leary, W. E. (1992a, February 1). U.S. panel backs approval of first condom for women. *The New York Times*, p. 7.

Leary, W. E. (1992b, December 10). Medical panel says most sexual impotence in men can be treated without surgery. *The New York Times*, p. D20.

Leary, W. E. (1992c, October 30). U.S. approves injectable drug as birth control. *The New York Times*, pp. A1, A14.

Leary, W. E. (1993a, September 9). Broader uses seen for abortion pill. *The New York Times*, p. A17.

Leary, W. E. (1993b, May 11). Female condom approved for market. *The New York Times*, p. C5.

Leary, W. E. (1993c, April 21). Maker of abortion pill reaches licensing pact with U.S. group. *The New York Times*, p. A18.

Leary, W. E. (1993d, April 28). Screening of all newborns urged for sickle cell disease. *The New York Times*, p. C11.

Leavitt, C. J. (1990). Sexual abuse of boys: A medical perspective. In M. Hunter (Ed.), *The sexually abused male: Prevalence, impact, and treatment*, (Vol. 1), (pp. 227–240). Lexington, MA: Lexington Books.

Leavitt, F. (1974). *Drugs and behavior*. Philadelphia: W. B. Saunders Co.

Leavitt, G. C. (1990). Sociobiological explanations of incest avoidance: A critical review of evidential claims. *American Anthropologist, 92*, 971–993.

Lechtenberg, R. (1984). *Epilepsy and the family*. Cambridge, MA: Harvard University Press.

Ledray, L. E. (1990). Counseling rape victims: The nursing challenge. *Perspectives in Psychiatric Care, 26*, 21–27.

Lee, A. L., & Scheurer, V. L. (1983). Psychological androgyny and aspects of self-image in women and men. *Sex Roles, 9*, 289-306.

Lee, J. A. (1988). Love-styles. In R. J. Sternberg & M. L. Barnes (Eds.), *The psychology of love* (pp. 38–67). New Haven: Yale University Press.

Lee, N. C., Rubin, G. L., & Borucki, R. (1988). The intrauterine device and pelvic inflammatory disease revisited: New results from the Women's Health Study. *Obstetrics and Gynecology, 72*, 1–6.

Leiblum, S. R., Pervin, L. A., & Campbell, E. H. (1980). The teatment of vaginismus: Success and failure. In S. R. Leiblum & L. A. Pervin (Eds.), *Principles and practice of sex therapy* (pp. 167–192). New York: Guilford.

Leiblum, S. R., & Rosen, R. C. (1991). Couples therapy for erectile disorders: Conceptual and clinical considerations. Special issue: The treatment of male erectile disorders. *Journal of Sex and Marital Therapy, 17*, 147-159.

Leiblum, S., & Rosen, R. (Eds.). (1988). *Sexual desire disorders*. New York: Guilford Press.

Leifer, M. (1980). *Psychological effects of motherhood: A study of first pregnancy*. New York: Praeger.

Leishman, K. (1987, February). Heterosexuals and AIDS. *The Atlantic Monthly*, pp. 39–58.

Leitenberg, H., Detzer, M. J., & Srebnik, D. (1993). Gender differences in masturbation and the relation of masturbation experience in preadolescence and/or early adolescence to sexual behavior and sexual adjustment in young adulthood. *Archives of Sexual Behavior, 22*, 87-98.

Leitenberg, H., Greenwald, E., & Tarran, M. J. (1989). The relation between sexual activity among children during preadolescence and/or early adolescence and sexual behavior and sexual adjustment in young adulthood. *Archives of Sexual Behavior, 18*, 299–313.

Leland, N. L., & Barth, R. P. (1992). Gender differences in knowledge, intentions, and behaviors concerning pregnancy and sexually transmitted disease prevention among adolescents. *Journal of Adolescent Health, 13*, 589-599.

Lemon, S. J., & Newbold, J. E. (1990). Viral hepatitis. In K. K. Holmes, P. Mardh, P. F. Sparling, & P. J. Wiesner (Eds.), *Sexually transmitted diseases* (2nd ed.) (pp. 449-466). New York: McGraw-Hill.

Lemp, G. F., et al. (1990). Survival trends for patients with AIDS. *Journal of the American Medical Association, 265*, 402–406.

Lenihan, G., Rawlins, M.E., Eberly, C.G., Buckley, B. & Masters, B. (1992). Gender differences in rape supportive attitudes before and after a date rape education intervention. Journal of College Student Development, 33, 331-338.

Lentz, S. L., & Zeiss, A. M. (1984). Fantasy and sexual arousal in college women: An empirical investigation. *Imagination, Cognition, and Personality, 3*, 185–202.

Lerner, R. M., & Gellert, E. (1969). Body build identification, preference, and aversion in children. *Developmental Psychology, 1*, 456–462.

Leshner, A. I. (1978). *An introduction to behavioral endocrinology*. New York: Oxford University Press.

Leslie, L. A., Huston, T. L., & Johnson, M. P. (1986). Parental reactions to dating relationships: Do they make a difference? *Journal of Marriage and the Family, 46*, 57–66.

Lesnik-Oberstein, M., & Cohen, L. (1984). Cognitive style, sensation seeking, and assortive mating. *Journal of Personality and Social Psychology, 46*, 112–117.

Letourneau, E., & O'Donohue, W. (1993). Sexual desire disorders. In W. O'Donohue & J. H. Geer (Eds.), *Handbook of sexual dysfunctions: Assessment and treatment.* (pp. 53-81). Boston: Allyn & Bacon.

LeVay, S. (1991). A difference in hypothalamic structure between heterosexual and homosexual men. *Science, 253*, 1034–1037.

Lever, J., et al. (1992). Behavior patterns and sexual identity of bisexual males. *Journal of Sex Research, 29*, 141-167.

Levin, R. J., & Stava, L. (1987). Personality characteristics of sex offenders: A review. *Archives of Sexual Behavior, 16*, 57–79.

Levine, G. I. (1991). Sexually transmitted parasitic diseases. *Primary Care: Clinics in Office Practice, 18*, 101–128.

Levine, M. (1951). Pediatric observations of masturbation in children. *Psychoanalytic Study of the Child, 6*, 117–124.

Levine, M. P., & Troiden, R. R. (1988). The myth of sexual compulsivity. *Journal of Sex Research, 25*, 347–363.

Levine, S., et al. (1989, April). Benefits and problems with intracavernosal injections for the treatment of impotence. *Medical Aspects of Human Sexuality, 14*, 38–40.

Levine, S. B., & Agle, D. (1978). The effectiveness of sex therapy for chronic secondary psychological impotence. *Journal of Sex and Marital Therapy, 4*, 235–258.

Levine, S. B., & Yost, M. A. (1976). Frequency of sexual dysfunction in a general gynecological clinic: An epidemiological approach. *Archives of Sexual Behavior, 5*, 229–238.

Levinger, G. (1980). Toward the analysis of close relationships. *Journal of Experimental Social Psychology, 16*, 510–544.

Levinger, G. (1983). Development and change. In H. H. Kelley et al. (Eds.), *Close relationships*. New York: W. H. Freeman.

Levitt, E. E. (1988). Alternative life style and marital satisfaction: A brief report. *Annals of Sex Research, 1*, 455–461.

Levy, D. S. (1991, September 16). Why Johnny might grow up violent and sexist. *Time*, pp. 16–19.

Levy, G. D., & Carter, D. B. (1989). Gender schema, gender constancy, and gender-role knowledge: The roles of cognitive factors in preschoolers' gender-role stereotype attributions. *Developmental Psychology, 25*, 444–449.

Levy, J. A. (1993). The transmission of HIV and factors influencing progression to AIDS. *The American Journal of Medicine, 95*, pp. 86-100.

Levy, J. A., et al. (1985). Isolation of AIDS-associated retrovirus from cerebrospinal fluid and brains of patients with neurological symptoms. *Lancet, 2*, 586–588.

Levy, J. (1985). Right brain, left brain: Fact and fiction. *Psychology Today, 19*, (5), pp. 38–44.

Levy, M. R., Dignan, M., & Shirreffs, J. H. (1987). *Life and health* (5th ed.). New York: Random House.

Levy, R. I. (1973). *The Tahitians.*. Chicago: University of Chicago Press.

Levy, R. M., et al. (1984). Central nervous system mass lesions in the acquired immune deficiency syndrome (AIDS). *Journal of Neurosurgery, 51*, 9–16.

Lewin, M. (1985). Unwanted intercourse: The difficulty of saying no. *Psychology of Women Quarterly, 9*, 184–192.

Lewin, T. (1991, February 8). Studies on teen-age sex cloud condom debate. *The New York Times*, p. A14.

Lewin, T. (1992, February 28). Canada court says pornography harms women. *The New York Times*, p. B7.

Lewin, T. (1992b, December 10). Sexual partners on increase for girls. *The New York Times*, p. D20.

Lewin, T. (1991, November 29). 5-year contraceptive implant seems headed for wide use. *The New York Times*, p. A1.

Lewin, T. (1992a, May 28). Parental consent to abortion: How enforcement can vary. *The New York Times*, pp. A1, B8.

Lewis, D. K., & Watters, J. K. (1991). Sexual risk behavior among heterosexual intravenous drug users: Ethnic and gender variations. *AIDS, 5,* 77-83.

Lewis, M., & Kagan, J. (1965). Studies in attention. *Merrill-Palmer Quarterly, 2,* 95–127.

Lewis, O. (1951). *Life in a Mexican village: Tepozlan revisited.* Urbana, IL: University of Illinois Press.

Libman, E. (1989). Sociocultural and cognitive factors in aging and sexual expression: Conceptual and research issues. *Canadian Psychology, 30,* 560–567.

Libman, E., Fichten, C. S., & Brender, W. (1985). The role of therapeutic format in the treatment of sexual dysfunction: A review. *Clinical Psychology Review, 5,* 103–117.

Lie, G., & Inman, A. (1991). The use of anatomical dolls as assessment and evidentiary tools. *Social Work, 36,* 396-399.

Liebowitz, M. (1983). *The chemistry of love.* Boston: Little, Brown.

Lief, H. (1989). Sexology. *Journal of the American Medical Association, 261,* 2888–2889.

Lief, H.I, & Hubschman, L. (1993). Orgasm in the postoperative transsexual. *Archives of Sexual Behavior, 22,* 145-155.

Lightfoot-Klein, H. (1989). The sexual experience and marital adjustment of genitally circumcised and infibulated females in the Sudan. *Journal of Sex Research, 26,* 375–392.

Lindermalm, G., Korlin, D., & Uddenberg, N. (1986). Long-term follow-up of "sex change" in 134 male to female transsexuals. *Archives of Sexual Behavior, 15,* 187–210.

Lindsey, R. (1988, February 1). Circumcision under criticism as unnecessary to newborn. *The New York Times,* p. A1.

Lindsey, R. (1984, April 4). Sexual abuse of children draws experts' increasing concern nationwide. *The New York Times,* p. A21.

Linn, S., et al. (1982). Salience of visual patterns in the human infant. *Developmental Psychology, 18,* 651–657.

Linsley, W. A. (1989). The case against censorship of pornography. In D. Zillmann & J. Bryant (Eds.), *Pornography: Research advances and policy considerations* (pp. 343–359). Hillsdale, NJ: Lawrence Erlbaum Associates.

Linz, D. (1985). *Sexual violence in the media: Effects on male viewers and implications for society.* Unpublished doctoral dissertation, University of Wisconsin-Madison.

Linz, D. (1989). Exposure to sexually explicit materials and attitudes toward rape: A comparison of study results. *Journal of Sex Research, 26,* 50–84.

Linz, D., Donnerstein, E., & Penrod, S. (1988). The effects of long-term exposure to violent and sexually degrading depictions of women. *Journal of Personality and Social Psychology, 55,* 758–767.

Linz, D., Donnerstein, E., & Penrod, S. (1984). The effects of multiple exposures to filmed violence against women. *Journal of Communciation, 34,* 130–147.

Lipovsky, J. A., Saunders, B. E., & Murphy, S. M. (1989). Depression, anxiety, and behavior problems among victims of father-child sexual assault and nonabused siblings. *Journal of Interpersonal Violence, 4,* 452–468.

Lisak, D. (1991). Sexual aggression, masculinity, and fathers. *Signs, 16,* 238–262.

Lisak, D., & Roth, S. (1990). Motives and psychodynamics of self-reported, unincarcerated rapists. *American Journal of Orthopsychiatry, 60,* 268–280.

Liskin, L., Wharton, C, & Blackburn, R. (1990). Condoms—now more than ever. *Population Reports, No. 8,* 1-36.

Liskin, L, & Blackburn, R. (1987). Hormonal contraception: New long-acting methods. *Population Reports, K(3).*

List, J. A., Collins, W. A., & Westby, S. D. (1983). Comprehension and inferences from traditional and nontraditional sex-role portrayals on television. *Child Development, 54,* 1579–1587.

Living alone and loving it. *Newsweek,* (1987, August 3). pp. 52–60.

Lloyd, S. A., Cate, R. M., & Henton, J. M. (1984). Predicting premarital relationship stability: A methodological refinement. *Journal of Marriage and the Family, 46,* 71–76.

Lodl, K. M., McGettigan, A., & Bucy, J. (1985, Spring). Women's responses to abortion: Implications for post-abortion support groups. *Journal of Social Work and Human Sexuality, 3,* 119–132.

Loewenstein, S. F. (1985). On the diversity of love-object orientations among women. *Journal of Social Work & Human Sexuality, 3,* 7–24.

Logan, D. D. (1978, August). *Variations on "the curse": Menstrual euphemisms in other countries.* Paper presented to the American Psychological Association, Toronto.

Lohr, J. (1989). The foreskin and urinary tract infections. *Journal of Pediatrics, 114,* 502–504.

Longo, D. J., & Clum, G. A. (1989). Psychosocial factors affecting genital herpes recurrences: Linear vs. mediating models. *Journal of Psychosomatic Research, 33,* 161–166.

LoPiccolo, J. (1978). Direct treatment of sexual dysfunction. In J. LoPiccolo & L. LoPiccolo (Eds.), *Handbook of sex therapy.* New York: Plenum Press.

LoPiccolo, J. (1977). Direct treatment of sexual dysfunction in the couple. In J. Money & H. Musaph (Eds.), *Handbook of sexology.* Amsterdam: Excerpta Medica.

LoPiccolo, J. (1985, September 19–22). *Advances in diagnosis and treatment of sexual dysfunction.* Paper presented at the 28th Annual Meeting of the Society for the Scientific Study of Sex, San Diego, CA.

LoPiccolo, J., & Friedman, J. (1988). Broad-spectrum treatment of low sexual desire: Integration of cognitive, behavioral, and systemic therapy. In S. Leiblum & R. Rosen (Eds.), *Sexual desire disorders.* New York: Guilford Press.

Loraine, J. A., et al. (1971). Patterns of hormone excretion in male and female homosexuals. *Nature, 234,* 552–555.

Lorch, D. T. (1993b, December 18). After years of ignoring AIDS epidemic, Kenya has begun facing up to it. *The New York Times,* p. A 5.

Lorch, D. (1993a, February 23). Uganda, scareed by AIDS, turns to its youth. *The New York Times,* pp. A1, A10.

Lorefice, L. S. (1991) Fluoxetine treatment of a fetish. *Journal of Clinical Psychiatry, 52,*

Lothstein, L. M. (1982). Sex reassignment surgery: Historical, bioethical, and theoretical issues. *American Journal of Psychiatry, 139,* 417–426.

Lott, B. (1981). A feminist critique of androgyny: Toward the elimination of gender attributions for learned behavior. In C. Mayo & N. M. Henley (Eds.), *Gender and nonverbal behavior.* New York: Springer.

Lott, B. (1985). The potential enhancement of social/personality psychology through feminist research and vice versa. *American Psychologist, 40,* 155–164.

Lottes, I. L., & Kuriloff, P. J. (1992). The effects of gender, race, religion, and political orientation on the sex role attitudes of college freshmen. *Adolescence, 27,* 675-688

Loucks, A., & Horvath, S. (1985). Athletic amenorrhea: A review. *Medicine and Science in Sports and Exercise, 17,* 56–71.

Lourea, D., Rila, M., & Taylor, C. (1986, January). *Sex in the age of AIDS.* Paper presented at the Western Region Annual Conference of the Society for the Scientific Study of Sex, Scottsdale, AZ.

Lovdal, L. T. (1989). Sex role messages in television commercials: An update. *Sex Roles, 21,* 715–724.

Lown, J., & Dolan, E. (1988). Financial challenges in remarriage. *Lifestyles: Family and Economic Issues, 9,* 73–88.

Lowry, T. P., & Williams, G. R. (1983). Brachioproctic eroticism. *Journal of Sex Education and Therapy, 9,* 50–52.

Loy, P. H., & Stewart, L. P. (1984). The extent and effects of the sexual harassment of working women. *Sociological Focus, 17,* 31–43.

Luciw, P. A., Leung, N. J. (1992). Mechanisms of retrovirus replication. In Levy, J. A. (Ed.), *The retroviridae: Vol. 1.* (pp. 159-298). New York: Plenum Press.

Luckenbill, D. F. (1985). Entering male prostitution. *Urban Life, 14,* 131–153.

Lui, K. J., et al. (1988). A model-based estimate of the mean incubation period for AIDS in homosexual men. *Science, 240,* 1333–1335.

Luker, K. (1984). *Abortion and the politics of motherhood.* Los Angeles: University of California Press.

Lundstrom, B., Pauly, I., & Walinder, J. (1984). Outcome of sex reassignment surgery. *Acta Psychiatrica Scandinavica, 70,* 289–294.

Lusk, R., & Waterman, J. (1986). Effects of sexual abuse on children. In K. MacFarlane et al. (Eds.), *Sexual abuse of young children: Evaluation and treatment* (pp. 101–118). New York: Guilford.

Lutjen, P., et al. (1984). The establishment and maintenance of pregnancy using in vitro fertilization and embryo donation in a patient with primary ovarian failure. *Nature, 307,* 174–175.

Lydon, J. E., Jamieson, D. W., & Zanna, M. P. (1988). Interpersonal similarity and the social and intellectual dimensions of first impressions. *Social Cognition, 6,* 269–286.

Lyons, B. (1991). Artistic freedom and the university. *Art Journal, 50, (4),* 77–83.

Lytle, C. D., et al. (1990). Virus leakage through natural membrane condoms. *Sexually Transmitted Diseases, 17,* 58-62.

Maccoby, E. E. (1990). Gender and relationships: A developmental account. *American Psychologist, 45,* 513–520.

Maccoby, E. E., & Jacklin, C. N. (1974). *The psychology of sex differences.* Stanford, CA: Stanford University Press.

Maccoby, E. E., & Jacklin, C. N. (1980). Sex differences in aggression: A rejoinder and reprise. *Child Development, 51,* 964–980.

MacDonald, A. P., Jr., & Games, R. G. (1974). Some characteristics of those who hold positive and negative attitudes toward homosexuals. *Journal of Homosexuality, 1,* 9–27.

MacDonald, A. P., Jr., et al. (1972). Attitudes toward homosexuality: Preservation of sex morality or the double standard? *Journal of Consulting and Clinical Psychology, 40,* 161.

MacDonald, J. M. (1971). *Rape: Offenders and their victims.* Springfield, IL: Charles C. Thomas.

MacDonald, N. E., et al. (1990). High-risk STD/HIV behavior among college students. *Journal of the American Medical Association, 263,* 3155–3159.

Mackinnon, J. (1974). *In search of the red ape.* New York: Holt, Rinehart & Winston.

Macklin, E. D. (1978). Nonmarital heterosexual cohabitation. A review of the recent literature. *Marriage and Family Review, 1,* 1–12.

Macklin, E. D. (1972). Heterosexual cohabitation among unmarried college students. *Family Coordinator, 21,* 463–472.

Macklin, E. D. (1974 November). Cohabitation in college: Going very steady. *Psychology Today.*

Macklin, E. D. (1980). Nonmarital heterosexual cohabitation. In A. Skolnick & J. H. Skolnick (Eds.), *Family in transition* (3d ed.). Boston: Little, Brown.

MacLean, P. M. (1976). Brain mechanisms of elemental sexual functions. In B. J. Sadock et al. (Eds.), *The sexual experience.* Baltimore: Williams and Wilkins.

Macrae, C. N., & Shepherd, J. W. (1989). Sex differences in the perception of rape victims. *Journal of Interpersonal Violence, 4,* 278–288.

Madonna, P. G., Van-Scoyk, S., & Jones, D. P. (1991). Family interactions within incest and nonincest families. *American Journal of Psychiatry, 148,* 46–49.

Mahoney, E. R., et al. (1986). Sexual coercion and assault: Male socialization and female risk. *Sexual Coercion and Assault, 1,* 2–8.

Major, B., & Cozzarelli, C. (1992). Psychosocial predictors of adjustment to abortion. *Journal of Social Issues, 48,* , 121-142.

Makepeace, J. M. (1987). Social factor and victim-offender differences in courtship violence. *Family Relations, 36,* 87–91.

Makinson, C. (1985). The health consequences of teenage fertility. *Family Planning Perspectives, 17,* 132–139.

Malamuth, N. M. (1989). The Attraction to Sexual Aggression Scale: Part 2. *Journal of Sex Research, 26,* 324–354.

Malamuth, N. M. (1984). Aggression against women: Cultural and individual causes. In N. M. Malamuth & E. Donnerstein (Eds.), *Pornography and sexual aggression* (pp. 19–52). Orlando, FL: Academic Press.

Malamuth, N. M. (1981). Rape proclivity among males. *Journal of Social Issues, 37,* 138–157.

Malamuth, N. M., & Ceniti, J. (1986). Repeated exposure to violent and nonviolent pornography: Likelihood of raping ratings and laboratory aggression against women. *Aggressive Behavior, 12,* 129–137.

Malamuth, N. M., & McIlwraith, R. D. (1988). Fantasies and exposure to sexually explicit magazines. *Communication Research, 15,* 753–771.

Malamuth, N. M., Heim, N., & Feshbach, S. (1980). Sexual responsiveness of college students to rape depictions: Inhibitory or disinhibitory effects. *Journal of Personality and Social Psychology, 38,* 399–408.

Malamuth, N. M., et al. (1991). Characteristics of aggressors against women: Testing a model using a national sample of college students. *Journal of Consulting and Clinical Psychology, 59,* 670–681.

Maletzky, B. M. (1980). Self-referred vs. court-referred sexually deviant patients: Success with assisted covert sensitization. *Behavior Therapy, 11,* 306–314.

Malhotra, H. K., & Wig, N. N. (1975). Dhat syndrome: A culture-bound sex neurosis of the Orient. *Archives of Sexual Behavior, 4,* 519–529.

Malinowski, B. (1929). *The sexual life of savages in north-western Melanesia.* New York: Eugenics.

Malinowski, B. (1927). *Sex and repression in savage society.* London: Kegan Paul, Trench, Trubner & Co.

Malloy, M. H., Hoffman, H. J., Peterson, D. R. (1992). Sudden infant death syndrome and maternal smoking. *American Journal of Public Health, 82,* 1380-1382.

Mammograms on rise, federal study finds. (1992, April 29). *The New York Times,* p. C13.

Maneker, J. S., & Rankin, R. P. (1985). Education, age at marriage, and marital duration: Is there a relationship? *Journal of Marriage and the Family, 47,* 675–683.

Mann, J., Tarantola, D., & Netter, T.W. (1992). *AIDS in the world 1992.* Cambridge, MA: Harvard University Press.

Mannarino, A. P., & Cohen, J. A. M. (1989). Emotional and behavioral difficulties in sexually abused girls. *Journal of Interpersonal Violence, 4,* 437–451.

Mansnerus, L. (1988, October 12). The darker side of the "baby blues." *The New York Times,* pp. C1, C8.

Mant, D. et al. (1987). Myocardial infarction and angina pectoris in young women. *Journal of Epidemiology and Community Health, 41,* 215–219.

Marchbanks, P., et al. (1988). Risk factors for ectopic pregnancy. *Journal of the American Medical Association, 259,* 1823–1827.

Marcus, T. L., & Corsini, D. A. (1978). Parental expectations of preschool children as related to child gender and socioeconomic status. *Child Development, 49,* 243–246.

Margolin, L., Miller, M., & Moran, P. B. (1989). When a kiss is not just a kiss: Relating violations on consent in kissing to rape myth acceptance. *Sex Roles, 20,* 231–243.

Margolin, L., & White, L. (1987). The continuing role of physical attractiveness in marriage. *Journal of Marriage and the Family, 49,* 21–27.

Marin, B., & Marin, G. (1992). Predictors of condom accessibility among Hispanics in San Francisco. *American Journal of Public Health, 82,* 592-594.

Marin, B. V., C. Gomez, A., & Hearst, N. (1993). Multiple heterosexual partners and condom use among Hispanics and non-Hispanic whites. *Family Planning Perspectives, 25,* 170-174.

Marks, G., Miller, N., & Maruyama, G. (1981). Effect of targets' physical attractiveness on assumption of similarity.*Journal of Personality and Social Psychology, 41,* 198–206.

Marmor, J. (1971). "Normal" and "deviant" sexual behavior. *Journal of the American Medical Association, 217,* 165–170.

Marshall, W. L. (1989). Pornography and sex offenders. In D. Zillmann & J. Bryant (Eds.), *Pornography: Research advances and policy considerations* (pp. 185–214). Hillsdale, NJ: Lawrence Erlbaum Associates.

Marshall, D. (1971). Sexual behavior on Mangaia. In D. Marshall & R. Suggs (Eds.), *Human sexual behavior: Variations in the ethnographic spectrum* (pp. 103–162). New York: Basic Books.

Marshall, W. L. (1988). The use of sexually explicit stimuli by rapists, child molesters, and nonoffenders. *Journal of Sex Research, 25,* 267–288.

Marshall, W. L., et al. (1991). Treatment outcome with sex offenders. *Clinical Psychology Review, 11,* 465–485.

Marsiglio, W. (1987). Adolescent fathers in the United States: Their initial living arrangements, marital experience and educational outcomes. *Family Planning Perspectives, 19,* 240–251.

Marsiglio, W. (1993b). Adolescent male's orientation toward paternity and contraception. *Family Planning Perspectives, 25,* 22-31.

Marsiglio, W. (1993a). Attitudes toward homosexual activity and gays as friends: A ntaional survey of heterosexual 15- to 19- year-old males. *Journal of Sex Research, 30,* 12-17.

Martens, M., & Faro, S. (1989, January). Update on trichomoniasis: Detection and management. *Medical Aspects of Human Sexuality,* 73–79.

Martin, C. E. (1977). Sexual activity in the aging male. In J. Money & H. Musaph (Eds.), *Handbook of sexology.* Great Britain: Elsevier.

Martin, C. L., & Halverson, C. F., Jr. (1981). A schematic processing model of sex typing and stereotyping in children. *Child Development, 54,* 1119–1134.

Martin, C. L., & Halverson, C. F., Jr. (1983). The effects of sex-typing schemas on young children's memory. *Child Development, 54,* 563–574.

Martin, D., & Martin, M. (1984). Selected attitudes toward marriage and family life among college students. *Family Relations, 33,* 293–300.

Martin, D. H. (1990). Chlamydial infections. *Medical Clinics of North America, 74,* 1367–1387.

Martin, D. J. (1992). AIDS-risk behavior among gay and bisexual men in the age of AIDS: Evidence of continued need for change. *Public Health Reports*

Martin, J. L. (1987). The impact of AIDS on gay male sexual behavior patterns in New York City. *American Journal of Public Health, 77,* 578–581.

Martin, J. L. (1988). Psychological consequences of AIDS-related bereavement among gay men. *Journal of Consulting and Clinical Psychology, 56,* 856–862.

Martinez, F. D., Cline, M., & Burrows, B. (1992). Increased incidence of asthma in children of smoking mothers. *Pediatrics, 89,* 21-26.

Martinson, F. M. (1976). Eroticism in infancy and childhood. *The Journal of Sex Research, 2,* 251–262.

Mason, R. T., et al. (1989). Sex pheromones in snakes. *Science, 245,* 290–293.

Masters, W. H., & Johnson, V. E. (1970). *Human sexual inadequacy.* Boston: Little, Brown.

Masters, W. H., & Johnson, V. E. (1966). *Human sexual response.* Boston: Little, Brown.

Masters, W. H., Johnson, V. E., & Kolodny, R. C. (1989). *Human sexuality.* (4th ed.). New York: HarperCollins.

Masters, W. H., & Johnson, V. E. (1976). *The pleasure bond.* New York: Bantam Books.

Masters, W., & Johnson, V. (1979). *Homosexuality in perspective.* Boston: Little, Brown.

Masters, W. H. (1980, October 20). *Update on sexual physiology.* Paper presented at the Masters & Johnson Institute's Postgraduate Workshop on Human Sexual Function and Dysfunction, St. Louis, MO.

Matek, O. (1988). Obscene phone callers. *Journal of Social Work and Human Sexuality, 7,* 113–130.

Matek, O. (1980 Fall/Winter). Teaching volunteers of a crisis phone service to respond therapeutically to callers with sex problems. *Journal of Sex Education and Therapy, 6,* 24–28.

Mathes, E. W., Adams, H. E., & Davies, R. M. (1985). Jealousy: Loss of relationship rewards, loss of self-esteem, depression, anxiety, and anger. *Journal of Personality and Social Psychology, 48,* 1552–1561.

Mathews, A., Whitehead, A., & Kellett, J. (1983). Psychological and hormonal factors in the treatment of female sexual dysfunction. *Psychological Medicine, 13,* 83–92.

Maticka-Tyndale, E. (1991). Sexual scripts and AIDS prevention: Variations in adherence to safer-sex guidelines by heterosexual adolescents. *Journal of Sex Research, 28,* 45-66.

Matlin, M. W. (1987). *The psychology of women.* New York: Holt, Rinehart and Winston.

Matthews, K. A., et al. (1990). Influences of natural menopause on psychological characteristics and symptoms of middle-aged healthy women. *Journal of Consulting and Clinical Psychology, 58,* 345–351.

Matthews, K. A., et al. (1989). Menopause and risk factors for coronary heart disease. *New England Journal of Medicine, 321,* 641–646.

May, J. L., & Hamilton, P. A. (1980). Effects of musically evoked affect on women's interpersonal attraction toward and perceptual judgments of physical attractiveness of men. *Motivation and Emotion, 4,* 217–228.

May, R. (1958). The origins and significance of the existential movement in psychology. In R. May, E. Angel, & H. R. Ellenberger (Eds.), *Existence.* New York: Simon & Schuster.

Mayer, J. P., Hawkins, B., & Todd, R. (1990). A randomized evaluation of smoking cessation interventions for pregnant women at a WIC clinic. (Women, Infants and Children). *American Journal of Public Health, 80,* 76-79.

Maykovich, M. K. (1976). Attitudes versus behavior in extramarital relations. *Journal of Marriage and the Family, 38,* 693–699.

Mays, V. M., & Cochran, S. D. (1988). Issues in the perception of AIDS risk and risk reduction activities by Black and Hispanic/Latina women. *American Psychologist, 43,* 944–957.

McArthur, M. J. (1990). Reality therapy with rape victims. *Archives of Psychiatric Nursing, 4,* 360–365.

McCabe, M. (1985). Dynamics of child sexual abuse. In M. McCabe, R. E. Cohen, & V. Weiss (Eds.), *Child sexual abuse.* New York: Goldner Press.

McCabe, M. P. (1987). Desired and experienced levels of premarital affection and sexual intercourse during dating. *Journal of Sex Research, 23,* 23–33.

McCabe, M. P., & Delaney, S. M. (1992). An evaluation of therapeutic programs for the treatment of secondary inorgasmia in women. *Archives of Sexual Behavior, 21,* 69-89.

McCaghy, C. H. (1980). Child molesters' "explanations." *Medical Aspects of Human Sexuality, 14,* 105.

McCance, A. A., Luff, M. C., & Widdowson, E. C. (1952). Distribution of coitus during the menstrual cycle. *Journal of Hygiene, 37,* 571–611.

McCann, K. (1992). The impact of receiving a positive HIV antibody test: Factors associated with the response. *Counseling Psychology Quarterly, 5,* 37-45.

McCarthy, B. W. (1989). Cognitive-behavioral strategies and techniques in the treatment of early ejaculation. In S. R. Leiblum & R. C. Rosen (Eds.), *Principles and practice of sex therapy* (2nd. ed.) (pp. 141–167). New York: Guilford Press.

McCarthy, B. W. (1982). Sexual dysfunctions and dissatisfactions among middle-years couples. *Journal of Sex Education and Therapy, 8(2),* 9–12.

McCarthy, J., & McMillan, S. (1990). Patient/partner satisfaction with penile implant surgery. *Journal of Sex Education and Therapy, 16,* 25–37.

McCary, J. L. (1971). *Sexual myths and fallacies.* New York: Van Nostrand Reinhold Co.

McCary, J. L, & McCary, S. P. (1978). *McCary's human sexuality.* (4th ed.). Belmont, CA: Wadsworth, Inc.

McCary, J. L., & McCary, S. P. (1982). *McCary's human sexuality.* (5th Ed.). Belmont, CA: Wadsworth, Inc.

McClintock, M. (1971). Menstrual synchrony and suppression. *Nature, 229,* 244–245.

McConaghy, N. (1987). Heterosexuality/homosexuality: Dichotomy or continuum. *Archives of Sexual Behavior, 16,* 411–424.

McConaghy, N., & Blaszczynski, A. (1980). A pair of monozygotic twins discordant for homosexuality: Sex-dimorphic behavior and penile volume responses. *Archives of Sexual Behavior, 9,* 123–124.

McConaghy, M. J. (1979). Gender performance and the genital basis of gender: Stages in the development of constancy of gender. *Child Development, 50* 1223-1226.

McCormack, W. M. (1990). Overview. *Sexually Transmitted Diseases, 57,* 187–191.

McCusker, J., et al. (1992). Maintenance of behavioral change in a cohort of homosexually active men. *AIDS, 6,* 861-868.

McCutchan, J. A. (1990). Virology, immunology, and clinical course of HIV infection. *Journal of Consulting and Clinical Psychology, 58,* 5–12.

McFalls, J. A. (1983). Where have all the children gone? The future of reproduction in the United States. In O. Pocs (Ed.), *Human sexuality.* Guilford, CT: Dushkin.

McGinnis, J. M., & Foege, W. H. (1993). Actual causes of death in the United States. *Journal of the American Medical Association, 270,* 2207-2212.

McGovern, F. J., & Nevid, J. S. (1986). Evaluation apprehension on psychological inventories in a prison-based setting. *Journal of Consulting and Clinical Psychology, 54,* 576–578.

McGuire, R. J., Carlisle, J. M., & Young, B. G. (1965). Sexual deviation as conditioned behavior: A hypothesis. *Behaviour Research and Therapy, 2,* 185–190.

McHale, S., & Huston, T. (1984). Men and women as parents: Sex role orientations, employment, and parental roles with infants. *Child Development, 55,* 1349–1361.

McKay, M., Davis, M., & Fanning, P. (1983). *Messages: The communication book.* Oakland, CA: New Harbinger.

McKillip, J., & Riedel, S. L. (1983). External validity of matching on physical attractiveness for same and opposite sex couples. *Journal of Applied Social Psychology, 13,* 328–337.

McKinney, K. (1989). Social factors in contraceptive and abortion attitudes and behaviors. In K. McKinney & S. Sprecher (Eds.), *Human sexuality: The societal and interpersonal context.* Norwood, NJ: Ablex Publishing Corporation.

McKinney, K., & Maroules, N. (1991). Sexual harassment. In E. Grauerholz & M. A. Koralewski (Eds.), *Sexual coercion: A sourcebook on its nature, causes, and prevention* (pp. 29–44). Lexington, MA: Lexington Books.

McKinney, R. E., et al. (1991). A multicenter trial of oral zidovudine in children with advanced human immunodeficiency virus disease. *The New England Journal of Medicine, 324,* 1018–1025.

McKusick, L., et al. (1987, June). *Prevention of HIV infection among gay and bisexual men: Two longitudinal studies.* Paper presented to the Third International Conference on AIDS, Washington, DC

McLaren, J., & Brown, R. E. (1989). Childhood problems associated with abuse and neglect. *Canada's Mental Health, 37(3),* 1–6.

McLaughlin, F. J., et al. (1992). Randomized trial of comprehensive prenatal care for low-income women: Effect on infant birth weight. *Pediatrics, 89,* 128–132.

McMullen, R. J. (1987). Youth prostitution: A balance of power. *Journal of Adolescence, 10,* 35–43.

McWhirter, D. P., & Madison, A. M. (1984). *The male couples–How relationships develop.* Englewood Cliffs, NJ: Prentice-Hall.

Mead, M. (1967). *Male and female: A study of the sexes in a changing world.* New York: William Morrow.

Mead, M. (1935). *Sex and temperament in three primitive societies.* New York: Dell.

Mead, B. T. (1975, June). Coping with obscene phone calls. *Medical Aspects of Human Sexuality, 9,* 127–128.

Meece, J. (1987). The influence of school experiences on the development of gender schemata. *New Directions for Child Development, 38,* 57–73.

Meeks, S., et al. (1986). Wives' employment status, hassles, communication, and relational efficacy: Intra- versus extra-relationship factors and marital adjustment. *Family Relations, 35,* 249–255.

Meeks, G. R. (1986). Easing the climacteric. *Medical Aspects of Human Sexuality, 20,* 88–107.

Mehrabian, A., & Stanton-Mohr, L. (1985). Effects of emotional state on sexual desire and sexual dysfunction. *Motivation and Emotion, 9,* 315–330.

Meiselman, K. C. (1978). *Incest: A psychological study of causes and effects with treatment recommendations.* San Francisco: Jossey-Bass.

Meisler, A. W., & Carey, M. P. (1990). A critical reevaluation of nocturnal penile tumescence monitoring in the diagnosis of erectile dysfunction. *Journal of Nervous and Mental Disease, 178,* 78–89.

Meisler, A., Carey, M., & Krauss, D. (1988). Success and failure in penile prosthesis surgery: Importance of psychosocial factors. *Journal of Sex and Marital Therapy, 14,* 108.

Melella, J. T., Travin, S., & Cullen, K. (1989). Legal and ethical issues in the use of antiandrogens in treating sex offenders. *Bulletin of the American Academy of Psychiatry and the Law, 17,* 223–232.

Melendy, M. R. (1901). *Maiden, wife, and mother: How to attain health, beauty, happiness.* Chicago: American Literary and Musical Association.

Melman, A., Tiefer, L., & Pedersen, R. (1988). Evaluation of first 406 patients in urology department–based center for male sexual dysfunction. *Urology, 32,* 6–10.

Melvin, S. Y. (1990). Syphilis: Resurgence of an old disease. *Primary Care: Clinics in Office Practice, 17,* 47–57.

Menaghan, E. G., & Lieberman, M. A. (1986). Changes in depression following divorce: A panel study. *Journal of Marriage and the Family, 48,* 319–329.

Menaghan, E. G. (1985). Depressive affect and subsequent divorce. *Journal of Family Issues, 6,* 295–306.

Mencken, J. (1972). The health and social consequences of teenage childbearing. *Family Planning Perspectives, 4,* 45–53.

Menedez, Barbara An entire country's men are dying. *New York Newsday,* pp. 101, 104.

Mengel, M., et al. (1989). The effectiveness of single-dose metronidazole therapy for patients and their partners with bacterial vaginosis. *The Journal of Family Practice, 28,* 163–171.

Merit Reports, Audits and Surveys. (1982). *National Sample Survey.* Storrs, CT: The Roper Center.

Mertz, G. J. (1990). Genital herpes simplex virus infections. *Medical clinics of North America, 74,* 1433–1454.

Mertz, G. J. , et al. (1985). Frequency of acquisition of first-episode genital infection with herpes simplex virus from symptomatic and asymptomatic source contacts. *Sexually Transmitted Diseases, 12,* 33–39.

Messenger, J. C. (1971). Sex and repression in an Irish folk community. In D. S. Marshall and R. C. Suggs (Eds.), *Human sexual behavior: Variations in the ethnographic spectrum* (pp. 3–37). New York: Basic Books.

Meston, C. M., & Gorzalka, B. B. (1992). Psychoactive drugs and human sexual behavior: The role of serotonergic activity. *Journal of Psychoactive Drugs, 24,* 1-40.

Metcalf, M. G., Braiden, V., & Livesey, J. H. (1992). Symptom cyclicity in women with the premenstrual syndrome: An 8-year follow-up study. *Journal of Psychosomatic Research, 36,* 237-241.

Meuwissen, I., & Over, R. (1990). Habituation and dishabituation of female sexual arousal. *Behaviour Research and Therapy, 28,* 217–226.

Meyer, J. P., & Pepper, S. (1977). Need compatibility and marital adjustment in young married couples. *Journal of Personality and Social Psychology, 35,* 331–342.

Meyer-Bahlburg, H. F. (1990-91). Can homosexuality in adolescents be "treated" by sex hormones? *Journal of Child and Adolescent Psychopharmacology, 1,* 231-235.

Meyer, C. L. (in press). Transmission of HIV through donor semen. *Rutger's University Women's Rights Law Reporter.*

Meyer, J. K., & Reter, D. J. (1979). Sex reassignment: Follow-up. *Archives of General Psychiatry, 36,* 1010–1015.

Meyer-Bahlburg, H. F. L. (1979). Sex hormones and female homosexuality: A critical examination. *Archives of Sexual Behavior, 8,* 101–120.

Meyer-Bahlburg, H. F. L. (1976). Book reviews. *Archives of Sexual Behavior, 5,* 259–261.

Meyer-Bahlburg, H. F. L. (1977). Sex hormones and male homosexuality in comparative perspective. *Archives of Sexual Behavior, 6,* 297–326.

Michael, R. P., Keverne, E. B., & Bonsall, R. W. (1971). Pheromones: Isolation of male sex attractants from a female primate. *Science, 172,* 964–966.

Michael, R. P., Bonsall, R. W., & Warner, P. (1974). Human vaginal secretions: Volatile fatty acid content. *Science, 186,* 1217–1219.

Michael, R. T., & Tuma, N. B. (1985). Entry into marriage and parenthood by young men and women: The influence of family background. *Demography, 22,* 515–544.

Michaels, D., & Levine, C. (1992). Estimates of the number of motherless youth orphaned by AIDS in the United States. *Journal of the American Medical Association, 268,* 3456-3461.

Mikawa, J. K., et al. (1992). Cultural practices of Hispanics: Implications for the prevention of AIDS. *Hispanic Journal of Behavioral Sciences, 12,* 421-433.

Mill, J. S. (1939). Utilitarianism. In E. A. Burtt (ed.), *The English philosophers.* New York: The Modern Library. (Original work published 1863.)

Miller, A. B., Baines, C. J., To, T., & Wall, C. (1992). Canadian national breast screening study: 2. Breast cancer detection and death rates among women aged 50 to 59 years. *Canadian Medical Association Journal, 147,* 1477-1488.

Miller, B. C., McCoy, J. K., & Olson, T. D. (1986). Dating age and stage as correlates of adolescent sexual attitudes and behavior. *Journal of Adolescent Research, 1,* 361–371.

Miller, B. C., et al. (1986). Parental discipline and control attempts in relation to adolescent sexual attitudes and behavior. *Journal of Marriage and the Family, 48,* 503–512.

Miller, C., & Boe, J. (1990). Tears into diamonds: Transformation of child psychic trauma through sandplay and storytelling. *Arts in Psychotherapy, 17,* 247–257.

Miller, H. G., Turner, C. F., & Moses, L. E. (Eds.) (1990). *AIDS: The second decade.* Washington, DC: National Academy.

Miller, J. (1991, March 10). Saudi Arabia: The struggle within. *The New York Times Magazine,* pp. 26–31, 38–39, 46.

Miller, J. (1992, December 27). Women regain a kind of security in Islam's embrace. *The New York Times,* Section 4, p. 6.

Miller, W. R., & Lief, H. I. (1976). Masturbatory attitudes, knowledge, and experience. Data from the Sex Knowledge and Attitude Test (SKAT). *Archives of Sexual Behavior, 5,* 447–468.

Miller-Perrin, C. L., & Wurtele, S. K. (1988). The child sexual abuse prevention movement: A critical analysis of primary and secondary approaches. *Clinical Psychology Review, 8,* 313–329.

Mills, J., et al. (1981, July 18). Should coitus late in pregnancy be discouraged? *Lancet,* 136.

Milsten, R. (1979). *Male sexual function: Myth, fantasy, & reality.* New York: Avon.

Minai, N. (1981). *Women in Islam: Tradition and transition in the Middle East.* London: John Murray.

Minkoff, H. L, et al. (1990) The relationship of cocaine use to syphilis and human immunodeficiency virus infections among inner city parturient women. *American Journal of Obstetrics and Gynecology, 163,* 521–526.

Minton, H. L., & McDonald, G. L. (1983). Homosexual identity formation as a developmental process. *Journal of Homosexuality, 9,* 91–104.

Mira, J. J. (1988). A therapeutic package for dyspareunia: A three case example. *Sexual and Marital Therapy, 3,* 77–82.

Mirotznik, J. (1991). Genital herpes: A survey of the attitudes, knowledge, and reported behaviors of college students at-risk for infection.*Journal of Psychology and Human Sexuality, 4,* 73-99.

Mirotznik, J., et al. (1987). Genital herpes: An investigation of its attitudinal and behavioral correlates. *Journal of Sex Research, 23,* 266–272.

Mishell, D. R., Jr. (1989). Medical progress: Contraception. *New England Journal of Medicine, 320,* 777–787.

Mohr, D. C., & Beutler, L. E. (1990). Erectile dysfunction: A review of diagnostic and treatment procedures. *Clinical Psychology Review, 10,* 123–150.

Mohr, J. W., Turner, R. E., & Jerry, M. B. (1964). *Pedophilia and exhibitionism: A handbook.* Toronto: University of Toronto Press.

Moi, H., et al. (1989). Should male consorts of women with bacterial vaginosis be treated? *Genitourinary Medicine, 65,* 263–268.

Monaghy, M. J. (1979). Gender performance and the genital basis of gender: Stages in the development of constancy of gender. *Child Development, 50,* 1223-1226.

Money, J. (1987a). Treatment guidelines: Antiandrogen and counseling of paraphiliac sex offenders. *Journal of Sex and Marital Therapy, 13,* 219–223.

Money, J. (1987b). Sin, sickness or status—Homosexual gender identity and psychoneuroendocrinology. *American Psychologist, 42,* 384–399.

Money, J. (1980). *Love and love sickness.* Baltimore: Johns Hopkins University Press.

Money, J. (1988). *Gay, straight, and in-between.* New York: Oxford University Press.

Money, J. (1968). *Sex errors of the body.* Baltimore: The Johns Hopkins University Press.

Money, J. (1977). Human hermaphroditism. In F. A. Beach (Ed.), *Human sexuality in four perspectives.* Baltimore: The Johns Hopkins University Press.

Money, J. (1990). Agenda and credenda of the Kinsey Scale. In D. P. McWhirter, S. A. Sanders, & J. M. Reinisch (Eds.), *Homosexuality/heterosexuality: Concepts of sexual orientation* (pp. 41–60.). New York: Oxford University Press.

Money, J., & Ehrhardt, A. (1972). *Man and woman, boy and girl.* Baltimore: The Johns Hopkins University Press.

Money, J., Jobaris, R., & Furth, G. (1977). Apotemnophilia: Two cases of self-demand amputation as a paraphilia. *Journal of Sex Research, 13,* 115–125.

Money, J., & Lamacz, M. (1989). *Vandalized lovemaps.* Buffalo, NY: Prometheus Books.

Money, J., Lehne, G., & Pierre-Jerome, F. (1984). Micropenis: Adult follow-up and comparison of size against new norms. *Journal of Sex and Marital Therapy, 10,* 105–116.

Money, J., & Wiedeking, C. (1980). Gender identity/role: Normal differentiation and its transpositions. In B. Wolman & J. Money (Eds.), *Handbook of human sexuality* (pp. 269–284). Englewood Cliffs, NJ: Prentice-Hall.

Monier, M., & Laird, M. (1989, April). Contraceptives: A look at the future. *American Journal of Nursing,* 496–499.

Mooney, K. M., Cohn, E. S., & Swift, M. B. (1992). Physical distance and AIDS: Too close for comfort? *Journal of Applied Social Psychology, 22,* 1442-1452.

Moore, K. A., Peterson, J. L, & Furstenberg, F. F. (1986). Parental attitudes and the occurrence of early sexual activity. *Journal of Marriage and the Family, 48,* 777–782.

Moore, K. A., & Stief, T. M. (1992). Changes in marriage and fertility behavior: Behavior versus attitudes of young adults. *Youth and Society, 22,* 362-386.

Moore, M. M. (1985). Nonverbal courtship patterns in women: Context and consequences. *Ethology and Sociobiology, 6,* 237–247.

Moore, R. D., et al. (1991). Zidovudine and the natural history of the acquired immunodeficiency syndrome. *New England Journal of Medicine, 324,* 1412–1416.

Moos, R. (1968). The development of the Menstrual Distress Questionnaire. *Psychosomatic Medicine, 30,* 853.

Moran, J. S., & Zenilman, J. M. (1990). Therapy for gonococcal infections: Options in 1989. *Reviews of Infectious Diseases,* (Suppl. 6.) S633–S644.

Morbidity and Mortality Weekly Report. (Sept. 28, 1990). v39.

More single mothers. (1993, July 26). *Time,* p. 16.

Morin, S. F., & Garfinkle, E. M. (1978). Male homophobia. *Journal of Social Issues, 34,* 29–47.

Morokoff, P. (1986). Volunteer bias in the psychophysiological study of female sexuality. *Journal of Sex Research, 22,* 35–51.

Morokoff, P. J., & Heiman, J. R. (1980). Effects of erotic stimuli on sexually functional and dysfunctional women: Multiple measures before and after sex therapy. *Behaviour Research and Therapy, 18,* 127–137.

Morrell, M., et al. (1984). The influence of age and cycling status on sexual arousability in women. *American Journal of Obstetrics and Gynecology, 148,* 66–71.

Morris, N., et al. (1987). Marital sex frequency and midcycle female testosterone. *Archives of Sexual Behavior, 7,* 157–173.

Morris, N. M., & Udry, J. R. (1978). Pheromonal influences on human sexual behavior: An experimental search. *Journal of Biosocial Science, 10,* 147–157.

Morrison, D. M. (1985). Adolescent contraceptive behavior: A review. *Psychological Bulletin, 98,* 538–568.

Morrison, E. S., et al. (1980). *Growing up sexual..* New York: Van Nostrand Reinhold Co.

Morse, E., et al. (1992). Sexual behavior patterns of customers of male street prostitutes. *Archives of Sexual Behavior, 21.,* pp. 347.

Moscarello, R. (1990). Psychological management of victims of sexual assault. *Canadian Journal of Psychiatry, 35,* 25–30.

Moser, C., & Levitt, E. E. (1987). An exploratory-descriptive study of a sadomasochistically oriented sample. *Journal of Sex Research, 23,* 322–337.

Mosher, D. L. (1988). Pornography defined: Sexual involvement theory, narrative context, and goodness-of-fit. *Journal of Psychology and Human Sexuality, 1,* 67–85.

Mosher, W. D., & Bachrach, C. A. (1987). First premarital contraceptive use. *Studies in Family Planning, 18,* 83.

Mosher, D. L., & O'Grady, K. E. (1979). Homosexual threat, negative attitudes toward masturbation, sex guilt, and males' sexual and affective reactions to explicit sexual films. *Journal of Consulting and Clinical Psychology, 47,* 860–873.

Moss, M., Frank, E., & Anderson, B. (1990). The effects of marital status and partner support on rape trauma. *American Journal of Orthopsychiatry, 60,* 379–391.

Moss, A. R., et al. (1988). Seropositivity for HIV and the development of AIDS or AIDS-related condition: Three-year-follow-up of the San Francisco General Hospital cohort. *British Medical Journal, 296,* 745–750.

Muehlenhard, C. L., & Falcon, P. L. (1990). Men's heterosocial skill and attitudes toward women as predictors of verbal sexual coercion and forceful rape. *Sex Roles, 23,* 241–259.

Muehlenhard, C. L., & Cook, S. W. (1988). Men's self-reports of unwanted sexual activity. *The Journal of Sex Research, 24,* 58–72.

Muehlenhard, C. L., & Linton, M. A. (1987). Date rape and sexual aggression in dating situations: Incidence and risk factors. *Journal of Counseling Psychology, 34,* 186–196.

Mueller, D. P., & Cooper, P. W. (1986). Children of single-parent families: How they fare as young adults. *Family Relations, 35,* 169–176.

Mueser, K. T., et al. (1984). You're only as pretty as you feel: Facial expression as a determinant of physical attractiveness. *Journal of Personality and Social Psychology, 46,* 469–478.

Munroe, R. H., Shimmin, H. S., & Munroe, R. L. (1984). Gender role understanding and sex role preference in four cultures. *Developmental Psychology, 20,* 673–682.

Murphy, Y., & Murphy, R. F. (1974). *Women of the forest.* New York: Columbia University Press.

Murray, A. D., et al. (1981). Effects of epidural anesthesia on newborns and their mothers. *Child Development, 52,* 71–82.

Murray, J. B. (1988). Psychopharmacological therapy of deviant sexual behavior. *Journal of General Psychology, 115,* 101–110.

Murray, J. L. (1979). False pregnancy. *Medical Aspects of Human Sexuality, 13(3),* 133–134.

Murray, T. E. (1985). The language of singles bars. *American Speech, 60,* 17–30.

Murstein, B. (1974). *Love, sex, and marriage through the ages.* New York: Springer.

Murstein, B. I. (1988). A taxonomy of love. In R. J. Sternberg & M. L. Barnes (Eds.), *The psychology of love.* (pp. 13–37). New Haven: Yale University Press.

Murstein, B. I. (1972). Interview behavior, projective techniques, and questionnaires in the clinical assessment of marital choice. *Journal of Personality Assessment, 36,* 462–467.

Murstein, B. I. (1986). *Paths to marriage.* Beverly Hills, CA: Sage.

Murstein, B. I., & Christy, P. (1976). Physical attractiveness and marital adjustment in middle-aged couples. *Journal of Personality and Social Psychology, 34,* 537–542.

Murstein, B., Merighi, J. R., & Vyse, S. A. (1991). Love styles in the United States and France: A cross-cultural comparison. *Journal of Social and Clinical Psychology, 10,* pp. 37-46.

Muster, N. J., (1992). Treating the adolescent victim-turned-offender. *Adolescence, 27,* 441-450.

Myer, M. H. (1985, Spring). A new look at mothers of incest victims. *Journal of Social Work and Human Sexuality, 3,* 47–58.

Myers, A. M., & Gonda, G. (1982). Utility of the masculinity-femininity construct: Comparison of traditional and androgyny approaches. *Journal of Personality and Social Psychology, 43,* 514–523.

Myers, D. G. (1987). *Social psychology* (2nd ed.). New York: McGraw-Hill.

Myers, L., & Leggitt, H. (1975). A positive view of adultery. In L. Gross (Ed.), *Sexual issues in marriage.* Englewood Cliffs, NJ: Spectrum Books.

Myers, M. B., Templer, D. I., & Brown, R. (1984). Coping ability of women who become victims of rape. *Journal of Consulting and Clinical Psychology, 52,* 73–78.

Myers, M. F. (1989). Men sexually assaulted as adults and sexually abused as boys. *Archives of Sexual Behavior, 18,* 203–215.

Nadeau, R., et al. (1993) Knowledge and beliefs regarding STDs and condoms among students. *Canadian Journal of Public Health, 84,* 181-185.

Nadler, R. D. (1976). Sexual behavior of captive lowland gorillas. *Archives of Sexual Behavior, 5,* 487–502.

Nadler, R. D. (1990). Homosexual behavior in nonhuman primates. In D. P. McWhirter, S. A. Sanders, & J. M. Reinisch (Eds.) *Homosexuality/heterosexuality: Concepts of sexual orientation* (pp. 138–170). New York: Oxford University Press.

Naeye, R. L. (1979). Coitus and associated amniotic-fluid infections. *New England Journal of Medicine, 301,* 1198–1200.

Naffziger, C. C., & Naffziger, K. (1974). Development of sex role stereotypes. *Family Coordinator, 23,* 251–258.

Nahemow, L., & Lawton, M. P. (1975). Similarity and propinquity in friendship formation. *Journal of Personality and Social Psychology, 32,* 205–213.

Nahmias, A. J., Josey, W. E., & Oleske, J. M. (1975). Epidemiology of cervical cancer. In A. S. Evans (Ed.), *Viral infections of man—epidemiological control.* New York: Plenum Press.

Nakamura, S. (1992, March 13). Cited in Advance reported on an AIDS cancer. *The New York Times,* p. A15.

Nakanishi, M. (1986). Perceptions of self-disclosure in initial interaction: A Japanese sample. *Human Communication Research, 13,* 167–190.

Namerow, P. B., & Philliber, S. G. (1982). The effectiveness of contraceptive programs for teenagers. *Journal of Adolescent Health Care, 2,* 189–198.

Nash, J. M. (1991, January 14). Tantalizing clues to a lethal legacy. *Time,* p. 55.

Nass, G. D., Libby, R. W., & Fisher, M. P. (1984). *Sexual choices: An introduction to human sexuality.* Monterey, CA: Wadsworth.

Nathan, S. G. (1986). The epidemiology of the DSM III psychosexual dysfunctions. *Journal of Sex and Marital Therapy, 912,* 267–281.

National Abortion Rights Action Fact Sheet. (1993, July). Washington, D.C.: Author.

National Academy of Sciences, Institute of Medicine. (1982). *Marijuana and health.* Washington, DC: National Academic Press.

National Research Council (1993). *Losing generations; Adolescents in high risk settings.* Washington, D.C.: National Academy Press.

National Center for Health Statistics. (1987). Births, marriages, divorces, and deaths for 1987. *Monthly Vital Statistics Report,* .

National Center for Health Statistics. (1983). *Advance report of final divorce statistics,* 1.

National Center for Health Statistics. (1985). *Health: United States 1985. Washington, DC: U.S. Department of Health and Human Services.*

Navarro, M. (1991, July 23). Women with AIDS virus: Hard choices on motherhood. *The New York Times,* pp. A1, B4.

Navarro, M. (1992, February 10). Agencies hindered in effort to widen definitions of AIDS. *The New York Times,* pp. 1, B11.

Navarro, M. (1993, February 18). New York needle exchanges called surprisingly effective. *The New York Times,* pp. A.1, B4.

Neimeyer, R. A., & Mitchell, K. A. (1988). Similarity and attraction: A longitudinal study. *Journal of Social and Personal Relationships, 5,* 131–148.

Nelson, R. (1988). Nonoperative management of impotence. *Journal of Urology, 139,* 2–5.

Nevid, J. S. (1984). Sex differences in factors of romantic attraction. *Sex Roles, 11,* 401–411.

Nevid, J. S. (1983). Exposure to homoerotic stimuli: Effects on attitudes and affects of heterosexual viewers. *The Journal of Social Psychology, 119,* 249–255.

New York Newsday (1992, December 3). The New York Newsday interview with Barbara Menendez: "An entire country's men are dying," pp. 101, 104.

Newcomb, M., & Bentler, P. (1980a). Assessment of personality and demographic aspects of cohabitation and marital success. *Journal of Personality Development, 4,* 11–24.

Newcomb, M., & Bentler, P. (1980b). Marital stability and satisfaction among cohabitators. *Journal of Personality Assessment, 44,* 147–154.

Newcomer, S. F., & Udry, J. R. (1985). Oral sex in an adolescent population. *Archives of Sexual Behavior, 14,* 41–46.

Newly found protein is sperm's key to egg. (1993, March 9). *The New York Times,* p. C5.

Newsweek (1985, March 18). The war against pornography, pp. 58–62.

Newton, N. (1979). Key psychological issues in human lactation. In L. R. Waletzky (Ed.), *Symposium on human lactation* (DHEW Publication No. HSA 79–5107). Rockville, MD: Department of Health, Education, and Welfare.

Nias, D. K. B. (1979). Marital choice: Matching or complementation? In M. Cook & G. Wilson (Eds.), *Love and attraction.* New York: Pergamon Press.

Nichols, M. (1990). Lesbian relationships: Implications for the study of sexuality and gender. In D. P. McWhirter, S. A. Sanders, & J. M. Reinisch (Eds.), *Homosexuality/heterosexuality: Concepts of sexual orientation* (pp. 350–364). New York: Oxford.

Nichols, M. (1990). Women and acquired immunodeficiency syndrome: Issues for prevention. In B. Voeller, J. Reinisch, & M. Gottlieb (Eds.), *AIDS and sex—an integrated biomedical and behavioral approach.* New York: Oxford University Press.

Nichols, P. L. (1977). *Minimal brain dysfunction: Associations with perinatal complications.* Paper presented to the meeting of the Society for Research in Child Development, New Orleans.

Nieberg, P., Marks, J. S., McLaren, N. M., & Remongton, P. L. (1985). The fetal tobacco syndrome. *Journal of the American Medical Association, 253,* 2998–2999.

Nock, S. L. (1982). Enduring effect of marital disruption and subsequent living arrangements. *Journal of Family Issues, 3,* 25–40.

Noller, P. (1987). Nonverbal communication in marriage. In D. Perlman & S. Duck (Eds.), *Intimate relationshps: Development, dynamics, and deterioration.* Newbury Park, CA: Sage.

Norman, C. (1986). Politics and science clash on African AIDS. *Science, 230,* 1140–1141.

Norman, J., & Harris, M. (1981). *The private life of the American teenager.* New York: Rawson Wade.

Norris, A. E., & Ford, K. (1991). AIDS risk behaviors of minority youth living in Detroit. *American Journal of Preventive Medicine, 7,* 416-421.

Norris, J., & Feldman-Summers, S. (1981). Factors related to the psychological impacts of rape on the victim. *Journal of Abnormal Psychology, 90,* 562–567.

Norton, A. J. (1983). Family life cycle: 1980. *Journal of Marriage and the Family, 45,* 267–275.

Norton, A. J., & Moorman, J. E. (1987). Current trends in marriage and divorce among American women. *Journal of Marriage and the Family, 49,* 3–14.

Notarius, C. I., & Johnson, J. S. (1982). Emotional expression in husbands and wives. *Journal of Marriage and the Family, 44,* 483–489.

Notzer, N., et al. (1984). Effect of religiosity on sex attitudes, experience, and contraception among university students. *Journal of Marriage and the Family, 10,* 57–62.

Notzon, F. C., Placek, P. J., & Taffel, S. M. (1987). Comparison of national Cesarean section rates. *New England Journal of Medicine, 316,* 386–389.

Novello, A. C. (1991). Women and HIV infection. *Journal of the American Medical Association, 265,* 1805.

Novello, A. C., et al. (1993). Condom use for prevention of sexual tranmission of HIV infection. *Journal of the American Medical Association, 269,* 2640.

Nowak, R. (1993, July). In Concorde's wake: Is the AIDS clinical-trials program flawed? *The Journal of NIH Research,* pp. 37-39.

Nuta, V. R. (1986). Emotional aspects of child-support enforcement. *Family Relations, 35,* 177–182.

Nutter, D. E., & Condron, M. K. (1985). Sexual fantasy and activity patterns of males with inhibited sexual desire and males with erectile dysfunction vs. normal controls. *Journal of Sex and Marital Therapy, 11,* 91–98.

Nutter, D. E., & Condron, M. K. (1983). Sexual fantasy and activity patterns of females with inhibited sexual drives vs. normal controls. *Journal of Sex and Marital Therapy, 9,* 276–282.

Nye, F. I. (1980). Family minitheories as special instances of choice and exchange theory. *Journal of Marriage and the Family, 42,* 479–489.

O'Carroll, R., & Bancroft, J. (1984). Testosterone therapy for low sexual interest and erectile dysfunction in men: A controlled study. *British Journal of Psychiatry, 145,* 146–151.

O'Connell, M. (1991, December 4). Cited in Pear, R. Larger number of new mothers are unmarried. *The New York Times,* p. A20.

Ochs, R. (1993b, December 7). Prostate cancer jolt: 16% increase attributed to wider screening. *New York Newsday,* p. 7.

Ochs, R. (1994, January 11). Cervical cancer comeback. *New York Newsday,* pp. 55, 57.

Ochs, R. (1993a, December 7). Breast cancer risk: What the numbers mean. *New York Newsday,* pp. 72-75.

O'Connor, J. C., & Koch, E. I. (1989). *His eminence and hizzoner.* New York: Morrow.

O'Donohue, W., Letourneau, E., & Geer, J. H. (1993). Premature ejaculation. In W. O'Donohue & J. H. Geer (Eds.), *Handbook of sexual dysfunctions: Assessment and treatment.* (pp. 303-333). Boston: Allyn & Bacon.

O'Gorman, E. C., & Bownes, I. T. (1990). Factors influencing behavioural change in response to AIDS educational programmes—the role of cognitive distortions. *Medical Science Research, 18,* 263–264.

O'Grady, K. E. (1982). Sex, physical attractiveness, and perceived risk for mental illness. *Journal of Personality and Social Psychology, 43,* 1064–1071.

O'Hara, M. W., et al. (1991). Prospective study of postpartum blues: Biological and psychosocial factors. *Archives of General Psychiatry, 48,* 801-806.

O'Hara, M. W., Neunaber, D. J., & Zekoski, E. M. (1984). Prospective study of postpartum depression: Prevalence, course, and predictive factors. *Journal of Abnormal Psychology, 93,* 158–171.

O'Hara, M. W., Zekoski, E. M., Philipps, L. H., & Wright, E. J. (1990). Controlled prospective study of postpartum mood disorders: Comparison of childbearing and nonchildbearing women. *Journal of Abnormal Psychology, 99,* 3-15.

O'Neill, N. (1978). *The marriage premise.* New York: Evans.

O'Neill, N., & O'Neill, G. (1972). *Open marriage.* New York: Evans.

Okami, P., & Goldberg, A. (1992). Personality correlates of pedophilia: Are they reliable indicators? *Journal of Sex Research, 29,* 297-328.

Oldenburg, R., & Brissett, D. (1980, April). The essential hangout. *Psychology Today,* pp. 81–84.

Olds, J., & Milner, P. (1954). Positive reinforcement produced by electrical stimulation of the septal area and other regions of the rat brain. *Journal of Comparative and Physiological Psychology, 47,* 419–427.

Olds, J. (1956). Pleasure centers in the brain. *Scientific American, 193,* 105–116.

Olson, P. E. (1990). The sexual abuse of boys: A study of the long-term psychological effects. In M. Hunter (Ed.), *The sexually abused male: Prevalence, impact, and treatment. (Vol. 1)* (pp. 137–152). Lexington, MA: Lexington Books.

Oriel, D. (1990). Genital human papillomavirus infection. In K. K. Holmes, P. Mardh, P. F. Sparling, & P. J. Wiesner (Eds.), *Sexually transmitted diseases.* (2nd ed.) (pp. 433-442). New York: McGraw-Hill.

Oro, A., & Dixon, S. (1987). Perinatal cocaine and methamphetamine exposure: Maternal and neonatal correlates. *Journal of Pediatrics, 111,* 571–578.

Orr, M. (1982). Sex education and contraceptive education in U.S. public high school. *Family Planning Perspectives, 14,* 304–313.

Osborne, N. G., & Adelson, M. D. (1990). Herpes simplex and human papillomavirus genital infections: Controversy over obstetric management. *Clinical Obstetrics and Gynecology, 33,* 801–811.

Oskamp, S., & Mindick, B. (1981). Personality and attitudinal barriers to contraception. In D. Byrne & W. A. Fisher (Eds.), *Adolescents, sex, and contraception.* New York: McGraw-Hill.

Osterhout, M. B., Formichella, A., & McIntyre, S. (1991). *Tell it like it is: Straight talk about sex.* (Preprint ed.). New York: Avon.

Ostrow, D. G., et al. (1989). Disclosure of HIV antibody status: Behavioral and mental health characteristics. *AIDS Education and Prevention, 1,* 1–11.

Ostrow, D. G., & Coates, T. J. (1987). Psychological counseling for LTLV-III antibody testing. In D. G. Ostrow (Ed.), *Biobehavioral control of AIDS* (pp. 124–134). New York: Irvington.

Oswalt, R., & Matsen, K. (1993). Sex, AIDS, and the sue of condoms : A survey of compliance in college students. *Psychological Reports, 72,,* 764-766.

Overholser, J. C., & Beck, S. (1986). Multimethod assessment of rapists, child molesters, and three control groups on behavioral and psychological measures. *Journal of Consulting and Clinical Psychology, 54,* 682–687.

Padesky, C. (1988). Attaining and maintaining positive lesbian self-identity: A cognitive therapy approach. *Women and Therapy, 8,* 145–156.

Padgett, V. R., Brislin-Slotz, J. A., & Neal, J. A. (1989). Pornography, erotica, and attitudes toward women: The effects of repeated exposure. *Journal of Sex Research, 26,* 479–491.

Padgett, V. R., & Brislin-Slotz, J. A. (1987). *Pornography, erotica and negative attitudes towards women: The effects of repeated exposure.* Unpublished manuscript, Marshall University, Huntington, WV.

Padian, N. S., Shiboski, S. C., & Jewell, N. P. (1991). Female-to-male transmission of human immunodeficiency virus. *Journal of the American Medical Association, 266,* 1664–1667.

Padilla, E. R., & O'Grady, K. E. (1987). Sexuality among Mexican Americans: A case of sexual stereotyping. *Journal of Personality and Social Psychology, 52,* 5–10.

Paige, K. E. (1978, July). The declining taboo against menstrual sex. *Psychology Today,* pp. 50–51.

Paige, K. E. (1977). Sexual pollution: Reproductive sex taboos in American society. *Journal of Social Issues, 33,* 144.

Paige, K. E. (1973, September). Women learn to sing the menstrual blues. *Psychology Today,* p. 41.

Paige, K. E. (1971). Effects of oral contraceptives on affective fluctuations associated with the menstrual cycle. *Psychosomatic Medicine, 33,* 515–537.

Painter, K. (1987, October 27). Poll challenges Hite's figures on fidelity. *USA Today,* p. D1.

Palenicek, J., et al. (1993). Comparison of clinical symptoms of human immunodeficiency virus disease between intravenous drug users and homosexual men. *Archives of Internal Medicine, 153,* 1806-1812.

Palmore, E. (1981). *Social patterns in normal aging: Findings from the Duke Longitudinal Study.* Durham, NC: Duke University Press.

Palson, C., & Palson, R. (1972). Swinging in wedlock. *Society, 9(4),* 28–37.

Papini, D., et al. (1988). An evaluation of adolescent patterns of sexual self-disclosure to parents and friends. *Journal of Adolescent Research, 3,* 387–401.

Park, B., & Flink, C. (1989). A social relations analysis of agreement in liking judgments. *Journal of Personality and Social Psychology, 56,* 506–518.

Parker, N. (1964). Homosexuality in twins: A report on three discordant pairs. *British Journal of Psychiatry, 110,* 489–495.

Parker, H., & Parker, S. (1986). Father-daughter sexual abuse: An emerging perspective. *American Journal of Orthopsychiatry, 56,* 531–549.

Parlee, M. B. (1982, September). New findings: Menstrual cycles and behavior. *Ms.,* 126–128.

Parmentler, M., et al. (1992). Expression of members of the putative olfactory receptor gene family in mammalian germ cells. *Nature, 355,* 453-455.

Parra, W. et al. (1990). Patients' counseling and behavior modification. In K. K. Holmes, P. Mardh, P. F. Sparling, & P. J. Wiesner (Eds.), *Sexually transmitted diseases.* (2nd ed.) (pp. 1057-1068). New York: McGraw-Hill.

Parsons, N. K., Richards, H. C., & Kanter, G. D. (1990). Validation of a scale to measure reasoning about abortion. *Journal of Counseling Psychology, 37,* 107–112.

Parsons, E. (1991, November 18). Women become top U.S. AIDS risk group. *The New York Times,* p. A14.

Patterson, C. J. (1992). Children of lesbian and gay parents. *Child Development, 63,* 1025-1042.

Patterson, G. (1982). *Coercive family process.* Eugene, OR: Castalia.

Pattison, E. M. (1974). Confusing concepts about the concept of homosexuality. *Psychiatry, 47,* 340–349.

Patton, D., & Waring, E. M. (1985). Sex and marital intimacy. *Journal of Sex and Marital Therapy, 11,* 176–184.

Paul, J. (1984). The bisexual identity: An idea without social recognition. *Journal of Homosexuality, 9,* 45–63.

Pauly, B., & Edgerton, M. (1986). The gender-identity movement. *Archives of Sexual Behavior, 15,* 315–329.

Pauly, I. B. (1974). Female transsexualism: Part 1. *Archives of Sexual Behavior, 3,* 487–508.

Pear, R. (1991, December 4). Larger number of new mothers are unmarried. *The New York Times,* p. A20.

Pearlin, L. I., & Johnson, J. S. (1977). Marital status, life strains, and depression. *American Sociological Review, 42,* 704–715.

Pearson, C. A. (1992, February 1). Cited in Leary, W. E. U.S. panel backs approval of first condom for women. *The New York Times,* p. 7.

Peat, Marwick & Partners. (1984, October 22). *Working papers on pornography and prostitution, report #6. A national population study of prostitution and pornography.* Ottawa, CA: Department of Justice.

Pelletier, L. A., & Herold, E. S. (1988). The relationship of age, sex guilt, and sexual experience with female sexual fantasies. *Journal of Sex Research, 24,* 250–256.

Penk, W. E., & Robinowitz, R. (1981). We agree: A rejoinder from Penk and Robinowitz to Sutker and Allain. *Journal of Abnormal Psychology, 90,* 177–178.

Penn, F. (1993, October 21). Cancer confusion: The risks and realities of human papilloma virus. *Manhattan Spirit,* pp. 14-15.

Peplau, L. A. & Cochran, S. D. (1990). A relationship perspective on homosexuality. In D.P. McWhirter, S.A. Sanders, & J.M. Reinisch (Eds.), *Homosexuality/heterosexuality: Concepts of sexual orientation* (pp. 321–349). New York: Oxford University Press.

Peplau, L. A., & Cochran, S. D. (1980, September). *Sex differences in values concerning love relationships.* Paper presented at the annual meeting of the American Psychological Association, Montreal, Canada.

Peplau, L., & Gordon, S. L. (1985). Women and men in love: Sex differences in close heterosexual relationships. In V. O'Leary, et al. (Eds.), *Women, gender, and social psychology.* Hillsdale, NJ: Erlbaum.

Perduta-Fulginiti, P. S. (1992). Sexual functioning of women with complete spinal cord injury: Nursing implications. Special Issue: Nursing roles and perspectives. *Sexuality and Disability, 10,*103-118.

Perilstein, R. D., Lipper, S., & Friedman, L. J. (1991). Three cases of paraphilias responsive to fluoxetine treatment. *Journal of Clinical Psychiatry, 52,* 169-170.

Perlez, J. (1992, April 12). Education effort fights AIDS in Zimbabwe. *The New York Times,* A.18.

Perlez, J. (1991, March 2). Ugandan wife confronts a custom to avoid AIDS. *The New York Times*, p. A2.

Perlman, J. D., & Abramson, P. R. (1982). Sexual satisfaction among married and cohabiting individuals. *Journal of Consulting and Clinical Psychology, 50*, 458–460.

Perlman, et al. (1993). To the editor. *Journal of the American Medical Association, 270*, 706-707. (Letter).

Perlmutter, L. H., Engel, T., & Sager, C. J. (1982). The incest taboo: Loosened sexual boundaries in remarried families. *Journal of Sex and Marital Therapy, 8*, 83–96.

Perry, D. G., & Bussey, K. (1979). The social learning theory of sex differences: Imitation is alive and well. *Journal of Personality and Social Psychology, 37*, 1699–1712.

Perry, J. D., & Whipple, B. (1981). Pelvic muscle strength of female ejaculation: Evidence in support of a new theory of orgasm. *Journal of Sex Research, 17*, 22–39.

Perry, S. W., et al. (In press). Psychological responses to HIV serological testing. *AIDS*.

Persky, H., et al. (1982). The relation of plasma androgen levels to sexual behaviors and attitudes of women. *Psychosomatic Medicine, 44*, 305–309.

Persky, H. (1974). Reproductive hormones, moods and the menstrual cycle. In R. C. Friedman et al. (Eds.), *Sex differences in behavior.* (pp. 455-466). New York: Wiley.

Person, E. S., et al. (1989). Gender differences in sexual behaviors and fantasies in a college population. *Journal of Sex and Marital Therapy, 15*, 187–198.

Peschel, E. R., & Peschel, R. E. (1987). Medical insights into the castrati in opera. *American Scientist, 75*, 578–583.

Peterman, D. J., Ridley, C. A., & Anderson, S. M. (1974). A comparison of cohabiting and noncohabiting college students. *Journal of Marriage and the Family, 36*, 344–354.

Peterman, T., Cates, W., & Curran, J. (1988). The challenge of human immunodeficiency virus (HIV) and acquired immunodeficiency syndrome (AIDS) in women and children. *Fertility and Sterility, 49*, 571–581.

Peters, S. D., Wyatt, G. E., & Finkelhor, D. (1986). Prevalence. In D. Finkelhor, et al. (Eds.), *A sourcebook on child sexual abuse* (pp. 15–59). Beverly Hills, CA: Sage.

Petersen, A. C. (1983). Menarche: Meaning of measures and measuring meaning. In S. Golub (Ed.), *Menarche*. Lexington, MA: Lexington Books.

Petersen, J. R., Kretchmer, A., Nellis, B., Lever, J., & Hertz, R. (1983, March). The *Playboy* reader's sex survey, part 2. *Playboy*, p. 90.

Petersen, W. (1975). *Population* (3rd ed.). New York: Macmillan.

Peterson, J. L., & Marin, G. (1988). Issues in the prevention of AIDS among Black and Hispanic men. *American Psychologist, 43*, 871–877.

Peterson, K., & Curran, J. P. (1976). Trait attribution as a function of hair length and correlates of subjects' preferences for hair style. *Journal of Psychology, 93*, 331–339.

Petit, E. J., & Bloom, B. L. (1984). Whose decision was it? The effects of initiator status on adjustment to marital disruption. *Journal of Marriage and the Family, 46*, 587–595.

Petitti, D., & Reingold, A. (1988). Tampon characteristics and menstrual toxic shock syndrome. *Journal of the American Medical Association, 259*, 686–687.

Pfeiffer, E., Verwoerdt, A., & Davis, G. (1972). Sexual behavior in middle life. *American Journal of Psychiatry, 128*, 1262–1267.

Pfeiffer, E., Verwoerdt, A., & Wang, H. S. (1974). Sexual behavior in middle life. In E. Palmore (Ed.), *Normal aging II*. Durham, NC: Duke University Press.

Pfeiffer, N. (1992). Long-term survival and HIV disease: Are there really any secrets? *AIDS Patient Care, 6*, 134-139.

Phillips, D., Fischer, S. C., Groves, G. A., & Singh, R. (1976). Alternative behavioral approaches to the treatment of homosexuality. *Archives of Sexual Behavior, 5*, 223–228.

Pillard, R. C. (1990). The Kinsey Scale: Is it familial? In D. P. McWhirter, S. A. Sanders, & J. M. Reinisch (Eds.) *Homosexuality/heterosexuality: Concepts of sexual orientation* (pp. 88–100). New York: Oxford University Press.

Pillard, R. C., & Weinrich, J. D. (1986). Evidence of familial nature of male homosexuality. *Archives of Sexual Behavior, 43*, 808–812.

Pillard, R. C. et al. (1982). A family study of sexual orientation. *Archives of Sexual Behavior, 11*, 511–520.

Pinching, A. J., & Jeffries, D. J. (1985). AIDS and HTLV-III/LAV infection: Consequences for obstetrics and perinatal medicine. *British Journal of Obstetrics and Gynecology, 92*, 1211–1217.

Pines, A., & Aronson, E. (1983). Antecedents, correlates, and consequences of sexual jealousy. *Journal of Personality, 51*, 108–109.

Pingree, S., et al. (1976). A scale for sexism. *Journal of Communication, 24 (4)*, 193–200.

Pinkerton, S. D., & Abramson, P. R. (1992). Is risky sex rational? *Journal of Sex Research, 29*, 561-568.

Pinney, E. M., Gerrard, M., & Denney, N. W. (1987). The Pinney Sexual Satisfaction Inventory. *Journal of Sex Research, 23*, 233–251.

Pinto, R. P., & Hollandsworth, J. G., Jr. (1984). A measure of possessiveness in intimate relationships. *Journal of Social and Clinical Psychology, 2*, 273–279.

Plan for wider use of Norplant by girls dividing Baltimore. (1993, February 11). *The New York Times*, p. B16.

Platt, O. S., et al. (1991). Pain in sickle cell disease—rates and risk factors. *The New England Journal of Medicine, 325*, 11–16.

Platt, R., Rice, P., & McCormack, W. (1983). Risk of acquiring gonorrhea and prevalence of abnormal adrenal findings among women recently exposed to gonorrhea. *Journal of the American Medical Association, 250*, 3205–3209.

Platz-Christensen, J., et al. (1989). Detection of bacterial vaginosis in Papanicolaou smears. *American Journal of Obstetrics and Gynecology, 160*, 132–133.

Pleck, J. H., Sonenstein, F. L., & Ku, L, (1993). Changes in adolescent males'; use of and attitudes toward condoms, 1988-1991. *Family Planning Perspectives, 25*, 106-110.

Plichta, S. B., et al. (1992). Partner-specific condom use among adolescent women clients of a family planning clinic. *Journal of Adolescent Health, 13*, 506-511.

Pliner, A. J., & Yates, S. (1992). Psychological and legal issues in minors' rights to abortion. *Journal of Social Issues, 48*, 203-216.

Podolsky, D. (1991, April 15). Charting premenstrual woes. *U.S. News & World Report*, pp. 68–69.

Poling, A., Redmon, W. K., & Burnette, M. M. (1990). Stigmatization of AIDS patients by college students in lower division psychology classes. *Journal of College Students Development, 31*, 64-70.

Polit-O'Hara, D., & Kahn, J. (1985). Communication and adolescent contraceptive practices in adolescent couples. *Adolescence, 20*, 33–43.

Pomeroy, W. B. (1966). Normal vs. abnormal sex. *Sexology, 32*, 436–439.

Pope, K. S., Keith-Spiegel, P., & Tabachnick, B. G. (1986). Sexual attraction to clients: The human therapist and the (sometimes) inhuman training system. *American Psychologist, 41*, 147–158.

Porter, F. S., Blick, L. C., & Sgroi, S. M. (1982). Treatment of the sexually abused child. In S. M. Sgroi (Ed.), *Handbook of clinical intervention in child sexual abuse*. Lexington, MA: Lexington Books.

Porter, N., Geis, F.L., Cooper, E., & Newman, E. (1985). Androgyny and leadership in mixed-sex groups. *Journal of Personality and Social Psychology*, p49, 808-823.

Porter, J. B., et al. (1982). Oral contraceptives and nonfatal vascular disease—recent experience. *Obstetrics and Gynecology, 59*, 299–302.

Porter, J. B., et al. (1985). Oral contraceptives and nonfatal vascular disease. *Obstetrics and Gynecology, 66*, 1–4.

Powell, E. (1991). *Talking back to sexual pressure*. Minneapolis: CompCare Publishers.

Powell, L., & Faherty, S. L. (1990). Treating sexually abused latency age girls: A 20 session treatment plan utilizing group process and the creative arts therapies. *Arts in Psychotherapy, 17*, 35–47.

Power, T. G., & Parke, R. D. (1982). Play as a context for early learning: Lab and home analyses. In L. M. Laosa & I. E. Sigel (Eds.), *The family as a learning environment*. New York: Plenum Press.

Power, T. G. (1985). Mother- and father-infant play: A developmental analysis. *Child Development, 56*, 1514–1524.

Powledge, T. M. (1981). Unnatural selection. In H. B. Holmes, B. B. Hoskins, & M. Gross (Eds.), *The custom-made child? Women-centered perspectives*. Clifton, NJ: Humana Press.

Pratt, C., & Schmall, V. (1989). College students' attitudes toward elderly sexual behavior: Implications for family life education. *Family Relations, 38*, 137–141.

Prentky, R. A., & Knight, R. A. (1991). Identifying critical dimensions for discriminating among rapists. *Journal of Consulting and Clinical Psychology, 59*, 643–661.

Press, A., et al. (1985, March 18). The war against pornography. *Newsweek*, pp. 58–66.

Press, A., et al. (1986, July 14). A government in the bedroom. *Newsweek*, pp. 36–38.

Preti, G., Cutler, W. B., et al. (1986). Human axillary secretions influence women's menstrual cycles: The role of donor extract of females. *Hormones and Behavior, 20*, 474–482.

Price, J. H. (1981, March). Update: Toxic shock syndrome. *The Journal of School Health, 51*, 143–145.

Price, V. A. (1989). Characteristics and needs of Boston street youth: One agency's response [Special Issue: Runaway, homeless, and shut-out children and youth in Canada, Europe, and the United States]. *Children and Youth Services Review, 11,* 75–90.

Price-Bonham, S., & Balswick, J. O. (1980). The noninstitutions: Divorce, desertion, and remarriage. *Journal of Marriage and the Family, 42,* 959–972.

Prince, V., & Bentler, P. (1972). Survey of 504 cases of transvestism. *Psychological Reports, 31,* 903–916.

Proctor, F., Wagner, N., & Butler, J. (1974). The differentiation of male and female orgasm: An experimental study. In N. Wagner (Ed.), *Perspectives on human sexuality.* New York: Behavioral Publications.

Prus, R., & Irini, S. (1980). Hookers, rounders, and desk clerks. Toronto, CA: Gage.

Pryde, N. A. (1989). Sex therapy in context. *Sexual and Marital Therapy, 4,* 215–227.

Pryor, J. B., et al. (1989). The instrumental and symbolic functions of attitudes toward persons with AIDS. *Journal of Applied Social Psychology, 19,* 377-404. Publicity about Magic Johnson may have led some to reduce their risky behavior, request HIV testing. (1993). *Family Planning Perspectives, 25,* pp. 192-193.

Purifoy, F. E., Grodsky, A., & Giambra, L. M. (1992). The relationship of sexual daydreaming to sexual activity, sexual drive, and sexual attitudes for women across the life-span. *Archives of Sexual Behavior, 21,* 369-375.

Purtillo, D. F., & Sullivan, J. L. (1979). Immunological basis for superior survival of females. *American Journal of Diseases of Children, 133,* 1251–1253.

Quackenbush, R. L. (1989). A comparison of androgynous, masculine sex-typed, and undifferentiated males on dimensions of attitudes toward rape. *Journal of Research in Personality, 23,* 318–342.

Quadagno, D., et al. (1991). Women at risk for human immunodeficiency virus. *Journal of Psychology and Human Sexuality, 4,* 97-110.

Quam, J. K., & Whitford, G. S. (1992). Adaptation and age-related expectations of older gay and lesbian adults. *Gerontologist, 32,* 367-374.

Quevillon, R. P. (1993). Dyspareunia. In W. O'Donohue & J. H. Geer (Eds.), *Handbook of sexual dysfunctions: Assessment and treatment.* (pp. 367-380). Boston: Allyn & Bacon.

Quinn, T. C., et al. (1990). The association of syphilis with risk of human immunodeficiency virus infection in patients attending sexually transmitted disease clinics. *Archives of Internal Medicine, 150,* 1297–1302.

Quinn, T. C. (1990). Unique aspects of human immunodeficiency virus and related viruses in developing countries. In K. K. Holmes, et al. (Eds.), *Sexually transmitted diseases* (2nd ed.) (pp. 355–369). New York: McGraw-Hill, Inc.

Quinsey, V. L., Chaplin, T. C., & Upfold, D. (1984). Sexual arousal to nonsexual violence and sadomasochistic themes among rapists and non-sex-offenders. *Journal of Consulting and Clinical Psychology, 52,* 651–657.

Rachman, S. (1966). Sexual fetishism: An experimental analogue. *Psychological Record, 16,* 293–296.

Radin, M. (1987). Market-inalienability. *Harvard Law Review, 100,* 1849, 1921–1936.

Radlove, S. (1983). Sexual response and gender roles. In E. R. Allgeier & N. B. McCormick (Eds.), *Changing boundaries: Gender roles and sexual behavior.* Palo Alto, CA: Mayfield.

Raffalli, M. (1992, November 11). PMS is a worldwide pheonomenon. *The New York Times,* p. C14.

Rajfer, J., et al. (1992). Nitric oxide as a mediator of relaxation of the corpus cavernosum in response to nonadrenergic, noncholinergic neurotransmission. *The New England Journal of Medicine, 326,* 90–94.

Raley, P. E. (1976). *Making love: How to be your own sex therapist.* New York: The Dial Press.

Ramirez, A. (1990, August 12). The success of sweet smell. *The New York Times,* p. 10F.

Ramsay, J., Latham, J. D., & Lindquist, C. U. (1978, August). *Long term same-sex relationships: Correlates of adjustment.* Paper presented at the annual meeting of the American Psychological Association, Toronto, Canada.

Rand, K. H., et al. (1990). Daily stress and recurrence of genital herpes simplex. *Archives of Internal Medicine, 150,* 1889–1893.

Rando, R. F. (1988). Human papillomavirus: Implications for clinical medicine. *Annals of Internal Medicine, 108,* 628–630.

Randolph, E. (1989, November 15). Female media workers from 38 nations discuss career-home conflicts. *Washington Post.*

Rao, K., DiClemente, R. J., & Ponton, L. E. (1992). Child sexual abuse of Asians compared with other populations. *Journal of the American Academy of Child and Adolescent Psychiatry, 31,* 880-886.

Rasmussen, P. K., & Kuhn, L. H. (1976). The new masseuse: Play for pay. In C. A. B. Warren (Ed.), *Sexuality: Encounters, identities, and relationships.* Beverly Hills, CA: Sage Publications.

Rate of teen-age pregnancy increases again. (1993, October 7). *The New York Times,* p. B14.

Rates of Caesarean delivery—United States, 1991. (1993). *Morbidity and Mortality Weekly Report, 42,* 285-289.

Rathus, S. A. (1988). *Understanding child development.* New York: Holt, Rinehart & Winston.

Rathus, S. A. (1978). Treatment of recalcitrant ejaculatory incompetence. *Behavior Therapy, 9,* 962.

Rathus, S. A. (1990). *Psychology* (4th ed.). Fort Worth, TX: Holt, Rinehart, and Winston.

Rathus, S. A., & Fichner-Rathus, L. (1991). *Making the most of college.* Englewood Cliffs, NJ: Prentice-Hall.

Rathus, S. A., & Nevid, J. S. (1992). *Adjustment and growth: The challenges of life* (5th ed.). Fort Worth, TX: Harcourt Brace Jovanovich.

Rathus, S. A., & Nevid, J. S. (1977). *Behavior therapy.* Garden City, NY: Doubleday.

Rathus, S. A. (1993). *Psychology* (5th ed.). Fort Worth, TX: Harcourt Brace Jovanovich.

Rathus, S. A., & Nevid, J. S. (1991). *Abnormal psychology.* Englewood Cliffs, NJ: Prentice-Hall, Inc.

Ratican, K. L. (1992). Sexual abuse survivors: Identifying symptoms and special treatment considerations. *Journal of Counseling and Development, 71,* 33-38.

Rawson, P. (1973). *Primitive erotic art.* London: Weidenfeld & Nicolson.

Raychaba, B. (1989). Canadian youth in care: Leaving care to be on our own with no direction from home [Special Issue: Runaway, homeless, and shut-out children and youth in Canada, Europe, and the United States]. *Children and Youth Services Review, 11,* 61–73.

Realmuto, G. M., Jensen, J. B., & Wescoe, S. (1990). Specificity and sensitivity of sexually anatomically correct dolls in substantiating abuse: A pilot study. 36th Annual Meeting of the American Academy of Child and Adolescent Psychiatry. *Journal of the American Academy of Child and Adolescent Psychiatry, 29,* 743–746.

Redfield, R. R., et al. (1991). A Phase I evaluation of the safety and immunogenicity of vaccination with recombinant gp160 in patients with early human immunodeficiency virus infection. *New England Journal of Medicine, 24,* 1677–1684.

Reichart, C. A., et al. (1990). Evaluation of Abbott Testpack Chlamydia for detection of chlamydia trachomatis in patients attending sexually transmitted diseases clinics. *Sexually Transmitted Diseases, 17,* 147–151.

Reid, R. L. (1991). Premenstrual syndrome. *The New England Journal of Medicine, 324,* 1208–1210.

Reid, S. T. (1987). *Criminal justice.* St. Paul, MN: West.

Rein, M. F., & Muller, M. (1990). *Trichomonas vaginalis* and trichomoniasis. In K. K. Holmes, P. Mardh, P. F. Sparling, & P. J. Wiesner (Eds.), *Sexually transmitted diseases.* (2nd ed.) (pp. 481-492). New York: McGraw-Hill.

Reingold, A. L., et al. (1982). Toxic shock syndrome surveillance in the United States, 1980 to 1981. *Annals of Internal Medicine, 96,* 875–880.

Reinisch, J. M., et al. (1992). High-risk sexual behavior among heterosexual undergraduates in a midwestern university. *Family Planning Perspectives, 24,* 116-121.

Reinisch, J. M. (1990). *The Kinsey Institute new report on sex: What you must know to be sexually literate.* New York: St. Martin's Press.

Reinisch, J. M., Sanders, S. A., & Ziemba-Davis, M. (1988). The study of sexual behavior in relation to the transmission of human immunodeficiency virus: Caveats and recommendations. *American Psychologist, 43,* 921–927.

Reiss, B. F. (1980). Psychological tests in homosexuality. In J. Marmor (Ed.), *Homosexual behavior* (pp. 296–311). New York: Basic Books.

Reiss, B. F. (1988, Spring/Summer). The long-lived person and sexuality. *Dynamic Psychotherapy, 6,* 79–86.

Reiss, B. F., Safer, J., & Yotive, W. (1974). Psychological test data on female homosexuality: A review of the literature. *Journal of Homosexuality, 1,* 71–85.

Reiss, I. L. (1980). *Family systems in America.* New York: Holt, Rinehart & Winston.

Reiss, I. L. (1981). Some observations on ideology and sexuality in America. *Journal of Marriage and the Family, 43,* 271–283.

Remafedi, G. (1990). Study group report on the impact of television portrayals of gender roles on youth. *Journal of Adolescent Health Care, 11(1),* 59–61.

Renshaw, D. (1987). Management of impotence: Psychological considerations. *Clinical Therapy, 9,* 142.

Renzetti, C. M., & Curran, D. J. (1989). *Women, men, and society: The sociology of gender.* Boston: Allyn and Bacon.

Research panel concludes AIDS has small impact on most of U.S. (February 5, 1993). *New York Times,* p. A11.

Resick, P. A., Jordan, C. G., Girelli, S. A., Hutter, C. K., & Marhoefer-Dvorak, S. (1988). A comparative outcome study of behavioral group therapy for sexual assault victims. *Behavior Therapy, 19,* 385–401.

Resick, P. A., & Schnicke, M. K. (1990). Treating symptoms in adult victims of sexual assault. *Journal of Interpersonal Violence, 5,* 488–506.

Reuters. (1991, July 10). Clean needles and AIDS. *The New York Times,* p. C11.

Rhoads, J. M., & Borjes, E. P. (1981). The incidence of exhibitionism in Guatemala and the United States. *British Journal of Psychiatry, 135,* 242–245.

Rhodes, F., N. H., et al. (1990). Risk behaviors and perceptions of AIDS among street injection drug users. *Journal of Drug Education, 20,* 271-288.

Rice, M. E., Harris, G. T., & Quinsey, V. L. (1990). A follow-up of rapists assessed in a maximum-security psychiatric facility. *Journal of Interpersonal Violence, 5,* 435–448.

Rice, M. E., Quinsey, V. L., & Harris, G. T. (1991). Sexual recidivism among child molesters released from a maximum security psychiatric institution. *Journal of Consulting and Clinical Psychology, 59,* 381–386.

Richardson, D. (1988). *Women and AIDS.* New York: Routledge, Chapman & Hall, Inc.

Richardson, L. (1985). *The new other woman: Contemporary single women in affairs with married men.* New York: The Free Press.

Riche, M. (1988, November 23–26). Postmarital society. *American Demographics, 60.*

Richgels, P. B. (1992). Hypoactive sexual desire in heterosexual women: A feminist analysis. Special Issue: Finding voice: Writing by new authors. *Women and Therapy, 12,* 123-135.

Richmond, D., & Hartman, T. P. (1982). Sex appeal in advertising. *Journal of Advertising Research, 22 (5),* 53–61.

Ricker, A. L. (1980, November). Sex for sale in Las Vegas. *Cosmopolitan,* pp. 280–315.

Rickert, V. I., et al. (1989). Adolescents and AIDS: Females' attitudes and behaviors toward condom purchase and use. *Journal of Adolescent Health Care, 10,* 313–316.

Riding, A. (1992, January 11). Paris and prostitutes: Withering love. *The New York Times,* p. 4.

Riding, A. (1990, July 29). Abortion politics are said to hinder use of French pill. *The New York Times,* pp. A1, 15.

Rieber, I., & Sigusch, V. (1979). Guest editorial: Psychosurgery on sex offenders & sexual "deviants" in West Germany. *Archives of Sexual Behavior, 8,* 523–528.

Riesman, P. (1977). *Freedom in Fulani social life: An introspective ethnography.* Chicago: University of Chicago Press.

Riggio, R. E., & Woll, S. B. (1984). The role of nonverbal cues and physical attractiveness in the selection of dating partners. *Journal of Social and Personal Relationships, 1,* 347–357.

Rindfuss, R. R. (1991, December 4). Cited in Pear, R. Larger number of new mothers are unmarried. *The New York Times,* p. A20.

Risman, B. J., et al. (1981). Living together in college: Implications for courtship. *Journal of Marriage and the Family, 43,* 77–83.

Roberto, L. G. (1983). Issues in diagnosis and treatment of transsexualism. *Archives of Sexual Behavior, 12,* 445–473.

Roberts, W. L. (1980). Significant elements in the relationship of long-married couples. *International Journal of Aging and Human Development, 10,* 265–271.

Robertson, J. A. (1988). Procreative liberty and the state's burden of proof in regulating noncoital reproduction [Special Issue: Forum on surrogate motherhood: Politics and privacy]. *Law, Medicine and Health Care, 16(1–2)* 18–26.

Robins, M. B., & Jensen, G. G. (1978). Multiple orgasm in males. *Journal of Sex Research, 13,* 21–26.

Robinson, B. W., & Mishkin, M. (1966). Ejaculation evoked by stimulation of the preoptic area in monkeys. *Physiology and Behavior, 1,* 269.

Robinson, D., & Rock, J. (1967). Intrascrotal hyperthermia induced by scrotal insulation: Effect on spermatogenesis. *Obstetrics and Gynecology, 29,* 217–223.

Robinson, M. H., & Robinson, B. (1979). By dawn's early light: Matutinal mating in a neotropical mantid. *Science, 205,* 825–826.

Rodin, J. (1976). Menstruation, reattribution, and competence. *Journal of Personality and Social Psychology, 33,* 345.

Roehl, J. E., & Gray, D. (1984). The crisis of rape: A guide to counseling victims of rape. *Crisis Intervention, 13,* 67–77.

Roehrich, L., & Kinder, B. N. (1991). Alcohol expectancies and male sexuality: Review and implications for sex therapy. *Journal of Sex & Marital Therapy, 17,* 45-54.

Rogan, H. (1984, October 30). Executive women find it difficult to balance demands of job, home. *The Wall Street Journal,* pp. 35, 55.

Rogers, A. S., et al. (1993). Investigation of potential HIV transmission to the patients of an HIV-infected surgeon. *Journal of the American Medical Association, 269,* 1795-1801.

Rogers, C. R. (1972). *Becoming partners: Marriage and its alternatives.* New York: Delacorte Press.

Rogers, M. F. (1985). AIDS in children: A review of the clinical, epidemiological and public health aspects. *Pediatric Infectious Disease, 4,* 230–236.

Rokach, A. (1990). Content analysis of sexual fantasies of males and females. *Journal of Psychology, 124,* 427–436.

Roland, B., Zelkart, P., & Dubes, R. (1989). MMPI correlates of college women who reported experiencing child/adult sexual contact with father, stepfather, or with other persons. *Psychological Reports, 64,* 1159–1162.

Rolfs, R. T., Goldberg, M., & Sharrar, R. G. (1990) Risk factors for syphilis: Cocaine use and prostitution. *American Journal of Public Health, 80,* 853–857.

Rolfs, R. T., & Nakashima, A. K. (1990). Epidemiology of primary and secondary syphilis in the United States: 1981 through 1989. *Journal of the American Medical Association, 264,* 1432–1437.

Rollins, J. (1986). Single men and women: Differences and similarities. *Family Perspective, 20,* 117–124.

Romenesko, K., & Miller, E. M. (1989). The second step in double jeopardy: Appropriating the labor of female street hustlers. *Crime and Delinquency, 35,* 109–135.

Ronald, A. R., & Albritton, W. (1990). Chancroid and *Haemophilus ducreyi.* In K. K. Holmes, P. Mardh, P. F. Sparling, & P. J. Wiesner (Eds.), *Sexually transmitted diseases.* (2nd ed.) (pp. 263-272). New York: McGraw-Hill.

Rooney, J., et al. (1986). Acquisition of genital herpes from an asymptomatic sexual partner. *New England Journal of Medicine, 314,* 1561–1564.

Roper Organization. (1985). *The Virginia Slims American Women's Poll.* New York: Roper Organization.

Rosen, I. (1967). *Pathology and treatment of sexual deviations.* London: Oxford University Press.

Rosen, R. C., & Beck, J. G. (1988). *Patterns of sexual arousal.* New York: Guilford.

Rosenberg, M. J., & Gollub, E. L. (1992). Commentary: Methods women can use that may prevent sexually transmitted disease, including HIV.

Rosenberg, M. J., Hill, H. A., & Friel, P. J. (1991, October). *Spermicides and condoms in prevention of sexually transmitted diseases: A meta-analysis.* Paper presented at the meeting of the International Society for Sexually Transmitted Disease Research, Banff, Canada.

Rosenfeld, A. (1992, May). The medical story of the century. *Longevity,* pp. 42-53.

Rosenkrantz, L., & Satran, P. R. (1988). *Beyond Jennifer & Jason: An enlightened guide to naming your baby.* New York: St. Martin's Press.

Rosenstock, I. M., & Kirscht, J. P. (1979). Why people seek health care. In G. C. Stone, F. Cohen, & N. E. Adler (Eds.), *Health psychology: A handbook.* San Francisco: Jossey-Bass.

Rosenthal, A. M. (1992, December 29). Female genital torture. *The New York Times,* p. A15.

Rosenthal, A. M. (1993, November 12). Female genital torture. *The New York Times,* p. A33.

Rosenthal, D. A., Hall, C., & Moore, S. M. (1992). AIDS, adolescents, and sexual risk taking: A test of the Health Belief Model. *Australian Psychologist, 27,* 166-171.

Rosenthal, E. (1991, July 10). Technique for early prenatal test comes under question in studies. *The New York Times,* p. C11.

Rosenthal, E. (1990, August 28). The spread of AIDS: A mystery unravels. *The New York Times,* pp. C1, C2.

Rosenthal, E. (1992, July 22). Her image of his ideal, in a faulty mirror. *The New York Times,* p. C12.

Rosman, J. P., & Resnick, P. J. (1989). Sexual attraction to corpses: A psychiatric review of necrophilia. *Bulletin of the American Academy of Psychiatry and the Law, 17,* 153–163.

Ross, E. A. (1914). *The old world in the new: The significance of past and present immigration to the American people.* New York: Century.

Ross, M., & Need, J. (1989). Effects of adequacy of gender reassignment surgery on psychological adjustment: A follow-up of fourteen male-to-female patients. *Archives of Sexual Behavior, 18,* 145–153.

Rossman, I. (1978). Sexuality and aging: An internist's perspective. In R. L. Solnick (Ed.), *Sexuality and aging.* (pp. 66–77). Los Angeles: University of Southern California, Ethel Percy Andus Gerontology Center.

Roth, S., Dye, E., & Lebowitz, L., (1988). Group therapy for sexual-assault victims. *Psychotherapy, 25,* 82–93.

Roth, S., Wayland, K., & Woolsey, M. (1989). Victimization history and victim-assailant relationship as factors in recovery from sexual assault. *Journal of Traumatic Stress, 3,* 169–180. *Roth v. United States.* 354 U.S. 4/6 (1957)

Rothenberg, K. H. (1988). Baby M, the surrogacy contract, and the health care professional: Unanswered questions [Special Issue: Forum on surrogate motherhood: Politics and privacy]. *Law, Medicine and Health Care, 16,* 113–120.

Rotheram-Borus, M. J., & Koopman, C. (1991). HIV and adolescents. Special Issue: Preventing the spread of the human immunodeficiency virus. *Journal of Primary Prevention, 12,* 65-82.

Rotheram-Borus, M. J., & Koopman, (1991). Sexual risk behaviors, AIDS knowledge, and beliefs about AIDS among runaways. *American Journal of Public Health, 81,* 209-211.

Rotheram-Borus, M. et al. (1992). Lifetime sexual behaviors among predominantly minority male runaways and gay/bisexual adolescents in New York City. *AIDS Education and Prevention, Fall Suppl.,* 34-42.

Rousso, H. (1982). Special considerations in counseling clients with cerebral palsy. *Sexuality & Disability, 5,* 78–88.

Rowan, E. L., Rowan, J. B., & Langelier, P. (1990). Women who molest children. *Bulletin of the American Academy of Psychiatry and the Law, 18,* 79–83.

Rowell, R. M., & Kusterer, H. (1991). Care of HIV infected Native American substance abusers. Special Issue: Counseling chemically dependent people with HIV illness. *Journal of Chemical Dependency Treatment, 4,* 91-103.

Rozin, P., & Fallon, A. (1988). Body image, attitudes to weight, and misperceptions of figure preferences of the opposite sex: A comparison of men and women in two generations. *Journal of Abnormal Psychology, 97,*342–345.

Rubenstein, H. (1992, February 23). Personal communication.

Rubin, A., & Adams, J. (1986). Outcomes of sexually open marriages. *Journal of Sex Research, 22,* 311–319.

Rubin, Z. (1982). Children without friends. In L. A. Peplau & D. Perlman (Eds.), *Loneliness: A sourcebook of current theory, research, and therapy.* New York: Wiley.

Rubin, Z. (1973). *Liking and loving.* New York: Holt, Rinehart & Winston.

Rubin, Z. (1970). Measurement of romantic love. *Journal of Personality and Social Psychology, 16,* 265–273.

Rubin, Z., Hill, C. T., Peplau, L. A., & Dunkel-Schetter, C. (1980). Self-disclosure in dating couples: Sex roles and the ethic of openness. *Journal of Marriage and the Family, 42,* 305–318.

Rubinow, D. R., & Roy-Byrne, P. (1984). Premenstrual syndromes: Overview from a methodologic perspective. *American Journal of Psychiatry, 141,* 163–172.

Rubinsky, H., et al. (1987). Early-phase physiological response pattern to psychosexual stimuli: Comparison of male and female patterns. *Archives of Sexual Behavior, 16,* 45–55.

Ruble, D. N., & Brooks-Gunn, J. (1979). Menstrual myths. *Medical Aspects of Human Sexuality, 13(6),* 110–121.

Ruble, D. N., & Ruble, T. L. (1982). Sex stereotypes. In A. G. Miller (Ed.), *In the eye of the beholder: Contemporary issues in stereotyping.* New York: Praeger.

Ruder, A. M., et al. (1990). AIDS education: Evaluation of school and worksitebased presentations. *New York State Journal of Medicine, 90,* 129–133.

Ruefli, T., Yu, O., & Barton, J. (1992). Sexual risk taking in smaller cities: The case of Buffalo, New York. *Journal of Sex Research, 29,* 95-108.

Ruff, G. A., & St. Lawrence, J. S. (1985). Premature ejaculation: Past research, progress, future directions. *Clinical Psychology Review, 5,* 627–639.

Ruppenthal, G. C., et al. (1976). A 10-year perspective of motherless-mother monkey behavior. *Journal of Abnormal Psychology, 85,* 341–349.

Rusbult, C. E. (1983). A longitudinal test of the investment model. *Journal of Personality and Social Psychology, 45,* 101–117.

Rusbult, C. E., & Zembrodt, I. M. (1983). Responses to dissatisfaction in romantic involvements: A multi-dimensional scaling analysis. *Journal of Experimental Social Psychology, 19,* 274–293.

Rusbult, C. E., Johnson, D. J., & Morrow, G. D. (1986). Impact of couple patterns of problem solving on distress and nondistress in dating relationships. *Journal of Personality and Social Psychology, 50,* 744–753.

Russell, D. (1986). *The secret trauma: Incest in the lives of girls and women.* New York: Basic Books.

Russell, D. (1982). The measurement of loneliness. In L. A. Peplau and D. Perlman (Eds.), *Loneliness: A sourcebook of current theory, research and therapy.* New York: Wiley.

Russell, D. E. H. (1983). The incidence and prevalence of intrafamilial and extrafamilial sexual abuse of children. *Child Abuse and Neglect, 7,* 133–146.

Russell, D. E. H. (1984). *Sexual exploitation.* Beverly Hills, CA: Sage.

Russell, D. E. H. (1982a). *The secret trauma.* New York: Basic Books.

Russell, D. E. H. (1982b). *Rape in marriage.* New York: Macmillan.

Russell, D. H. (1976, September). Obscene phone calls by women. *Medical Aspects of Human Sexuality, 10,* 11.

Russell, D., Peplau, L. A., & Cutrona, C. E. (1980). The revised UCLA Loneliness Scale: Concurrent and discriminant validity evidence. *Journal of Personality and Social Psychology, 39,* 472–480.

Russo, N. F., Horn, J. D., & Schwartz, R. (1992). U.S. abortion in context: Selected characteristics and motivations of women seeking abortions. *Journal of Social Issues, 48,* 183-202.

Rust, J., Golombok, S., & Collier, J. (1988). Marital problems and sexual dysfunction: How are they related? *British Journal of Psychiatry, 152,* 629–631. *Rust v. Sullivan* 111 S. Ct. 1759 (1991).

Rutter, M. (1980). *Changing youth in a changing society: Patterns of development and disorder.* Cambridge, MA: Harvard University Press.

Saadawi, N. (1980). *The hidden face of Eve: Women in the Arab world* (S. Hetata, Trans. and Ed.). Boston: Beacon Press.

Sachs, B. P., et al. (1983). Caesarean section. *Journal of the American Medical Association, 250,* 2157–2159.

Sack, A. R., Keller, J. F., & Hinkle, D. E. (1984). Premarital sexual intercourse: A test of the effects of peer group, religiosity, and sexual guilt. *Journal of Sex Research, 20,* 168–185.

Sack, W. H., & Mason, R. (1980). Child abuse and conviction of sexual crimes: A preliminary finding. *Law and Human Behavior, 4,* 211–215.

Sadalla, E. K., Kenrick, D. T., & Vershure, B. (1987). Dominance and heterosexual attraction. *Journal of Personality and Social Psychology, 52,* 730–738.

Sadava, S. W., & Matejcic, C. (1987). Generalized and specific loneliness in early marriage. *Canadian Journal of Behavioural Science, 19,* 56–66.

Sadker, M., & Sadker, D. (1985). Sexism in the schoolroom of the 1980s. *Psychology Today, 19,* pp. 54–57.

Sagan, C. (1977). *The dragons of Eden: Speculations on the evolution of human intelligence.* New York: Random House.

Sagan, C., & Dryan, A. (1990, April 22). The question of abortion: A search for answers. *Parade Magazine,* pp. 4–8.

Sagarin, E. (1973). Power to the peephole. *Sexual Behavior, 3,* 2–7.

Sagarin, E. (1977). Rape of one's wife. *Medical Aspects of Human Sexuality, 12,* 153.

Sagarin. E. (1977). Incest: Problems of definition and frequency. *Journal of Sex Research, 13,* 126–135.

Saghir, M. T., & Robins, E. (1973). *Male and female sexuality.* Baltimore: Williams and Wilkins.

Sakheim, D. K. (1984). *Waking assessment of erectile potential: The validation of a laboratory procedure to aid in the differential diagnosis of psychogenic and organic impotence.* Unpublished doctoral dissertation, State University of New York at Albany.

Sakheim, D. K. (1987). Distinguishing between organogenic and psychogenic erectile dysfunction. *Behaviour Research and Therapy 25,* 379–390.

Sales, E., Baum, M., & Shore, B. (1984). Victim readjustment following assault. *Journal of Social Issues, 40,* 117–136.

Saluter, A. F. (1992). Marital status and living arrangements: March 1992. *Current Population Reports,* Series P20-468.

Samuels, M., & Samuels, N. (1986). *The well pregnancy book.* New York: Simon & Schuster, Inc.

Sanday, P. R. (1981). The socio-cultural context of rape: A cross-cultural study. *Journal of Social Issues, 37,* 5–27.

Sanders, S. A., Reinisch, J. M., & McWhirter, D. P. (1990). Homosexuality/heterosexuality: An overview. In D. P. McWhirter, S. A. Sanders, & J. M. Reinisch (Eds.) *Homosexuality/Heterosexuality: Concepts of sexual orientation* (pp. xix–xxvii). New York: Oxford University Press.

Sandross, R. (1988, December). Sexual harassment in the Fortune 500. *Working Woman*, p. 69.

Sanger, D. E. (1992, January 27). History scholar in Japan exposes a brutal chapter. *The New York Times*, p. A4.

Sanger, M. (1938). *Margaret Sanger: An autobiography.* New York: Norton.

Santee, R. T., & Maslach, C. (1982). To agree or not to agree: Personal dissent amid social pressure to conform. *Journal of Personality and Social Psychology, 42,* 690–700.

Santiago, J. M., et al. (1985). Long-term psychological effects of rape in 35 rape victims. *American Journal of Psychiatry, 142,* 1338–1340.

Santrock, J. W. (1970). Paternal absence, sex typing, and identification. *Developmental Psychology, 2,* 264–272.

Sargent, T. O. (1988). Fetishism. *Journal of Social Work and Human Sexuality, 7,* 27–42.

Sarrel, P., & Masters, W. (1982). Sexual molestation of men by women. *Archives of Sexual Behavior, 11,* 117–131.

Sauer, M. V., Paulson, R. J., & Lobo, R. A. (1990). A preliminary report on oocyte donation extending reproductive potential to women over 40. *The New England Journal of Medicine, 323,* 1157–1160.

Sauzier, M. (1989). Disclosure of child sexual abuse: For better or for worse. *Psychiatric Clinics of North America, 12,* 455–469.

Savitz, L., & Rosen, L. (1988). The sexuality of prostitutes: Sexual enjoyment reported by "streetwalkers." *Journal of Sex Research, 24,* 200–208.

Saywitz, K. J., et al. (1991). Children's memories of a physical examination involving genital implications for reports of child sexual abuse. *Journal of Consulting and Clinical Psychology, 59,* 682–691.

Schachter, J. (1990). Biology of *Chlamydia trachomatis.* In K. K. Holmes, P. Mardh, P. F. Sparling, & P. J. Wiesner (Eds.), *Sexually transmitted diseases.* (2nd ed.) (pp. 161-180). New York: McGraw-Hill.

Schachter, J. (1989). Why we need a program for the control of *Chlamydia trachomatis. New England Journal of Medicine, 320,* 802–804.

Schafer, R. (1974). Problems in Freud's psychology of women. *Journal of the American Psychoanalytic Association, 22,* 459–485.

Schafer, R. B., & Keith, P. M. (1990). Matching by weight in married couples: A life cycle perspective. *Journal of Social Psychology, 130,* 657–664.

Schaller, G. B. (1972). *The Serengeti lion: A study of predator-prey relations.* Chicago: University of Chicago Press.

Scharlach, A. S. (1986). From supermoms to superdaughters. *Marriage and Divorce Today, 11(3),* 1–2.

Schecter, M., et al. (1984, June 9). Changes in sexual behavior and fear of AIDS. *Lancet,* 1293.

Schenker, J. G., & Evron, S. (1983). New concepts in the surgical management of tubal pregnancy and the consequent postoperative results. *Fertility and Sterility, 40,* 709–723.

Schiavi, R. C. (1990). Chronic alcoholism and male sexual dysfunction. *Journal of Sex and Marital Therapy, 16,*23–33.

Schiavi, R. C., et al. (1990). Healthy aging and male sexual function. *American Journal of Psychiatry, 147,* 766–771.

Schiedel, D. G., & Marcia, J. E. (1985). Ego identity, intimacy, sex-role orientation, and gender. *Developmental Psychology, 21,* 149–160.

Schinke, S., Holden, G., & Moncher, M. (1989). Preventing HIV infection among Black and Hispanic adolescents. *Journal of Social Work and Human Sexuality, 8,* 63-72.

Schmalz, J. (1993, November 28). Whatever happened to AIDS? *The New York Times Magazine,* pp. 56-61, 81, 85-86.

Schmalz, J. (1992, August 14). Toll so far: a dreadful gain for women. *The New York Times,* pp. L.1, L.10.

Schmidt, G. (1975). Male-female differences in sexual arousal and behavior during and after exposure to sexually explicit stimuli. *Archives of Sexual Behavior, 4,* 353–364.

Schmidt, G., & Schorsch, E. (1981). Psychosurgery of sexually deviant patients: Review and analysis of new empirical findings. *Archives of Sexual Behavior, 10,* 301–323.

Schmidt, G., Sigusch, V., & Schafer, S. (1973). Responses to reading erotic stories: Male-female differences. *Archives of Sexual Behavior, 2,* 181–199.

Schmidt, G., & Sigusch, V. (1970). Sex differences in response to psychosexual stimulation by films and slides. *Journal of Sex Research, 6,* 268–283.

Schmidt, G., & Sigusch, V. (1973). Women's sexual arousal. In J. Zubin & J. Money (Eds.), *Contemporary sexual behavior: Critical issues in the 1970's.* Baltimore: Johns Hopkins University Press.

Schmidt, K. W., et al. (1992). Sexual behaviour related to psychosocial factors in a population of Danish homosexual and bisexual men. *Social Science and Medicine, 34,* 1119-1127.

Schneemann, C. (1991). The obscene body/politic. *Art Journal, 50(4),* 28–35.

Schnell, D. J., O'Reilly, K. R. (1991). Patterns of sexual behavior change among homosexual/bisexual men—selected U.S. sites, 1987-1990. *Mortality and Morbidity Weekly Report, 40, 46,* 792-794.

Schoendorf, K. C., & Kiely, J. L. (1992). Relationship of sudden infant death syndrome to maternal during and after pregnancy. *Pediatrics, 90,* 905-908.

Schreiner-Engel, P., et al. (1989). Low sexual desire in women: The role of reproductive hormones. *Hormones and Behavior, 23,* 221–234.

Schreiner-Engle, P., & Schiavi, R. (1986). Lifetime psychopathology in individuals with low sexual desire. *Journal of Nervous and Mental Disease, 174,* 646–651.

Schultz, N. R., Jr., & Moore, D. W. (1984). Loneliness: Correlates, attributions, and coping among older adults. *Personality and Social Psychology Bulletin, 10,* 67–77.

Schultz, T. (1980, June). Does marriage give today's women what they really want? *Ladies' Home Journal,* pp. 89–91, 146–155.

Schur, E. M. (1984). *Labeling women deviant.* New York: Random House.

Schwartz, I. M. (1993). Affective reactions of American and Swedish women to their first premarital coitus: A cross-cultural comparison. *Journal of Sex Research, 30,* 18-26.

Schwartz, L. L. (1989). Surrogate motherhood: III. The end of a saga? *American Journal of Family Therapy, 17,* 67–72.

Schwartz, M. F., & Masters, W. H. (1984). The Masters and Johnson treatment program for dissatisfied homosexual men. *American Journal of Psychiatry, 141,* 173–181.

Schwartz, M., & Masters, W. H. (1988). Inhibited sexual desire: The Masters and Johnson Institute treatment model. In S. Leiblum and R. Rosen (Eds.), *Sexual desire disorders.* New York: Guilford Press.

Scott, J., & Schuman, H. (1980). Attitude strength and social action in the abortion dispute. *American Sociological Review, 53,* 785–793.

Scott, J. E., & Cuvelier, S. J. (1993). Violence and sexual violence in pornography: Is it really increasing. *Archives of Sexual Behavior, 22* 357-371.

Scott, W. J., & Morgan, C. S. (1983). An analysis of factors affecting traditional family expectations and perceptions of ideal fertility. *Sex Roles, 9,* 901–914.

Scully, D., & Marolla, J. (1985). Riding the bull at Gilley's: Convicted rapists describe the rewards of rape. *Social Problems, 32,* 251–263.

Sears, A. E. (1989). The legal case for restricting pornography. In D. Zillmann & J. Bryant (Eds.), *Pornography: Research advances and policy considerations.* Hillsdale, NJ: Lawrence Erlbaum Associates.

Sears, R. R., Maccoby, E. E., & Levin, H. (1957). *Patterns of child rearing.* New York: Harper & Row.

Seattle-King County Department of Public Health (1991). The AIDS Prevention Project. *The Seattle Star: A report to the communiity on what we're learning from the "Be A Star Study."* Seattle: Author.

Seftel, A. D., Oates, R. D., & Krane, R. J. (1991). Disturbed sexual function in patients with spinal cord disease. *Neurologic Clinics, 9,* 757-778.

Segal, M. W. (1974). Alphabet and attraction: An unobtrusive measure of the effect of propinquity in the field setting. *Journal of Personality and Social Psychology, 30,* 654–657.

Segal, S. J. (1990). Mifeprisone (RU 486). *The New England Journal of Medicine, 322,* 691–693.

Segal, Z. V., & Marshall, W. L. (1985). Heterosexual social skills in a population of rapists and child molesters. *Journal of Consulting and Clinical Psychology, 53,* 55–63.

Segraves, K., Segraves, R., & Schoenberg, H. (1987). Use of sexual history to differentiate organic from psychogenic impotence. *Archives of Sexual Behavior, 16,* 125–137.

Segraves, K. B., & Segraves, R. T. (1991b). Hypoactive sexual desire disorder: Prevalence and comorbidity in 906 subjects. *Journal of Sex & Marital Therapy, 17,* 55-58.

Segraves, R. (1989, April). Presurgical psychological evaluation for penile prosthesis surgery. *Medical Aspects of Human Sexuality,* 5–53.

Segraves, R. (1988). Drugs and desire. In S. Leiblum & R. Rosen (Eds.), *Sexual desire disorders.* New York: Guilford Press.

Segraves, R. T. (1988). Sexual side-effects of psychiatric drugs. *International Journal of Psychiatry in Medicine, 18,* 243–252.

Segraves, R. T., & Segraves, K. B. (1991a). Diagnosis of female arousal disorder *Sexual and Marital Therapy, 6,*. 9-13.

Segraves, R. T., & Segraves, K. B. (1993). Medical aspects of orgasm disorders. In W. O'Donohue & J. H. Geer (Eds.), *Handbook of sexual dysfunctions: Assessment and treatment.* (pp. 225-252). Boston: Allyn & Bacon.

Seibel, M. (1988). A new era in reproductive technology. *The New England Journal of Medicine, 318,* 828-834.

Seligmann, J. (1993, July 26). Hsubands no, babies yes. *Newsweek,* p. 53.

Selik, R. M., Castro, K. G., & Pappaioanou, M. (1988). Racial/ethnic differnces in risk of AIDS. *American Journal of Public Health, 78,* 1539-1545.

Selkin, J. (1975, January). Rape. *Psychology Today,* pp. 71–72, 74–76.

Seltzer, R. (1992). The social location of those holding antihomosexual attitudes. *Sex Roles, 26.* 391-398.

Selvin, B. W. (1993, June 1). Transsexuals are coming to terms with themselves and society. *New York Newsday,* pp. 55, 58, 59.

Semans, J. (1956). Premature ejaculation: A new approach. *Southern Medical Journal, 49,* 353–358.

Seng, M. J. (1989). Child sexual abuse and adolescent prostitution: A comparative analysis. *Adolescence, 24,* 665–675.

Senn, C. Y., & Radtke, L. H. (1990). Women's evaluations of and affective reactions to mainstream violent pornography, nonviolent pornography, and erotica. *Violence and Victims, 5,* 143–155.

Severn, J., Belch, G. E., & Belch, M. A. (1990). The effects of sexual and non-sexual advertising appeals and information level on cognitive processing and communication effectiveness. *Journal of Advertising, 19,* 14–22.

Shabsigh, R., Fishman, I., & Scott, F. (1988). Evaluation of erectile impotence. *Urology, 32,* 83–90.

Shafer, M. A., et al. (1993). Evaluation of urine-based screening strategies to detect *Chlamydia trachomatis* among sexually active asymptomatic young men. *Journal of the American Medical Association, 270,* 2065-2070.

Shah, F., Zelnik, M., & Kantner, J. (1975). Unprotected intercourse among unwed teenagers. *Family Planning Perspectives, 7,* 39–44.

Shanteau, J., & Nagy, G. (1979). Probability of acceptance in dating choice. *Journal of Personality and Social Psychology, 37,* 522–533.

Shapiro, H. I. (1988). *The new birth-control book: A complete guide for women and men.* Englewood Cliffs, NJ: Prentice-Hall.

Shapiro, J. P. (1992, July 13). The teen pregnancy boom. *U.S. News & World Report,* p. 38.

Shaver, P., Hazan, C., & Bradshaw, D. (1988). Love as attachment. In R. J. Sternberg & M. L. Barnes (Eds.), *The psychology of love* (pp. 68–99). New Haven: Yale University Press.

Shaw, J. (1989). The unnecessary penile implant. *Archives of Sexual Behavior, 18,* 455–460.

Shaw, J. S. (1982). Psychological androgyny and stressful life events. *Journal of Personality and Social Psychology, 43,* 145–153.

Shaywitz, S., Cohen, D., & Shaywitz, B. (1980). Behavior and learning difficulties in children of normal intelligence born to alcoholic mothers. *The Journal of Pediatrics, 96,* 978–982.

Shenon, P. (1992, November 8). After years of denial, Asia faces scourge of AIDS. *The New York Times,* p. A1.

Sherman, M. A., & Haas, A. (1984, June). Man to man, woman to woman. *Psychology Today,* pp. 72–73.

Sherman, B. (1985, October 23). A new recognition of the realities of date rape. *The New York Times,* pp. C1, C14.

Sherman, K. J., et al. (1990). Sexually transmitted diseases and tubal pregnancy. *Sexually Transmitted Diseases, 17,* 115–121.

Sherwin, B. B., Gelfand, M. M., & Brender, W. (1985). Androgen enhances sexual motivation in females: A prospective, crossover study of sex steroid administration in the surgical menopause. *Psychosomatic Medicine, 47,* 339–351.

Sherwin, R., & Corbett, S. (1985). Campus sexual norms and dating relationships: A trend analysis. *Journal of Sex Research, 21,* 258–274.

Shettles, L. (1982, June). Predetermining children's sex. *Medical Aspects of Human Sexuality, 172.*

Shilts, R. (1988). *And the band played on: Politics, people, and the AIDS epidemic.* New York: Penguin Books.

Shipp, E. E. (1985, November 4). Teen-agers taking risks: When pregnancy is the result. *The New York Times,* p. A16.

Shorter, E. (1982). *A history of women's bodies.* New York: Basic Books.

Shortle, B., & Jewelewicz, R. (1986). Psychogenic vaginismus. *Medical Aspects of Human Sexuality, 20,* 82–87.

Shostak, A., McLouth, G., & Seng, L. (1984). *Men and abortions: Lessons, losses and love.* New York: Praeger.

Sidi, A. A., et al. (1986). Intracavernous drug-induced erections in the management of male dysfunction: Experience with 100 patients. *Journal of Urology, 135,* 704–706.

Siegal, B., & Short, J. (1974). Post-partum depression. *Marriage and Divorce, 1,* 77–83.

Siegel, K., et al. (1988). Patterns of change in sexual behavior among gay men in New York City. *Archives of Sexual Behavior, 17,* 481–497.

Siegel, J. M., et al. (1990). Reactions to sexual assault: A community study. *Journal of Interpersonal Violence, 5,* 229–246.

Siegel, J. M., et al. (1987). The prevalence of childhood sexual assault: The Los Angeles Epidemiological Catchment Area Project. *American Journal of Epidemiology, 126,* 1141–1153.

Siegelman, M. (1974). Parental background of male homosexuals and heterosexuals. *Archives of Sexual Behavior, 3,* 3–18.

Siegelman, M. (1972). Adjustments of male homosexuals and heterosexuals. *Archives of Sexual Behavior, 2,* 9–25.

Siegelman, M. (1978). Psychological adjustment of homosexual and heterosexual men: A cross-national replication. *Archives of Sexual Behavior, 7,* 1–11.

Siegelman, M. (1979). Adjustment of homosexual and heterosexual women: A cross-national replication. *Archives of Sexual Behavior, 8,* 121–126.

Signorielli, N. (1990). Children, television, and gender roles: Messages and impact. *Journal of Adolescent Health Care, 11(1),* 50–58.

Silber, S. J. (1980). *How to get pregnant.* New York: Charles Scribner's Sons.

Silber, S. J. (1991). *How to get pregnant with the new technology.* New York: Time Warner.

Silbert, M. H. (1989). The effects on juveniles of being used for pornography and prostitution. In D. Zillmann & J. Bryant (Eds.), *Pornography: Research advances and policy considerations* (pp. 215–234). Hillsdale, NJ: Lawrence Erlbaum Associates.

Silvestre, L., et al. (1990). Voluntary interruption of pregnancy with mifepristone (RU 486) and a prostaglandin analogue: A large-scale French experience. *The New England Journal of Medicine, 322,* 645–648.

Simenauer, J., & Carroll, D. (1982). *Singles: The new Americans.* New York: New American Library.

Simon, W. A., Berger, A. S., & Gagnon, J. H. (1972). Beyond anxiety and fantasy: The coital experiences of college youth. *Journal of Youth and Adolescence, 1,* 203–222.

Simonds, R. J., et al. (1992). Transmission of human immunodeficiency virus type 1 from a seronegative organ and tissue donor. *The New England Journal of Medicine, 326,* 726–732.

Simons, M. (1993, November 23). Mutilation of girls' genitals: Ethnic gulf in French court. *The New York Times,* p. A13.

Simonsen, J. N., et al. (1988). Human immunodeficiency virus infection among men with sexually transmitted diseases: Experience from a center in Africa. *The New England Journal of Medicine, 319,* 274–278.

Simpson, J. A., Campbell, B., & Berscheid, E. (1986). The association between romantic love and marriage: Kephart (1967) twice revisited. *Personality and Social Psychology Bulletin,* 363–372.

Sims, C. (1991, December 7). H.I.V. tests up 60% since the disclosure from Magic Johnson. *The New York Times,* p. A1, A28.

Sinclair, A. H., et al. (1990). A gene from the human sex-determining region encodes a protein with homology to a conserved DNA-binding motif. *Nature, 346,* 240–245.

Sinding, S. W., & Segal, S. J. (1991, December 19). Birth-rate news. *The New York Times,* p. A31.

Singer, J., & Singer, I. (1972). Types of female orgasm. *Journal of Sex Research, 8,* 255–267.

Singer, K. I. (1989). Group work with men who experienced incest in childhood. *American Journal of Orthopsychiatry, 59,* 468–472.

Singer, M., et al. (1990). Owning AIDS: Latino organizations and the AIDS epidemic. *Hispanic Journal of Behavioral Sciences, 12,* 196-211.

Singh, G. (1985). Dhat syndrome revisisted. *Indian Journal of Psychiatry, 27,* 119–122.

Sirles, E. A., & Franke, P. J. (1989). Factors influencing mother's reactions to intrafamily sexual abuse. *Child Abuse & Neglect, 13,* 131–139.

Sirles, E. A., Smith, J. A., & Kusama, H. (1989). Psychiatric status of intrafamilial child sexual abuse victims. *Journal of the American Academy of Child and Adolescent Psychiatry, 28,* 225–229.

Sivin I. (1988). International experience with Norplant and Norplant-2 contraceptives. *Studies in Family Planning, 19,* 81–94.

Slaby, R. G., & Frey, K. S. (1975). Development of gender constancy and selective attention to same-sex models. *Child Development, 46,* 849–856.

Slattery, M. L., & Kerber, R. A. (1993). A comprehensive evaluation of family history and breast cancer risk: The Utah population database. *Journal of the American Medical Association, 270,* 1563-1568.

Slonim-Nevo, V. (1992). First premarital intercourse among Mexican-American and Anglo-American adolescent women: Interpreting ethnic differences. *Journal of Adolescent Research, 7,* 332-351.

Small comfort for gay soliders. (1993, December 24). *The New York Times*, p. A 26.

Smith, E. A., & Udry, J. R. (1985). Coital and non-coital sexual behaviors of white and black adolescents. *American Journal of Public Health, 75,* 1200–1203.

Smith, L. G., & Smith, J. R. (1974). Co-marital sex: The incorporation of extramarital sex into the marriage relationship. In J. R. Smith & L. G. Smith (Eds.), *Beyond monogamy.* Baltimore: Johns Hopkins University Press.

Smith, R. E. (1979). The movement of women into the labor force. In R. E. Smith (Ed.), *The subtle revolution: Women at work.* Washington, DC: The Urban Institute.

Smith, T. F., et al. (1988). The phylogenetic history of immunodeficiency viruses. *Nature, 33,* 573–575.

Smith, T. W. (1987). The polls—a review: The use of public opinon data by the Attorney General's Commission on Pornography. *Public Opinion Quarterly, 51,* 249–257.

Smolowe, J. (1993, June 14). New, improved and ready for battle. *Time,* pp. 48-51.

Snyder, A., LoPiccolo, L., & LoPiccolo, J. (1975). Secondary orgasmic dysfunction. II. Case study. *Archives of Sexual Behavior, 4,* 239–247.

Snyder, D. (1979). Multidimensional assessment of marital satisfaction. *Journal of Marriage and the Family, 41,* 813–823.

Sobel, J. D. (1990). Vaginal infections in adult women. *Medical Clinics of North America, 74,* 1573–1602.

Solano, C. H., Batten, P. G., & Parish, E. A. (1982). Loneliness and patterns of self-disclosure. *Journal of Personality and Social Psychology, 43,* 524–531.

Solberg, D., Butler, J., & Wagner, N. N. (1974). Sexual behavior in pregnancy. In N. Wagner (Ed.), *Perspectives on human sexuality.* New York: Behavioral Publications.

Soley, L. C., & Kurzbard, G. (1986). Sex in advertising: A comparison of 1964 and 1984 magazine advertisements. *Journal of Advertising, 15,* 46–54, 64.

Solkin, C. (1990, November 23). AIDS and the hospital crisis. *New York Perspectives,* p. 13.

Sommer, B. (1983). How does menstruation affect cognitive competence and psychophysiological response. In S. Golub (Ed.), *Lifting the curse of menstruation* (pp. 53–90). New York: Haworth Press.

Sommer, B. (1972). Menstrual cycle changes and intellectual performance. *Psychosomatic Medicine, 34,* 267–269.

Sonenstein, F. L., Pleck, J. H., & Ku, L. C. (1989). Sexual activity, condom use and AIDS awareness among adolescent males. *Family Planning Perspectives, 21,* 152–157.

Sonenstein, F. L., Pleck, J. H., & Ku, L. C. (1990, May). *Patterns of sexual activity among adolescent males.* Paper presented at the Annual Meeting of the Population Association of America, Toronto, Canada.

Sorensen, R. C. (1973). *Adolescent sexuality in contemporary America.* New York: World.

Sorensen, T., & Snow, B. (1991). How children tell: The process of disclosure in child sexual abuse. *Child Welfare, 70,* 3–15.

Sorenson, S. B., et al. (1987). The prevalence of adult sexual assault: The Los Angeles Epidemiologic Catchment Area Project. *American Journal of Epidemiology, 126,* 1154–1164.

Sorrenti-Little, I., Bagley, C., and Robertson, S. (1984). An operational definition of the long-term harmfulness of sexual relations with peers and adults by young children. *Canadian Child, 9,* 46–57.

South, S. J. (1991). Sociodemographic differentials in mate selection preferences. *Journal of Marriage and the Family, 53,* 928-940.

Southerland, D. (1990, May 27). Limited "sexual revolution" seen in China: Nationwide survey shows more liberal attitudes developing in conservative society. *Washington Post.*

Spanier, G., & Furstenberg, F. (1982). Remarriage after divorce: A longitudinal analysis of well-being. *Journal of Marriage and the Family, 44,* 709–720.

Spanier, G. B. (1983). Married and unmarried cohabitation in the United States: 1980. *Journal of Marriage and the Family, 45,* 277–288.

Spanier, G. B, & Castro, R. F. (1979). Adjustment to separation and divorce: A qualitative analysis. In G. Levinger & L. C. Moles (Eds.), *Divorce and separation: Context, causes and consequences.* (pp. 211–227). New York: Basic Books.

Spark, R. F. (1991). *Male sexual health: A couple's guide.* Mount Vernon, NY: Consumer Reports Books.

Specter, M. (1991, November 9). When AIDS taps hero, his "children" feel pain. *The New York Times,* pp. A1, A32.

Specter, M. (1991, November 8). Magic's loud message for young black men. *The New York Times,* p. B12.

Spector, I. P., & Carey, M. P. (1990). Incidence and prevalence of the sexual dysfunctions: A critical review of the empirical literature. *Archives of Sexual Behavior, 19,* 389–408.

Spees, E. R. (1987). College students' sexual attitudes and behaviors, 1974–1985: A review of the literature. *Journal of College Student Personnel, 28,* 135–140.

Spence, J. T., Helmreich, R., & Stapp, J. (1975). Ratings of self and peers on sex-role attributes and their relation to self-esteem and concepts of masculinity and femininity. *Journal of Personality and Social Psychology, 32,* 29–39.

Sperber, N. D. (1989). Bite marks, oral and facial injuries: Harbingers of severe child abuse? *Pediatrician, 16,* 207–211.

Speroff, L., Blas, R., & Kase, N. (1985). *Clinical gynecologic endocrinology and infertility.* Baltimore: Williams & Wilkins.

Spezzano, C. (1981). Prenatal psychology: Pregnant with questions. *Psychology Today, 15(5),* pp. 49–57.

Spiess, W. F., Geer, J. M., & O'Donohue, W. T. (1984). Premature ejaculation: Investigation of factors in ejaculatory latency. *Journal of Abnormal Psychology, 93,* 242–245.

Spira, A., et al. (1992). AIDS and sexual behavior in France. *Nature, 360,* 407-413.

Spiro, M. E., (1965). *Children of the kibbutz.* New York: Schocken Books.

Spitz, R. (1949). Autoeroticism: Some empirical findings and hypotheses on three of its manifestations in the first year of life. *Psychoanalytic Study of the Child, 2,* 313–342.

Spitzer, P. G., & Weiner, N. J. (1989). Transmission of HIV infection from a woman to a man by oral sex. *Journal of the American Medical Association, 320,* 251.

Spitzer, R. L., et al. (1989). *DSM-III-R casebook.* Washington, DC: American Psychiatric Press.

Spock, B., & Rothenberg, M. B. (1985). *Dr. Spock's baby and child care* (40th Anniversary ed.). New York: Dutton.

Sporacino, J., et al. (1983). Self-monitoring and blood pressure. *Journal of Personality and Social Psychology, 44,* 365–375.

Sprecher, S. (1989a). The importance to males and females of physical attractiveness, earning potential, and expressiveness in initial attraction. *Sex Roles, 21,* 591–607.

Sprecher, S. (1989b). Premarital sexual standards for different categories of individuals. *Journal of Sex Research, 26,* 232–248.

Spring-Mills, E., & Hafez, E. (1980). Male accessory sexual organs. In E. Hafez (Ed.), *Human Reproduction.* New York: Harper & Row.

Stafford, R., Backman, E., & Dibona, P. (1977). The division of labor among cohabiting and married couples. *Journal of Marriage and the Family, 39,* 43–57.

Stamm, W. E., & Holmes, K. K. (1990). *Chlamydia trachomatis* infections of the adult. In K. K. Holmes, P. Mardh, P. F. Sparling, & P. J. Wiesner (Eds.), *Sexually transmitted diseases.* (2nd ed.) (pp. 181-194). New York: McGraw-Hill.

Stampfer, M. J., et al. (1988). A prospective study of past use of oral contraceptive agents and risk of cardiovascular diseases. *The New England Journal of Medicine, 319,* 1313–1317.

Stampfer, M. J., et al. (1991). Ten-year follow-up study of estrogen replacement therapy in relation to cardiovascular disease and mortality. Paper presented at the 24th annual meeting of the Society for Epidemilogic Research, Buffalo, New York, June 11-14, 1991.

Stangor, C., & Ruble, D. N. (1989). Differential influences of gender schemata and gender constancy on children's information processing and behavior. *Social Cognition, 7,* 353–372.

Stanley, L. A. (1991). Art and "perversion": Censoring images of nude children. *Art Journal, 50(4),* 20–27.

Staples, R. (1986). Black masculinity, hypersexuality, and sexual aggression. In R. Staples (Ed.), *The Black Family* (pp. 57–63). Belmont, CA: Wadsworth Publishing.

Staples, R. (1972). Research on black sexuality: Its implication for family life, education, and public policy. *The Family Coordinator, 21,* 183–188.

Stark, E. (1986, October). Young, innocent, and pregnant. *Psychology Today, 20,* pp. 28–35.

Starr, B. D., & Weiner, M. B. (1981). *The Starr-Weiner report on sex and sexuality in the mature years.* New York: Stein & Day.

Starr, B. D., & Weiner, M. B. (1982). *The Starr-Weiner report on sex and sexuality in the mature years.* New York: McGraw-Hill.

Stavros, M. K. (19??) Family systems approach to sexual dysfunction in neurologic disability. Special Issue: Sexuality and neurologic disability. *Sexuality and Disability, 9,* 69-85.

Steadman, H. J. (1979). *Beating a rap: Defendants found incompetent to stand trial.* Chicago: University of Chicago Press.

Steege, J., Stout, A., & Carson, C. (1986). Patient satisfaction in Scott and Small-Carrion penile implant recipients: A study of 52 patients. *Archives of Sexual Behavior, 15,* 393–400.

Steele, C. M., & Southwick, L. L. (1985). Alcohol and social behavior I: The psychology of drunken excess. *Journal of Personality and Social Psychology, 48,* 18–34.

Steffensmeier, D., & Steffensmeier, R. (1974). Sex differences in reactions to homosexuals: Research continuities and further developments. *Journal of Sex Research, 10,* 52–67.

Stein, Z., et al. (1975). *Famine and human development: The Dutch hunger-winter of 1944–1945.* New York: Oxford University Press.

Steinberg, J. (1993). CDC broadens AIDS definition. *The Journal of NIH Research, 5.* p. 32.

Steinbock, B. (1988). Surrogate motherhood as prenatal adoption [Special Issue: Forum on surrogate motherhood: Politics and privacy]. *Law, Medicine and Health Care, 16,* 44–50.

Stenchever, et al. (1981). Possible relationship between in utero diethylstilbestrol exposure and male fertility. *American Journal of Obstetrics and Gynecology, 140,* 186–193.

Stengle, R. (1986, July 21). Sex busters. *Time,* pp. 12–21.

Stephan, C. W., & Langlois, J. H. (1984). Baby beautiful: Adult attributions of infant competence as a function of infant attractiveness. *Child Development, 55,* 576–585.

Stephens, T. (1991a). AIDS hemophiliacs in tough court battles. *The Journal of NIH Research, 3,* 46–51.

Stephens, T. (1991b). AIDS in women reveals health-care deficiencies. *The Journal of NIH Research, 3,* 27–30.

Stephens, W. N. (1982). *The family in cross-cultural perspective.* Washington, DC: University Press of America.

Stephens, W. N. (1963). *The family in cross-cultural perspective.* New York: Holt.

Stericker, A., & LeVesconte, S. (1982). Effect of brief training on sex-related differences in visual-spatial skill. *Journal of Personality and Social Psychology, 43,* 1018–1029.

Stermac, L. E., & Segal, Z. V. (1989). Adult sexual contact with children: An examination of cognitive factors. *Behavior Therapy, 20,* 573–584.

Sternberg, R. J. (1987). Liking versus loving: A comparative evaluation of theories. *Psychological Bulletin, 102,* 331–345.

Sternberg, R. J. (1988). *The triangle of love: Intimacy, passion, commitment.* New York: Basic Books.

Sternberg, R. J., & Barnes, M. L. (1988). An introduction to the psychology of love. In R. J. Sternberg & M. L. Barnes (Eds.), *The psychology of love* (pp. 3–12). New Haven: Yale University Press.

Sternberg, R. J. (1986). A triangular theory of love. *Psychological Review, 93,* 119–135.

Sternberg, R. J., & Grajek, S. (1984). The nature of love. *Journal of Personality and Social Psychology, 47,* 312–329.

Sterngold, J. (1992, September 8). Japan confronts sudden rise in AIDS. *The New York Times,* p. L13.

Stevens, W. K. (1994, January 2). Poor lands' success in cutting birth rate upsets old theories. *The New York Times,* p. A1, A8.

Stevenson, R. W. (1991, November 8). Magic Johnson ends his career, saying he has AIDS infection. *The New York Times,* pp. A1, B12.

Stewart, F. H. (1992, February 1). Cited in Leary, W.E. U.S. panel backs approval of first condom for women. *The New York Times,* p. 7.

Stier, D. S., & Hall, J. A. (1984). Gender differences in touch: An empirical and theoretical review. *Journal of Personality and Social Psychology, 47,* 440–459.

Still no pill for Japan. (1992, March 22). *The New York Times* section 4, p. 7.

Stock, W. (1993). Inhibited female orgasm. In W. O'Donohue & J. H. Geer (Eds.), *Handbook of sexual dysfunctions: Assessment and treatment.* (pp. 253-301). Boston: Allyn & Bacon.

Stock, W. E. (1991). Feminist explanations: Male power, hostility, and sexual coercion. In E. Grauerholz & M. A. Koralewski (Eds.), *Sexual coercion: A sourcebook on its nature, causes, and prevention* (pp. 61–73). Lexington, MA: Lexington Books.

Stoler, R. (1968). *Sex and gender.* New York: Science House.

Stoller, R. J. (1977). Sexual deviations. In R. Beach (Ed.), *Human sexuality in four perspectives.* (pp. 190–214). Baltimore: Johns Hopkins University Press.

Stoller, R. J. (1969). Parental influences in male transsexualism. In R. Green & J. Money (Eds.), *Transsexualism and sex reassignment.* Baltimore: Johns Hopkins University Press.

Stoller, R. J. (1972). Etiologic factors in female transsexualism. *Archives of Sexual Behavior, 2,* 47–64.

Stoller, R. J., & Herdt, G. H. (1985). Theories of origins of male homosexuality. *Archives of General Psychiatry, 42,* 399–404.

Stone, K. M., & Whittington, W. L. (1990). Treatment of genital herpes. *Reviews of Infectious Diseases* (Suppl. 6), S633–S644.

Stone, S. (1989). Assessing oral contraceptive risks. *Medical Aspects of Human Sexuality,* 112–122.

Storms, M. (1979). Sexual orientation and self-perception. In P. Pliner et al. (Eds.), *Advances in the study of communication and affect,* (Vol. 5). New York: Plenum Press.

Storms, M. D. (1978). Sexual orientation and self-perception. In P. Pliner, et al. (Eds.), *Advances in the Study of Communication and Affect* (Vol. 5). New York: Plenum.

Storms, M. D. (1980). Theories of sexual orientation. *Journal of Personality and Social Psychology, 38,* 783–792.

Story, M. D. (1982). A comparison of university student experiences with various sexual outlets in 1974 and 1980. *Adolescence, 17,* 737–747.

Story, M. D. (1985). A comparison of university-student experience with various sexual outlets in 1974 and 1984. *Journal of Sex Education and Therapy, 11,* 35–41.

Strassberg, D. S., et al. (1990). The role of anxiety in premature ejaculation: A psychophysiological model. *Archives of Sexual Behavior, 19,* 251–257.

Strassberg, D. S., et al. (1987). The psychophysiological nature of premature ejaculation. *Archives of Sexual Behavior, 16,* 327–336.

Straus, S. E., et al. (1984). Suppression of frequently recurring genital herpes: A placebo-controlled double-blind trial of oral acyclovir." *New England Journal of Medicine, 310,* 1545–1550.

Straus, S. E. (1985). Herpes simplex virus infections: Biology, treatment, and prevention. *Annals of Internal Medicine, 103,* 404–419.

Streissguth, A. P., Barr, H. M., & Martin, D. C. (1983). Maternal alcohol use and neonatal habituation assessed with the Brazelton scale. *Child Development, 54,* 1109–1118.

Streissguth, A. P., Herman, C. S., & Smith, D. W. (1978). Intelligence, behavior, and dysmorphogenesis in the fetal alcohol syndrome: A report on 20 patients. *Journal of Pediatrics, 92(3),* 363–367.

Streissguth, A. P., et al. (1980). Teratogenic effects of alcohol in humans and laboratory animals. *Science, 209,* 353–361.

Streissguth, A. P., et al. (1984). Interuterine alcohol and nicotine exposure: Attention and reaction time in 4-year-old children. *Developmental Psychology, 20,* 533–541.

Struckman-Johnson, C. (1988). Forced sex on dates: It happens to men, too. *The Journal of Sex Research, 24,* 234–241.

Strunin, L., & Hingson, R. (1987). AIDS and adolescents: Knowledge, beliefs, attitudes and behavior. *Pediatrics, 79,* 825–828.

Stuart, F., Hammond, C., & Pett, M. (1987). Inhibited sexual desire in women. *Archives of Sexual Behavior, 16,* 91–106.

Study suggests menopause doesn't affect mental health. (1990, July 26). *The New York Times,* p. B7.

Study finds many heterosexual are ignoring serious risk of AIDS. (1992, November 13). *The New York Times,* p. A16.

Sue, D. (1979). Erotic fantasies of college students during coitus. *Journal of Sex Research, 15,* 299–305.

Sue, D., Sue, D.W., & Sue, S. (1981).*Understanding abnormal behavior.* Boston: Houghton Mifflin Co.

Sullivan, T. (1987). Juvenile prostitution: A critical perspective. *Marriage and Family Review, 12,* 113–134.

Suman, H. C. (1990). Attraction behavior of young women in relation to their perceived physical attractiveness and self-concept characteristics. *Journal of the Indian Academy of Applied Psychology, 16,* 21–25.

Suman, H. C. (1989). Attraction behaviour of young women in relation to their perceived physical attractiveness and characteristic self. *Social Science International, 5,* 42–48.

Suman, H. C., & Kureshi, A. (1988). Interpersonal attraction as a function of physical attractiveness, personality similarity-dissimilarity, and reciprocity. *Psychologia: An International Journal of Psychology in the Orient, 31,* 234–238.

Summers, R. J. (1991). Determinants of the acceptance of co-workers with AIDS. *Journal of Social Psychology, 131,* 577-578.

Sunday, S., & Lewin, M. (1985, April). *Integrating nuclear issues into the psychology curriculum.* Paper presented at the annual meeting of the Eastern Psychological Association, New York, NY.

Suomi, S. J. (1977). Peers, play, and primary prevention in primates. In *Proceedings of the Third Vermont Conference on the Primary Prevention of Psychopathology: Promoting Social Competence and Coping in Children.* Hanover, NH: University Press of New England.

Sussman, N. (1976). Sex and sexuality in history. In B. J. Sadock, H. I. Kaplan, & A. M. Freedman (Eds.), *The sexual experience* (pp. 7–70). Baltimore: Williams & Wilkins.

Sutker, P. B., & Allain, A. N. (1981). Comments on voluntarism: Reply to Penk & Robinowitz. *Journal of Abnormal Psychology, 90,* 175–176.

Sutton-Smith, B., & Rosenberg, B. G. (1970). *The sibling.* New York: Holt, Rinehart and Winston.

Swahn, M. L., et al. (1985). Pharmacokinetic and clinical studies of RU 486 for fertility regulation. In E. E. Baulieu & S. J. Segal (Eds.), *The antiprogestin RU 486 and human fertility control* (pp. 249–258). New York: Plenum Press.

Swann, W. B., Jr., et al. (1987). Cognitive-affective crossfire: When self-consistency meets self-enhancement. *Journal of Personality and Social Psychology, 52,* 881–889.

Sweet, R. (1985). Chlamydia, group B streptococcus, and herpes in pregnancy. *Birth, 12,* 17–24.

Symons, D. (1979). *The evolution of human sexuality.* New York: Oxford University Press.

Szasz, G., et al. (1987). Induction of penile erection by intracavernosal injection: A double-blind comparison of phenoxybenzamine versus papaverine-phentolamine versus saline. *Archives of Sexual Behavior, 16,* 371–378.

Szasz, G., & Carpenter, C. (1989). Clinical observations in vibratory stimulation of the penis of men with spinal cord injury. *Archives of Sexual Behavior, 18,* 461–474.

Szasz, T. (1980). *Sex by prescription.* New York: Anchor Press/Doubleday.

Taffel, S. M., & Keppel, K. G. (1986). Advice about weight gain during pregnancy and actual weight gain. *American Journal of Public Health, 76,* 13.

Takefman, J., & Brender, W. (1984). An analysis of the effectiveness of two components in the treatment of erectile dysfunction. *Archives of Sexual Behavior, 13,* 321–340.

Talese, G. (1980). *Thy neighbor's wife.* New York: Doubleday.

Talmadge, L. D., & Talmadge, W. C. (1986). Relational sexuality: An understanding of low sexual desire. *Journal of Sex and Marital Therapy, 12,* 3–21.

Tanfer, K., & Horn, M. C. (1985). Contraceptive use, pregnancy, and fertility among single American women in the '20s. *Family Planning Perspectives, 17,* 10–19.

Tanfer, K. (1987). Patterns of premarital cohabitation among never-married women in the United States. *Journal of Marriage and the Family, 40,* 483–497.

Tanfer, K., Grady, W. R., Klepinger, D. H., & Billy, J. O. G. (1993). Condom use among U.S. men, 1991. *Family Planning Perspectives, 25,* 61-66.

Tanfer, K., & Rosenbaum, E. (1986). Contraceptive perceptions and method choice among young single women in the United States. *Studies in Family Planning, 17,* 269–277.

Tannahill, R. (1980). *Sex in history.* Briarcliff Manor, NY: Stein & Day.

Tannen, D. (1990). *You just don't understand.* New York: Ballantine Books.

Tannenbaum, J. (1991). Robert Mapplethorpe: The Philadelphia story. *Art Journal, 50(4),* 71–76.

Tart, C. (1971). *On being stoned.* Palo Alto, CA: Science and Behavior Books.

Tavris, C., & Sadd, S. (1977). *The Redbook report on female sexuality.* New York: Delacorte.

Taylor, R. (1993c). Sex surveys help map AIDS risk. *The Journal of NIH Research, 5,* p. 31-32.

Taylor, R. (1993b, July). Dentist-to-patient HIV-1 transmission: More heat, no light. *The Journal of NIH Research,* p. 50.

Taylor, R. (1993a, July). Asia now second only to Africa in total HIV infections. *The Journal of NIH Research,* pp. 48-50.

Telushkin, J. (1991). *Jewish literacy.* New York: Morrow.

Temin, H. M. (1992). Origin and nature of retroviruses. In Levy, J. A. (Ed.), *The retroviridae: Vol. 1. (pp. 1-18). New York: Plenum Press.*

Tempest, R. (1993, February 18). Ancient traditions vs. the law. *The Los Angeles Times,* p. A1, A10.

Teen-agers and aids: The risk worsens. (1992, April 14). *The New York Times,* p. C3.

Terkel, S. N. (1988). *Abortion: Facing the issues.* New York: Franklin Watts.

Terman, L. (1916). *The measurement of intelligence.* Boston: Houghton Mifflin.

Tessler, A., & Drahn, H. (1966). Varicocele and testicular temperature. *Fertility and Sterility, 17,* 201–203.

Tharinger, D. (1990). Impact of child sexual abuse on developing sexuality. *Professional Psychology: Research and Practice, 21,* 331–337.

The AIDS "plot" against blacks. (1992, May 12). *The New York Times,* p. A22. (Editorial)

Thomas, S. B. (1991, November 1). Cited in Associated Press. Syphilis study seen causing blacks to distrust AIDS efforts. *The Hartford Courant,* p. A11.

Thomason, J. L., & Gelbart, S. M. (1989). Trichomonas vaginalis. *Obstetrics and Gynecology, 74,* 536–541.

Thomlison, B., et al. (1991). Characteristics of Canadian male and female child sexual abuse victims. Special Issue: Child sexual abuse. *Journal of Child and Youth Care, Fall,* 65-76.

Thompson, A. P. (1983). Extramarital sex: A review of the research literature. *Journal of Sex Research, 19,* 1–22.

Thompson, A. P. (1984). Emotional and sexual components of extramarital relations. *Journal of Marriage and the Family, 46,* 35–42.

Thompson, D. S. (1993) (Ed.). *Every woman's health: The complete guide to body and mind.* New York: Simon & Schuster.

Thompson, I. (1989). Carcinoma of the prostate. *Southern Medical Journal, 82,* 335–337.

Thompson, J. K., & Tantleff, S. (1992). Female and male ratings of upper torso: Actual, ideal, and stereotypical conceptions. *Journal of Social Behavior and Personality, 7,* 345-354.

Thompson, L. (1991, January 15). Health status of Hispanics: Nation's fastest-growing minority lacks access to medical care. *Washington Post.*

Thompson, M. E. (1991). Self-defense against sexual coercion: Theory, research, and practice. In E. Grauerholz & M. A. Koralewski (Eds.), *Sexual coercion: A sourcebook on its nature, causes, and prevention (pp. 111–121).* Lexington, MA: Lexington Books.

Thornburg, H. D., & Aras, Z. (1986). Physical characteristics of developing adolescents. *Journal of Adolescent Research, 1,* 47–78.

Thornhill, N. W., & Thornhill, R. (1987). Evolutionary theory and rules of mating and marriage pertaining to relatives. In C. Crawford, M. Smith, & D. Krebs (Eds.), *Sociobiology and psychology: Ideas, issues, and applications* (pp. 373–400). London: Lawrence Erlbaum.

Thornhill, N. W., & Thornhill, R. (1990). An evolutionary analysis of psychological pain following rape: II. The effects of stranger, friend, and family-member offenders. *Ethology and Sociobiology, 11,* 177–193.

Thornton, A., & Camburn, D. (1987). The influence of the family on premarital sexual attitudes and behavior. *Demography, 24,* 323–340.

Thornton, A., & Freedman, D. (1983, October). The changing American family. *Population Bulletin,* 1–43.

Thornton, A., & Freedman, D. (1982). Changing attitudes toward marriage and single life. *Family Planning Perspectives, 14,* 297–303.

Tiefer, L., & Melman, A. (1989). Comprehensive evaluation of erectile dysfunction and medical treatments. In S. R. Leiblum & R. C. Rosen (Eds.), *Principles and practice of sex therapy* (2nd. ed.) (pp. 207–236). New York: Guilford Press.

Tiefer, L., Pederson, G., & Melman, A. (1988). Psychosocial follow-up of penile prosthesis implant patients and partners. *Journal of Sex and Marital Therapy, 14,* 184–201.

Tierney, J. (1994, January 9). Porn, the low-flung engine of progress. *The New York Times,* Section 2, pp. 1, 18.

Tietze, C. (1979). The pill and mortality from cardiovascular disease: Another look. *Family Planning Perspectives, 11,* 80–84.

Ting,-David; Carter,-James-H. Behavioral change through empowerment: Prevention of AIDS. Human Behavior Seminar (1990, Durham, North Carolina). *Journal of the National Medical Association, 84,* 225-228.

Tobias, S. (1982). Sexist equations. *Psychology Today, 16(1),* pp. 14–17.

Toll of American AIDS orphans put at 80,000 by end of decade. (1992, December 23). *The New York Times,* p. B6.

Tollison, C. D., & Adams, H. E. (1979). *Sexual disorders: Treatment, theory, and research.* New York: Gardner Press.

Tolstedt, B., & Stokes, J. (1983). Relation of verbal, affective, and physical intimacy to marital satisfaction. *Journal of Counseling Psychology, 30,* 573–580.

Tomasson, R. (1980). *Iceland: The first new society.* Minneapolis: University of Minnesota Press.

Tomlinson, J. A. (1991). Burn it, hide it, flaunt it. *Art Journal, 50(4),* 59–64.

Toner, J. P., et al. (1991). Basal follicle-stimulating hormone level is a better predictor of in vitro fertilziation performance than age. *Fertility and Sterility, 55,* 784-791.

Toomey, K. E., & Barnes, R. C. (1990). Treatment of chlamydia trachomatis genital infection. *Reviews of Infectious Diseases* (Suppl. 6), S645–S655.

Touchette, N. (1993, July). Maternal-fetal HIV-1 transmission continues to confound. *The Journal of NIH Research,* pp. 44-47.

Touchette, N. (1991). HIV-1 link prompts circumspection of circumcision. *The Journal of NIH Research, 3,* 44–46.

Toufexis, A. (1993, February 15). The right chemistry. *Time,* pp. 49-51.

Touhey, J. C. (1974). Effects of additional women professionals on ratings of occupational prestige and desirability. *Journal of Personality and Social Psychology, 23,* 8–10.

Touhey, J. C. (1972). Comparison of two dimensions of attitude similarity on heterosexual attraction. *Journal of Personality and Social Psychology, 23,* 8–10.

Toussie-Weingarten, C., & Jacobwitz, J. (1987). Alternatives in childbearing: Choices and challenges. In L. Sherwen (Ed.), *Psychosocial dimensions of the pregnant family.* New York: Springer.

Travin, S., Cullen, K., & Protter, B. (1990). Female sex offenders: Severe victims and victimizers. *Journal of Forensic Sciences, 35,* 140–150.

Trenton State College. (1991, Spring). Sexual Assault Victim Education and Support Unit (SAVES-U) Newsletter.

Trieschmann, R. (1989). Psychosocial adjustment to spinal cord injury. In B. W. Heller, L. M. Flohr, & L. S. Zegans (Eds.), *Psychosocial interventions with physically disabled persons.* (pp. 117-136). New Brunswick, NJ: Rutgers University Press.

Trieschmann, R. (1988). *Spinal cord injuries: Psychological, social, and vocational rehabilitation.* New York: Demos Publications.

Trinkaus, J., & Chow, M. B. (1990). Misgivings about AIDS transmission: An informal look. *Psychological Reports, 66,* 230-254.

Trocki, K. F. (1992). Patterns of sexuality and risky sexuality in the general population of a California county. *Journal of Sex Research, 29,* 85-94.

Troll, L. E., Miller, S. J., & Atchley, R. C. (1979). *Families in later life.* Belmont, CA: Wadsworth.

Tross, S., & Hirsch, D. A. (1988). Psychological distress and neuropsychological complications of HIV infection and AIDS. *American Psychologist, 43,* 929–934.

Trost, J. (1975). Married and unmarried cohabitation: The case of Sweden, with some comparisons. *Journal of Marriage and the Family, 37,* 677–682.

Trotter, R. J. (1986, September). The three faces of love. *Psychology Today,* pp. 46–54.

Trovato, F. (1986). The relationship between marital dissolution and suicide: The Canadian case. *Journal of Marriage and the Family, 48,* 341–348.

Trudgill, E. (1976). *Madonnas and Magdalens: The origins and development of Victorian sexual attitudes.* New York: Holmes & Meier.

Trumbach, R. (1977). London's sodomites: Homosexual behavior and western culture in the eighteenth century. *Journal of Social History, 11,* 1–33.

Trunnell, E. P., Turner, C. W., & Keye, W. R. (1988). A comparison of the psychological and hormonal factors in women with and without premenstrual syndrome. *Journal of Abnormal Psychology, 97,* 429–436.

Trussell, J., Strickler, J., & Vaughan, B.(1993). Contraceptive efficacy of the diaphragm, the sponge, and the cervical cap. *Family Planning Perspectives, 25,* 100-105.

Trussell, J. (1988). Teenage pregnancy in the United States. *Family Planning Perspectives, 20,* 262–273.

Trussell, J., Warner, D. L., & Hatcher, R. (1992). Condom performance during vaginal intercourse: Comparison of Trojan-ENZ and Tactylon condoms. *Contraception, 45,* 11.

Tsai, M., Feldman-Summers, S., & Edgar, M. (1979). Childhood molestation variables related to differential impact of psychosexual functioning in adult women. *Journal of Abnormal Psychology, 88,* 407–417.

Turner, C. F., Miller, H. G., & Moses, L. E. (Eds.) (1989). *AIDS: Sexual behavior and intravenous drug use.* Washington, DC: National Academy Press.

Turner, L. A., et al. (1989). Self-injection of papaverine and phentolamine in the treatment of psychogenic impotence. *Journal of Sex and Marital Therapy, 15,* 163–176.

Tutty, L. M. (1992). The ability of elementary school children to learn child sexual abuse prevention concepts. *Child Abuse and Neglect, 16,* 369-384.

Two viewfinders, two views of Gay America. (1993, June 27) *The New York Times,* Section 4, p. 10.

U.S. Bureau of the Census. (1991a). *Fertility of American women.* Washington, DC: U.S. Government Printing Office.

U.S. Bureau of the Census. (1991b). Marital status and living arrangements: March 1990. *Current Population Reports,* Series P-20, No. 450. Washington, DC: U.S. Government Printing Office.

U.S. Bureau of the Census. (1991c). *Statistical abstract of the United States.* Washington, DC: U.S. Government Printing Office.

U.S. Bureau of the Census. (1990a). Marital status and living arrangements: March 1990. *Current Population Reports,* Series P-20, No. 450. Washington, DC: U.S. Government Printing Office.

U.S. Bureau of the Census. (1990b). *Statistical abstract of the United States.* Washington, DC: U.S. Government Printing Office.

U.S. Bureau of the Census. (1988). Marital status and living arrangements: March 1987. *Current Population Reports,* Series P-20, No. 423. Washington, DC: U.S. Government Printing Office.

U.S. Bureau of the Census. (1987). *Statistical abstract of the United States.* Washington, DC: U.S. Government Printing Office.

U.S. Bureau of the Census. (1985). *Marital status and living arrangements.* Current Population Reports. Washington, DC: U.S. Government Printing Office.

U. S. Department of Health and Human Services. (USDHSS). (1992). *Smoking and health in the Americas.* (DHHS Publication No. (CDC) 92-8419). Atlanta: Public Health Service, Center for Disease Control, National Center for Chronic Disease Prevention and Health Promotion. Office on Smoking and Health.

U.S. Department of Health and Human Services (USDHHS). (1991). *Strategies to control tobacco use in the United States: A blueprint for public health action in the 1990's.* (NIH Publication No. 92-3316). Washington, D.C.: National Cancer Institute, Public Health Service, National Institutes of Health.

U.S. Department of Health and Human Services. (USDHHS). (1990). *The health benefits of smoking cessation: A report of the Surgeon General.* (DHHS Publication No. CDC 90-8416). Rockville, MD: Public Health Service, Centers for Disease Control, Center for Chronic Disease Prevention and Health Promotion, Office on Smoking and Health.

U.S. Department of Health and Human Services, U.S. Public Health Service. (1986). *Surgeon general's report on acquired immune deficiency syndrome.* Washington, DC: U.S. Government Printing Office.

U.S. Department of Health and Human Services, Public Health Service, Centers for Disease Control, Operational Research Section, Behavioral and Prevention Research Branch, Division of STD/HIV Prevention, Center for Prevention Services (1992a). *What we have learned from the AIDS Community Demonstration Projects.* Atlanta, GA: Centers for Disease Control.

U. S. Department of Justice. (1982). *A national crime survey report, NCJ 84015.* Washington, DC: U.S. Government Printing Office.

U.S. Department of Justice. (1986). *Attorney general's commission on pornography: Final report.* Washington, DC: U.S. Government Printing Office.

U.S. Department of Justice, Bureau of Justice Studies. (1985). *The crime of rape.* Washington, DC: U.S. Government Printing Office.

U. S. Department of Justice, Federal Bureau of Investigation. (1987). *Uniform crime reports.* Washington, DC: U.S. Government Printing Office.

U. S. Department of Justice, Federal Bureau of Investigation. (1990). *Uniform Crime Reports.* (1990). Rape statistics. Washington, DC: U. S. Government Printing Office.

U.S. Merit Systems Protection Board. (1981). *Sexual harassment in the federal workplace: Is it a problem?* Washington, DC: Office of Merit Systems Review and Studies.

U.S. Says 349,000 Caesareans in 1991 were not necessary. (1993, April 23), *The New York Times,* p. A16.

U.S. Senate Committee on the Judiciary. (1991). Violence against women: The increase of rape in America 1990. *Response to the Victimization of Women and Children, 14,, (79, No 2),* 20-23.

Udry, J. R., & Morris, N. M. (1978). Relative contribution of male and female age to the frequency of marital intercourse. *Social Biology, 25,* 128–134.

Udry, J. R., & Billy, J. O. G. (1987). Initiation of coitus in early adolescence. *American Sociological Review, 52,* 841–855.

Udry, J. R., Talbert, L., & Morris, N. M. (1986). Biosocial foundations for adolescent female sexuality. *Demography, 23(2),* 217–230.

Udry, J. R., et al. (1985). Serum androgenic hormones motivate sexual behavior in adolescent boys. *Fertility and Sterility, 43,* 90–94.

Ulbrich, P. M., Coyle, A. T., & Llabre, M. M. (1990) Involuntary childlessness and marital adjustment: His and hers. *Journal of Sex & Marital Therapy, 16,* 147-158.

Ullman, S. E., & Knight, R. A. (1992). Fighting back: Women's resistance to rape. *Journal of Interpersonal Violence,* 31-43.

Ullman, S. E., & Knight, R. A. (1991). A multivariate model for predicting rape and physical injury outcomes during sexual assaults. *Journal of Consulting and Clinical Psychology, 59,* 724–731.

Ullrich, H. E. (1977). Caste differences between Brahmin and non-Brahmin women in a South Indian village. In A. Schlegel (Ed.), *Sexual stratification: A cross- cultural view.* New York: Columbia University Press.

Umberson, D., & Hughes, M. (1984, August). *The impact of physical attractiveness on achievement and psychological well-being.* Paper presented at the meeting of the American Sociological Association, San Antonio, Texas.

Unger, R. K., Hilderbrand, M., & Madar, T. (1982). Physical attractiveness and assumptions about social deviance: Some sex-by-sex comparisons. *Personality and Social Psychology Bulletin, 8,* 293–301.

Unsettling report on an epidemic of rape. (1992, May 4). *Time,* p. 15.

Upton, G. (1987). Contraception for the perimenopausal patient. *Obstetrics and Gynecology Clinics of North Americas, 14,* 207–227.

Urquiza, A. J., & Capra, M. (1990). The impact of sexual abuse: Initial and long-term effects. In M. Hunter (Ed.), *The sexually abused male: Prevalence, impact, and treatment* (Vol. 1) (pp. 105–135). Lexington, MA: Lexington Books.

Vaginal yeast infection can be an HIV warning. (1992, November 24). *New York Newsday,* p. 51.

van Lawick-Goodall, J. (1971). *In the shadow of man.* Boston: Houghton Mifflin.

Van den Hoek, A., Van Haastrecht, H. J., & Coutinho, R. A. (1990). Heterosexual behaviour of intravenous drug users in Amsterdam: Implications for the AIDS epidemic.*AIDS, 4,* 449–453.

Van den Berghe, P. L. (1983). Human inbreeding avoidance: Culture in nature. *Behavioral and Brain Sciences, 6,* 91–123.

Van de Perre, P., et al. (1991). Postnatal transmission of human immunodeficiency virus type 1 from mother to infant: Aa prospective cohort study in Kigali, Rwanda. *The New England Journal of Medicine, 325,* 593–598.

Van der Kwaak, A. (1992). Female circumcision and gender identity: A questionable alliance? Special Issue: Gender, health and development. *Social Science and Medicine, 35,* 777-787.

Vance, C. (1984). *Pleasure and danger: Exploring female sexuality.* London: Routledge & Kegan Paul.

Vance, E. B., & Wagner, N. N. (1976). Written descriptions of orgasm: A study of sex differences. *Archives of Sexual Behavior, 5,* 87–98.

Vander Mey, B. J., & Neff, R. L. (1982). Adult-child incest: A review of research and treatment. *Adolescence, 17,* 717–735.

Vanggaard, T. (1972). *Phallos: A symbol and its history in the male world.* London: Jonathan Cape.

Vaughan, E., & Fisher, E. (1962). Male sexual behavior induced by intracranial electrical stimulation. *Science, 137,* 758.

Vazi, R., Best, D., Davis, S., & Kaiser, M. (1989). Evaluation of a testicular cancer curriculum for adolescents. *Journal of Pediatrics, 114,* 150–162.

Veitch, R., & Griffit, W. (1976). Good news, bad news: Affective and interpersonal effects. *Journal of Applied Social Psychology, 6,* 69–75.

Ventura, S. J. (1991, June 15). Cited in Quarter of newborns in U.S. were born to single women. *The New York Times,* p. 9.

Vicenzi, A. E., & Thiel, R. (1992). AIDS education on the college campus: Roy's adaptation model directs inquiry. *Public Health Nursing, 9,* 27-276.

Vinacke, W., et al. (1988). Similarity and complementarity in intimate couples. *Genetic, Social, and General Psychology Monographs, 114,* 51–76.

Vinick, B. (1978). Remarriage in old age. *The Family Coordinator, 27,* 359–363.

Vinovskis, M. A. (1988). *An "epidemic" of adolescent pregnancy? Some historical and policy considerations.* New York: Oxford University Press.

Voeller, B. (1991). AIDS and heterosexual anal intercourse.*Archives of Sexual Behavior, 20,* 233-276.

Voeller, B. (1990). Some uses and abuses of the Kinsey Scale. In D. P. McWhirter, S. A. Sanders, & J. M. Reinisch (Eds.), *Homosexuality/heterosexuality: Concepts of sexual orientation* (pp. 32–38). New York: Oxford University Press.

Volberding, P. A., et al. (1990). Zidovudine in asymptomatic human immunodeficiency virus infection. *New England Journal of Medicine, 322,* 941–949.

von Reyn, C. F., et al., (1993). Absence of HIV transmission from an infected orthopedic surgeon: A 13-year look-back study. *Journal of the American Medical Association, 269,* 1807-1811.

Von Krafft-Ebbing, R. (1978). *Psychopathia sexualis.* Philadelphia: F. A. Davis. (Original work published 1886.)

Von Krafft-Ebbing, R. (1965). *Psychopathia sexualis, 1886.* New York: Putnam.

Wachter, R. M. (1992). AIDS, activism, and the politics of health. *The New England Journal of Medicine, 326,* 128–133.

Waigandt, A., et al. (1990). The impact of sexual assault on physical health issues. *Journal of Traumatic Stress, 3,* 93–102.

Wakefield, J. (1988). Female primary orgasmic dysfunction: Masters and Johnson versus DSM-III-R on diagnosis and incidence. *Journal of Sex Research, 24,* 363–377.

Walfish, S., & Myerson, M. (1980). Sex role identity and attitudes toward sexuality. *Archives of Sexual Behavior, 9,* 199–204.

Wallace, H. M., & Vienonen, M. (1989). Teenage pregnancy in Sweden and Finland. *Journal of Adolescent Health Care, 10,* 231–236.

Wallerstein, J. S., & Blakeslee, S. (1989). *Second chances: Women and children a decade after divorce.* New York: Ticknor & Fields.

Wallerstein, J. S., & Kelly, J. B. (1980). *Surviving the breakup: How children and parents cope with divorce.* New York: Basic Books.

Wallis, C. (1991a, January 14). A puzzling plague: What is it about the American way of life that causes breast cancer? *Time,* 48–52.

Wallis, C. (1987, October 12). Back off, buddy: A new Hite report stirs up a furor over sex and love in the '80s. *Time,* pp. 68–73.

Wallis, C. (1991b, January 14). The rough road to recovery. *Time,* 53–54.

Wallis, C. (1984, August 27). Can science pick a child's sex? Doctors challenge new methods of granting an ancient wish. *Time,* p. 59.

Walsh, J. (1990, December 2). Asian women, Caucasian men. *The San Francisco Examiner, Image Magazine.*

Walsh, R. N., et al. (1981). The menstrual cycle, sex and academic performance. *Archives of General Psychiatry, 38,* 219–221.

Walster, E., & Walster, G. W. (1978). *A new look at love.* Reading, MA: Addison-Wesley.

Walt, V. (1993, July 26). Some 2nd thoughts on depo. *New York Newsday,* p. 13.

Walter, H. J., & Vaughan, R. D. (1993). AIDS risk reduction among a multiethnic sample of urban high school students. *Journal of the American Medical Association, 270,* 725-730.

Ward, J. W., et al. (1988). Transmission of human immunodeficiency virus (HIV) by blood transfusions screened as negative for HI antibody. *New England Journal of Medicine, 318,* 473–478.

Ward, I. L. (1972). Prenatal stress feminizes and demasculinizes the behavior of males. *Science, 175,* 82–84.

Wardlaw, G. M., & Insel, P. M. (1990). *Perspectives in nutrition.* St. Louis: Times Mirror/Mosby College Publishing.

Warner, E., & Strashin, E. (1981). Benefits and risks of circumcision. *Canadian Medical Association Journal, 125,* 967–976, 992.

Warren, C. W., et al. (1990). Assessing the reproductive behavior of on- and off-reservation American Indian females: Characteristics of two groups in Montana. *Social Biology, 37,* 69–83.

Washington, A. C., Rosser, P. L., & Cox, E. P. (1983). Contraceptive practices of teenage mothers. *Journal of the National Medical Association, 75,* 1059–1063.

Wassenberg, L., & Nass, G. D. (1977). In G. D. Nass, R. W. Libby, and M. P. Fisher (Eds.), *Sexual choices.* Monterey, CA: Wadsworth.

Waterman, J. (1986a). Family dynamics of incest with young children. In K. MacFarlane, et al. (Eds.), *Sexual abuse of young children: Evaluation and treatment* (pp. 204–219). New York: Guilford.

Waterman, J. (1986b). Overview of treatment issues. In K. MacFarlane et al. (Eds.), *Sexual abuse of young children: Evaluation and treatment.*(pp. 197–203). New York: Guilford.

Waterman, J., & Lusk, R. (1986). Scope of the problem. In K. MacFarlane, et al. (Eds.), *Sexual abuse of young children: Evaluation and treatment* (pp. 3–14). New York: Guilford Press.

Waterman, J., et al. (1986). Challenges for the future. In K. MacFarlane, et al. (Eds.), *Sexual abuse of young children: Evaluation and treatment* (pp. 315–332). New York: Guilford.

Watkins, C. E. (1990). Psychiatric epidemiology II: The prevalence and aftermath of sexual assault. *Journal of Counseling & Development, 68,* 341–343.

Watson, R. E. L. (1983). Premarital cohabitation vs. traditional courtship: Their effects on subsequent marital adjustment. *Family Relations, 32,* 239–147.

Watson, R. E. L., & DeMeo, P. W. (1987). Premarital cohabitation vs. traditional courtship and subsequent marital adjustment: A replication and followup. *Family Relations, 36,* 193–197.

Watters, W. W. (1986). Supra-biological factors in the assessment of males seeking penile prostheses. *Canadian Journal of Psychiatry, 31,* 25–31.

Waugh, M. A. (1990). History of clinical developments in sexually transmitted diseases. In K. K. Holmes, et al. (Eds.), *Sexually transmitted diseases* (2nd ed.) (pp. 3–16). New York: McGraw-Hill, Inc.

Wayne, D. M., Adams, M., & Rowe, L. (1947). A study of military prisoners at a disciplinary barracks suspected of homosexual activities. *Military Surgeon, 101,* 499–504.

Webb, S. L. (1992). *Step forward: Sexual harassment in the workplace.* MasterMedia.

Weideger, P. (1977). Menstruation and menopause : The physiology and psychology, the myth and the reality. New York: Dell.

Weinberg, M. S., & Williams, C. J. (1988). Black sexuality: A test of two theories. *Journal of Sex Research, 25,* 197–218.

Weinberg, M. S. & Williams, C. J. (1974).*Male homosexuals: Their problems and adaptations.* New York: Oxford University Press.

Weinberg, T. S. (1987). Sadomasochism in the United States: A review of recent sociological literature. *Journal of Sex Research, 23,* 50–69.

Weinberg, T., & Bullough, V. L. (1988). Alienation, self-image, and the importance of support groups for the wives of transvestites. *Journal of Sex Research, 24,* 262–268.

Weinberg, T. S., & Bullough, V. L. (1986). *Women married to transvestites: Problems and adjustments.* Paper presented at the annual meeting of the Society for the Study of Social Problems, New York.

Weinberg, T. S., Williams, C. J., & Moser, C. (1984). The social constituents of sadomasochism. *Social Problems, 31,*379–389.

Weiner, J., et al. (1951). Carcinoma of the cervix in Jewish women. *American Journal of Obstetrics and Gynecology, 61,* 418.

Weingarten, H. (1985). Marital status and well-being: A national study comparing first-married, currently divorced, and remarried adults. *Journal of Marriage and the Family, 47,* 653–662.

Weinstock, H. S., et al. (1993). Factors assocaited with condom use in a high-risk heterosexual pouplation. *Sexually Transmitted Diseases, 20,* 14-20.

Weisberg, D. K. (1985). *Children of the night: A study of adolescent prostitution.* Lexington, MA: D. C. Heath.

Weiss, R.D., & Mirin, S.M. (1987). *Cocaine.* Washington, D.C. American Psychiatric Press.

Weiss, D. L. (1983). Affective reactions of women to their initial experience of coitus. *Journal of Sex Research, 19,* 209–237.

Weiss, D. L., & Jurich, J. (1985). Size of community of residence as a predictor of attitudes toward extramarital sexual relations. *Journal of Marriage and the Family, 47,* 173–178.

Weiss, R. S. (1975). *Marital separation.* New York: Basic Books.

Weitzman, L. (1985). *The divorce revolution: The unexpected social and economic consequences for women and children in America.* New York: The Free Press.

Welch, M. R., & Kartub, P. (1978). Socio-cultural correlates of incidence of impotence: A cross-cultural study. *Journal of Sex Research, 14,* 218–230.

Wells, J., & Kline, W. (1987). Self-disclosure of homosexual orientation. *Journal of Social Psychology, 127,* 191–197.

Werner, D. (1984). Paid sex specialists among the Makranoti. *Journal of Anthropological Research, 40,* 394–405.

Werner, D. (1979). A cross-cultural perspective on theory and research on male homosexuality *Journal of Homosexuality, 4,* 345–362.

Werner, D., & Cohen, A. (1990). Instructor's edition. In C. R. Ember & M. Ember, *Anthropology.* (6th ed.). (pp. I-1 to I-146). Englewood Cliffs, NJ: Prentice-Hall.

Westoff, C. F., & Jones, E. F. (1977). The secularization of U.S. Catholic birth control practices. *Family Planning Perspectives, 9,* 203–207.

Westrom, L. V. (1990). Chlamydia trachomatis—clinical significance and strategies of intervention. *Seminars in Dermatology, 9,* 117–125.

Whalen, R. E., Geary, D. C., & Johnson, F. (1990). Models of sexuality. In D. P. McWhirter, S. A. Sanders, & J. M. Reinisch (Eds.), *Homosexuality/Hetero*sexuality: Concepts of sexual orientation (pp. 61–70). New York: Oxford University Press.

Wharton, C., & Blackburn, R. (1988, November). Lower-dose pills. *Population Reports,* Series A, No. 7.

Whiffen, V. E. (1988). Vulnerability to postpartum depression: A prospective multivariate study. *Journal of Abnormal Psychology, 97,* 467–474.

Whiffen, V. E. (1992). Is postpartum depression a distinct diagnosis? *Clinical Psychology Review, 12,* 485–508.

Whipple, B., & Komisaruk, B. R. (1988). Analgesia produced in women by genital self-stimulation. *Journal of Sex Research, 24,* 130–140.

Whitam, F. L. (1977). Childhood indicators of male homosexuality. *Archives of Sexual Behavior, 6,* 89–96.

Whitam, F. L., Diamond, M., & Martin, J. (1993). Homosexual orientation in twins: A report on 61 pairs and three triplet sets. *Archives of Sexual Behavior, 22,* 187–206.

Whitam, F., & Mathay, R. M. (1985). *Male homosexuality in four societies: Brazil, Guatemala, the Philippines, and the United States.* New York: Praeger.

Whitcher, S. J., & Fisher, J. D. (1979). Multidimensional reaction to therapeutic touch in a hospital setting. *Journal of Personality and Social Psychology, 37,* 87–96.

White, L. K., Booth, A., & Edwards, J. N. (1986). Children and marital happiness: Why the negative correlation? *Journal of Family Issues, 7,* 131–147.

White, S., et al. (1988). Behavioral comparisons of young sexually abused, neglected, and nonreferred children. *Journal of Clinical Child Psychology, 17,* 53–61.

White, G. L. (1980). Physical attractiveness and courtship progress. *Journal of Personality and Social Psychology, 39,* 660–668.

White, G. L. (1981). Some correlates of romantic jealousy. *Journal of Personality, 49,* 129–146.

White, J. W. (1983). Sex and gender issues in aggression research. R. G. Green & E. I. Donnerstein (Eds.), *Aggression: Theoretical and empirical reviews,* Vol. 2. New York: Academic Press.

White, S. D., & DeBlassie, R. R. (1992). Adolescent sexual behavior. *Adolescence, 27,* 183-191.

Whitehead, A., Mathews, A., & Ramage, M. (1987). The treatment of sexually unresponsive women: A comparative evaluation. *Behaviour Research & Therapy, 25,* 195–205.

Whitley, B. E., & Hern, A. L. (1991). Perceptions of vulnerability to pregnancy and the use of effective contraception. *Personality and Social Psychology Bulletin, 17, 104-110.*

Whitley, B. E., Jr. (1988). Sex differences in heterosexuals' attitudes toward homosexuals: It depends upon what you ask. *Journal of Sex Research, 24,* 287–291.

Whitley, B. E., Jr. (1983). Sex role orientation and self-esteem: A critical meta-analysis. *Journal of Personality and Social Psychology, 44,* 765–788.

Whitley, R., et al. (1991). Predictors of morbidity and mortality in infants with herpes simplex virus infections. *The New England Journal of Medicine, 324,* 450–454.

Whittemore, A. S., et al. (1992). Characteristics relating to ovarian ccancer risk: Collaborative analysis of 12 U.S. case-control studies: II. Invasive ovarian cancers in white women. *American Journal of Epidemiology, 136,* 1184-1203.

Whitten, C. F. (1992). Sickle cell anemia and African-Americans. In R. L. Braithwaite, & S. E. Taylor (Eds.), *Health issues in the black community.* (pp. 192-205). San Francisco: Jossey-Bass.

Whyte, W. W. (1956). *The organization man.* New York: Simon & Schuster.

Widom, C. S. (1989). Child abuse, neglect, and adult behavior: Research design and findings on criminality, violence, and child abuse. *American Journal of Orthopsychiatry, 59,* 355–367.

Wiest, W. (1977). Semantic differential profiles of orgasm and other experiences among men and women. *Sex Roles, 3,* 399–403.

Wiggins, J. S., Wiggins, N., & Conger, J. C. (1968). Correlates of heterosexual somatic preference. *Journal of Personality and Social Psychology, 10,* 82–90.

Wilcox, B. L. (1987). Pornography, social science and politics: When research and ideology collide. *American Psychologist, 42,* 941,943.

Wilcoxon, L. A., Schrader, S. L., & Sherif, C. W. (1976). Daily self-reports on activities, life events, moods, and somatic changes during the menstrual cycle. *Psychosomatic Medicine, 38,* 399.

Wildman, B. G., & White, P. A. (1986). Assessment of dysmenorrhea using the Menstrual Symptom Questionnaire: Factor structure and validity. *Behaviour Research & Therapy, 24,* 547–551.

Wilentz, R. N. (1988). In the matter of Baby M: Case report. *Conciliation Courts Review, 26,* 69–77.

Wilford, J. N. (1992, November 17). Clues etched in bone debunk theory of a plague's spread. *The New York Times,* p. C1, C8.

Wille, R., & Beier, K. M. (1989). Castration in Germany. *Annals of Sex Research, 2,* 103–133.

Williams, G. C. (1975). *Sex and evolution.* Princeton, NJ: Princeton University Press.

Williams, J. G., & Solano, C. H. (1983). The social reality of feeling lonely: Friendship and reciprocation. *Personality and Social Psychology Bulletin, 9,* 237–242.

Williams, S. S., et al. (1992). College students use implicit personality theory instead of safer sex. *Journal of Applied Social Psychology, 22,* 921-933.

Wilson, C. (1985, April 11). Ad bares all about jeans. *Advertising Age,* pp. 11, 31

Wilson, E. O. (1975). *Sociobiology: The new synthesis.* Cambidge, MA: Harvard University Press.

Wilson, G., & Cox, D. (1983). Personality of pedophile club members. *Personality and Individual Differences, 4,* 323–329.

Wilson, G. T., Lawson, D. M., & Abrams, D. B. (1978). Effects of alcohol on sexual arousal in male alcoholics. *Journal of Abnormal Psychology, 87,* 609–616.

Wilson, G. T., & Lawson, D. M. (1978). Expectancies, alcohol, and sexual arousal in women. *Journal of Abnormal Psychology, 87,* 358–367.

Wilson, J., George, F., & Griffin, J. (1981). The hormonal control of sexual development. *Science, 211,* 1278–1284.

Wilson, J. D. (1982). Gonadal hormones and sexual behavior. In G. M. Besser & L. Martini (Eds.), *Clinical neuroendocrinology* (pp. 1–29). New York: Academic Press.

Wilson, M. L., & Greene, R. L. (1971). Personality characteristics of female homosexuals. *Psychological Reports, 28,* 407–412.

Wilson, M. R., & Filsinger, E. E. (1986). Religiosity and marital adjustment: Multidimensional interrelationships. *Journal of Marriage and the Family, 48,* 147–151.

Wilson, S. M., & Medora, N. P. (1990). Gender comparisons of college students' attitudes toward sexual behavior. *Adolescence, 25,* 615–627.

Wilson, S. N., & Sanderson, C. A. (1988). The sex report curriculum: Is "just say no" effective? *SIECUS Report, 17,* 10–11.

Wilson, W. C., & Abelson, H. I. (1973). Experience with and attitudes toward explicit sexual materials. *Journal of Social Issues, 29,* 19–39.

Wincze, J. P. (1981). Sexual dysfunction (distress and dissatisfaction). In S. M. Turner, K. S. Calhoun, & Henry E. Adams (Eds.), *Handbook of clinical behavior therapy.* New York: John Wiley & Sons.

Wincze, J. P., et al. (1988). A comparison of nocturnal penile tumescence and penile response to erotic stimulation during waking states in comprehensively diagnosed groups of males experiencing erectile difficulties. *Archives of Sexual Behavior, 17,* 333–348.

Wincze, J. P., Hoon, E. F., & Hoon, P. W. (1976). Physiological responsivity of normal and sexually dysfunctional women during erotic stimulus exposure. *Journal of Psychosomatic Research, 20,* 445–451.

Windsor, R. A., & Orleans, C. (1986). Guildelines and methodological standards or smoking cessation intervention research among pregnant women: Improving the science and art. *Health Education Quarterly, 13,* 131-161.

Winick, C. (1985). A content analysis of sexually explicit magazines sold in an adult bookstore. *Journal of Sex Research, 21,* 206–210.

Winkelstein, W., Jr., et al. (1987). The San Francisco Men's Health Study. III. Reduction in human immunodeficiency virus transmission among homosexual/bisexual men. *American Journal of Public Health, 77,* 685–689.

Winn, R. L., & Newton, N. (1982). Sexuality in aging: A study of 106 cultures. *Archives of Sexual Behavior, 11,* 283–298.

Wise, T., & Meyer, J. (1980). Transvestism: Previous findings and new areas for inquiry. *Journal of Sex and Marital Therapy, 6,* 116–128.

Wise, T. N. (1985). Fetishism—etiology and treatment: A review from multiple perspectives. *Comprehensive Psychiatry, 26,* 249–257.

Wisell, T. E., et al. (1987). Declining frequency of circumcision: Implications for changes in the absolute incidence and male to female sex ratio of urinary tract infections in early infancy. *Pediatrics, 79,* 338–342.

Wolfe, J., & Baker, V. (1980). Characteristics of imprisoned rapists and circumstances of the rape. In C. G. Warner (Ed.), *Rape and sexual assault* (pp. 265–278). Germantown, MD: Aspen Systems Co.

Wolfe, L. (1981). *The cosmo report.* New York: Arbor House.

Wolman, T. (1985). Drug addiction. In M. Farber (Ed.), *Human sexuality* (pp. 277–285). New York: MacMillan.

Women under assault. (1990, July 16). *Newsweek,* p. 23.

Woodard, C. (1993, January 12). Minorities hit harder by AIDS, panel says. *New York Newsday,* p. 4.

Woodard, C. (1993, June 7). Cases among young women rise, hint at vulnerability. *New York Newsday,* p. 17.

Woods, N., et al. (1987). Women's health: The menstrual cycle/premenstrual symptoms: Another look. *Public Health Reports,* 106–112.

Wooldridge, W. E. (1991). Syphilis: A new visit from an old enemy. *Postgraduate Medicine, 89,* 199–202.

Wortman, C. B., et al. (1976). Self-disclosure: An attributional perspective. *Journal of Personality and Social Psychology, 33,* 184–191.

Wright, J. T., et al. (1983, March 26). Alcohol consumption, pregnancy, and low birthweight. *The Lancet,* 663–665.

Wu, Z., & Balakrishnan, T. R. (1992). Attitudes towards cohabitation and marriage in Canada. *Journal of Comparative Family Studies, 23,* 1-12.

WuDunn, S. (1991, June 16). China, with ever more to feed, pushes anew for small families. *The New York Times,* pp. 1, 10.

Wyatt, G. E. (1988). The relationship between child sexual abuse and adolescent sexual functioning in Afro-American and white American women. *The Annals of the New York Academy of Sciences, 528,* 111–122.

Wyatt, G. E., & Lyons-Rowe, S. (1990). African American women's sexual satisfaction as a dimension of their sex roles. *Sex Roles, 22,* 509–524.

Wyatt, G. E., Peters, S. D., & Guthrie, D. (1988a). Kinsey revisited, Part I: Comparisons of the sexual socialization and sexual behavior of white women over 33 years. *Archives of Sexual Behavior, 17(3),* 201–209.

Wyatt, G. E., Peters, S. D., & Guthrie, D. (1988b). Kinsey revisited, Part II: Comparisons of the sexual socialization and sexual behavior of black women over 33 years. *Archives of Sexual Behavior, 17(4),* 289–332.

Wyatt, G. E., Notgrass, C. M., & Newcomb, M. (1990). Internal and external mediators of women's rape experiences. *Psychology of Women Quarterly, 14,* 153–176.

Wyatt, G. E. (1985). The sexual abuse of Afro-American and white American women in childhood. *Child Abuse and Neglect, 9,* 507–519.

Wyatt, G. E. (1990). The aftermath of child sexual abuse of African American and white American women: The victim's experience. *Journal of Family Violence, 5,* 61–81.

Wyatt, G. E., (1991). Examining predictors of sex guilt in multiethnic samples of women. *Archives of Sexual Behavior, 20,* 471-485.

Wyatt, G. E. (1989). Reexamining factors predicting Afro-American and white American women's age at first coitus. *Archives of Sexual Behavior, 18,* 271–298.

Wyatt, G. E., & Newcomb, M. (1990). Internal and external mediators of women's sexual abuse in childhood. *Journal of Consulting and Clinical Psychology, 58,* 758–767.

Wyer, R. S., Jr., Bodenhausen, G. V., & Gorman, T. F. (1985). Cognitive mediators of reactions to rape. *Journal of Personality and Social Psychology, 48,* 324–338.

Xu, D., et al. (1988). Clinical safety of long-term administration of gossypol in 32 cases. *Contraception, 37,* 129–135.

Yamaguchi, K., & Kandel, D. B. (1985). Dynamic relationships between premarital cohabitation and illicit drug use: An event-history analysis of role selection and role socialization. *American Sociological Review, 50,* 530–546.

Yamanouchi, K., & Arai, Y. (1990). The septum as origin of a lordosis-inhibiting influence in female rats: Effect of neural transection. *Physiology and Behavior, 48,* 351-355.

Yankelovich, S. (1983). *The Yankelovich monitor.* Yankelovich Institute.

Yarber, W. L., Torabi, M. R., & Veenker, C. H. (1989). Development of a three-component sexually transmitted diseases attitude scale. *Journal of Sex Education & Therapy, 15,* 36–49.

Yarber, W. L. (1985). *STD: A guide for today's young adults.* Waldorf, MD: American Alliance Publications.

Yarber, W. L., & Parillo, A. V. (1992). Adolescents and sexually transmitted diseases. *Journal of School Health, 62,* 331-338.

Yarchoan, R., Mitsuya, H., & Broder, S. (1988). AIDS therapies. *Scientific American, 259,* 110–119.

Yates, G. L., et al. (1991). A risk profile comparison of homeless youth involved in prostitution and homeless youth not involved. Special Issue: Homeless youth. *Journal of Adolescent Health, 12,* 545-548.

Yogev, S., & Vierra, A. (1983). The state of motherhood among professional women. *Sex Roles, 9,* 391–397.

Young, A. (1973). Gay gringo in Brazil. In L. Richmond and G. Noguera (Eds.), *The gay liberation book* (pp. 60–67). San Francisco: Ramparts Press.

Young, J. E. (1982). Loneliness, depression, and cognitive therapy. In L. A. Peplau & D. Perlman (Eds.), *Loneliness: A sourcebook of current theory, research, and therapy.* New York: Wiley.

Zabin, L. S., et al. (1986). Evaluation of a pregnancy prevention program for urban teenagers. *Family Planning Perspectives, 18,* 119–126.

Zaslow, M. J., et al. (1985). Depressed mood in new fathers: Association with parent-infant interaction. *Genetic, Social and General Psychology Monographs, 111(2),* 133–150.

Zaviacic, M., & Whipple, B. (1993). Update on the female prostate and the phenomenon of female ejaculation. *Journal of Sex Research, 30,* 148-151.

Zaviacic, M., et al. (1988a). Concentrations of fructose in female ejaculate and urine: A comparative biochemical study. *Journal of Sex Research, 24,* 319–325.

Zaviacic, M., et al. (1988b). Female urethral expulsions evoked by local digitial stimulation of the G-spot: Differences in the response patterns. *Journal of Sex Research, 24,* 311–318.

Zaviacic, M. (1986). Argyrophil and argentaffin APUD cells in the human female prostata homologue and urethra. *Acta Histochemica, 79,* 93–96.

Zaviacic, M. (1985). The adult human female prostate homologue and the male prostate gland. Comparative enzyme-histochemical study. *Acta Histochemica, 77,* 19–31.

Zelnick, M., & Kantner, J. F. (1980). Sexual activity, contraceptive use, and pregnancy among metropolitan-area teenagers: 1971–1979. *Family Planning Perspectives, 12,* 230–237.

Zelnick, M., & Kantner, J. F. (1977). Sexual and contraceptive experience of young unmarried women in the United States, 1976 and 1971. *Family Planning Perspectives, 9,* 55–71.

Zelnick, M., & Kantner, J. F. (1972). Sexuality, contraception, and pregnancy among young unwed females in the United States. In U.S. Commission on Population Growth and the American Future, *Demographic and Social Aspects of Population Growth.*

Zelnick, M., & Kantner, J. F. (1974). The resolution of teenage first pregnancies. *Family Planning Perspectives, 6,* 74.

Zelnick, M., & Shah, F. K. (1983). First intercourse among young Americans. *Family Planning Perspectives, 15,* 64–70.

Zelnik, M., Koenig, M. A., & Kim, Y. J. (1984). Sources of prescription contraceptives and subsequent pregnancy among young women. *Family Planning Perspectives, 16,* 6–13.

Zelnik, M., & Kim, Y. J. (1982). Sex education and its association with teenage sexual activity, pregnancy and contraceptive use. *Family Planning Perspectives, 14,* 117–126.

Zeman, N. (1990, Summer/Fall). The new rules of courtship (Special Edition). *Newsweek,* 24–27.

Zenker, P. N., & Rolfs, R. T. (1990). Treatment of syphilis, 1989. *Reviews of Infectious Diseases* (Suppl. 6), S590–S609.

Zgourides, G. D., & Warren, R. (1989). Retarded ejaculation: Overview and treatment implications. *Journal of Psychology and Human Sexuality, 2,* 139–150.

Zhang, J., & Fried, D. B. (1992). Relationship of maternal smoking during pregnancy to placenta previa. *American Journal of Preventative Medicine, 8,* 278-282.

Zilbergeld, B. (1978). *Male Sexuality.* Boston: Little, Brown.

Zillman, D., & Bryant, J. (1982, Autumn). Pornography, sexual callousness, and the trivialization of rape. *Journal of Communication,* 10–21.

Zillmann, D., & Bryant, J. (In press). Effects of prolonged consumption of pornography on family values. *Journal of Family Issues.*

Zillmann, D., & Weaver, J. B. (1989). Pornography and men's sexual callousness toward women. In D. Zillmann & J. Bryant (Eds.), *Pornography: Research advances and policy considerations* (pp. 95–125). Hillsdale, NJ: Lawrence Erlbaum Associates.

Zillmann, D. (1989). Effects of prolonged consumption of pornography. In D. Zillmann & J. Bryant (Eds.), *Pornography: Research advances and policy considerations* (pp. 127–157). Hillsdale, NJ: Lawrence Erlbaum Associates.

Zillmann, D., & Bryant, J. (1984). Effects of massive exposure to pornography. In N. M. Malamuth & E. Donnerstein (Eds.), *Pornography and sexual aggression* (pp. 115–138). New York: Academic Press.

Zimmer, D. (1983). Interaction patterns and communication skills in sexually distressed, maritally distressed, and normal couples: Two experimental studies. *Journal of Sex and Marital Therapy, 9,* 251–265.

Zimmer, D., Borchardt, E., & Fischle, C. (1983). Sexual fantasies of sexually distressed and nondistressed men and women: An empirical investigation. *Journal of Sex and Marital Therapy, 9,* 38–50.

Zinik, G. (1985). Identity conflict or adaptive flexibility? Bisexuality reconsidered. *Journal of Homosexuality, 11,* 7–20.

Zuckerman, S. (1981). *The social life of monkeys and apes* (2nd ed.). London: Routledge & Kegan Paul. (Original edition published 1932.)

Zuger, B. (1989). Homosexuality in families of boys with early effeminate behavior: An epidemiological study. *Archives of Sexual Behavior, 18,* 155–166.

Zuger, B. (1984). Early effeminate behavior in boys: Outcome and significance for homosexuality. *Journal of Nervous and Mental Disease, 172,* 90–97.

Zuger, B. (1976). Monozygotic twins discordant for homosexuality: Report of a pair and significance of the phenomenon. *Comprehensive Psychiatry, 17,* 661–669.

NAME INDEX

SUBJECT INDEX

Behaviorist, defined, 29
Benign, defined, 83
Bestiality, 571-573
    defined, 14
Bias
    observer, 53-54
    sample, 42, 46-47, 49, 52
Birth centers, 339
Birth-control pill. See Oral contraceptives
Bisexuality, 278-279
    defined, 13, 272
Blastocyst, 322
Blended orgasm, 155
Blindness, sexuality and, 448
Body decoration, 179
Body type, ad physical attractiveness, 197-198
Body Collage, 645, 646
Bondage, 566
Bondage and discipline (B&D), 568
Bottle-feeding, 342
Brain
    geography of, 140-141
    pleasure centers in, 142
    prenatal sexual differentiation of, 165, 180
    role in erection, 123
    role in sexual function, 141-142
Braxton-Hicks contractions, 334
Brazil, AIDS in, 529
Breast cancer
    detection of, 82-84
    incidence of, 81-82
    treatment of, 84-86
Breast-feeding, 342
Breasts
    age-related changes in, 443
    cancer of, 81-86
    changes during sex, 147, 152
    cultural attitudes towards, 79-80
    cysts in, 83
    morphological variations in, 80
    and physical attractiveness, 197
    reconstruction after mastectomy, 86
    self-examination of, 82-83
    self-image and, 85
    stimulation of, 81, 254, 256
Breech presentation, 325, 338
Brothel prostitution, 627
    male, 634
Brother-sister incest, 610
Building stage in ABCDE model, 219
Bulbourethral glands, 116
Bupropion, 136
Butch-femme relationship, 287

Caesarean section, 338-339
Calendar method, 367
Call boys, 634
Call girls, 628
Call tracing, 564
Caller ID, 564
Calymmatobacterium granulomatus, 503
Cancer
    breast, 81-86
    cervical, 75, 489, 508, 511-512
    endometrial, 76
    ovarian, 77-78
    prostate, 119-120, 144
    testicular, 117-118
Candida albicans, 504
Candidiasis, 494, 504-505
Canterbury Tales, 637
Cantharidin, 136
Caring, defined, 228
Case study
    defined, 57
    limitations of, 57-58
Castration, 144-145

to treat sex offenders, 614
Castration anxiety, in psychoanalytic theory, 291
Catcher in the Rye, 637
CD4 cells, 526
Ceftriaxone, 497, 503
Celibacy, 423
    early Christian attitude towards, 15
Cephalic presentation, 325
Cephalocaudal development, 323
Cerebellum, 140
Cerebral palsy, sexuality and, 446
Cerebrum, 140, 141
Cervical cap, 362-363
Cervical mucus method, 368
Cervicitis, 497
Cervix, 75
    cancer of, 489, 508, 511-512
    changes in childbirth, 334-335
    examination of, 79
Chancre, 499
Chancroid, 502-503
Chattel, defined, 14, 427
"Chemical castration," 581
Chewu people, sexual attitudes among, 392
Child pornography, 637
Child sexual abuse
    effects of, 610, 611-612, 630
    defined, 605-606
    incest, 609-611
    incidence of, 605
    patterns of, 606
    pedophilia, 608-609
    prevention of, 612-613
    reporting of, 605, 607
    treatment of, 613
    treatment of abusers, 614
    types of abusers, 607
Childbirth
    facilities for, 339
    methods of, 336-339
    preliminaries to, 334
    problems with, 339-341
    stages of, 334-335, 336
Childbirth Without Fear, 337
Childhood
    sex play in, 8
    sexuality in, 393-395
Chimpanzees, kissing behavior in, 52
China
    ancient, sexual attitudes in, 15-16
    communication conventions in, 222
    infanticide in, 310
    premarital sex in, 9
    sexual behavior in, 50
Chinese-Americans, attitudes towards adolescent sexuality, 408-409
Chlamydia, 488, 494
    diagnosis and treatment of, 502
    incidence of, 500-501
    symptoms of, 501-502
    transmission of, 501
Chlamydia trachomatis, 488, 501, 503
Chorion, defined, 333
Chorionic villus sampling (CVS), 333
Choroti people, 568
Christianity
    ancient, sexual attitudes of, 14-15
    attitudes towards homosexuality, 279-280
    circumcision in, 109
    views on marriage, 427
Chromosomal abnormalities, 331-332
    averting, 333
Chromosomes, 306
    defined, 23, 162
    sex, 162-163, 165, 306
Chuckchee people, sexual attitudes of, 437, 441
Cilia, 116

Circumcision, 109
    effects of, 109-110
    female, 68-69
    Pharaonic, 68
Climacteric, 95
Clitoral orgasm, 154, 155
Clitoridectomy, 68-69, 71
Clitoris, 66-67
    changes during sex, 147, 148, 149
    manual stimulation of, 255, 256
    masturbation of. See Masturbation
Cloaca, 107
Clomiphene, 89
Close couples, defined, 301
Clotrimazole, 504
Coca-Cola, 139
Cocaine
    effect on fetus, 328
    sexual effects of, 139, 466-467
Cognition, gender differences in, 176-177
Cognitive-developmental theory, view of gender typing, 184
Cohabitation, 423-424
    incidence of, 424-425
    and marriage, 425
    reasons for, 425
    styles of, 425
Coitus
    defined, 5
    duration of, 434
    fantasy during, 264, 266-267
    frequency in elderly, 445
    in marriage, 433-433
    positions for, 22, 260-264, 477
    resumption after childbirth, 343
    techniques of, 260-264, 434
Coitus interruptus, 245, 349, 366
Colpotomy, 371
Comanche people
    gender typing among, 178, 179
    sexual attitudes of, 437
Comarital sex, 438
Combination birth control pills, 351, 352
Coming out
    to oneself, 297-298, 418
    to others, 298-299
Commercial sex
    pornography, 635-649
    prostitution, 624-635
Commission on Obscenity and Pornography, 640
Commitment, as component of love, 209
Communication
    aspects of, 233-239
    in building romance, 219-220
    cohabitation and, 426
    criticism, 237-239
    cultural perspectives on, 222
    date-seeking, 194-195, 221
    difficulties in, 232-233
    gender and style of, 177
    I-talk, 236-237
    impasse in, 239-240
    of information, 235-236
    in intimacy, 229-230
    making requests, 236-237
    mechanics of, 229
    about needs, 234
    in prevention of STDs, 490-491
    sex education, 398-399
    sexual desire and, 457
    sexual dysfunction and, 469-470
Companionate love, 211, 212-213, 213
Complete hysterectomy, 76
Conception, 306-307
    justifications for and against, 318-319
    optimizing chance of, 307-308
Concordance, defined, 288
Concubine, defined, 14

Hawaii, ancient, incestuous marriage in, 12
HCG (human chorionic gonadotropin), 315
Health care provider referral, 539
Health, sexuality and, 7
Hearing, arousal and, 135
Hebrews
  ancient, sexual attitudes in, 12
  ancient, views on marriage, 426
  ancient, views on rape, 587
Hedonism, 657
Hegar's sign, 315
Height, and physical attractiveness, 197
Hemophilia, 331, 332-333
Hemophilus ducreyi, 502
Hepatitis, viral, 495, 510-511
Hermaphroditism, 166-167
Heroin, effect on fetus, 329
Herpes, 495, 506-507
  chronic, and AIDS, 527
  coping with, 509-510
  diagnosis and treatment of, 509
  ocular, 508
  oral, 495, 509
  symptoms of, 508-509
  transmission of, 507-508
Herpes simplex, types of, 507
Heteroerotic, defined, 274
Heterosexual behavior
  in adolescence, 403-407, 410-417
  in early childhood, 394-395
  by gay males and lesbians, 274
  in preadolescence, 395-396
Heterosexual orientation, 272
Hinduism, sexual attitudes in, 16
Hispanic Americans
  AIDS and, 524, 535, 549
  attitudes towards adolescent sexuality, 408-409
  machismo/marianismo and, 174-175
Hite Report, 45
Hite Report on Male Sexuality, 45
HIV
  coping with, 541-542
  diagnosis of, 537-539
  discovery of, 520
  effects of, 526
  epidemic status of, 528-529, 530
  iatrogenic transmission of, 533-534
  incidence of, 521-524
  issues concerning testing for, 538-539
  minimizing risk of, 268, 549-551
  myths about, 532-533
  prevention of, 542-549
  progression of, 526-528
  prostitution and, 633, 634-635
  risk factors for, 531-533
  sources for information about, 548-549, 550
  transmission of, 529-531
  transmission through placenta, 327
  treatment of, 540-541
  types of, 526
Home births, 339
Homoerotic, defined, 274
Homogamy, 429
Homologous, defined, 67
Homophobia, 283
Homosexual orientation, 272
Homosexual in America, 273
Homosexualities, 45, 299
Homosexuality
  in ancient Greece, 13-14
  attitudes towards, 273, 282-285
  behavior vs. orientation, 273-274
  biological perspectives on, 288-290
  changing attitudes towards, 557
  cross-species perspectives on, 281-282
  cultural perspectives on, 280-281
  defined, 13

early Christian attitude towards, 15
  fantasies about, 253
  gender nonconformity and, 294-295
  genetics of, 288-290
  historical perspectives on, 279-281
  hormones and, 290
  laws on, 284-285
  learning theories on, 293
  lifestyles in, 299-302
  psychoanalytic theory on, 291-293
  self-discovery of, 418
  stereotypes of, 286-287
  studies of, 45, 53
  treatment of, 296-297
Homosexuality in Perspective, 53
Honesty, in intimacy, 228
Hopi, sexual attitudes among, 26
Hormone-replacement therapy (HRT), 95
Hormones
  androgens, 113, 145-146
  defined, 87
  effect on fetus, 329
  estrogens, 77
  and menstrual cycle, 87-89, 91
  pituitary, 88, 112-113
  prostaglandins, 97
  "raging," 99
  sex, 142-146
  and sexual differentiation, 163
  and sexual orientation, 290-291
  testosterone, 112-113, 136-137
  to treat erectile disorders, 482
Hot flashes, 95, 96
HPV, 488, 496
  effects of, 489
  incidence of, 489
  symptoms of, 511-512
  treatment of, 512
Huckleberry Finn, 635, 636
Hudood Ordinance, 9
Human chorionic gonadotropin (HCG), 315
Human immunodeficiency virus. See
  AIDS; HIV
Human papilloma virus. See HPV
Human sexuality. See Sexuality
Human Potential Movement, 21
Human Sexual Inadequacy, 472
Human Sexual Response, 432
Huntington's chorea, 331
  detection of, 333
Hustler, defined, 632
Hyaluronidase, 307
Hymen, 70
  imperforate, 71
Hypersexuality, 571
  gender and, 572-573
Hypertension, sexual effects of, 466
Hypoactive sexual desire disorder, 456-457
Hypogonadism, 145
  hypoactive sexual desire disorder in, 457
Hypothalamus, 140, 141
  defined, 87
  sensitivity to sex hormones, 165
Hypothesis
  defined, 36
  testing of, 37
Hypoxyphilia, 567
Hysterectomy, 76, 371
Hysteria, etymology of term, 100
Hysterosalpingogram, 313
Hysterotomy, 384

Id, defined, 27
Immune system, 525-526
  effects of HIV on, 526
Impasse, coping with, 239-240
Imperforate hymen, 71
Implicit personality theories, 547

Impotence, defined, 246, 458
In vitro fertilization (IVF), 313
  donor, 313, 314
Incas, incestuous marriage in, 12
Incest
  in Dahomey culture, 37
  family factors in, 611
  perpetrators of, 608
  types of, 609-611
Incest taboo, 12, 429
  perspectives on, 609
Incestuous marriage, 12
Incidence, defined, 43
Independent variable, defined, 54
India
  AIDS in, 528
  ancient, sexual attitudes in, 16
Individuality, in intimacy, 229
Induced abortion, 376
Infancy, sexuality in, 390-393
Infatuation, 207-208, 210, 213
Inference, defined, 37
Infertility, 310-311
  female, 312-314
  male, 311-312
Infibulation, 68
Infidelity. See Extramarital sex
Inflammation, defined, 525-526
Informed consent, defined, 59
Infundibulum, 76
Inguinal canal, 165
Inhibited female orgasm, 461-462
  treatment of, 475-478
Inhibited male orgasm, 461
  treatment of, 478-479
Inhibited sexual desire, 456
Inis Beag, 464
Injecting drug users, and AIDS, 520, 549
Intellectualization, as defense mechanism, 28
Intercourse. See Coitus
Internal sexual organs
  female, 73-78
  male 112-117
Internalized homophobia, 283
Interstitial cells, 112, 113
Interstitial-cell-stimulating-hormone (ICSH), 113
Intimacy
  as component of love, 209
  defined, 226
  features of, 228-231
  individuality within, 229
  prerequisites for, 227-228
  types of, 227
Intra-amniotic infusion, 383
Intrapsychic conflict, defined, 293
Intrauterine devices (IUDs)
  advantages and disadvantages of, 357-358
  effectiveness of, 357
  mechanism of, 356-357
  reversibility of, 357
  types of, 356, 357
Introitus, 70, 71
Invisible Lives, 298
Irrational beliefs
  communication about, 232
  and sexual dysfunctions, 470-471
Islam
  circumcision in, 109
  sexual attitudes in, 15
Isthmus, 76
IVF (in vitro fertilization), 313
  donor, 313, 314
Ivory Coast, AIDS in, 536

Janus Report, 44
Japan
  AIDS in, 529

attitudes towards abortion, 9, 384-385
communication conventions in, 222
Jaundice, 510
Jealousy, 223
Joy of Sex, 433
Judaism
attitudes towards homosexuality, 279
circumcision in, 109
views on marriage, 426

Kama Sutra, 16
Kaposi's sarcoma, 520, 527
Kegel exercises, 73
Kenya, AIDS in, 528, 536
Kept boys, 633
Kinsey Reports, 42-43
Kissing
animal analogues to, 37, 52
body, 254
cultural perspective on, 8, 26
types of, 254
Klinefelter's syndrome, 165
Klismaphilia, 574
Kukukuku people, sexual attitudes among, 280
Kung people, gender typing among, 180
Kurdish people, gender typing among, 179
Kwoma people, sexual attitudes among, 393

L-dopa, 136
Labia majora, 65
age-related changes in, 443
changes during sex, 147, 148, 149
Labia minora, 65
changes during sex, 147, 149
Labor, 334-335
anesthetics and, 337
false, 334
Laboratory observation, 52-53
Lactation, 80, 342
Lady Chatterley's Lover, 20, 432, 635
Lamaze childbirth, 338
Laparoscopy, 313, 371, 372
Larynx, 401
Lateral-entry coital position, 262-263
Learning theories, 29-30
on homosexuality, 293
on paraphilias, 575-576
Learning Tree, 637
Lecha people, sexual attitudes among, 393
Legalism, 655-656
Lesbians
adjustment of, 295-297
attitudes towards, 273, 282, 283
defined, 272
heterosexual activity by, 274
lifestyles among, 299-302
relations with family, 294, 298
relationships involving, 296, 300-302
self-discovery in adolescence, 418
types of sexual activity among, 299
Lesu people, sexual attitudes among, 392, 393
Leukocytes, defined, 525
Levirate marriage, 245
Leydig's cells, 112, 113
LH (luteinizing hormone), 88, 112
LH-releasing hormone (LH-RH), 113
Librium, effect on fetus, 329
Lice, 512-513
Lifelong erectile dysfunction, 459
Liking, 211, 213
Limbic system, 140, 141, 142
Listening, active, 233-234
Liu Report, 50
Local anesthesia, 337
Lochia, 342
Loneliness

causes of, 225
components of, 209
coping with, 225-226
defined, 225
Greek heritage of, 205
literature about, 204
"look" of, 231
models of, 208-214
romantic, 205-208
styles of, 208-209
types of, 209, 211-212
Lovemap, 578
Low-birth-weight infants, 340
LSD
effect on fetus, 329
sexual effects of, 139
Lumpectomy, defined, 84
Luteal phase of menstrual cycle, 9
Luteinizing hormone (LH), 88, 112
and conception, 308
Lymphocytes, 526
Lymphogranuloma venereum, 503

Machismo, 174-175
jealousy and, 223
Maja desnuda, 643
Maja vestida, 643
Male erectile disorder, 459
Male pill, 375
Male rape, 592-593
Male sexuality, surveys of, 50
Male strippers, 624
Male-superior coital position, 186, 260-261
Malignant, defined, 83
Mammary glands, 80
Mammography, 81
controversies about, 84, 86
Mangaia, 464-465
"Manopause," 114
Mardi Gras, 437
Marianismo, 174-175
Marijuana
effect on fetus, 328, 329
sexual effects of, 139
Marital conflict
and inhibited desire, 457
and sexual dysfunctions, 469-470
Marital fidelity, cultural perspectives on, 8
Marital rape, 587-588, 593-594
Marriage
age differences and, 200, 201
alternative forms of, 440-441
candidates for, 429-432
cohabitation and, 425-426
history of, 426-428
incestuous, 12
incidence of, 426
levirate, 245
modern vs. traditional, 428
reasons for, 428-429
reproduction and, 431-432
sexuality in, 432-435
types of, 429
Marshall Islanders
gender typing among, 178
sexual attitudes of, 437
Mashing, 570
Masochism, 565-567
theories on, 575, 577, 577-578
Massage parlors, 627-628
Mastalgia, defined, 98
Mastectomy, defined, 84
Masturbation, 5
in adolescence, 402
cross-cultural perspective on, 26
defined, 244
in early childhood, 394
early Christian attitude towards, 15

in elderly, 445
fantasies in, 251-253
historical views on, 245-248
in infancy, 391
incidence of, 246-247
in preadolescence, 395
reasons for, 248
Taoist attitude towards, 16
techniques of female, 249-251
techniques of male, 248-249
types of, 244-245
uses and justifications for, 151, 477
Matching hypothesis, 202-203
Mate-swapping, 21, 436
Mating gradient, 430-431
Mattachine Society, 285
Median, defined, 247
Medicated childbirth, 337
Medulla, 140
Meese Commission, 640-641
Men
cross-cultural views of, 178-179
external sexual organs of, 106-112
internal sexual organs of, 112-117
qualities desired in, 230
sex hormones and, 144-145
sexual response cycle of, 148
Menarche, 399
age of, 400
cultural attitudes towards, 404
defined, 87, 400
Menopause
defined, 94
male, 114
myths about, 96-97
physiology of, 95
Menstrual cycle, 86-87
body changes during, 90
phases of, 88-94
regulation of, 87-88
sexual behavior during, 146
Menstrual phase of menstrual cycle. See Menstruation
Menstruation
coitus during, 94
defined, 86
described, 91-94
discomfort during, 100-102
disorders of, 97-100
distinguished from estrus, 87
resumption after childbirth, 342
sanitary considerations of, 92-94
synchrony of, 132-133
Mescaline, sexual effects of, 139
Mesoderm, 323, 324
Mesopotamia, ancient, prostitution in, 625
Metastasize, defined, 82
Methadone, effect on fetus, 329
Metronidazole, 504
Miconazole, 504
Middle Ages, sexual attitudes in, 16-17, 71
Midwives, 336
Miller v. California, 636-637
Minilaparotomy, 371
Minipills, 351, 353
Miscarriage, 315
caused by syphilis, 326
Missionary coital position, 260
Mittelschmerz, 91
Modeling, defined, 30
Molluscum contagiosum, 512
Mongolism, 332
Moniliasis, 504
Monogamy, 12, 429
cultural perspective on, 26
serial, 423
Monozygotic twins, 288
Mons pubis, manual stimulation of, 255
Mons veneris, 65

Physical attractiveness, 196-197
  cultural aspects of, 197-198
  perceptions of, 198
PID, from IUDs, 358
Pill, the. See Oral contraceptives
Pimps, 626-627
Pituitary gland
  defined, 87
  in menopause, 95
Placenta, 324
Plateau phase, 147
Playboy Foundation Survey, 43-44
Plumpness, and physical attractiveness, 197
PMS (premenstrual syndrome), 99-100
  coping with, 101
Podophyllin, 512
Polyandry, 429
  defined, 26
Polygamy, 12, 429
Polygyny, 429
  defined, 26
Polymorphously perverse, in psychoanalytic
  theory, 291
Ponapean people, 568
Pons, 140
Pope v. Illinois, 637
Population, defined, 41
Pornography
  classified, 636
  computer-based, 639
  defined, 635
  effects of, 639-641, 646-648
  gender differences in response to, 638
  laws on, 636-638
  prevalence of, 638-639
Positions, coital, 22, 260-264, 477
Possessive love, 209
POSSLQ, 423-424
Post-traumatic stress disorder (PTSD), after
  rape, 599-600
Postpartum, defined, 319
Postpartum depression, 341-342
Potatoes, 136
Power rape, 597-598
Power, sexuality and, 31
Pragmatism, gender and, 431-432
Preadolescence, sexuality in, 395-398
Preeclampsia, 327
Pregnancy
  attitudes towards, 314
  early effects of, 315
  early signs of, 314
  ectopic, 77, 328
  psychological changes in, 320-321
  sexual activity during, 315, 318-320
  teenage, 411-417. See also Teenage preg-
    nancy
  tests for, 315
  uterus in, 75
Prehistoric sexuality, 11-12
Premarital intercourse
  in China, 9
  contraceptive use in, 414-415
  cultural attitudes towards, 408-409
  factors in, 407
  the first time, 410-411
  incidence of, 405-406
  motives for, 406-407
  pregnancy and, 411-417
Premature ejaculation, 110, 124, 462
  causes of, 470
  treatment of, 479
Premenstrual syndrome (PMS), 99-100
  coping with, 101
Prenatal care, 341
Prenatal development
  embryonic stage, 322-324
  environmental influences on, 325-331
  fetal stage, 323, 324-325

germinal stage, 321-322
  organ development, 163-164, 327
  sexual development, 290
  sexual differentiation, 162-165
Preovulatory phase of menstrual cycle, 89
Prepared childbirth, 338
Prepuce, 66
Preterm infants, 340-341
Priapism, 125
Primary amenorrhea, defined, 98
Primary dysmenorrhea, defined, 97
Primary erogenous zones, 134
Primary sex characteristics, 399
Probability sample, defined, 41
Prodromal symptoms, defined, 508
Progesterone, 77, 78
Progestin, effect on fetus, 329
Projection, as defense mechanism, 28
Prolactin, 88, 342
Proliferative phase of menstrual cycle, 89
Prophylactic, defined, 363
Prostaglandins, 334
  defined, 97
Prostate gland, 116
  cancer of, 119-120, 144
  changes during orgasm, 148
  enlargement of, 118-119
  inflammation of, 120
Prostate test, 119
Prostatitis, 120
Prostitutes and prostitution
  AIDS and, 633, 634-635
  characteristics of female, 629-630
  characteristics of male, 633-634
  cultural perspective on, 8-9
  customers of, 630-631
  history of, 624-625
  incidence of, 625
  male, 632-634
  types of female, 626-628
Provider referral, 539
Proximodistal development, 323
Prurient, defined, 635
Pseudohermaphroditism, 166, 167
  and gender identity, 167-169
Psychoactive drugs, sexual effects of, 137-
  139
Psychoanalytic theory
  defense mechanisms and, 28
  defined, 27
  dream interpretation in, 29
  on homosexuality, 291-293
  on paraphilias, 575
  on transsexualism, 170-171
  view of gender typing, 181-182
  view of psychosocial development, 30
Psychological androgyny, 186-189
Psychological disabilities, sexuality and, 448-
  449
Psychopathia Sexualis, 19
Psychosexual development
  defined, 28
  psychoanalytic view of, 30
Psychosexual therapy, 472
Psychosexual trauma, 467
Psychotherapy, to treat paraphilias, 579
Puberty, 399-400
  in female, 400, 402
  in male, 401, 403
Pubic lice, 512-513
Pubococcygeus muscle, 72
  exercises for, 73
Pudendal block, 337
Pudendum, defined, 64
Puerto Rico, AIDS in, 529
Punks, 634

Queen, defined, 286

Radiotherapy, defined, 75
Random sample, defined, 41
Rape
  animal analogues to, 22
  blaming the victim, 9
  coping with, 599-601
  cross-cultural studies of, 597
  defined, 587
  historical views on, 587-588
  incidence of, 588-589
  legal types of, 587-588
  motives for, 597-598
  myths and attitudes condoning, 594
  perpetrators of, 595-597
  prevention of, 601-603
  reactions to, 599-601
  reporting, 599
  sadism in, 558
  sociocultural factors in, 594-595
  treatment of, 601
  types of, 589-594
Rape trauma syndrome, 600
Rapid orgasm, 462
Rapists, 595-597
  coping with, 602-603
  motives of, 597-598
  treatment of, 614
Rationalism, 658
Rationalization, as defense mechanism, 28
Reaction formation, as defense mechanism,
  28
Rear-entry coital position, 263-264
Recessive trait, defined, 333
Reciprocity, 204
Recto-vaginal examination, 79
Reflex
  defined, 121
  spinal, 22
Reflex arc, 122
Reformation, sexual attitudes in, 18
Refractory period, 150
Regional anesthesia, 337
Relationship
  fantasy in, 266
  marriage, 426-441
  sexual dysfunctions in, 457, 469-470
  stages in, 218-224
  traits conducive to, 198, 200
Reliability, defined, 43
Religion, prehistoric, 11
REM sleep, 121
Remarriage, prognosis for, 440
Representative sample, defined, 41
Repression
  as defense mechanism, 28
  defined, 27, 28
Reproductive system
  female, 70
  male, 108
Requests, making, 236
Research
  case study, 57-58
  correlational, 56-57
  ethical, 56, 58-60
  experimental, 54-56
  observational, 51-54
  survey, 40-50
Resolution phase, 149-150
Respiratory distress syndrome, 340
Reticular activating system, 140
Retina blastoma, 331
Retrograde ejaculation, 126
Retroverted, defined, 75
Retroviruses, 526
Reverse transcriptase, 526
Rh incompatibility
  detection of, 333
  effect on fetus, 328
Rhogan, 328

sexual attitudes among, 25, 26, 29, 393, 557
Trophoblast, 322
Tropic of Cancer, 432, 635
Trukese people, 568
  sexual attitudes among, 393
Trust, defined, 228
TSS (toxic shock syndrome), 93-94
Tubal sterilization, 371
Tumescence, defined, 466
Tupinamba people, gender typing among, 178
Turner's syndrome, 165
Twin studies, of homosexuality, 288-290
Twins, types of, 288

Uganda, AIDS in, 528, 535, 536
Ultrasound, 333, 334
  temporary sterilization from, 376
Umbilical cord, 324
Unconscious mind, defined, 27, 28
Urethra, changes during orgasm, 149
Urethral bulb, 125, 126
  changes during orgasm, 148-149
Urethral opening, 67
Urethritis, 117
Urinary bladder, changes during orgasm, 148, 149
Urogenital system, diseases of, 117-120
Urologist, defined, 117
Urophilia, 574
Uterine orgasm, 155
Uterus, 75-76
  changes in childbirth, 334
  changes during orgasm, 149
  changes during sex, 147, 149
Utilitarianism, 657

Vacuum aspiration, 381, 383
Vacuum constrictor device, 483
Vagina, 73-74
  age-related changes in, 442
  changes during orgasm, 149
  changes during sex, 147, 149
  infections of, 503-506
  inflammation of, 74-75
  manual stimulation of, 255, 256
  mucus of, 308
Vaginal opening, 70-71
  changes during sex, 147
  parous, 71
Vaginal orgasm, 154, 155
Vaginal photoplethysmograph, 39, 40
Vaginal ring, 373
Vaginismus, 463
  treatment of, 480
Vaginitis, 74, 503-506
  prevention of, 74-75
Validity, defined, 43
Valium, effect on fetus, 329
Value systems, 655-658
Values
  defined, 6
  sexuality and, 6-7, 654-655
Variables
  defined, 38
  dependent vs. independent, 54
Vas deferens, 112, 115
  changes during orgasm, 148
Vascular surgery, for erectile disorders, 482
Vasectomy, 115, 369-370
  reversibility of, 370-371
Vasocongestion, 146, 458
  defined, 40
  measurement of, 39
VDRL test, 500
Venereal disease, 489. See also STDs
Venereal warts, 511

Ventral-ventral position, defined, 22
Venus of Willendorf, 11
Verbal cues, 235
Vestibular bulbs, 72
Vestibule, 67
Viable, defined, 378
Vibrators, in masturbation, 249, 250
Victimization surveys, 588
Victorian era, 18-19
Vietnam war, 21
Violence in pornography, 637
  effects of, 640, 641, 646-647
Viral hepatitis, 495, 510-511
Virginity, 70-71
  early Christian attitude towards, 15
Virtual sex, 639
Viscosity, defined, 368
Vision, arousal and, 130-131
Vitamins, effect on fetus, 329
Volunteer bias, 42, 46-47
Voyeurism, 564-565
  causes of, 578
Vulgarity, 232
Vulva, 65
  morphology of, 66
Vulval orgasm, 155

Wasting syndrome, 527
Webster v. Reproductive Health Serv., 379-380
West Side Story, 204, 206
Whore-madonna complex, 63125
Women
  AIDS and, 534-535, 537
  cross-cultural views of, 178-179
  external sexual organs of, 65-73
  internal sexual organs of, 73-78
  medieval attitudes towards, 17
  rape by, 594
  self-image of, 85
  sex hormones and, 145-146
  sexual response cycle of, 150-151
Wyatt Survey, 48, 610

X Portfolio, Patrice, 644
X-rays, effect on fetus, 331

Yeast infection, 504
Yogurt, as anti-candidiasis drug, 504
Yohimbine, 136
Yungur people, 71

Zaire
  AIDS in, 536
  art of, 642
Zambia, AIDS in, 536
Zidovudine, to treat HIV, 540
ZIFT (zygote intrafallopian transfer), 313, 314
Zona pellucida, 307
Zoophilia, 571-573
Zygote
  defined, 89, 306
  development of, 163
Zygote intrafallopian transfer (ZIFT), 313, 314

Running/Black Star; (right) Kim Newton/Woodfin Camp & Associates; p. 50: Owen Franken/Stock Boston; p.51: © Chris Steele Perkins/ © Magnum; p.53: © Elliott Erwitt/ ©Magnum; **Chapter 3**: p. 77: John Giannicchi/Photo Researchers Science Source; p. 81: Lynn Johnson/Black Star; p. 84:Courtesy of Cable News Network, Inc.; p. 85: Lynn Johnson/Black Star;p. 93: The Bettmann Archive; p. 96: Catherine Karnow/Woodfin Camp & Associates; p. 99: John Coletti; **Chapter 4**: p.113: Professor P. Motta/Dept. of Anatomy/Rome University/ Science Photo Library/Photo Researchers; p. 115: Dr. Rom Verma/Phototake; p. 119: Courtesy of Cable News Network, Inc.; **Chapter 5**: p. 131: Nicholas DeVore III /Photographers Aspen; p. 132: Larry Lawfer/Black Star; p. 137: Robert Frerck/Odyssey; p. 143: Bob Daemmrich/Stock Boston; **Chapter 6**: p. 166: Courtesy of Dr. John Money; p. 168: (both) Courtesy of Dr. John Money; p. 170: (both) AP/ Wide World Photos; p. 172: Martin Rotker/Phototake; p. 173: (top) Martin Rotker/Phototake; (bottom) Ellis Herwig /Stock Boston; p. 175: Robert Floyd/Creative Image; p.179: (left) Robert Azzi /Woodfin Camp & Associates; (right) Lindsay Hebberd/Woodfin Camp & Associates; p. 180: G & J Raith/Black Star; **Chapter 7**: p. 196: (top left) Adam Wolfitt/Woodfin Camp & Associates; (top center) Richard Falco/Black Star; (top right) Claus Meyer/Black Star; (bottom left) Mitch Kezar/Black Star; (bottom right) Nicholas DeVore III /Photographers Aspen; p. 197: Guy Marineau/Black Star; p. 203: © Paul Fusco/ © Magnum; Lisa Quinones/Black Star; **Chapter 8**: p. 222: © S. Franklin/ © Magnum; p. 224: Richard Hutchings/Photo Researchers; p. 227: (top) Catherine Karnow/Woodfin Camp & Associates; (bottom) Fritz Hoffman/JB Pictures; p. 229: Nicholas DeVore III /Photographers Aspen; p. 233: Robert Harbison; **Chapter 9**: p. 250: Frank Siteman; p. 252: Laurie Platt Winfrey, Inc.; p. 255: Lou Jones; p. 267: Robert Floyd; **Chapter 10**: p. 273: Donna Binder/Impact Visuals; p. 288; © 1992, Newsweek, Inc. All rights reserved. Reprinted by permission; p. 293: Stephen Marks; p. 295: Courtesy of Cable News Network, Inc.; p. 301: Jacques Chenet/Woodfin Camp & Associates; **Chapter 11**: p. 307: Francis LeRoy/Bio Cosmos/ Photo Researchers Science Source; p. 317: Annie Griffith Belt; p. 320: Robert Frerck/Odyssey; p. 325: (all) Petit Format/Nestle/Photo Researchers Science Source; p. 329: Courtesy of The Fetal Alcohol & Drug Unit/Pregnancy & Health Studies; p. 333: Will & Deni McIntyre /Photo Researchers; p. 337: (all) SIU/ Photo Researchers; p. 340: Courtesy of Cable News Network, Inc.; p. 341: Courtesy of Cable News Network, Inc.; p. 344: Courtesy of Jeffrey Nevid; **Chapter 12**: p.352: Courtesy of Cable News Network, Inc.; p. 354; Courtesy of Planned Parenthood Federation of America; p. 357: Martin Rotker/Phototake; p. 361: Courtesy of Whitehall Robins; p.362: Courtesy of Cervical Cap Ltd.; p. 364: Biophoto Assoc. /Photo Researchers Science Source; p. 373: (top) Courtesy of Wyeth Ayerst Laboratories; (bottom) Courtesy of Wisconsin Pharmaceutical Co.; p. 375: Alon Reininger/Contact/Woodfin Camp & Associates; p. 376: Courtesy of Cable News Network, Inc.; p. 380: Robert Harbison; **Chapter 13**: p. 391: Robert Harbison; p. 394: © Josef Koudelka/ © Magnum; p. 401: Jeff Parsons/Stock Boston; p. 409: Robert Fried Photography; p.413: Gale Zucker/Stock Boston; p. 414: Jeff Lowenthal/Woodfin Camp & Associates; **Chapter 14**: p. 423: Courtesy of Cable News Network, Inc.; p. 427: (left) David Moore/Black Star; (center) Nicholas DeVore III /Photographers Aspen; (right) Michel Setboun/JB Pictures; p.: 435: Lou Jones; p. 443: © Paul Fusco/ © Magnum; p. 446 Christopher Springman/The Stock Market; **Chapter 15**: p. 457: Bob Daemmrich/Stock Boston; p. 458: Shackman/Monkmeyer; p. 465: Nicholas DeVore III /Photographers Aspen; p. 469: Roy Morsch/The Stock Market; p. 482: G. Thomas Bishop/Custom Medical; **Chapter 16**: p. 489: David Butow/Black Star; p. 497: Courtesy of Dr. Nicholas J. Fiumara; p. 499: Custom Medical/CMSP//NIAID/NIH; p. 509: Phototake /CNRI; p. 512: Bio Photo Assoc/Photo Researchers; p. 513: E.Gray/Photo Researchers Science Photo Library; p. 516: Courtesy of Cable News Network, Inc.; **Chapter 17**: p. 526: Bill Longcone/Photo Researchers Science Source; p. 533: AP/Wide World; p. 534: Phil Schermeister/Photographers Aspen; p. 541: Alon Reininger/Woodfin Camp & Associates; p. 547: John Nordell/JB Pictures; **Chapter 18**: p. 559: Alon Reininger/Contact/Woodfin Camp & Associates; p. 560: Donna Binder/Impact Visuals; p. 562: Matusow/Monkmeyer; p. 569: Custom Medical Stock; p. 573: North Wind Picture Archives; p. 577: Fredrik D. Bodin; **Chapter 19**: p. 586: AP/Wide World Photos; p. 587: Roy Morsch/The Stock Market; p. 590: © Steve McCurry/ © Magnum; p. 596: Bob Daemmrich /Stock Boston; p. 601: Gale Zucker /Stock Boston; p. 603: Clark Jones/Impact Visuals; p. 606: Courtesy of the LaPorte County Child Abuse Prevention Council; p. 613: Courtsey of Western Psychological Services; p. 617: John Coletti; **Chapter 20**: p.624: Gerd Ludwig//Woodfin Camp & Associates; p. 626: Tony O'Brien/JB Pictures; p. 627: Mike Yamashita/Woodfin Camp & Associates; p. 633: Paul Chesley /Photographers Aspen; p. 637: Jim Anderson /Woodfin Camp & Associates; p. 642: (left) Marc Morrison/Shooting Star; (right) Carolee Schneemann; p. 643: (all) Art Resource; p. 644: *Patrice*, 1977 Copyright © 1977 The Estate of Robert Mapplethorpe; p. 645: (top) Sue Coe: *Bedford Rape*, Copyright © 1983 Sue Coe, Courtesy of St. Etienne, New York; (top left) Joan Lyon, (bottom both) Carolee Schneemann; p. 646: (both) Carolee Schneemann; p. 648: Steven Rubin/JB Pictures.